Parícutin, newly formed Mexican volcano.

THE BOOK OF
POPULAR
SCIENCE

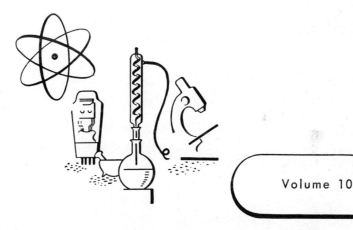

Volume 10

INCORPORATED

New York

Distributed in the United States by
THE GROLIER SOCIETY INC.

Distributed in Canada by
THE GROLIER SOCIETY OF CANADA LIMITED

Cover photograph: radio telescope at Jodrell Bank, near
Manchester, England. It receives and records radio waves
originating in space; it also
tracks man-made satellites.

David Moore—Black Star

13 ☼

X

CONTENTS OF VOLUME X

THE UNIVERSE

RECORDING THE FLEETING DAYS 171
The Development of the Calendar

THE EARTH

MOUNTAIN STOREHOUSES 18
Ranges and Peaks That Hold Water Reserves

THE MAKING OF MOUNTAINS 213
The Cycles of Building and Decay

LIFE

LAND AND SEA HABITATS 135
The Natural Abodes of Animals and Plants

PLANT AND ANIMAL COMMUNITIES 181
How Living Things of a Region Dwell Together

PLANT LIFE

THE TREATMENT OF PLANTS 143
The Use of Surgery in the Garden

ANIMAL LIFE

THE ANIMALS OF THE ZOO 154
Sidelights on Modern Zoological Collections

THE TAMING OF THE WILD 239
How Animals Have Become Man's Allies

MAN

EXERCISE AND REST 85
How the Body Expends and Renews Energy Stores

HEALTH

A FIRST-AID PRIMER 5
What to Do While Waiting for the Doctor

MAN AND THE MOSQUITO 30
The War against Malaria

A HOME NURSING PRIMER 55
How to Care for the Sick or Injured at Home

KEEPING FIT 75
How to Care for the Body in Health

ATOMIC MEDICINES 98
Battling Disease with Radioactive Isotopes

PROGRESS IN MEDICINE 127
Important Landmarks of Modern Research

MATTER AND ENERGY

RADIOCARBON DATING 92
How the Relics of the Past Reveal Their Age

THE MIGHTY MIDGET OF ELECTRONICS 102
The Transistor—What It Is and Can Do

PRESERVING FOOD BY ATOMIC RADIATION 114
Using Gamma Rays to Sterilize Foodstuffs

ELECTRONICS 168
Its Effects on Daily Living

ATOMIC FARMING 251
How Radioactivity Is Put to Work for Agriculture

INDUSTRY

POWER-DRIVEN TOOLS 105
Machines by Which Men Build Other Machines

INDUSTRIAL DESIGN 117
A Striking Twentieth-Century Development

THE RISE OF AUTOMATION 235
The Industrial Revolution Takes a Step Forward

TRANSPORTATION

THE STORY OF ROCKETS 1
Swift Travelers in Air and Space

SPACE TRAVEL 40
Man's Future Journeying beyond Our Atmosphere

SUPERSONIC FLIGHT 228
Velocities That Exceed That of Sound in Air

COMMUNICATION

MICROFILMING 68
First Aid to Crowded Archives

PHOTOGRAPHY AT WORK 163
A Pictorial Record of Recent Developments

SCIENCE THROUGH THE AGES

TWENTIETH CENTURY (1895–   ) IX 191
  The Making of a Scientist
  Careers in Science — A Bird's-Eye View

TWENTIETH CENTURY (1895–   ) X 224
  The Road Ahead in Scientific Research

PROJECTS AND EXPERIMENTS

EXPLORING THE PLANT WORLD 203
Interesting Finds and How to Preserve Them

EXPLORING THE ANIMAL WORLD 254
How to Find and Study Our Animal Neighbors

SELECTED READINGS IN SCIENCE 267

SCIENTIFIC FACTS AND FIGURES 293

FULL-COLOR PICTURES 311

GENERAL OUTLINE 319

ALPHABETICAL INDEX 331

THE STORY OF ROCKETS

Swift Travelers in Air and Space

UP TO a comparatively short time ago, most people thought of the rocket only as a kind of fireworks. Today it has come into its own. It is one of the world's deadliest weapons; it is a valued tool of the meteorologist; it is being seriously considered for interplanetary flight.

The principle of the rocket is simple enough. If we fill a toy balloon with hydrogen gas under high pressure, the gas will press equally upon every part of the balloon. If we prick it with a pin, the gas will begin to escape through the hole, and there will be less pressure in this area. The pressure in the opposite side will therefore be relatively greater and the balloon will move away in that direction. In the rocket, high-pressure gases are produced by the combustion of fuel. These gases make their way through an opening at the rear of the rocket and consequently give it a forward thrust.

The Chinese began to use rockets for fireworks displays several hundred years before the birth of Christ. This kind of rocket is still popular. It generally consists of a cardboard case, closed at one end and fastened to a stick. For the greater part of its length the rocket is filled with gunpowder; an open space is left in the middle. An explosive charge and a number of "stars" made of inflammable material are set in the head. The charge is ignited and the rocket shoots upward. When the charge in the head explodes, the stars are ignited and fall in showers.

Rockets served as weapons at least as far back as the eighteenth century. Tippoo Sahib, who was sultan of Mysore in the last years of the eighteenth century, fired a number of rocket projectiles at his English foes. Greatly impressed by Tippoo's rockets, the English decided to adopt the weapon; and several English rocket ships took part in the attack on the American stronghold of Fort McHenry in September 1814. Francis Scott Key, who was an eyewitness of the battle, immortalized the "rockets' red glare" in a line of THE STAR SPANGLED BANNER.

The rocket of those days was very erratic in flight, but it could compete with round shot, grape shot and chain shot because they too were hit-and-miss projec-

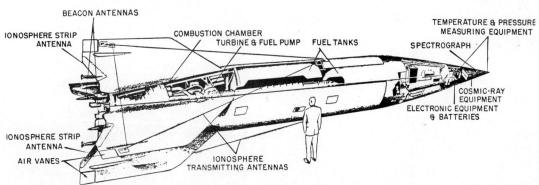

U. S. Navy

Diagram of a V-2 rocket that soared some 100 miles into the upper air over White Sands Proving Ground, Las Cruces, New Mexico. A number of scientific instruments were carried in the rocket's warhead (forward section), which would be loaded with high explosives if it were used against a foe.

Rockets launched in vertical flight are made to deviate a bit from a straight upward path, so that they will not crash too near the launching site.

tiles. When the far more accurate rifled shell came into general use the rocket was abandoned as a military weapon, but continued to be used in other ways. It was still a favorite kind of fireworks; it was employed for signaling purposes; and it served to carry lines between wrecked ships and the shore.

In the course of World War II the rocket was restored to military favor. The Russians used a rocket-firing gun, the Katiusha, which launched a considerable number of projectiles at the same time. The United States developed the rocket-firing bazooka; with a comparatively small rocket, this weapon could knock out a good-sized tank. Rockets were also launched from ships and airplanes and added greatly to their firepower.

The most deadly of all rocket weapons

was the gigantic German V-2, an aerial bomb with which the Germans showered London in the early months of 1945. The V-2 rockets were over 45 feet long and weighed 12 tons at the take-off. Fired from the Dutch coast, they reached an altitude of 65 miles and bridged a horizontal distance of 200 miles. The great damage they inflicted was all the more frightful because, traveling faster than sound, they gave no warning of their approach.

The rocket projectile is now a standard weapon for modern armies, navies and air forces. Its main parts are the warhead, containing the explosive charge; a fuse for exploding the warhead when it reaches the target and finally the motor. This contains the fuel, an igniter and a venturi or nozzle through which the exhaust gases pass. The projectiles are often provided with fins in order to assure stability in flight.

Military men are particularly interested in long-range rockets, for they are a devastating offensive weapon. They can pepper an enemy with high explosives from a distance of several hundred miles; and their range is being steadily increased.

Both photos, General Electric

Crater made by a crashing V-2 rocket at the White Sands Proving Ground. As there was no explosive in the rocket's warhead, the size of the crater shows with what force it struck the desert floor.

In recent years, research in rocketry has been speeded up as military authorities have sought to perfect guided missiles. They are particularly interested in the development of the IRBM (Intermediate Range Ballistics Missile) with a range of 1,500 miles and the ICBM (Intercontinental Ballistics Missile) with a range of 5,000 miles. Carrying atom bombs, these weapons could deliver devastating blows to an enemy force or installation.

Rockets are also being used in high-atmosphere observations of weather, cosmic rays, solar activity and ionospheric magnetic disturbances.

Progress in
rocket engineering

Because of this renewed interest in rocketry, rocket engineering has developed amazingly. Already scientists have been able to hurl man-made satellites into orbits around the earth. A small United States satellite reached an altitude of 2,400 miles in one part of its orbit. Manned space rockets are believed to be less than a generation away. (See Index, under Satellites, artificial.)

In order to achieve this progress, engineers and scientists have had to solve many technical problems involving the design of the rocket and its propulsion.

Air resistance to a space-bound rocket is very great as it shoots upward through the dense air of the lower atmosphere. To minimize this "air drag," scientists have resorted to the long, streamlined shape of our present rockets. The sharp, pointed cylinder knifes its way up through the air like the prow of a ship in a heavy sea. But in using this shape, designers have had to sacrifice fuel capacity. A long, slender rocket holds much less fuel than a squat, wide-diameter cylinder of the same weight.

Weight is one of the most important factors to be considered in the design of any rocket since the main force affecting the rocket's flight is gravity. One of the weight factors taken into account in the design of the rocket is the "mass ratio." This is the ratio of the weight of the rocket when fully loaded with fuel at take-off to its weight after all its fuel has been burned. Once the fuel has been used up, there is no longer any need for the tanks or engines, which become excess weight. Engineers have sought to discard this excess weight by building rockets consisting of two or more stages. Each stage is really a rocket in itself; the rockets of the different stages ride one on top of the other. As one rocket exhausts its fuel, it drops off, thus reducing the weight. The disadvantage of this arrangement is that it adds greatly to the complexity of the rocket.

The United States Naval Research Laboratory made a theoretical analysis of the gains in velocity by the use of an increasing number of stages and found that the three-stage rocket was the most practical on the whole. The velocity gain over a single-stage rocket was 33 per cent for two stages, 45 per cent for three stages and only 70 per cent for an infinite number of stages.

The air in the lower atmosphere generates tremendous heat because of friction with the surface of the fast-moving rocket. To reduce this friction, very smooth materials have to be provided for the surface of the rocket. These materials have to be able to withstand very high temperatures; they also have to insulate the delicate instruments within the rocket. For this purpose, silicones (organic silicon compounds) and other artificial substances have been used. Other possible surface materials now under development include several heat-resistant chromium alloys, beryllium metal and high-melting-point ceramics.

Another method of getting rid of the heat produced by friction is to coat the rocket with a radiant skin which will cause the heat to radiate away from the surface of the rocket as fast as it is produced. One of the most promising radiant skin materials is the so-called honeycomb sandwich panel. This consists of two very thin sheets with a corrugated material, forming a honeycomb pattern, between them. The "meat" of the sandwich has spaces which tend to insulate the inside of the rocket from the heat produced on the surface by friction.

Engineers have made great progress in rocket design and in providing suitable rocket materials. The development of rocket fuels, however, has lagged far behind. Our present rockets are powered by ordinary chemical fuels such as hydrazine, gasoline, kerosene, alcohol and other low-energy hydrocarbons. Not only are these fuels heavy but they are also often hard to handle, dangerous and unreliable.

The chemical fuels now in use are either solid or liquid. Each form has certain advantages and disadvantages; there has been much controversy over which is better. Solid fuels are generally more reliable than those in liquid form. They take up less room; they do not require the complex engines and pumps of liquid-fuel propulsion mechanisms. In general they have a better mass ratio. On the other hand liquid fuels have a higher specific impulse.* They are easier to control because their rate of burning can be regulated. It is generally believed that solid fuels will be used in the smaller short-range rockets while the liquid fuels will be used in the larger long-range ones.

The so-called "exotic," high-energy fuels are much more powerful than our present ones. The most promising of these exotic fuels are the boranes, simple compounds of the elements boron and hydrogen. Rocket men are particularly interested in decaborane ($B_{10}H_{14}$) which burns with a very hot flame, giving off about 28,000 British thermal units per pound.

Another potential exotic fuel under development is hydrogen burned in fluorine instead of oxygen. It would be twice as powerful as our current fuels. The main drawback is that it is so difficult to handle. Fluorine is the most corrosive substance known and cannot be transported or stored in the ordinary manner. It will be necessary to find a safe way to handle the fuel before it can be put to practical use. It is believed that the problem can be solved by having the hydrogen combine with a compound of fluorine instead of with fluorine itself. Scientists are working on

several such compounds. In one, an atom of oxygen is combined with two atoms of fluorine; in another, three atoms of oxygen and two of fluorine are combined.

Most authorities maintain that man will never be able to travel great distances through space (to one of the distant planets, for example) in a rocket powered by a chemical fuel because too much fuel would have to be carried. That is why scientists are working on the idea of a rocket driven by atomic energy. In one atomic engine under consideration, the heat from a nuclear reactor would be applied to liquid hydrogen. The hydrogen would vaporize, expanding greatly, and would be forced out through a nozzle, thus producing tremendous thrust.

Another proposed atomic engine is the so-called ionic jet. In this, the heat produced by the atomic reactor would be used to vaporize and ionize liquid cesium. The ions produced would be accelerated in electric grids in much the same way as atomic particles are accelerated in an atom smasher (see Index, under Atom smashers). The cesium ions would then be driven out of the nozzle jet at a fantastic speed — perhaps 450,000 miles per hour.

The great difficulty in developing any atomic engine for manned rockets is that a heavy shield would be required to protect the crew and instruments against atomic radiation. A solar engine would not require such a shield. A rocket using this type of engine would carry giant concave mirrors, which would focus the sun's rays on a tube carrying liquid hydrogen. The hydrogen would vaporize and expand and would be forced out of the nozzle of the rocket in much the same way as in the nuclear-hydrogen engine and the ionic jet that we mentioned above.

Some scientists believe that the ultimate method of propulsion of a rocket traveling through space would be the use of pure energy in the form of photons of light. To make this power source available, it would first be necessary to convert matter directly into light — a task that is at present beyond our powers.

* The specific impulse of a fuel is the number of pounds of thrust per pound of fuel.

See also Vol. 10, p. 286: "Space Travel."

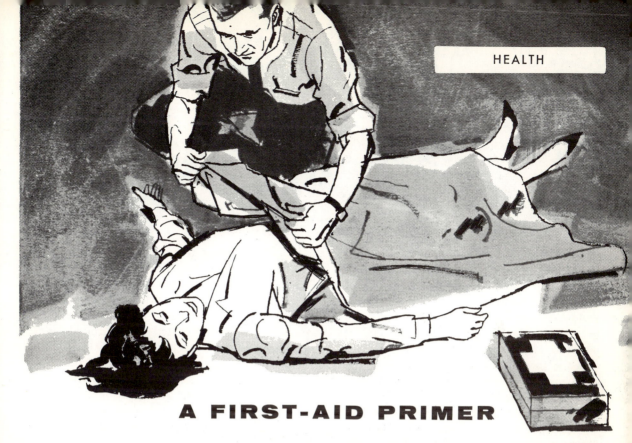

A FIRST-AID PRIMER

What to Do While Waiting for the Doctor

WHEN we say that we give first aid, we mean that we provide *immediate* and temporary care, of limited extent, for the victim of an accident or sudden illness. It is the care he must have until he can receive the attention of a physician. Immediate action is required only (1) when there is severe bleeding (hemorrhage); (2) when breathing has stopped for any reason; (3) when poison has been swallowed; and (4) when irritating chemicals come in contact with the skin or get in the eyes. A person who has had even elementary first-aid training should be able to cope with any of these emergencies. He may be able to save a life by applying first-aid principles.

First-aid training has certain definite aims. (1) It seeks to prevent accidents by making people aware of dangerous conditions and by showing them how to follow safe practices. (2) It protects the victim of accident or sudden illness from his own unwise actions and those of others. Well-meaning but misguided efforts to help him may aggravate what otherwise would be a minor injury. (3) It teaches that accident

and sudden illness may temporarily dull or disturb the mind. Hence victims need reassurance and encouragement as well as treatment for physical injuries.

In first aid, the words "signs" and "symptoms" are frequently used. "Signs" refer to what the giver of first aid can see on the body of the victim or at the scene of the accident; "symptoms" refer to the feelings of the victim. For example, in shock, typical signs are perspiration, dilated eyes, shallow and irregular breathing, weakness and absence of pulse. Among the symptoms of shock are feelings of weakness, nausea and dizziness.

CONTROL OF BLEEDING

Hemorrhage

When a large artery or vein is severed, a person can lose so much blood within even a minute's time that he may die. In cases of severe bleeding, you should immediately apply pressure directly over the wound. It is preferable to place a sterile or clean cloth against the spot where the

* Article prepared by the technical staff of the American Red Cross.

5

Controlling bleeding by direct pressure. Place the cleanest material available against the bleeding point and apply firm pressure with your hand until a bandage can be applied.

bleeding occurs, pressing it tightly with your hand. However, it is more important to stop the bleeding than to use a clean cloth; if necessary, apply pressure to the wound with your bare hand. If a cloth is being used to apply pressure and it becomes saturated with blood, do not remove it; merely place another one on top of it. If you remove the saturated cloth, you may disturb the normal clotting process and thus make the bleeding more severe.

Large arteries lie close to the surface of the body along the long bones of the arms and legs. Sometimes pressure applied over the blood vessel which supplies the wounded part, together with pressure directly over the wound as described above, may be helpful in controlling bleeding. For example, pressure over the artery in the arm about midway between the armpit and the elbow will sometimes reduce the flow of blood into the part below. If pressure is applied over the artery where it crosses the groin, the flow of blood should be lessened in the limb below that point.

Tourniquet

A tourniquet is a device for stopping bleeding by shutting off the flow of blood; it is most easily improvised from a bandage which is kept twisted tight around the limb by a stick. We mention it here principally to discourage its use. For one thing, it usually causes tissue injury in the area where it is applied. It should be used only when it is necessary to shut off the *entire* blood supply to the area immediately below the point where it is applied. This should be done only when life-threatening bleeding cannot be controlled by the methods described above, or when an arm or leg has been partly or completely severed. The tourniquet cannot be applied to the trunk; its use is restricted to the arms and legs.

If it is necessary to use a tourniquet, it should be placed close above the wound, toward the heart, but not at the wound's edge. There should be normal uninjured skin between the tourniquet and the injury. If the wound is near a joint, application

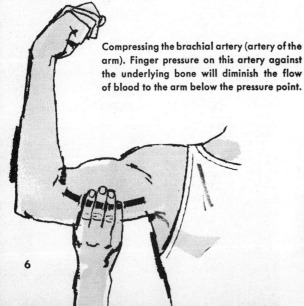

Compressing the brachial artery (artery of the arm). Finger pressure on this artery against the underlying bone will diminish the flow of blood to the arm below the pressure point.

Compressing the femoral artery (artery of the thigh). Finger pressure on this artery against the underlying bone will diminish the flow of blood in the leg below the pressure point.

should be made at the nearest practical point above the joint. Make sure that the tourniquet is applied tightly enough to stop bleeding. Improperly applied, it is likely to increase venous bleeding.

Improvised tourniquets should be made of flat material about two inches wide. Never use a rope, wire or sash cord since it will cut into and damage the underlying tissues and blood vessels. When applying an improvised tourniquet, first wrap the material tightly around the limb, twice if possible. Tie a half knot. Then place a short stout stick or similar article on the half knot and tie a full knot; twist the stick to tighten the tourniquet until the flow of blood ceases. Finally, tie the stick in place with the loose ends of the tourniquet or another strip of cloth.

Once a tourniquet is applied, the victim should be taken as soon as possible to a physician. The tourniquet should be released only by a physician who is prepared to control hemorrhage and replace blood volume by transfusion if necessary. Experience has shown that a properly applied tourniquet can be left in place one or two hours without causing undue tissue damage. However, if the first aider does not accompany the patient to the hospital or physician's office, he should attach a note to the victim, giving the location of the tourniquet and the time it was applied. Clothing or bandages should never be allowed to cover the tourniquet, as it may be forgotten.

Minor cuts and scratches

The best source of information concerning home care for minor cuts and scratches is your family physician. If you cannot reach a doctor, follow these recommendations: (1) Wash your hands thoroughly with clean water and soap. (2) Cleanse the wound carefully, using plain soap and boiled water cooled to room temperature, or soap and clean running tapwater. (3) Use a sterile or at least a clean piece of cloth to apply the soap and water. (4) Apply a dry sterile dressing, or a dressing made from clean cloth, and bandage it into place. (5) Be sure to tell the victim to see his doctor promptly if soreness develops.

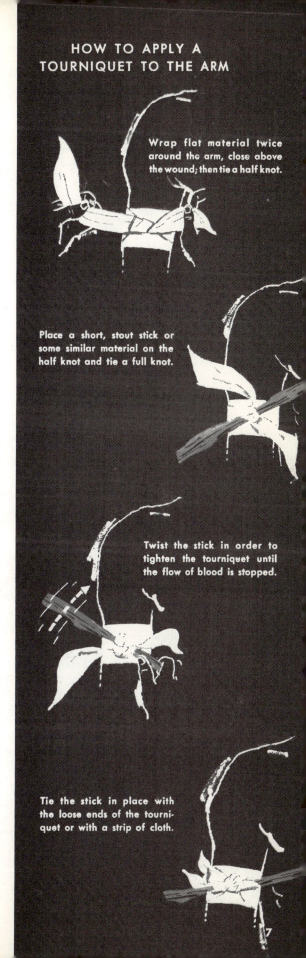

HOW TO APPLY A TOURNIQUET TO THE ARM

Wrap flat material twice around the arm, close above the wound; then tie a half knot.

Place a short, stout stick or some similar material on the half knot and tie a full knot.

Twist the stick in order to tighten the tourniquet until the flow of blood is stopped.

Tie the stick in place with the loose ends of the tourniquet or with a strip of cloth.

MOUTH-TO-MOUTH RESUSCITATION

Using middle finger of one hand, clear child's mouth of foreign matter. With same finger, hold tongue forward.

Place child face down, head down. Pat his back firmly. This helps to dislodge foreign objects in child's air passage.

Place the child on his back. Using both middle fingers, lift his lower jaw from beneath and behind so it "juts out."

Using only one hand, hold the child's jaw in this jutting-out position. Let the fingers support the jaw on one side.

Cover child's mouth and nose with your mouth; breathe into him. Press his abdomen to keep air from filling stomach.

WHEN BREATHING STOPS

When breathing stops, immediate action is necessary; this may mean the difference between life and death. A person may cease to breathe as a result of either disease or an accident. If breathing stops as a result of disease, artificial respiration efforts are of questionable value. On the other hand, if breathing has stopped because of an accident, it is often possible to revive the person if there has not been too long an interval between the time the patient stopped breathing and the time the treatment is applied.

The causes of asphyxiation (suspended breathing) may be divided into four groups: (1) The supply of air is shut off completely, as in drowning, choking and strangling. (2) There is an insufficient supply of oxygen in the air, as when a person is caught in an abandoned icebox, an empty silo, a vat, a well or a cistern. (3) The oxygen in the circulating blood has been displaced by other gases. This occurs in carbon-monoxide poisoning; also when a person is exposed to certain combinations of gases. (4) In some cases, there is paralysis or depression of the breathing center, as from electric shock or drugs used to induce sleep.

Nonmedical people usually do not have the training and experience to enable them to tell whether breathing has stopped because of disease or an accident. It is best, therefore, to apply some form of artificial respiration in all cases until the cause of the condition can be determined by a competent physician.

An airway must be kept open from the lungs to the mouth if any form of artificial respiration is to be successful. It is important to clear the patient's throat if it is blocked by foreign matter. The mouth must also be kept free from obstructions. If the person is discovered soon after his breathing has stopped and if artificial respiration is started immediately, his muscles usually retain enough tone * so that

---

* Even when muscles seem to be relaxed, some of the fibers are contracting. This partial contraction is called muscle tone, or tonus. It holds the bones in place and keeps the muscles taut and ready for use.

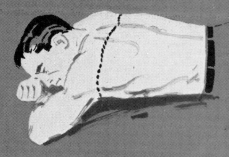

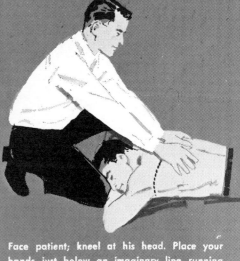

Place patient in a face-down, prone position. Bend his elbows; place hands one on the other. Turn his face so cheek rests on his hands. Be sure tongue does not block the air passage.

Face patient; kneel at his head. Place your hands just below an imaginary line running between his armpits. Spread your fingers downward and outward with tips of thumbs touching.

To force air out of the patient's lungs, rock forward until your arms are vertical, with elbows straight. Allow weight of upper part of your body to press down upon the patient's back.

Rock slowly backward, gradually releasing the pressure your hands have applied on patient's back. Avoid a final thrust. Place your hands on the patient's arms just above his elbows.

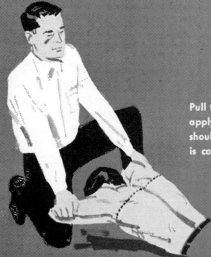

Pull the patient's arms upward and toward you, applying enough lift to feel tension at his shoulders. Lower his arms to the ground. Cycle is completed. Repeat twelve times per minute.

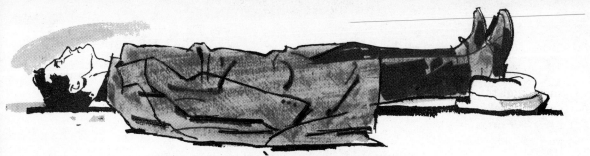

Shock accompanies nearly all injuries. Keep the patient
lying down; cover him to prevent the loss of body heat.

it is not too hard to keep an airway open into the lungs. Alternately increasing and decreasing the size of the chest will force air in and out of the victim's lungs if his throat and mouth are not obstructed.

If air is not quickly moved in and out of the lungs and if the person is not revived, the throat closes up because of internal conditions. As muscle tone goes, the tongue's base, which weighs approximately a quarter of a pound, relaxes against the windpipe and shuts off the flow of air. Since the tongue is attached to the lower jaw, if the first aider tilts the head of the victim backward and stretches the neck muscles as tightly as possible, the small opening is created that allows air to pass in and out. In addition, if the rescuer lifts the lower jaw upward, the air passage usually opens completely, in spite of the relaxation process.

Once a passage for air has been guaranteed, any action that alternately increases and decreases the size of the chest cage will revive a person if body conditions permit life. This increase and decrease can be accomplished either by blowing directly into the lungs through the mouth or nose or by alternately compressing and expanding the chest. The victim's body position is relatively unimportant.

WHEN POISON IS SWALLOWED

Poisonous substances, such as household cleaners, disinfectants and an overdose of medicine, are accidentally taken by many people. In all cases, first have the victim drink large amounts of plain water or milk in order to dilute the poison. The antidote for the poison is often printed on the label of the container of the poisonous material. It should be given to the victim if it is readily available. However,

diluting the poison will usually be sufficient until medical advice can be obtained. If there is a delay, it may be wise to induce vomiting — *except* when the victim is known to have taken an acid, an alkali or a petroleum product such as kerosene. In these cases vomiting should *not* be induced. If an acid substance has been taken, it should be diluted and a weak alkali, such as milk of magnesia or baking soda, should be given to counteract the acid. If an alkali has been swallowed, have the victim drink a weak acid, such as lemon juice or vinegar. If a petroleum product has been taken, it should be diluted *only*. It is more dangerous to take a chance on fumes entering the lungs than it is to allow the poison to pass through the digestive tract and be absorbed into the blood stream.

In cases where the poison is unknown, a universal antidote is recommended. It is made up of magnesium oxide, activated charcoal and tannic acid and is available commercially in most parts of the country. You can make up your own universal antidote by using one part milk of magnesia, two parts crumbled burned toast and one part strong tea, measured in terms of volume rather than by weight.

SHOCK

Nearly all injuries are accompanied to some degree by a condition called shock. If the injury involves blood loss, the circulatory system sets up an automatic, self-regulating action that tries to keep the blood in the deeper parts of the body near the vital organs. The skin often becomes cold, wet and clammy. This reaction to injury should not be confused with electric shock or the temporary shock of simple fainting or with neurogenic (shell) shock.

The first-aid measures dealing with shock and the prevention of shock are the same. The most important first-aid measure is to keep the patient in a lying-down position and thus help the flow of blood to the brain. Unless there are head or chest injuries, the victim may be placed with his head a little lower than his feet.

In treating shock, the main objective is to prevent a large loss of body heat. You will have to use your judgment, after examining the patient, to decide whether or not external heat should be applied to the body surface. If it is applied, care must be taken not to burn the patient. You should not make the victim sweat; it is better for him to be slightly cool than toasty warm.

If there must be a long wait between the onset of shock and medical care and if the patient is conscious, it may help to give him a mixture of common baking soda and table salt, one-half level teaspoon of each in a quart of water. This mixture may be given in small sips at fifteen-minute intervals. All handling of the victim should be as gentle as possible; rough handling will add to shock.

INJURIES TO BONES, MUSCLES AND JOINTS

Fractures

A fracture is a break in the bone. If there is no wound accompanying the break, it is called a simple fracture; it is known as a compound fracture if there is a wound associated with the break. A compound fracture might be caused either by the sharp ends of the bone pushing out through the flesh, or by a missile, such as a bullet, penetrating the body. Needless to say, compound fractures are more dangerous than simple fractures, because there is the danger of infection as well as the break to contend with. Signs of a fracture are an odd position or distortion of the limb. The patient will also complain of pain when he attempts to move it.

In all fractures, the broken bone ends as well as the adjacent joints must be kept still. This will help prevent further damage to the flesh by the broken bone. If materials are available and if the first aider is skillful, he may wish to splint the injured limb. The best splints are made of rigid materials such as wood. However, newspapers, magazines and even pillows may be used to give temporary support. They should be placed in such a way as to limit movement of the joints. If the first aider has not had extensive training, the best thing to do is leave the fracture alone and to move the patient as little as possible. In almost every case the broken bone ends can be kept from moving by using the hands alone. If ambulance service and a physician are near at hand, it is usually best to use only the hands and wait for the doctor to give further attention to the injury. In case of an injury to the bones of the back or neck, be especially careful not to move the person or to allow his spine to be twisted.

Dislocations

Dislocations are difficult to identify because they often resemble simple fractures. The signs and symptoms are similar to those of fractures. Usually a dislocation should be given the same type of support that a fracture requires; the part should be kept as still as possible until the arrival of the physician. Generally speaking,

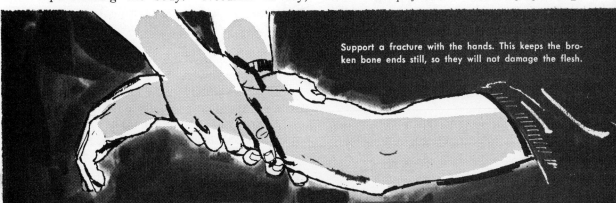

Support a fracture with the hands. This keeps the broken bone ends still, so they will not damage the flesh.

only a doctor should attempt to put a dislocation back in place (this is called reducing a dislocation). The only exceptions to this rule are possibly dislocations of the lower jaw and the first joint of the fingers and toes. To reduce dislocation of the first joint of a finger or toe, pull firmly parallel to the hand or foot.

Sprains

The word "sprain" should be associated with the word "joint" since sprains occur at joints, most frequently at the ankle and the wrist. When there is a sprain, the

or is charred, depending upon the degree of heat and the length of contact. These evidences of heat, which represent signs, are frequently referred to as degrees; we speak of first-degree, second-degree and third-degree burns. The severity of a burn is judged not only by the degree but also by its extent. It is said to be of limited extent when less than 10 per cent of the body surface is involved; when 10 per cent or more of the surface of the body is burned, the injury is referred to as extensive. A person with extensive burns should be taken to a hospital as soon as possible. The

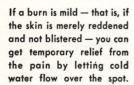

If a burn is mild — that is, if the skin is merely reddened and not blistered — you can get temporary relief from the pain by letting cold water flow over the spot.

joint is greatly enlarged and is sometimes discolored; if it is moved, there is pain. The symptoms are similar to those of fractures and are often mistaken for them. Sprains should be treated like fractures until they are properly identified. The joint should be kept as still as possible.

Strains

Strains occur when the muscles are overstretched. Although a strain is uncomfortable, it is not usually serious. Application of heat to the injury and bed rest will generally be sufficient. There are usually no obvious signs of a strain; there is only soreness and discomfort when the muscle area is touched or when movement is attempted.

BURNS AND COLD INJURIES

Thermal burns (burns due to heat)

When the skin comes in contact with heat, the skin reddens, becomes blistered

symptoms of a thermal burn are intense pain, nausea and fear.

The most essential job for the first aider is to reduce pain and the possibility of infection. You should cover the burned part as quickly as possible with layers of clean, dry, lint-free material to exclude air (the chief cause of the pain associated with burns) and to protect the burned area from contamination. If there are blisters, wrap the part so that you do not break them. If a part such as a finger, an arm or a leg is merely reddened, quick relief can be given by letting cold running water cover the burned area. This treatment gives momentary relief from pain because the water keeps air away from the burn. Do not apply ointments, salves, butter or lard to the burned area. Such coverings may not only be absorbed into the subcutaneous tissues (those under the skin) but they also invariably interfere with the physician's examination of the burn and with his choice of treatment.

Sunburn

Sunburn is caused by exposure to ultraviolet rays. The small blood vessels in the skin dilate and the skin becomes red. Prolonged exposure to the rays of the sun may even cause blisters to appear.

Commercial preparations are available to protect the skin from the effects of ultraviolet rays. Some are highly effective but many cause allergic reactions. The best first-aid practice is to prevent overexposure to the sun's rays. The first sunbathing periods of the season should be short and the length of exposure only gradually increased.

Heat exhaustion

Anyone working under conditions that cause a great amount of perspiration and loss of body fluids and certain minerals can suffer heat exhaustion. It is more prevalent in hot weather and among old people, fat people and those who suffer from systemic diseases (affecting the body as a whole). The signs of heat exhaustion are profuse perspiration, pale damp skin, a nearly normal body temperature and, rarely, unconsciousness. The person will complain of unusual fatigue and, sometimes, of headache and nausea. He should be put to bed at once.

In order to prevent heat exhaustion, persons working for long periods in poorly ventilated areas should increase their intake of water. Taking extra salt occasionally may be helpful. A well-balanced diet also helps prevent heat exhaustion.

Heatstroke

Elderly people are more prone than others to develop heatstroke, a condition caused by overexposure to the sun. The body temperature may rise as high as 109° F.; and the patient will have a dry skin and rapid pulse. He may complain of headache, dizziness and nausea; in severe cases he may become unconscious. Medical attention should be given as soon as possible. While waiting for the physician or ambulance, bring the patient indoors, put him to bed and sponge his body freely with alcohol or lukewarm water to reduce his temperature. If a thermometer is not at hand, take his pulse. A rate below 110 per minute usually means an endurable temperature.

Chemical burns

Certain chemicals cause severe irritation or burns when they come in contact with the skin and eyes. Among the irritating substances in common use are acids, alkalies, turpentine, cleansing agents, lime and cement, petroleum products and some asphalt preparations. Immediate action should be taken to wash the affected area with large amounts of clean running water until medical assistance can be obtained. Putting salve, ointment or other medication on the skin or in the eye is not recommended as a first-aid method, because it will obstruct the physician's view of the damaged area. Besides, the presence of medication will make the physician's cleansing of the part more painful than it would otherwise be.

Cold injuries

Heat affects the skin surface and so does cold. Parts of the body that are the furthest from the heart — that is, the nose, ears, fingers and toes — are most frequently affected by what is known as frostbite. It was formerly believed best to warm frostbitten and frozen parts slowly. We know now, however, that the parts should be warmed quickly as long as they do not come in direct contact with heat.

The victim himself is usually not aware of the onset of frostbite. Hence, whenever people are out in the cold together, they should notice the color of one another's ears and noses. If any of these parts have become grayish white, warming should start as soon as possible, if only with warm scarves and clothing. The frostbitten part should be immersed frequently at short intervals in warm water — if it is available — not exceeding 90° F. to 100° F. If the victim's entire body is affected, bring him into a warm room and wrap him in warm blankets. Give artificial respiration if he has stopped breathing. If water is available, immerse him in a tub of warm (78

degrees F. to 82 degrees F.) water; then dry his body thoroughly. When he revives, give him a hot drink.

COMMON EMERGENCIES

Heart attack

About 10,000,000 people in the United States alone have heart disease of some kind. A great many of them are well acquainted with their condition and can tell the first aider what to do in the event of a heart attack. However, because there are large numbers of people whose first experience with a heart attack is sudden, the ability of the first aider to handle the situation well is important.

There are many kinds of heart attack, but the two most common are congestive heart failure and coronary thrombosis. In heart failure, the signs are shortness of breath, occasional bluish color of the lips and fingernails, and swelling of the ankles. The symptoms are chest pain and extreme fright. In coronary thrombosis, the signs are quite often negligible. Since the symptoms are indigestion and nausea, the illness is often mistaken by friends and first aiders for simple indigestion and upset stomach.

In all cases where heart attack is suspected, you should first reassure the victim with encouraging words. Then allow him to select the position he finds most comfortable. He may either lie on his back or be propped up at any comfortable angle that gives some relief. Except for these two services, the first aider's main responsibility is to see that the victim gets medical attention. If he is taken to the hospital by ambulance or other vehicle, the driver should be instructed to drive slowly.

If you find an epileptic having a seizure, put something between his teeth to prevent him from biting his tongue.

Apoplexy

Apoplexy, or stroke, is usually brought about by a blood clot or hemorrhage involving a blood vessel in the brain. People who suffer from high blood pressure are most often victims of apoplexy. The signs of this condition are paralysis on one side of the body, lack of muscle tension and heavy, audible breathing (snoring). The victim is nearly always unconscious. Stroke, like all cases involving heart action, calls for prompt medical attention. While awaiting the arrival of the physician, keep the victim as quiet as possible and lying down, face up or face down. If mucus tends to collect in the mouth, put him slightly on his side and turn his head completely to the side to drain the fluids.

Simple fainting

Simple fainting is a nervous-system reaction that causes temporary lack of sufficient blood supply to the brain and brings about unconsciousness. It can be caused by injury, by the sight of injury or by lack of sufficient concentration of oxygen in a room.

Fainting does not occur if the brain is receiving an adequate supply of oxygenated blood (blood that has received a fresh oxygen supply from the lungs). Therefore, recovery follows when the victim gets his head lower than his heart by bending over or lying down. From time to time many kinds of medication have been recommended. It does not really help, however, to give aromatic spirits of ammonia and the like or to hold smelling salts under the victim's nose.

If recovery of consciousness is not prompt, medical attention is needed because the underlying cause of the unconsciousness is a matter of great concern.

Epileptic seizures

Until recent years, epilepsy was not well understood. Its cause was not known, and there was very little relief for its victims. Although more effective medical treatment is available today, untreated patients and occasionally even some of those

under care are subject to periods of unconsciousness. These episodes may last for only a moment or for a long time. They may be accompanied by convulsions involving the entire body. Epileptics who recognize the symptoms that precede an attack usually seek a quiet place and lie down with something between their teeth to prevent injury to the tongue.

If you find a person having an epileptic seizure, do not try to restrict his convulsive motions. Try to keep him from injuring himself and, if possible, gently place something — a book cover or a spoon handle wrapped with clean cloth — between his teeth. When the convulsive motions have ceased, loosen the clothing about his neck and allow him to lie flat with his head turned to one side. He may have vomited during his seizure, and any stomach contents remaining in his mouth are not so likely to be drawn into his lungs if his head is kept in a sideways position. Let him rest undisturbed during the deep sleep that follows a seizure.

Unconsciousness — cause unknown

Unconsciousness is associated with many injuries and illnesses. When its cause is unknown, a first aider can distinguish only between those cases which require artificial respiration and those where breathing is adequate. The accident scene nearly always provides a good clue to the cause of unconsciousness. If it does not, the first aider, in the presence of reliable witnesses, should search the victim for a written statement concerning specific diseases that may be the cause, such as diabetes, heart disease or others.

If breathing is not adequate, start artificial respiration immediately and have someone notify a physician or police officer.

Injuries to the eye

Injuries to the eye include damage to the soft tissue around the eye, scratching of the eye surface and puncturing of the eyeball. No matter what the injury to the eye may be, first-aid care should be held to a minimum. If the soft tissue about the eye is damaged, first give normal first-aid

care for wounds. Then place a fairly tight bandage over the eye and the affected area. When the eye itself is involved, cover it with moist cotton held in place with a bandage until medical assistance can be obtained.

Occasionally small foreign bodies become lodged on the inner surface of the upper lid. You can remove these by pulling the upper lid outward and downward over the lower lid so that the small object will be picked up on the outer surface of the lower lid.

Foreign body in the throat or air passage

If a foreign body lodges in the throat or air passage, violent choking and spasm will likely occur. These reactions alone often eliminate the object, but in other cases it must be removed by the instrument called the bronchoscope or by an operation.

First, let the victim try to cough up the object. Do not probe with your fingers down his throat because you may force the object deeper. If the person's breathing stops, give him artificial respiration and have someone get medical assistance quickly.

Foreign body in the alimentary canal

Most foreign objects that have been swallowed pass harmlessly along the digestive tract and are excreted. However, some objects require extraction either by special instruments or by an operation. Medical care, therefore, should be gotten as soon as possible. Try to remain calm so that you do not excite the victim. Do not give him a cathartic or, in general, any food. If the victim is an infant or small child and feeding is necessary, do not give him cereal or other bulky foods.

BANDAGES, DRESSINGS AND TRANSPORTATION

A dressing is a sterile or clean piece of cloth that is placed directly over a wound. A bandage is a piece of cloth or other material used to hold a dressing in place. Bandage compresses combine the benefits of both in that a large gauze pad

is attached to strips of cloth which may be used to encircle the part in opposite directions. A sterile compress of this type can be applied as snugly or as loosely as you wish. You should be careful in bandaging injuries not to make the bandage too tight and thus interfere with the circulation of the blood in the part.

First aiders do not have to acquire intricate bandaging skills. It is sufficient for them to know how to cover a dressing so that it will stay in place until medical aid can be reached. They should know how to do a circular turn, how to anchor the bandage and how to tie it off when completed.

If the body surface to be covered is tapered, as a forearm, a closed spiral turn is used. If the part tapers sharply, the turn will have to be an open spiral. In this type of bandaging, gaps will appear, but as long as the bandage holds the dressing in place it is satisfactory. If the body part to be covered is angular, a figure-of-eight turn — two loops crossing each other in opposite directions — should be used. Knees, elbows, shoulders, and the like can best be covered by this type of turn. If an ovoid surface — fingers, toes, or head — must be covered, a recurrent turn is first used: that is, the bandage goes back and forth over the ovoid surface and is then held in place by a circular turn. We show these different types of bandages in the drawings on this page and on the following one.

Unless first aiders are careful, they may cause more harm by moving accident victims than by leaving them where they are. If you must move the victim, you should prevent the injured parts of his body from twisting or bending.

LEARNING FIRST-AID SKILLS

Although you may be able to help in an emergency by studying suggestions and diagrams, it is best to learn first-aid skills under a competent instructor, so that you will be able to provide help when needed — a responsibility of citizenship.

If you would like to learn more about first aid, we suggest that you consult the AMERICAN RED CROSS FIRST AID TEXT-BOOK, published by Doubleday, Garden City, New York, fourth edition, 1957.

SPIRAL TURNS

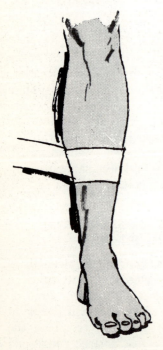

A. Anchoring the bandage.

B. The closed spiral turn.

C. The open spiral turn.

FIGURE-OF-EIGHT TURNS

This bandage consists of two spiral loops, one up and one down and crossing each other.

A. First, anchor the bandage.

B. Then cover the injured area.

C. Complete figure-of-eight turn.

D. Tie the finished bandage.

RECURRENT TURNS

These bandages wind back and forth over a part and are held in place by circular turns.

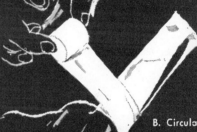

A. Start of recurrent turn.

B. Circular turn holds it.

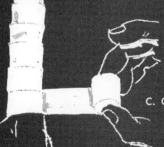

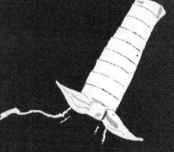

C. Circular turn continued.

D. Finished bandage tied off.

THE CIRCULAR TURN

This bandage simply encircles the part; each layer of bandage is put on top of the last.

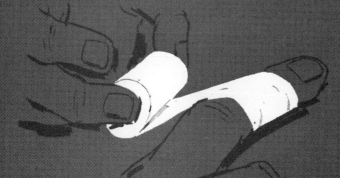

17

The Matterhorn (14,780 feet), in the Pennine Alps, is on the Swiss-Italian border, near Zermatt.

MOUNTAIN STOREHOUSES

Ranges and Peaks That Hold
Water Reserves for Mankind

MEN at all times and in all lands have looked up to mountains with great reverence and awe, and even superstition. The gods of Greece were said to live on Mount Olympus; the Muses dwelt on Parnassus, far to the south. On Mount Meru sat the gods of ancient India.

Even in our modern, matter-of-fact times, mountains have power to arouse sublime emotions. Thousands of people go each year to the Rockies of Canada or the United States, to the Alps and other ranges, not only to enjoy the revivifying air of the heights but also to gain spiritual refreshment.

Some of the noblest passages in literature and some of the great works of art have been inspired by mountains. The Psalms, for example, abound in references to hills and mountains; the most famous, perhaps, is "I will lift up mine eyes unto the hills, from whence cometh my help."

It would almost seem as if the mountain locale affected the character of the people living there, for mountaineers are notably brave, vigorous and independent. Probably, however, the highland character is the result of struggle with an adverse environment.

Difficulties and dangers attract the combative spirit of man, and so mountain climbing appeals to many a stout heart. One by one the world's lofty peaks are being scaled. The grandest of all, Everest, was attained in 1953, after a number of unsuccessful attempts.

The mountains serve us in countless ways. Observatories are often built on them, among other reasons so that the heavens may be studied with less atmosphere to distort the picture. (The air, of course, is more rarefied the higher one goes.) Weather stations on heights have proved valuable; so have stations for the study of cosmic rays.

The pure mountain air is appreciated in certain types of illness, and so we find sanatoria there. In olden times peaks were good signaling stations. Beacon fires and smoke signals at night, sun flashes in the daytime, warned of approaching danger and carried other messages in wartime and in peace.

Mountains can be unfriendly, too, to mankind. A sudden avalanche of snow can bury a town; a volcano can spurt hot ashes and volcanic mud upon a community.

The mountains are not all of the same age. Mountain building has gone on for more than a billion years. Great ranges have been thrust above the surface of the land and above the sea floor, only to be worn down slowly by the wind, the water, glaciers and other forces. Geologists have determined, from study of radioactive minerals, that there were at least seven great periods of mountain building over the world in Pre-Cambrian times, but not one of these archaic peaks remains. As old mountains wear away, new ones appear. In our own century we have seen volcanic mountains form in a matter of months, as in Mexico, where Parícutin piled up, day by day, in a farmer's field.

But what, in the first place, is a mountain? At what height does a mound become a mount? This is a question that each land must answer for itself, for no standards exist. A small hill in a flat country, rising abruptly from the plain, may seem a veritable mountain to the dwellers on the plain.

Philip Gendreau

Mount Monadnock, in New Hampshire. It has given its name to the type of hill called a monadnock.

Thus, as Reclus points out, a hill only 780 feet high which rises from the level plains of Lower Pomerania impresses the inhabitants so much that they have named it the Mountain of Hell, while a smaller hill in Denmark but 557 feet high is named by the cheerier Danes the Mountain of Heaven. In a general way, however, to deserve the name, mountains must be some thousands of feet in height.

As a rule, the higher mountains of the world are congregated into groups, and are arranged linearly in ranges and chains. Thus we have the Rockies, the Pacific ranges, the Alps, the Apennines, the Andes, the Himalayas. But, in some instances, a high mountain stands in splendid isolation, like Roraima (8,740 feet) in Venezuela, and, 50 miles away, Mount Kukenaam (over 8,500 feet). These isolated hills are

The Mountain of Heaven, the highest elevation in Denmark, is really a hill, only 557 feet in height.

colossal earth pillars which resisted the river waters that cut down the surrounding country. They are called monadnocks, after the New Hampshire mountain of that name. Other isolated mountains, such as Vesuvius, Fujiyama and Stromboli, are of volcanic origin. Solitary peaks such as these are the exception; most peaks are combined in immense groups.

Though most of the valleys run in the same direction as the mountains, there are numerous passes and transverse valleys that interrupt the linear continuity of the ranges. There are many hundreds of distinct valleys in the Alps. There are five hundred in the canton of Grisons alone; they form a regular labyrinth.

The mountain range of the Pyrenees runs between France and Spain, forming a great barrier between the two countries. From a double rampart of mountains running east and west, transverse mountain chains running north and south are given off. These chains give off secondary chains, which are parallel to the principal ramparts.

Most of the peaks of the Pyrenees are sharp and pointed. Their average height is about 8,000 feet, which is something like 300 feet more than the average height of the Alpine peaks. The Pyrenees are much less picturesque than the Alps, however, because none of the peaks in the range are particularly outstanding. The tallest one, the Pico de Aneto, which rises to a height of 11,168 feet, is surpassed by a number of peaks in the Alpine system.

The Alps form a much more labyrinthine system of mountains than the Pyrenees. Though the general trend of the range is east and west, it has numerous branches which run in different directions. The Alps are commonly divided into many more or less distinct systems, each with characteristics of its own.

The central mass is the St. Gotthard group, from which the principal chains radiate. The most magnificent group, perhaps, is the mighty Monte Rosa rampart, whose peaks exceed 13,000 feet, the highest being the Dufourspitze (15,200 feet). Mont Blanc, 15,777 feet in height, is the loftiest peak of the Alps; but the average height of the mountains of its group is only about 12,600 feet. Other striking Alpine peaks are the Dom (14,909 feet), the Weisshorn (14,778 feet), the Matterhorn (14,686 feet), the Finsteraarhorn (14,032 feet) and the Jungfrau (13,639 feet).

National Film Board

Mount Rundle, in Canada's Banff National Park, towers above beautiful Lake Vermillion.

The Himalaya range is the southernmost of a triple rampart of mountain ranges running east and west across Asia, to the north of India. The most northerly of these ranges is the Kunlun, or Kuenlun, Shan; the middle range is the Karakoram. This threefold rampart extends for a distance of 2,000 miles and its breadth in certain places is over 600 miles. The height of the rampart is truly breath-taking. The peaks of the Karakoram have the greatest mean height; next come those of the Himalaya and, lastly, those of the Kunlun. In the Himalaya range

loftiest peak in the Andes, is quite outtopped.

From this gigantic triple rampart flow the Indus and the Brahmaputra. Between the Himalaya and the Kunlun is the plateau of Tibet, which is some 13,000 feet above sea level; it measures 2,000 miles from east to west and 1,700 miles from north to south. Though the peaks of the Himalaya are grander than those of Switzerland, the scenery is not so picturesque and varied. "In all its grandeur, the Himalaya is uniform, its peaks are loftier, its snows more extensive, its forests deeper, but there are fewer cas-

Screen Traveler, from Gendreau

The Route of the Pyrenees, winding high above sea level amid tall peaks, connects Spain and France.

there are a great many peaks that are higher than Mont Blanc; Mount Everest (29,028 feet) is almost twice the height of that king of European mountains. Mount Everest, of course, is the highest known mountain in the world. But Mount Godwin Austen (28,-250 feet), in the Karakoram, and Kanchenjunga (28,146 feet), in the Himalaya, are not very far behind; while Mount Dhaulagiri (26,795 feet), in the Himalaya, is a quite worthy rival. No other peaks in any other ranges can compete with giants like these; even Aconcagua (22,835 feet), the

cades and lakes; there are no pleasant lawns and scattered groves, and we fail to note the picturesque chalets nestling down in the glens, or hanging over the brims of the precipices." Because of the height of these mountains and because they are situated in a land with a warm climate, every climate is represented as we ascend them. First, we have a tropical climate with tropical fauna and flora; then a temperate one, with corresponding animal and plant life; finally, there is a forbidding arctic climate, with perpetual snows decking the mountains.

Though Mount Kenya, shown above, is only eight miles from the equator, it is snow-capped.

Since the Himalayan range runs roughly east and west, it constitutes an immense natural barrier between the regions to the north and those that lie to the south. Winds are constantly intercepted by this barrier; as a result, the climates of the areas lying on either side of the mountains are profoundly modified.

The Rocky Mountains form the principal mountain system of North America. They extend from Alaska to Mexico; in the east they generally rise abruptly from the plains, while in the west they are bounded by high plateaus and by various mountain ranges. The loftiest mountain of the Rockies — Mount Elbert, in Colorado — is 14,431 feet in height; a number of other peaks in Colorado are more than 14,000 feet high. The Rockies form the Continental Divide; they separate Pacific drainage from Atlantic and arctic drainage.

South of the Rockies lies Mexico's Sierra Madre. This mountain system is divided into three main branches — eastern, western and southern; they enclose the great central plateau of Mexico. The Sierra Madre boasts two lofty volcanic peaks — Orizaba, or Citlaltepetl (18,700 feet), and Popocatepetl (17,887 feet). A subrange of the Mexican mountain system extends into Guatemala. South of this subrange is the main cordillera of Central America, which connects with the Andes near the Panama-Colombia boundary.

The Sierra Nevada, to the west of the Rockies, lies mainly in eastern California. It extends more than 400 miles from Tehachapi Pass (about 40 miles from Bakersfield) to the gap south of Lassen Peak. It contains the loftiest mountain in the United States (not including Alaska) — Mount Whitney, towering to the height of 14,495 feet. North of the Sierra Nevada is the Cascade Range, which extends more than 700 miles north from Lassen Peak through California, Oregon, Washington and British Columbia. The Cascade Range is continued by the Coast Mountains, which are not to be confused with the Coast Ranges. The Alaska Range, which represents the continuation of the Coast Mountains, contains the highest peak in the North American continent — Mount McKinley (20,270 feet).

Half Dome, on the Alice Lake side of the rugged Sawtooth Mountains, which lie in the central portion of Idaho.

The Coast Ranges are a rambling mountain belt extending along the Pacific coast south from Alaska through British Columbia, Washington, Oregon and California and into Lower California. The section of the Coast Ranges lying in southeastern Alaska and southwestern Yukon — it is called the St. Elias Mountains — contains the lofty peaks Mount Logan (19,850 feet) and Mount St. Elias (18,008 feet).

The Appalachian Mountains form the principal mountain system in the eastern part of the United States; they run more than 1,600 miles from Alabama through New York and New England to the Canadian province of Quebec. The Appalachians include the Alleghenies, the Blue Ridge Mountains, the Cumberland Mountains, the Black, Green and White Mountains and the Catskills. This system is quite narrow; at no point is it more than 100 miles wide. There are no great elevations; the highest mountain is Mount Mitchell (6,684 feet), in North Carolina.

South America has the longest mountain system in the world — the Andes Mountains. They extend along the western coast of the continent for a distance of some 4,500 miles from Panama to Cape Horn. In the north, the Andes consist of three ranges. One of these runs along the western coast from Panama through Colombia; another runs southwest from Venezuela; the third lies between these two.

The central Andes
consist of two ranges

The central Andes are made up of two ranges that enclose a great plateau, partly in Peruvian and partly in Bolivian territory — a tableland that lies something like 12,000 feet above the level of the sea. Among the highest peaks of the central Andes are Illampu (21,490 feet), Sajama (21,390 feet), Illimani (21,185 feet) and Chimborazo (20,577 feet).

Farther south, the Andes form three parallel ranges at first; these three then merge into a single range. The tallest mountain in this section of the Andes is Aconcagua, in eastern Argentina. Rising to a height of 22,835 feet, it is the loftiest peak in the New World.

The Atlas Mountains, the
longest African mountain system

Africa has no mountain chain that can compare with the Andes. The longest range — the Atlas Mountains — lies in the north of the continent. These mountains extend about 1,500 miles across Morocco, northern Algeria and Tunisia, more or less parallel to the Mediterranean Sea. The Atlas Mountains, which form an imposing barrier between the Sahara and the Mediterranean, are a rugged group; they are made up of a veritable maze of high peaks and plateaus. They are divided into a number of branches, including the High, or Great, Atlas, the Middle Atlas, the Anti-Atlas, the Tell Atlas and the Saharan Atlas. The highest peak of the range is the Djebel Toubkal (13,665 feet), in Morocco.

The Ethiopian highlands, in eastern Africa, are divided into a northwest section and a southeast section by the Great Rift Valley, a deep and steeply walled depres-

The Stelvio Road zigzagging down a precipitous alpine slope on the Austrian side.

A mountain landscape in Kashmir — Liddar Valley, a cool spot not far from Srinagar.

sion in the earth's crust, extending south-west from the Red Sea. The loftiest point in the Ethiopian highlands is the peak known as Ras Dashan (15,158 feet). The highest peaks of Africa, found farther south on the east African Plateau, are Mount Kilimanjaro (19,565 feet) and Mount Kenya (17,040 feet).

The range of the Drakensberg, which lies mainly in the Union of South Africa, extends about 700 miles in a southwesterly direction from the Transvaal to the southern part of Cape Province. It forms the southeastern border of Basutoland and the western border of Swaziland. The Drakensberg is an important watershed; it is the source of the Orange River, flowing into the Atlantic, and the Tugela River, which empties into the Indian Ocean. The highest peak of the range is Thabantshonyana (11,425 feet), in Basutoland.

Such, then, are the great mountain chains of the world. They play an important part in insuring a constant water supply. Perhaps their most vital function is to condense the water vapor that results from evaporation and thus to bring about rainfall and other forms of precipitation.

Precipitation would be far more evenly distributed in the various regions of the world if there were no mountains. There would be less rain and snow in the areas where mountains now exist; there would be more in wastelands that are now arid. The state of Washington would no longer boast the highest annual precipitation in the United States — 146 inches — at a point on the seaward slope of the Cascade Range, and the lowest annual precipitation — less than 6 inches — at another point to the east of that range. If all the mountains were leveled, the water falling upon the earth in the form of precipitation would not be adequately drained off because of the lack of declivity; a considerable proportion of the earth's surface would be transformed into marsh land.

When mountains concentrate rainfall in downhill currents, as torrents, rivulets and streams, they add enormously to its effective mechanical power. Rain falling from the heavens could not be used as

a power source; but concentrated in appropriate channels, it can turn the turbines of a mighty hydroelectric development and thus provide the power that will light a city or run a factory.

Mountains bring about precipitation in two ways. The water vapor contained in a warm, moist wind is condensed as it blows against a cold mountain summit. Again, a wind blowing against the base of a mountain is deflected upward into the rarer atmosphere. There it expands; since expansion brings about cooling, the air is cooled and ultimately deposits its load of moisture as precipitation. The tremendous rainfall at Cherrapunji, India, is due to a combination of these two factors. It results not only from the contact of the warm, moist monsoon with the icy Himalayan crests but also from the fact that the monsoon is forced upward by the Khasi Hills, to the south of the Himalayas.

Mountains do more than cause the water vapor in the air to condense, thereby contributing to the water supply used for drinking purposes, agriculture, industrial operations and the generation of electricity. They also hoard up water for mankind.

The snow-laden summits of the Alps, the Himalayas and the Andes represent an enormous reserve, which is made available for widespread areas of the earth's surface.

The Po, the Rhone, the Rhine and the Danube would be mere brooks in summer if it were not for the Alps. "But for those barren fields of ice," wrote the English geologist Thomas George Bonney, "high up among the silent crags [of the Alps], the seeming home of winter and death, these great arteries of life would every summer dwindle down to paltry streams, feebly meandering over stone-strewn beds. Stand, for example, on some mountain spur and look down on the Lombardy plain, all one rich carpet of wheat and maize, of rice and vine; the life of these myriad threads of green and gold is fed from these icy peaks, which stand out against the northern sky in such strange and solemn contrast. As it is with the Po, so is it with the Rhine and the Rhone, both of which issue from the Alps as broad, swelling streams; so, too, with the Danube, which, although it does not rise in the Alps, receives from the Inn and Drave almost all the drainage of the eastern [areas]."

Beautiful Inca Lake, in the Andes Mountains, is surrounded by towering, snow-clad peaks.

Mountains, therefore, provide vast reserves of water for the use of living things. They also serve as a bountiful source of soil for low-lying areas. As water courses down the mountainside in swiftly flowing streams, it erodes the rock formations over which and past which it flows. The impact of the water loosens and dislodges a great many fragments, ranging from boulders to small particles, of weak rock or rock mantle. As these fragments are transported downstream, they serve as a sort of gouging tool, carving out the beds and sides of the stream that transports them. The flowing water also dislodges rock fragments by dissolving soluble materials in limestone or similar formations.

The fragments that have been broken off from the mountainside, together with animal and plant debris and many kinds of organic substances, are carried along by rivers for considerable distances, sometimes for hundreds of miles. As the velocity of the stream decreases, it deposits its load at various places along its course, particularly toward its mouth.

Mountains play an important part in the circulation of air. After nightfall their crests are cooled more rapidly than the lower-lying land; the cold, dense air that is formed has a tendency to flow downhill under the influence of gravity. The cool air borne by the gravity wind, as it is called, collects in various pockets of valley bottoms. That is why valleys are apt to be cooler in the morning than mountainsides, when these are warmed by the sun. During the day, the heating of the floor and slopes of a valley brings about an expansion of the air and a movement of warm air up the valley and often up the mountainside. A strong valley breeze — one blowing upward from a valley — may develop. Toward the middle of the afternoon, the breeze may reach a velocity of as much as twenty miles an hour. Updrafts of this kind are particularly likely to occur over rocky slopes that have sparse vegetation or that are entirely lacking in vegetation.

When a warm wind blows strongly across a mountain range, frictional drag may cause it to be deflected downward as it reaches the lee side of the range. By the time it has reached the valleys and plains beyond the range, it has become a gusty wind, as dry as it is warm. This is known as a foehn. The one that develops east of the North American continental divide may be so warm that it will melt up to two feet of snow in one day. That is why the foehn in this area is known as a chinook — the Indian word for "snow-eater."

H. Armstrong Roberts

Irrigating California's Imperial Valley. The Colorado River, whose tributaries rise in the mountains of Wyoming, Colorado and Utah, provides the water for this vast irrigating project.

Bridalveil Falls, Yosemite National Park, California. Water, dropping 1,000 feet, has long eroded the slope underneath and deposited rock fragments and debris in the valley.

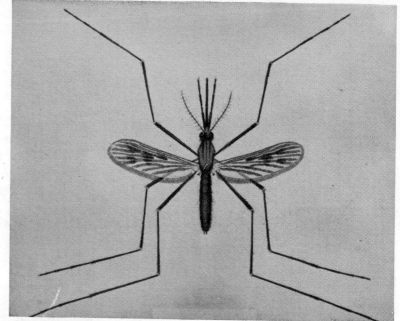

This mosquito, called *Anopheles quadrimaculatus,* is the principal vector, or transmitter, of malaria in the United States.

Below we see a skilled laboratory worker carefully examining the salivary gland of a mosquito under a powerful microscope.

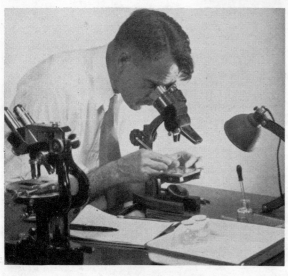

MAN'S WAR AGAINST
AN INSECT FOE

Photos, U. S. Public Health Service

This plane is spraying kerosene over marshes where the malaria-transmitting anopheles mosquito flourishes.

MAN AND THE MOSQUITO

The War against Malaria and Yellow Fever

THE fight against malaria makes one of the most thrilling tales in human history. It has all the elements of suspense, mystery, danger and heroism, disappointment, and, finally, it has a bright and hopeful ending. Not that we have reached the end; malaria is not yet wiped off the face of the earth. But there are now vast areas where the disease, once rampant, is virtually extinct, and new areas of safety are being added, year by year.

Malaria is one of the oldest of the plagues that have beset mankind. Some authorities believe that it was malaria that caused the slow decay of Greek civilization. This could well be true, indeed, for malaria is a disease that attacks and destroys the red cells of the blood, thus causing, of course, anemia, and a nation of anemic people can scarcely hope to prolong a Golden Age. In Italy, malaria was endemic until a few years ago. (An endemic disease is one that occurs constantly in a certain region.)

Today malaria is endemic in India and other parts of southern Asia and in the Pacific Islands, in warm, humid areas of Africa and in tropical South America. Before World War II it was said that one-third of the earth's population was afflicted with the malady. During the war synthetic drugs were produced to supplement the supply of the one specific that had previously been known, quinine. Since the war, drugs many times as powerful as quinine have been developed. These, together with war against mosquitoes, give promise of bringing malaria completely under control. There is no longer any excuse for the existence of this pest.

Although malaria is infectious, one human cannot pass the infection directly to another in the way tuberculosis or diphtheria can be transmitted. The agent travels a two-way street — from man to a mosquito, then back to another man. Louis Pasteur smoothed the way to the scientific discovery of this strange life cycle. (The mosquito's role as carrier had been guessed earlier.) In the eighties of the nineteenth century, Pasteur established in Paris the institute that bears his name, for the study of parasitic diseases. Students flocked to the Pasteur Institute from all over the civilized world. Among them was a French Army surgeon, Alphonse Laveran, who was especially interested in malaria. He had good reason to be interested, for malaria was causing havoc with the health of French colonial soldiers stationed in tropical Africa.

Laveran found that a certain parasite was invariably associated with malarial attacks. He discovered, too, that the parasite contained a pigment known to be present in the livers of malarious individuals. In 1880, largely on the basis of these two observations, Laveran published a famous work called PALUDISM, in which he advanced a new theory concerning the cause of malaria. Paludism is a technical term meaning "malarial disease," and is from the Latin *palus:* "marsh." The name was applied to the disease because it seemed to be associated with marshes or swamps. It was believed that in such places a mysterious kind of air, or vapor, caused malarial attacks. In fact, the word "malaria" comes from the Italian *mal'aria,* or "bad air."

Laveran argued that the disease was caused by a parasite which lived in the blood of the patient, destroying red blood cells and liberating poisonous substances

into his blood stream. In 1886, Camillo Golgi, an Italian physician, published a paper in which he pointed out that the course of the disease followed the life cycle of the parasites in the human blood stream. The fever reached its peak when the organisms broke out of the red blood cells in which they developed. This liberated toxins (poisons), which caused the chills and fevers of malaria. The poisons gradually lost their potency until the next crop of parasites in the cells made their escape, releasing a fresh supply of toxins.

How did the malaria-causing parasite enter the human body? For years, it had been suspected that the mosquito transmitted it. As early as 1853, the Frenchman Beauperthuy suggested that both malaria and yellow fever were carried by mosquitoes to man and that neither disease could be transmitted directly from one human to another. Beauperthuy's analysis, which was amazingly accurate, was not based on experiment and was not taken seriously.

In 1884, Patrick Manson, a well-known English doctor, also expressed the belief that the mosquito was the vector, or transmitter, of malaria. Manson was particularly noted for his study of filariasis, a tropical disease caused by a very small worm. He suspected that the worm might be transferred to man by something that could pierce the skin and inject the worm directly into the body. After a prolonged investigation, he found that this was indeed the case. Mosquitoes infected man with the disease by injecting the disease-producing organisms into his body. If a person were protected from mosquitoes, he could not possibly contract filariasis.

Manson believed that the mosquito was also responsible for malarial infection, but he had no idea how this condition was brought about. He thought that perhaps dead mosquitoes contaminated water supplies with malaria parasites. At his suggestion, another English physician, Ronald (later Sir Ronald) Ross began a series of researches that greatly clarified the situation. He set off for India with the idea of learning how the mosquito transmitted malaria — that is, if it really did.

This is a model of a malarial mosquito, belonging to the genus *Anopheles*. It carries the protozoan parasites (genus *Plasmodium*) that cause malaria. A person may be infected with the disease when he is bitten by a mosquito carrier of this type.

Amer. Mus. of Nat. Hist.

His experiments were carried on under trying conditions. For one thing, the British government was continually sending him off to doctor sick Indians in regions where there were no mosquitoes. Then too, though a man of great energy and enthusiasm, Ross was not the most systematic of workers. He had trouble duplicating his results; besides, he was not too sure about which of the many types of mosquitoes he should study. His work, in many respects, was that of the talented amateur rather than the rigorous, systematic professional.

Manson, back in England, kept up a steady correspondence with Ross to encourage him, but offered little guidance. He did suggest, however, that Ross work with birds, since they too can contract malaria.

When Ross finally turned his attention to birds, it was as a last resort. About all that he had managed to learn was that mosquitoes that had fed on victims of malaria harbored microscopic organisms that might represent one stage of the parasite's development. He had learned little else about the relationship between mosquito and parasite. In fact, he had so much difficulty in confirming whatever results he

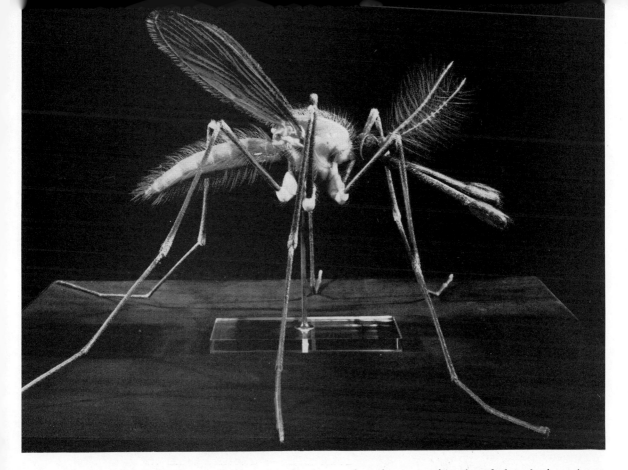

achieved that he was no longer certain that the parasite, in whatever stage of development, actually occurred in mosquitoes.

Ross was not very optimistic about obtaining results when he began to work with birds. However, probably to his great surprise, his researches soon bore fruit. He observed the malaria parasite in mosquitoes that had bitten malarious birds, and then he set up a classically simple experiment. He exposed three birds — one free of malaria, one slightly infected and one very badly infected — to a swarm of mosquitoes. The insects biting the healthy birds showed no malaria organisms after dissection; those biting the slightly infected birds had only a few parasites. But there was a horde of parasites in the stomachs of the mosquitoes that had attacked the sick birds. Through systematic dissections, Ross traced the path of the malaria parasite until he learned how it traveled to its new host. Though he had not shown how malaria is transmitted to *man,* Ross had laid the foundation for our present knowledge of the malaria parasite.

Not long after, an Italian bacteriologist, Giovanni Battista Grassi, showed that the mosquito *Anopheles claviger* (now called *Anopheles maculipennis*) was responsible for malaria in Italy. He did so by traveling all over Italy, observing where malaria occurred and determining the type of mosquito that was to be found in that area. He established that wherever *Anopheles claviger* appeared, malaria was a serious problem. He also proved that this mosquito, popularly known as the zanzarone, had to bite a malarious person in order to be able to transmit the disease. If the offspring of malaria-carrying mosquitoes were raised in the laboratory, where they could not bite persons suffering from malaria, they were harmless.

Grassi obtained a grant from the Italian government to carry out his work in the plain of Carpaccio, where malaria was rampant. He screened the houses of a selected group of railroad workers, kept them indoors at night and found that no new cases of malaria developed among them. In nearby unprotected areas, nearly everyone came down with the disease. Thus he proved conclusively that the mosquito was the carrier of malaria. Grassi's experiments were simple and he succeeded more by

hard work than by brilliant research, but he did establish his point beyond any doubt.

The story of malarial infection was not yet complete. In 1897, W. G. MacCallum discovered that the organisms Ross had seen in the mosquito were male and that they fertilized the female parasites in the mosquito's stomach. He realized that the parasite had both a sexual and asexual phase. In the mosquito, male and female parasitic cells combined to form new individuals. In the human host, only asexual reproduction occurred, each new cell being an exact replica of its parent.

The significance of this discovery was great. It is well known that if a patient is not exposed to the source of malaria for several years, he will be freed of the symptoms of the disease. Apparently, the sexual phase is necessary to maintain the proper vigor in the parasite. Not only does the mosquito serve to transport the parasite, but it also provides a medium for part of the organism's life cycle. As a matter of fact, the parasite will become extinct after only a few years if the particular genus of mosquito to which it is adapted is not available to it.

The life cycle of the malaria parasite

The researches of Ross and MacCallum cleared up most of the mysteries surrounding the malarial parasite's life cycle. This cycle is complex, and we can give only the barest outline of it here. Spores are injected into the human body as the mosquito feeds upon a victim. Some of the spores give rise to sexual organisms, others to asexual. All these organisms, sexual and asexual alike, ultimately lodge in red blood cells. As each grows in its cell, it develops into the protozoan *Plasmodium malariae*. The protozoan soon occupies the whole cell. If it was derived from a spore giving rise to asexual forms, the protozoan splits into many spores. In time, these burst out of the blood cell and pass to new cells, where the splitting process is repeated. In other cases, the developing protozoan is a male or female organism. If a mosquito bites the human host, these organisms are

sucked into the mosquito's stomach. Here fertilization takes place. The product of fertilization, the zygote, produces numerous spores, which find their way to the salivary glands of the mosquito. When the mosquito bites a person, the spores pass into the blood stream of the human host, and the cycle is repeated.

It should be made clear that not all species of mosquitoes transmit malaria. There are about 1,500 known species of these insects. As far as we know, only the group called the anophelines can transmit malaria. Some 175 anopheline species exist; of these, approximately 70 are considered to be important vectors of malaria.

Once the malaria parasite's life cycle was known, it was possible to combat malaria much more effectively than before. A famous antimalaria campaign was undertaken by Sir Ronald Ross himself.

A famous anti-malaria campaign

In 1902, Ross received an urgent call for help from Prince Auguste d'Arenberg, president of the Suez Canal Company. The administrative seat of the company was Ismailia, located about a mile from the canal. Swarms of mosquitoes had caused such terrible malaria epidemics that the company was on the verge of abandoning the town entirely. Ross accepted the Prince's call and soon was lodged in the royal residence at Ismailia. To his surprise, few mosquito larvae * could be found anywhere near the town and yet at night huge numbers of mosquitoes appeared. Where and how did the deadly insects breed?

Ross was puzzled by this apparent paradox until he discovered that sewage was emptied into deep pits called *puits perdus* (lost wells), dug under the houses of the town. The top of each pit was covered with a piece of flagstone; a long ventilation pipe led from the pit to the roof. The mosquitoes bred in the pits, and at night swarmed up through the ventilation pipes. Since there was a *puits perdu* under

---

* It should be explained that the mosquito lays its eggs in slow-moving or stagnant water. Here the eggs develop into free-floating larvae and ultimately into adult mosquitoes after passing through an intermediate stage.

almost every house in Ismailia, the mystery of the mosquito hordes was solved.

Ross knew that, though the mosquito larva lives in water, it has to draw in air through a breathing tube extending above the surface. If the larva could be deprived of air by means of a film of oil spread over the surface of the water, it would be suffocated. Ross ordered that a cup of oil should be poured down each well once a week. The victory was complete; the mosquitoes disappeared as if by magic. Of course, it was easier to eliminate mosquitoes in a place like Ismailia, where breeding sites were so concentrated, than it would have been in open country. However, Ross's successful campaign showed what could be accomplished in the war against the mosquitoes that transmitted malaria.

At the turn of the present century, malaria was one of the most dreaded of diseases. Ross has left a dramatic description of its ravages. "Malaria," he wrote, "strikes down not only the indigenous barbaric population, but with still greater certainty the pioneers of civilization — the planter, the trader, the missionary and the soldier. It is therefore the principal ally of barbarism. No wild deserts, no savage races, no geographical difficulties, have proved so inimical to civilization as this disease. We may also say that it has withheld an entire continent from humanity — the immense and fertile tracts of Africa. What we call the Dark Continent should be called the Malarious Continent; and for centuries the successive waves of civilization which have flooded and fertilized Europe and America have broken themselves in vain upon its deadly shores."

In the twentieth century (particularly during and after World War II) vigorous efforts were made to wipe out malaria. Several methods have been employed to combat the disease. The basic technique is to interrupt the parasite's life cycle by killing its host, the mosquito. This is done through the use of insecticides and by means of oil spread upon the water where the mosquito larvae develop. Natural enemies of the mosquito can also be used. In Barbados, an island in the British West Indies, malaria is unknown despite the fact that the island abounds in pools that should be ideal for the breeding of mosquitoes. The reason is that these pools are populated by a kind of "toy minnow," whose staple food is the mosquito larva.

Dwellings can be protected by screening; individuals, by mosquito netting.

Sir Ronald Ross, British physician and bacteriologist, who was awarded the Nobel prize in medicine in 1902 for his researches in the transmission of malaria. He verified by extensive investigation the theory that mosquitoes carry the microscopic parasites causing the disease and he succeeded in tracing the life cycle of the parasites.

Brown Bros.

The photos on this page show scenes from an anti-mosquito campaign in Greece — a campaign carried on by the World Health Organization of the UN. Above: spraying marshes from the air with DDT and oil.

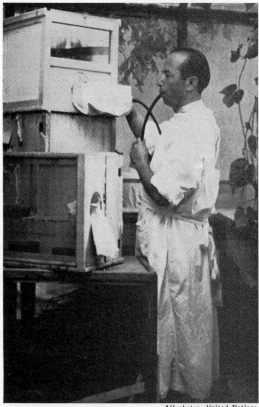

Two members of a World Health Organization team examining marsh water to see if it contains mosquito larvae.

This technician is breeding mosquitoes. The insects will be used in an extensive series of insecticide tests.

Swamps can be drained so that the mosquito is denied its breeding place. Antimalaria drugs can be used to combat the disease. Quinine has been employed for this purpose for a long time. During World War II, atabrine and totaquine were developed as quinine substitutes. These drugs serve to treat the disease and also for prevention. In the latter case, the drug is taken in small, regularly spaced doses so that there is a continual supply in the blood stream to check the development of the parasite as soon as it is introduced by the mosquito.

Since its foundation, the World Health Organization (WHO), an agency of the United Nations, has conducted world-wide antimalaria campaigns in many parts of the world. As a result, the disease has been wiped out in many areas and greatly reduced in others. Nevertheless, it still strikes many millions of people every year and much remains to be done before it is conquered. According to a recent WHO publication, it is responsible for about one million deaths a year. Besides, the weakness caused by malaria makes sufferers susceptible to the attack of other diseases.

It has been found that with repeated sprayings of insecticide, the mosquito develops resistance to the insecticide and soon cannot be controlled by it. The present theory is that the mosquito population should be subjected to a very great insecticide concentration for a short period. As a result, the insects will become comparatively rare, at least for a time. If antimalaria drugs continue to be used while disease-carrying mosquitoes are few in number, the disease may be virtually wiped out. Then, when the mosquito population is built up again, there will be no source from which it can acquire the parasite. Hence, if a sizable area can be kept free from malaria for a few years, it will remain free permanently, unless the disease is introduced from outside.

Malaria has been pretty effectively controlled in British Guiana, Ceylon, Greece, Italy and Thailand. In the southern United States, malaria was once common; it has been wiped out through the use of sprays and drugs. The larger the area in which malaria has been eradicated, the more likely it is that when the antimalaria campaign is over, the disease will not return. If national and international antimalaria programs continue, it should be possible to wipe out the disease entirely.

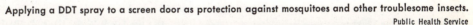

Applying a DDT spray to a screen door as protection against mosquitoes and other troublesome insects.
Public Health Service

The yellow
fever problem

Shortly after the cause of malaria had been definitely determined, yellow fever became a major problem for United States medical officers in the Caribbean. After the Spanish-American War, it decimated the American troops stationed in Cuba and Puerto Rico; it claimed more victims among them than the war itself. Yellow fever began with headache and prostration; the patient's face soon became suffused with blood. Later, his blood turned a blackish color, and there were also other less obvious physiological changes. The crisis would then be at hand. Often the disease proved fatal; at times up to 80 per cent of the soldiers who contracted the disease succumbed to it. If a patient survived, he would acquire lifelong immunity.

Dr. Walter Reed of the Army Medical Corps was sent to Cuba in 1900 to seek a cure for this disease, which was killing thousands and making it almost impossible for the Americans to remain in possession of the islands. Reed's investigations soon ran into a complete dead end. Search as he might, he could find no protozoan or bacterium that could possibly be the cause of yellow fever. Examination of the blood and tissues of men desperately ill with the disease revealed no clue to the enigma. Since the cause of the disease was unknown, any attempt at medication was futile.

Reed now met Dr. Carlos Juan Finlay, a Cuban physician, who for many years had been insisting that yellow fever was carried by mosquitoes. Although the idea was generally scoffed at, Reed became convinced that the doctor might very well be right.

For one thing, the nurses who worked in the yellow fever wards did not come down with the disease, as one would expect in the case of an ordinary contagious disease. Again, the disease struck at all classes of society. Disease usually is more prevalent among those living in crowded or unsanitary places. Yellow fever, however, attacked staff officers living in fine quarters and protected by elaborate sanitary measures as readily as it did peasants and the residents of Havana's slums. Besides, the disease seemed to skip about erratically. It might strike one family and then another many blocks away — a family that had no contact with the first one. All this pointed to the possibility that yellow fever was carried by an insect and that it was caused by the bite of that insect. Reed decided to put Finlay's idea to the test. Unfortunately, man was the only known victim of the disease at that time and experimental animals could not be used.

Reed instructed his staff to try to induce yellow fever in men by causing them to be bitten by mosquitoes. The technique was to allow specially bred mosquitoes to feed upon yellow fever patients and then, some time later, to feed upon experimental subjects. James Carroll, a doctor on Reed's staff, and William Dean, a private, allowed themselves to be bitten by Reed's laboratory-bred mosquitoes. They both came down with yellow fever and were very ill; however, somewhat against the prevailing odds at the time, both survived.

The role of the mosquito as the carrier of the disease was proved in a more tragic fashion by Jesse Lazear, a biologist on Reed's staff. While he was working in the hospital wards, a mosquito settled on his hand. It was a stray, and not even one of the species they were investigating. Lazear was busy with other things and did not bother to brush the insect off. When he became ill of yellow fever, he carefully noted the incident; he soon succumbed.

The experiments
at Camp Lazear

Reed now determined to prove once and for all that the mosquito carried yellow fever. He set up an experimental station, appropriately called Camp Lazear. There he isolated men so that yellow fever could not possibly reach them by contagion. After a waiting period, he exposed them to infected mosquitoes. All of the eight volunteers in the project became ill with the fever, though only one died of it.

Another all-important experiment was devised to prove that there was no other cause of yellow fever. Reed completely

screened a house and provided it with a double door so that no mosquito could fly in when someone entered or left. Three volunteers were installed in the house; they wore the clothing of victims who had died of yellow fever and used the bedding of these victims. Not a single one of the volunteers became ill. Several other three-man teams of volunteers lived in this house. Despite the fact that they were exposed to contagion from the yellow fever ward, not one of them developed the disease. Finally Reed put one volunteer in an absolutely clean building, one that had been fumigated and made as nearly germ-free as possible. After a suitable time, mosquitoes were introduced; as expected, the man was stricken with yellow fever.

The results of these tests showed that in Cuba the disease was transmitted solely by the mosquito. An extensive mosquito extermination campaign was now launched in Havana. In an astonishingly short time, the city was free from yellow fever.

Discovery of the yellow fever virus

Since then, the disease has been practically wiped out in the northern part of the Western Hemisphere. The discovery that yellow fever is transmitted by mosquitoes was the key factor in this triumph of modern science. There were other factors. After a good deal of careful research, some of it by Reed, it was disclosed that yellow fever is the product of a filterable virus, an infective agent so small that it can pass through a fine clay filter. This accounted for the fact that Reed, in his first microscopic researches, had been unable to detect the organism that caused yellow fever. Some time later, researchers discovered that the Rhesus monkey, the marmoset (a small monkey species) and the white mouse were susceptible to the yellow fever virus. Hence they could be inoculated with the virus and then studied by researchers.

Once the path was open to extensive laboratory investigation, it was not long before a yellow fever vaccine was produced.

Live viruses, belonging to a strain called 17D, are actually injected into the person being vaccinated. Careful breeding has made them so weak that, while they stimulate the production of antibodies, they do not do the subject any observable harm. The combination of vaccine and mosquito extermination has made the campaign against yellow fever increasingly effective.

A great many mosquitoes can carry the yellow fever virus. The chief carrier in Cuba was *Aedes aegypti*. In Brazil, the genus *Haemagogus* has been found to harbor the virus; *Aedes simpsoni* is a vector in Uganda, in Central Africa.

See also Vol. 10, p. 278: "Public Health Movement."

Standard Oil Co. (N. J.)

An effective mosquito control measure: spreading oil in a Colombia ditch to kill mosquito larvae that infest it.

SPACE TRAVEL

Man's Future Journeying
beyond Our Atmosphere

BY WILLY LEY

LIKE nuclear physics, the science of space travel, or astronautics, is a product of the twentieth century. The *idea* of space travel, however, goes back many centuries. There have been numerous accounts of fanciful trips to other worlds, and in particular to the moon, whose silvery disk has always stirred the imagination of men.

In the earlier accounts of space flight, it was assumed that the earth's atmosphere reached all the way to the moon and to the other visible heavenly bodies; the only problem, therefore, was to perfect a flying craft that could make the trip. We now realize, however, that the atmosphere is a film of air that extends only a short distance above the ground. At twenty miles up, 99 per cent of the earth's atmosphere lies below; at an altitude of 100 miles, even a body moving with cosmic speeds does not find much resistance. Because the earth's atmosphere is only a thin film, airborne devices such as balloons, blimps, propeller planes and jets have not been stepping stones to space, since none of them can stay aloft without a supporting atmosphere.

Yet, curiously enough, a device that can bridge the gulf of space between the earth and other heavenly bodies has been known to mankind for many centuries. This device is the rocket. It is based upon Sir Isaac Newton's Third Law of Motion, which states that for every action there must be a reaction, equal in force but opposite in direction. This law explains the recoil of a gun or rifle; corresponding to the forward thrust, there is a backward thrust, which in the case of a big gun is very formidable. In a rocket, the firing of the fuel causes gases to be expelled at high velocity from the rear; the recoil causes the rocket to dart forward in the opposite direction.

As long as the rocket fuel burns and shoots out billions and billions of molecular bullets — the combustion gases — there will be recoil that will push the rocket ahead. Its thrust does not depend on the presence of air; the device would function even more efficiently in an absolute vacuum. For one thing, there would be no air to resist the rocket's forward motion. What would be even more important, air resistance would not impede the exhaust. Hence the exhaust velocity would increase, and with it the thrust. The thrust of the rocket depends on only two factors: the quantity of combustion gases produced (which, of course, corresponds to the amount of fuel being burned) and the speed with which these gases are ejected.

The jet-propelled plane of the turbojet type (see the article Jet-Propulsion Progress, in Volume 7) is also based on the recoil principle. But this type of flying craft could never be used for space flight, because it is dependent upon the oxygen provided by the outer air. In a jet, air is drawn from the atmosphere through intakes; it is compressed, led into a combustion chamber, mixed with injected fuel and ignited. The gases resulting from combustion are then forced rearward and the reaction provides the thrust. Obviously if a jet plane penetrated beyond the atmosphere there could be no oxygen to combine chemically with the fuel, and combustion could not take place. The typical rocket

Launching of an *Atlas* rocket, carrying a space capsule, at Cape Canaveral, Florida. This launching formed part of Project Mercury, the manned space-exploration program conducted by the United States.

engine, however, does not draw air from the atmosphere; it carries its own oxygen in the form of liquid oxygen or as a compound, such as nitric acid. Hence it is the only kind of power plant known to us that could possibly fly beyond the atmosphere of our planet.

The first man to realize the possibilities of the rocket in space flight was a German inventor by the name of Hermann Ganswindt, who began to lecture on space travel in 1890. Unfortunately he did not grasp the mathematical relationships involved. Konstantin Eduardovich Tsiolkovsky, a Russian who began writing about rocket-propelled vehicles in 1903, understood something of the mathematics of space flight; but his knowledge of engineering was scanty.

Though Ganswindt and Tsiolkovsky led the way, the science of astronautics was really launched, shortly after the end of World War I, with the publication of three basic works on space flight. Each of these books was less than a hundred pages in length; each was strongly mathematical in treatment. The first, A METHOD OF REACHING EXTREME ALTITUDES, by Robert H. Goddard (1919), was primarily a mathematical investigation of rocket motion; it also contained a report on experiments with various types of gunpowders. THE ROCKET TO INTERPLANETARY SPACE (*Die Rakete zu den Planetenräumen*), by Hermann Oberth, published three years later, discussed hypothetical rockets burning liquid fuels; it investigated the possibility of piloting such rockets. In THE ATTAINABILITY OF HEAVENLY BODIES (*Die Erreichbarkeit der Himmelskörper*), which appeared in 1925, Walter Hohmann investigated the motion of piloted rockets outside the earth's atmosphere. These classic works laid the theoretical foundation of astronautics.

We now have a large and quite generally accepted body of theory concerning the nature of travel beyond our atmosphere. For one thing, we must take into account both liquid-fuel and solid-fuel rockets. Modern solid fuels mostly consist of synthetic rubber (which burns well) with ox-idizing chemicals kneaded in during the manufacturing process. Both liquid-fuel and solid-fuel rockets have their advantages. The liquid-fuel rockets are more complicated, but are more flexible in use. The solid-fuel rockets are simple and also cheaper. However, once a rocket charge consisting of solid fuel has been ignited, there is no way of stopping it or modifying it in any way, whereas the flow of a liquid fuel can be governed by the opening or closing of a valve. In a solid-fuel rocket, the charge is set off in a container, which to all intents and purposes is the rocket itself. Hence the whole rocket has to be strong enough to withstand the great pressures resulting from the combustion of the fuel. In a liquid-fuel rocket, the burning of the fuel takes place only in the motor, which is a small part of the device. The rocket as a whole does not have to withstand the pressures of combustion and so it can be kept quite light.

The factor that is called mass-ratio is supremely important in rocket performance and space flight. To explain what mass-ratio is, let us first point out that any rocket's weight is the sum of three "units." The first of these is the pay load, which is the reason for the flight. The pay load may be a warhead, filled with high explosive; it may be a compartment containing scientific instruments; in future spaceships, it will be the cabin for the pilot and passengers. The second "unit" is dead weight — the total weight of the rocket structure, plus the rocket motor and any auxiliary devices, such as fuel pumps. The third "unit" is the fuel load.

The pay load, dead weight and fuel load combined make up what is known as the take-off mass. After the fuel has been used up, the pay load and dead weight form the remaining mass. If you divide the take-off mass by the remaining mass, you obtain the mass-ratio. For example, if the take-off mass is 45 tons and the remaining mass is 15 tons, the mass-ratio is 3:1. The higher the mass-ratio, the greater the fuel load and the greater the range of the rocket. A rocket with a mass-ratio of 4:1 will outperform a rocket with a mass-ratio of 3:1

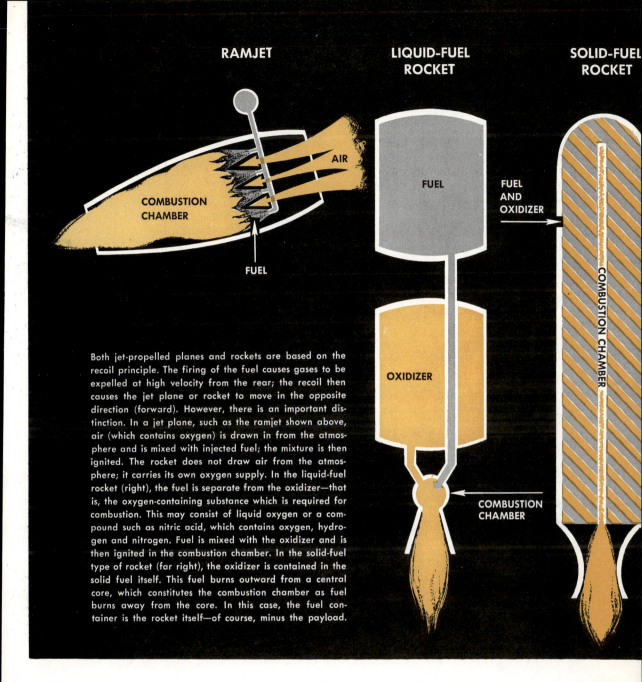

RAMJET

COMBUSTION CHAMBER

AIR

FUEL

LIQUID-FUEL ROCKET

FUEL

OXIDIZER

FUEL AND OXIDIZER

COMBUSTION CHAMBER

SOLID-FUEL ROCKET

COMBUSTION CHAMBER

Both jet-propelled planes and rockets are based on the recoil principle. The firing of the fuel causes gases to be expelled at high velocity from the rear; the recoil then causes the jet plane or rocket to move in the opposite direction (forward). However, there is an important distinction. In a jet plane, such as the ramjet shown above, air (which contains oxygen) is drawn in from the atmosphere and is mixed with injected fuel; the mixture is then ignited. The rocket does not draw air from the atmosphere; it carries its own oxygen supply. In the liquid-fuel rocket (right), the fuel is separate from the oxidizer—that is, the oxygen-containing substance which is required for combustion. This may consist of liquid oxygen or a compound such as nitric acid, which contains oxygen, hydrogen and nitrogen. Fuel is mixed with the oxidizer and is then ignited in the combustion chamber. In the solid-fuel type of rocket (far right), the oxidizer is contained in the solid fuel itself. This fuel burns outward from a central core, which constitutes the combustion chamber as fuel burns away from the core. In this case, the fuel container is the rocket itself—of course, minus the payload.

if both have the same dimensions and take-off mass.

The step principle in space flight

Another important factor in space flight is the step principle. By this we mean that the pay load of one rocket is another rocket — a much smaller rocket, of course, since it must fit into the first one. When the fuel of the first step, or stage (the larger rocket), has been used up, the second stage takes over. This stage is moving rapidly before it even begins to operate on its own; hence it attains a much greater speed than the first stage. We could add a third, or fourth or fifth stage if need be.

To penetrate into the boundless space that lies beyond our atmosphere, a rocket has to overcome the mighty force of gravity pulling it toward the center of the earth. It has been calculated that the rocket must attain a velocity of about seven miles a second to escape from the gravitational pull of the earth. This is called escape

How a three-stage rocket works. The payload is stage 3, which is a space capsule. At the start of this flight, the three stages fit into one another, as shown in the diagram at the right. Stage 1 gives the initial thrust. The whole assembly rises in a huge arc. When the first stage has used up its fuel, it is jettisoned and the second stage is ignited, either automatically or by radio command from the ground. When stage 2 has also burned up its fuel, after having given the payload the final boost, it too is jettisoned. The capsule, representing stage 3, is now quite on its own in space.

velocity. If a body were catapulted from the earth at less than escape velocity it would in many cases fall back to the surface again after it had attained a certain height.

There is another type of escape — not from our planet, but from the ground. If a rocket moved horizontally (and outside the atmosphere) with a velocity of slightly less than five miles per second, it would continue to circle the earth indefinitely as an artificial moon. Being a satellite of the earth it would still "belong" to the earth in a manner of speaking, but it would probably never touch the ground again. The velocity required for this purpose is known as circular velocity.

The early rocket experimenters were handicapped by lack of funds; few people took them seriously. Nevertheless, the research team of the Society for Space Travel (*Verein für Raumschiffahrt*) in Germany succeeded in sending primitive liquid-fuel rockets to heights of 3,000 and 4,000 feet in 1931 and 1932. A somewhat more elaborate rocket, designed by Robert H. Goddard, climbed to 7,500 feet in May 1935.

As soon as the military possibilities of rockets became known, more funds became available to experimenters. The German Army embarked on a large-scale rocket-research program and established a special experiment station, which became world-famous, at Peenemünde. Here the first large liquid-fuel rocket was developed. Its designers called it the *A–4*; but it became much better known in time as the *V–2*, Germany's most dreaded weapon in World War II. This rocket, provided with a warhead containing high explosive, was used against targets in England in 1944–45. Launched from sites on the western European coast, it produced devastating effects, particularly in the London area.

After the war, extensive experiments with large rockets were carried on in the United States, Great Britain, Russia and other countries. These experiments were made originally for military purposes or else in research on the upper levels of our atmosphere. But they served the added purpose of developing craft that could be launched on flights to outer space. Today, the long-range rocket capable of space flight has passed beyond the experimental stage. Unmanned rockets have soared to the moon and even beyond; manned rockets have orbited around the earth.

Certain basic features are common to all large-scale, liquid-fuel rockets. They are all rather thin-skinned, in the most literal meaning of the word. For this reason they cannot be put into a firing tube like the small and strongly built solid-fuel bombardment rockets; only rarely can they be set in a launching rack. They have to take off vertically, standing freely on their tail fins on a firing table.

The skyward-pointing nose constitutes the pay load. The section immediately below the pay load is the instrument section; it contains the devices that compute the rocket's speed, activate the guiding and control surfaces and so on. Below this is the fuel-tank section, which takes up most room; it usually accounts for at least two thirds of the take-off mass when the tanks are full. At the very bottom, between the tail fins, there is the section housing the rocket motor and auxiliary equipment.

Ignition is truly automatic in certain instances — if, for example, the fuel employed is aniline and if the oxygen required for combustion is contained in the compound called nitric acid. The two substances (both are liquids) burst into flame as soon as they touch each other. Certain rocket types require a special ignition device in order to bring about the combustion reaction. If the fuel is alcohol and if liquid oxygen is used for combustion, ignition may be provided in the form of "fireworks," set off by electricity and burning inside the rocket motor. When the fuel catches fire, this crude but effective ignition system is simply blown out of the motor with the gases of combustion.

When a large rocket lifts itself off the firing table, it travels less than its own length during the first second. The velocity mounts rapidly, however. It is about 40 feet per second at the end of the first second, 80 at the end of the second, 120 at the end of the third and so on. Very soon the velocities become awe-inspiring, partly because the rocket is losing weight steadily, as its fuel is rapidly consumed, partly because the thrust of the motor increases as the rocket reaches thinner and thinner layers of the atmosphere. (As we have pointed out, a rocket motor would work best in a vacuum.) As a result of all these factors, the rocket, one minute after take-off, is moving slightly faster than a mile per second. At the end of the first minute it has attained a height of about 20 miles; if the motor is shut off at that point, the rocket

may coast to a total height of about 100 miles.

The first rocket to reach the 100-mile mark was a *V–2*, fired from a German island in the Baltic Sea in 1944. Since that time, rocket altitude records have been broken again and again. The single-stage Viking rocket went up 158 miles. The first all liquid-fuel two-stage rocket, known as *Project Bumper No. 5*, rose to 250 miles in February 1949. Nowadays, with three- and four-stage rockets available, any altitude (distance from the earth) can be reached.

A milestone on the road to space flight was the development of artificial satellites, orbiting around the earth. Most of these satellites are packages of scientific instruments which are coupled with a radio transmitter so that the readings taken by the instruments can be received on the ground and studied at leisure. Some artificial satellites carry television cameras so that the ground stations may receive pictures of how the world looks when seen from a distance of 300 or 400 miles. To put an artificial satellite into orbit, a three- or four-stage rocket is normally used. The first stage puts the whole assembly into a long arc.

The highest point of this arc is above the atmosphere. When the peak of the arc is reached and the rocket moves parallel to the ground, the upper stages are ignited, either automatically or by radio command from the ground, and they bring the artificial satellite up to the necessary velocity. This velocity, for an orbit 300 miles above sea level, is about 4½ miles per second. All satellite orbits are elliptical; some of the ellipses are long and narrow, while others resemble a circle. The question of how long a satellite will stay in orbit, however, does not depend on the shape of the orbit. It depends on the question of whether the point of the orbit closest to the ground, called the perigee, is inside the upper atmosphere. If it is not, the so-called lifetime of the satellite is indefinite, which means that it will stay in orbit for a very long time, measured in centuries. This is a so-called permanent orbit. If the perigee is inside the upper atmosphere the orbit will slowly shrink and finally the satellite will re-enter the atmosphere; it will burn up when it reaches the denser levels of the atmosphere. Generally speaking, scientists prefer these "temporary orbits" because "dead" satellites which have done their duty are cleared out of space.

The first artificial satellite was launched on October 4, 1957, by the Soviet Union. Its weight was 183 pounds and its orbit had its perigee just 155 miles from the ground. The farthest point of its orbit, the apogee, was 560 miles up. The Russians called it *Sputnik*. When this word is used in everyday life, it means "somebody who accompanies one on a trip." However, since the beginning of this century, astronomers have used the word to refer to *small* satellites (natural ones) of planets. The second artificial satellite, called *Sputnik II*, was launched on November 3, 1957. It weighed over 1,000 pounds and carried a capsule holding a dog named Laika ("barker") for the purpose of finding out how an animal would be able to stand conditions in space when properly protected. Since it was impossible at the time to get a satellite back from orbit, the dog was painlessly put to death after some 95 hours of circling the globe.

The first artificial satellite orbited by the United States was *Explorer I*. It was fired from Cape Canaveral in the late evening hours of January 31, 1958, and took on an orbit with the apogee 1,570 miles from the ground and a perigee 224 miles up. Its weight was nearly 31 pounds; by the end of 1961 it was still in orbit.

During the first four years since the first artificial satellite began to circle the earth, the United States put more than fifty satellites into orbit successfully. It was an ambitious program, conducted by the NASA (National Aeronautics and Space Administration) and also by the Air Force. The program was designed to find out about conditions in nearby space and also to create satellites which would be useful for everyday purposes.

Among these was the *Tiros* project. The first of the *Tiros* satellites was launched in April 1960. The *Tiros* satel-

lites carry TV cameras for the purpose of giving observers on the ground an over-all picture of cloud conditions. They carry devices measuring the amount of heat radiated by clouds, by the sea, by dry land and so on. Experiments with satellites for communication purposes were also conducted. The satellite *Echo I*, placed in orbit in August 1960, is a 100-foot aluminum-coated balloon. It is used to reflect radio and television signals sent out from transmitters on earth. Messages routed in this way have been relayed for great distances. The Air Force satellites *Discoverer XIII* and *XIV* were launched in August of 1960; they ejected instrument-carrying capsules, which sped through the air back to earth and were captured. They represent the first man-made objects ever to be recovered from satellites orbiting in space (not merely from rockets fired out into space).

Another advance has been to send rockets beyond the earth's gravitational pull. Unmanned, instrumented vehicles have already reached the moon or gone past it, to circle the sun as artificial planets. The United States made the first attempts, beginning in 1958, with its *Pioneer* space probes. Most failed of their prime objective — to reach or circle the moon — but they uncovered many new facts about space. *Pioneers IV* and *V*, however, escaped earth's gravity to orbit the sun. The Soviets, in 1959, fired three "shots" at the moon. The first of their so-called *Luniks* swung around the lunar body and went into orbit around the sun; the second hit the moon; the third took photographs of the far side of the moon and transmitted them to earth.

The first manned flight into outer space took place on April 12, 1961. The five-ton U.S.S.R. space vehicle *Vostok I*, with Y. A. Gagarin on board, was launched by a multi-stage rocket. It went into orbit around the earth, reaching a height of 188 miles. Toward the end of one revolution, it headed toward the earth and landed safely after a flight of 108 minutes. About four months later, another Russian spaceship, *Vostok II*, with G. S. Titov at the controls, also went into orbit and made

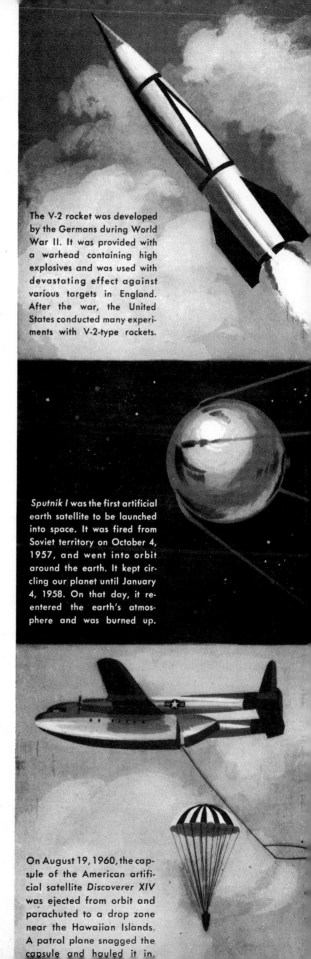

The V-2 rocket was developed by the Germans during World War II. It was provided with a warhead containing high explosives and was used with devastating effect against various targets in England. After the war, the United States conducted many experiments with V-2-type rockets.

Sputnik I was the first artificial earth satellite to be launched into space. It was fired from Soviet territory on October 4, 1957, and went into orbit around the earth. It kept circling our planet until January 4, 1958. On that day, it reentered the earth's atmosphere and was burned up.

On August 19, 1960, the capsule of the American artificial satellite *Discoverer XIV* was ejected from orbit and parachuted to a drop zone near the Hawaiian Islands. A patrol plane snagged the capsule and hauled it in.

seventeen revolutions before landing. In the period between these flights, the Americans sent A. B. Shepard, Jr., and V. I. Grissom aloft in space vehicles, and since then have sent men into orbit.

More ambitious space flights are being planned. Special precautions must be taken to protect the pilots and the passengers (if any) from the unusual conditions encountered in a flight to space. One of the most serious strains confronting those who travel in spaceships is produced by the tremendous acceleration required to escape from the atmosphere.

We all feel the effects of a certain degree of acceleration even when we are earth-bound. The mighty force of gravity is constantly pulling us toward the center of the earth with a force equivalent to an acceleration of about 32.16 feet per second. The rate of acceleration is called 1 g ("g" stands for gravity). We are no more aware of it than we are of the fact that the atmosphere weighs down upon us with a pressure of about 14.7 pounds per square inch; such conditions are normal in our lives. But if we are subjected to an acceleration of 2 g's, we experience a very curious sensation — as if we had suddenly become twice as heavy. This effect is heightened as the acceleration increases.

Let us suppose that the crew and passengers of a spaceship set out on a voyage to some far-off objective. At the moment the ship rises from the firing platform, there will be an acceleration of 2 g's. Acceleration will increase as the rocket loses weight with the consumption of fuel; it will reach the 8-g level as the fuel supply of the first stage is almost exhausted.

When the first stage drops off and the second stage takes over, the acceleration will drop to about 3 g's; within the following eight minutes it will climb to 8 g's again. The second stage will then drop off and the third stage will take over, again with an acceleration of 3 g's. This time the acceleration will climb to only 5 or 6 g's, until finally the ship will begin to coast in space with the motors shut off.

One can reproduce acceleration rates of 3 or 5 or 8 g's by substituting centrifugal force (see Index) for acceleration. A volunteer enters a gondola suspended from the end of a large arm, which in turn is attached to a rotary motor. As the motor is set going, the gondola speeds round and round at ever increasing velocity; the centrifugal force, corresponding to acceleration, increases apace.

Test volunteers have endured an acceleration of 8 g's — about the maximum to which one would be subjected in a spaceship. One volunteer withstood 17 g's for a minute. If a volunteer remains in a seated position under extreme acceleration conditions, the blood circulation slackens alarmingly. When it fails to reach certain vital areas of the brain, the volunteer blacks out: that is, becomes unconscious. It has been found, however, that if he lies supine (on his back), with head slightly raised and knees slightly bent, the physical effects of acceleration are not nearly so pronounced. The best position, then, for enduring high accelerations is to lie on one's back. American astronauts who have been sent up in space craft have assumed this position, resting on specially contoured couches, and have reported no ill effects from increased acceleration.

Those who go aloft in space craft have to endure not only highly increased acceleration but also a strange sensation of weightlessness. It is sometimes erroneously assumed that objects and persons in space are weightless because the pull of gravity beyond the atmosphere is insignificant. As a matter of fact, at a height of even two hundred miles or so the force of gravity is about 90 per cent as strong as at sea level. It becomes half as strong only when we have risen to a height of more than sixteen hundred miles above the earth's surface. Even far beyond that point, the force of gravity would make itself felt. After all, the moon goes around the earth only because the earth's gravity holds it at an average distance of 239,000 miles.

But there is a big difference between being under the gravitational influence of a body and feeling weight. Weight is felt *only* if the pull of gravity is resisted. If a body follows the pull of gravity freely

without resisting it in any way, it is weightless. A satellite winging around the earth does follow the gravitational pull — if it did not it would go off into deep space along a straight line — and therefore it is weightless. If the satellite were a spaceship in a satellite orbit, everything inside it would feel weightless too.

To reproduce the condition of weightlessness, experimenters have sent pilots aloft on a series of "parabolic flights." In a flight of this sort, the pilot goes into a power dive from a safe altitude in order to gather speed. He pulls out of the power dive, pointing the nose of the plane up and cutting the engine simultaneously. The plane then moves through a curve that leads upward at first, then levels out and finally points downward at a medium-steep angle; the curve is roughly a parabola. (See Index, under Parabolas.) From the instant the pilot cuts off the engine until the moment he pushes the ignition button again, the airplane and everything it contains are weightless. The faster the plane, the longer the curve and the longer the time during which the zero-g, or weightless, condition is experienced. In the experiments actually performed, the duration was about half a minute. During the first test of this kind,

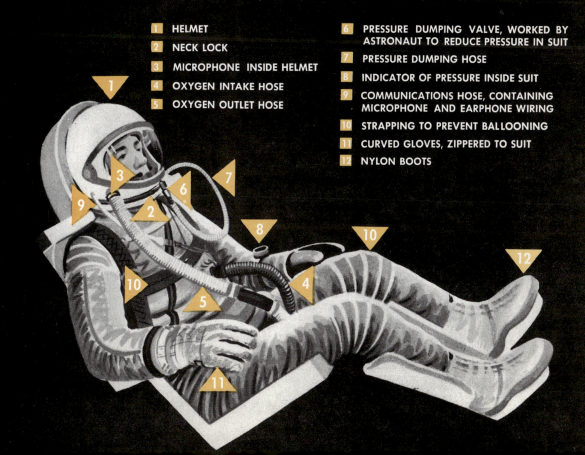

American astronauts—voyagers in space—wear a specially designed pressurized suit made of airtight rubberized material. Oxygen is supplied from "bottles," or tanks; the same gas serves for pressurizing and breathing. It enters the suit through an intake hose at a waist connection, circulates upward, is breathed by the astronaut and is discharged through a hose outlet. Discharged oxygen passes through a circuit containing a carbon-dioxide sep-arator, a solids trap, an odor absorber and a water separator; it is then returned to the suit, together with oxygen from the tanks. The suit can be pressurized to any desired extent; strapping at various places prevents it from ballooning. In actual flight, the astronaut communicates with the outer world by means of a microphone and earphones. He rests on a specially contoured couch, to which he is fastened by a restraint-strap system.

1 HELMET
2 NECK LOCK
3 MICROPHONE INSIDE HELMET
4 OXYGEN INTAKE HOSE
5 OXYGEN OUTLET HOSE

6 PRESSURE DUMPING VALVE, WORKED BY ASTRONAUT TO REDUCE PRESSURE IN SUIT
7 PRESSURE DUMPING HOSE
8 INDICATOR OF PRESSURE INSIDE SUIT
9 COMMUNICATIONS HOSE, CONTAINING MICROPHONE AND EARPHONE WIRING
10 STRAPPING TO PREVENT BALLOONING
11 CURVED GLOVES, ZIPPERED TO SUIT
12 NYLON BOOTS

a. pencil that had been lying loose hovered in the cabin in front of the pilot's face.

One of the pilots taking part in the "parabolic flights" reported that he felt decidedly uncomfortable while weightless. Others "didn't mind"; one pilot remarked that "in time he might get to like it." Astronauts in actual space flight have been able to adjust to weightlessness without much difficulty.

Special measures have to be taken to offset the condition of weightlessness in a space craft. Everything moveable has to be battened down. Various precautions have to be taken in eating foods and drinking liquids. Also, ways and means have to be provided to enable crew and passengers to move about within a spaceship.

It will be no problem to supply the cabin of a spaceship with oxygen for breathing, since the amount of oxygen a small crew would use up is not very large. The oxygen will be carried in its liquid state and released by evaporation. It would be only slightly more difficult to eliminate the carbon dioxide exhaled by the crew. It would be unnecessary for a trip of only a few hours' duration.

Outside the atmosphere the occupants of a spaceship will be subjected to several dangers. The most obvious one is that the ultraviolet rays of the sun will strike the ship with full force, undiminished by the filtering action of the atmosphere. However, ultraviolet radiation can be stopped by any kind of sheet metal, which can be very thin.

Various other kinds of radiation will be encountered in space. One of these is known as impact radiation. When freely moving electrons hit the wall of a satellite or a spaceship, they produce X rays by their impact, just as they do when they hit the metal plate called the "target" in an X-ray tube. Since these X rays are not very powerful, shielding is possible. The so-called cosmic rays are another story. Cosmic rays, in spite of their name, are particles — the nuclei of hydrogen atoms (protons) or other atomic nuclei. They cannot be stopped by anything a ship could carry, but fortunately they are quite rare

except in certain places, including the Van Allen Belt (see Index, under Van Allen radiation belt), and at certain times. Scientists feel sure that the cosmic-ray danger can be avoided with proper planning.

Still another danger would be that of meteors, but this has been grossly exaggerated. The vast majority of meteors are the size of dust grains. It has been calculated that a ship would not encounter a meteor an inch in diameter in thousands of years of flight through space.

Setting up a manned space station

Artificial satellites and rocket probes have informed us about conditions in nearby space, so that the next step can now be contemplated. That is the construction of a manned space station. The term "space station" means an artificial earth satellite which is in a permanent orbit and has a crew inside to do necessary work. The orbit of a space station will be as nearly circular as it can be made. Perhaps it will be at a height of a thousand miles above the level of the sea.

The first experimental space station will probably be small, with a crew of only five or eight men. Such a small station could probably be carried into orbit by a powerful rocket such as the *Saturn*. It will not be carried fully assembled; the assembly will have to take place after the rocket has gone into orbit. The bigger space stations that will be set up later will have to be carried as several rocket pay loads and will also have to be assembled in orbit.

The men who work on this assembly project will have to leave the rocket ship, of course, and step out into space. Each man will have to wear a special space suit — a self-contained unit that will supply the wearer with oxygen, maintained at the proper pressure, and will keep him comfortable whatever the extremes of heat or cold. Provision will have to be made to carry off the carbon dioxide and moisture constantly released in exhalation. The crew will propel themselves from place to place by mechanical means — perhaps by means

Proposed space station, as described by Wernher von Braun, famous German-American space-age pioneer. The station would constitute an artificial earth satellite, making a complete circuit of our planet every two hours at an altitude of something like a thousand miles. The station proper would consist of a number of flexible sections, making up an enclosed ring; this would be inflated to a little less than normal atmospheric pressure. As a substitute for gravity, centrifugal force would be produced by making the big wheel turn slowly about its hub. The hub itself would be the center for all entrances, loadings and departures. Within the big wheel, there would be living quarters, supplies and equipment, as well as a great variety of essential services. The space station would serve, among other things, as a center for the observation of the earth; as an astronomical observatory for the study of the heavens; and as a building site and also launching station for voyages far out into space.

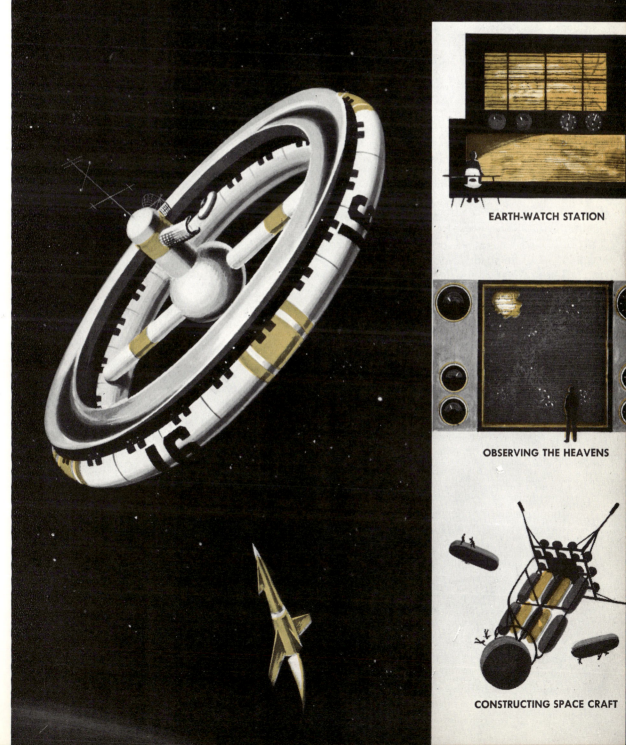

EARTH-WATCH STATION

OBSERVING THE HEAVENS

CONSTRUCTING SPACE CRAFT

America's Project Apollo aims at sending a manned spacecraft to the moon. The vehicle is to consist of three sections: a nose cone, or flight center; a central section to serve as a booster for the return trip from the moon; and a rear section with retrorockets for braking.

Upon approaching the surface of the moon, the pilot will turn the spaceship around and fire off retrorockets to slow it down; he will also cause the retractable landing pods to be extended from the craft. The latter will then be able to make a "soft" landing on the moon's surface.

of tiny rocket motors attached to the space suits. All this may seem to smack of science fiction; but it presents no problems that cannot be quite readily solved.

The space station will be wheel-shaped. The entrance will be in the hub, but the working and sleeping quarters will be located in the rim. It would be quite unpleasant to live in such quarters under conditions of weightlessness for a prolonged period. But the crew will not be subjected to such conditions. The large wheel of the station will keep spinning slowly and centrifugal force will be substituted for gravity. The synthetic gravity produced by the spinning of the station will probably be less than the 1 g we experience on the ground, but it will suffice to make the crew feel at ease.

In all probability, the air the crew will breathe will be somewhat different from that which we breathe on earth near sea level. The atmosphere is a mixture of gases: approximately 78 per cent nitrogen, 21 per cent oxygen and 1 per cent of other gases. The air in the space station will probably have an oxygen content of between 30 and 35 per cent. The remainder will be helium instead of nitrogen, if only because it will take less fuel to transport the much lighter helium to the space sta-

tion. Near sea level, the pressure of the atmosphere is about 14.7 pounds per square inch. A pressure of about 9 pounds per square inch will suffice in the space station, especially if the oxygen content is higher than in the atmosphere.

Without the atmosphere to temper its rays, the sun will shine much more brightly upon the station than it does on the ground: the earth will reflect additional sunlight. Besides, the members of the crew will all generate a certain amount of heat. Air conditioning, therefore, will be needed. The sun itself will provide all the energy needed for the purpose. There are several ways of converting sunlight into electric current. For small amounts of current, silicon solar batteries have proved very useful; for larger amounts, other systems are available. The current will be used in electric motors which will drive the compressors of the conditioning apparatus. The heating of the space station will not represent any particular difficulty.

The chief task of the station will be to keep watch upon doings on our planet. As the man-made satellite revolves around the earth, a large part of the surface will be visible at any given time; each area will be visible at least once every twenty-four hours. No iceberg can intrude upon the

After several days of exploration, the Apollo nose cone will take off from the moon with the aid of its booster (central) section. The last section, containing retrorockets and landing pods, will serve as a launching pad for the nose and the booster, and will be left behind.

On the homeward journey to the earth, the booster section will be jettisoned when its fuel is exhausted. As the nose cone approaches the earth, it will be slowed down by retrorockets. Upon nearing its destination—perhaps an ocean rendezvous—parachutes will be broken out.

shipping lanes, no hurricane develop anywhere, no expedition be lost, no ship wrecked without being spotted from the station in a matter of hours. Likewise no road can be built, no railroad track laid and no armed force concentrated without the knowledge of those in the space station.

Such "earth watch" will represent only a part of the station routine. There will also be a "sky watch." Astronomers will be able to view the heavens under ideal conditions; for the first time they will be able to scan the skies with their powerful telescopes without being hampered by the distorting effects of the atmosphere. They will almost certainly learn many hitherto unsuspected facts about our planet neighbors and the stars of our own galaxy and other galaxies.

In the space station, it will be possible to carry on scientific research under conditions hard to duplicate on the ground. Researchers will be able to heat anything to almost any desired temperature by concentrating the sun's rays on it; they will be able to cool anything to very nearly absolute zero (about $-459°$ F.) by placing it in the shadow of the station and leaving it there for a time. They will be able to work with vacuums that could not be duplicated on earth.

The space station will also serve as a base for trips to heavenly bodies out in space. The ships making such flights will be transported in sections to the vicinity of the space station. The crew that assembles the ship will use the station as a base.

Probably most of the spaceships that will be used for far-off space objectives will never touch the ground; hence they might have any weird design that would make for efficiency. Some believe that they will have a framework upon which to hang fuel tanks and rocket motors; the passenger cabin will be put in an appropriate location. According to some authorities, each ship will consist of two sections, which will be separated in flight and will be connected only by an immensely strong wire rope. The two parts will be set spinning around each other to produce synthetic gravity during the flight.

The motive power of the long-range spaceships will undoubtedly be based on the recoil principle. In the calculations that have been made up to now, we have assumed that ships will be propelled by fuels that are now known. It seems quite likely that other fuel types will be developed. Even with new and more powerful chemical fuels, however, trips will probably follow the general pattern that experts have predicted.

A trip to
the moon

It seems quite certain that the first trip to an objective in outer space will be to our satellite, the moon, because it is so near to us as celestial distances go — about 239,000 miles, on the average. Both the United States, with its Project Apollo, and the Soviet Union are planning manned voyages to the moon.

The spaceship that will make the trip to the moon will be set in flight by the combustion of fuel and will be headed toward our satellite. Upon approaching the moon, the pilot will turn the craft around and fire off retrorockets (braking rockets) to slow it down. Retractable landing pods will be extended from the craft, which will make a "soft" landing on the moon's surface. For the return trip, a section of the craft will serve as a launching pad, and will be left behind. Power will be supplied by a booster section, which will be jettisoned when its fuel is exhausted. When the remaining section of the craft approaches the earth, it will be slowed down by retrorockets and parachutes.

After spaceships have made several trips to the moon, venturesome astronauts will be ready to launch on other trips in space. It is probable that the second heavenly body to be visited will be the asteroid, or minor planet, Eros. It comes closer to us at perihelion (the point in its orbit nearest to the sun) than either Mars or Venus, our neighboring planets. Since Eros is tiny, its gravitational field should not present any other serious problems to a spaceship approaching it. The first-hand investigation of a minor planet would be of enormous scientific interest.

Perhaps the most intriguing goal for space explorers would be the planet Mars. We have learned quite a good deal about this planet. We know that it has polar caps whose size varies with the seasons; that there are barren areas probably like our deserts; that there are certain dark regions that undergo seasonal changes and that probably contain vegetation. We can make out certain markings that some astronomers have taken to be canals constructed by intelligent beings. It will be most gratifying to add to our knowledge of Mars. We shall want to learn what kind of deserts it has and what kind of vegetation. We shall want to find out if there are intelligent beings on the planet. We shall want to solve the mystery of the so-called canals. According to present calculations a trip to Mars would take about 258 days.

Our other planetary neighbor, Venus, would also attract space travelers sooner or later, not because it is so well known but because we know so little about it. Because of the clouds that constantly cover it, no man has ever viewed its surface even with the most powerful telescope. An astronaut who would succeed in exploring the surface of this mysterious planet and who would return to earth to present his findings would win undying fame. It would take something like 146 days, according to present calculations, to make the trip to Venus.

We expect atomic energy to play a part in space travel in the fairly near future, say by about 1967 and 1968. Preliminary experiments have shown that an atomic rocket engine can be built. This is how it works. In an atomic reactor, uranium or plutonium is permitted to fission until the whole reactor is nearly white-hot. Then hydrogen gas, which has been carried in a separate tank in liquid form, is pumped into the reactor. The gas heats up to very high temperatures. But it does not burn, because no oxygen is present; it is just heated up to develop high pressure. Finally, the hot gas is expelled from a nozzle to drive the rocket. For various reasons, an atomic rocket would not take off from the ground directly; it will first be carried into an orbit, or at least to a very high altitude by a chemical booster.

While the atomic rocket would have a number of advantages with respect to the weight of the pay load, the program of space exploration could be carried out without atomic energy. Even the chemical fuels we now have, if used properly, could do it.

See also Vol. 10, p. 286: "Space Travel."

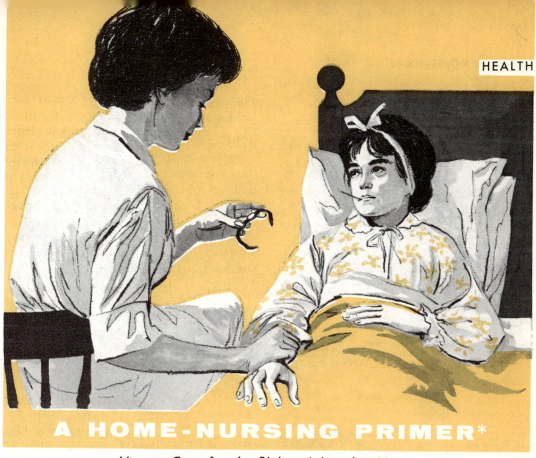

A HOME-NURSING PRIMER*

How to Care for the Sick or Injured at Home

AT SOME time in nearly every family there is a case of illness or injury. Much of the worry and confusion that often result can be reduced if a member of the family has the knowledge and skill required to give simple home-nursing care to the sick and injured. More and more doctors are recommending home care, when conditions are favorable, rather than hospital care for many patients. Then, too, hospitals are often overcrowded and patients are sent to their homes as soon as the acute stage of their illness is over. It makes good sense, therefore, to have at least one person in every home trained in home nursing. He should be able to recognize and make use of the fundamentals of nursing as they apply to safety, effectiveness of treatment, economy of time, effort and material, and neatness and cleanliness of patient and surroundings. Civil-defense authorities urge people to learn how to give first aid in order to provide nursing care for themselves and, if necessary, for others in shelters.

* Adapted from the *American Red Cross Home Nursing Textbook*.

How to recognize the signs and symptoms of illness

The home nurse should be able to recognize the symptoms and signs of illness so that the doctor can be told what to expect when he is called. There are certain symptoms than can be noted readily, such as the color of the skin, rash, if any, cough, discharge from eyes, nose or ears, vomiting, diarrhea, listlessness, unusual irritability or bleeding. Except in the case of an infant, the patient can tell about other symptoms, such as pain, nausea, dizziness, spots before the eyes or sore throat. When a sick person feels unusually warm, fever — a rise in temperature — is suspected and can be measured accurately by taking the body temperature with a clinical thermometer. The severity of a symptom is not always a true guide because it is possible for a mild symptom to be the forerunner of a serious illness that might be communicable, or infectious. Hence no symptoms should be ignored, no matter how trivial they may seem to be to the home nurse.

Careful washing of the hands is a *must* in caring for a patient.

Guarding the patient and his family against infection

Because disease-producing germs may be present in the mucous membranes of the nose and throat or in the intestinal tract of healthy people, we should all consider ourselves possible carriers of germs. Sick people are especially in need of protection against further illness since their powers of resistance to certain germs may have been weakened. It is important, too, to protect the members of the patient's family.

Since the hands are the greatest single offender in the spread of infection, they must be kept clean when nursing the sick. Hands should be washed not only when they become soiled, but also before and after handling food, after going to the toilet and before and after giving direct care to a patient.

In instances where water is at a premium, as in a disaster, knowing how to handle both clean and soiled articles and materials may have to take the place of hand washing.

The careless handling of body waste and materials used in the care of the patient can result in particularly serious infection. All body discharges should be disposed of in the toilet immediately. Materials such as soiled tissues, cotton pledgets (compresses) and throat swabs should be placed carefully in a paper bag and then taken from the room and disposed of by burning, if possible. Materials that will be used again should be placed in a paper bag and carefully handled until laundered to prevent the spread of infection. If paper bags are not available, a substitute bag can be fashioned readily from newspapers.

When nursing a patient with a communicable disease, the home nurse must realize that the care may be subject to regulations established by health authorities.* The health officer or his representative may visit the home to confirm the diagnosis or to make arrangements for quarantine or

* Measures for the control of communicable diseases are established either by law or regulation in the various states and communities. This includes immunization, or the giving of serums or vaccines for specific infectious diseases. Each adult is responsible for co-operating with health authorities in helping prevent the spread of disease.

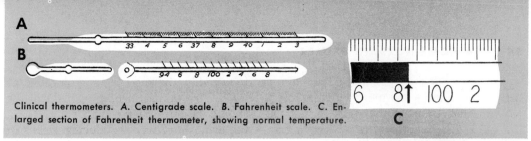

Clinical thermometers. **A.** Centigrade scale. **B.** Fahrenheit scale. **C.** Enlarged section of Fahrenheit thermometer, showing normal temperature.

isolation. In any event, the doctor will give specific instructions about the care of the patient with a communicable disease and the directions should be carefully followed for the protection of the patient, family and community.

Taking the patient's temperature

In the case of adults, the temperature is usually taken by mouth; in babies, young children and, sometimes, the aged, it is taken by rectum. The heat of the body causes the mercury in the bulb of the thermometer to expand and push up in the tube. The point at which the mercury stops indicates the temperature of the body at the time.

If the temperature is taken by mouth, a reading of 98.6° Fahrenheit indicates the average normal temperature, although this may vary in different individuals. Slight variations are unimportant. If the mercury rises to a degree or more above the point marked normal (98.6° F.), we say that the person has a fever. The temperature taken by rectum is usually slightly higher than that taken by mouth; hence the home nurse must always record, for the doctor's information, whether the reading was oral (by mouth), rectal (by rectum) or axillary (by armpit). Some diseases are characterized by a high temperature, others by a low temperature; in still others, the temperature remains normal.

Whenever a member of the family complains of feeling ill, or the home nurse observes symptoms of illness, readings should be taken once or twice a day as a matter of routine. A doctor may order a more frequent taking of the temperature. Readings should not be taken within a half hour after the patient has swallowed food, drink or any medicines he is required to take.

Taking the temperature by mouth. Wash the hands carefully before taking the temperature. Grasp the thermometer firmly

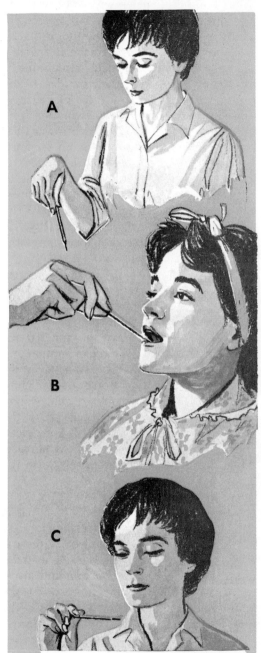

Above we show how to take the temperature by mouth. A. Shake down the thermometer. B. Insert it in the patient's mouth. C. Read the thermometer. D. Clean it.

by the end opposite the bulb. (The bulb is the end containing the mercury reservoir.) With a quick snap of the wrist, shake the mercury down below the 95° F. mark. Rinse the thermometer with cold water to lubricate and then place the bulb in the patient's mouth, well under the tongue to the side. Instruct him to keep the lips firmly closed. Let the thermometer remain in the mouth for 3 minutes; then remove it and wipe off moisture with a piece of gauze or cleansing tissue, using a rotary motion from the end opposite the bulb down toward the bulb. To read, hold the thermometer horizontally with the bulb to the left. Locate the mercury, a silver ribbon, by looking at the ridge between the numbers and the lines. The ridge acts as a magnifying glass. Write down the reading (where the mercury ribbon ends) on a piece of paper or on the patient's record.

After each taking of temperature, carefully cleanse the thermometer. Hold the thermometer firmly by the tip with the bulb down. Wash it with cold soapy water. Rub it down once with cotton, toilet tissue or facial tissue, using a circular motion and getting well into the grooves and over the bulb; then discard the cotton or tissue. Rinse the thermometer with clear, cold water; repeat the soaping and rinsing. Dry the thermometer well so that it is both clean and dry before it is returned to the case. After cleansing the thermometer, wash the hands with soap and water.

Taking the temperature by rectum. Lubricate the thermometer (which has a stubby bulb) with an oily substance for ease in inserting and for the comfort of the patient. Turn the patient on the side in order to see the opening of the rectum and insert the thermometer far enough to cover the bulb. Stay with the patient and hold the thermometer in place for 3 minutes. Cleanse the thermometer in the manner described above.

Taking the armpit temperature. Axillary, or armpit, temperature is considered less accurate than temperature taken by mouth or rectum. It registers about one-half to one degree lower than mouth temperature; when it is recorded, it is always followed by the letter *A* (standing for "axillary"). In taking armpit temperature, one should be sure that the thermometer and the armpit are dry. Place the bulb of the thermometer in the hollow of the armpit. Fold the patient's arm closely over his chest with his hand over the opposite shoulder to hold the thermometer in place about 10 minutes. Remove, read, record and cleanse, as outlined for taking the temperature by mouth or rectum.

Counting the pulse and respiration

Taking the patient's pulse is a method of counting the heartbeat. The rate, volume and rhythm of the pulse vary with individuals, with exercise and with illnesses; generally, the pulse rate increases as fever rises. The normal rate is usually between 70 and 90 beats per minute. The pulse may be taken where large arteries come near the surface. The pulse at the wrist is the usual place. Have the patient lie or sit down and place his arm and hand in a relaxed position, thumb up, supported on a chair arm, table or bed. Locate the pulse by placing two fingers on the thumb side of the patient's wrist between the tendons and the wrist bone.* Count the pulse beats for one-half minute; then check by counting for another half minute.

The breathing rate is sometimes hard to measure because the patient is able to

* One should never use one's thumb in taking a pulse, because the thumb itself pulsates.

Taking the patient's pulse.

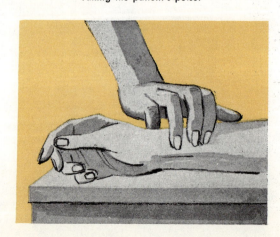

control it to some extent. There is a variation in the rate, volume and rhythm of respiration; it generally increases as fever rises. The normal rate is usually between 12 and 29 breaths per minute. Count the respiration unobtrusively; if the patient realizes what is going on, he may breathe more rapidly. If the respiration is counted immediately after the pulse while the wrist is still being held, the patient is not apt to know about the count.

Keeping the patient comfortable in bed

The doctor nearly always orders a sick person to bed because the patient's body must have relief from activity while it builds up its defenses and makes its repairs. There are other reasons why those who are ill should be put to bed at once. Even if we cannot recognize a sick person's symptoms, there is always the chance that he may have contracted a serious illness. Again, if the patient has a communicable disease, he may infect other members of the family unless he is kept away from them.

It is desirable that a patient have a room by himself; it is absolutely necessary that he be separated from others in the family if he has a communicable disease. When a long illness is anticipated, all articles of furniture that are not actually needed should be removed from the room; only furniture that can be easily cleaned should be used. A comfortable bed, a small table, a chest of drawers and one or two chairs

Setting drawsheet in place.

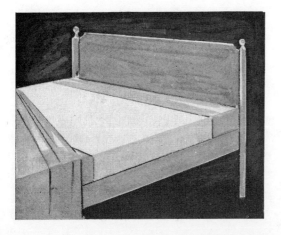

are necessary. Medicines and toilet articles should be covered with a clean towel to protect them from dust and to keep them from the view of the patient. Soiled dishes and linens should be taken from the room and placed where well people will not come in contact with them before they are properly cleaned. An atmosphere of harmony and cheer in the sick room is beneficial.

A clean and comfortable bed is of vital importance. There should be a good thick mattress pad between the sheet and the mattress, both for the added comfort it gives and to protect the mattress from body discharges. If there is likely to be vomiting, or if the bedpan or wet dressings will be used, the most exposed part of the bed should be protected by a rubber sheet or other waterproof material.

The bed should be snugly and smoothly made; there should be no wrinkles in the lower sheet. As a protection for the lower sheet to avoid changing it too often, a drawsheet may be used. The drawsheet can be a regular-sized sheet folded in half and placed across the upper part of the bed. It should be put on the bottom sheet; the folded edge should be well above the shoulders and the other edge well below the hips. While the bedding over the patient should be tucked in carefully at the foot so that it will not pull out easily, it should be loose enough to allow for toe space and free movement of the feet. A box pleat may be folded into the bedding (lengthwise) before tucking it under the mattress, to give more fullness over the feet. Bear in mind that the patient should be provided with supports for all body joints. The top cover on the bed should be light in weight but provide the necessary warmth.

Moving the patient in bed

The home nurse will be able to work efficiently in moving the patient in bed, if the latter is raised. It is possible to improvise a safe way to raise the bed to a convenient working height by using bed blocks or something similar. The following instructions on moving a patient will also serve when one makes an occupied bed.

ance. Help the patient to flex his knees so that he can push his feet against the mattress and aid in the moving. Place both arms and hands, palms up, under and well across the shoulders and, on a prearranged signal, pull slowly toward the near side of the bed. Place both hands, palms up, under and well across the buttocks and again pull toward the near side of the bed; then bring legs and feet to the near side of bed. Adjust the patient's body for comfort.

Rolling the patient to his side, using a drawsheet. Instruct the patient; loosen the covers; get the proper balance; have the patient flex his knees. Grasp the rolled-up drawsheet over the patient's body at the shoulders and buttocks. At a given signal, pull him steadily toward you and gently roll him to his side. Adjust his head, shoulders, hips, legs and feet for comfort.

Rolling the patient to his back when he is lying on his side. Instruct the patient; loosen the covers; stand properly for balance and leverage. Place one hand on his shoulder and the other on his hip and on

Raising the patient to a sitting position.

To get the proper balance and leverage, stand with one foot advanced in order to move easily toward and from the bed. Bend at the knees, keeping the back straight in order to avoid strain on the back muscles. To gain the patient's co-operation, tell him what is about to be done. Loosen the covers on both sides. Help the patient flex his knees so that he can support himself by pushing his feet against the mattress. Move only on a prearranged signal so that he will be ready to move, too.

Moving the patient from the center of the bed to either side. Get the proper bal-

a given signal gently roll him back. Adjust his body for comfort.

Raising the patient to a sitting position. Help the patient to flex his knees. Bending at the hip, place one arm under the patient's near arm and use the other arm to support the head and shoulders; have him grasp your near shoulder. When ready to move, tell the patient to push with his feet and raise him slowly to a sitting position. Pause until he is comfortable. Have him support himself by placing his hands behind him against the mattress. Later, lower him slowly in the same way.

Moving the patient toward the foot or the head of the bed. Raise the patient to a sitting position, and have him support himself with his hands at the back, keeping his knees flexed. Place one hand and arm under and well across the patient's thighs close to the buttocks, the other low at the patient's back. Ask him to help by digging his hands against the mattress, and on a signal swing him toward the foot of the bed. Use the same procedure to move him to the head of the bed.

A back rest
for the patient

When the patient is well enough to sit up in bed, he will need a back rest. Several types can be improvised from articles at hand. A straight chair may be used, bottom side up, with its front legs against the head of the bed so that its back forms an inclined plane; the chair may then be covered with pillows. A folded card table or large breadboard may be set on a slant, with one edge leaning against the head of the bed and the other resting on the bed in back of the patient; it should then be covered with pillows. Overstuffed cushions from a chair or davenport may be protected by pillowcases or other cloth and used for support when the patient sits up. Care must always be taken that the back rest is secure.

Perhaps the most satisfactory kind of back rest is one made from a paper carton, approximately 20 by 20 by 18 inches. Cut down along the edges of one of the short sides of the carton. This side will lie flat. Then, with a knife, crease the two longer sides diagonally from the back top to the lower front; bend in at the crease, side flaps and all. Bend the flap down. Pull the front side over and up; make a crease and bend over any excess at the top. Tie the carton back rest with strong cord; then cover it with cloth to keep the bedding clean and for a neat appearance. Place the back rest with the slanting side toward the patient; put pillows on it for comfort. This box may also serve as a footrest.

When the patient is sitting up in bed on a back rest, adjust supports for the arms and hands, using extra pillows or rolled-up blankets. Provide a flat support under the knees to relieve abdominal strain. Also adjust a footrest about 2 inches higher than the toes. It will keep the feet in a walking position, and will prevent toe-drop or foot drop; it will also serve as a cradle for the top covers draped over the footrest.

Giving support and
protection to joints and bony parts

The bony parts of a patient — his heel, his elbow or the end of his spine — may become tender because of continued pressure; the circulation may then become poor in that part, causing a pressure sore. Keep the area clean and dry and give frequent gentle circular rubbing to stimulate the circulation. Placing a soft support under the part will also give relief and prevent a sore. The support may be made from absorbent cotton and gauze or sponge rubber.

Bathing the
patient in bed

Bathing is necessary in sickness as in health. The bath will refresh the patient; it will aid in the elimination of waste, such as perspiration and dead skin; it will stimulate the circulation of the blood; and it will provide a mild form of exercise. The

How to make a bed rest, as explained on this page.

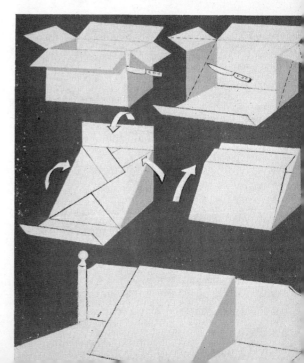

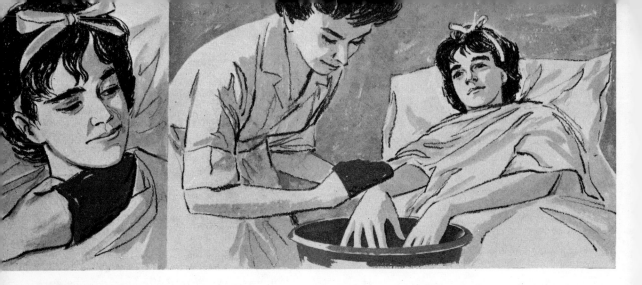

patient should be encouraged to bathe himself whenever possible.

Principal points to keep in mind when giving a bath. Protect the patient by keeping him covered to avoid chilling. Use a towel to protect the bedding; keep the water comfortably warm and wash only a small area at a time. Provide support for the patient's body while bathing him so that he will be comfortable; use long, firm strokes in order to stimulate circulation and to give passive exercise. Select a time that is free from interruption and is convenient for the patient and the household. The room should be comfortably warm and free from drafts. Collect and place at the bedside all the necessary equipment, including toilet articles, and work from one side of the bed in order to save energy. Wear a coverall to protect yourself and the patient.

In order to gain his co-operation, especially when it is necessary to move or lift him, tell him at each step what is about to be done.

Procedure for giving a bed bath. Wrap a washcloth around the hand about mid-palm. Anchor the top under the thumb and tuck in the loose ends; this prevents dragging. Squeeze dry to prevent dripping. Supporting the head, first wash the eyes from the nose outward with clear water, using a clean part of the cloth for each eye. Wash the forehead from the center to each side, using long firm strokes and the flat of the hand; the cheeks from the bridge of the nose and up each cheek; the upper lip, lower lip and under the chin with an **S** motion. If soap is used, rinse the cloth well and use the same motions to remove all soap. Dry well, holding the towel in such a way as to prevent dragging over the face.

Soap, rinse and dry the front of the neck and the ears, washing well in the creases and behind the ears. Continue with the chest, then with the abdomen, arms and hands, protecting the bedding and keeping the patient covered to avoid exposure and chilling. His hands may be immersed in the basin of water.

Turn the patient on his side to wash his back. Change the bath water at this time. (It may be changed at any time when it becomes cool, dirty or soapy.) Soap, rinse and dry, using long firm strokes, first washing the back of the neck and then continuing down over the back of the buttocks. Before turning the patient, use alcohol, powder or some lubricant on the hand, and rub the back with long firm strokes in order to stimulate circulation and to give some passive exercise. Any reddened areas may be given extra circular rubbing.

Wash the legs and feet, covering the patient well. Flex the knees and soak the feet in a basin of water if desired.

Place the basin, washcloth, soap and towel within the patient's reach and allow him to wash his genitals; place a towel under his buttocks to protect the bed. If the patient is helpless, finish the bath for the patient. Replace the gown and bedding.

The use of the bedpan

Warm the bedpan if necessary and sprinkle the seat with powder to avoid having the pan stick to the patient's skin. The seat may be padded if the patient is very

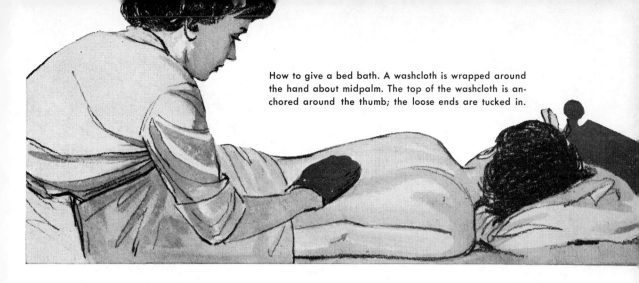

How to give a bed bath. A washcloth is wrapped around the hand about midpalm. The top of the washcloth is anchored around the thumb; the loose ends are tucked in.

thin. Protect the bedding with a bed pad. A serviceable bed pad may be made of about 10 full sheets of newspaper, covered with cloth. Turn the bedcovers back far enough to make it easy to place the pan. Keep the bedpan out of sight in a covered container when it is not in use; keep it covered when presenting it and after use. Cleanse the pan immediately after it has been used.

Placing the bedpan. Have the patient .flex his knees; hold the bedpan in one hand by the side to slide it under the buttocks, open end toward the foot of the bed. Put the other hand under the small of the back; on a signal, have the patient raise his buttocks and place them on the pan. Adjust the pan for comfort. The patient may be placed in a sitting position if desired; have him support himself, or give him safe back support. Place a newspaper or other extra protection in front of the pan between the patient's knees. Allow him to use toilet tissues if he is able to do so. If he cannot cleanse himself, do this for him.

Removing the pan. Have the patient lie down and flex his knees. Place one hand under the small of the patient's back; raise him on a signal and with the other hand remove the pan, holding it carefully at the sides to avoid soiling the bed or the hands. Cover the patient at once and make him comfortable.

Cleansing the pan. Remove the pan; inspect the contents in order to make a report if necessary. Add cold water to keep the contents from sticking; use a swab (toilet paper, newspaper or other) to help remove any material adhering to the pan before emptying. Clean well with hot soapy water, using additional swabs as needed. Rinse well; dry the outside of the pan and replace it in its container. Wash the hands. It may be necessary to wash the patient's hands, too.

Incontinence, or the inability to retain urine or bowel content, presents a nursing problem, especially with aging and chronically ill patients. Every effort must be made to keep a patient's skin in good condition. An incontinent patient needs more frequent bathing, drying and extra rubbing of reddened areas of the back to prevent pressure sores. Encouraging the patient to sit up in a chair or even walk about, if allowed, or offering the bedpan or the use of the commode * at regular hours may help the incontinent patient regain control.

How to give medicine

Medicine should be given exactly as prescribed. The following procedure is recommended. Wash the hands, assemble all the needed materials and carefully read the label on the medicine bottle; check the dosage with the doctor's orders. If the medicine is a liquid, shake the bottle in order to mix the contents thoroughly; then remove the cork or cap and place it topside down on the table to keep it clean. Hold the bottle with the label toward the palm and pour the medicine from the opposite side to avoid dampening or soiling the label. It is important to keep the label dry and clean because the directions cannot be followed accurately if they cannot be read, and the patient may be endangered. Measure

* This is a stool holding a chamber pot.

Hold a medicine bottle with the label toward the palm when pouring medicine, so as to avoid soiling the label.

the amount of medicine accurately according to the doctor's instructions, and read the label a second time as an extra precaution against mistakes.

After measuring the medicine, follow carefully any specific orders as to the addition of water or fruit juices. Give the medicine to the patient, helping him as much as necessary; then wash the glass, or spoon or other equipment with the greatest possible care and put it away.

The same precautions should be followed when giving drops, pills, tablets, capsules or powders. Pills, tablets and capsules should always be presented to the patient in a teaspoon and not from the fingers of the nurse.

Medicines should be kept out of sight of the patient, in a safe place where children cannot reach them. When the patient recovers, leftover prescribed medicines should be destroyed by throwing into the toilet or burning, unless the doctor advises otherwise. Many drugs grow stronger or deteriorate with age; they may be useless or dangerous if taken some months later. Under no circumstances should medicine prescribed for one patient be given to another unless the doctor orders it. It is extremely dangerous to assume that the medicine benefiting one patient will be good for another sick person.

The feeding of the patient

Feeding the sick is always an important part of medical treatment. The doctor must decide what kind of diet the patient should have. It is the nurse's duty to see (1) that the food is well prepared and served so that the patient will want to eat it; (2) that the patient has help, if necessary, in eating his food; (3) that the doctor is kept informed about the patient's appetite and the effects of the diet, if any are ap-

If fresh flowers or a little favor are placed upon the tray, the patient will look forward eagerly to mealtime.

parent. In some cases, the doctor will give specific instructions about the foods the patient may have; in others, he may say that the patient should be kept on a liquid diet or a soft diet.

The home nurse must know the liquids that provide the most nourishment and the foods that are included in a soft diet. She must also know which foods will provide the necessary variety to give the patient a well-balanced and adequate diet. Liquid diet usually includes:

Fruit juices, strained
Milk—whole, evaporated, malted, buttermilk
Thin gruels, strained
Soups, clear or creamed and strained
Ice cream, plain
Ices
Cocoa or chocolate

Milk may be prohibited for some illnesses. If allowed, it provides more nourishment than any other natural liquid food. Fruit and vegetable juices are especially refreshing to the feverish patient and have good nutritive value. It is important to remember that many liquids are low in food

A patient who is being fed with a spoon should be given food slowly so as to catch her breath between swallows.

value and for this reason the patient on a liquid diet must be fed much more often than when on solid foods. Unless the doctor orders otherwise, a glassful of liquid should be given every 2 or 3 hours.

As the patient's condition improves, semisolid or soft foods may be permitted. Fruit juices, cereals and soups need no longer be strained, and light, easily digested foods are added to the diet. Soft food usually includes all foods in the liquid diet, plus:

> Fruits, stewed and strained
> Cereals, well-cooked and sieved
> Bread, plain or toasted
> Soda crackers
> Eggs, poached
> Cheese, cottage
> Meats—scraped beef, white meat
>   of chicken, fish
> Potatoes, baked or mashed
> Vegetables, cooked and sieved
> Gelatin desserts, plain
> Puddings, rice, bread,
>   tapioca, cornstarch

The meals of a sick person should be served regularly. Since the appearance of the tray may affect the appetite favorably or unfavorably, dishes should be attractive; the tray cloth and napkins should be spotless, whether they are paper or fine linen. The practice of placing a fresh flower or an interesting little favor on the tray is likely to make the patient anticipate mealtime with pleasure. Liquids or light refreshments should be served as carefully as the mealtime tray.

It is best to avoid asking the patient in advance about what he wants to eat, but consider his likes and dislikes when preparing his food. Serve the food in small amounts; cover hot food to keep it hot and serve cold food cold.

Before serving the tray, allow the patient to use the bedpan, if desired. After this, wash his face and hands to help him feel relaxed and comfortable for the meal. Put the room and bed in order; adjust the back rest and pillows to his comfort and arrange the bed table conveniently.

Water is generally an essential part of the treatment in illness. Unless the doctor issues orders to the contrary, keep a pitcher or bottle of fresh cool water and a glass on a table beside the patient. If he is not able to help himself, offer water to him frequently, whether he asks for it or not.

It is generally considered advisable for a sick person to take food in small amounts and to have light nourishment between meals. A glass of fruit juice or some other liquid will serve this purpose.

When feeding a helpless patient, always protect the gown and pillows with a towel or large napkin. If the patient is too ill to be propped up with pillows in a sitting position, the nurse may place her hand under the pillow, raise the head slightly and hold a glass to the lips. If the head cannot be raised or if the patient prefers, use a glass or drinking tube.

If the patient must be fed with a spoon or a fork, the nurse should sit by the bedside. She should not hurry the patient; he should have enough time to get his breath between swallows and to chew his food well.

When the patient has finished his meal, flush all liquid waste down the toilet; place all solid matter in paper bags and

burn, if possible. Wash dishes with hot soapy water; rub thoroughly all rims of glasses and cups, tines of forks and bowls of spoons because these surfaces have been in direct contact with mouth secretions that may contain infectious germs. Stack the dishes so that all surfaces are exposed and rinse them with scalding water. Allow them to drain dry or use a clean towel. The dishes from any sickroom should be washed in this manner unless special instructions are given by the physician or public health nurse.

Keeping a daily record

A patient's condition is apt to vary from day to day. The doctor is helped considerably if the home nurse can give him certain facts. Keep a written record, as it is not good practice to trust the information to memory. The following form shows how such a record might be kept:

DAILY RECORD					JANE JONES
Date & hour	Temp.	Diet, medicine & treatments	U.	B.M.	Remarks

Note: U stands for urination; B.M. for bowel movement.

Giving simple treatments ordered by the doctor

The doctor will often order treatments to make the patient more comfortable and to hasten recovery. Heat and cold are used in many instances. Whatever the treatment ordered, take special precautions to safeguard the patient, home nurse and surroundings adequately.

Giving steam inhalation. Move the patient to the near side of the bed and cover his hair with a towel. Place a well-protected table, chair or stool in a convenient place near the patient. Make a tent of the bed covering or some similar material, using the head of the bed or an umbrella for a support. Bring a steaming kettle or container to the bedside and place it carefully on the table or stool, below the level of the mattress, for safety. Adjust a funnel made of newspaper and direct it into the tent but away from the patient's face.

The water level in the kettle must be below the inside opening of the spout of the kettle in order to allow the steam to escape. If medication is ordered, it may be placed in an open, weighted jar or can inside of the kettle, above water level to avoid staining the kettle. It will be necessary to add fresh boiling water to keep the steam up during the period for which it was ordered.

Stay with the patient continuously if there is any danger that the kettle will be tipped over. For small children, make a crib tent. It is safer to remain at the bedside during the entire period of inhalation. When the inhalation is finished, dry the patient's face, remove the tent, adjust the bed clothes and put away the equipment.

When the patient is up and around, the inhalation may be given by using a paper bag. Cut an opening in the bag to fit around the nose and mouth. Place the bag over a container of steaming water that has been set on a tray or in a basin for safety.

Filling a hot-water bag. Inspect the hot-water bag to see that the washer is in place and that the stopper fits snugly. Test the temperature of the water before filling the bag. The water should not be hot enough to burn the patient or damage the bag; it should be just hot enough to be momentarily bearable to the fist of the person who is testing.

Pour the water into the bag slowly so that air may escape as the water enters. Fill the bag half to two-thirds full so that it will be light in weight and comfortable to the patient. Expel air by squeezing and pressing the bag until there is water in the neck. Fasten the top so that it will be tight; hold the bag upside down to test for leaks. Dry the bag and cover it with a cloth or towel; then apply it as ordered, taking care that the patient does not lie on the hard neck of the bag.

After removing the bag, empty it and hang it upside down to drain. When the bag has dried, inflate it by pulling the sides

How to give steam inhalation. An impromptu tent is made of the bed covering or of some similar material. A steaming kettle or other type of container is then brought to the bedside. A funnel made of newspaper is set over the kettle, as shown above, and is directed into the tent, but away from the face of the patient.

apart and then insert the stopper; if this is done, the sides will not stick together. If a hot water bag is not available, a glass bottle or a heated brick or heavy plate can be used. When using a glass bottle, take great care to see that it is well stoppered and covered and that it does not break. No matter which type of heat appliance is used, the home nurse must make sure that it is not hot enough to burn the patient. Take special care when applying heat to a helpless patient.

Filling an ice bag. Crush ice in pieces small enough to go into the mouth of the bag; a little water poured over the ice will remove sharp edges that may pierce the rubber. Fill the bag half to two-thirds full of ice to make it light in weight. To make the bag pliable, expel the air by laying the bag on the table and pressing gently until the ice comes to the mouth of the bag. Screw the cap on firmly and test for leakage. Dry the bag and cover it before applying. The bag should be removed for a short time every few hours to allow the blood to come back and nourish the tissues.

After the ice bag is removed, allow it to dry thoroughly inside; then inflate it and replace the stopper to keep the sides from sticking together.

You will find more information about home nursing in the AMERICAN RED CROSS HOME NURSING TEXTBOOK, published by Doubleday, Garden City, New York. However, we have to point out to our readers that it is impossible to learn through reading all that there is to know about home nursing. The best results will be obtained by taking the home-nursing courses offered by the American Red Cross and by other health or educational agencies. Courses of this kind provide expert instruction and opportunities for supervised practice.

Filling a hot-water bag. The temperature of the water should be tested before the bag is filled.

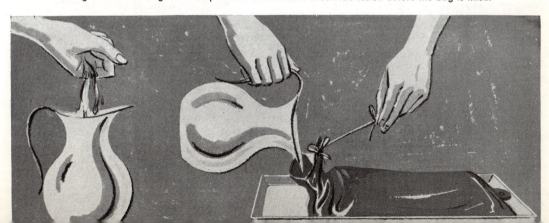

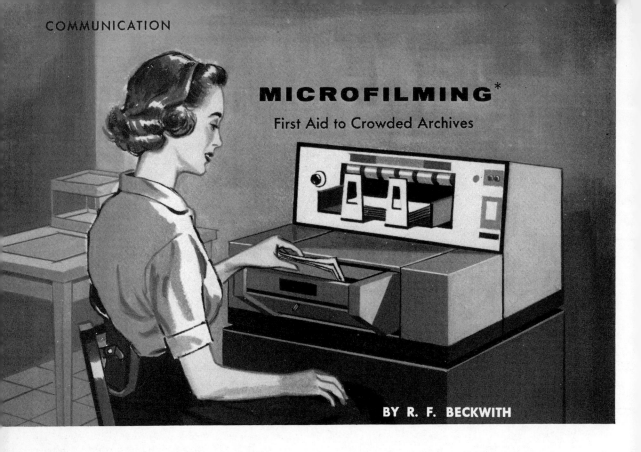

MICROFILMING*

First Aid to Crowded Archives

BY R. F. BECKWITH

IN THE year 1870, when the Prussians and their German allies were besieging Paris, the inhabitants could neither receive nor send messages through the ordinary channels. Yet the flow of news into and out of the city was kept up throughout the siege because of the ingenuity of a French photographer named Dagron. He had conceived the idea of photographing messages on narrow strips of film. These were developed and flown over the enemy lines by carrier pigeons. At the destination points, the tiny pictures were projected upon walls or other suitable surfaces, or else those receiving the messages read them through magnifying glasses. To Dagron's brilliant improvisation, we owe the basic idea of microfilming, one of the outstanding duplicating developments of the present century. By microfilming we mean recording documents — book pages, letters, checks, maps, contracts and the like — on a narrow ribbon of film. The film is developed and stored away until needed; then it is enlarged by special reading devices.

* Editor's note: The drawings and diagrams in this article were adapted from material supplied by the Life picture collection, the Minox Corporation, the Recordak Corporation, the United States Army (Technical Manual 12–257) and the United States Department of Justice.

Men have always been concerned with the problem of duplicating records. A lost will may lead to years of bickering among the prospective heirs of an estate. A lost receipt may mean endless trouble for a man; an entire community may be affected by a missing town charter. More than one business firm has been forced into bankruptcy because its records were destroyed by fire, flood or earthquake. The only way to prevent mishaps like these is to make duplicate records, which will serve if originals are lost.

Up to the end of the Middle Ages, duplicating of documents of all kinds, in the Western world at least, was by hand. (It is said that the Chinese used movable wooden blocks to print official proclamations.) In the fifteenth century Gutenberg's invention of printing from movable type enabled men to make thousands of copies of books and other documents in a fraction of the time formerly required.

Printing has been used since Gutenberg's time for the duplicating of documents, but only when a considerable number of copies are desired. It costs as much to set type for one copy of a letter, say, as for

a thousand copies; the cost of making a single printed copy would be very much higher than the cost of typing it. The duplicating methods known as mimeographing and multigraphing are also practical only when a considerable number of copies of an original are desired.

Up to a comparatively short time ago, the duplicating of records, in cases where one wished to have only one or a few copies, was entirely by hand — by writing or typing. Such duplication was time-consuming; errors sometimes crept in, for the copyist could not do his work with the accuracy of a machine.

Photocopying, or the creation of a copy on a sensitized surface by the action of light, has proved far more satisfactory. There are various photocopying methods, including the Photostat, the Verifax, the Electrofax, xerography and smokeprinting. The thermographic method, which has become quite popular, is not, strictly speaking, a photocopying method, since it uses the heat of infrared rays, instead of light, for exposure.

All of the copying methods mentioned in the preceding paragraph result in duplicates that take up about as much space as the original. Now the problem of finding adequate space for industrial, educational, scientific and other records is becoming more and more acute. Government bureaus and business offices alike have been swamped with documents that in some cases have been piling up for hundreds of years. As libraries grow, they find it more and more difficult to provide shelfroom for new books, pamphlets, magazines and newspapers. Yet one cannot simply destroy old records in order to make way for new ones.

Microfilming, which is a photocopying process, has solved the problem, for it makes it possible to store records in a fraction of the space formerly required. As we have seen, the idea itself goes back at least as far as 1870; but the first practical microfilming apparatus was developed in the twenties of the present century by a New York banker, George L. McCarthy.

The film used is made of cellulose acetate. It comes in two widths: 16 milli-

In order to get messages out of Paris while the city was being besieged by the Prussians and their German allies in 1870, René Dagron photographed the messages on narrow strips of film. These were then developed and placed inside a goose quill, which was tied to the tail or wing of a carrier pigeon. The pigeon would fly over the enemy lines. When the tiny pictures reached their destination, they were projected on a wall or other surface or else they were read through magnifying glasses.

meters (about ⅔ of an inch) and 35 millimeters (about 1⅜ inches). Sixteen-millimeter film, which is like that used in home movie cameras, serves for ordinary business documents, such as bank checks, cards, letters and legal papers. Bound books and large documents, such as newspapers and engineering drawings up to 37½ by 52½ inches, are recorded on 35-millimeter film, the size used by many amateur photographers for their miniature cameras.

A reel of microfilm is loaded in the camera and the document to be photographed is brought into focus. As the roll unwinds, a small section of film is brought into position opposite the camera lens. An exposure is made, that bit of film is wound away from the lens, a new section takes its place and another document is brought forward to be photographed.

In the case of small documents, such as checks or receipts, the operator of the microfilm apparatus has only to feed the documents into the machine as rapidly as he can. In a single automatic operation the shutter clicks and the film is advanced the correct amount for the next exposure.

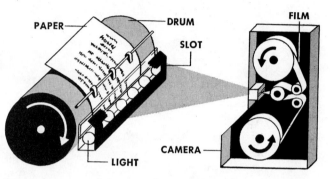

Left: large documents are laid on a flat surface and photographed by a special camera unit that can be raised or lowered as desired. Below is shown a rotary camera. It differs from the flat-bed camera in that the paper, which is wrapped around a drum, is in motion while it is being photographed. The camera film is moved at the same relative rate of speed. A given section of the paper is photographed in passing the slot shown below; and ultimately there is a photograph of the whole paper.

PAPER — DRUM — FILM

SLOT

CAMERA —

LIGHT

Focus, light intensity, distance from lens to subject, diaphragm opening — all are fixed and require no adjustment.

Large documents are laid on a flat surface and photographed by a special camera unit that can be raised or lowered on a supporting platform. Bound volumes can be photographed without removing the bindings. For this purpose the machine is provided with a mechanical book cradle that automatically brings the individual pages in turn beneath the camera lens. It is possible to photograph two pages simultaneously. Before the exposure is made, a beam of light is projected downward and outlines the exact area that is to be photographed. In this way, only the precise amount of film required is used for each exposure.

When the reel of film has been entirely exposed, it is removed from the camera and developed. We now see on the film a series of tiny images, separated from each other by a narrow border. Each image is greatly reduced from the size of the original; a document ten inches square can be reproduced on a tenth of a square inch of film.

When the film is developed, it is in the form of a negative; what is dark in the original is light in the negative and vice versa. Generally the developed film is left

in negative form; it is wound on a reel and enclosed in a cardboard box, measuring about 4 inches by 4 inches by 1 inch. If a roll contains a number of unconnected items, it is sometimes cut into comparatively short lengths, which are placed, flat, in long, thin envelopes or transparent plastic jackets and stored in labeled boxes or filing cabinets. Sometimes cut film is placed in cloth pockets, sewn on the backs of filing cards; the cards are stored in ordinary filing cabinets.

The tiny pictures are much too small to be read with the naked eye. Special projectors, called film readers, are used to magnify the images to a convenient size for reading. The enlarged image is projected on a translucent screen, where every detail of the original record is clearly and accurately reproduced. The reader can work the film back and forth through the film reader by means of winding cranks; in this way he can refer to any part of the film that he wishes.

In some readers, the film is run forward and backward by means of an electric motor. One such device, the Recordak Lodestar Reader, operates with 16-millimeter microfilm, which is placed in special containers called magazines after the film

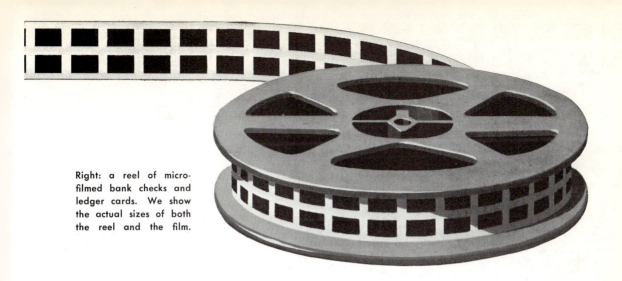

Right: a reel of micro-filmed bank checks and ledger cards. We show the actual sizes of both the reel and the film.

is processed. A single magazine measuring 4½ by 4½ inches can contain the equivalent of 2,400 pages of printed matter. Inserting a magazine in the reader automatically starts the motor, lights the screen and threads the film. By means of an ingenious coding system, any given page on a 100-foot roll of film in a magazine can be located in 20 seconds and flashed on the screen.

Positive film prints may be made from a microfilm negative, of course. Paper prints in any size up to that of the original document, or even larger, can easily be produced from the negative by the ordinary photographic enlarging processes.

Microfilming offers many advantages over other methods of duplication. For one thing it is very rapid — far more so than any other duplicating method. It is error-proof, because documents are copied with the absolute accuracy of photography. It is economical, because the microfilm is inexpensive and because so many documents can be recorded on a single roll. It is durable; according to the United States Bureau of Standards at Washington, microfilm made of cellulose acetate will last as long as the best grade of all-rag paper.

Perhaps the greatest advantage of microfilm is that it occupies astonishingly little space. An operator can reproduce 28,000 cards measuring 3 by 5 inches, or 10,700 8½-by-11½-inch business letters, on a 100-foot roll of 16-millimeter film that can be held in the palm of your hand. A 1,600-page dictionary can be reproduced on a part of a roll of film of the same size. A 4-drawer filing cabinet full of microfilm reels holds the equivalent of 50,000 bound

volumes of ordinary size. A single safety-deposit box in the vault of a bank could hold all the confidential records of a great business enterprise, reproduced in the medium of microfilm.

Microfilming has so far found its widest use in business and industry. Banks microfilm canceled checks and bank statements, thus protecting both the bank and the depositors against loss and fraud. Business houses microfilm their correspondence files and their accounts-receivable records. Engineering departments record their mechanical drawings and other data. When a leading electrical manufacturer microfilmed 2,000,000 old shop orders, sketches, draw-

Below: diagram of a microfilm reader. The film is wound on spools and can be moved forward or backward by means of a winding crank. A beam of light is passed to the upper mirror, set at a 45° angle, and is reflected on through the film to a projection lens. The picture is enlarged by this lens and is reflected by the lower mirror to the reading screen. When the lower mirror is swung upward, as indicated by the dotted line, an enlarged print of any part of the negative can be made on sensitized paper, which is placed on the paper holder.

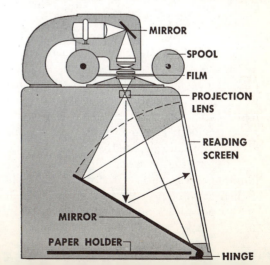

MIRROR
SPOOL
FILM
PROJECTION LENS
READING SCREEN
MIRROR
PAPER HOLDER
HINGE

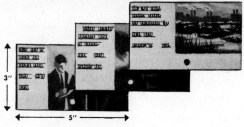

Left: bound volumes of the back issues of a newspaper and the three rolls of microfilm on which these issues have been photographed. Above: three-inch by five-inch catalogue cards used to index the picture files of *Life* magazine. On each card there appears a print that has been made from a microfilm of the original picture; appropriate descriptive material is also included here.

ings and charts, he saved an acre of floor space!

In some instances, original business documents continue in everyday use after microfilms have been made of them, while the negatives are stored in safety-deposit boxes. In other cases, the bulky originals are destroyed, positives serving in the office or plant while negatives are stored safely.

Some business houses and factories have their microfilming done by companies that specialize in this sort of service. The camera is generally set up in the place where the records are and reproductions are made while the ordinary business of the firm is being carried on. The films are developed by the company that provides the service. Other firms rent or buy their own microfilming equipment and train their employees to do all the work involved.

Federal government bureaus in the United States and Canada microfilm many of their records; so do state (or provincial), county and municipal agencies. Quantities of old records have been recorded on microfilm and then destroyed, thus releasing valuable space.

Picture research in the files of magazines and other publications is made easier by means of microfilming. The picture files of one large publishing company are indexed mainly by 3-inch-by-5-inch catalogue cards. Each of these cards features a print made from a microfilm negative and also appropriate descriptive data.

Before the development of the microfilming process, libraries were seriously concerned with the problem of keeping up their newspaper files. Such files are very bulky

and it is difficult to find space for them. Besides, newspapers have for years been printed on fragile sulfite and wood-pulp paper, instead of on rag paper, with the result that many of the old newspapers in the files have crumbled away.

Nowadays a number of leading newspaper publishers are having all current editions microfilmed; some of them have had all their old issues recorded on microfilm. Newspapers sell positive film prints to other newspapers, local libraries and historical societies. *The New York Times*, for instance, now distributes over a hundred sets of positive film prints of its negatives.

Every library has a certain number of rare books and manuscripts and also books that are too badly worn to be used by the general public. Formerly, only a few people were permitted to consult them. Now a good deal of this material has been reproduced in microfilm and is available to all.

It often happened, in the past, that scholars wishing to consult rare books or manuscripts in their own country or in other lands had to visit the libraries where these books or manuscripts were kept; or else they had to pay somebody to copy the contents by hand. When the photostatic method of reproduction was developed, scholars could have photostats made. However, the cost was far too high for the average scholar if he had to have many documents reproduced in this way. Nowadays a number of libraries are equipped to supply microfilm reproductions of any item included on their shelves or on the shelves of near-by libraries. The cost comes to only a few cents a page.

Microfilm book-charging systems are used in many circulating libraries. The microfilmer (microfilming machine) photographs at one and the same time the book card, the borrower's card and the date on which the book is due. With such a system, it is not necessary to stamp the date on the borrower's card, or to write the borrower's serial number on the book card or to file the book cards in the library. The microfilmer can be operated by clerks, who can be taught how to run it in a few minutes. This releases trained librarians for more important library work.

Sometimes microfilming of old manuscripts is done on a tremendous scale. The year 1950 saw the completion of such a project. Microfilm reproductions were made of over 2,000,000 pages of ancient manuscripts in the library of St. Catherine's Monastery, at Mount Sinai in Egypt. These documents, some of which go back 1,200 years, were made available for the first time to the scholars of the world.

Often, when we seek to learn about the civilization of past ages, we have to grope

During World War II, letters sent to men on far-off fronts and from these men to their homes were often photographed on microfilm. The films were sent by plane to their destinations, where they were enlarged and then printed on paper. This system was called Airgraph by the British and V-mail by the United States. The equivalent of two sacks of mail could be photographed on the single roll of microfilm we show in the drawing.

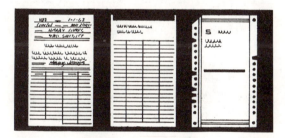

Above: borrower's card, book card and date-due card used in charging books at a circulating library. When these cards are all photographed together in the microfilming machine shown in the picture below, they provide an accurate record in a very short period of time.

in the dark because so many ancient documents have been destroyed. Microfilming will make it possible to preserve for posterity a remarkably complete record of our own civilization and those that follow. A dramatic example of how this may be done was provided in 1939, at the New York World's Fair. The Westinghouse Time Capsule, a receptacle containing various exhibits of our civilization, was lowered into a crypt at the Fair; it was not to be opened again until 6939 A.D. — 5,000 years later. Among the contents of the capsule were three and one-half reels of microfilm. On these had been photographed more than 30,000 pages of printed matter dealing with language, literature, science, government, industry, religion, entertainment — in short, a cross section of man's way of life in the year 1939.

During the early years of World War II, the libraries of England suffered terribly from aerial bombs; some of their most precious treasures were lost to mankind. To prevent further loss, a great number of books and manuscripts were microfilmed under the direction of the American Council of Learned Societies, with the full cooperation of the English authorities. The microfilmed material dealt with a wide variety of subjects — American and European history, law, the fine arts, music and literature. Copies of each microfilmed reel were

The use of microfilm in espionage. The spy, with his miniature camera, shown at the left, gains access to classified material, and photographs the documents from the file (immediately below). He then develops the film. Afterwards, the spy inserts the microfilm inside a hollowed-out coin, shown at the bottom of the picture. He can then pass the coin to a comrade without arousing suspicion.

deposited in Great Britain and in the Library of Congress in Washington, D. C.

Microfilming was put to use in various ways in World War II to further the war effort. Early in the spring of 1942, to speed mail *to* men fighting far away and *from* these men to their homes, the British began photographing letters on microfilm. The films were sent by plane to their destination, and there they were enlarged and printed on paper. The British called this system Airgraph. In June of the same year, the United States adopted the system, giving it the name of V-mail. During the war 321,000,000 letters were sent by Airgraph; 1,500,000,000 letters by V-mail.

Microfilming made it possible for the United States Navy to repair damaged warships with the utmost speed. Navy men had to have blueprints of damaged ships in order to make satisfactory repairs. Such prints are stored in the Washington headquarters of the Navy. They are very bulky; if the blueprints for a comparatively small ship like a destroyer were spread out, they would cover a quarter of an acre. Plans for a battleship would weigh more than a ton and would fill a boxcar.

If blueprints like these had been sent by ship, it might have meant a long wait before they reached their destination; or they would have used up a great deal of space on planes, at a time when such space was at a premium. Microfilming solved the problem. In Washington, the drawings were microfilmed, and an officer was able to carry them by hand — and by air — to the repair station. In one instance, at least, this method proved so efficient that by the time the damaged vessel reached the port where it was to be repaired, new sections had already been fabricated and were ready to be installed!

Microfilming has been widely used in espionage work. Of course, microfilm is an ideal medium for such activities, since it is absolutely accurate and takes up so little space.

In peace and war, then, microfilming has proved its worth; it has become indispensable in many operations and new uses are constantly being found for it.

KEEPING FIT

How to Care for the Body in Health

by RUTH E. GROUT

NO TWO humans are alike. Some persons inherit strong, healthy bodies; if such people are properly guided in childhood and give their bodies proper care later on, they will enjoy good health, barring serious accidents or diseases. Others will never attain a full measure of health, no matter how careful they are.

Each person should learn what his own health assets and liabilities are and how to give his body the attention it requires, so that he may enjoy as great a degree of health as possible.

How to judge physical condition

The Health Examination. Thorough health examinations at definite intervals provide the most dependable method for finding out about one's physical condition. Children under one year of age should be taken to a physician for an examination every month. The preschool child should be examined every three months; the school child, at least once a year.

The young man (or woman) between twenty and thirty-five years of age ordinarily does not need a complete examination more than once in two years. He has reached his full growth, for one thing, and he is not likely to be affected by the common ailments of later years. By the time he is thirty-five, an annual examination is desirable. Beyond the age of fifty, when cancer, heart disease, kidney trouble and similar diseases are most likely to occur, a checkup twice a year is advisable.

The Dental Examination. Dental examinations are essential in order to control tooth decay. They should be made by a competent dentist annually or at more frequent intervals, starting at the age of two and continuing throughout life. It is poor policy to visit your dentist only when you have a toothache.

Taking the Body Temperature and the Pulse Rate. Body temperature and the pulse rate are clues to the state of health. The physician uses them to aid his diagnosis; a layman, to decide whether or not it is advisable to consult a physician.

Body temperature is taken with a clinical thermometer. The temperature of adults and older children is nearly always taken by placing the thermometer in the mouth. A special kind of thermometer, which is inserted in the rectum, is used for babies and small children. In health, the temperature will read about 98.6° when taken by mouth; however, the reading will generally vary slightly from this standard at different times. In children, rectal temperatures of 99 degrees are within the

---

The Signs of Good Health

There are certain signs of good health:

Hair: glossy; clean.

Eyes: bright; clear; move normally; vision normal.

Ears: free from infection; no discharge or pain; hearing not impaired.

Skin: good color; smooth texture; free from blemishes.

Teeth: clean; no unfilled cavities; properly aligned.

Muscles: firm; well-conditioned.

General Appearance: alert; good posture; no nervous symptoms; not too thin or too fat.

Other Signs: good appetite; no undue fatigue after exertion, refreshed by rest.

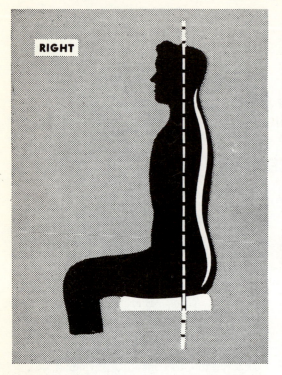

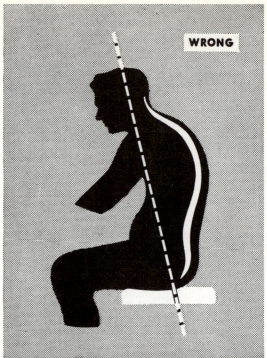

Correct posture helps young and old to keep fit.   Incorrect posture may bring about bodily ills.

limit of normal variation. Body temperatures also vary with different individuals. Generally speaking, one should consult a physician if the temperature is 100° or more; however, in certain cases, medical care is required even if the temperature is not so high as that. In other words, body temperature is only *one* of the factors that should be considered.

The expansion and contraction of the arteries as the blood flows through them is known as the pulse; it can be felt best in the arteries that lie near the surface and close to a bone, as at the wrist or the temples. Pulse rates vary according to age. They are higher in children, until the age of puberty (sexual maturity) is reached, than in adults. Women have higher rates than men. The rate for women averages about seventy-five to eighty beats per minute; for men, about seventy beats a minute. Anger, fear, excitement and increased physical activity will cause the pulse rate to increase; the rate will also be faster when the body temperature rises. If the pulse rate is far above the average, a physician should be consulted.

The Use of Height-Weight Tables. A common method of determining one's general physical condition has been to compare one's height and weight with standard tables of average heights and weights at different ages. Any wide deviation from so-called "normal" height and weight is supposed to show that something is wrong. The tables have also been used to determine whether a child is growing properly.

Scientists now know that deviations from the average weight for a given height and age, as shown by these tables, may be perfectly normal for an individual. Some people who appear to be underweight may be small in build but are in excellent health; others who seem to be overweight have large skeletons and they too are healthy. Still others who have "normal" weight, according to the standard height-weight tables, may really weigh too little for their build, or they may display certain symptoms that indicate poor health.

Growth as an Index of Health in Children. The study of a child's own growth record or the growth records of other children is now considered the most dependable

method of judging his physical progress. Regular gain in weight and in height is a sign that he is developing as he should, while failure to gain in weight for three successive months or more usually means that something is wrong. In keeping records, weights should be recorded monthly; heights, two or three times a year.

The care of the teeth and mouth

Sound teeth and a clean mouth add to personal attractiveness and contribute to good health. Poor teeth and gums interfere with the digestion of food. Missing or crooked teeth may cause speech defects; unpleasant facial expressions may result.

If food becomes lodged between the teeth and is not removed, it gradually disintegrates and produces bad breath. (Bad breath may also be caused by conditions that have nothing at all to do with the teeth, such as indigestion, diseased tonsils and nose infections.)

The most common cause of poor teeth is dental decay, known as dental caries. It is particularly widespread in children. It has been said that 97 per cent of the people in America at some time or other have cavities, caused by decay, in their teeth.

At the present time, there is no known method of care that will wholly prevent dental caries, but certain things may be done, nevertheless, to control its effects.

Early and frequent dental care is the most dependable method of dealing with this condition. As we remarked before, regular visits to the dentist should begin as early as the age of two. The dentist will fill any cavities he finds before they have had a chance to cause too much damage to the teeth. When decay is left unchecked, it spreads through a tooth much as rot spreads through an apple; it may finally cause the loss of the tooth.

Frequent visits to the dentist during childhood are advisable for another reason. The dentist will have a chance to see whether or not the child's teeth are coming in straight. If necessary, they can be straightened through orthodontia (dentistry dealing with irregularities of the teeth),

so that each tooth will have room to grow as it should.

Particular attention should be paid to the six-year molars. These are the first permanent teeth to appear in the mouth; as the name implies, they come through about the sixth year. They should be preserved at all costs. If any one of them is extracted, it leaves a gap so that the other permanent teeth come in crooked.

A good diet is necessary for the formation of good teeth during growth. After the teeth have been formed, a well-balanced diet is essential for good general health, including the health of teeth and mouth. The diet should include adequate amounts of milk, vegetables, fruits, meat or fish and whole-grain cereals.

There is increasing evidence that a diet that is rich in sweets favors the growth of germs that cause dental decay. Cutting down on candy, pastries, sweet drinks and sugar-coated gum will help to check caries.

Brushing the teeth may help prevent a certain amount of dental decay. The teeth should be brushed after every meal. Unfortunately, the old saying that "a clean tooth never decays" is not very accurate.

Mothers should begin to brush their chil-

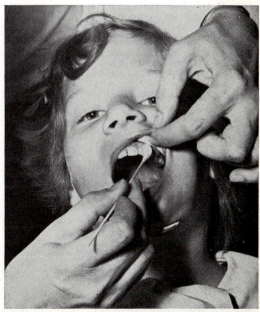

U. S. Public Health Service

Applying a 2 per cent solution of sodium fluoride to children's teeth will reduce tooth decay.

dren's teeth by the age of two years. By the age of three, children should be able to brush their own teeth. The toothbrush should be small. An approved type for any age is one that is no more than six bristle-tufts long and two wide.

Commercial tooth powders and tooth-pastes are pleasant to use, but have no special virtue in the cleansing of teeth. Many dentists recommend finely precipitated chalk or bicarbonate of soda as safe and inexpensive substitutes.

It is said that rinsing the mouth (water is sufficient) after eating — particularly after eating substances containing sugar — will cut down caries. Mouth washes have little effect in the control of dental decay. They do help to remove particles of food from between the teeth; but, after all, a water rinse will have the same effect.

No matter how carefully the teeth are cleaned at home, tartar and other deposits or stains will accumulate on them. The only satisfactory way to have these stains removed is to have the teeth cleaned by the dentist, once or twice a year.

An interesting development in the control of caries is the use of a fluoride (compound of fluorine). It may be taken internally through properly treated drinking water, or it may be applied directly to the teeth by the dentist. Experiments have shown that dental caries in children whose teeth are developing has been reduced as much as 60 per cent by the use of the treatment. It does not check caries in adults. It is important to note that it should be used only under expert supervision.

Ammoniated toothpastes and powders, which set ammonia free in the mouth, have also been used as antidecay agents.

The care of the eyes

In general, the eyes furnish their own hygienic care. Eyelids cover the eyes when there is danger; when the eyes close, a protective secretion is spread over the inside of the lids. Tears and eyelashes provide further protection and help to keep the eyes clean. All of these mechanisms work automatically.

General body health has an important bearing on good eye health; when the body is in a run-down condition, the eyes likewise are below par.

Eyes should be examined periodically by a qualified physician and if possible by an oculist, or ophthalmologist — a physician specializing in the treatment of defects and

Better Light Better Sight Bureau

A poor lighting arrangement: the lamp produces a comparatively small circle of light on the desk.

diseases of the eye. If visual defects are discovered, they should be corrected at once. Otherwise, they may cause great discomfort to the eyes and may also produce dizziness and other disturbances.

Adequate lighting is important; there should be enough light and also the right kind of light, so that the eyes do not have to strain in order to see. Light is measured in terms of foot-candles. A foot-candle represents the amount of light that a sperm candle, made according to a definite formula, will throw at a distance of a foot. A minimum of fifteen foot-candles of light is needed for ordinary reading in the home; at least twenty-five foot-candles are required for close work such as sewing.

Glare has a very fatiguing effect on the eyes. Opaque lighting fixtures that reflect the light upward as well as outward help to prevent glare; exposed electric-light bulbs and clear-glass oil-lamp shades produce glare and cause much eye discomfort and strain.

Prolonged use of the eyes produces eye fatigue. It is a good idea to lift one's eyes occasionally from close work and look off into the distance, or to rest one's head on the desk or table. Sleep and other forms of rest and relaxation also help to reduce or eliminate eye fatigue.

The introduction of television in many homes has produced a new cause for eye fatigue. A clear image on the screen will minimize such fatigue. There should not be too great contrast between the light on the screen and in the room. Moderate, indirect lighting makes a good background for viewing television. Shifting the gaze away from the screen at frequent intervals will cut down eye fatigue considerably.

Many eye difficulties arise from infections and injuries. External infections often are spread as a result of careless personal habits, such as using another person's towel or rubbing the eyes with unclean hands.

Suitable precautions should be taken to protect the eyes from injury on the playground, in the factory or wherever they are exposed to danger.

A physician should be consulted whenever there is trouble. Granulated eyelids (trachoma), styes, conjunctivitis (an inflammation of the membranes covering the front of the eyeballs and lining the eyelids), foreign particles in the eye, continuous headaches and red eyes are among the abnormal conditions that demand medical attention. The use of eyedrops and eye-

Better Light Better Sight Bureau

A good lighting arrangement: the light, effectively diffused, illuminates every part of the desk.

washes should be avoided, unless the physician orders them. If glasses are prescribed, they should be worn as directed.

The care of the ears

The saying that "nothing smaller than the elbow should be placed in the outer ear" is not so nonsensical as it might appear to be. Certainly, the practice of cleaning the ear with hairpins, toothpicks or other sharp instruments should be avoided. It may re-

and treatment of an ear infection are extremely important. If left untreated, not only may the ear itself become permanently damaged but the infection may spread to the mastoid bone and from there to the brain.

Periodic hearing tests will reveal early hearing losses. These tests should be given frequently enough so that any defects in hearing may be detected before they have progressed too far to benefit from treatment. The instrument known as the audi-

Sonotone Corp.

Giving a hearing test with an audiometer. The instrument detects and measures hearing losses.

sult in the infection of the ear canal or in damage to the eardrum.

Wax that accumulates in the outer ear should be removed by syringing it out gently with lukewarm water. Before attempting to do so, a person should obtain instructions from a physician or a nurse.

Infection of the middle ear, the part that lies behind the eardrum, may be the result of a spread of infection from the nose and throat through the Eustachian tube to the middle ear. The ear will ache, and hearing will be affected. Early medical diagnosis

ometer is particularly useful in detecting hearing losses; communities should purchase the instrument for schools and health centers. All those who are found to have hearing loss should be referred to a physician for further examination and for treatment if necessary.

The care of the nose

The nose serves as a passageway for air to the lungs. As the air passes through, it is warmed and moistened; it is also cleaned

Cleanliness Bureau

A scrubbing brush is useful in washing the hands.

by means of a great number of tiny cilia, or hairs, within the nose. These protective devices are more efficient than any that we can provide.

Blowing the nose is helpful in removing mucous secretions, dust and various other particles. The nose should be blown with both nostrils open.

Self-medication by means of jellies, sprays, drops and douches is a dangerous procedure. Preparations like these may give temporary relief, but have no lasting value. They may even interfere with the normal protective activities of the nose and they may cause chronic irritation.

The nose is connected by small passageways to the sinuses; these are cavities within the skull, located in the vicinity of the eyes and nose. Infection in the nose can spread rapidly to the sinuses. Although acute infections of this sort often clear up spontaneously, chronic infections may cause much discomfort and ill health. Diagnosis and treatment of sinus infections should be entrusted to a physician.

Children often stuff pennies, chalk, buttons or various other foreign bodies in the nose. Parents should never attempt to remove foreign objects like these themselves, but should seek the aid of a physician.

The care of the hands

Cleanliness of hands and nails is important from the standpoint of good grooming and, to a certain extent, from the stand-

point of good health. Hands should be washed as often as necessary; the number of times a day will depend on the person's occupation. Hands should be washed before handling food, before eating and after going to the toilet. They should be rubbed thoroughly; plenty of soap and warm water should be used.

Too-frequent hand washing may result in the removal of natural oils and may cause rough, cracked hands. Lotions help to keep the hands soft.

The care of the nails

Nails reflect the state of a person's health. Diseases like diabetes, typhoid fever, valvular heart disease, asthma and syphilis may cause changes in the color, texture and shape of nails. Brittle, cracked nails may be due to a deficiency of vitamins, iron or other elements in the diet; they may also be caused by too frequent use of nail-polish remover. Nervous persons are apt to bite their nails. Before this particular habit can be broken, the underlying conditions that cause it must be corrected.

Regular manicuring will help to prevent hangnails. The cuticle (the skin around the base and sides of the nail) should be pushed back frequently, especially after washing the hands, while the cuticle is soft.

The care of the feet

Foot difficulties are the cause of much fatigue and also of various other disturbances. Comfortable, properly fitted shoes will help keep the feet in good condition. Good general body health, good posture and cleanliness are also important.

Shoes for everyday use should fit properly. A shoe that is too short will cramp the foot; one that is too long will be just as uncomfortable. In general, shoes should have round toes and straight inner borders; they should be of medium width. The heels should be neither too high nor too low. High heels for women are all right for dress occasions, but they are bad for the feet if worn every day. Very low-heeled shoes, like moccasins, do not give the foot

The hair should be brushed thoroughly twice a day.

enough support. Most feet require the firm support that is provided by rigid shanks.

Faulty shoes may cause ingrown toenails, corns and calluses and other defects. Ingrown toenails occur usually on the big toe; the edge of the nail penetrates the flesh and often causes infection. Treatment for this condition is a local operation, with partial removal of the nail. To prevent ingrown toenails, the nails should be cut straight across. When troubled with corns, one should find out which piece of footwear is causing the difficulty and promptly stop wearing it. Corns are not easy to cure; they are likely to reappear when pressure is applied again.

Weight control has a definite bearing on foot hygiene; people who weigh too much are likely to have foot difficulties, as the feet cannot support the extra load. Proper posture in standing and walking are also important; so is cleanliness. The feet should be bathed daily with a nonirritating soap, and they should be dried thoroughly. Tired feet should be soaked alternately in hot and cold water.

The care
of the hair

Dirt, dead skin cells and oil secreted by the scalp accumulate on the scalp and in the hair. They can be removed by brushing and shampooing.

The hair should be brushed thoroughly twice a day; this not only helps to remove

dirt but it also serves to stimulate the scalp. A stiff brush, with its bristles set apart, is desirable.

Frequency of shampooing depends upon the condition of the scalp and the amount of exposure to dust and dirt. Oily hair should be washed once a week or oftener; dry hair may not have to be washed more than once every two weeks.

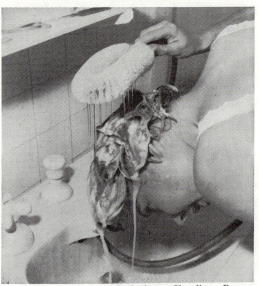

Both photos, Cleanliness Bureau

For sparkling cleanliness, the hair should be rinsed thoroughly in warm, then cold water. Plenty of clear water should be poured over the hair.

Use plenty of soap (or detergent) and of warm water. The soap may be in the form of a solution, a cream or a powder. Soap cake rubbed directly onto the hair is hard to remove later when the hair is rinsed. Usually two soapings are desirable, the first to remove the excess oil and the second to clean the hair and scalp thoroughly. Several rinsings are necessary to remove all the soap. Clean, wet hair will "squeak" when rubbed between the fingers. Excessive heat should be avoided in drying the hair; it is better to use a towel or simply to expose the hair to the air.

Permanent waving has become a very common practice among women today. Are permanent waves harmful to the hair or scalp? The following statement by the Bureau of Investigation of the American Medical Association answers the question:

"Both the machine- and machineless-wave solutions consist chiefly of ammonia, the machineless solutions also containing various sulfates, as a rule. The cold-wave preparations do not greatly differ from one another in composition, usually depending on ammonium salts for softening the hair and ammonia for the waving effects.

"Though all three types have been reported to have caused injuries in individual cases, considering the millions of such treatments given to American women annually, it seems likely that the proportion of injuries is small, though, of course, not all of them may have been reported.

"The cold-wave solutions apparently have come into popularity in very recent years, as the inquiries about them are now more numerous than those about the heat-wave preparations. A government agency which investigated some of them expressed the belief that most of the difficulties resulting from their use are due to carelessness on the part of the beauty-shop operator or of the user in applying them, chiefly because proper warnings are not given with the directions that accompany the products. The government agency further warned that care should be taken not to let the solutions touch the scalp or skin, lest they enter the system and cause some internal injury."

The problem
of elimination

Body wastes are eliminated through the intestines and kidneys and also by way of the skin and lungs. The healthy body handles its eliminative processes with a minimum amount of attention.

Ordinarily, constipation, or delay in elimination, can be avoided by a balanced diet, regularity of eating habits, the drinking of plenty of fluids, adequate rest, exercise and freedom from emotional strain.

Each person has his own bowel habits. For some persons it is perfectly natural to have a bowel movement only once in two or three days; for others, it is normal for the bowels to move two or three times a day. It is important to heed the call of nature whenever it occurs; ample time should be allowed for complete evacuation.

Laxatives and cathartics may give temporary relief, but they often do more harm than good. They should never be used if there is any abdominal pain. Such pain may be the first symptom of appendicitis; purgatives may cause irritation and even rupture of the appendix. Special drugs to aid elimination should be used only as directed by a physician.

The care
of the skin

A simple, well-balanced diet helps to keep the skin smooth, free from blemishes, in good color and functioning properly.

Cleanliness is essential for a healthy skin and a good complexion. In general, the average person should take a cleansing bath with mild soap and warm water daily. This removes the waste materials excreted by the body through the skin; it also eliminates excessive oil and the dirt that has collected during the day.

The face and hands should be washed oftener than the rest of the body. Hand washing has been discussed earlier in the chapter. Wash the face very thoroughly at least once a day, preferably at night, with a mild soap and warm water applied with a wash cloth. In the morning, a rinsing with warm water, followed by cool water, may be enough.

Oily skins will need more frequent cleansing than dry skins. If the skin is bathed too often, it may become excessively dry, chapped or inflamed; this is true particularly during cold weather. The skin will become similarly irritated when the soap used in bathing is not rinsed off completely.

Soap is the most satisfactory of all cleansing agents. In former years, soaps contained free alkalis, which caused considerable irritation, but such alkalis are generally absent in the complexion soaps sold today.

The skin disorder called acne is common in young people. In acne, the pores of the skin and the openings of the oil glands become clogged, and this condition results in pimples and blackheads. It is now be-

lieved that glandular secretions within the body play a very important part in the development of acne. In mild cases, thorough washing with plenty of soap and warm water is helpful. Severe cases require expert treatment by a physician.

The use of cosmetics

Many millions of dollars are spent annually on cosmetics. Though many of these products serve a useful purpose, nothing can take the place of health as a source of genuine beauty. Good health produces fresh complexions and smooth, firm skin; it also causes cheeks to glow and the eyes to shine. Cosmetics may be used to enhance these effects; they should never be used as a substitute for nature's methods.

Most of the cleansing creams, cold creams and lotions that are now on the market are harmless to the normal skin. Cleansing creams are of different kinds. Some of them are merely soap and water in cream form; others contain mineral oil; still others contain chemicals known as emulsifiers, which serve to keep the cream from separating into its component parts. These make particularly effective cleansing creams; they are gradually replacing the other kinds. According to advertising claims, hormone creams preserve youth; they are dangerous and should be avoided.

Cold creams and face lotions have been used to cleanse or lubricate the skin since time immemorial. These cosmetic preparations do not cause superfluous growth of hair, as some people believe, but they definitely cannot bring about the miracles that are sometimes claimed for them. Names like "nourishing creams," "wrinkle eradicators," "skin tonics," "contour creams" and "tissue creams" are quite inaccurate and misleading.

The use of deodorants

Body odors are caused by an accumulation of sweat or oil on the body's surface. Regular bathing to remove these substances and change of underclothing following the bathing are the best methods to keep down the odors. When sweating becomes excessive, as under the arms, it may be desirable to use a deodorant. Some deodorants cut down the action of the sweat glands; others merely reduce or counteract the odor of sweat. A simple, inexpensive underarm deodorant of the latter type is ordinary baking soda.

Many people can use deodorants without harmful effects. If they irritate the skin, one should either change the product or seek medical advice.

The use of depilatories

Excessive hair on the face, legs and armpits often causes annoyance to women. Various methods, both temporary and permanent, are used to remove this hair.

The only safe method for the permanent removal of hair is electrolysis, in which an electric needle is used. It is important to note that this method should be employed only by skilled operators.

Hair is sometimes removed temporarily by chemical or mechanical devices. The chemical method, which involves the application of a substance that dissolves the hair, may damage the skin. The chemicals may also be absorbed and do harm to the body. They are not recommended.

Hair may be removed mechanically by means of tweezers, by shaving and by a mild abrasive, such as sandpaper or pumice. The tweezers method is satisfactory for removing single hairs. Over wide surfaces, shaving or the use of an abrasive is preferable. Another procedure is to cover the surface of the skin with wax and then to strip off the hardened wax, thus pulling out the enmeshed hair. This method may be irritating; it is not more effective than the rest.

Keeping abreast of new developments in medicine and public health

New developments in medicine and public health add constantly to our understanding of the care of the body. Everybody should try to keep abreast of these developments and to apply them if possible.

See also Vol. 10, p. 277: "General Works."

EXERCISE AND REST

How the Body Expends and Renews Its Energy Stores

by A. C. BURTON

IN CERTAIN respects, at least, the human body is like a locomotive or the motor of an automobile, because it is constantly transforming the chemical energy contained in its "fuel" — that is, the food it swallows — into heat energy and mechanical energy. The toast you eat for breakfast is burned in the body just as truly as coal is burned beneath the boiler of a steam engine or gasoline is burned in the cylinders of an automobile. Part of the chemical energy supplied by the toast is changed into the heat energy that keeps your body warm; part of it, into the mechanical energy that makes it possible for your muscles to pump blood through your body or to move your chest in breathing.

Even if you lie idly in bed all day, your body continues to transform a certain minimal amount of the chemical energy provided by food into mechanical energy and heat energy. The heart keeps on pumping blood in the circulation; the diaphragm continues to contract and expand in order to draw oxygen into the lungs and force carbon dioxide and water vapor from them; the movements of the intestines continue as food is digested and absorbed into the tissues. The body must be kept at its normal temperature so that activities such as these may be carried out as effectively as possible.

The rate at which your body transforms energy when it is at rest is called its basal metabolic rate. (Metabolism refers to those processes that build up protoplasm and those that break it down into simpler substances with the accompanying release of energy.) In the basal, or resting, state of the body, most of the chemical energy

provided by food is changed into heat energy and only a little into mechanical energy, since most of the muscles are relaxed and inactive.

When you rise from your bed and go about your daily activities — moving the arms and fingers in the act of eating, walking briskly to the train or bus, playing eighteen holes of golf — the rate at which energy is transformed by the body increases greatly. Even when you are simply standing still, the muscles that have to do with posture must exert themselves in order to hold the body upright.

The transforming of chemical energy into mechanical energy by the muscles is called muscular exercise. We generally think of exercise as the kind of activity that is involved in playing a game of tennis or running a race or carrying the puck in a hockey game. Scientifically, however, the word exercise has a far broader meaning; it refers to any kind of muscular activity, violent or gentle, from lifting a heavy weight to threading a needle.

No engine is perfectly efficient, since a good deal of its chemical energy is transformed into heat energy instead of mechanical energy. In the case of the human body, only about one-quarter of the energy we obtain from food is changed into the energy required for breathing, talking, walking, writing and the like. The rest is changed into heat energy.

When the muscles become active, more chemical energy is required so that increased mechanical energy may be made available. The following table shows the energy increase involved in different kinds of muscular exercise:

Table 1. Rate of Energy Transformation by the Body in Different Kinds of Muscular Exercise

Type of Exercise	Rate in Mets *	Type of Exercise	Rate in Mets
Resting, or basal	1.0	Fast walking (4 miles per hour)	4
Sleeping	0.8		
Standing quietly	1.2	Mining coal	4
Dressing and undressing	1.4	Sawing wood	5
Dishwashing	1.6	Skiing	6 to 10
Slow walking (2 miles per hour)	2	Running (5½ miles per hour)	7
Cycling	3 to 7	Long-distance running	10 to 12
Rowing	3 to 10	100-yard dash in 10 seconds	100

* A Met represents the resting, or basal, rate of energy transformation of an average man. The word comes from metabolism. It is about equal to the rate of energy used in a 100-watt electric bulb.

The figures in this table are only roughly accurate, since the actual rate of energy transformation will depend on the strenuousness with which a given activity is carried out. The energy required to perform a task is much greater if it is done rapidly than if it is done slowly. Friction has to be overcome in the different muscles that are involved; the higher the speed of movement, the greater the forces of friction. This is true also of mechanisms like automobiles. You use up more gasoline when you drive your car a distance of 5 miles at 50 miles per hour than when you drive the same distance at 30 miles per hour.

Naturally, more food will be required as the rate of energy transformation increases. A modest amount of food will suffice for an invalid resting quietly in bed all day long. A miner will have to eat much more if he is to do his job effectively. Athletes must also be well fed. Many American colleges and universities have a special training table where football players eat carefully selected food in adequate

Standard Oil Co. (N. J.)

The fuel that is being pumped into this car will be burned in the cylinders, thus releasing energy.

quantities. As a result, the coach can feel reasonably certain that his charges will have enough energy for their violent play.

What happens in the body during exercise?

When you step on the accelerator of your car, the carburetor feeds more gasoline to the engine. The engine runs faster — that is, the chemical energy of the fuel is changed into heat energy and mechanical energy at an increased rate. But it is not enough to supply the engine with more gasoline; if that were all, your car would soon be on the scrap heap. A great many other factors are involved.

In order to burn the fuel, a greater supply of oxygen is needed; hence, the carburetor must suck in air to the engine in greater quantities than before. A good deal more heat is generated at high speeds. To keep the engine from becoming overheated, more cooling must be provided by the water pump, which circulates water through the engine jacket, and by the fan, which blows air over the radiator. The ignition must produce more sparks per minute to fire the fuel in the cylinders; more oil must flow in order to lubricate the working parts. Many

operations are required, therefore, in order to bring about an increased rate of energy transformation in your automobile.

So it is with the human body when it passes from rest to exercise. The muscles must transform chemical energy into mechanical energy at a faster rate than before, but a good many other things must happen, too.

To burn more fuel, the muscles need a greater supply of the oxygen that is carried to them by the circulation of the blood. Therefore, the flow of blood to the muscles must increase greatly. To charge the increased blood flow with sufficient oxygen, the lungs must pump more air. Notice that your breathing becomes deeper and faster the minute you start exercising.

As the muscles become more active, more chemical energy is transformed into heat energy. This extra heat would quickly raise the body temperature to fever pitch if effective cooling were not provided.

The increased circulation of blood to the surface of the body — that is, the skin — helps to carry the heat away faster than normally. The sweat glands all over the body surface burst into activity and drench the body with perspiration; as the sweat

Standard Oil Co. (N. J.)

The food that we eat is a fuel, like gasoline; it will release energy when it is burned in the body.

Wide World

In this 50-meter run, much of the energy of the racers comes from accumulating a big oxygen debt.

evaporates, the body loses heat to its surroundings. These cooling devices are quite effective, but they do not suffice if a person engages in particularly strenuous activity. The body temperature of the most perfectly trained athlete is bound to rise if he runs a mile race, or plays several fast sets of tennis or boxes ten rounds.

The increase in oxygen supply required for muscular exertion

The human mechanisms that take part in exercise are linked up by the action of the nervous system, which governs the action and the co-operation of all the parts of the body in muscular exercise. We still do not fully understand just what is involved. For example, what brings about the increase in the oxygen supply that is required for muscular exertion? We know that the rate and depth of breathing are controlled by the amount of carbon dioxide in the blood, but this is by no means the whole story. Nerve impulses from the muscles to the brain undoubtedly play a part. It is probable, too, that when the motor cortex — the part of the brain that controls the activity of the muscles — goes into action, it sends nerve messages to the various muscles that control breathing.

In exercising, we "live on income" or "go into debt"

In exercise, as we have seen, the supply of oxygen to the muscles increases as they become more and more active. There is a limit, however, to the rate at which the lungs can breathe air and the heart can pump blood. The maximum rate for each individual depends on his fitness and his training for a particular form of exercise.

Professor Archibald V. Hill, of England, a Nobel Prize winner in physiology, measured the rate at which a group of athletes breathed in air and absorbed oxygen. He found that an athlete of average size, at rest, uses nearly half a pint of oxygen each minute; when doing violent exercise, he can take in roughly 15 times as much oxygen, or more than 7 pints a minute. This would correspond to 15 Met units in Table 1. Yet how can we say that 15 Mets is the maximum rate for taking in and using oxygen, when the table shows that a sprinter in the 100-yard dash transforms energy at the rate of 100 Mets?

Here our comparison of the human body with the engine of an automobile breaks down. The car engine can only "live on its income"; it can burn only as much gasoline as the fuel pump supplies, together with as much oxygen as the carburetor can draw in. This, of course, sets a definite limit to the speed of a car. If it has a maximum speed of 100 miles per hour on a certain track, it cannot go faster than this, even for a very short time. The maximum speed for a 1-mile race will be the same as for a 10-mile race; it will be 100 miles per hour.

This is not true in the case of the human machine. The average speed of a sprinter in a 100-yard dash is not the same as that of a miler or a ten-mile runner, as a glance at the following table will show. In it we have given the world's running records in hours, minutes and seconds; in each case we have also calculated the average speed in terms of miles per hour.

TABLE 2. WORLD RUNNING RECORDS RECOGNIZED BY THE INTERNATIONAL
AMATEUR ATHLETIC FEDERATION, MARCH, 1957

Distance	Record Time Hrs.	Min.	Sec.	Average Speed in Miles per Hour	Record Holder	Date
100 yds.			9.3	20.4 (25 for last 50 yds.)	M. E. Patton, U.S.A.	1948
					H. D. Hogan, Australia	1954
					James Golliday, U.S.A.	1955
					Leamon King, U.S.A.	1956
					David Sime, U.S.A.	1956
220 yds.			20.0	22.5	David Sime, U.S.A.	1956
440 yds.			45.8	19.7	Jim Lea, U.S.A.	1956
880 yds.		1	47.5	16.7	Lon Spurrier, U.S.A.	1955
1 mile		3	58.0	15.1	John Landy, Australia	1954
2 miles		8	33.4	14.0	Sandor Iharos, Hungary	1955
3 miles		13	14.2	13.7	Sandor Iharos, Hungary	1955
6 miles		27	43.8	13.0	Sandor Iharos, Hungary	1956
10 miles		48	12.0	12.8	Emil Zatopek, Czechoslovakia	1951
15 miles	1	14	1.0	12.2	Emil Zatopek, Czechoslovakia	1956

The table shows that the shorter the distance the greater the average speed that a human can attain. There is an apparent exception in the case of the 100-yard dash, since the average speed here is lower than that for the 220-yard run. But this is not really an exception; the comparatively low average speed for the 100-yard dash is due to the fact that the time lost in getting up speed counts for much more in a short race than it does in a longer one. Actually, the speed recorded in the last 50 yards of the 100-yard dash is close to 25 miles per hour, the figure in brackets in Table 2.

For distances longer than a mile, the speed does not decrease greatly. The rate of energy transformation of the long-distance runner turns out to be close to fifteen Mets; it corresponds to the maximum rate at which the body can take in oxygen.

In this long-distance race, there is a fairly steady balance between energy output and oxygen intake.

YMCA

In this basketball game, the players are piling up tremendous oxygen debts, which must be paid later.

Evidently, in the case of sprinters, the muscles can transform energy at a much greater rate than this. In other words, the muscles are not limited, as is the automobile engine, to living on income, but for a short time at least they can pile up an "oxygen debt." That is, they can transform chemical energy into mechanical energy and heat energy without any reaction with oxygen. They can do this by breaking down the glycogen, or animal starch, stored up in the muscles and liver, to form lactic acid — a reaction that does not require oxygen.

Extra oxygen will have to be taken in later to pay back this oxygen debt when the heavy exercise is over. This extra oxygen will then react with the lactic acid that has accumulated in the muscles. Part of the lactic acid will be reconverted into glycogen,

which will be stored anew in the muscles and liver; part of it will yield carbon dioxide and water, which will be passed out of the body with other waste products.

The total oxygen debt that can be accumulated is strictly limited. It is about twenty-nine pints of oxygen for a trained athlete. When he has piled up the maximum oxygen debt, the store of glycogen in his muscles has been practically used up and excessive quantities of lactic acid have accumulated. His muscles are now completely exhausted, and his legs will buckle under him.

In the 100-yard dash, much of the energy comes from piling up an oxygen debt, since a good sprinter does not take a single breath from start to finish. In contrast, in long-distance runs, there is a more or less steady balance between the output of energy and the intake of oxygen; the runner accumulates an oxygen debt only in the final sprint for the tape. When a new record is established, it is often because the winner has found a better method — for him, that is — of spending both his income of oxygen and his borrowed oxygen, so that he arrives almost completely "bankrupt" at the tape.

Look at Table 2 again. You will note that almost all the records for distances up to one mile are held by Americans, but records for longer distances are all held by Europeans. This has been more or less true for years. Apparently, while other races excel at "running on income," Americans excel at bursts of activity, piling up tremendous oxygen debts that have to be paid later. Consider the all-out spurts and big oxygen debts in America's favorite autumn sport — football. If it were not for the interval between halves, more or less frequent time-outs, wholesale substitutions, the marking off of penalties and the like, the players would be in a state of complete collapse at the end of a game.

The recovery period — paying back the debt

When you stop doing a violent exercise, your body does not return at once to its normal state. For quite a while you will breathe fast and deeply, your heart will

pound and your skin will perspire. In fact, you will not feel up to par again until practically all the oxygen debt has been paid. The period during which this debt is made good is called the recovery period.

The longer the heavy exercise has continued and the more violent it has been, the bigger the oxygen debt that you must pay and the longer the recovery period will last. Physical fitness and training are exceedingly important in this connection. The fit person will have less oxygen debt to pay, because he has been more efficient in producing mechanical energy; he will also require less time to pay the debt in the recovery period.

Professor Hill measured, in three different men, the time required to recover from the effects of marking time at the double-quick. For a man of 35, it took 20 minutes for full recovery; for a 24-year-old student, it took 12 minutes; for a very fit young student, who was a champion swimmer, only 8 minutes.

After violent exercise that lasts longer, it may be an hour or more before the body is back to its normal resting state. In our laboratory, we once recorded the heartbeat of a student lying on a bed; we were puzzled to find that for nearly an hour it kept getting steadily slower. The mystery was solved when we found that he had just played in a basketball game and that he was not very fit.

The body must make up its "water debt"

During the recovery period following heavy exercise, you will note that you become very thirsty. The body is serving notice in this way that it has lost a great deal of water in perspiration during the exercise and that this "water debt" must be made up. The total weight of water lost in this way may amount to several pounds.

In long-continued heavy work, especially in hot surroundings, it is a good idea to drink not pure water but water with salt added (a teaspoonful to a gallon). The reason is that, together with water, the body has lost a considerable amount of salt as a result of perspiring freely.

There does not seem to be any salt-craving sensation in the human body, corresponding to the water-craving sensation, or thirst. This deficiency is really most unfortunate, since it may cause trouble. For example, for many centuries miners used to suffer from severe cramps in the muscles (miners' cramps). Then it was discovered that they simply needed salt to make up for the salt that they had lost in sweat; salt was supplied and this particular ailment practically disappeared. Curiously enough, animals seem to realize when they require salt. Deer or cattle will travel miles in search of it, and they will gather eagerly at the salt licks in our reservations.

In very violent exercise, though the oxygen debt may be paid back in an hour or so, the muscles may not fully recover for days. The body may be stiff and sore, blisters may form and there may be other distressing symptoms. All this indicates that the exercise in question is altogether too violent for the sufferer, at least in his present state of training.

The restorative effect of sleep

It has long been considered that the activity of the muscles and the brain and nervous system throughout the day results in the gradual accumulation, in the body, of chemicals that have something to do with tiredness, or fatigue. We do not know just what these chemicals are, although much research has been done trying to find them in the blood. The removal of these products of fatigue is probably very slow and not complete in the usual recovery period we have discussed. It is thought that only after a good night's sleep is the body really back to normal and ready for another day's exercise and work.

In sleep, the muscles are probably more relaxed than at any other time, except when the body is under the influence of a total anesthetic. The rate of metabolism is reduced up to 20 per cent below the basal, or resting, level. When we awake at last, renewed and refreshed, our muscles are ready for the stresses of the following day.

See also Vol. 10, p. 277: "Exercise."

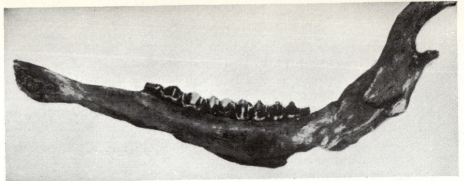

Lower jawbone of red deer found at the human occupation site at Star Carr, Yorkshire, England. The birchwood platform at this site has been dated by the radiocarbon method.

British Inf. Serv.

The funerary ship from the tomb of King Sesostris III of Egypt. A sample for radiocarbon dating was obtained by sawing a hole in the deck of this ship.

Chicago Nat. Hist. Mus.

Huge monumental stones at Stonehenge, in Wiltshire, England. A charcoal sample from a hole outside these stones was dated by the radiocarbon method.

British Inf Serv.

PRACTICAL APPLICATIONS
OF RADIOCARBON DATING

RADIOCARBON DATING

How the Relics of the Past Reveal Their Age

by WILLARD F. LIBBY

ALL living things, plants and animals alike, contain the chemical element carbon. Green plants obtain carbon from the carbon dioxide existing in gaseous form in the air; they combine this substance with water in the presence of sunlight and manufacture food. They become the source of carbon for other plants and also for animals, which eat plants or plant-eating animals.

A comparatively insignificant number of the carbon atoms existing in all living things are radioactive: that is, their nuclei disintegrate sooner or later, sometimes after a long span of time. Radioactive carbon atoms continue to exist in animals and plants (and in objects made from them) for thousands of years after death has taken place. We find radioactive carbon in the bones and meat and manure of animals that died long ago, in peat (derived from dead vegetation), in wooden boats and platforms, in cotton and linen garments, in leather shoes and bags and in many other things.

In recent years certain scientists (including the author of this article) have found a practical application for the radioactive carbon atoms existing in dead organic matter. By carefully measuring the radioactivity of samples derived from such matter, they have developed a method for dating objects that go back to early antiquity and even to prehistoric times.

The radioactive carbon atoms that make possible the new dating method are atoms with mass number 14 (see Index under Mass number); they are known as carbon 14 atoms. The vast majority of carbon atoms are isotopes with mass number 12; they are not radioactive.

How is radioactive carbon 14 produced? The answer is to be found in the upper reaches of the earth's atmosphere. This area, filled with tenuous gases, is constantly bombarded by cosmic rays — mysterious radiations coming from outer space, probably from beyond our galaxy. As the rays strike the atmosphere, they disintegrate the nuclei, or cores, of some of the numberless atoms that are found there. Among the building blocks that make up the nuclei are the particles called neutrons. When nuclei are smashed by cosmic rays, free neutrons are scattered in the air.

They are very quickly absorbed by the nitrogen atoms, with mass number 14, that make up about 78 per cent of the atmosphere by volume. When a nitrogen atom absorbs a neutron, a proton is emitted; thus the atom keeps its mass number, 14, but instead of remaining a stable nitrogen atom, as it had been before, it becomes an unstable, radioactive carbon atom.

University of Chicago

The author in his laboratory.

The material that is to be dated is shipped to a well-equipped laboratory.

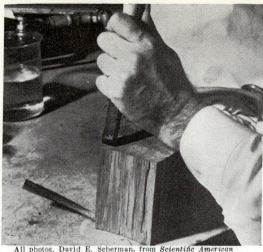

All photos, David E. Scherman, from *Scientific American*

Splitting a sample from wood that is to be dated by the radiocarbon method.

Radioactive carbon, or radiocarbon, as it is often called, has a half-life of 5,600 years. By that we mean that if we start with 100 atoms of radiocarbon, at the end of 5,600 years we shall have only 50 atoms, or half as many; the rest will have decayed. In the next period of 5,600 years, one half of the remaining 50 atoms — that is, 25 atoms — will also decay and so on.

Cosmic rays have been bombarding the atmosphere for millions of years, and they have been constantly producing new supplies of radiocarbon. At the same time the radiocarbon atoms that have already been formed are steadily disintegrating. It is as if water were being pumped into a tank with a hole in its bottom. A steady level will be reached in the tank when the amount of water entering it will be equal to the amount of water flowing out of it. By analyzing the corresponding "level" of carbon 14 atoms, scientists have calculated that there are about 100 tons of radiocarbon on the earth at any given time. In each second upon each square centimeter of the earth's surface something like 2.4 disintegrations of radiocarbon are taking place — that is, 2.4 atoms of radiocarbon are decaying. This represents a considerable amount of radioactivity, and it is surprising that it is not noticed ordinarily. The reason for this state of affairs is that the radiocarbon that is produced in the atmosphere is always diluted with a tremendous amount of ordinary carbon.

What happens to the radioactive carbon atoms on the earth's surface? We know that under the appropriate circumstances ordinary carbon atoms combine with the oxygen atoms in air and burn, forming carbon dioxide molecules (or carbon monoxide molecules, if combustion is incomplete). That is what happens, for example, when we set fire to coal, which is made up largely of carbon. We take it for granted, therefore, that the radiocarbon atoms upon the earth will combine sooner or later with oxygen atoms and will produce radioactive carbon dioxide molecules (plus a certain quantity of carbon monoxide molecules).

How plants and animals assimilate radiocarbon

There is a considerable amount of nonradioactive carbon dioxide in the air at all times. Winds thoroughly mix together the radioactive and nonradioactive molecules of carbon dioxide. Plants assimilate small amounts of radioactive carbon dioxide together with large amounts of ordinary carbon dioxide. That is why they and the animals that feed upon them, directly or indirectly, contain radiocarbon.

As long as plants and animals live, they keep replenishing their stores of radioactive carbon; they can no longer absorb it, however, after they die. The radiocarbon atoms they contain at the moment of death will disintegrate at the rate of 50

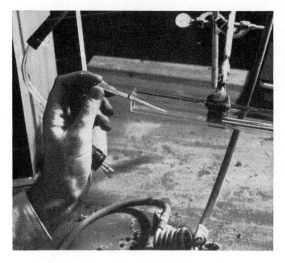

The sample, which is to be converted into carbon dioxide, is put in a tube.

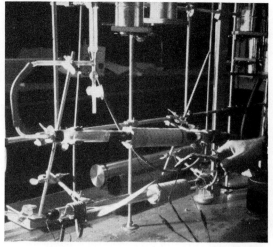

The sample is now burned and yields a certain quantity of carbon dioxide.

per cent every 5,600 years, and they will not be replaced.

While the organism is alive, there are 15.3 disintegrations per minute for every gram of carbon that it contains; 5,600 years from the time of death there will be 7.65 disintegrations (half of 15.3) per minute; 11,200 years from the time of death there will be 3.83 disintegrations (half of 7.65) per minute and so on. At the end of 20,000 or 30,000 years, the disintegrations will be so few that it will be exceedingly difficult to measure them. By noting the rate at which the radiocarbon atoms in a given sample decay, we can estimate the age of the sample — that is, age in the special sense of "time that has elapsed since death." That is the principle of radiocarbon dating.

In order to measure the rate of disintegration of radiocarbon atoms, we use a special Geiger counter. This instrument is shaped like a cylinder and has a wire extending down its center; it is filled with gas. An electrical potential is maintained between the wire and cylinder walls, which have been appropriately charged. The radiocarbon dating sample is placed on the inside surface of the Geiger counter.

As an atom disintegrates, it emits a beta particle. When this particle passes through the gas-filled space of the counter, a tiny spark is produced; an electrical impulse is recorded by electronic equipment connected to the Geiger counter. The

The carbon dioxide is dried by freezing, and is stored in glass bottles.

Finally, a Geiger counter measures the amount of radioactivity in the carbon.

sensitive instrument detects every disintegrated particle that passes through the gas within it.

Unfortunately the radiocarbon in the sample is not the only source of radiation that affects the Geiger counter. Even before the radioactive sample has been placed in it, the instrument records some 600 counts a minute, produced by external radiation.

The radiations from uranium and thorium deposits and their disintegration products can be effectively absorbed by placing six or eight inches of iron around the Geiger counter. But cosmic rays, which are an important source of external radiation, are so penetrating that they cannot be warded off by a shield of iron. Hence, instead of trying to shield the Geiger counter from these rays, we must "erase" them from the record. Within the external iron shield, we place a set of Geiger counters, in close contact, around the central counter that contains the radiocarbon sample. The outside counters are then connected electronically so that whenever cosmic radiation passes through one of them, the central counter is turned off for a fraction of a second.

By utilizing the iron shield and the concentric Geiger counters, the 600 counts per minute produced by external radiation can be reduced to 5 or 6 per minute, and a reasonably accurate analysis of the sample can be obtained.

By measuring a given sample for about forty-eight hours, it is possible to determine its age, with a certain margin allowed for error. The symbol $\pm$ is used to indicate this margin. For example, if the age of a given sample is given as 11,044 $\pm$ 500 years, the age-range will be from 10,-544 years to 11,544 years.

If we measure the radioactivity of samples whose antiquity is known through historical records, we find that the age indicated by radiocarbon dating corresponds pretty closely to the known age of the sample. Radiocarbon dating, therefore, affords a fairly accurate method of determining the age of material up to 5,000 years old. (Our earliest historical records go back about 5,000 years.) There is no direct method of checking the results obtained with samples that go back to prehistory. About the only thing we can do is to measure a wide variety of samples and to observe whether the results that we obtain are consistent and logical.

The sample used for radiocarbon dating may be a piece of wood or a handful of organic soil, such as peat; it may be a fragment of cloth; it may be a well-preserved shell. The sample should contain at least one-half ounce of elementary carbon; of course that means that the size of the sample will depend upon its carbon content. The average sample used for radiocarbon dating weighs about an ounce.

Already scientists have estimated the age of a good many objects by means of radiocarbon dating. The interpretation of their findings is entrusted to competent archaeologists. The table that follows will give an idea of some of the results that have been obtained:

SITE	NATURE OF SAMPLE	AGE (years)
		determined by radiocarbon dating
EGYPT	A piece of acacia wood beam in an excellent state of preservation from the tomb of Zoser at Sakkara. This tomb has a known age of 4,650 $\pm$ 75 years.	3,979 $\pm$ 350
	Wood from the deck of the great funerary ship from the tomb of King Sesostris III. Known age: 3,750 years. This remarkable boat is now in the Chicago Museum of	

	Natural History; it is about 12 feet long and has a beam of about 6 feet. The sample was obtained by sawing a hole in the deck.	3,621 ± 180
EGYPT	Wheat and barley grain found in a granary in the province of Faiyum.	6,095 ± 250
PALESTINE	Sample of the linen wrapped around the manuscript of the Book of Isaiah recently found in Palestine. From the nature of the writing, scholars have calculated that the manuscript goes back to the time of Christ.	1,917 ± 200
FRANCE	Charcoal sample from the floor of the Lascaux Cave, near Montignac, in the department of Dordogne. This cave is famous for its colored paintings (of animals) executed in the Old Stone Age.	15,516 ± 900
ENGLAND	Birchwood platform from the human occupation site at Lake Pickering, in Yorkshire.	9,488 ± 350
"	Charcoal sample from the famous stone monument of Stonehenge in Wiltshire, England. The holes outside the outer circle of immense stone blocks were probably used for some kind of ritual. The charcoal sample referred to above was discovered in one of the holes.	3,798 ± 275
UNITED STATES	Near Las Vegas, Nevada, is an ancient cave closed by accident many thousand years ago. In this cave the floor is covered to a depth of some eight feet with the manure of the extinct giant sloth. Manure from the lower part of the pile was used as a sample.	10,455 ± 340
" "	Crater Lake, in Oregon, was created by the eruption of an ancient volcano. Apparently the eruption blew off the top of the mountain, covering the whole countryside with lava and pumice and burning or charring the nearby forests. The sample used in this case was charcoal from a tree charred by glowing pumice.	6,453 ± 250
" "	In a cave known as Fort Rock Cave in Oregon were found some 300 pairs of woven rope sandals. The beautifully made sandals were used directly for the measurement of radiocarbon content.	9,053 ± 350

ATOMIC MEDICINES

Battling Disease with Radioactive Isotopes

ALMOST all elements exist in several forms that have the same chemical and physical properties but different atomic weights. About a thousand isotopes, as these different forms of elements are called, have been found in nature or are prepared artificially. While some are stable and do not decompose easily, many are radioactive.

Those that are radioactive are called radioisotopes. They give off one or more types of radiation — alpha particles, gamma rays or beta rays. The alpha particle is really a charged helium atom; because it cannot penetrate other forms of matter, it is of little value in medicine. The gamma ray acts much as the X ray does, and penetrates deeply into body tissues or other kinds of matter. It may be used to produce the same biological effects as the X ray. The beta ray is composed of electrons (negatively charged particles) that travel at very high speed. It penetrates matter, but somewhat less easily than the gamma ray does.

Certain radioisotopes are being increasingly used in diagnosing medical troubles of one kind and another. Those used medically are harmless in the minute quantities that are necessary.

One of the most useful of the radioisotopes is radioiodine (I 131). If a small amount of I 131 is introduced into the center of the thyroid gland, all of the beta energy given off by the I 131 is used up within the gland. It can be used to damage, or even destroy, hyperactive, or cancerous, cells of the thyroid tissue. It does this efficiently; no significant amount of the radiation goes beyond the thyroid to harm the nearby parathyroids, which are essential to life. The gamma rays of the radioactive iodine affect the thyroid and parathyroids very little. The net result, then, is selective damage or destruction of the unwanted hyperactive, or cancerous, cells of the thyroid. Fortunately, certain types of tumor cells are much more sensitive to radiation than are normal, healthy cells.

The thyroid is unique because it quickly traps any iodine, even if given by mouth. The iodine stays in the gland for several days before it is released into the blood. As a part of the hormone thyroxine, iodine is important in regulating the metabolism of the body. (Metabolism is the sum of the life processes by which protoplasm is built up and broken down and energy is stored and released.)

The only practical method of producing the large and continuous supply of radioisotopes needed in medicine is through the operation of nuclear reactors. Fortunately, this can be done side by side with the manufacture of materials for military purposes with little increase in basic cost. Therefore chemical and irradiation services are available to all users at a tiny fraction of the real value.

About 2 per cent of the products produced during uranium fission in the nuclear reactor is radioiodine. The great amount of I 131 produced in this way makes it possible to use radioiodine widely in medicine. It is separated quite readily in a pure state and has a fairly short half life, eight days. (The half life of a radioactive element is the time required for half of its atoms to disintegrate.)

The short half life of I 131 is important for medical use. Any long-lived radioisotope such as radium 226 (about 1,700 years), carbon 14 (about 5,700

years) or strontium 90 (25 years) might remain in the body of the patient and might bring about long-term damage that could not be repaired.

Progress in electronics has kept pace with the development of radioisotopes. This science has provided us with extremely sensitive devices for detecting and recording minute amounts of radiation. Let us see how one of these devices works. We place a special sodium iodide crystal, about an inch in diameter, a foot or so away from the neck of a patient. The patient has previously received a very small and harmless amount of sodium radioiodide. The gamma rays from the sodium radioiodide in the patient's body reach the crystal and cause tiny invisible flashes of ultraviolet light. These flashes can be picked up by an ultraviolet-sensitive photomultiplier tube and recorded electrically. We can then measure the percentage of any dose of radioiodine that has been taken up by the thyroid. The measure of uptake is a better indication of the metabolic state of an individual than is the older basal metabolism test. This newer test, because of its accuracy, is being widely used in diagnoses at the present time.

Detecting cancer by means of radioiodine

If the patient has thyroidlike cancer cells elsewhere in his body, they too may take up I 131. They can also be detected and located by the new testing procedure.

Radioiodine can be used to determine whether a patient needs blood transfusions or intravenous fluids. Its use in this way has undoubtedly saved many lives. It is particularly valuable when much blood has been lost in accidents, surgery or wounds received in battle and the amount of blood left in the body is not known.

The chemist takes a small sample of blood and separates out the serum albumin, which is the principal protein in the blood. With this he combines an amount of I 131 so small that it cannot even be weighed. The radioiodine makes the serum albumin radioactive without changing any of its properties. The volume of the serum albumin is known and the amount of radiation given off by it can be measured by means of a Geiger counter. Then it is injected into the blood stream of the patient, where it mixes intimately with the blood in a few minutes' time. The next step is to take a sample of the patient's blood which is now very mildly radioactive. With the Geiger counter the amount of radiation given off by this sample of blood is measured. The amount of radiation in this sample is much less than that of the original sample of radioactive serum albumin because the I 131 has been diluted throughout the whole blood stream of the patient. The radiation counts of the two samples are now compared and we are able to determine the amount of blood in the patient.

Radioactive chromate, containing radiochromium, Cr 51, is used in medicine to find out certain facts about the red cells of the blood. We mix a trace of this substance with a sample composed of red cells and allow the sample to stand briefly. The cells then become radioactive and remain so during their entire life span. The radioactive cells are then reinjected into the blood, where they behave normally. On each of several successive days we remove a given volume of red cells from the patient's blood. We find that these samples, all of the same volume, show less and less radioactivity from day to day, and we know that red cells are being lost. If this rate of loss is greater than the normal rate, it may be due to bleeding or abnormal destruction of the cells, as in some kinds of anemia. Bleeding from ulcers into the gastrointestinal tract has been studied by this method. It is also used to measure the life span of red cells in various types of anemia.

If we increase by a hundred or a thousand times the amount of the radioisotope used and find ways of keeping it localized in a tumor, we can, as in the case of the thyroid, cause the destruction of cancer cells, or render them inactive. It is as though we placed a tiny but powerful X-ray machine inside the tumor, instead of bringing the X rays in from outside the

body. For this purpose we generally use colloids (minute particles suspended in liquid) that have been made radioactive. This gives us billions of tiny sources of radiation per gram of tissue, because each colloidal particle is radioactive. Moreover, these colloids are picked up by the lymph system and carried to the lymph nodes, where they continue to damage cancer cells in those areas as well.

Fortunately, we are able to choose, for medical purposes, from among the many isotopes those that have the best combination of radiation intensities, half lives and body tolerances.

One of the most unusual and valuable of these is radiogold (Au 198). To produce Au 198 we place a piece of thin gold foil, less than the size of a postage stamp, in the Oak Ridge nuclear reactor, for instance. In one week, it will have as much

A patient with goiter has received radioiodine (I 131) and is being tested with a Geiger counter at a clinic of Canada's McMasters University.

National Film Board of Canada

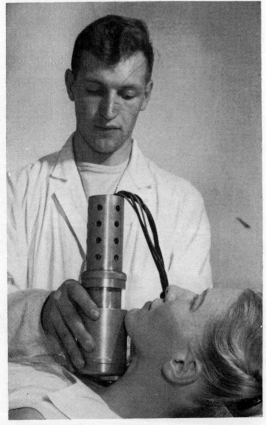

radioactivity as one gram of radium and at a tiny fraction of the cost. The amount that can be produced is almost unlimited. Au 198, converted into colloid form (Aurcoloid), is being used successfully in the treatment of tumors.

Aurcoloid has another perhaps more important application, also. Many patients, after tumor cells have grown, rapidly accumulate fluid in the chest and abdomen. Aurcoloid can be injected in the cavity and in over 50 per cent of the cases there is at least temporary improvement in these symptoms and in the general condition of the patient. Because of the short half life of Au 198 (2.8 days) 95 per cent of the effect takes place in ten to eleven days, and there is no need to remove the spent residue of the radioactive substance.

Radiophosphorus is another radioisotope that has become the standard treatment for certain diseases.

Much has been said and written about radiocobalt (Co 60). As is true of other radioisotopes, almost unlimited amounts are available if needed. Because its half life is 5 years, it must be used carefully. One way is to render thin, solid wires radioactive and to enclose one or more of these wires in a needle or cell. The Co 60 can also be enclosed in nylon tubing; this can be sewn surgically through tumors, as thread is sewn through material.

The use of these radioisotopes is under strict government control. In spite of the fact that about a hundred thousand shipments have been made, there have been no reports of serious contamination or of harm to users or patients.

Radioistopes are also used in studying how drugs act; they make it possible, for instance, to show that the intravenous anesthetic Pentothal is quickly broken down in the body into some ten different products. Not one of these is either toxic or anesthetic by itself. The use of radioisotopes is making necessary the development of new concepts regarding the way drugs act in the body. Many medical groups engaged in research and clinical medicine use radioactive materials.

See also Vol 10, p. 280: "Atomic Energy."

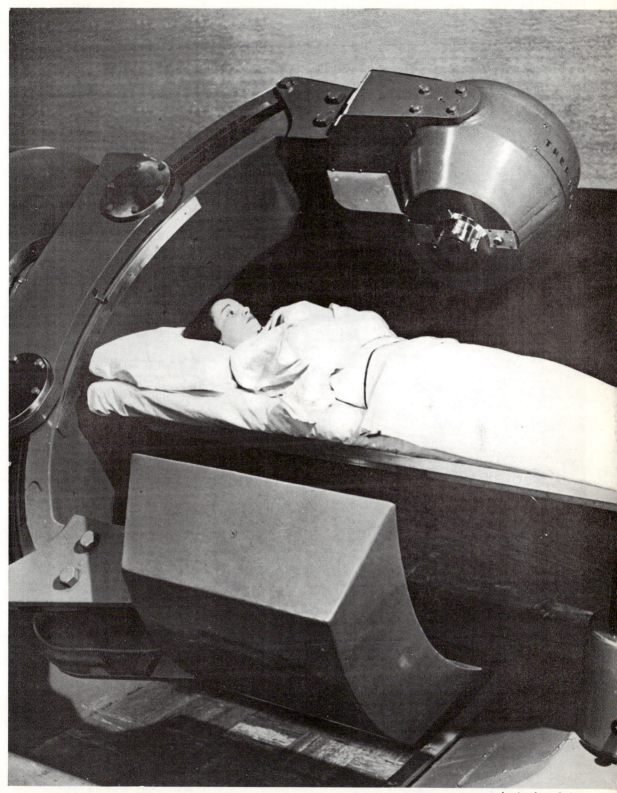

Radiation from Cobalt 60, equal to the radiation from a 3,000,000-volt X-ray machine, is used to fight cancer. The cobalt source in the housing can be revolved around the patient.

This tiny electronic instrument — a point contact transistor — can perform nearly all the functions of a standard vacuum tube many times as large. Contained in the simple metal cylinder of the transistor are two extremely fine wires, whose points rest on a small dot of semiconductive material.

THE MIGHTY MIDGET OF ELECTRONICS

The Transistor—What It Is and What It Can Do

A TINY germanium crystal set within a blob of plastic or a wee metal cylinder bids fair to revolutionize the giant electronics industry. This device is called a transistor; it was developed in the Bell Telephone Laboratories by a research group headed by Dr. William Shockley. The transistor is so small that a hundred can easily be held in the palm of the hand. Yet it can perform most of the tasks of the vacuum tube that now operates electronic devices — radio and television sets, radar apparatus, electronic calculating machines, magnetic wire recorders and electron microscopes, to mention only a few.

The vacuum tube has served, and served well, since it was developed in the first decades of the twentieth century. It consists of a glass tube from which air has been evacuated so as to form a high vacuum. A metal filament, heated within the tube, causes millions of electrons to boil off. Since there is practically no air in the tube to hold back the electrons, they can be made to respond freely to different electrical forces that are brought to bear upon them. Utilizing these electrons, the vacuum tube can amplify weak electric currents; it can turn alternating current into direct current; it can serve as a relay — that is, it can switch an independent electric circuit on and off. A specially coated vacuum tube, acting as a photoelectric cell, can transform light into electricity.

The transistor achieves these effects by utilizing a tiny, suitably prepared germanium crystal. Germanium, a by-product of the smelting and refining of zinc and cadmium, is a metallic element; it is grayish in appearance and it is hard and brittle. It is a semiconductor — that is, it can take on the properties of a conductor or an insula-

tor, depending upon the way in which it is treated.

In the article on Inside the Atom, in Volume I, we explained that the electrons that revolve around the nucleus of atoms occupy one or more shells. The outer shell of the germanium atom contains four electrons. In a germanium crystal practically all the electrons in the outer shells are tied to other atoms; there may be only one free current-carrying electron for every million atoms. But suppose we build a small amount of phosphorus into the crystal. Phosphorus has five electrons in its outer shell; one of these electrons would be free to move freely through the crystal.

Instead of adding phosphorus to the crystal, we might add an element that has only three electrons in its outer shell. An electron from a germanium atom can fill this gap under certain conditions. As a result, this particular germanium atom will now have only three electrons in its outer shell, and it will have a "hole." Every time an electron moves in to fill such a gap, it leaves a new gap behind it. To all intents and purposes, the "holes" moving through the germanium crystal produce the effect of a flow of free electrons; they can carry current.

In the first transistor model, known as a "point contact" transistor, two hair-thin wires were set upon a tiny speck of germanium; the apparatus was housed in a small metal cylinder. A "junction transistor" was also developed, based on quite a different principle. It consisted of a tiny rod-shaped piece of germanium treated so that it was made up of a thin electrically positive layer sandwiched between the two electrically neutral ends. It derived its name from the junctions between the neu-

tral ends and the positive layer. The entire rod was encased in a tiny plastic bead about 3/16 of an inch in diameter; wire leads connected to each of the three regions extended outside the bead. Both the point contact and junction transistors are being developed at the present time.

The moving electrons or moving "holes" within the germanium crystal of a transistor can be regulated, just as free electrons can be regulated in a vacuum

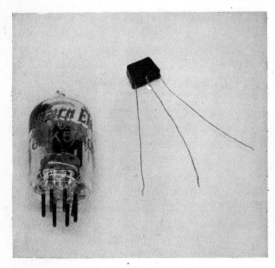

Above: a junction transistor is shown, for size comparison, with a commercial vacuum tube, which does about the same job. Right: a point contact type of transistor, set in a metal cylinder casing. The casing is cut away here, to show details.

tube. But what an amazing difference there is between the two devices! Compared with the conventional vacuum tube, the transistor is a most uncomplicated device; its manufacture is a relatively simple matter. To be sure, germanium is a pretty expensive substance, costing over $100 a pound; but such a small fragment of germanium is used in a transistor that the cost of the material is a very small part of the manufacturing cost.

As to the power requirements of the vacuum tube and the transistor, there is really no comparison. It takes a watt of electric power to amplify an electric current in a vacuum tube. In the case of complicated electronic devices, in which there are hundreds — sometimes thousands — of vacuum tubes, the problem of providing

adequate power is often a serious one. But the power problem does not exist in the case of a transistor; only a millionth of a watt is required to operate one.

When a vacuum tube is in operation, considerable heat is generated. When hundreds of tubes are used in an apparatus, overheating must be avoided; the tubes must be kept far enough apart and they must be cooled by an air stream. The amount of heat generated by a transistor, with its tiny power requirement, is infinitesimal. Hence, hundreds of transistors may be set close together, and no precautions need be taken to avoid overheating.

It is expected that when transistors have been fully developed, their uses will

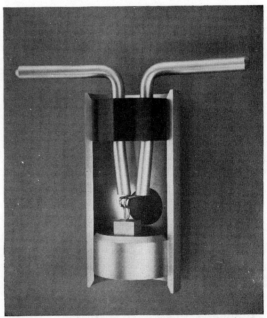

All photos, Bell Telephone Laboratories, Inc.

be legion. Already they are used on a large scale in radios, hearing aids, telephone-dial-switching equipment, electronic computers and other devices. By replacing electronic tubes with transistors in airplanes and guided missiles, it will be possible to install most elaborate electronic equipment, which will occupy little space and which will be almost shockproof. It is safe to assume that transistors will play an important part in the rocket ships that may someday conquer outer space.

See also Vol. 10, p. 281: "Electronics."

POWER-DRIVEN TOOLS

Machines by Which Men Build Other Machines

by JUSTUS PEARSON

WE STAND in awe as we watch the great handlike claw of a hoisting crane snatching up a ton of rocks and moving it to a conveyer with dexterity and apparent ease. We are just as dumfounded when we see a gigantic machine pick up a car containing hundreds of tons of coal and dump its contents in the hold of a vessel. Devices such as these are the products not only of master engineers and skillful craftsmen but of a host of special tools. The tools are often more intricate in construction and operation than the massive and sturdy machines that they fashion and that impress us so readily.

The history of man's toilsome journey from savagery to civilization is to be found only partly in the chronicles of kings and princes. It is to a large extent the story of the development of man's tools and of his skill in handling them. Because of this progress, man has spanned the immeasurable distance between the stone ax and the riveting hammer or the turret lathe; between the small boat gouged out of a tree log, and the modern ocean liner; between the rude shelter of a cave and the comfort of a heated and lighted home filled with labor-saving appliances.

Until approximately the middle of the eighteenth century, tools remained comparatively simple. They included guiding tools, such as straightedges, squares, spirit levels, plumb levels, compasses and calipers; holding tools — pincers, vises and clamps; rasping tools — saws, files and rasps; edge tools — chisels, gouges and planes; sharpening tools — grindstones, emery wheels and oilstones; boring tools — awls, gimlets, augers, bits, braces and drills; striking tools — hammers and mallets; chopping tools — axes, hatchets and adzes. Fashioning the products of industry with these hand tools was a laborious and painfully slow process.

When steam was introduced to drive machinery, a revolution was brought about in the methods of industry. For one thing, because of the great and continuous power supplied by steam, it became possible to use many machines, all built upon the same design, in the same place. For example, the single wooden loom used at home and operated by hand or foot power, was replaced in time by a whole row of looms, made chiefly of metal and driven by steam power, in a single factory. Laborers and craftsmen were brought together in the factory to run these newfangled devices.

Machines now had to be particularly sturdy in order to withstand the terrific thrust of the power supplied by steam. Therefore they were made principally of the strong metals, such as steel and iron. Craftsmen needed special tools to cut and shape these metals, particularly because there was not enough time to shape each piece carefully by hand. Therefore machine tools were developed — mechanical, power-driven devices that could be held and guided so that they could perform their work rapidly and accurately.

The term "machine tool" is often misunderstood because "machine" suggests an appliance that is not actually a tool. If we used the term "mechanical tool" instead of "machine tool," we should be describing the device more aptly. We might compare a machine tool with a toy truck, provided with a system of wheels and le-

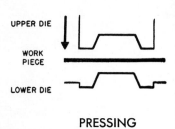

UPPER DIE

WORK PIECE

LOWER DIE

PRESSING

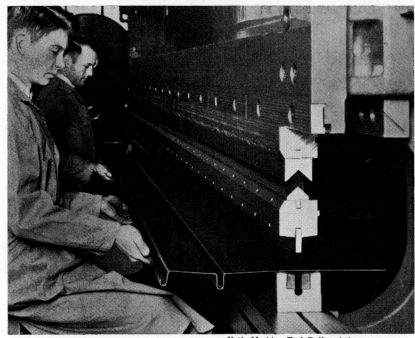

Natl. Machine Tool Builders' Assn.

A press brake forming sheet steel into roofing panels. This powerful tool is employed to bend strips or sheets of metal.

vers and set in motion when a taut spring unwinds. This sort of toy requires very little effort on the part of the child owner; he has only to wind the spring "motor" and to set the toy on the floor. The machine tool is vastly more complicated than a child's mechanical toy truck, yet it follows the same general principles. It is controlled by means of gears and shafts and levers; it is power-driven and not operated by hand.

Steam was formerly the chief source of power in factories or plants; power was supplied to individual machine tools from a jungle of moving belts and pulleys overhead. Nowadays all modern machine tools are powered by electricity; each of them has at least one built-in motor.

In the early years of the modern industrial era, many different kinds of machinery were built by machine tools in the same large room or factory. Later, it was found more convenient and economical to perform only certain machining operations or to construct only certain types of machines in one place. Machining operations are becoming continually more specialized; whole factories may be devoted to cutting gears, or manufacturing axles or fashioning automobile bodies.

Practically every product known to mankind requires the use of machine tools.

They make the working parts of the machinery upon which we depend for our industrial processes — steelmaking machinery, papermaking machinery, textile machinery and the like. Machine tools are also used in producing household appliances such as the refrigerator, the vacuum cleaner and the toaster. Transportation depends upon machine tools, which fashion the working parts of airplanes, automobiles, trucks, diesel-electric engines and freight cars. These tools are also an essential factor in agriculture; they are used in turning out steel plows, cultivators and combines.

Machine tools play an all-important part in mass production, which involves the assembly of accurately machined and freely interchangeable parts. Mass production based on the use of machine tools has greatly raised our standards of living; it has made thousands of useful products available to all at moderate cost and it has provided work for millions of persons.

Machine tools have become so complicated and so elaborate that a visitor to a plant in which they are in operation might be quite confused. He would see batteries of machine tools, known by different names and apparently performing different and unrelated operations. Yet many of these devices might be doing the same kind of

work, such as removing small bits of metal from an object. As a matter of fact, machine tools, for all their bewildering variety, perform only a limited number of basic operations; they hammer, or press, or shear, or saw, or shave, or drill or grind.

It is interesting to note that these operations are also used in shaping articles made of wood. There are, however, several important differences in the working of metal and wood. Metal can be melted and poured into molds, while fire causes wood to undergo a radical chemical change, reducing it to gases and a powdery solid residue. Again, the metal that is worked by machine tools must be held rigidly in place in vises, clamps and similar devices while it is being machined; wood can often be held by the hand as cutting tools are applied to it.

An important group of machine tools — the metal-forming tools — prepare the metal by squeezing, hammering, shearing or forging it. They perform much the same work as the tools in the old-fashioned smithy; but they are incomparably more powerful.

The mechanical press makes blanks out of a sheet of metal; it then squeezes these blanks into the desired shape in a die. The hydraulic press does the same work by applying hydraulic power. The drop hammer is used to hammer red-hot

Big shafts for ships, gate stems for dams and enormous ordnance parts are forged by this massive 8-ton hammer.

Internat. Nickel Co., Inc.

metal on an anvil. The cutting jaws of the shearing press do the same kind of work as the shears used to cut cloth or paper. In the press punch, one die is forced through the material into a hollow mating die, thus cutting a hole of the desired shape; this is the principle used in the familiar paper punch. In the forging machine, a piece of red-hot metal is squeezed in a die under great pressure, so that it flows into every part of the die and assumes the desired shape.

When we pass beyond the metal-forming stages, machine tools become more complicated. Yet, whether they drill, plane, hob, broach or grind, they are performing the same basic operation — they are removing metal from the piece that is being worked. Sometimes the machine tool acts like a carpenter's plane or chisel, whittling metal away in chips as though it were wood; sometimes it does the work of sandpaper or of pumice stone. All of these operations could be done by hand; but the machine tool, working more or less automatically and applying tremendous force,

can perform its tasks in a fraction of the time that would otherwise be required.

A large number of metal-removing operations are carried on by the machines called lathes. The word "lathe" refers to the way in which the object that is to be machined is held, rather than to any particular operation that is performed upon it. A lathe is a device in which the work is clamped, as in a vise, and rotated about a horizontal axis while it is formed to size and shape by a cutting tool; this operation is called turning. The lathe is quite similar to the ancient potter's wheel; the chief differences are that the lathe generally turns about a horizontal axis instead of a vertical axis, and its spindle is turned by a motor or other source of power. The common alternative to the use of a lathe, in machining work, is to clamp the metal object to a flat surface and to hold

Chips pile up as a hobbing machine cuts teeth in a huge gear over 8 feet in diameter. The hob makes deep grooves in gears, racks and so on.

Westinghouse

it securely, while the tool is drawn over it or rotated upon it.

A number of cutting tools can be used at one time on the lathe known as the turret lathe. This machine is equipped with a six-side tool-holder, called a turret, to which a number of different cutting tools are attached. The device makes it possible to swing the different cutting tools into position one at a time as needed, and

the cutting edge to become dull. When several holes are to be made simultaneously, a "gang" of drills may be employed, with drills properly spaced and adjusted for the depth of hole. Two dozen or more drills may be used at the same time, cutting as many holes in a single piece of metal.

Occasionally a drill is used on a lathe; the work turns and the drill remains

Natl. Machine Tool Builders' Assn.

to repeat the sequence of operations over and over again without resetting the tools. The turret lathe is exceedingly flexible; it can be adjusted so that the change of tools is automatic.

To speed up production on a lathe when the identical parts to be turned out number many thousands, an automatic multiple-spindle bar machine is used; it works on six parts at one time. Once the machine is set up, all the operator has to do is feed long bars of metal into it and take away the finished parts.

In the process called drilling, the work is generally fixed in position; the tool is pressed into the work. Drilling is a basic machine technique that goes back, it is believed, to primitive man; it consists of cutting a round hole by means of a rotating tool.

It is often necessary to cool the drill and the metal that is to be drilled by a stream of liquid, for excessive heat will take the temper out of the tool and cause

GRINDING

A master toolmaker grinding a broaching cutter. It takes him many hours to grind the 380 teeth of the tool.

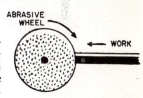

fixed, except that it moves slowly into the work. This method offers no particular advantage; it is generally adopted only as a matter of convenience, as, for example, when the work is already fixed in the lathe.

In the boring process a cutting tool is used; in some machines it rotates, while in others the tool is stationary and the work revolves. A hole may be bored in solid metal; sometimes a hole that has already been drilled is finished by boring. Reaming and tapping are both boring operations. Reaming consists of finishing, to very close tolerances, a hole that has already been drilled. Tapping is the process of cutting a thread inside the hole so that a bolt may be screwed in.

When a large, round hole is to be bored in the end of the piece — say, in the lengthwise direction in a solid cylinder — it would be impractical to use a drill that would be big enough to bore the hole. In this case, the lathe is used to turn the work against a cutting tool, perhaps no bigger around than a pencil and with one end slightly rounded or cut back. The cutting tool can be adjusted to move into the work at an angle, so as to increase the bore of the hole gradually. The tool is held in place by a rigid carriage, and is moved in one or more directions through the action of gears and of a shaft that is provided with screw threads. The threads are comparatively fine, so that a complete turn of the shaft moves the carriage only a short distance. This method of drilling is comparatively slow.

The process called milling consists of machining a piece of metal by bringing it into contact with a rotating cutting tool — a wheel with a succession of cutting edges on its outer rim. A narrow milling cutter resembles the familiar circular saw; other cutters have spiral edges and look like huge screws. When a milling cutter is rotated rapidly against a metal surface and is properly guided, it removes metal quite rapidly.

The milling tool called a hob is often used to make the deep grooves required for gears, racks and other serrated (saw-like) pieces. The hob resembles a stubby ear of corn with alternate kernels removed. The "kernels" that remain are sharp and accurately spaced.

The planer is a machine tool that cuts metal in much the same way as a carpenter's hand plane; in the planer, however, the cutting tool is held stationary and the parts to be planed are moved back and forth underneath it. Planers are often very large; some may work on huge pieces of metal twenty feet wide and thirty feet long. In the case of certain machine tools performing planing operations, the work is held stationary while the cutting tool is moved back and forth. Machines of this kind are called shapers; they are used for comparatively short cuts. In the planing machine called the slotter, the cutting tool moves up and down instead of back and forth. Slotting machines are used chiefly when a large, heavy table is required to support the work piece.

The broach is generally classed with the planing tools. It consists of a tapering bar, whose surface is provided with a great many cutting teeth; these teeth increase in size as the cross section of the broach becomes larger. The broach is generally either pushed or pulled through a hole that has been previously formed. The smaller end of the broach is drawn through first; as the tool passes through the hole, metal is removed by the teeth.

Internat. Nickel Co., Inc.

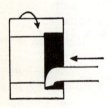

BORING

Collapsible cutting tool that can be inserted through a small hole to counterbore a large hole inside a Monel forging.

DRILLING

Radial drill being used to drill holes in an end frame for a big printing press. The basic drilling technique is very ancient.

Broaching is applied in some cases to the machining of outer surfaces, such as those of automobile cylinder blocks.

Planing tools such as planers, shapers and slotters can cut remarkably elaborate surfaces. They are frequently used to prepare other cutting tools, particularly when complicated shapes are required. A skilled operator can manipulate a planing tool with as much ease as an old tar whittling a block of wood with a jackknife.

A piece of metal that has been machined to approximate size may be finished to a close degree of accuracy by grinding. This operation consists of shaping the metal by bringing it in contact with a rotating abrasive wheel. The grinding operation is often performed to finish a part that has been heat treated to make it very hard. Grinding corrects any distortion that may have resulted from the heat treatment.

A great deal of heat is generated in the grinding operation; consequently, the grinding wheel and the metal that is being finished are often flushed with a liquid coolant (cooling agent) that carries away the heat. The cooling process is particu-

larly necessary when a high degree of accuracy is required, because metal at a high temperature will not have the same measurements when it is cool. The milky coolant also helps flush away the particles of metal removed by the grinding wheel; it helps eliminate the danger of flying emery dust and metal bits, which menace the operator's eyes.

Finishing a metal piece within close tolerances by the process of grinding is a delicate operation, requiring close attention on the part of the workman. He must check the work periodically with micrometer calipers, or a plug gauge or other measuring apparatus. By the time the metal piece has gone through all the preliminary stages of forging or casting, milling to rough proportions, heat treatment and the like, a good deal of labor has gone into it and it represents a sizeable investment. One slip of the grinding wheel and the piece may be reduced to scrap.

The limit, or
difference, gauge

The special instruments used to test finished work have to be accurate, yet not so delicate that they will easily break or get out of order. A typical testing device used to check the size of round holes that have been machined to close tolerances is the limit, or difference, gauge. It consists of a solid cylinder, with a round plug at either end. One of the plugs is marked "go," the other "no go" or "not go." Let us suppose that the hole is to be machined to the diameter of 1.00 inch with a tolerance of ± .005; this means that the diameter of the hole may be as much as 5/1000 of an inch smaller or larger than 1.00 inch. The inspector uses a limit gauge whose "go" end has a diameter of .995 inches and whose "no go" end has a diameter of 1.005 inches. He inserts the "go" plug in the hole that has been bored in the metal. If the hole is not large enough, the plug will not fit in the hole. If the "go" plug fits readily in the hole, the inspector tries to insert the "no go" plug also. If this passes through, it means that the diameter of the hole is greater

Natl. Machine Tool Builders' Assn.

MILLING

Skilled operator milling the top and sides of a block of metal and cutting a slot down the middle in one operation.

than 1.005 inches and that the piece is ruined. A worker or inspector can use a testing device like a limit gauge with great ease and rapidity. This is extremely important, since time is money in a busy factory

The cutting tools that we have just described vary in size from small bits of metal about as big as match sticks to chunks perhaps as large as a man's forearm. They are characterized by fine molecular structure and hardness. A cutting tool must withstand great heat, especially at its cutting edge; this edge must resist wear and retain its contour. The cutting tool is made of selected metal, specially treated to make it as tough and durable as possible. After it has been cut to the proper shape while in a comparatively soft and workable condition, it undergoes heat treatment so that the finished tool will be hard enough to resist wear.

The machine that holds the cutting tools must also be carefully constructed in order to give long and dependable service.

A breakdown of equipment in a factory will upset production schedules and may endanger human lives. Often one part of a machine is purposely made weaker than the rest, so that it will break before more vital parts of the machine are damaged; this weak part serves much the same purpose as an electric fuse in an electric circuit. If this part breaks, as the result of an excessively heavy work load, it can be readily replaced and there will be little or no loss of production.

Workers must be protected from injury when operating machine tools. They may become thoughtless or careless; because they work on the same machine day after day, they are likely to forget that it is capable of maiming or killing. To protect operators, many machines are equipped with safety devices. For example, the electrical or hydraulic controls of a huge stamping press may be so arranged that the operator's hands must be placed on the handles, out of harm's way, before the machine will operate. The smaller machines cannot limit the worker in such a way, for his hands must be free to move. Fac-

tory safety engineers often see to it that screens, or goggles or special gloves are used. If the worker's services are lost through accident, it is a serious matter not only to the worker himself but also to his employer, for it may be difficult to find a replacement.

The fact is that a machine-tool operator is a skilled craftsman, who has undergone extensive training for his job. Apprentices are given a well-rounded program of shop and classroom work; sometimes they take night-school or correspondence courses. They are shifted from department to department so that they may develop all-round skills. When they have completed their training, they are assigned to the specific tasks for which they seem to be best fitted. As full-fledged machine-tool operators, they take immense pride in the perfection of their finished products.

See also Vol. 10, p. 283: "Machine Tools."

PLANING

Convertible openside planer which can work on huge pieces of metal.

G. A. Gray Co.

An assistant places a sample of food in a "cave," or irradiation vault, which houses radioactive cobalt 60.

Cutaway view of the irradiation vault, showing the 10,000-curie source of cobalt 60 below a deep water shield.

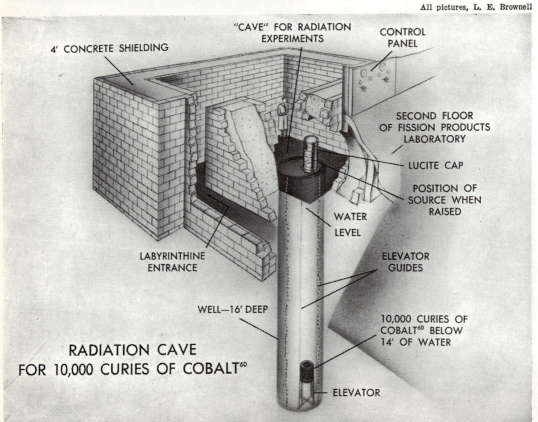

4' CONCRETE SHIELDING

"CAVE" FOR RADIATION EXPERIMENTS

CONTROL PANEL

SECOND FLOOR OF FISSION PRODUCTS LABORATORY

LUCITE CAP

POSITION OF SOURCE WHEN RAISED

WATER LEVEL

LABYRINTHINE ENTRANCE

ELEVATOR GUIDES

WELL—16' DEEP

10,000 CURIES OF COBALT⁶⁰ BELOW 14' OF WATER

RADIATION CAVE FOR 10,000 CURIES OF COBALT⁶⁰

ELEVATOR

Preserving Food by Atomic Radiation

How Deadly Gamma Rays Are Used to Sterilize Foodstuffs

by L. E. BROWNELL

THE destructive effects of atomic energy have been evident to all since the first atomic bomb was exploded over Hiroshima on August 6, 1945. Fortunately, energy from the atom has also been used to benefit mankind. Radioactive isotopes, produced in nuclear reactors (atomic piles), have been effectively employed in the treatment of disease; they have also proved valuable in experimental medicine, biology, chemistry, physics and engineering. Already atomic fission has supplied power for the propulsion of submarines. It is believed that in the years to come atomic energy will be a major source of industrial power.

Researchers at the University of Michigan are now working on another method of using nuclear energy to serve man. They are investigating the preservation of food by atomic radiation at the memorial center known as the Phoenix Project of the University of Michigan. This food-preservation research is based on the effects of the radiations called gamma rays.

In nuclear reactions large quantities of gamma rays are emitted. This radiation, in sufficiently large doses, is deadly to all forms of life. Its lethal power, however, can be so controlled as to destroy only certain living things that are harmful to man. Gamma radiation can be used, among other things, to kill the molds, yeasts and bacteria that cause foods to spoil. Once food has been treated in this way it is sterile; it can be preserved for a long time if it is protected from the outer air by being put in sealed cans or packages.

The successful use of radiation in sterilizing food involves the solution of many problems. Food spoils for a number of reasons. Microscopic organisms may make it poisonous for man; chemical reactions may change its flavor; loss of moisture may cause it to deteriorate; long storage may bring about unpleasant changes. In certain cases, these problems have to be considered separately for different kinds of food. Even if food can be safely sterilized by gamma rays or by any other process, this does not necessarily completely solve the problem of preserving it.

It is very important to find out whether food exposed to gamma rays is safe to eat. Thus far there has been no evidence that food treated in this way becomes radioactive. However, we do not know as yet whether irradiated food — food exposed to gamma rays — will support normal growth without harmful effects when used as a major part of the diet for some generations. Long-term feeding experiments are now being carried out in which several generations of animals will be fed a diet consisting principally of irradiated foods. It is hoped that the experiments will show that such foods are perfectly safe.

Another problem is to obtain at reasonable cost enough radioactive material to process foods on a commercial scale by gamma radiation. There is a possible solution to this problem. Large amounts of radioactive waste materials result from the production of plutonium in nuclear reactors. These materials are the products of uranium fission — the splitting of the nucleus of the uranium atom. Since such wastes are radioactive, they cannot be disposed of as ordinary industrial wastes, by

dumping on the ground or into streams, because of the danger of contaminating food materials and water supplies. At the present time, radioactive wastes are being stored in underground tanks designed to hold their contents for as long as five hundred years. As the number of reactors increases, particularly through the peacetime production of power from nuclear energy, these waste products will also increase. If they could be used to preserve food, an expensive storage problem might be turned into an asset.

The Fission Products Laboratory of the University of Michigan has provided two powerful sources of gamma radiation which are being used in the experimental studies on the preservation of food. The first source consists of 1,000 curies of cobalt 60, stored in a lead container. (A curie is a standard unit of radiation.) This container is a lead bottle with a wall about 10½ inches thick and a lead stopper at the top. The second gamma-ray source consists of 10,000 curies of cobalt 60. The radiation from this source is so intense that concrete walls four feet thick are necessary to absorb the rays. Operators can safely

enter the "cave" that houses the cobalt 60, in order to put in or take out food samples, only when the source is shut off. This is done by lowering it into a well of water 16 feet deep, which absorbs the gamma rays.

Cooked and raw carrots, partly cooked broccoli, asparagus, spinach and cooked potatoes have been preserved by gamma radiation. These vegetables undergo only slight change in flavor. Unfortunately, some other perishable foods, such as milk, become very unpleasant to the taste when they undergo irradiation.

Various meats have also been tested. It has been found that those that have been cured, such as corned beef, ham and bacon, have the best flavor after irradiation. The fresh meats that have been irradiated have not proved so palatable. Treatment with chemicals may make such flavor changes less pronounced.

Researchers are now experimenting on food irradiation not only at the University of Michigan but also at the Brookhaven National Laboratory, the Massachusetts Institute of Technology, the University of Nebraska and elsewhere. It will probably take years before scientists determine all the advantages and limitations of this revolutionary method of food preservation.

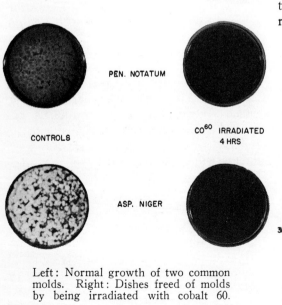

Left: Normal growth of two common molds. Right: Dishes freed of molds by being irradiated with cobalt 60.

A potent source of gamma radiation (cobalt 60), used in sterilizing food, is stored in a lead-bottle container.

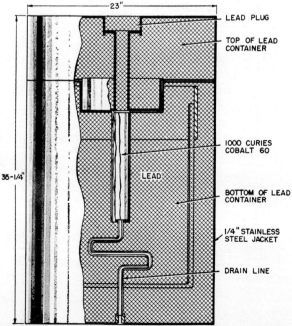

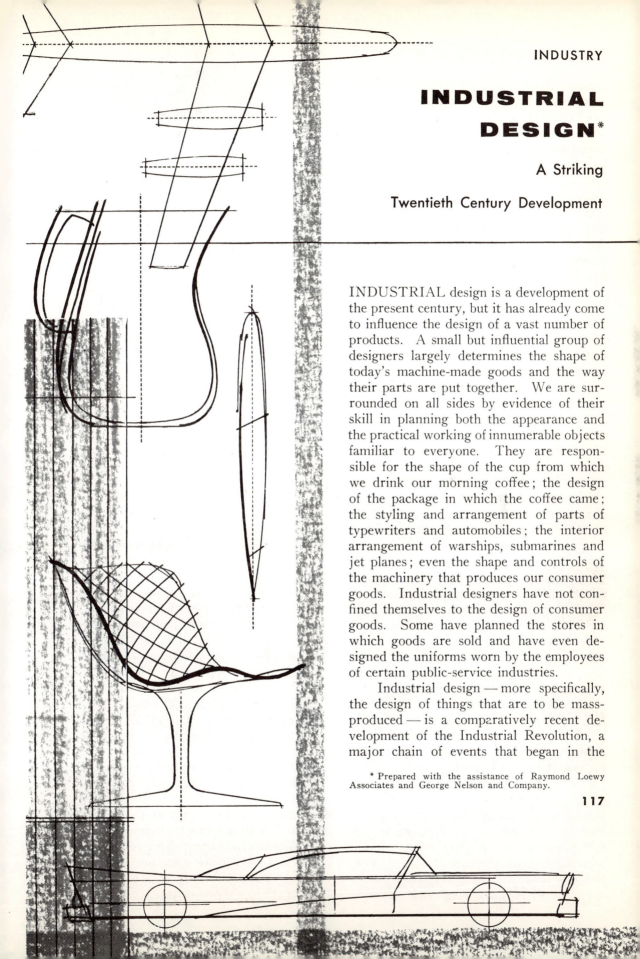

INDUSTRIAL DESIGN*

A Striking

Twentieth Century Development

INDUSTRIAL design is a development of the present century, but it has already come to influence the design of a vast number of products. A small but influential group of designers largely determines the shape of today's machine-made goods and the way their parts are put together. We are surrounded on all sides by evidence of their skill in planning both the appearance and the practical working of innumerable objects familiar to everyone. They are responsible for the shape of the cup from which we drink our morning coffee; the design of the package in which the coffee came; the styling and arrangement of parts of typewriters and automobiles; the interior arrangement of warships, submarines and jet planes; even the shape and controls of the machinery that produces our consumer goods. Industrial designers have not confined themselves to the design of consumer goods. Some have planned the stores in which goods are sold and have even designed the uniforms worn by the employees of certain public-service industries.

Industrial design — more specifically, the design of things that are to be mass-produced — is a comparatively recent development of the Industrial Revolution, a major chain of events that began in the

* Prepared with the assistance of Raymond Loewy Associates and George Nelson and Company.

117

second half of the eighteenth century. It was marked by a gradual change-over from hand labor (sometimes aided by the horse) to powered machinery as the chief method of production. The individual craftsman had to give way to the factory, in which each worker performed an operation representing only one step in the making of a given product. This is the system known as mass production. Its efficiency has made possible a vast increase in the quantity and variety of products available to consumers. The Industrial Revolution is discussed more fully elsewhere in THE BOOK OF POPULAR SCIENCE (see Index).

From the point of view of the industrial designer, the most important effect of this historical development was the displacement of the craftsman as the shaper of products. Formerly, it had always been the man who made an object who decided how it was to be shaped and how it was to work. The wagonmaker or carriage builder, for example, designed his product (with, perhaps, some suggestions from his customer) as he built it. His training almost always consisted of a long period of apprenticeship to an older craftsman, who had himself served his apprenticeship under a craftsman of a previous generation.

As a consequence of this state of affairs, the designs of most objects tended to remain unaltered over long periods of time. Changes would occur very gradually and usually in response to slow changes in taste. For instance, the craftsmen making furniture would alter their products to match changing styles of architecture. The designs developed by such eighteenth-century furniture makers as Chippendale, Sheraton and Hepplewhite underwent the influence of the Georgian architecture of the period and remained basically unchanged for over a hundred years.

The designs for the earliest machine-made products marked no break with the past. Factories usually turned out products more or less identical with those of the earlier craftsmen. A chair factory would reproduce handmade chairs (indeed some factories still do so); a textile factory would copy hand-woven materials. Even in

Herman Miller Furniture Co.

This strikingly original creation — a molded plywood chair — was designed by Charles Eames for Herman Miller.

the manufacture of new products for which no handmade prototypes existed, the tendency was to imitate some older product. An automobile could be made to look somewhat like a horse-drawn carriage; in linoleum design, rug patterns were used.

The designer was usually a rather unimportant factory employee — perhaps a draftsman — who made the drawings necessary for the production of a given article. The only training available to such designers was given in a few art and trade schools under the name of "applied art." This name, which originally meant "art applied to some practical purpose," came to stand for the art of decoration, "applied" or added as an afterthought. The resulting decorations were often quite grotesque, at least from our modern viewpoint. There were sewing machines with cast-iron bases shaped like woven branches; there were radios which looked like small Gothic churches.

The shortcomings of this system of designing became apparent very early. It could not be applied to such inventions as the railway locomotive or, later, the airplane because they were quite different from anything previously known. New products of this kind were usually made in accordance with the ideas of the inventor or the builder (who was often the same man).

Russel Wright

Russel Wright is famous for his "American Modern" dinnerware designs, of which this pitcher is a fine example.

In the latter part of the nineteenth century, the English poet and artist William Morris was one of the most caustic critics of the chaotic designs employed in the machine age. He played an important part in the formation of the Arts and Crafts Movement, which aimed to bring about the abandonment of machine production and a return to the simplicity of craft production. The Arts and Crafts Movement could not stay the development of the Industrial Revolution, but it did have the effect of calling attention to the inadequacy of the design efforts of the time. Morris stressed the need for new designers.

In Europe, particularly in France and Germany, architects became aware of the problems raised by new developments in building construction. At first, materials such as steel and concrete were used in buildings that were no different in design from those constructed hundreds of years before. Some architects realized the absurdity of the situation as early as the 1890's. It was not until after the first World War, however, that a definite break was made with the past. A strong group of so-called "modern architects" appeared on the scene. Men such as Le Corbusier * in France and

* Le Corbusier was the pseudonym of Charles-Edouard Jeanneret, a Swiss.

Walter Gropius in Germany designed and constructed edifices that did not imitate previous styles of architecture. These architects designed not only buildings but also special products suitable for use in their buildings — products such as lighting fixtures and hardware.

Gropius founded a school called the Bauhaus (House of Architecture) in Dresden, Germany. It was there that the teaching of industrial design was first seriously undertaken. Design was no longer thought of as applied art; it was considered to be a matter of serious planning for industrial production. Instructors and students of the Bauhaus were concerned not only with architecture but with designs for textiles, chinaware, glassware, furniture and light fixtures. Some of the Bauhaus designs were used by German manufacturers; the tubular chairs manufactured by Marcel Breuer became particularly popular.

With the rise of Nazism in Germany, the Bauhaus came into disfavor. Many of its teachers were forced to leave Germany and the school was eventually closed. Its influence has been great. Many of its former students have become respected teachers of industrial design. There is hardly a design school whose teaching methods do not owe much to the doctrines of the Bauhaus. (For an account of the architectural innovations of the Bauhaus school, see the chapter Glass Houses in Volume 8.)

During the 1920's, a few American pioneers began to practice industrial design. They included Raymond Loewy, Henry Dreyfus, Norman Bel Geddes and Walter Dorwin Teague. These men had been recruited from various fields. Loewy, for example, had been trained as an electrical engineer, and had developed a career in fashion illustration. Dreyfus and Bel Geddes had worked as set designers for the theater. Teague had been an advertising-design specialist and a type designer. Other pioneers in the new field had specialized in art, architecture and silversmithing.

All these men had one thing in common: they sensed the emergence of a new art form peculiar to machine production. They felt that the principles of art relating

to painting and sculpture could be applied to all products made by man. They did not believe, however, that it was necessary to sacrifice mechanical efficiency in order to achieve beauty in design. They were convinced, too, that improved appearance, coupled with mechanical efficiency, would result in greater profits for the manufacturer. To bring this about, they studied the public's wants and desires. They trained themselves to understand not only manufacturing methods but also the factors that determined mass acceptance.

For the most part, the first industrial designers stumbled on the field more or less by accident. For example, Raymond Loewy happened to meet Sigmund Gestetner, a British manufacturer, at a friend's house in 1927. Gestetner was turning out a famous duplicating machine, whose design had not been changed in thirty years. Loewy inspected the device and told Gestetner that he could improve its design. He took the duplicator to his apartment, covered it with clay and sculptured a new design over the old. In the new design, the machine was provided with short, straight legs, instead of the curved, spreading ones of the original device; there would no longer be any danger of a person's tripping over them. Loewy put many of the working parts of the machine inside a shield; they could be left unfinished and this would lower manufacturing costs. Covering the parts also prevented the accumulation of dust and ink. Gestetner was delighted with Loewy's innovations. The design was adopted by the manufacturer and served for the next fifteen years.

Another one of Loewy's early assignments was the redesigning of the Coldspot refrigerator, sold by Sears Roebuck and Company. He moved the motor from the top of the icebox to the bottom where it could be hidden by a shield. He chopped off the legs, so that dust no longer accumulated under the machine, and installed the first nonrusting aluminum shelves ever to be used in a refrigerator.

In 1926, Walter Dorwin Teague redesigned the Eastman Company's Brownie camera and produced an attractive streamlined model. He also restyled various optical instruments produced by Bausch and Lomb. Henry Dreyfus worked on the styling of telephones for the Bell System and of clocks for Westclox. It was this designer who put the numerals and letters outside the dials of telephones; in this position, they would not be obscured by the dialer's finger.

The coming of the depression in 1929 called greater attention to the efforts of industrial designers. People were not able to buy so many things as before and they became more discriminating. Producers realized that they would have to employ the sales appeal of good design. The manufacturers who survived those bleak days of intense competition were the ones who re-

Basic storage component, designed by George Nelson for the Herman Miller Furniture Company.

Herman Miller Furniture Co.

peatedly put their products to the test, making improvements in their appearance as well as in their workings.

Nearly all the work that industrial designers did in those days represented basic simplification of consumer goods. They began by doing away with superfluous decoration and rearranging the parts of devices in a simplified, logical order. Simplification is still the goal of the industrial designer. It usually means fewer parts and lighter weight; consequently less labor is required and freight costs are lower.

Most mass-produced articles received at least some styling. The more imaginative industrial designers now began to apply their talents to new fields. They wanted to do more than to develop a new look for products; they wanted to shape them from the very earliest stages. It was their aim not only to provide attractive appearance and lower cost but also to make products more useful and easier to maintain. Industry was slow to accept the services of the designers in this broadened role.

Then came the second World War. The government, which is usually conservative, took the unexpected step of hiring industrial designers to solve "human engineering" and basic design problems. They were given the task of making instruments of war fit the men who were to use them. Triggers were to be shaped to be in exactly the right position for the human finger; gunstocks were to fit the shoulders; tank

interiors would accommodate their crews with at least a reasonable amount of comfort. In this way, it was felt, the most efficient use could be made of both men and weapons — a most important point in wartime. The industrial engineers met this challenge brilliantly.

Since World War II, the pioneer industrial designers in America have been joined by a number of younger men representing various backgrounds and points of view. Several of them are architects who have concentrated on industrial design. Such men as Charles Eames, George Nelson and Eliot Noyes belong to this group. Eames is best known for certain furniture designs; a plastic chair he created has become one of the most widely used pieces of furniture ever produced. He has strongly influenced the design profession through certain highly original educational films. George Nelson has been active in the design of furniture, household accessories and appliances, interiors and packaging. Eliot Noyes prepared a strikingly original design for a well-known electric typewriter manufactured in the United States.

For the most part, the industrial designer is a phenomenon of the most highly industrialized countries, particularly the English-speaking countries. There has been far less demand for his services elsewhere. However, industrial designers have appeared in Europe and South America. Loewy has a thriving Paris office and rep-

Left, RCA; right, Raymond Loewy Associates

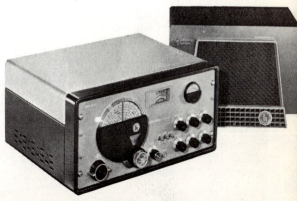

Left: a portable television set, designed by H. Rundle of the RCA staff. Right: tuner and loud-speaker unit of a short-wave Hallicrafters radio, designed by Raymond Loewy to reflect its function as a mechanism.

resentation in Belgium and Puerto Rico. In the pages that follow, we shall devote ourselves particularly to conditions in the United States, where the industrial-design movement has reached its peak.

How industrial
designers are employed

Industrial designers may be divided into two groups. (1) Some work full time for companies that set up their own design departments. (2) Others operate on a freelance basis, setting up offices of their own. They may work under contract for a number of clients at the same time. Usually they can accept any kind of job, provided that the product involved is not in direct competition with the product of another client. Sometimes they will be called on by companies that have their own design staffs. This happens when the company designers feel the need of independent stimulation, criticism or assistance.

It is estimated that there are rather less than three hundred independent industrial-design offices in the United States today. These offices may employ from two or three persons up to two hundred or more; the average number is eight. The principal industrial designers have many specialists on their staffs. There are artists, architects, draftsmen, engineers, psychologists, interior decorators, economic analysts and, of course, office workers. The specialty of each office is usually determined by the talents and taste of the head of the organization and the needs of clients. One designer may be known for his packaging, another for his interiors or industrial architecture; still another for his appliances.

The independent designer may be paid for his services in various ways. A common arrangement is a retainer. This is a fee paid to ensure prior claim on the services of the designer, so that he will not work for a direct competitor of the manufacturer and also so that he will be continuously available. In addition to the retainer, the company may pay the designer for the time actually spent on a job. A client may give a designer a certain percentage of the profits realized from the sales of a product in whose planning the designer has played a significant part.

Frigidaire's "Kitchen of Tomorrow," designed by Alexander Kostellow and the General Motors staff, offers a most convenient arrangement. In the center is an "island" sink. Behind is the range, with table-top cabinets. At the right of the photograph, we see the refrigerator and food freezer, in cabinets with horizontal doors.

Frigidaire Division, Gen. Motors Corp.

Services rendered by modern industrial designers

Today's industrial designer performs a wide variety of services for the company that employs him. As we saw, the pioneers in the field were primarily concerned with the design of manufactured products. This still forms an important part of the designer's work. Generally speaking, any product that goes through a designer's hands is expected to work better and to look better.

The vacuum cleaner is a familiar example. This machine consists of three main parts — a motor-driven air pump which produces suction, a separating tank where dust and dirt are removed from the incoming air and a nozzle or motor-driven brush which passes over the surface to be cleaned.

When the first vacuum cleaner appeared on the market in 1901, it was a heavy, clumsy machine. Its working parts were placed one on top of the other so that the "business" part of the machine stood nearly waist-high. The cleaner had to be almost totally dismantled for any repairs.

However, when the vacuum cleaner passed through the hands of the industrial designers, the motor, air pump and brush were all placed inside a "head" unit, which was mounted on wheels. This eliminated the tower of component parts which had characterized the earlier machines. Since all the working parts were more easily accessible in this arrangement, repair and part replacement were made much simpler.

An interesting vacuum-cleaner design for the Singer Sewing Machine Company was completed by Loewy in 1949. The cleaner featured an automatic cord reel, a thin head which enclosed all motor parts in an easily accessible arrangement, a light in the head and a handle which folded flat to allow the machine to go under low furniture and to hang in a storage closet. This design proved so successful that it is still used by Singer.

It would require hundreds of pages simply to list the manufactured products that have been handled by industrial designers. They include kitchen appliances, dinnerware, vacuum cleaners, decanters, sofas, cameras, pressure cookers, refrigerators and air conditioners. Designers have turned their attention to automobiles, buses, planes, trains, ocean liners and outboard motors. They have designed not only bottles for soft drinks but also the dispensers and coolers in which they are sold and the six-pack cartons in which they are carried.

The industrial designer has worked on machines used by industry, such as die-cutting machines and spinning frames. He has designed automatic vending machines, scales and prescription balances.

He may be called on to design buildings such as service stations and self-service supermarkets. Walter Dorwin Teague was given the task of laying out the interiors of the United States Air Force Academy's plants in Denver, Colorado. Loewy has designed a cultural center for Montreal and the Norfolk and Western Railway station at Roanoke, Virginia.

The analysis of market problems may also occupy the industrial designer. One designer analyzed the products that Turkey and Israel could best produce with their existing raw materials and equipment resources. Another made a marketing analysis of four countries in the Far East for the International Co-operation Administration. Loewy has done a study of supermarkets, to help them in selling nonfood items.

A designer is often employed to give a "new look" to an entire corporation. Such a job may take in everything from the product and its package to the company's delivery trucks, driver uniforms and identification badges for conventions. Again, a designer may do research to discover new uses for basic manufacturing materials. He may suggest a novel product for a company that wants to get into a profitable sideline.

New opportunities have been created for industrial designers by a revolution in distribution methods. In recent years, the self-service store has become widely established; more and more goods are being sold on the serve-yourself basis. Formerly, a clerk could suggest to a customer that he buy one or the other of several competing brands. Now, different brands of the same commodity are stacked side by side, and the

Brown Bros.

Above, we see one of the first electric vacuum cleaners, which was put on the market toward the turn of the century. This cumbersome machine was very hard to handle.

product literally has to sell itself. Hence it is more important than ever that it be properly packaged and displayed.

The present trend in advertising is to stress the producer's reputation. It is to any manufacturer's advantage, therefore, to have all his products in easily recognized packages, all having a certain family resemblance. "Family" packages of this type help the customers identify all the products that a manufacturer makes.

The industrial designer has made a thorough study of package design. He does not consider the package by itself; instead, he analyzes the ways in which it resembles and differs from other packages.

Designers want to know why a person picks up one package instead of another. Many shoppers parade past the rows of goods without a list, buying on impulse. More than half of such "impulse sales" in supermarkets are triggered by a picture of the product in full color on the package or by a glass container showing the contents. Other packages may remind the customer of the producer's advertisements or there may be some special feature to help sell the product — for instance, the package may be re-usable.

There are other things to be considered in package design. It has been found, for example, that as a person walks down the

supermarket aisle, each product stays in his line of vision for only four and a half seconds. Hence, the package will have to sell itself to him in that amount of time. Again, more than 65 per cent of the shoppers do not get beyond one word identifying a package on display in the supermarket. In fact, they may recognize the package they want not even by a single word, but by its over-all image, or the general impression it makes. Hence, a subtle approach to package design is out of the question. The package must fairly leap out at the prospective customer.

Different approaches to industrial design

Industrial designers employ widely differing methods. Some of the largest design offices have built their reputations on their ability to help their clients sell more merchandise. They emphasize research; they seek to find out what the potential purchaser would like best. They may make up sample packages or products in a number of different designs and ask many average customers for their preferences. Sometimes specialists in marketing research are called in (or become part of the designer's staff) and spend many hours trying to find out how the consumer decides on a purchase; this method suggests new designs.

Other designers question the value of certain types of market research. They point out that the preferences of the majority do not necessarily lead to the best design solutions. Certain highly respected designers believe that they should work for the best possible solution to a given problem and should then wait for the product to be gradually accepted as the public becomes familiar with it. The chinaware designed by Russel Wright in the mid-1930's illustrates this point of view. When these dishes were first introduced, it was almost impossible to sell them because of their unfamiliar appearance; yet eventually (some years later) they became best sellers.

How an industrial-design project is carried out

Every design office has its own particular way of working. In what follows, we shall describe the procedure that would be fairly typical for most offices.

In the first meeting between client and designer, several members of the client's firm will usually be present; among them will be representatives of different departments, including manufacturing and sales. They meet with the head of the design office, or a partner or a chief designer. Usually, one person in the design organization takes charge of a particular assignment and

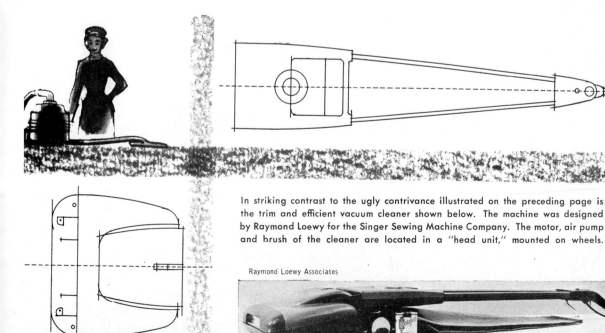

In striking contrast to the ugly contrivance illustrated on the preceding page is the trim and efficient vacuum cleaner shown below. The machine was designed by Raymond Loewy for the Singer Sewing Machine Company. The motor, air pump and brush of the cleaner are located in a "head unit," mounted on wheels.

Raymond Loewy Associates

works with the specialists required for the job. After the problem has been presented in all its details, the design organization will usually do some research. This may consist simply of looking at a few competitive products, or it may be a major study, leading to an elaborately written and illustrated report.

The design office will then begin to make sketches and rough models, illustrating various possible solutions to the problem. A meeting is usually arranged to show the preliminary designs to the client so that he may have a voice in the selection of the ideas to be finally developed. Some designers prefer to offer only one proposal, feeling that a problem can have only one correct solution; others will show dozens of alternative proposals; still others will present one preferred solution and a few alternatives. After a basic scheme has been selected, the design is developed in detail, and usually a three-dimensional model is made. It is full-size, if possible. Of course, if the product is very large (if, say, it is a ship, or train or bus), it can be shown only in scale models or drawings.

After the design has been fully approved, all the details needed for manufacture are worked out. Some products may be manufactured in small quantities and "test-marketed" at first so that any needed changes may be made before full production begins.

Most designers ask to follow through with the design of packaging, displays and advertising, so that these may be related to the product they have just designed. An ideal situation develops when a client and his designer work together closely.

Training programs
in industrial design

Industrial designers may acquire the necessary background for their profession in colleges, universities and art schools. Industrial-design degrees were first offered in 1936. Such degrees today are generally granted after the completion of a four-year program. Students study technical subjects concerned with techniques and treatments of materials, liberal-art subjects and art and design subjects planned to stimulate original thinking. The completion of such a program is a great help in obtaining employment in the field. However, any top designer will hire promising young people if they show extraordinary aptitude and talent for design, regardless of training.

The young designer usually works under supervision on minor assignments at first, and gradually is given more responsibility as he acquires experience. He may stay with one organization or may change jobs several times in order to broaden his experience. Eventually, he may be put in charge of one or more important projects. His goal will usually be to start an independent organization. However, only a small percentage of the persons who enter the field of industrial design establish successful offices of their own. The majority remain with a large organization or join the staff of a manufacturer's design department.

Museums and
professional organizations

A number of art museums have established departments of industrial design. These museums organize exhibits of outstanding work, publish books and in various other ways further the cause of high standards in industrial design. The Museum of Modern Art in New York City was a pioneer in this field; it has remained a leader in acquainting the intelligent layman with the best designing work in America and other countries. Some other museums, including the Albright Gallery in Buffalo, the Institute of Contemporary Art in Boston and various city museums, have also shown special interest in industrial design.

There are two national industrial designers' organization in the United States: the Industrial Designers' Institute and the American Society for Industrial Designers. The former group was organized in 1936; the latter, in 1944. They serve the same purpose — to establish and maintain ethical standards of practice, encourage training in the field and promote the interests of all their members. Both of these organizations have a number of chapters throughout the United States.

PROGRESS IN MEDICINE

Important Landmarks of Modern Research

THE year 1935 marked a milestone in the history of chemotherapy — the treatment of internal disease by chemical agents. In February of that year a distinguished German chemist, Gerhard Domagk, published an article called "A Contribution to the Chemotherapy of Bacterial Infections" in the GERMAN MEDICAL WEEKLY. In this article he revealed that he had arrested deadly streptococcic and staphylococcic infections in rabbits with a red dye called prontosil. This dye contained sulfanilamide, a chemical belonging to the sulfonamide group. Would it not be possible to use prontosil in treating infections in human beings? If so, Domagk had discovered a new weapon in the fight against disease.

After the discovery of the curative properties of prontosil, French researchers tried to obtain the dye from German sources, but were rebuffed. They therefore synthesized the substance themselves, calling it rubiazol. They used prontosil (or rubiazol) to treat infected animals; their experiments generally confirmed the findings of Domagk. These French investigators were the first to discover that the curative agent was not prontosil itself but the sulfanilamide that it contained. When they administered sulfanilamide to animals, they found it was as effective as prontosil.

American research workers — including Eli K. Marshall, Jr., of the Johns Hopkins School of Medicine, and his associates — began treating various infections in human beings with sulfanilamide. They developed effective methods of determining the distribution of the drug in the body after it was taken by mouth or injected in the blood stream. Sulfanilamide proved very effective in the treatment of a number of serious diseases. A new and startlingly effective weapon had now been made available to doctors. Sulfanilamide was the first of the sulfonamides, or sulfa drugs, to be used in the treatment of disease. Later other sulfa drugs were developed, including sulfapyridine, sulfathiazole, sulfadiazine, sulfamerazine, sulfaguanidine and succinyl sulfathiazole.

The sulfa drugs are especially effective in combatting streptococcic bloodstream infection, streptococcic meningitis, erysipelas, certain types of pneumonia, gonorrhea and dysenteric infections. These drugs interfere with the growth and reproduction of bacteria and make it possible for the white cells of the blood to destroy them.

If sulfa drugs are taken in large doses, the mucous membranes may become bluish and the skin may acquire a grayish tinge. This discoloration does not appear to be harmful; it generally disappears when treatment with the drugs comes to an end. In the case of some people the sulfa drugs have toxic effects — that is, they act as poisons. The symptoms of such reactions vary greatly. There may be fever, rashes and considerable pain in the chest and abdomen. In extreme cases, dosage with sulfonamides may result in blood destruction, jaundice, anemia, diminution in the number of white blood corpuscles and injuries to the kidneys.

The rise of the antibiotics

Among the physician's most potent weapons at the present time are the chemical substances called antibiotics. They are able to check the growth of bacteria and various other microorganisms and in some

cases can destroy them. The antibiotics are produced by living organisms, such as molds and bacteria.

The first of the antibiotics to attract world-wide attention was penicillin,* an acid produced by the mold *Penicillium notatum.* An English scientist, Sir Alexander Fleming, discovered in 1928 that his cultures of bacteria would not grow in the presence of this mold. He found that the mold produced a substance — penicillin — that was toxic to various disease-causing organisms. Fleming did not carry forward his investigation of penicillin, and his epoch-making discovery was all but forgotten.

Several years later Sir Howard W. Florey, Ernst Boris Chain and others in England decided to investigate the possibilities of penicillin in the treatment of various infections. In 1941, the drug was first administered to human beings with amazingly successful results. In the summer of that year Florey came to the United States to seek help in producing penicillin in quantity. This goal was achieved by the following year through the efforts of America's drug industry and the Northern Regional, Research Laboratory of the United States Department of Agriculture. Penicillin was employed extensively in World War II to prevent infection of wounds and it saved many lives. Since that time many billions of units have been used in the treatment of disease.

Penicillin is generally given by injection; it is given by mouth in some cases. It is active chiefly against Gram-positive bacteria **; these include the streptococci and the staphylococci. It is not effective when used against most Gram-negative bacteria or the bacterialike organisms called rickettsiae. Penicillin is useful in the treat-

ment of bronchitis, meningitis, osteomyelitis, tonsilitis, tetanus and various other diseases; it also combats infection in burns and wounds.

Another important antibiotic is streptomycin. It is derived from *Streptomyces griseus,* a microorganism growing in the soil. Streptomycin was isolated in 1943 by Selman A. Waksman and his assistant Albert Schatz at Rutgers University; it was first used on human beings in 1945. It is particularly effective in treating tuberculosis; it has also been used to combat meningitis, peritonitis, abscesses of the liver and infections of the urinary tract and lungs. Streptomycin is much more toxic than penicillin; it sometimes produces certain unfortunate side reactions. The antibiotic called dihydrostreptomycin, derived from streptomycin, is less toxic and is sometimes used in place of streptomycin.

Chloromycetin (chloramphenicol), also produced by a soil microorganism, is called a broad-spectrum antibiotic, because it is effective against a much wider range, or spectrum, of organisms than either penicillin or streptomycin. The chemical formula of chloromycetin is quite simple, and the substance has been successfully synthesized. Aureomycin and terramycin are also effective broad-spectrum antibiotics. Terramycin has been employed with considerable success in the treatment of tuberculosis.

Neomycin has been used to combat infections of the skin, eyes and intestinal tract. Viomycin has been added to the drugs used in fighting tuberculosis. It has been found valuable in treating tuberculous patients who have developed resistance to other drugs, such as streptomycin and isoniazid. Bacitracin is sometimes the best drug for wound and postoperative infections. Its internal use is limited, since it may damage the kidneys.

The antibiotics have also proved their worth in animal medicine; they have saved the lives of thousands of pets and livestock animals. They have revolutionized animal nutrition, for it has been found that they have an extraordinary effect on animal growth. Small quantities of terramycin, penicillin and other antibiotics are

---

* Contrary to general belief, penicillin was not the first antibiotic to be used in treating human disease. The first was tyrothrycin, derived from *Bacillus brevis,* a soil bacterium, and isolated by René Dubos of the Rockefeller Institute for Medical Research. Tyrothrycin is still used, but on a very modest scale, since it is highly toxic. It serves only in treating infections on the surface of the body.

** This name is given to bacteria that hold a purple dye when stained by a method developed by the Danish physician Hans C. J. Gram. Bacteria that do not hold the dye when stained by Gram's method are called Gram-negative.

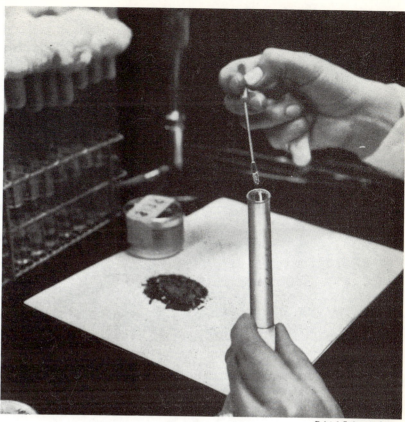

A technician in the laboratory of a big drug company analyzes a soil sample mailed by a collector. The antibiotic Bryamycin was obtained from soil sent in from Hawaii.

often added to livestock feeds; they bring hogs, chickens, turkeys and other livestock to market weight weeks sooner than before.

Researchers have discovered that the antibiotics offer a promising means of controlling halo blight of beans, fire blight of apples and peaches and other crop diseases. It has been found, too, that small amounts of terramycin speed the germination and early growth of sweet corn and some other crop plants by as much as 100 per cent.

The story of antibiotics is not one of uninterrupted success. For one thing, they have not been effective against most virus diseases. Then too, various antibiotics may produce undesirable side reactions. These effects may make themselves felt with the very first dose; sometimes they develop after a person has received repeated doses. When broad-spectrum antibiotics are given by mouth, the growth of many of the bacteria normally found in the stomach is checked, and there is an overgrowth of various undesirable yeastlike or funguslike organisms.

What is even more serious, perhaps, infectious bacteria gradually develop re-sistance to various antibiotics, so that in time these have little or no effect. It was thought at one time that such bacterial resistance would cut short man's splendid new triumph over disease. Since then, however, the development of new antibiotics and the use of older ones and other drugs in combination have kept us a jump ahead of resistant microbes.

The war against poliomyelitis

The disease known as poliomyelitis, or polio or infantile paralysis, most often attacks children but also claims considerable numbers of adult victims. The disease is caused by a virus too small to be seen under the ordinary microscope. There are various strains of this virus, any one of which can bring on an attack of polio. However, only three of them can cause paralysis in man: these are known as the Brunhilde strain, the Lansing strain and the Leon strain. Immunity to one of these types does not provide immunity to the other two. That is why a person may have more than one attack of crippling polio —

Dr. Jonas E. Salk, above, developed a vaccine that has proved to be effective against paralytic poliomyelitis.

a development that puzzled early investigators of the disease.

The polio viruses attack the body by invading the digestive organs or the lungs. As they come in contact with the body defense mechanisms, they bring about the formation of antibodies — substances that neutralize the effects of the viruses. (See Index, under Antibodies.) If the viruses are not held in check by the antibodies, they may reach nerve cells in the spinal cord or brain. If that happens, numbers of these cells may be destroyed; the disease may result in wasting away of muscles, or permanent paralysis or death. The severity of an attack depends upon the extent of the cell destruction in the affected areas. The great majority of polio cases are not serious.

One method of treating polio is to keep the affected limbs in casts or splints during the early stage of the disease. Afterward, in less severe cases, massage or electrotherapy is applied in order to stimulate the affected muscles. Swimming exercises are also employed for the same purpose. Another method of treatment was developed by Elizabeth Kenny, an Australian nurse. She put hot packs on the affected parts and combined this treatment with gentle massage and exercise. Although the Kenny method was endorsed by the American National Foundation for Infantile Paralysis in 1941, many specialists are not convinced that it should supersede the other method described above.

If paralysis of the muscles of respiration sets in as a consequence of the disease, it is necessary to apply artificial respiration, particularly with the aid of the machine known as the Drinker respirator, or "iron lung." (See Index, under Drinker respirators.) In extreme cases such respiration must be applied throughout the life of the patient.

Extensive efforts have been made in recent years to bring about the prevention of the disease. It has been found that the fraction of the blood known as gamma globulin contains antibodies that may serve to keep the polio viruses in check. In the course of World War II methods were devised to concentrate this fraction of the blood. In 1951 and 1952 Dr. William McD. Hammon of the University of Pittsburgh conducted a series of controlled tests with gamma globulin, injecting a number of children in the states of Utah, Texas and Iowa. According to Dr. Hammon, these tests showed that mass injections of gamma globulin could prevent paralytic

IMPORTANT ANTIBIOTICS

The chemical substances called antibiotics have marked a revolution in the fight against disease. These substances are derived from living organisms, such as molds and bacteria. The first important one to be developed was penicillin, an acid produced by the mold *Penicillium*. (illustrated above). It was first given to human beings in 1941. Since that time many antibiotics have been developed. Here are a few organisms that yield antibiotics; we show how they are grown and tested.

In their search for new antibiotics, scientists grow soil organisms, such as molds, yeasts and bacteria, in sterile culture plates, known as Petri dishes. The organisms grow in distinct colonies, as shown here.

Chas. Pfizer & Co., Inc.

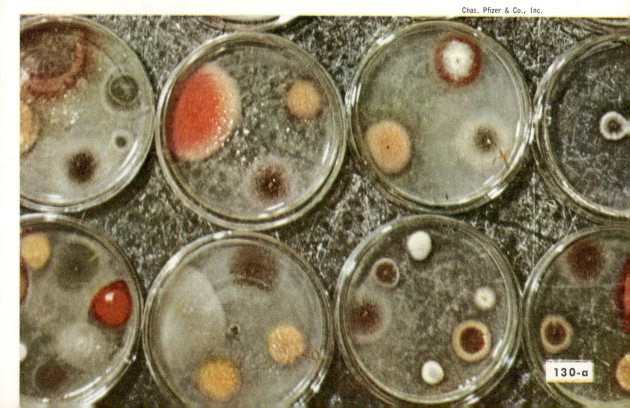

Important antibiotics are derived from some of the molds in the microscopic "jungle" at the right. (This "jungle" is an artist's conception.) Below we provide a key to the molds, as follows: (1) *Isaria*, often parasitic on insects. (2) *Aspergillus giganteus*, which produces oxalic acid from sugar. (3) *Pilobolus*, a light-sensitive mold. (4) *Streptomyces*, which yields such antibiotics as streptomycin and Terramycin. (5) *Aspergillus glaucus*, a common mold of foods, textiles and tobacco. (6) *Monilia sitophila*, one of the commonest bread molds. (7) *Aspergillus clavatus*, which produces the antibiotic called clavacin. (8) *Aspergillus versicolor*. (9) *Aspergillus terreus*; from it is derived itaconic acid, an industrial chemical. (10) *Gliocladium roseum*. (11) *Penicillium italicum*, a major cause of fruit rot. (12) *Aspergillus Wentii*. (13) *Aspergillus niger*, which produces citric acid. (14) *Mucor racemosus*; it produces alcohol, though not on a commercial scale. (15) *Penicillium chrysogenum*, which now produces all the world's commercial penicillin. (16) *Aspergillus effusus*.

Chas. Pfizer & Co., Inc.

Scientist examining a culture of an antibiotic-producing organism at the Institute of Microbiology, Rutgers University. Much important antibiotic research has been carried on at this university. It was here that Selman A. Waksman and his assistant Albert Schatz first isolated the major antibiotic streptomycin in the year 1943.

Rutgers University

Right: finding out how powerful an antibiotic is by the "cup-plate" method. Disease-causing bacteria are put in a glass-covered dish; the antibiotic to be tested is fed into the dish by means of a tube. At the end of a 24-hour period, the potency of the antibiotic can be determined by its effect on the bacteria in the dish.

Below: paper discs containing samples of new antibiotics are put in culture plates on which disease-producing bacteria are growing. We show one of the discs in the left-hand plate. Four discs have been placed in the right-hand plate. Note the havoc caused among the germs in the culture by the two discs in the center.

Chas. Pfizer & Co., Inc.

Merck & Co.

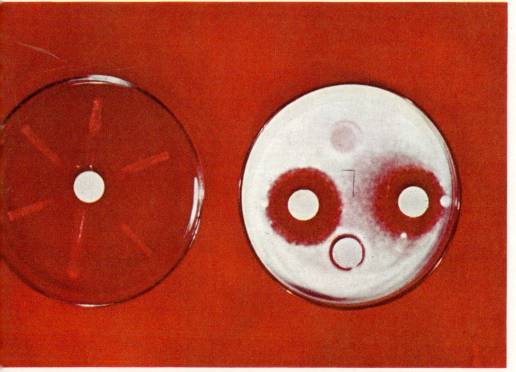

polio in about 70 per cent of the cases if the injections were given in the early stages of an epidemic.

Gamma globulin is not an ideal preventive. It does not stimulate the body to produce antibodies of its own; it provides protection for six weeks, at most. Even Dr. Hammon conceded that "the use of gamma globulin is certainly not a panacea for the prevention of paralytic poliomyelitis." Certain scientists are even more skeptical. A report issued in February 1954, under the auspices of the United States Public Health Service, maintained that gamma globulin was useless as a preventive in close-contact cases and that it did not reduce the severity of the disease.

An antipolio vaccine that causes the

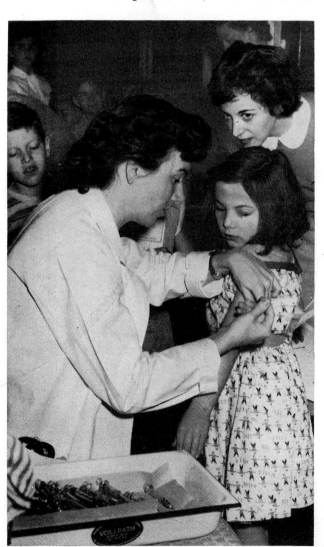

body to produce its own antibodies has been developed by Dr. Jonas E. Salk of the University of Pittsburgh School of Medicine. To prepare this vaccine, polio viruses are grown on monkey-kidney tissue. The viruses are killed by formalin and then mixed with mineral oil. Various tests are performed to see whether any of the viruses are still alive. The Salk vaccine is intended to provide protection against all three strains of paralysis-producing viruses for a period of seven months or longer.

The Salk vaccine
is put to the test

During the spring of 1954 the National Foundation for Infantile Paralysis began a series of extensive field trials to find out how effective the Salk vaccine was. In eighty-four areas of eleven states, 200,745 children received injections of the vaccine while another 201,229 were injected with a fluid containing no killed viruses (known as placebo). Only the persons conducting the tests knew which children were actually receiving the vaccine. An additional group of 338,778 received no inoculations but were observed as controls. Another type of test was carried out in 127 areas of thirty-three states. Here, a total of 221,998 children in the second grade received injections of Salk vaccine. A group of 848,778 children in the first, second and third grades were not injected and were observed as controls. All the inoculated children received three injections.

The results of the tests were studied at a Poliomyelitis Vaccine Evaluation Center at the University of Michigan. In April 1955, Dr. Thomas Francis, Jr., director of the Center, issued a report on the tests. Of the 1,829,916 who took part in the tests, including those who took the vaccine and those who served as controls, 863 were attacked by polio. In the vaccinated group there were 113 cases of polio, including seventy-one cases of par-

Physician giving a Salk antipolio vaccine inoculation to a little girl in a school in Baltimore, Maryland.

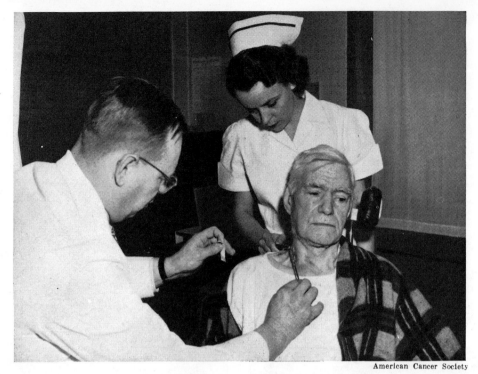

Placing a capsule of radium in position for treating cancer of a gland in the neck.

ACTH is obtained from the anterior lobe of the pituitary gland (the segment to which the pencil eraser points).

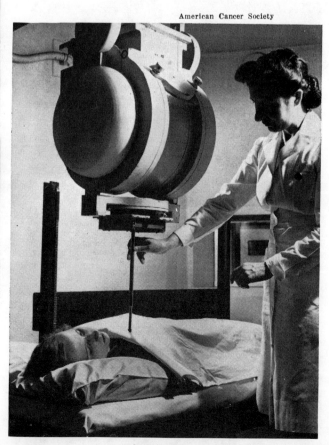

Treating cancer with X rays — technician using an attachment that concentrates the rays onto a small area.

alytic polio. In the unvaccinated group there were 744 cases of polio; of these 609 involved paralysis. Dr. Francis came to the conclusion that the vaccine was 80 to 90 per cent effective against paralytic polio. Following the report, the United States Public Health Service approved a license for the vaccine.

The Salk vaccine has been employed on a wide scale and the number of cases of acute paralytic polio has been reduced as a consequence. The disease is still a menace, however. Some authorities believe that the best way to conquer it is to use a safe live-virus vaccine. Already, three such vaccines have been developed: one by Dr. H. R. Cox, of the Lederle Laboratories in Pearl River, New York; another by Dr. H. Koprowski, of Philadelphia's Wistar Institute; a third by Dr. A. B. Sabin, of the University of Cincinnati.

Mass inoculation with live-virus vaccine has taken place in the Soviet Union, with apparently favorable results. In August 1960, United States Surgeon General Leroy E. Burney announced that the live-virus vaccine developed by Dr. Sabin had been officially approved as suitable for use in the United States.

Live-virus vaccine is given by mouth, while the Salk killed-virus vaccine must be injected with a hypodermic needle. There are other differences. Live-virus vaccine produces antibodies against virulent viruses more rapidly, and its effects are more lasting. Obviously, the killed viruses in the Salk vaccine cannot multiply in a person's body; viruses used in live-virus vaccines *can* multiply there. This may have unfortunate results. Originally harmless live viruses in a person's body may become virulent in time and may bring on the very disease they were supposed to prevent.

Hormones that
serve as medicines

It has been known since the time of the nineteenth-century English physician Thomas Addison that the adrenal glands are essential to life. In 1930, scientists at Princeton and the University of Buffalo prepared extracts from the adrenal cortex (the outer layer of the adrenal glands) that showed unmistakable hormone activity. By 1933, researchers of the Upjohn Company had worked out a commercial process for manufacturing extracts from the cortex of the adrenal glands.

Soon afterwards, the biochemists Edward C. Kendall of the Mayo Foundation and Tadeus Reichstein of Switzerland, working independently, isolated a number of hormones from the adrenal cortex. In 1948, Philip S. Hench of the Mayo Clinic found that one of these hormones, cortisone (17-hydroxy-11-dehydrocorticosterone; also called Compound E), was extraordinarily effective in treating rheumatoid arthritis. It was soon discovered that the substance could be used to treat various other diseases. Similar effects were produced by stimulating the adrenal cortex with ACTH (adrenocorticotropic hormone), which was first extracted from the pituitary gland in 1943 by scientists at Yale and the University of California.

Since that time ACTH and several hormones of the adrenal cortex — particularly cortisone and hydrocortisone (17-hydroxycorticosterone; also called Compound F) have been used in treating arthritis and other diseases. Hydrocortisone has much the same physiological effects as cortisone. Since it is more potent, it can be given in smaller doses. It is more expensive than cortisone.

ACTH, cortisone and hydrocortisone have provided relief for thousands of sufferers from rheumatoid arthritis. These hormones lessen or eliminate stiffness, aching and tenderness of joints and muscles. However, the beneficial effects that the drugs provide are only temporary; the disease is suppressed only as long as they are administered.

If these hormones are given uninterruptedly and in large doses in the treatment of rheumatoid arthritis, they often bring about certain undesirable side reactions, which usually disappear when the hormones are no longer administered. Among these reactions are fluid retention, abnormal fatty deposits on the face, abnormal hair growth in women, acne, fa-

tigue, headache and dizziness. To avoid such complications, physicians try to keep the dosage to a safe level, even if complete relief is not obtained.

ACTH, cortisone and hydrocortisone are very helpful in the treatment of rheumatic fever. If they are given early enough, they may prevent the development of rheumatic carditis, a heart condition that is sometimes a sequel of rheumatic fever. These hormones provide relief from various skin diseases; they have been employed in cases of eye inflammation. Small doses of cortisone have been effective in treating Addison's disease, which involves the degeneration of the adrenal cortex.

In 1960, the University of Pittsburgh announced that Dr. Klaus Hofmann and his associates at the University's Health Center had succeeded in synthesizing an artificial substance that would carry on all the biological activities of the natural ACTH. The latter hormone is a protein, made up of thirty-nine amino acids (see Index). The new artificial ACTH contained only the first twenty-three of these thirty-nine amino acids, and yet displayed the full activity of the natural hormone. It was the largest moleculelike substance ever synthesized up to that time, with a molecular weight of 3,200.

It was believed that the achievement of the University of Pittsburgh scientists would ultimately have far-reaching effects. It might lead to the production of man-made ACTH in large quantities, bringing about a marked reduction in cost. It might also point the way to the synthesis of still larger proteins, such as insulin.

The vexing cholesterol problem

The fatty alcohol called cholesterol is found in the cells of the body as well as in the blood stream; it is also present in bile salts and is one of the chief constituents of gallstones. In the blood stream, it protects the red blood cells from bacterial poisons, bile salts and other agents. If, however, it is present in excessive amounts, it can have certain undesirable effects. It may be deposited on the blood vessels and

may lead to the serious condition called atherosclerosis,* in which waxy cholesterol deposits are built up on the arterial linings. Gradually, they come to protrude into the lumen, or passageway, of arteries and thus reduce the supply of blood to a given organ.

One method of dealing with this condition has been to reduce the intake of foods rich in cholesterol, such as animal fats and egg yolk, and to substitute foods such as corn oil, cottonseed oil and fish oils. It is by no means certain that such a diet will bring about a decrease in the amount of cholesterol in the body, since this substance is built up in the tissues (particularly in the liver) from various types of foods — carbohydrates, fats and proteins.

Researchers have sought to develop drugs that will lower the cholesterol level. One of these, triparanol, has been used with quite favorable results. It blocks the synthesis of cholesterol at the final stage, when the substance is being formed from desmosterol. However, this might lead to an accumulation of desmosterol in the body and might conceivably cause trouble.

Thyroxine, the hormone of the thyroid gland, has also been effective in reducing the cholesterol level. Unfortunately, it also has certain unfortunate side effects; it unduly stimulates the nervous system and it speeds up metabolism. Biochemists are working on various thyroxinelike compounds that will lower the cholesterol level as effectively as thyroxine and that will be free from undesirable effects.

There is some evidence that tension and stress may lead to a rise (at least a temporary rise) in the quantity of cholesterol in the blood. Tension causes the release of the hormone adrenaline; this hormone, in turn, triggers the release of fatty materials from storage depots in the body, so that they may be available for conversion into energy. It would seem advisable, therefore, for sufferers from atherosclerosis to avoid excitement as much as possible.

See also Vol. 10, p. 278: "Medicine, Progress of."

* This is a form of arteriosclerosis, or hardening of the arteries.

LAND AND SEA HABITATS

The Natural Abodes of Animals and Plants

by F. L. FITZPATRICK

A HUGE whale bowling along the surface of the sea, a tiny field mouse gnawing away at a stalk of wheat in a field, a palm tree in an oasis — these living things are obviously where they belong. Just as clearly, they are not where they belong when the whale is stranded on a beach; when the field mouse is in the air, firmly clutched in the talons of a hawk; when the palm tree, set in a tub, adorns a hotel lobby. In each case a living thing has been removed from the place where it normally lives, the place we call its habitat.

In the long course of time, plants and animals have made themselves at home in different regions of the earth. Some live on the surface of the land. Others are found in the soil or in fresh-water ponds, streams or lakes. Still others live in the shallow sea, in the deep sea, in the trees or in the air. Generally, living things are well adapted for life in their habitats.

The land habitat is best known to us because it is the one in which we normally spend our own lives. Most centers of human population are in places where the annual rainfall is moderate and where variations in temperature are not extreme. We ourselves are reasonably well adapted to such habitats; if not, we would not survive. A great variety of plants and animals also are adapted to life on the land.

A forest tree is a good example. Its root system penetrates deep down into the soil and forms a secure anchorage so that the tree may withstand the uprooting effects of gales. At the same time, the tiny branch roots far below the surface can absorb soil water and mineral compounds that the tree must have in order to maintain life. The trunk of the tree holds up the branches and leaves; it also houses a vast number of ducts, which afford passage to water and dissolved minerals taken in from the soil and to food products manufactured in the leaves. For the green leaves are food-making centers, which take carbon dioxide from the air and water from the soil and which make use of the energy furnished by sunlight. Thus, roots, trunk, branches and leaves work together in an environment of soil, air and sunlight.

Not all land habitats are alike by any means. Some of them present extreme conditions that can be met only by unusual adaptations. The desert, for instance, is a dry habitat in which only a few of our more familiar plants and animals can live. Camels, however, are well suited to life in a dry country; so much so, indeed, that they are called "ships of the desert." They have padlike feet which are very effective in walking upon the shifting desert sands. Special stomach pouches, which are closed by ringlike muscles, store reserve supplies of water. A camel can live without drinking for several days, drawing upon its reserve store of liquid while it makes its way over the desert between two oases.

A camel may be required to go without food for a time, because vegetation in a desert habitat is likely to be scanty. The animal is also equipped to meet an emergency of this kind. One species, the dromedary of Arabia, has a hump on its back that can hold a reserve food supply of stored fat. The Bactrian camel of central Asia has two humps of fat-storing cells.

A considerable number of the world's land animals spend all or part of their

N. Y. Zoological Society

This female gibbon and her baby are in their natural habitat, in a forest area of Pegu, in Burma.

lives in trees; these are called arboreal animals. A good example is the three-toed sloth, found in the tropical jungles of Central and South America. This ungainly animal clings to the branches of a tree in an upside-down position with its curved claws, which are turned inward. A sloth may spend most of its life in the same tree. As it hangs suspended from a limb, it eats near-by leaves and shoots and laps the moisture that collects upon leaves during tropical downpours. In the warm, moist environment of such a forest, tiny green plants sometimes grow upon the coarse hair of the sloth and thus shield this relatively defenseless animal from the gaze of its enemies.

Another animal that lives almost entirely in the trees is an ancient and perhaps primitive type of bird, the South American hoactzin. It is about the size of a common robin. In the adult state it has feathered wings, but it rarely uses them except to fly feebly from tree to tree along the banks of the tropical river where it makes its home. The hoactzin climbs about among the branches, and feeds upon vegetation and fruit. The young bird is especially well adapted for this climbing habit because its wings bear two claws which are used in clinging to the branches. As the young bird develops, the claws are lost, and the wing feathers appear.

There are many plants that live in and upon the trees. The wild grape of eastern North America develops a climbing vine; eventually the leaves of the grape plant are spread out over the top of the tree host. In this position, the grape leaves receive the direct rays of the sun, and may shade the leaves of the tree host to such an extent that the tree is killed.

Like this grapevine the mistletoe also grows as a climbing plant and pushes its way into the sunlight. The mistletoe takes even greater advantage of its tree host, for its roots grow into the tissues of the tree, where they obtain liquids containing food substances. Thus it is not necessary for the mistletoe plant to emulate its tree host by manufacturing all its own food.

Black Star

This young chimpanzee, learning to ride a tricycle in a public zoo, is far from his natural habitat.

Many plants and animals live in the soil; they are known as subterranean or underground species. An interesting example is the pocket gopher, found in the midwestern area of the United States. This little animal spends almost all its life burrowing about in the soil, where it feeds upon the

roots of crop plants and other vegetable materials. If a colony of gophers makes its home in a field, its members will soon create an astonishingly extensive system of burrows.

The industrious pocket gopher has a subterranean habitat

The pocket gopher lives in total darkness most of the time. It has very small eyes, as we would expect, and it depends very little upon the sense of sight. It has short, powerful front legs and its feet and claws are very efficient digging tools. Like all rodents, it has chisel-like front teeth, just the thing for cutting off the roots of plants. Infolded pockets of skin, one on each side of the neck, serve as food-bearing pouches. The gopher uses its forelegs, chest and head to push dirt from its burrow to the surface, where it is dumped into "hills."

Many other plants and animals live in the soil most or all the time. Some of them dig burrows of their own; others live in burrows which they find ready-made. Still others, which are too tiny to be seen without the aid of a microscope, make their homes amid soil particles.

Among the smallest of these underground dwellers are various species of soil bacteria. These are single-celled types which do not contain chlorophyl, the green coloring matter of plants, and therefore are unable to make their own food. Many of them feed upon the bodies of dead animals and plants. These bacteria are beneficial, for they break down, or decay, the remains of animals and plants into compounds that enrich the soil; moreover, the surface of the earth would be badly cluttered up by now if these remains did not decay.

A great many organisms are found above the surface of the earth

The air also has its inhabitants, which are sometimes known as aerial organisms. We at once think of birds, of course, but birds are by no means the only living things that invade the atmosphere. As a matter of fact, the forms of life most commonly found above the surface of the earth are

Davey Tree Expert Co.

This photograph shows the extensive root system of trees. Roots penetrate far below the surface.

a host of microscopic animals, plants, spores and pollens, which drift along with the air currents, sometimes at great heights. Some of them have been picked up by special balloon-trapping devices at an altitude of ten miles. Even spiders have been found in the upper air, riding upon their floating webs. None of these little organisms is able to fly in the ordinary sense of the word; they remain aloft because they are so light that they are supported by air currents. They are very hardy, too; they survive drying, changes in pressure and extremes of temperature.

The first inhabitants of the air were probably one-celled organisms

When a pond dries up during the long, hot days of midsummer, certain single-celled animals that formerly lived in the water secrete tiny protective coverings about themselves. These animals, together with bacteria and spores, may be swept up into the air by winds, like so many dust particles, and carried to great heights and distances before chance brings them back to the surface of the earth again. Together with simple plant cells, they probably were the first inhabitants of the air. They had this element to themselves throughout long eras, until the larger flying animals finally appeared upon the scene.

The first true flyers probably were developed among members of the insect group, millions of years ago. They gave rise to a long line of descendants, including our modern insects, many of which are aerial to some extent. Some present-day insects cannot fly, but the vast majority of species possess either one or two pairs of wings in the adult state.

The wings of insects are not like those of birds or bats

The wings of insects are most unusual. An insect's body is covered with a hard, protective and supporting material called chitin. Within its body is a system of branching tubes through which the oxygen of the air reaches the various tissues. When wings are developed, they arise as outpushings of the chitin layer surrounding

N. Y. Zoological Society

The sloth is well adapted to its arboreal habitat. It is able to cling upside-down to tree branches.

the body, and the ends of some of the air tubes grow into the wings to become supporting structures or veins. Thus, the wings of an insect, unlike those of bats or birds, are in no way derived from limbs.

Except for a few species, birds are capable of true and sustained flight. The wings are fore limbs that bear feathers, thus forming flying surfaces. They are the main supports in flight, but bird tails are also important because they act as rudders and as balancers and may be used to brake forward motion when a bird alights. The bird's body, more or less spindle-shaped, meets a minimum of air or wind resistance when in flight. Bird bodies are compact and light when compared with the wing surface that must support them.

However, sustained flight would be impossible if the birds did not have a highly efficient muscular system. This system is firmly attached to the skeleton, which is strong and rigid, especially in the back shoulder regions. But if the bird's bone structure is strong, it is also extremely light—a great advantage to a flying animal. The long bones are usually hollow. The skull is thin; it is strong because many of the small bones are fused together.

A powerful muscular system needs a large and steady supply of food materials and oxygen. Birds eat relatively large amounts of food, and digest the food quickly. They have highly developed sys-

tems of arteries and veins, which promptly supply the products of digestion to muscle cells. Two small, compact lungs are supplemented by a number of air sacs lying beneath the skin. In some species the air sacs are connected with the cavities of the hollow bones. This adaptation makes the bird's respiration very efficient and provides a steady supply of oxygen to the body cells.

Among mammals the bats furnish the best example of aerial organisms. Many species of these night flyers are found in both the New and the Old Worlds. Their wings are fleshy membranes which extend from the fore limbs to the hind limbs and the tail. The muscular, circulatory and digestive systems of bats are probably not so efficient as those of birds, even though bats are warm-blooded animals. Bats, however, are unsurpassed in zigzagging, darting flight, which takes them in and out

These three camels are laying in a supply of water that may have to last them for several days.

Standard Oil Co. (N. J.)

American Museum of Natural History

Grape vines twine themselves around other plants.

of small spaces safely when they are pursuing their insect prey.

To perform such flights requires amazing muscular co-ordination. It also requires ability to detect the exact whereabouts of possible obstacles. Experiments have shown that even when bats are blindfolded, they can fly about in rooms without striking walls or any other obstacles. They can do so because they have a radar-like detecting apparatus. As a bat flies, it emits a series of very high-pitched squeaks. The resulting sound-waves move out rapidly from the animal's body; when they strike any solid object, they are reflected back. The bat's delicate sense organs receive the reflected sound-waves, and as a result the animal is warned when it is in danger of a collision.

Many different organisms are found in the habitats provided by the shallow waters of ponds, lakes, streams and certain areas of the sea. Practically all our well-known aquatic, or water-dwelling plants and animals come from these shallow waters. ("Shallow" in the scientific sense includes water up to several hundred feet in depth.)

Green plants living in shallow water have one requirement in common: they must maintain contact with sunlight. Sunlight penetrates into the water to various depths, depending upon the clarity of the water and

Both photos, Fish and Wildlife Service

The little pocket gopher, shown above, spends almost all its life burrowing about in the soil.

The dirt in this mound has been carried to the surface of the ground by a burrowing pocket gopher.

the motion of its surface. However, sufficient sunlight for the food-making needs of plants seems to be limited, in most cases, to a zone within fifty feet of the surface. Very few living green plants are found at depths greater than a hundred feet.

Oxygen is one of the chief requirements of animals living in shallow water. A few of them come to the surface to breathe air. However, most species living beneath the water are either simple types that can take in oxygen dissolved in water through the surfaces of their bodies, or more complex varieties that develop gills.

Most common fish, for example, obtain oxygen from the water by means of gills. These are fleshy, branching structures in which the small end processes of blood vessels come close to the surface. When water containing oxygen passes over the gills, oxygen is taken into the fish's blood vessels. Through the same gills carbon-dioxide waste is discharged into the water.

The ocean provides a number of habitats which differ greatly from one another. There may be variation in the type of bottom, in the temperature of the water, in the presence or absence of waves or currents and in the available food supply for particular forms of life.

Certain fishes have been brought to the surface from depths of 12,000 feet, and

National Audubon Society

The powerful wings of birds are really fore limbs that bear feathers, thus forming flying surfaces.

other simpler varieties of animals from depths of 23,000 feet. In fact, a number of fish families appear to be represented only by species that are found more than 6,000 feet below the surface.

Down in the abyss, sunlight is absent, and so, as we have said, are living green plants. The familiar waves and ocean cur-

L. W. Brownell

Water lilies are green plants that maintain contact with sunlight through their broad floating leaves. These leaves, like those of land plants, utilize the energy of the sun in manufacturing food.

rents are also missing and the temperature does not vary to any great degree but remains just above the freezing point. In some places the bottom is covered with an ooze made up of the dead and partly decomposed bodies of various plants and animals that once lived at or near the surface of the sea. After death they sank to the bottom where they were preserved after a fashion, in a natural cold-storage locker. Wherever there is such a basic supply of food to be had for the eating, one may expect to find animals as well.

Only a particular type of animal can exist in such a habitat, for pressure at a depth of even 6,000 feet is terrific. Living at sea level we are accustomed to an air pressure of 14.7 pounds per square inch. In salt water, pressure increases another 14.7 pounds per square inch for every 33 feet of depth. At 6,000 feet, therefore, the total pressure is well over 2,500 pounds per square inch. A deep-sea animal has pressures in the cells of its body equal to the water pressure upon the animal. When a deep-sea fish is caught in a dredge and hauled up to the surface, the sudden lessening of pressure upon it may cause its air-filled swim bladder to burst; that is, the fish is literally blown up by pressure from within its body.

Feeding habits of animals living in a deep-sea habitat

Some of the animals in a deep-sea habitat feed upon the ooze or the larger morsels of food that drop down from the surface. Others appear to be carnivorous, or flesh-eating, and live, no doubt, at the expense of their smaller and more helpless neighbors.

In such a dark environment there would seem to be little need for eyes. In truth, some deep-sea animals are blind and depend upon organs of touch to find their way about. However, light is present even in the abyss; it comes from phosphorescent organs that emit light without noticeable heat.

The explanation of phosphorescence in deep-sea animals

A phosphorescent organ usually consists of a group of cells covered by a lens-like structure. The cells beneath the "lens" secrete a substance that is luminous, and the glow produced by a group of these organs may permit a deep-sea fish to see near-by objects. Not only fish but also many of the simpler animals found in the deep sea are also phosphorescent. Some deep-sea fish have unusually large eyes, well adapted for making the most of such feeble illumination. Certain species of deep-sea fish also bear phosphorescent organs on projecting stalks. Such glowing baits may serve to lure unwary animals within easy reach of a waiting mouth and an empty stomach.

Every living thing, then, lives in a habitat—in the soil, in the air or in the water—for which it is well adapted. If it is removed from that habitat, it may perish.

See also Vol. 10, p. 271: "Ecology."

American Museum of Natural History

A phosphorescent deep-sea fish, *Chauliodus sloani,* pursuing some melamphids. Phosphorescence is produced by cells covered by a lens-like structure.

THE TREATMENT OF PLANTS

The Use of Surgery in the Garden

LIKE all living things, bushes and trees are subject to a considerable variety of injuries. A heavy fall of snow or sleet may blanket the trees, causing overladen branches to break off or split. Violent winds may rip off well-developed boughs. Insects, such as bark beetles, bore into the bark; gnawing animals, such as beavers, may strip off pieces of living tissue. With their cultivating tools, or pruning shears or saws, gardeners may sometimes unwittingly produce grievous wounds. Most of the injuries caused by such mishaps are ragged, open sores, which may become avenues of infection for rot-producing fungi and deadly disease germs. The bush or tree is likely to succumb to its injuries unless man lends a helping hand.

In caring for injured plants, we must bear in mind that under the proper conditions they can produce new tissue in the damaged areas. The source of supply is the healthy tissue that grows around the site of the wound. Generally the first sign that healing is taking place is the appearance of a whitish substance over the surface of the injured area. This substance, which is called the callus, is formed from the inner bark and other tissues; it protects the wound surface from drying out and also guards it against the entry of insects and fungus growths. From the callus tissue there eventually develops a new mass of special cells; these replace the ones that have been lost by injury.

Many times, when limbs are broken off, new ones are regenerated from buds. These special organs are made up of tissue that can grow rapidly and that will develop into different plant parts. In a normally growing plant, many buds remain inactive, or dormant. The food supply of the plant is sent to the actively growing stems, leaves or flowers, and the dormant buds receive only enough to keep alive.

When a branch is removed from a tree, the food supply to that member is naturally cut off. It is diverted to the dormant buds located on the main branch or on the trunk in the vicinity of the injury. With an increase in food supply, accompanied by stimulation from various hormones, the once dormant buds enter upon an active career and begin to develop into new branches. Often a severe injury to a tree will cause buds to form in areas where formerly there were no buds at all. For example, a tree may be cut down so that only a stump is left. In the course of time a number of buds, called adventitious buds, will develop and give rise to new stems.

Both the healing of injured tissue and the regeneration of lost limbs can take place only if the proper conditions are provided. Harmful insects and other organisms must be kept at bay with adequate spraying. The soil in which the plant grows must be fertilized so as to provide the basic food elements. There must be an adequate supply of water; the chemical substances called hormones, which initiate and control growth, must be present. The plant must have sufficient food reserves, in the form of the carbohydrates and proteins that it has itself manufactured in the green leaf. Plants must be transplanted from the area if it is so crowded that individual plants do not obtain enough water and essential food elements. In other words, man must often supplement nature. He may even find it necessary to substitute his own methods for natural processes if healthy plants are to thrive and injured plants are to be restored.

In the following pages we shall deal with some of the methods that man has devised to treat the injuries and diseases of plants. Tree surgery has made great progress in recent years. Outstanding progress has been made, too, in the preparation of preventive or curative sprays, washes and paints that are used to combat plant diseases and insect pests.

Tree surgery differs from human and animal surgery, particularly because trees are far more plastic than animals and because they possess to a far greater degree the faculty of rejuvenation.

When we say that trees are more plastic than animals, we mean that they are capable of more variation. In animals, the size, weight and outward appearance of each species is more or less stable. In plants, while the specific characters of cells, tissues, flowers and seeds remain unaltered,

A remarkably vigorous growth of pitch pine sprouts at the base of a tree that has been badly scorched by fire.

The stump sprout of a black cherry. The stump is that of a tree that was chopped down eighteen years before.

outward appearance and size show surprising variations. These depend upon the climate, the altitude and the presence or absence of certain minerals.

Even more remarkable, perhaps, is a plant's powers of rejuvenation, compared with those of animals. In most vertebrates, limbs that have been lost will not grow again. If large masses of tissues are destroyed, the resulting cavities will not be filled up; what tissue regeneration does occur is superficial and serves rather as a protection to the remaining tissue than as a replacement. Plants can repair damaged tissue much more effectively than animals; they can also replace lost parts.

Trees are subjected to all kinds of accidents and various other mishaps. Wind storms frequently break off their limbs, leaving jagged stumps. Heavy snows weigh down branches and may cause them to snap off. Trees are struck by lightning; they are attacked by frost and drought and insects. Sometimes, it is true, a tree's gaping wounds offer a pathway for infection by bacteria and fungi — infection that is responsible for the cavities, large and small, found on most old trees. In the great majority of cases, however, the injuries that a tree receives in the course of its long life heal rapidly.

Trees repair injuries by growing new tissue and new bark. Some trees seal up their wounds almost immediately with certain secretions, such as resin (as in the pine and fir trees) and latex (as in *Hevea brasiliensis* — the rubber tree — and the sumac). This secretion rapidly covers the wound with a varnishlike coating and protects it from infection, in much the same way as court plaster protects a cut on a human finger or leg.

Even when an old tree has been overwhelmed during a violent storm and has been reduced to a mere stump, it is surprising to note how soon it will come to life again. (The time required will depend upon the particular species of tree.) Generally within a year a clump of young shoots will appear around the stump of the shattered tree and will start to grow. Some of the shoots will be eliminated in the competition for sunlight and air. The rest will develop very rapidly, and when they have reached a respectable size, very little will be seen of the old stump. This is what happens when the rejuvenation process is left entirely to nature. Recovery is even more remarkable when man takes a hand. If one lops off all the shoots except the most promising one, this will rise straight and strong. After a time it will match its predecessor, or rather its own self before it was so severely damaged. It will have been completely rejuvenated.

We can speed up in various ways the recovery of a tree that has suffered a major accident. If we saw the stump off near the ground and "freshen up" (bruise) the edge near the bark with a knife or an axe, depending upon the size of the stump, we will ensure a strong growth of shoots from which to choose. An application of disinfectant, followed by a coat of wax or paint, will eliminate the chance of infection. Care in suppressing the lower limbs as the sprout grows will ensure a straight and rapidly growing bole, such as is generally sought for in timber or shade trees.

In the avenue Denfert-Rochereau, in Paris, trees are trimmed like this every three or four years so that they may be kept uniform in size and shape.

Standard Oil Co. (N. J.)

The discussion on the preceding page has shown that a tree is exceedingly tenacious of life. Because of this fact a tree surgeon, or, more properly, tree expert, may perform a number of operations without endangering the organism. Probably the observation of some such fallen tree springing into new life led the primitive agriculturist to devise the various methods of pruning that have been in existence for ages. He found that branches that were broken off or twigs that were shed were in due time replaced by others; thus would arise a belief that surgical interference with the parts of a tree might be pushed to extreme limits.

Tree care is an ancient art

The art of horticulture goes back to antiquity. Records show that gardeners of ancient Babylonia, Assyria and Persia pruned trees, transplanted them and treated their wounds. Theophrastus, the Greek philosopher and scientist of the fourth century B.C., wrote a HISTORY OF PLANTS in which he describes the cultivation and care of trees and speaks of plastering tree wounds with mud to prevent decay.

Today, tree care has become an exact science. The tree expert must know something about plant physiology and about tree diseases. He should be acquainted with the insects that attack trees and with the methods for eradicating them. He must know how to determine the acidity and alkalinity of soils, what to use in the way of fertilizers and how to judge the effects of drainage, soil texture and climate on trees. He should be aware of the species of trees that do best in a given environment. Moreover, he must practice tree sanitation. This entails cutting away dead, diseased and insect-ridden parts and destroying the debris so that no breeding places for insects and disease remain.

The care of tree wounds, even apparently insignificant ones, prevents the inroads of infection and improves the tree's appearance. Small wounds may enlarge into cavities, which ultimately weaken the structure of the tree and afford a breeding

Tree showing neglected pruning wounds.

place for insects and destructive fungi. Years ago tree surgeons, for the most part, cleaned out larger tree cavities and filled them with concrete or other materials. This was often a costly procedure and frequently the tree died a lingering death in spite of it. Nowadays experts attempt to prevent large cavities from forming by attending promptly to the small wounds made by wind breakage and pruning cuts. Furthermore, they increase the tree's chances of recovery by spraying against insects and fungi, fertilizing the soil and keeping the tree well watered.

The principle of treating an old wound is to clean out the wounded area and apply

a protective coating to stop further decay. If the stub of a broken branch remains, it is cut off flush with the trunk or limb from which it extended. The tree expert then follows the procedure used in the treatment of all old wounds. First, he removes decayed, diseased, insect-eaten, discolored and water-soaked wood by means of a mallet and hand chisel or by air-driven drills or chisels. After this operation only the sound wood remains.

The surface of the cavity is then made smooth; if the cavity is likely to hold water, it is shaped so that the water will drain out. The top and bottom edges of the wound are tapered to promote callus formation. Final trimming cuts are made with a sharp knife, and the cut edges of the bark, cambium (layer of actively growing cells beneath the bark) and sapwood are immediately painted with shellac. The surface of the cavity is then protectively coated with a tree-wound dressing compound. A good dressing is made from resin

A large pruning wound, smoothed, trimmed and treated with a tree-wound dressing compound.

Photos, The Davey Tree Expert Co.

and sardine or raw linseed oil. Other dressing compounds usually have a coal-tar or creosote base; these substances sometimes retard callus formation, however. The cavity need not be filled with concrete, but a filling often improves the appearance of the wound and gives a surface on which the callus can grow.

Fresh wounds are trimmed of any ragged edges and shaped so that the wound tapers at top and bottom. The surface of the wound is made smooth. If the injury is small, a coating of shellac or grafting wax usually suffices. Large wounds are treated with the more permanent tree-wound dressing compounds. A fungicidal, or fungus-killing, paint made by mixing dry Bordeaux mixture with raw linseed oil protects the wound from fungus growths. When cankers, caused by certain fungi, form on limbs, the cankers are cut out and the wound coated with an asphaltum paint containing a small amount of the fungicidal phenylmercury nitrate. All of these dressed surfaces have to be inspected from time to time for any blistering or cracking. If irregularities are found, the surface is repainted. Even if no abnormalities occur, a dressing is applied at least once every year until the wound completely heals.

Pruning is a necessary operation in tree care. The tree expert does not go about it in a haphazard fashion but removes branches and limbs for a specific purpose. Sometimes they interfere with telephone wires, endanger house roofs or create a traffic hazard by arching low over a highway. Often dead or dying limbs impair the beauty and threaten the health of a tree. Quite frequently a tree is structurally weak and requires shaping to preserve its strong limbs and rid it of unsound ones. Damage from wind, ice storms and heavy snow is considerably reduced if a tree is properly pruned. The cutting away of excessive growth allows for greater circulation of air and deeper penetration of light into the center of the tree. Cutting back of branches often revitalizes old trees and induces the formation of blossoms in those that flower. It must be emphasized, however, that pruning is not a cure-all for

Newly planted tree after being pruned.

Same tree after ten years of growth.

sickly trees. If the plants are not adequately watered and fertilized, no amount of pruning is going to be of great value.

Pruning is accomplished with several tools. For cutting small branches up to one-half inch in diameter, hand pruning shears are adequate. For larger branches up to one inch across, lopping shears are employed. These tools have handles from two to two and one-half feet long. If the branches are high on the trunk or far out on a high limb, the tree expert uses a pole pruner, which has the cutting parts at the end of a long, perhaps twelve-foot, pole. Pruning saws of various designs are used to cut through the larger limbs.

All branches and limbs are removed flush with the trunk or stem from which they extend. The smaller branches can be cut off smoothly in one action. Larger limbs require three cutting operations. The first sawing cut is made on the underside of the limb about a foot from the main stem. This cut goes in until the saw binds. The second cut is made a few inches beyond the first, going through until the limb falls. The original undercut stops the falling limb

from stripping a piece of bark from the main stem. The stub that remains is then cut off flush and the wound trimmed, shaped and dressed. Growth of the callus depends upon the amount of food substances — manufactured in the leaves — that is carried down through the inner bark to the wound. More rapid healing results when heavy foliage occurs above the wound. Tree experts prune limbs so that the wounds are below substantial leaf growth.

The season for pruning varies with the climate, locality and species of tree; generally late-winter or early-spring, when the plants are still dormant, seems to be the most opportune time for pruning. Severe freezing temperatures can injure freshly pruned trees, so pruning is best delayed until danger of intense cold is past. On the other hand, if it is put off until after spring growth commences, the tree may be devitalized. The first growth is activated by food materials stored by the plant through the winter. When pruned early, the tree diverts its stored food reserves to the buds and young stems that remain and

Photos, Bureau of Plant Industry, USDA

These apples fell before harvest time from a tree that was not sprayed with plant-growth regulator.

Sprayed with plant-growth regulator, this fine tree retains its apples until they have ripened.

J. Horace McFarland

Far more fruit and much less wood growth are produced by the pruned pear tree that is shown above.

vigorous growth results. Once spring buds have opened and growth has started, pruning cuts off much of the food materials that have circulated into the wood and new growth that are removed.

Tree expert and orchardist
train trees in a similar manner

When new trees are cared for, young trees shaped and older trees revitalized, the tree expert and orchardist follow similar methods. A young tree that is fresh from the nursery is pruned of any damaged roots, and its top growth is cut back, sometimes leaving only the central stem that eventually becomes the trunk.

Once side branches have a good start, selection is made of those that in time form the firm framework that supports foliage, smaller branches and fruits. Probably the most important principle of selection is to get rid of any branch that eventually would lead to a weak crotch. Such a branch, if allowed to mature on the tree, would split from the trunk under the weight of a moderate amount of snow or fruit or under the stress of a heavy wind. The limbs that branch from the trunk must be smaller in diameter than the trunk itself. Furthermore, the greater the angle between the trunk and a limb issuing from it, the stronger will be the crotch. Consequently, those branches that are larger than the trunk in cross section or that form but a small angle with it are pruned away. Once these branches are removed, selection depends upon the distribution of those that remain. No two branches are allowed to remain at the same height on the trunk; a vertical distance of at least six inches is maintained between them. Branches, too, must be spaced so that they extend equally from all sides of the trunk. Careful selection of firm and properly spaced limbs on young trees prevent drastic pruning operations in the future.

As the tree reaches maturity, most prunings consist of cutting out weakly growing wood and any limbs damaged by storm or disease. If the tree is thinly branched, the expert can often remedy this condition by removing many of the growing points.

This causes food materials to be diverted to side, or axillary, buds; this stimulates them to burst forth into new shoots. Often a mature tree will have a weak crotch. If the process of removing one of the faulty limbs would cause too large a pruning wound, the best technique is to prune one of the limbs of many of its foliage-bearing branches. This has the effect of cutting off part of the food supply and curtailing the growth of the limb, thus reducing its size in respect to the other limb with which it forms the crotch.

Sometimes the tree expert resorts to braces and cables to help support weak crotches or overloaded limbs. To brace a crotch, holes are drilled at the same level through the two limbs forming the crotch. A steel rod threaded at both ends is then fixed — one end through each hole — so that it forms a connection between the limbs. Washers and bolts tighten the rod in place. Cables are often used to keep a recently planted tree in the upright state until its root system has established a firm hold in the soil. Braces, too, are employed on the inside of large cavities to prevent any further splitting.

Girdling roots
cause a tree to weaken

Girdling roots are occasionally the cause of a weakened tree. Such roots, in the course of their development, deviate from their true path in the soil to wind around the base of the trunk. This strangling gradually cuts off the food supply destined for the lower roots. The roots slowly starve and fail to function properly. If this condition is diagnosed in time, the tree expert can cut away the faulty roots and restore the tree to health.

Lightning is another hazard to which large trees are often subject, and the tree expert is called upon to protect them before damage occurs. Copper conductors are secured to a number of the upper limbs of a tree. These conductors are led downward, and each is connected to a wide copper mesh, which is fastened to the trunk and extended some distance into the ground. With such an arrangement, light-

ning bolts pass harmlessly from the outer branches down into the soil.

Besides supplying the ordinary fertilizers to the soil in which a tree grows, the tree expert can force feed a tree if it shows signs of improper nourishment. Sometimes soil augers are used to bore holes in the ground around the tree. A dry plant food is then poured into these holes where it mixes quite readily with the constituents of the soil. In an emergency, a solution of properly balanced chemical nutrients is introduced directly to the roots. This is done without digging up the soil, by using specially designed drills that penetrate to the roots. The chemicals are forced under pressure into the surrounding soil. Either the tree responds to this kind of treatment very quickly by showing better leaf color, or else it does not respond at all. If the treatment appears to have helped, regular feeding follows and perhaps complete cultivation and rebuilding of the soil is put into effect.

Tree moving is another job for the tree expert

Tree experts are often expected to transplant a tree — that is, uproot the whole organism and move it to an entirely new environment. This frequently calls for several experienced men and specially designed hauling equipment. Generally a large ball of earth is dug up along with the roots. The long main roots are uncovered and wrapped with moist burlap. Then these roots, the smaller roots and the accompanying ball of earth are covered with burlap or canvas, which is firmly held in place by laced ropes. The limbs of the tree are bent in toward the trunk and secured with belts to avoid breakage while the tree is in transit. At all times care is taken to prevent bruising or other injuries to roots, trunk and limbs.

Trees are moved at any season, but the preferable time is during dormancy. They are more easily handled at this time, and, in the case of deciduous trees, there is little loss of water from the plant because the leaves are absent. Evergreens must have a larger ball of earth around the roots than other trees require, for their leaves lose water during the whole transplanting process. When broad-leaved deciduous trees are moved during the growing season, the tree expert usually prunes back foliage-bearing branches to prevent excessive water loss from leaves while the tree adjusts to its new environment.

Chemicals are used to control insects and disease

Chemicals have been used for some time to eradicate insect pests and stop the ravages of bacterial and fungus infections. These chemicals are applied by spraying or dusting, methods that have met with a varying degree of success. Compounds containing nicotine or arsenic, when spread directly on foliage, act as stomach poisons to leaf-eating beetles and caterpillars. Insects, such as aphids, that suck the juices from leaves are killed by contact poisons that either enter the insect's body through the breathing pores or clog the breathing tubes. Compounds with nicotine, sulfur, chlorine or oils of various kinds are efficient contact poisons.

Fungi and bacteria are controlled by substances containing copper, sulfur, coal tar or creosote. These chemicals merely serve as a protective coat on the plant parts to prevent the entry of fungi or bacteria. They are not a cure for the diseases caused by these organisms and must be applied before the parasites have a chance to invade their host.

Chemotherapy — a new kind of plant treatment

Recently a new type of chemical treatment — chemotherapy — has come into use. This entails the introduction of chemicals directly into the plant's circulatory system. Therapeutic chemicals may be given to a tree in three ways — by feeding the roots, by spraying the plant and by direct injection into the sapwood.

Antitoxins, or chemicals that neutralize the poisons secreted by parasites, are introduced into the soil around the tree's roots. The fine root hairs take up the chemicals, which then circulate throughout the tree.

Tomatoes, often plagued by the pest known as tomato fruitworm, are being dusted with a bellows-type hand duster at the Columbus, Ohio, Entomology and Plant Quarantine Station.

A speed sprayer covers orange trees with insecticides. The air blast is produced by a modi-fied airplane propeller which rotates at high speed. Such applicators save time and labor.

Both photos, USDA

Moving a tree for transplanting. The ball of earth is wrapped to prevent drying of the roots.

The Dutch elm disease has been combatted fairly successfully in a certain number of cases by forcing various compounds under pressure into the soil. However, better results occur, at least in young elm seedlings, when compounds are sprayed on the plants, which then absorb the chemicals into their systems.

Injecting trees directly with chemicals calls for a sound knowledge of plant physiology and expert techniques in bringing about the desired end. The point on the trunk for injection is carefully selected and a hole is drilled through the bark into the sapwood. A bottle containing a specific chemical solution is then attached above the hole and a tube is led from the bottle to the hole. The chemical is slowly taken up into the tree's circulation. When chemicals are injected into the trunk in this manner, accurate measurements can be taken on the amount of drug absorbed and the amount needed for controlling a specific disease. A case history of the tree is kept, and frequent inspections make certain that the disease does not reoccur.

Chemical injection has proved effective in treating bleeding canker, a disease of hardwoods. Chlorosis, another malady of trees, has been overcome by the use of iron injections. This disease occurs when there is insufficient iron in the plant for the manufacture of chlorophyll; the leaves display a mottled yellowish green color. If water-soluble iron salts are introduced into the sapwood, the condition quickly clears up. Even the depredations of bark beetles have been moderately checked by injecting zinc chloride, copper sulfate and other chemicals. Considerable research and experimentation are now being applied to the techniques of chemotherapy. It is believed that this science will revolutionize the treatment of many plant infections.

See also Vol. 10, p. 272: "Diseases of Plants," *and p. 273:* "Insects and Plants."

A moated-island exhibit in a modern zoo. The lions are separated from the browsers in the foreground by ha-has — sunken fences — set in ditches. This accounts for the peaceful attitude of the lions!

THE ANIMALS OF THE ZOO

Sidelights on Modern Zoological Collections

by R. MARLIN PERKINS

FEW people think of the zoo as an educational institution; yet that is just what it is. The modern zoological collection is no hit-or-miss assortment of animals gathered together to amaze and amuse the casual observer. Rather, the collection is carefully planned and arranged to bring to the visitor the story of nature and its wonderful works.

The size and range of the animal collection in any zoo are subject to certain limitations. When space is at a premium, there will be fewer large animals, like elephants and rhinoceroses, in order that there may be enough smaller animals. The size of the budget and particularly the portion allotted for the purchase of new animals will also have a bearing on the number and kinds of exhibits the zoo will present.

The zoologist must take all these considerations into account in planning his collection and that is why no two zoos are alike. In every case, however, one cardinal principle is kept in mind — the collection must be as representative of the animals of the world as possible. Most zoos include at least one elephant among their attractions. Some zoos, with large budgets and sufficient space, feature several elephants and other members of the pachyderm family, such as rhinoceroses and hippopotamuses. Lions and tigers are also universally associated with the zoo and they, too, are almost invariably found in the collection.

Of course, the carnivore section can be extended to include leopards, jaguars, ocelots, pumas and many other members of the cat family. The anthropoid-and-monkey department is even more popular with zoo visitors and is an important educational feature as well. The well-rounded zoo will have a bird section. This will include domestic birds native to the area in which the zoo is located, and it may include birds from far-off areas of the world — land and water fowl, flightless birds and some of the more spectacular members of the feathered world. Practically all zoological collections also include exhibits of reptiles, bears, small mammals and hoofed stock (deer and other four-footed hoofed animals).

Unlike the museum operator, the zoo man faces the problem of constantly replacing animals since, obviously, they do not live forever. The director, in addition to being a zoologist and an educator, must also be a businessman — a purchasing agent, constantly on the lookout for new animals for his collection. He knows from training and experience the average zoo-life expectancy of most animals under his care, and he anticipates his replacement needs.

The most important single source of animals for a zoological collection is the

The author of this article with a furry friend.

Arrival at Chicago of four baby gorillas, bound for the Lincoln Park Zoo. Air transportation has helped zoos to round out their collections.

Members of the Lincoln Park Zoo staff on the annual snake-hunting expedition that is sponsored by the zoo in the southern and southeastern states.

the animal dealer must settle for a quick sale in order to decrease the risk of loss involved.

The ability of a particular animal to survive transportation to another part of the world also affects its price. In most cases a sale is not considered final until the animal is safely delivered by the dealer or his agents; the dealer covers this risk to himself in setting the price. When the zoo undertakes the risk involved in transporting the animal from the dealer to its own location, the price is correspondingly decreased.

Trades with other zoos constitute another source of animals for the zoo. A zoo

animal dealer. Most zoos are in constant touch with a number of dealers in many parts of the world. The dealers, who buy from independent hunters or who commission the capture of animals as they need them, keep the zoo informed of the animals currently available for purchase and the market price of such animals. Many times, a zoo will circularize the various dealers asking whether a particular type of animal is currently available, or else it will request a dealer to obtain such an animal at the earliest opportunity.

Animal prices fluctuate according to supply and demand; they are affected, too, by the health, appearance and disposition of individual specimens. Certain factors tend to keep prices down. An animal dealer with a large supply of lions on hand cannot wait too long for the lion market to develop high prices, since the cost of maintaining the animals in stock for any period of time could easily wipe out any price advantage gained through holding his stock. Also, in the case of some animals which require special treatment and diet in captivity,

located in the southwestern United States will obviously have easy access to the reptiles of the area: rattlesnakes, lizards and so on. It will pay comparatively little for these animals because they are readily available. A European zoo would also be plentifully supplied with animals native to its region and could buy them very cheaply. But if the European zoo tried to buy rattlesnakes and if the American zoo tried to buy European badgers in the world animal market, the prices would be high. In many instances, such zoos correspond regularly and are able to bring about mutually profitable exchanges of animals for little more than the cost of transportation from one country to the other.

Many zoos maintain a debit-and-credit

system. Zoo "A," which is in the United States, sends six rattlesnakes to Zoo "B," in Europe. Zoo "B" has no animals on hand at the moment that are of interest to Zoo "A," and therefore it credits Zoo "A" with the transaction. Later Zoo "A" needs a European badger to replace one that died. At the earliest opportunity Zoo "B" sends the badger to Zoo "A" and the

Babies of the zoo — leopard cubs. They must be handled carefully because of their sharp claws.

debt is entirely or partially cancelled — depending on the valuation set on the various animals involved. The same procedure is sometimes followed in dealings between zoos and animal dealers.

Other sources of animals are less productive and only partially fill current needs. Births at the zoo are a minor source of supply, since many animals do not reproduce in captivity; in some cases, when young are born they fail to survive. There are many types of animals, of course, which reproduce successfully. In these cases, the young may be numerous enough to be used for trading purposes with other zoos or dealers.

Some zoos regularly sponsor and conduct animal-collecting expeditions. A successful snake-collecting expedition could fill out the gaps in the sponsor zoo's reptile collection. The sponsor zoo might also acquire specimens commanding sizable sums in the world market.

Donations of animals to the zoo by private individuals or organizations represent the least productive source of supply. It is true that many zoos have acquired important and valuable additions to their collections through such donations, but they are generally so infrequent that the zoo director does not consider this source of supply in his plan of animal replacement. Most often, private donations consist of offers of personal pets by individuals who have lost interest in the animals, or who consider their upkeep too expensive or who have found it inconvenient to keep the animals in the home. If zoos accepted all such donations, they would have on hand an embarrassing oversupply of rabbits, monkeys, guinea pigs, raccoons, alligators, snakes and other former pets. The cost of maintenance of such animals would be completely out of proportion to their value to the zoo; besides, they would take up space which could be used in making the general collection more representative of the animals of the world.

Probably the most important single factor in successful zoo operation is the care given to the animals. A sick animal, unable to communicate its symptoms, presents a special problem; a sick wild animal, unapproachable because of its ferocity, is a complex problem indeed. Hence, the zoo makes every effort to keep its exhibits in good health.

Cleanliness is the first rule of disease prevention, and in most zoos this rule is strictly observed. Cages and other exhibit areas are cleaned daily wherever possible. In many instances, animals, too, are cleaned and are protected, where possible, from insects and vermin. In the zoo commissary, where diets are prepared and issued, an especially high degree of sanitation is rigidly enforced.

In addition to general cleanliness throughout, many special precautions must be taken to protect the health of the animal collection. This is especially true in the case of the animals which have been transplanted into climates foreign to their native habitat. The anthropoids, for example, are liable to contract respiratory diseases, such

as the common cold and pneumonia. Unlike man, they have failed in the natural state to develop any appreciable degree of immunity to these diseases. The average zoo visitor would be surprised to learn that the glass partition separating the apes from the public is there for the protection of the animals against possible infection from sniffling visitors! Other special precautions include a wire mesh screen around the exhibits featuring ostriches or crocodiles, since these animals are notorious swallowers of almost any object that fits into their mouths. Many other measures are taken by various zoos to protect the health of their charges.

The animal keeper plays an important part in the preventive medical program. In addition to the routine duties to be fulfilled each day — cleaning quarters, feeding his charges and checking their condition — he contributes companionship. The sense of security that this gives the animals has a direct bearing upon their health. Animals, like people, have a morale problem; when their morale is low, through neglect or abuse, they are easy marks for any ailment that happens along. Conversely, the animal with high morale and an active interest in its surroundings is better fitted to fight off the normal hazards of day-to-day living.

A recent case illustrates this point. A certain zoo imported some young gorillas from Africa and a keeper was assigned to their care. In a very short time, the animals, particularly the youngest ape, had transferred their affection to their new keeper, who filled the void caused by their separation from their gorilla mothers. As a result of this keeper's attitude toward his charges, all the youngsters throve in their new surroundings.

Animal keepers are trained to observe closely the physical appearance, actions and reactions of the animals charged to their care. They must be able to spot any irregularity in appearance or behavior the moment it shows itself. Revealed early enough by this method, most illnesses can be treated effectively by seeking the cause and eliminating it, by mild medication or

by corrective diet, as the case may be.

One must realize that individual animals have personalities of their own. One monkey may be normally active, friendly, noisy and playful; another of the same species may have just the opposite traits. Symptoms of the same illness in each animal would differ. The gay monkey might become morose and inactive and might repel the advances of the keeper. The normally antisocial monkey might become restless and therefore abnormally active; he

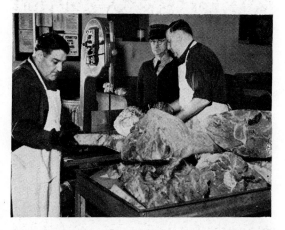

Hundreds of pounds of government-inspected horse meat are used daily for meat-eating animals.

might seek out his keeper for solace in his misery and might become noisy. In the case of both animals the keeper would read the early signs correctly. On the other hand, the veterinarian, who cannot possibly become familiar with each of the hundreds of animals in the collection, might consider an ailing animal's behavior as entirely normal. Its illness might well reach a serious stage before there would be unmistakable symptoms.

In a zoo containing hundreds or thousands of animals, even the most thorough preventive medical program cannot eliminate all sickness. In addition to the common ailments brought on by old age there are the various accidents, small or large, which are beyond the control of the staff. Young monkeys may fall and injure themselves; an animal may scratch itself and develop an infection. All these incidents are recognized as probable happenings in the daily routine of the zoo and are pro-

vided for as completely as possible.

When an animal shows by its actions and appearance that it is ailing, it is isolated and placed under close observation in the zoo "hospital." Most zoos have segregated cages or areas for this purpose. The isolation protects other animals against the spread of whatever ailment is causing the symptoms. It also gives the sick animal the rest and quiet it needs for recovery.

Animals which can be handled are given medication with very little trouble. Various devices and methods are employed for immobilizing and treating the larger and more dangerous animals. Veterinarians use drugs to produce unconsciousness only in dire emergency, since it is not always possible to determine beforehand whether or not the drug will aggravate the sick animal's condition. Hence the squeeze cage is used where possible. The walls of such a cage can be compressed upon the animal, restricting its movement and permitting close examination and treatment.

ment and exertion imposed on the animal in immobilizing it may easily aggravate its condition.

Visitors to the zoo find the feeding of the animals a fascinating process. Many zoos cater to this natural interest by staggering the feeding hours in the various sections so as to permit the visitor to see all the animals fed in a single afternoon. If the visitor could look behind the scenes and see the complex preparations required for a single day's feeding of the zoo population, he would be truly amazed. Here is an operation involving the diets of hun-

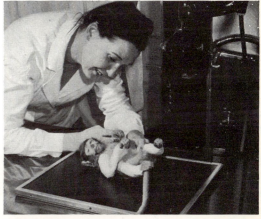

This sorrowful little Patas monkey, which broke both legs and an arm in a fall from the top of its mother's cage, is being given an X-ray check.

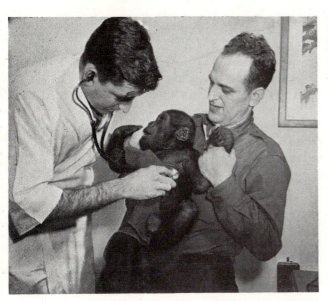

A veterinarian makes a routine examination of a young gorilla. Gorillas, once an uncertain risk in zoo operation, now generally thrive in zoos.

In other instances, where the squeeze cage is impractical, the animal is caught and bound. These measures, however, are resorted to only if the veterinarian has completed his diagnosis and has decided upon a specific form of treatment, or when the animal's condition is so serious that immediate action must be taken. The excite-

dreds, perhaps thousands, of animals, in varied amounts and utilizing an impressive variety of ingredients.

Wherever possible, the type of food the individual animal would ordinarily eat in the wild state is duplicated in the zoo commissary. Usually this natural diet is supplemented with vitamins and other elements in order to offset possible deficiencies in sunlight and exercise and to meet other conditions.

In the natural state, lions, tigers and other carnivorous predators obtain their vitamin and mineral requirements from their kills by feeding on the viscera and other vital organs which contain these ele-

ments. After their natural craving for these parts of the animals is satisfied, they gorge themselves on the meat of the animal. In captivity, powdered or capsulated vitamins and minerals are imbedded in the meat ration and are absorbed in this manner.

In many cases, special foods must be obtained to meet the dietary requirements of certain animals. Pandas must have bamboo shoots, which are obtainable only in tropical and semitropical regions; certain birds require special types of insects and worms for a well-balanced diet. In cases where the food requirement falls into a general category — such as cereals, vegetables, fruits or meats — local products can be given with wholly satisfactory results. Thus, apes, which require a certain amount of cereal foods, vegetables and fruits, are given various kinds of bread, oranges, apples, grapes, lettuce, cabbage, celery and milk. Many of these items are actually foreign to the animal in the native state. However, they contain the same essential elements as the fruits, vegetables and cereals found by the animal in its normal habitat and are therefore eminently suitable.

Only through experience over a long period of time does the individual zoo learn which foods and what quantities of food are desirable for every type of animal. This information is carefully noted and exchanged with other zoos. Here again the keeper is an important factor. He observes the reaction of the animal to its food and works closely with the zoo veterinarian and the commissary in arriving at a satisfactory diet.

The food distributed to the animals must be of good quality. The meat served to the carnivores and other animals is usually government-inspected horse meat, fit for human consumption. Stale bread is used because most animals prefer it; however, it must not be moldy or in any other way unfit for use as a food. Often zoos are offered spoiled or slightly contaminated foods by restaurants or dealers, who are under the impression that the animals will eat anything and that the donation will

Bushman, famous gorilla of the Lincoln Park Zoo, attained the weight of 550 pounds in his prime.

bring about savings in food costs. The zoo politely but firmly declines these offers, since only certain carrion-eating animals could subsist on such food. It would be injurious and might even prove fatal if given to the other animals.

The methods of exhibiting animals have undergone certain drastic changes in the present century. Originally animals were kept either in cages or in open pits where the public could look down on them. The cage type of exhibit remains the backbone of the average zoo display; the pit type, with many variations, is still widely used.

At the turn of the century a new trend in zoo exhibits was introduced in Germany and was soon adopted in many other parts of the world, particularly in America, where the original idea was greatly expanded. This was the so-called barless-cage exhibit. Barless cages operate on the principle of presenting the animals to the public with the necessary barriers hidden or camouflaged. One of the most popular and familiar forms of barless cages is the moated-island exhibit. Here the animals are gathered on an "island" surrounded by

either a dry or water-filled ditch, or moat. The exhibit is closed off at the back by a steep wall or fence separating it from other exhibits on the same island, and the public views the exhibit from across the moat.

Zoo visitors are familiar with the popular monkey-island exhibits of some of the larger zoos. Certain types of monkeys refuse to enter water; hence all that is required to restrain these animals is a water-filled moat with perhaps a guard rail for the visitors. Other monkeys show no aversion for water — indeed they prove on occasion to be excellent swimmers! These animals must be restrained not only by a water moat but by a fairly high, inwardly inclined parapet, from which the visitors may view them.

The great cats, too, are often displayed in moated units. Here again, the combination of moat and parapet is the restraining element of the exhibit. Zoos have found, through experience and study, that tigers can leap as far as thirty feet in a horizontal line and six feet upward (in the same leap). Therefore, moats surrounding tiger exhibits must exceed thirty-five feet in width and the visitors' parapet should be at least ten feet above the level of the exhibit floor. Leopards and mountain lions, because of their great agility, are not usually displayed in moated units.

Another variation of the moated unit is one in which the "island" is occupied by several animal exhibits. One zoo features lions, tigers, zebras and antelopes in one such exhibit, grouping various types of animals — the hunted and the hunter of a particular region of the world — behind the same moat. The individual exhibits are separated by ha-has, or sunken fences; these are set in ditches which divide the island into different areas. Since the ha-has are practically invisible, visitors are often startled at the sight of all these animals apparently living peaceably together.

Many zoos are slow in adopting the new trend in animal exhibits, since it in-

This indoor aviary contains many species of waterfowl. It permits free movement, including flight.

volves rebuilding or replacing the animal quarters. The newer zoos, however, are incorporating the modern exhibit design into their plans. The most up-to-date exhibits not only feature barless cages but also pay close attention to the background and setting of the displays. They try to reproduce as faithfully as possible the animals' native habitats, including vegetation and rock formations.

The grouping of animals is a factor in the effectiveness of the zoo as an educational institution. The most natural grouping — the one followed by most zoos in assembling their exhibits — is to place animals of a particular type in a single area, building or group of buildings. Such major divisions consist of reptiles and amphibians, primates, the great cats, birds, small mammals, large mammals, hoofed animals, bears and so on. If animals are grouped in these divisions, the zoo visitor can compare the animals of the same group and can appreciate the zoological development of the various species.

Such groupings also simplify the zoo's problems in housing, feeding and caring for the animals of the collection. Desert reptiles generally require hot, dry housing; amphibians need warm, humid quarters. Both groups require similar diets and care; hence, assembling them in one building

makes for maximum operating convenience and economy. The same holds true for the other groups of animals. Larger zoos with extensive animal collections may make even further divisions of the general classifications mentioned above. Thus, animals native to tropic, temperate and arctic climates may be grouped according to habitat. Occasionally zoos set up special exhibits, such as a "Mother Goose Zoo" or a "Domestic Zoo."

As the visitor passes before the various animals in the zoo, he automatically looks for the labels identifying the exhibits and giving information about them. In most cases the facts about the particular animal on display are taken from the zoo records.

Such records are often quite extensive, since many zoos, in addition to maintaining animal exhibits, conduct serious studies in the field of zoology. The studies cover the longevity and gestation periods of various animals, diet requirements and reactions to diet, special care, medical histories and so on. Zoo records are primarily of interest to other zoos, since the easy exchange of such information makes a wide field of experience available to every zoo contemplating new animal exhibits. However, some of the studies originating at zoos have proven of value directly and indirectly to the human medical profession as well.

The age-old question of "Are the animals really happy in their captivity at the zoo?" is one that often crops up. Zoo men point to the fact that on the average, the various inhabitants of the zoo enjoy a longer span of life than could be expected in the natural or wild state. There are many reasons for this. First, the protection the animal enjoys in captivity from various beasts of prey encourages a sense of security. A steady food supply, the companionship and the daily ministrations of the keepers, medical care and clean, adequate quarters all contribute to longer life. Zoo men further point out that, in the rare instance when an animal is loosed, it almost always tries, after a few hours of freedom, to return to its familiar cage.

See also Vol. 10, p. 276: "Zoos."

All photos, unless otherwise stated, Chicago Park District

This fearless young visitor is handling a snake in the Children's Zoo, a special and extremely popular summer feature of the Lincoln Park Zoo.

Bell Aircraft Corp.

Taking a news photograph from a helicopter, which hovers almost motionless above the scene of action.

PHOTOGRAPHY AT WORK

The camera is a never failing source of entertainment for those who desire to keep a pictorial record of their own doings and those of their relatives and friends. But it is much more than a satisfying hobby for amateurs; it is an indispensable tool in the work of the newsman, the surveyor, the astronomer, the metallurgist, the botanist and a host of others. It provides them with a wide variety of data; it brings before them the infinitely large, the infinitely small and all that lies between. In these pages we show some of the ways in which the camera has served.

The Royal Canadian Air Force has worked since 1921 at the monumental task of photographing Canada from the air. Shown below is an RCAF Vedette, used for this type of work in the 1920's and 1930's.

RCAF

Upper photo, E. I. du Pont de Nemours & Co.

Among the most valuable contributions of photography to science are photomicrographs, which are enlarged photographs of microscopic objects taken by attaching a camera to a microscope. Above we see a metallurgist making a photomicrograph of a test sample of ore. Below are two photomicrographs. Left: cross section of the stem of a basswood tree. Right: gum of a newborn baby. The upper tooth shown here under the surface of the gum is the temporary tooth; the lower one is the permanent tooth. Of course the upper tooth, closer to the surface of the gum, will erupt first.

Lower photos, Julius Weber

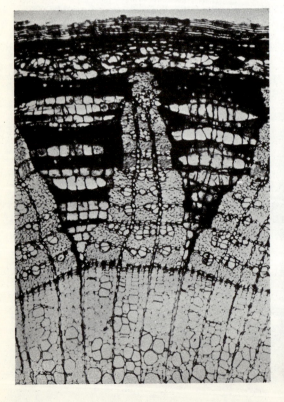

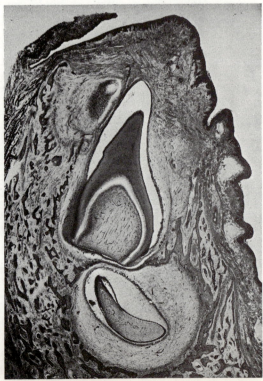

Those who make a special study of gases are able to see them by means of an ingenious device called the schlieren apparatus. (*Schlieren* is a German word meaning "striations" or "streaks.") The schlieren apparatus was first used by August Toepler, a German scientist, in 1864; its basic principle has remained unchanged. In this apparatus a curved mirror focuses a narrow beam of light so that all the rays are parallel. As the rays pass through the gas that is being studied, they are bent as a result of differences in density, temperature and pressure in the gas. The bent rays are then focused on a viewing screen. Cameras can be used with a schlieren apparatus to make photographs of gases. Below we see the equipment used in making such pictures. Above are shown two schlieren photographs. At the left, heavy acetone vapor is flowing out of a bottle. At the right, air currents are rising above a gas flame; the core of unburned gas shows in the center of the picture.

All photos, Battelle Memorial Institute

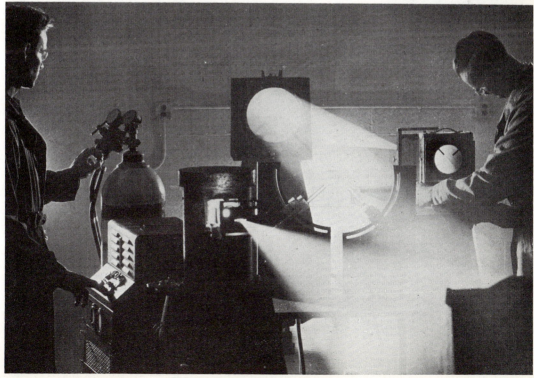

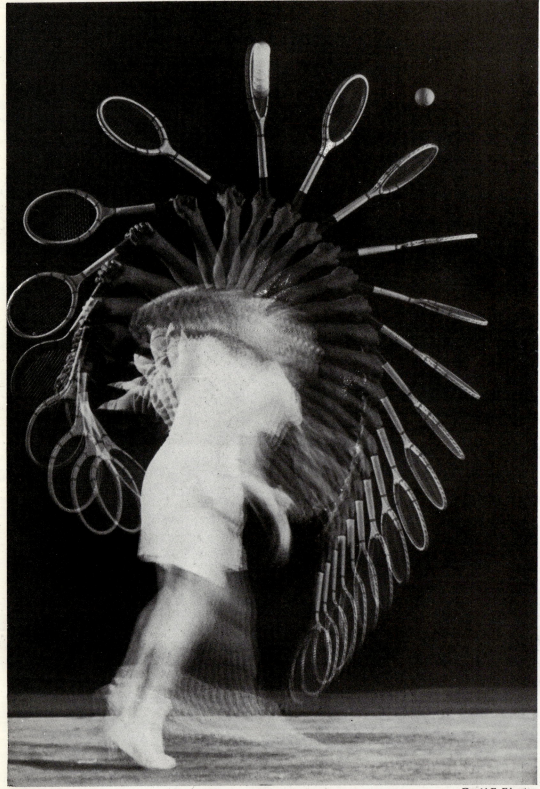

Harold E. Edgerton

The light for this striking high-speed photograph of a tennis player in action was provided by a stroboscope, a device that illuminates any given object with a rapid succession of bright flashes.

The camera has been used for many years to record the wonders of underseas plant and animal life. At the right is seen a particularly effective type of underwater camera, known as the underwater blimp from its superficial resemblance to the aircraft of that name. This camera is provided with wings and a rudder, which help to stabilize it. Here the photographer-diver is adjusting the lens diaphragm. The lower photograph, taken with an underwater blimp at a depth of thirty feet, shows the fish that is called the puffer because it can inflate its body.

Both photos, USN

Westinghouse

This Phototroller is a finger-saving device. If the operators of the punching-press reach too far into the machine, they automatically break the beam of light and the machine does not start.

ELECTRONICS

Electrons are atomic particles with a negative charge of electricity. When they flow along a conductor, like a copper wire, they produce an electric current. For many years men have been utilizing these flowing electrons, imprisoned in a conductor, in such devices as the electric motor, the dynamo, the electromagnet, the electric light, the telegraph and the telephone.

When men succeeded in separating electrons from conductors and producing currents of electrons moving outside of any conductor, the science of electronics was born. These unchanneled streams of electrons have revolutionized modern living. They have given us radio, television, radar, the photoelectric cell, the electron microscope and a host of other supremely useful devices. On this page and those which follow we show some of the ways in which electronics has benefited mankind.

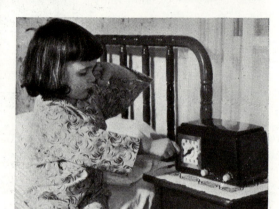

RCA

The stylus for this reading aid for the blind converts printed words into recognizable sounds.

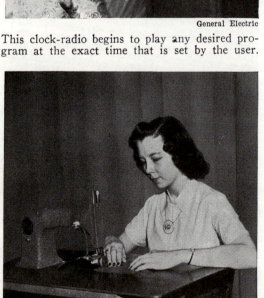

General Electric

This clock-radio begins to play any desired program at the exact time that is set by the user.

RCA

The electronic "sewing machine" produces a strong and water-tight seam in plastic-coated fabrics.

Standard Oil Co. (N. J.) photo by *Corsini*

The electron microscope, shown above, has made it possible to magnify objects up to 100,000 times. In this device, beams of electrons, focused by electric and magnetic forces, pass through an object and produce a highly enlarged image of it on a photographic plate or fluorescent screen.

National Bureau of Standards

A micrograph of a specimen of toilet soap, magnified about 25,000 times by the electron microscope. (A micrograph is a photograph of an object as seen through the microscope.) By examining the hills and dales shown in the picture, a skilled viewer can tell what the soap contains.

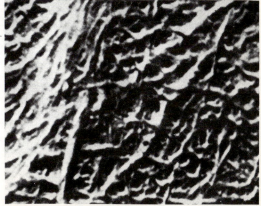

A super-sensitive electronic detector that ferrets out all impurities in a sample of metal.

The Sterilamp, high on the wall, kills bacteria in the air with "bullets" of ultraviolet light.

The automatic arc-welding equipment shown here is being used to make axle housings. An electronic device is used to control the rate of feed of the electrode coil that is used in the equipment.

Recording the Fleeting Days

The Development of Calendars That Fit the Seasons

by ELISABETH ACHELIS

IF WE asked the average man to name the things that are most essential in the daily round of his activities, the chances are that he would not include the calendar among them. Yet in every civilized age, ancient and modern, the calendar has been indispensable. It enabled the men of early times to plan ahead for the sowing, growing and harvesting of crops and for various other activities as well. In our own far more complex civilization, the calendar is even more important. Our complicated industrial structure, with its system of contracts, drafts, checks and promissory notes, is dependent upon it; so is the political structure; so is the tapestry of history.

The calendar of today is the product of a great many centuries of patient study and of constant trial and error. When man first looked to heavenly bodies for a yardstick for the measurement of time, he observed that the sun seemed to make a constantly repeated journey in the heavens, always returning to the same place after many days. (Actually, of course, it is the earth that makes a yearly revolution around the sun.) He observed, too, that the moon went through a cycle in the course of which it waned until it could no longer be seen and then waxed until it became once more a bright disc in the sky.

Most of the earliest calendars were based on moon cycles, which were made to fit as best they could within the larger framework of the sun cycle. The year, in these calendars, generally consisted of twelve moon cycles, or months. Since twelve moon cycles are not quite equal to a solar year, an extra month — called an intercalary, or inserted, month — was added

from time to time. A number of ancient peoples, including the Babylonians, Hebrews, Greeks and Romans, adopted this method of computation.

The Egyptians were the first to base their calendar on the sun cycle and to make the month a purely arbitrary unit, not corresponding to the actual lunar cycle. They worked out a year of 360 days, with 12 months of 30 days each. Since, according to their reckoning, it took 365 days for the sun to complete its journey in the heavens, they added 5 days to the end of the 360-day year. These added days were "feast days"; the Egyptian priests were entrusted with the task of arranging for them.

The Egyptians observed that the inundation of their land by the Nile River lasted four months, that the planting and cultivating of the crops took up four more months and that it took another four months to complete the harvesting. They remarked, too, that the bright star Sirius began to rise in the sky together with the sun at just about the time that the Nile began to overflow. Therefore the Egyptians divided the year into three seasonal periods of four months each; and they began their calendar with the day on which Sirius began to rise in the east with the sun. (This corresponds to July 19.)

This Egyptian 365-day calendar was adopted in the year 4236 B.C., according to the reckoning of the great American archaeologist James Henry Breasted (1865–1935). According to Breasted, it was the "earliest known and practically convenient calendar of 365 days"; as for the year 4236 B.C., it marked "not only the earliest fixed date in history but also the earliest date in

the intellectual history of mankind." This Egyptian calendar was the ancestor of the Gregorian calendar of today.

In the course of the centuries that followed, it was discovered that the year really consisted of 365 days and about a quarter of a day. This additional quarter of a day was causing a gradual shift of the seasons as recorded in the calendar. It meant that the first month of the Egyptian calendar came to coincide not with the flooding of the Nile but with the harvest period, and, later, with the period of the planting of the crops. In 238 B.C. the pharaoh Ptolemy III, also known to history as Euergetes I, tried to correct this obvious error in calculation by adding another day to the calendar every four years. It was to be a religious holiday and was to be known as the Festival of the Good-Doing Gods. Unfortunately, this edict, which was known as the Decree of Canopus, was not generally adopted. The priests, whose duty it was to adjust the feast days, were unwilling to accept the extra day since it was not in keeping with the traditions built up

Days of the Month	Martius Maius Quintilis October	Januarius Sextilis December	Aprilis Junius September November	Februarius
1	Calendae	Calendae	Calendae	Calendae
2	6	4	4	4
3	5	3	3	3
4	4	Prid. Nonas	Prid. Nonas	Prid Nonas
5	3	Nonae	Nonae	Nonae
6	Prid. Nonas	8	8	8
7	Nonae	7	7	7
8	8	6	6	6
9	7	5	5	5
10	6	4	4	4
11	5	3	3	3
12	4	Prid Idus	Prid Idus	Prid Idus
13	3	Idus	Idus	Idus
14	Prid Idus	19	18	16
15	Idus	18	17	15
16	17	17	16	14
17	16	16	15	13
18	15	15	14	12
19	14	14	13	11
20	13	13	12	10
21	12	12	11	9
22	11	11	10	8
23	10	10	9	7
24	9	9	8	6
25	8	8	7	[6]
26	7	7	6	5
27	6	6	5	4
28	5	5	4	3
29	4	4	3	Prid. Cal Mart
30	3	3	Prid. Calen.	
31	Prid.Calen.	Prid.Calen.		
DAYS	31	31	30	28-29

The Julian calendar. The Latin names for the months are given; they are easily recognizable, since all but two of them have been retained, with certain changes, in our calendar.

under the old arrangement; and the people were just as reluctant to make the change. As a result the Egyptian calendar continued to be defective as a measure of the seasons.

The Mayan calendar

Another seasonal sun calendar that was used in antiquity was that of the Mayas of Mexico. It probably goes back to the year 580 B.C. According to a renowned American archaeologist, Sylvanus Griswold Morley, it was the first seasonal and agricultural calendar in America.

The Mayan calendar was similar in some respects to that of the Egyptians. It consisted of 360 days, with a period of 5 days, necessary to complete the year, added as a short month. As we saw, the Egyptians dedicated the 5 extra days in the year to the gods, but the Mayas considered them as evil days upon which no work could be done, no journey undertaken and no marriage performed. As in Egypt, arrangements for the extra days were left to the priesthood.

The Mayan calendar was arranged differently from that of the Egyptians. The year had 18 months of 20 days. The 20 days within each month were divided into four 5-day series, corresponding to our weeks; each day had its own name. The 20

days of the month began with a cipher; hence the days were numbered from 0 to 19 inclusive, not from 1 to 20 inclusive, as we would count the days in our months.

Dovetailed with the Mayan sun calendar was another imposed by the priests, who used a time system of their own for ceremonial rites and purposes. This was the permutation system, or tzolkin. In this system there were 20 months of 13 days each existing within the framework of the 18-month 20-day year. It was as if we were to have a 260-day year start on January 1. The 260th day would correspond to September 17; the first day of the new 260-day year would then correspond to September 18.

The calendar of the Aztecs was based upon that of the Mayas. The Aztecs realized that a year consisted of 365 days plus a quarter of a day, approximately. Each year they stored away the additional quarter-day for future reference. The slack was finally taken up when a cycle of 52 years had been reached. It is thought that the Aztecs came to realize that an intercalation of 13 days was too long and a 12-day intercalation too short. Hence a 12½-day insertion completed the 52-year cycle. In a period of 104 years (twice 52) 25 such days were added. By this method the Aztecs adjusted their calendar to the seasons.

The Julian calendar

The Egyptian sun calendar was most carefully guarded by rulers and priests and consequently remained unknown to the outside world for more than thirty centuries. Only during Julius Caesar's stay in Egypt did he learn of this calendar, which was immensely superior in every respect to the one used in Rome.

As we have seen, the ancient Romans had a moon calendar; it was complicated and most confusing. There were 12 months; a thirteenth month, called Mercedonius, was occasionally inserted in a haphazard way. The 12 months of the Roman year consisted of 7 months of 29 days each, 4 months of 31 days each and one month, Februarius (February) with 28 days, making a year of 355 days. The names of the 12 months of the Roman year were as follows:

Name of month	*Origin of name*
Martius	Month of Mars
Aprilis	"Opening" month, when the earth opens to produce new fruits
Maius	Month of the great god (Jupiter)
Junius	Month of the Junii (a Roman *gens* or clan)
Quintilis	Fifth month
Sextilis	Sixth month
September	Seventh month
October	Eighth month
November	Ninth month
December	Tenth month
Januarius	Month of the god Janus
Februarius	Month of the Februa (a purification feast)

In 153 B.C., January was designated as the first month of the year instead of Martius.

The Romans used a complicated system of reckoning within the month. There were three more or less fixed dates—the calends, the ides and the nones. (Our word "calendar" is derived from calends.) The calends always fell on the 1st of the month. The ides came on the 15th in Martius, Maius, Sextilis and October and on the 13th in other months. The nones always came on the 8th day before the ides. In designating a particular day of the month, Romans always reckoned backward from the calends, the ides or the nones, as the case might be. Thus the 15th of March would be referred to as the ides of March; the 14th as "the day before the ides of March"; the 13th as "the 3rd day before the ides of March" (more exactly, the 3rd day, counting backward, of the ides period).

The calendar was entrusted to a council of priests—the College of Pontiffs, presided over by a *pontifex maximus*. The pontiffs were not priests in our sense of the word; they were state officials charged with the regulation of certain religious matters. Among their duties was the fixing of dates for ceremonies and feast days. That is why the calendar was under their control;

This old Scandinavian calendar was made of wood.

gave it 365 days, plus a quarter-day of six hours. Quarter-days were withheld from the year until a full day had accumulated; the day was then added to the common year as a leap-year day. This happened once every four years.

Further changes had to be made to adjust the short moon year of 355 days to the 365-day sun year. Ten days had to be added to the year, of course; these were distributed among the various months. Seven months now had 31 days each and four months 30 days each. February still had 28 days. It was also allotted the extra day

The Bettmann Archive

Aztec stone calendar of the fifteenth century.

and they flagrantly misused this power for their own selfish purposes.

Their corruption was most apparent in the way in which they inserted the thirteenth month, Mercedonius. Since there were no fixed rules for its intercalation, the pontiffs followed their own interests and those of their friends in the matter. They would sometimes insert Mercedonius in years where it did not belong in order to keep their friends longer in political office.

As a result, when Julius Caesar became virtual dictator of Rome, the calendar was in utter confusion.

Caesar was elected *pontifex maximus* in 63 B.C., but it was not until 47 B.C. that he took the first steps to reform the calendar. He called upon a famous Greek astronomer, Sosigenes, to undertake this momentous task. Sosigenes wisely counseled the Roman dictator that it would be futile to try to reconcile the old Roman moon-cycle calendar with the more scientific solar calendar developed by the Egyptians. Following the suggestions of Sosigenes, Caesar adopted the solar year for the Roman calendar; he

every leap year; but instead of becoming the 29th day of February, as in our calendar, it became an additional 24th day. This repetition of the 6th day before the calends of March (March 1) gave rise to the name "bissextile [twice sixth] year" for what we now call leap year.

The year 46 B.C. bridged the old and the new calendar by having 445 days. Contemporary historians ruefully referred to it as the "year of confusion." The following year, 45 B.C., was actually the first one of this reformed calendar. Caesar retained the complicated system of calends, nones and ides within the months; January continued to be the first month of the year. The Roman Senate changed the name of

the month Quintilis to Julius (our July) in honor of Caesar. The new calendar, shown on page 172, was known as the Julian calendar; it was used for many centuries after the downfall of the Western Roman Empire.

Caesar was assassinated in 44 B.C. After his death the pontiffs disregarded the leap year provisions that had been established by Caesar. They inserted a leap-year day every three years instead of every four; as a result the calendar again began to be out of step with the seasons. Augustus Caesar, the first Roman emperor, was compelled to correct the error by dropping leap-year days from 8 B.C. to 8 A.D. On 8 A.D. the leap-year series was resumed on the basis of one leap year in every four-year period.

To honor the Emperor Augustus, the Roman Senate changed the name of the month Sextilis to Augustus (August). This month had formerly had thirty days. The story goes that the Emperor persuaded the Senate to increase the number of days in August by one, so that his month would have as many days as July, named after Caesar. Some scholars hold, however, that Caesar established the length of the months as we know them before Augustus became emperor.

Constantine introduces the seven-day week

In 321 A.D. the Emperor Constantine issued an edict introducing the seven-day week in the calendar, doing away once and for all with the system of calends, ides and nones. Constantine established Sunday as the first day of the week and set it aside as the Christian day of worship.

There are three theories about the reason for the Emperor's selection of the seven-day week. Some scholars say that it is based on the story of creation in the Book of Genesis: the world, according to this account, was created in six days and a seventh day was set aside as a day of rest. Others believe that the number of days in the week was based on the number of the "planets" known at that time—Mars, Mercury, Jupiter, Venus, Saturn, the sun and the moon. (Of course, we know now that the sun is not a planet but a star and that the moon is a satellite of the earth.) Still others believe that the week originated with the phases of the moon, each being of about seven days' duration.

Although the introduction of the week greatly sim-

The Gregorian calendar. It must borrow one or two days from another week to complete the year; hence it changes every year.

plified matters, it brought about a serious defect in the calendar. Both the Egyptian and Julian calendars had been stabilized: that is, in them every year had been like every other year. Through Constantine's reform the Julian calendar became a shifting one. Now that there were 52 seven-day weeks, totaling 364 days, there was always one day left over in ordinary years and 2 days in leap years. This meant that in successive years, the Julian calendar began on different days of the week. Suppose that January 1 of a given year fell on a Sunday. The 30th of December would come on a Saturday; the 31st would be Sunday. The new year would begin on Monday and not on Sunday, as in the preceding year.

The Gregorian calendar

The true length of the solar year is a trifle less than 365 and a quarter days—it is 365.242199 days, or 365 days, 5 hours, 48 minutes and 46 seconds, to be exact. Therefore the Julian calendar was too long by about 11 minutes; after a number of centuries the error in question amounted to several days. Once again the calendar began to drift from its seasonal moorings.

In the year 1582 another momentous calendar reform took place. Pope Gregory XIII determined to adjust the calendar to the seasons; for this purpose he called upon the services of the mathematician Christopher Clavius and the astronomer-physician Luigi Lilio Ghiraldi, also known by the Latinized version of his name—Aloysius Lilius. They found that the error caused by the excessive length of the Julian calendar now amounted to ten days. To set the year aright, they canceled ten days from the Julian calendar, so that October 4, 1582, was followed by October 15. This was how the month looked on the calendar:

1582		OCTOBER				1582
SUN	MON	TUE	WED	THUR	FRI	SAT
	1	2	3	4	15	16
17	18	19	20	21	22	23
24	25	26	27	28	29	30
31						

Naturally this loss of ten days in the month of October created a certain amount of confusion. For example, according to the calendar, little Thingumbob, born on October 4, 1582, was eleven days old on the following day, the 15th! To avoid confusion, dates prior to October 15, 1582, were often given thereafter (and are still often given) as O.S. (old style) or N.S. (new style). In the case of Thingumbob, his date of birth could be given as either October 4 (O.S.) or October 14 (N.S.). If neither O.S. nor N.S. is given after a date, the presumption is that it is N.S.

To avoid further error in the calendar, the leap-year rule was changed. In the case of centurial years (those ending in "00"), only the ones that were divisible by 400 were to be leap years. Thus, of the four centurial years since the establishment of the Gregorian calendar, 1600 was a leap year, while 1700, 1800 and 1900 were not. Non-centurial leap years continued to receive an extra day. The year still began on January 1. No attempt was made to equalize the lengths of the months or to stabilize the calendar. This Gregorian calendar is the one that we use today.

All Roman Catholic countries adopted the Gregorian reform, but other groups in Christendom were slow in accepting it. The English kept on using the Julian calendar for over a century and a half; they did not adopt the Gregorian calendar until 1752. In doing so, they had to cancel eleven days instead of ten, because the year 1700 was a leap year in the Julian calendar, but not in the Gregorian. The eleven lost days were canceled in September, thus:

1752		SEPTEMBER				1752
SUN	MON	TUE	WED	THUR	FRI	SAT
		1	2	14	15	16
17	18	19	20	21	22	23
24	25	26	27	28	29	30

France, like the other Catholic countries of Europe, had adopted the Gregorian calendar in 1582. But in the course of the French Revolution, the legislative body known as the National Convention issued a decree (November 24, 1793) providing for a new calendar. In this, the year was to consist

Conde Museum, Chantilly

The month of February in the Book of Hours, a masterpiece that goes back to the fifteenth century.

The Bettmann Archive

This medieval calendar enabled readers to calculate the holidays.

purposes Jews employ the Hebrew calendar, which begins with the year of creation, set at 3,760 years before the beginning of the Christian Era. This calendar is based on the cycles of the moon; there are 12 months, which are alternately 29 and 30 days in length. An extra month of 29 days is intercalated 7 times in every cycle of 19 years; whenever this is done, one of the 29-day months receives an extra day. The year begins in the autumn.

Another important calendar is the Islamic, or Mohammedan, calendar. It also is based on the cycles of the moon; there are 354 days and 12 months, half of which have 29 days and the other half 30. Thirty years form a cycle; 11 times in every cycle an extra day is added at the end of the year. The months and the seasons do not correspond; the first day of the Moslem year falls on different seasons in different years. The Mohammedan calendar begins with the first day of the year of the Hegira—that is, the flight of Mohammed to Medina. This date corresponds to July 15, 622, of the Christian Era.

Modern calendar reform

The Gregorian calendar has served man and served him well for almost four centuries. Yet some thoughtful people have not been satisfied with it; they have tried to bring about reforms that would restore stability to the calendar within the framework of the seasonal year and at the same time rearrange it on a more orderly and practical basis.

In 1834, Abbé Marco Mastrofini, a Roman Catholic priest, put forward a plan by

of 12 months with 30 days each; to complete the full number of days, 5 feast days (in leap years, 6) were to be added at the end of the year. The new reckoning was to begin with September 22, 1792, when the first decree of the new French Republic had been issued; the date corresponding to September 22 was to be the first day of the year I. This calendar was abolished, at the command of Napoleon, by a decree of the Senate on September 9, 1805; the Gregorian calendar was re-established on January 1 of the following year.

Japan adopted the Gregorian calendar in 1873, China in 1912, Greece in 1924 and Turkey in 1927. Russia began to use the calendar in 1918, replaced it by a calendar of her own when the Bolsheviks took over the country and returned to the Gregorian calendar in 1940.

The Gregorian calendar is not the only one used at the present time. For religious

which every year would be perpetually the same and the lost stability of the calendar would be restored. In his calendar, there were 364 days in the year—a number easily divisible in various ways. The 365th day and the 366th, in leap years, were inserted as extra days within the year. Each year would begin on Sunday, January 1. The Abbé's idea was so simple and practical that most modern calendar reformers have made it the basis of their own proposals.

Calendar reform lagged until the League of Nations took up the question in 1923. Acting upon a request made by the International Chamber of Commerce in 1920, the league turned over the matter of calendar reform to its Advisory and Technical Committee for Communications and Transit. A preparatory meeting was held at Geneva in June 1931; and in October of that year a full-fledged international Conference on Calendar Reform took place.

More than 500 plans were submitted to the conference. Some of these were based on the decimal system; others, on a 5-day, 6-day or 10-day week. One project introduced 4 long 35-day months and 8 short 28-day months; another, a 364-day year, with occasional "leap weeks" added every 5, 6 or 11 years. Of all the plans submitted to the conference, only 2 received serious consideration. These were the Thirteen-Month Calendar and the World Calendar. Both plans called for intercalated or extra days; both conformed to the seasons.

Each of the 13 months in the Thirteen-Month Calendar has 4 weeks each; there are 13 weeks in each quarterly season. That makes a total of 364 days. To bring the total up to 365, a "year day" is added, correspond-

ing to December 29. The names of the 12 months of the Gregorian calendar are kept; the thirteenth month, set between June and July, is called Sol. The Thirteenth-Month Calendar is shown on this page.

This calendar met with serious objections. Americans were unwilling to accept a calendar in which their Independence Day would come, not on the traditional date of July 4, but on Sol 17. Businessmen complained that it would complicate matters for them; that, for example, they would have to issue statements to all their customers thirteen times a year instead of twelve times. As a result the Thirteen-Month Calendar is now no longer seriously considered as a successor to the Gregorian calendar.

But the World Calendar, based on the easily divisible number 12, has become increasingly popular. In this calendar each

JANUARY							FEBRUARY							MARCH						
S	M	T	W	T	F	S	S	M	T	W	T	F	S	S	M	T	W	T	F	S
1	2	3	4	5	6	7	1	2	3	4	5	6	7	1	2	3	4	5	6	7
8	9	10	11	12	13	14	8	9	10	11	12	13	14	8	9	10	11	12	13	14
15	16	17	18	19	20	21	15	16	17	18	19	20	21	15	16	17	18	19	20	21
22	23	24	25	26	27	28	22	23	24	25	26	27	28	22	23	24	25	26	27	28

APRIL							MAY							JUNE						
S	M	T	W	T	F	S	S	M	T	W	T	F	S	S	M	T	W	T	F	S
1	2	3	4	5	6	7	1	2	3	4	5	6	7	1	2	3	4	5	6	7
8	9	10	11	12	13	14	8	9	10	11	12	13	14	8	9	10	11	12	13	14
15	16	17	18	19	20	21	15	16	17	18	19	20	21	15	16	17	18	19	20	21
22	23	24	25	26	27	28	22	23	24	25	26	27	28	22	23	24	25	26	27	28

LEAP DAY
June 29

SOL						
S	M	T	W	T	F	S
1	2	3	4	5	6	7
8	9	10	11	12	13	14
15	16	(17)	18	19	20	21
22	23	24	25	26	27	28

JULY							AUGUST							SEPTEMBER						
S	M	T	W	T	F	S	S	M	T	W	T	F	S	S	M	T	W	T	F	S
1	2	3	4	5	6	7	1	2	3	4	5	6	7	1	2	3	4	5	6	7
8	9	10	11	12	13	14	8	9	10	11	12	13	14	8	9	10	11	12	13	14
15	16	17	18	19	20	21	15	16	17	18	19	20	21	15	16	17	18	19	20	21
22	23	24	25	26	27	28	22	23	24	25	26	27	28	22	23	24	25	26	27	28

OCTOBER							NOVEMBER							DECEMBER						
S	M	T	W	T	F	S	S	M	T	W	T	F	S	S	M	T	W	T	F	S
1	2	3	4	5	6	7	1	2	3	4	5	6	7	1	2	3	4	5	6	7
8	9	10	11	12	13	14	8	9	10	11	12	13	14	8	9	10	11	12	13	14
15	16	17	18	19	20	21	15	16	17	18	19	20	21	15	16	17	18	19	20	21
22	23	24	25	26	27	28	22	23	24	25	26	27	28	22	23	24	25	26	27	28

YEAR DAY
DECEMBER 29

The Thirteen-Month Calendar. Each month has 4 weeks and 28 days. There is also a Year Day and, in leap years, a Leap Day.

equal quarter year of 91 days, or 13 weeks or 3 months, corresponds to a seasonal period. The three months within each quarter-year have respectively 31, 30 and 30 days; every month has 26 weekdays plus Sundays. Every year in this calendar is like every other year; the first of every year, for example, falls on a Sunday; Christmas, December 25, falls on a Monday.

Since each quarter-year consists of 91 days, the total number of days in all four quarter-years is 364. To provide the necessary 365th day, another day—known as Worldsday—has been inserted. It is placed after December 30 and before January 1; it belongs to the month of December. Worldsday is a world holiday.

The 366th day in leap years is inserted between June 30 and July 1; it is called Leapyear Day and is also considered as a world holiday. Worldsday and Leapyear Day are dated respectively December W or December 31 and June W or June 31; the letter "W" is preferred. These two stabilizing days keep the calendar on an even keel with the seasons. The Gregorian four-hundred centurial leap-year rule is retained. In fact, the World Calendar differs but little from the Gregorian calendar; the two are identical for the period between September 1 and February 28, bearing in mind, of course, that Worldsday, December W, is equivalent to December 31. The World Calendar is shown on this page.

In 1937, when the League of Nations asked the different member and non-member nations to give their opinion of the World Calendar, 14 nations approved it, 6 rejected it, 8 abstained from replying, 10 said that they were not prepared to reply and 7 believed that the time was premature for a new calendar. The result was considered unsatisfactory; besides the league felt that so momentous a step as the introduction of a world calendar should not be taken with political conditions as unsettled as they were throughout the world. (Continued Axis aggression had brought about great tension.) Therefore the new calendar was set aside. It has been revived in recent years in the United Nations.

FIRST QUARTER

JANUARY	FEBRUARY	MARCH
S M T W T F S	S M T W T F S	S M T W T F S
1 2 3 4 5 6 7	1 2 3 4	1 2
8 9 10 11 12 13 14	5 6 7 8 9 10 11	3 4 5 6 7 8 9
15 16 17 18 19 20 21	12 13 14 15 16 17 18	10 11 12 13 14 15 16
22 23 24 25 26 27 28	19 20 21 22 23 24 25	17 18 19 20 21 22 23
29 30 31	26 27 28 29 30	24 25 26 27 28 29 30

SECOND QUARTER

APRIL	MAY	JUNE
S M T W T F S	S M T W T F S	S M T W T F S
1 2 3 4 5 6 7	1 2 3 4	1 2
8 9 10 11 12 13 14	5 6 7 8 9 10 11	3 4 5 6 7 8 9
15 16 17 18 19 20 21	12 13 14 15 16 17 18	10 11 12 13 14 15 16
22 23 24 25 26 27 28	19 20 21 22 23 24 25	17 18 19 20 21 22 23
29 30 31	26 27 28 29 30	24 25 26 27 28 29 30 ✶✶W

THIRD QUARTER

JULY	AUGUST	SEPTEMBER
S M T W T F S	S M T W T F S	S M T W T F S
1 2 3 4 5 6 7	1 2 3 4	1 2
8 9 10 11 12 13 14	5 6 7 8 9 10 11	3 4 5 6 7 8 9
15 16 17 18 19 20 21	12 13 14 15 16 17 18	10 11 12 13 14 15 16
22 23 24 25 26 27 28	19 20 21 22 23 24 25	17 18 19 20 21 22 23
29 30 31	26 27 28 29 30	24 25 26 27 28 29 30

FOURTH QUARTER

OCTOBER	NOVEMBER	DECEMBER
S M T W T F S	S M T W T F S	S M T W T F S
1 2 3 4 5 6 7	1 2 3 4	1 2
8 9 10 11 12 13 14	5 6 7 8 9 10 11	3 4 5 6 7 8 9
15 16 17 18 19 20 21	12 13 14 15 16 17 18	10 11 12 13 14 15 16
22 23 24 25 26 27 28	19 20 21 22 23 24 25	17 18 19 20 21 22 23
29 30 31	26 27 28 29 30	24 25 26 27 28 29 30 ✶W

The World Calendar. The W with a single asterisk before it is Worldsday; the W that has two asterisks before it is Leapyear Day.

See also Vol. 10, p. 268: "Calendar."

PLANT AND ANIMAL COMMUNITIES

How the Living Things of a Region Dwell Together

BY N. E. BINGHAM

WHEN we speak of a community, we ordinarily have in mind a definite group of people, living together in a certain area and bound together by common laws, customs and traditions. The different members of the community take part in a wide variety of activities. Some grow crops or raise animals; others manufacture machines of various kinds; still others are engaged in a wide variety of business and professional pursuits. Each individual plays a particular role in the total life of the community and what he does affects every other individual directly or indirectly.

Human beings form part of a larger community, made up not only of men but of all the animals and plants dwelling in the same locality. In this article, we shall be particularly concerned with the many interrelationships that exist among all of the plants and animals (including man) that live together in selected communities. We shall also consider the relationship between these living things and the physical environment that serves as their home.

In animal and plant communities, all the members, large or small, active or anchored, ferocious or passive, play a definite part. The green plants convert the energy of sunlight, in a many-stage operation, into sugars and other substances, and these products are the source of all the energy used by themselves and the other members of the community. There are animals that feed upon these plants, and other animals that prey upon the plant-eaters in their turn. Certain small parasites fasten upon the bodies of larger animals and feast upon the living flesh of their victims. Animal scavengers feed upon carcasses; plant scav-

engers, upon animals and plants and organic wastes. There are thousands of such natural communities.

Human communities are separated from one another by natural or political boundaries and sometimes by barriers of language, custom and tradition. Plant and animal communities are set apart no less effectively. In their case, of course, only natural boundaries hem them in — the lay of the land, the climate, geologic factors, their own physical make-up.

The natural features of the landscape — land, water, deserts, jungles, mountains and the like — act as barriers to certain species and not to others. For marine forms of life, like fishes and octopuses and seaweeds, the land is a barrier; the sea is just as effective a barrier for land forms, including the great majority of mammals. The deserts keep out plants which require a good deal of moisture — sphagnum moss, cypress trees, rushes and the like. On the other hand, cacti, sagebrush, yuccas and other plants that flourish in dry areas cannot thrive in waterlogged swamps. A natural barrier may extend for hundreds of miles, or it may be comparatively small. Thus the Androscoggin River, in southwestern Maine, forms the southern boundary of the ranges of many animals of northern Maine and lower Canada.

Temperature also serves as a barrier for natural communities. For example, in a short climb of 5,000 feet up Mount Washington, in New Hampshire, one passes through four different zones of life, bounded by increasingly low temperatures. The valleys belong to the Eastern Transition Zone; in them we find maple, beech, black oaks, birches and such animals as cottontails, wood thrushes and blue jays. On the slopes, we find plants and animals that are characteristic of the Canadian Zone. There are evergreen forests of spruce and fir, northern jack rabbits, hermit thrushes and juncos. Still higher up we see the animals, hardy flowers and low shrubs of the Hudsonian Zone, so called because it is characteristic of Canada's Hudson Bay region. Finally, the barren windswept area around the top of the mountain forms what is called

Upper photo, USDA; lower photo, U. S. Forest Service

The natural features of the landscape act as a barrier to certain species and not to others. Black gum trees (upper photo) thrive in swampy areas; they could not survive in dry regions, such as those in which the cholla (lower photo), a variety of cactus plant, flourishes.

the Arctic-Alpine Zone. There are algae, lichens and a few flowering plants, together with insects and other animals that are commonly associated with such vegetation.

The effects of temperature are sometimes intensified by high or low relative humidity. (See Index, under Humidity.) Thus, humidity affects the transpiration of plants — that is, their loss of water. The dryer the air is, the more rapidly water vapor will pass from the leaves. When low relative humidity is combined with high temperature, the rate of transpiration is very high — so high, indeed, that few plants can survive the resulting loss of water. Only those species that are specially adapted for life in desert regions can grow under

such conditions. The cactus is one of these plants. It has no broad leaves through which it could lose quantities of water to the outer air; hence it is able to retain a good deal of the moisture that comes from rare showers or the melting of scanty winter snows, and it survives the dry season.

Plant and animal communities are profoundly affected by rain, snow, hail and other forms of precipitation. It takes at least forty inches of rainfall to sustain a forest and thus to provide shelter for animal life within it. Twenty inches of rainfall are required for a prairie; ten inches, for a subhumid grassland.

The habitats and niches of living things

In any plant and animal community, the different species live in the same general area but play different roles. The place where a given organism lives (a desert, say, or a fresh-water pond) is known as its habitat. The part it plays in the habitat is called its niche.

Consider, for example, the birds known as Darwin's finches, which dwell in the isolated island group of the Galápagos. There are fourteen different species in all. Some of these species live together in the same habitat — the arid coastal regions of the Galápagos or the moist forests of the interior. But each species has developed its particular food habits and so each occupies a particular niche.

What is an ecosystem?

A plant and animal community and the environment in which it lives are linked together to form a so-called ecosystem. Each ecosystem, then, is made up of living

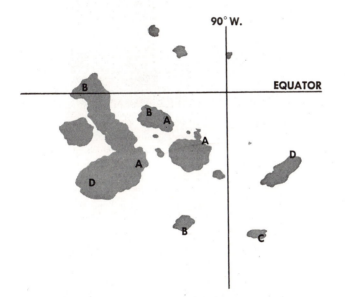

90° W.

EQUATOR

The birds known as Darwin's finches, found in the isolated Galápagos Islands (shown in the map), have evolved into fourteen species. Note the differences in the beaks of the four species shown below: *Geospiza scandens* (A), *Geospiza difficilis debilirostris* (B), *Geospiza fortis* (C) and *Platyspiza crassirostris* (D). The dwelling places of these species are indicated on the map.

Drawings of birds adapted from photo by Amer. Mus. of Nat. Hist.

A   B   C   D

NONLIVING (ABIOTIC) SUBSTANCES, SUCH AS WATER, OXYGEN AND NITROGEN, ARE UTILIZED BY PLANT AND ANIMAL LIFE

PRODUCERS ARE PLANTS THAT MAKE FOOD FROM INORGANIC SUBSTANCES

PRIMARY CONSUMERS ARE PLANT-EATING ANIMALS (HERBIVORES)

DECOMPOSERS ARE TINY ORGANISMS THAT TURN PLANT AND ANIMAL WASTES INTO MATERIALS FOR FUTURE PLANT USE

things — animals and plants — and nonliving, or abiotic, substances. It can be broken up conveniently into four different components: (1) nonliving substances; (2) producers; (3) consumers; (4) decomposers.

Nonliving (abiotic) substances. These are inorganic materials such as water, carbon dioxide, oxygen, nitrogen and various minerals. Water is required by all living things, plants and animals alike. Both water and carbon dioxide are raw materials used by plants in their manufacture of food. Oxygen is required for the respiration of both animals and plants. Nitrogen and minerals are employed by plants in the manufacture of various organic substances.

Producers. The producers of an ecosystem are the plants that make food from

inorganic substances — foods essential for both animals and plants. In a forest, the trees are the dominant producers; in a prairie, the grasses; in a fresh-water lake, the algae and other plants.

Consumers are the organisms that eat other organisms. The vast majority of consumers are animals.* Those that feed on the primary producers — that is, plants — are the primary consumers; they are also known as herbivores, or vegetation-eaters. Insects that devour garden foliage are herbivores; so are cattle; so are protozoans that feed on algae in a pond.

Animals that feed on other animals are known as secondary consumers, or carni-

* A few plants trap and devour insects; among them are Venus's-flytraps and pitcher plants. See the Index, under the names of these plants.

ECOSYSTEM
(AFRICAN VELD)

SECONDARY CONSUMERS ARE FLESH-EATING ANIMALS (CARNIVORES)

SCAVENGERS, SUCH AS HYENAS, VULTURES AND VARIOUS INSECTS, KEEP THE WILDS FROM BEING CLUTTERED UP

vores (flesh-eaters). They include the birds that devour insects, the coyotes that prey on rabbits and the fish that eat protozoans and crustaceans. Animals that eat other animals are also known as predators. They are often eaten by other predators in their turn; thus a bird that has dined on an earthworm may later become the victim of a snake.

A predator may be smaller than the animal that it kills. Wolves hunt in family groups and so can run down and slay a deer that is larger than any individual wolf in the family. Generally speaking, however, the predator is markedly smaller than the victims on which it feasts.

In fact, a prospective prey may be immune from the attentions of large predators

because it is too small to be easily caught and because it would not begin to make a full meal. That is why mice do not reckon lions among their natural enemies. The lion in Aesop's famous fable could have caught the mouse only by sheerest accident; and the little animal would have been about as satisfying a morsel as a single pea to a hungry man.

There are exceptions, though. Certain species of whales feed upon plankton — minute plant and animal organisms floating in the water. Of course the whale does not nibble away daintily at one microscopic animal or plant after another. The big seagoing mammal has a special straining device that enables it to separate the plankton from the water in which they float; thus a mouth-

ful may consist of billions of the tiny creatures. The anteater is also far larger than the ant, which is the anteater's prey; but the anteater satisfies its hunger by drawing in considerable numbers of its ant victims at a time with its long tubular tongue.

Certain animals satisfy their food requirements not by devouring smaller and weaker animals but by becoming parasites —that is, by fastening on the body of a much larger animal and feeding upon it for a period of days or weeks or even years. The animal that harbors the parasite is called the host. There are parasites, too, among plants. The mistletoe, for example, is parasitic on a wide variety of trees and shrubs, including the poplar, the willow, the maple and the mountain ash.

The larger the host, the more parasites it can support. A lion may have ticks in its skin, protozoans and flukes in its blood, tapeworms in its intestines, moth larvae in its fur and fungi between its toes. It may also suffer from illnesses caused by the parasitic activities of bacteria or viruses.

Nature's community of living things has its scavengers, too. When an animal dies of natural causes in the wilds, its carcass may be devoured by a hyena or a jackal or a vulture or a great variety of insects.

Decomposers. The decomposers are made up chiefly of tiny organisms such as bacteria and various fungi. They obtain their food, in part, at least, from the dead bodies or waste products of other organisms. Decomposers prevent the wild from being cluttered up with organic debris. But some of them serve an even more useful purpose. Bacteria, for example, release the chemical materials locked within the remains of trees, grasses, vertebrates and the like and make such materials available for a new generation of plants.

Food chains
among living things

Plants, herbivores, predators, parasites, scavengers and decomposers are all linked together by their food requirements to form food chains. These provide a most intimate bond between the various members of the natural community.

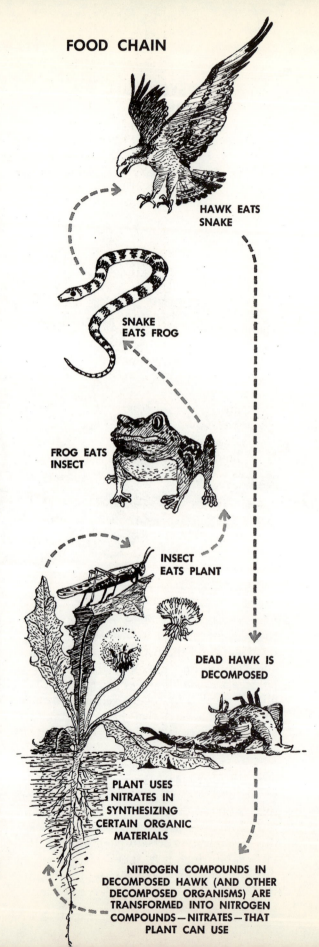

FOOD CHAIN

HAWK EATS SNAKE

SNAKE EATS FROG

FROG EATS INSECT

INSECT EATS PLANT

DEAD HAWK IS DECOMPOSED

PLANT USES NITRATES IN SYNTHESIZING CERTAIN ORGANIC MATERIALS

NITROGEN COMPOUNDS IN DECOMPOSED HAWK (AND OTHER DECOMPOSED ORGANISMS) ARE TRANSFORMED INTO NITROGEN COMPOUNDS—NITRATES—THAT PLANT CAN USE

Examples of food chains among land animals and plants are legion. Plants manufacture food in sunlight; insects devour plants; frogs devour insects; snakes devour frogs; hawks devour snakes; beetles and other insects devour the carcasses of hawks. Aphids, or plant lice, which feed on cabbage plants, are the food of lady-bird beetles, which are eaten by birds. Zebras live on grasses; they are infested with ticks and are the staple fare of lions; hyenas, jackals and vultures clean up the remains of the zebras.

We find much the same sort of food chains among water animals and plants. In a fresh-water pond, say, there are plants that provide food; there are also herbivores, predators, parasites and scavengers. Small plants, including the one-celled diatoms, serve as the primal source of food, just as plants do on land. Protozoans, rotifers, mosquito larvae, May-fly nymphs, caddisfly larvae, small crustaceans, tadpoles and snails devour the tiny plants. In their turn, these animals serve as food for predators, such as the larvae of the damsel fly and the dragonfly, water scorpions, diving beetles, frogs, water snakes and fish. There are parasites in the ponds, too; they include the leeches and lampreys that suck the blood of the larger carnivores, as well as bacteria, fungi and protozoa. Various roundworms, flatworms and insect larvae act as scavengers, cleaning up organic wastes in the pond; certain species of bacteria and fungi act as decomposers.

If one link in a food chain is affected by some unfavorable development or other, the other links will also be affected. A case in point is the lichen-caribou-Eskimo food chain. The Eskimos of Alaska feed upon the caribou, which in turn feed upon lichens. Unfortunately, the radioactive fallout resulting from nuclear-weapon tests have caused the lichens to absorb notable quantities of strontium 90, a long-lived radioactive isotope that is found in fallout. When strontium 90 is absorbed into the body of man or beast, it seeks out living bone and keeps bombarding the bone cells with beta rays. If such irradiation is prolonged and heavy, it may lead to cancer.

Even now Alaskan caribou, because of their lichen diet, are reported to have from four to six times as much strontium 90 as cattle raised on the Nevada Atomic Test Site. The meager data available indicate that the bones of the Alaskans who feed upon caribou contain more strontium 90 than the bones of Americans living in the temperate zone.

Communal partnerships — symbiosis

In a community of plants and animals, therefore, hunger brings about never-ending slaughter. Species A is devoured by species B, which in turn falls victim to species C, which is the favorite food of species D, upon which species E feeds with zest. Yet this constant round of eat-and-be-eaten is not by any means the whole story of communal life. In many cases, two organisms of different species live together in a mutually beneficial partnership. We give the name of symbiosis ("living together," in Greek) to this relationship.

Lichens furnish a striking example of symbiosis. Some of these plants form a crusty covering on barren rocks and tree trunks; others are leaf-like; still others are branched and bushy. Each lichen plant consists of a fungus and, within the fungus, a number of microscopic one-celled plants called algae. The fungus obtains its food from the algae, which, like other green plants, manufacture it from carbon dioxide, water and other materials. But the algae also benefit by their association with the fungus. For the larger plant absorbs and retains the water and mineral salts that the algae use in their food-making activities. Under such favorable conditions the algae produce sufficient food for their own growth and for that of their partner, the fungus. As a matter of fact, algae grow more luxuriantly when associated with fungi.

Another good example of symbiosis involves certain bacteria that live in the roots of legumes, such as clover, peas and alfalfa. These plants supply the bacteria with shelter, water and food elements. But the legumes also benefit by the relationship, for the bacteria draw nitrogen from the air

The ant called *Formica rufa* feeds the beetle *Atemeles cava* and "milks" it by collecting a secretion from the beetle's abdomen.

SYMBIOSIS

Lichens (right) are composite organisms, consisting of fungi and algae living together. In making food, the algae use water and mineral salts collected by the fungi; the fungi obtain food from the algae.

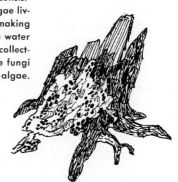

The Nile plover feeds on the leeches that suck blood from the crocodile's gums. Thus it obtains a meal and is helpful to the crocodile.

and use it to prepare nitrogen compounds that the plants need.

An unusual partnership exists between termites and certain protozoans. The termite makes its home in dead wood; it chews a passageway through the wood and swallows the tiny chips. Within its digestive tract lie several varieties of protozoans, which digest the cellulose of the wood, converting it into sugars. Both the termites and the protozoa derive their energy from these sugars.

The tick birds that pick ticks from the hides of antelopes, zebras and rhinoceroses assure themselves of an ample food supply and at the same time relieve the big animals of their parasites. A similar relationship exists between the Nile plover and the crocodile; the bird enters the gaping mouth of the crocodile and picks off the leeches that suck blood from the big reptile's gums. Aphids, which pump juices from leaves, are cared for by ants, which procure a sweetish secretion from their "ant cows" by stroking them. There are many other cases of symbiosis in nature.

The climax
stage in nature

In every natural community there is a constant trend toward a balance between the various species. This balance is reached when there are just the right numbers of each successive species of the food chain to maintain a constant population. This is called the climax stage. It may continue for a long time. Sooner or later, however, the balance is disturbed as the environment undergoes a change. The ocean and the land shift their boundaries; erosion changes the features of the landscape; temperature and moisture conditions are modified. The climax stage then comes to an end.

Succession in the
natural community

When the environment changes, plant and animal communities undergo a series of regular and orderly changes known as succession. Whether succession occurs in a small pond or in a land area of several thousand square miles, the principles involved are the same. With changed environment comes a change in the plant and animal inhabitants. In turn, each group modifies the environment by living in it. Different communities of organisms develop until finally a stable climax stage is reached.

Succession would occur even if all life were wiped out from an area. Let us suppose that a level, barren rock surface suddenly appeared in the midst of luxuriant surroundings. It would not be long before living forms would populate it. The first residents to move in would be the lichens, which would spread over the barren rock and begin the work of capturing the energy of sunlight. Organic acid from these lichens

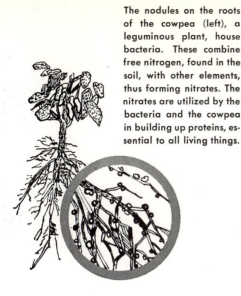

The nodules on the roots of the cowpea (left), a leguminous plant, house bacteria. These combine free nitrogen, found in the soil, with other elements, thus forming nitrates. The nitrates are utilized by the bacteria and the cowpea in building up proteins, essential to all living things.

The tick birds that pick ticks from the hide of a rhinoceros free the animal of its parasites. At the same time, they obtain an abundant supply of food.

would begin to dissolve and break up parts of the rock. Wind and rain would move these beginnings of soil into slight depressions. Algae, mosses and ferns would grow in the small patches of sòil. Their growth would produce increased amounts of organic acids; rock would break up at an increasing rate with an ever increasing yield of soil. In time, small flowering plants, grasses and various herbs would get started. ·

If the barren rock were in a region where the dominant climax plant is prairie grass, it would become a grassy expanse in the course of time; if it were in a more humid climate, it would develop into a forest. The process would be a long one, with many setbacks. Ultimately, however, there would be a climax stage, with the vegetation and the animals characteristic of the region.

This is not a mere theoretical statement of what might happen; we have witnessed such succession at work again and again. Within the past century, the volcanic Indonesian island of Krakatoa has provided a dramatic example. In May 1883, one, of the most violent eruptions of all time took place on the island. A mass of rocks, small stones, ashes and dust was hurled high in the air. The disturbance created a series of monstrous sea waves which swept over the shores of Java and Sumatra, destroyed many villages and caused the loss of more than 30,000 lives. More than half of Krakatoa was destroyed, including the highest

mountain. Every vestige of life was wiped out on the island and on two others in the vicinity.

The nearest land from which new life could come was another island some fifteen miles away. Yet less than three years after the eruption the ashy soil, from sea level to mountain tops, had been covered with a gelatinous layer of blue-green algae, diatoms and bacteria. A number of mosses and ferns, developed from wind-blown spores, had appeared upon this layer; wind-blown seeds and ocean-borne seeds had given rise to a few species of flowering plants. Ten years later, thirteen years after the eruption, there were about fifty species of flowering plants. In some places, both flowering plants and ferns completely covered the soil. Inland, there were stretches of tall grasses. Scattered here and there were a few shrubs and trees.

Twenty-three years after the eruption, the island was covered with rich vegetation. Along the shores, there was a forest containing several kinds of fig trees and coconut palms. Other forests extended into the ravines of the interior. There were over ninety varieties of flowering plants and fifteen varieties of ferns. Mosquitoes, ants, wasps, birds, bats and lizards flourished. Life did not yet approach the variety and luxuriance of a climax tropical rain forest, such as had existed on Krakatoa before the eruption of 1883. Still, the changes that

In his unceasing war against insect pests and rats, man has sometimes set their natural enemies against them. Thus the *Polistes* wasp has been introduced into tobacco-growing areas to combat the tobacco hookworm. The mongoose was brought into Jamaica in the 1870's to rid the island of its rats. Unfortunately, when the rat supply dwindled, the mongoose turned its attention to poultry and various other kinds of animal life useful to man.

had already taken place showed that the island was well on its way to the climax stage.

Man and the balance of nature

Man is forever disturbing the orderly balance of the climax stage. Alone of all living creatures, he has sought to make over nature. He has destroyed forests and drained swamps in order to make room for his crops. He has waged constant warfare against weeds, which are simply the plants that would normally occupy at least a part of the area given over to crops. He has threatened the normal soil-building cycle by repeated cultivation of a single crop. His careless methods of planting have exposed the soil to erosion by wind and water.

By adding greatly to the numbers of the animals and plants that are useful to him, man has provided insects and vermin of all kinds with an endless variety and quantity of their natural foods; therefore they have increased and multiplied. He has added to their number by unwittingly importing insect pests from foreign lands, without likewise introducing the natural enemies that had kept them in check. The European corn borer, the gypsy moth and the cottony cushion scale, among other American insect pests, are examples.

As if this were not enough, man has sometimes knowingly introduced predators from other areas to solve an immediate problem, without any thought of the consequences. Thus the mongoose was brought into Jamaica and other islands of the West Indies in the seventies of the last century in the hope that it would overcome the plague of rats on the sugar plantations. The mongoose fulfilled its mission by killing vast numbers of the rodents. But when its rat food supply dwindled, the mongoose turned its attention to other animals that were useful to man. It killed off such great numbers of poultry and of insect-eating birds, reptiles and mammals that it became a dangerous pest in its turn.

Again and again, man has had to pay the penalty for upsetting the balance of nature to further his own ends. Only at the cost of eternal vigilance can he protect his crops and his farm animals from insects and other natural enemies which are simply trying to re-establish the balance of nature. We discuss elsewhere the methods that he has adopted in the never-ending struggle. In part this campaign consists of trying to keep insect enemies and other pests out of a particular region, and of waging relentless war upon them once they have entered. In part, too, it consists of re-establishing the balance of nature as far as possible by conserving and adding to forest resources, by restoring the fertility of the soil and by helping maintain a fair balance among wild animal life. Thus man for his own survival attempts to make his peace with plant and animal communities.

See also Vol. 10, p. 271: "Ecology."

THE TWENTIETH CENTURY (1895-) IX

BY JUSTUS SCHIFFERES

THE MAKING OF A SCIENTIST

SOME young people who read these pages may find themselves drawn to a career in science. As scientists they will find themselves in most distinguished and also most varied company. As the preceding chapters of this group reveal, men and women of different races, walks of life, temperaments, creeds and professions have become famous scientists. Leonardo da Vinci was an artist; Sir William Herschel, a band leader; Lavoisier, a tax collector; Priestley, a clergyman; Marie Curie, a political exile; Joule, a brewer; Edison, a telegraph operator; Ruth Benedict, a teacher of English; Scheele, an apothecary; Einstein, a patent-office clerk; Faraday, a bookbinder; Halley, a gourmet; Newton, a recluse; Von Humboldt, an explorer; Leeuwenhoek, a lens-grinder; Pascal, a child prodigy; Darwin, an unpromising lad; Paracelsus, an alchemist; Kepler, an astrologer; Carver, a slave.

These men and women had in common their passionate devotion to science. The career of the great Negro chemist George Washington Carver offers a particularly striking example. It illustrates the important point that anybody with the necessary ability and the necessary ambition can become a first-rate scientist, no matter how humble his origin or how discouraging the circumstances under which he must work.

Carver was born of slave parents toward the close of the American Civil War (about 1864). His mother lived on the plantation of Moses Carver near the village of Diamond Grove in the extreme southwest corner of Missouri, not far from the Arkansas line; his father belonged to a neighboring farmer. One night slave raiders from Arkansas carried off little George and his mother from the Carver plantation. Moses Carver followed the raiders over the state line and ransomed George for a race horse worth about $300. The whereabouts of the child's mother remained unknown.

After the defeat of the South and the freeing of the slaves, George continued to live on the Carver plantation, which had been devastated by Union troops in the war. Since he was extremely frail, he did women's work about the house — he washed, ironed, cooked and sewed. A bright lad, he memorized a little blue-backed Webster's speller.

When he was about ten years old, George asked the master of the plantation to let him attend the one-room log schoolhouse at Neosho, Missouri, eight miles away. Carver told the lad that he was free to go but that he would have to shift for himself. The boy went off to Neosho without a penny in his pocket. He slept in barns, did odd jobs for his meals and eagerly devoured every bit of book learning that was available to him. A few years later, he worked his way with a mule train going sixty miles west to Fort Scott, Kansas, where he enrolled in the high school. Here, too, his life was a constant struggle with grinding poverty; he took in "white folks' washing" in order to pay his way. Then he went to Simpson College, in Indianola, Iowa. He attended this school for three years, supporting himself by doing odd jobs and running a laundry.

In the year 1890, when he was about twenty-six years old, he enrolled at Iowa

State College at Ames, and four years later he received the degree of Bachelor of Science in agriculture.   In 1896 he obtained his master's degree.   Meanwhile his wonderful skill with plants had attracted the admiring attention of his professors.   He was given a regular job at the college; he took care of the greenhouse and did a certain amount of teaching.

The speeches and teachings of the famous Negro educator Booker T. Washington greatly influenced young Carver, who resolved to help his people — the Negroes

of the South.   In 1896 he accepted a teaching position at an Alabama Negro college — Tuskegee Institute — which at that time was a pitiful collection of shacks.   His work at this school was destined to change the agriculture and much of the economy of the South.

His first task was to introduce diversified agriculture to the cotton-impoverished soil of the South.   He urged farmers to plant peanuts and sweet potatoes, which, he said, had tremendous industrial possibilities.   To realize these possibilities to

GEORGE
WASHINGTON
CARVER

USDA

the full, he began a series of infinitely patient and persistent researches. He drew inspiration from early morning walks in the woods, where he would meditate and pray to God for the solution of scientific mysteries.

Carver analyzed the components of peanuts — fats, oils, gums, sugars, resins and so on. He showed how these sub-

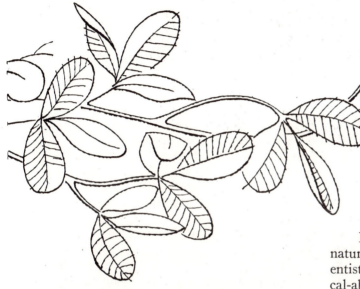

stances could be chemically transformed into synthetic milk, butter and coffee and also into such varied products as flour, breakfast food, salad oil, shaving lotion, cosmetics, ink, wallboard and axle grease. He made 300 different substances from peanuts and 118 different products from sweet potatoes.

National and international honors came to this modest slave-born scientist — the "peanut man," as he was called. He received many fabulous bids from industry (including an offer of a $25,000-a-year job from Thomas A. Edison), but he refused them all. Living simply and piously, amusing himself with painting (with pigments that he made himself) and handicraft arts (he wove his own neckties), Carver had no need for vast sums of money. He was content in the knowledge that his work would help uncounted millions. He died in 1943. His story is an inspiration to young people seeking a career in science.

How can you know that you have the natural ability to become a first-rate scientist? Aptitude tests, including mechanical-ability tests, will be helpful; so will a heart-to-heart talk with a successful scientist or a science teacher. But, in the last analysis, only you can judge whether you have the qualities that characterize the genuine scientist. These qualities are:

(1) The capacity to work alone for hours, days and years, if need be.

(2) The willingness to shoulder responsibility.

(3) Courage — the ability to keep your head and to stick to your guns in a crisis.

(4) The ability to co-operate with other people — to understand the problems on which they are working.

(5) Curiosity — especially about the ways of man and nature.

(6) A liking for experiments and a feeling for accuracy.

(7) Independence — the willingness to map out your own path of investigation.

(8) A willingness not only to look after the details of your job but also to see it whole.

(9) A sense of deep personal satisfaction as you seek a scientific goal, despite lack of immediate glory, applause or financial reward.

(10) Imagination — the same quality that animates great writers, artists and musicians.

You cannot expect to possess in the highest degree all the qualities that are listed here. Certain great scientists have been strikingly deficient in one or more of them. Leeuwenhoek was content to peer eternally through his microscopes, caring little about general theories. Newton did not co-operate well with other people. Sir Humphry Davy was avid for personal glory, and this led him to be unjust to possible rivals. But, by and large, the qualities mentioned above describe the attitude of the genuine scientist.

Since science is built upon the combined wisdom of dead and living scientists, this wisdom must be sought out in books and museums as well as in the laboratory; in other words, a prospective scientist must acquire a thoroughgoing education. This education need not necessarily be entirely formal, but it must be effective. There may be self-taught scientists — though these have been few and far between — but there are no ignorant scientists.

Generally speaking, it is advisable to begin your scientific training in high school and to continue it in college and in a graduate school. The common sequence of degrees you will seek is B.S. (Bachelor of Science) or B.A. (Bachelor of Arts);

M.S. (Master of Science); and Ph.D. (Doctor of Philosophy) or D.S. (Doctor of Science; also written Sc.D.). Usually four years of undergraduate work and three or more years of graduate work at an accredited college or university are necessary to obtain the Ph.D. and D.S. degrees. Other degrees are granted to scientists specializing in certain branches of science. For example, the degree of M.D. (Doctor of Medicine) is granted in medicine; the degree of D.D.S. (Doctor of Dental Surgery) in dentistry.

Your high-school training should include mathematics, at least one foreign language and several science courses, as well as English, history and other subjects. You will want to choose a college that has a good science department; the name "Institute of Technology" or "Scientific School" may be a clue. Or you may select a college on the strength of the teachers. For example, you may have been greatly influenced by a book written by a botany professor in a particular college; if you wish to major in botany, it might be a good idea to go to that college and to study with that professor. Incidentally, good science departments usually grow up around eminent scientists.

You may not be able to enter the college you have selected immediately. You can, however, usually make arrangements to go to a local college or junior college near your home and then transfer in the second or third year to the school of your choice. It is often easier to be admitted

to a particular college as a transfer student than as an incoming freshman.

Most universities have certain scholarship funds available to able students in all departments. You can find out about these funds by consulting university catalogues (often available in public libraries) or by writing to admission officers or deans. In both the United States and Canada, qualified veterans are provided by the government with funds to carry on college work. The amount of help given to each veteran depends on the length of his service, his family status and so on.

In the United States certain other scholarships are available on a limited scale. Most widely known, perhaps, are those offered through the organization known as Science Service, with headquarters in Washington, D. C. Science Service conducts an annual Science Talent Search on behalf of the Westinghouse Electrical Corporation. This contest is promoted through the Science Clubs of America. There are 10,000 or more of these clubs, many of them connected with high schools.

Do not specialize too narrowly at college. Your course of study should include literature, philosophy, art and other cultural subjects. If you neglect your general education, you may find it difficult to make up the lost ground later on.

If you have had a satisfactory undergraduate record, you will generally find it easy to get into any graduate school of your choice. By this time you should have a pretty good idea of the field of science in which you will specialize. In seeking suitable subjects for your master's and doctor's theses, you will, of course, freely consult your professors.

As you acquire your basic training in science you may feel drawn to a career in pure scientific research. Or perhaps you may be particularly interested in some field of applied science — chemical engineering, electrical engineering and the like. Even if you later decide to transfer to a non-scientific activity, your scientific training will have developed in you qualities of observation, accuracy and method which will serve you well in any field.

CAREERS IN SCIENCE — A BIRD'S-EYE VIEW

When you have completed your scientific training, you will have to look for a job. Of course you will not ask a prospective employer for a job as a "scientist"; you will apply for a specific position in a specific field — as a junior chemist, or an instructor in mechanical drawing, or a medical-laboratory technician, or a

petroleum geologist, or a forester or a research assistant.

It is important not to be misled by the label of this or that position. When you are seeking employment, ask for a *job analysis* or *job description* from your employer; it will explain what is expected of you. Do not turn down a job merely be-

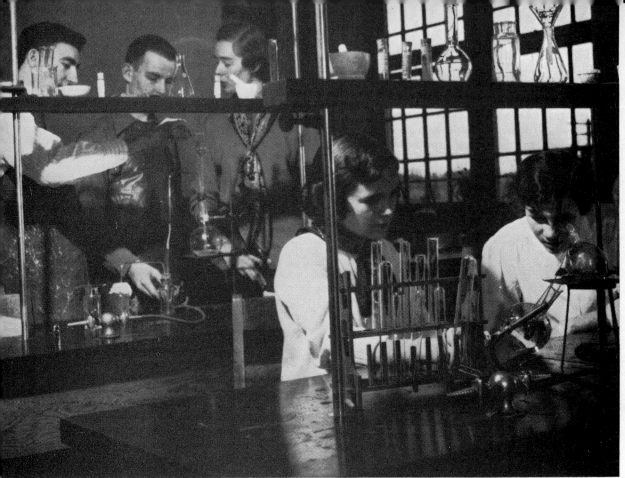

Members of a high-school chemistry class working in the laboratory.
High-school science teaching offers fine opportunities for advancement.

cause it seems to involve too much petty detail. Every scientific position has research possibilities, no matter how humdrum it may seem. After you have shown your ability to carry out routine tasks, you will be given jobs that require greater initiative. In time, you may become a project director, with laboratory facilities and technical assistants working under you.

Sometimes a young scientist does not *find* a job — he *creates* a job through his special knowledge and skill. That is particularly true when a young scientist-in-training opens a new field of inquiry or devotes himself to some new development in applied science. For example, Lee De Forest created his own opportunities in the field of electronics because of his achievements as a pioneer in this field. That was also true of such electronic experts as Philo T. Farnsworth, Edwin H. Armstrong and Vladimir Zworykin. Not only did these men achieve success in their

chosen field but they created positions for a great many other men.

What should you expect of a job in science? A leading personnel expert (a man whose task it is to keep other people happy and efficient in their work, so far as possible) maintains that, to be really satisfactory, a job should provide:

(1) An employer whom you respect, whose praise you treasure and whose criticism you accept because you realize that it is meant both for your good and the good of your job.

(2) Congenial associates with whom you get along well, whose teamwork and co-operation make your job more desirable.

(3) Reasonable security. In this respect university positions and civil-service jobs offer definite advantages over industrial jobs.

(4) Opportunities for advancement. Industry is particularly quick to reward initiative on the job.

(5) An adequate salary. Few scientists get rich, but they can usually look forward to enjoying a comfortable income.

Positions for men and women with good scientific training fall into three major classifications: (1) teaching in high schools, colleges and universities, (2) positions in government agencies and (3) industrial research.

High-school teaching offers a richly satisfying career to those who like to work with young people. The opportunities in this field are increasing, since high-school curriculums are being constantly enlarged. To teach science in high school, one must have at least an A.B. from an accredited college and, preferably, an M.S.; certain courses in education are required in most cases. An increasing number of high-school teachers have gone forward with their graduate studies and have obtained their doctorates in science. Such teachers have a particularly good chance of becoming heads of science departments in their schools.

The Ph.D. or D.S. degree is practically a necessity for a successful career as a college or a university teacher of science. Occasionally a topnotch research man or technologist without a doctor's degree obtains an important teaching job, but this does not happen very often.

Steps in college teaching usually are assistant, instructor, assistant professor, associate professor, full professor, head of department. It usually takes ten to twenty years — or more — to become a full professor and to obtain a salary that may range from $5,000 to $15,000 a year. University science professors often add to their incomes by serving as consultants to industry or to government. A few particularly prominent professors, especially in the field of engineering, set up their own offices, and occasionally their own research laboratories, as independent consultants; they are paid regular retaining fees or special-project fees for their services.

When university teachers of science write for learned publications, they receive a certain number of reprints of their ar-

USDA

A scientist of the United States Department of Agriculture examining perennial rye grass, which has been fertilized with radioactive phosphorus. Many biologists find jobs with the government.

ticles, but they are seldom paid for their contributions. On the other hand, they are paid, and sometimes quite handsomely, for articles in popular magazines and newspapers. If they write science textbooks, they receive royalties, generally amounting to 10 per cent of the retail price. If a textbook is unusually successful, the royalties may represent a considerable amount.

Government service generally means employment under Civil Service in one of the numerous agencies of the Federal Government. Both the United States Civil Service Commission and the Civil Service of Canada announce competitive examinations for various science positions through posters displayed in post offices and elsewhere.

United States government service, in particular, offers opportunities galore to young scientists. The United States Department of Agriculture, for example, employs a great many persons trained in biological sciences. Many important scientific jobs are under the jurisdiction of the Army, Navy or Air Force. When scien-

Industry offers a wide variety of positions for qualified men and women scientists. At the right, a lighting engineer, employed by a large American manufacturer of electrical equipment, is testing a big street light In a snow-white room with twenty sides.

Westinghouse

tists enter United States government service, they are given professional classifications by the Civil Service Commission. Salaries range from about $2,500 to $10,000, as one moves from P1 (Professional, first grade) to P6 (Professional, sixth grade) or P7 classifications. Government jobs provide generous leave provisions and steady salary increases.

There are a number of jobs in science in state (provincial, in Canada) governments and in such local governments as cities, school districts, sanitary districts

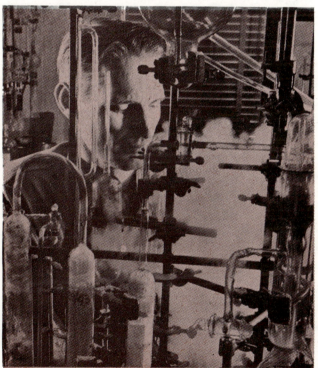

Standard Oil Co. (N. J.)

This laboratory technician is engaged in soil-analysis work in the well-equipped laboratory of an oil company.

and so on. Chemists, technologists, sanitary engineers and others find satisfying careers in such service.

Industry offers innumerable positions for qualified men and women scientists. Such persons generally find a place in an industrial research laboratory. In the United States, for example, there were only about 300 industrial research laboratories in 1920. Thirty years later, accord-

ing to a bulletin of the National Research Council, there were 2,845 in all and they employed something like 100,000 people.

There are three kinds of industrial research laboratories:

(1) Plant laboratories. These analyze and control (often by statistical as well as by experimental methods) the materials, processes and products that are handled in a given factory.

(2) Development laboratories and "pilot plants." Here attention is directed to improvements in the company's product and to economies that will make it possible to lower the costs of production. Such improvements and economies have brought about mass production of radios, washing machines, automobiles, cellophane and so on.

(3) Basic research laboratories. These laboratories carry on research in fundamental sciences bearing on a given industry. Great industrial leaders have long recognized the need for such research. George Eastman once said: "The future of photography is in the laboratory."

Salaries of scientists in industry generally start at $3,000 a year (or more) and may range up to $25,000. Of course, if a scientist becomes a partner in a large firm, the figure is much higher.

The labor market for scientists in industry fluctuates with the times. In depression days, for example, physicists had a rather lean time of it in the field of industry. After World War II broke out, there was a steady demand for young physicists, particularly for those with training in electronics and nucleonics (the science dealing with atomic energy).

Industry offers particularly rich rewards to skillful research scientists with marketable ideas. The main job of a research director in industrial laboratories is to keep his eye open for such scientists. If he can add a few really productive research workers to his staff, his reputation is established.

Most large industrial firms make a special canvass of colleges at the end of each year to seek out and hire the most likely men among the crop of new gradu-

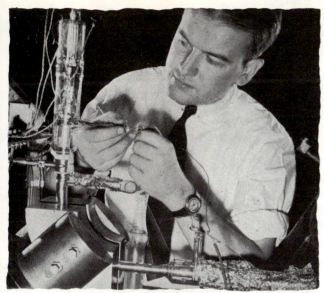

Photos on this page, Westinghouse

There are opportunities galore in the fields of nucle-onics (the study of the phenomena of the atomic nucleus) and electronics (dealing with the emission and behavior of electrons, particularly in electron tubes, photoelec-tric cells and so on). In the large photograph at the left, we see a million-volt atomic generator for research in nucleonics. The inset shows the operation of a "ro-bot chemist," a form of mass spectrometer. This elec-tronic device is used to analyze the chemical content of gases and vapors. Above is Dr. John A. Hipple, who developed the apparatus. The photograph at the right shows another electronic device — a cathode-ray oscillo-graph, which uses an electron beam to measure voltages. The variations in voltage cause the electron beam to move in different patterns across a fluorescent screen in a tube, which traces the motions by emitting light.

cially coal and petroleum), (7) industrial and engineering chemistry, (8) the leather and gelatin industries, (9) medicinal prod-ucts (pharmacological chemistry), (10) metallurgical chemistry, (11) organic chemistry, (12) the paint and varnish in-dustry, (13) photochemistry, (14) physi-cal chemistry and inorganic chemistry, (15) rubber, (16) sugar, (17) water sup-ply, sewage and sanitation and (18) nu-clear chemistry.

There are also many jobs in industry for physicists. You may become a civil, mechanical or automotive engineer. You may get into aviation—as a power-plant designer, an aeronautical engineer or a meteorologist. Electrical engineering of-fers many opportunities; so does electronic research in such fields as radio, radar and television. Your research or development job may be in the fields of optics, lighting or acoustical engineering. As a mathe-matical physicist you may do research in nucleonics. You may be a transportation engineer, an instrument designer, a clima-tologist on a soil-conservation project, a

ates. Your chances of being selected are improved if you can obtain a good letter of recommendation from a professor in your chosen field or if you are near the top of your class. Prospective employers are also bound to be impressed if you have completed a special research job or if you have had an article published in a recog-nized scientific journal.

There are more jobs in industry for chemists than for any other scientific group. The field of chemistry (and chemi-cal engineering) offers opportunities in (1) agricultural and food chemistry, (2) biological chemistry, (3) cellulose chemis-try (plastics and explosives), (4) dyes, (5) fertilizers, (6) gas and fuel (espe-

← British Info. Services; (inset) Gen. Elec. Co.

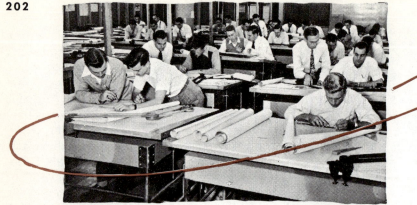

Glen L. Martin Co.

specialist in glass manufacture, a mining engineer or a consultant in the manufacture of X-ray tubes.

Geologists are in great demand in industry, particularly to search for raw materials and to exploit them efficiently. This applies to the vast petroleum industry and to the industries based on coal, gold, copper, lead, uranium and so on. Geologists carry on prospecting activities; they often direct mining and drilling operations. They play an important part, too, in engineering projects. They locate the most convenient sources of building materials, such as rock for road construction and also the gravel and broken stone used in the preparation of concrete. They test foundations for railroad beds, bridges,

Hundreds of men like those who are shown in the above photograph are employed to create the original design drawings of any new airplane. It very often takes a number of years before a new type of aircraft is ready to be produced commercially on a large-scale basis.

dams and airfields and the possibilities for water supply and drainage.

There are other careers in science besides those in teaching, in government work or in industry. Medicine and dentistry, for example, offer unparalleled opportunities for service to mankind as well as for financial success. There are many opportunities, too, in the writing field for persons who combine scientific knowledge with the ability to write clearly, interestingly and simply for the public at large. We might note, perhaps, that some of those who have been most successful in this field have not devoted all their time to writing; they have also occupied positions as government biologists, directors of research departments, roving editors of magazines, professors of astronomy and what not.

People who devote their lives to science generally derive a vast amount of satisfaction from their jobs. Sometimes, indeed, research workers may be so engrossed in their particular project that they may lose all interest in the world at large. They would do well to heed the warning of Albert Einstein that the chief interest of the scientist should be concern for man himself and his fate. "The creations of our mind," said he, "should be a blessing and not a curse to mankind. Never forget that in the midst of your diagrams and equations!"

Standard Oil Co. (N. J.)

Geologists are in great demand in a number of different industries. The young geologist in the above illustration is operating a gravity meter, a delicate device that is used to study the nature of subsurface structures. This and other methods are used to discover oil.

Continued on page 224.

Exploring the Plant World

Interesting Finds and How to Preserve Them

by THOMAS GORDON LAWRENCE

TO EXPLORE the plant world, it is not necessary to seek out the redwood groves of California, nor the mangrove thickets of the Malay Archipelago nor caverns where strange mushrooms loom like ghosts as you search for the path with your flashlight. You will find natural marvels galore in a vacant lot covered with a confused tangle of wild plants or in a perfectly conventional meadow where thousands of flowers are serving refreshments of nectar and pollen, cafeteria style, to hordes of bees and butterflies.

In fact, you can start your journey of exploration in your own back yard. You will make some surprising discoveries. For example, in a small back yard, I found 300 hopeful baby trees, and over 200 more in the still smaller front yard; you can imagine what a jungle there would be if all these little trees continued to grow. The variety of wild flowers in your back yard may be quite amazing: red clover, yellow dande-

lion, blue chicory, orange butterfly weed, tiny star-shaped chickweed, to name only a few. Even the plants of your vegetable garden will produce striking flowers, ranging from the large bell-shaped flowers of squash to the diminutive blossoms of tomato and eggplant.

When you have exhausted the possibilities of your back yard, you will be ready to explore the areas that lie beyond — meadows brimful of wild flowers, brooding woods, dim swamps. You will be particularly fascinated, perhaps, with the striking changes that the seasons bring with them in the course of the year.

Exploring the plant world in winter

Except in regions with very mild climates, most plants go into hiding in winter; the trees, except the pines, spruces and other evergreens, are bare. On cold days, even the cedars lose their bright, deep

green and take on a brown or purple tint. Under an overcast sky the whole world out-of-doors turns gloomy — dull gray bushes and vines clustered about the trees, tall dead grass in the fields and acres of stiff and awkward dead stems of golden-rod, aster and other wild flowers.

As soon as the sun shines, however, the winter fields and woods are beautiful. The dead grasses gleam in bright red, yellow, rich brown. Many of them wave clusters of silver-colored, feathery seeds; others offer the hungry birds meals of richly colored, polished grains. If you look at the base of the wild grasses or separate the tufts with your hand, you discover that the grass is not really dead; the lower blades, protected by the dried-up parts above, are green and juicy.

On a mild January day, especially after rain, the tough, thorny stems of black-berry bushes glow in beautiful red, purple and green tints as if they could hardly restrain themselves from bursting out with leaves and flowers. In sheltered places clumps of grass look green and vigorous. There are vivid green rosettes of evening primrose and dandelion and woolly blanket-like leaves of mullein. You may even find golden dandelion blooming and in some moist spot hundreds of tiny white stars of chickweed. The softest green of winter hides itself along the shores of brooks in deep woods. Deep green leaves of the evergreen Christmas fern grow down to the water's edge. Where the snow has left uncovered places here and there, moss carpets the soft ground, sometimes glistening even fresher than in summer.

Exploring the plant world in spring

The best place to look for the first spring flowers is in swampy woods, because plenty of moisture is there and the trees protect the smaller plants from biting winds. The skunk cabbage pushes its big cabbagelike leaves through the mud of icy ponds and swamps in February. Its strange cluster of evil-smelling flowers may even bloom before the end of winter. Later, when the tremendous leaves spread out, the plant looks like a husky growth of some tropical jungle. As a matter of fact, the skunk cabbage belongs to the arum family, which thrives mostly in the tropics.

Some of the trees are among the early bloomers. These, too, are generally found along streams and in swamps. The earliest tree blossoms are delicately colored. In some places the woods display the golden stamens of pussy willow, the bright crimson clusters of red maple flowers dangling from tall branches and the soft green blossoms of silver maple. If you find a shrub that looks as if it were sprinkled with bright golden stars, it is probably a spice-bush.

The misty appearance of spring woods is due to millions of tiny tree and shrub flowers appearing before the leaves. Later, when the sun hits tiny leaves just beginning to grow, the trees look as if thousands of green flames were dancing on each branch. Even before the first leaf buds burst open on trees and shrubs, the forest floor begins to be dotted with bright early spring flowers. Crowding close on the heels of the skunk cabbage comes the he-

patica with its lovely blossoms of blue or white. Cold bothers the hepatica very little; sometimes its three-lobed leaves are still green and juicy under a slab of ice in January.

You will see such early flowers as bloodroot, Dutchman's-breeches and spring beauty, as well as those that come later in the spring — shining-leaved marsh marigold, white-flowered wild strawberry, wild geraniums, white and blue violets, trillium with its three bright petals and May apple with petals of waxy white and leaves like green umbrellas.

Exploring the
plant world in summer

As summer comes on, you will find fewer flowers in the woods and more and more in the fields, along roadsides and in vacant lots. Some of the beautiful little flowering plants that sparkled in the spring woods may seem to disappear entirely. But if you keep a sharp lookout as you prowl along leafy paths, you will see little shriveled stems here and there, some bare, some with one or two fading leaves. Carefully loosen the soil around them and dig; up comes a bulb or fleshy rootstock. In this guise the plant sleeps through most of the summer, fall and winter; it will send up delicate green leaves and bright petals again when the snows melt next spring.

The tulip trees and locust trees bloom early in June. Both trees are magnificent at this time — the locust with dangling clusters of small white flowers and the great tulip tree with all its branches loaded with tuliplike blossoms. Meadows, old

fields and roadsides are even more exciting; note how they change color from month to month. A meadow that is red or yellow with seeds and dead grass in winter turns bright green in spring, then may become yellow with mustard, blue with bluets, white with wild daisies, reddish purple with joe-pye weed toward the end of August and finally deep gold with tall goldenrod.

Sometimes the plants growing in a field or wood will offer you a glimpse of the future. If you find goldenrod, with blue asters and eastern ragweed together, you are safe in predicting that in several years — providing no human agency disturbs the field — the goldenrods and asters will make the ragweed disappear.

This is a striking example of underground warfare. Ragweed is an annual; it has to start all over again as a weed every spring. Asters and goldenrods, on the other hand, are perennials. This means that their roots and underground stems remain alive all winter, plump and juicy with rich supplies of stored food. When the ragweed seed sprouts, the little plant has to send its tiny roots down into soil where a mass of perennial roots are already twisting and squirming, poking their tips into every cranny as they grow.

If seedling trees have started to grow in a meadow, you can safely predict (provided again, that nature is allowed to have her own way) that the meadow will become a forest. Consequently, the flowers that flourish in strong sunlight, such as Queen Anne's lace, blue chicory and milkweed, will disappear while ferns, moss,

Solomon's-seal and bloodroot will thrive. You can even tell sometimes that one forest will change into another kind of forest, as when young beeches and oaks, which can stand a good deal of shade, grow under pines, whose seedlings cannot endure it.

Exploring the plant world in autumn

Some of the most beautiful colors of fall are shown by weeds and other small wild plants. Amaranth (also called pigweed) often blazes into deep red; the smooth green leaves of pokeweed, a much taller plant, turn scarlet. The stems of these plants change to beautiful reds and purples. Leaves of common milkweed take on a dull gold color, often flecked with beautiful patterns of black specks.

Some flowers bloom far into the fall season — white snakeroot, New England aster, Michaelmas daisy (really another aster) and, in the woods, the mysterious thin yellow petals of witch hazel. In most of the United States and Canada the aster continues to bloom bravely as the days grow chillier and its few remaining friends among the butterflies and bees limp as if the cool nights gave them rheumatism. One twilight in late November, I found that another late survivor was one of our commonest flowers. Plodding home from a day's tramp I plunged into an icy swamp to capture a yellow flower that gleamed on an elevation surrounded by cold water. Had I discovered a new species of plant? I found that it was the familiar evening primrose.

Preserving your finds

You can derive a great deal of pleasure from simply watching the ever changing pageant of the plant world. You can add to your enjoyment immeasurably by bringing home mementos of your jaunts through wood and meadow and swamp, whether you intend to make a permanent collection of flowers or leaves or plants, or to grow live plants or to set up beautiful floral displays.

A fine collection of flowers and leaves is a source of never ending satisfaction and entertainment. Leaves often look more beautiful after they have been pressed, dried and mounted on paper than they did while alive. One reason is that we do not pay so much attention to any particular plant or leaf when it is surrounded by thousands of others. But when we see mounted leaves of fern and meadow rue and Queen Anne's lace, we become fully aware of their intricate and delicate designs. Flowers are a bit harder to prepare than leaves, but are often even more effective. The most interesting specimens of all are entire small plants, or the tops of larger plants, showing flowers and leaves still on the main stem.

A vasculum (shown at the left) keeps flowers, leaves and entire small plants fairly fresh.

Unless you keep your flowers and leaves sufficiently moist, they will be crumpled and faded long before you reach home; if this happens, you are not likely to prepare worthwhile mounts. Professional plant collectors carry a long, oval metal box, called a vasculum, which is sold by biological supply houses. The vasculum keeps the plants fairly fresh; it is particularly valuable if you wish to study a whole plant or to grow it later. Instead of using a vasculum, you can wrap your plants in waxed paper as you gather them. In either case, you must freshen the specimens when you come home by putting them in water if they have become crumpled or faded.

You can even start to press and dry leaves, flowers and small plants as you collect them by carefully inserting them between the leaves of a pulp-paper magazine. (Pulp paper is much more absorbent than smooth or slick paper.) Spread out the plants or plant parts as you put them between the pages and be sure that different specimens do not touch one another. Number the plants as you collect them, writing on the paper that holds each specimen; add the name (if you know it) and the place and date of collection. If you put this information in your notebook, set down the number of the plant beside the facts.

To dry your specimens when you get home, you can use a plant press, which you can purchase from any biological supply house. You can easily make your own plant press. Place specimens individually between sheets of newspaper or other absorbent paper. Separate the sheets that are in direct contact with the specimens with several other sheets of newspaper. Make a stack 6 inches high, or less, put it between 2 sheets of plywood, each 12 inches by 18 inches, and then apply pressure by means of 2 cloth or leather straps, one at each end of the plywood sheets. Every 24 hours open up the press, remove and replace the moist sheets of paper and repeat the process with fresh paper. Continue until the sheets of paper are dry when you remove them from the press. Your specimens are now ready to be mounted.

An even simpler method of drying plants or leaves is to spread out your speci-

Plant press made of two sheets of plywood and two straps. Place specimens between newspapers that are separated from other specimens by additional sheets of paper.

Above: Plant specimen mounted on herbarium paper by first dipping the specimen in a film of glue that has been spread over a sheet of glass. Right: Herbarium sheet on which the specimens are taped down by strips of paper.

mens flat between sheets of newspaper, build your stack and put your heaviest books on top of the stack. Renew the papers every twenty-four hours. Some of the plants and leaves I prepared in this way have remained in perfect condition for twenty years.

Professional botanists mount their specimens on regular herbarium paper — thin cardboard cut to standard size of 11½ by 16½ inches. However, you can do an excellent job with any fairly stiff paper or thin cardboard. Before you apply the glue, move your dry specimen around on the mounting paper until you have the best arrangement. Do not allow leaves to overlap; if necessary, trim off some leaves or parts of leaves.

You can use either glue or "tin paste," which is used to glue labels on tin cans. Rubber cement is not so satisfactory, since it will eventually discolor. The glue should be rather thin; dilute it with a little water if it seems too thick. To do the best job get a piece of glass as large as your mounting paper and spread a thin layer of glue on the glass with a broad brush. Pick up your specimen with forceps and place it on the glue. Use the forceps to remove the specimen from the glass and place it, glue side down, on the paper. Remove any superfluous glue. To avoid getting glue on your fingers, lay a sheet of wax paper over the specimen while you press down to make sure that the glued side is firmly attached. Put newspapers over the mount

and place your heaviest books on top. Let them remain in position until the specimen is firmly attached to the paper. All of your specimens should be labeled with the name of the plant, the date, the place where the collection was made and your name as collector.

You can protect your mounted leaves and flowers with cellophane covers. Cut the cellophane to a size a bit larger than your specimen and then fasten the sheet neatly in place with Scotch tape. Better still, lay a sheet of cellophane over the mounting sheet, fold an inch of the cellophane at the top and glue this to the back of the mounting sheet. Then fasten the lower edge of the cellophane to the mounting sheet with Scotch tape.

If you want to be able to examine both sides of the specimen, you can make a cellophane "sandwich" without mounting the specimen on paper. Cut two sheets of cellophane to suitable size, spread the leaf or flower between them and finish your "sandwich" by pressing it gently with a warm (not hot) iron.

Leaf skeletons are beautiful and instructive. One of our worst pests, the Japanese beetle, is the best skeletonizer. You can gather hundreds of fine specimens of leaf skeletons under any of the plants upon which this insect feeds, since it eats only the soft parts of the leaf, leaving the tough midrib and veins. If you wish to process your own leaf skeletons, select leaves with tough, prominent veins. First

Left: Leaf prints, created by inking the veined side of the leaf. Above: Spatter prints are made by silhouetting a leaf on paper with India ink.

flatten and dry the leaf; then place it on a cloth and tap it repeatedly with a stiff brush. In this way you will pick away the softer tissues, leaving only the intricate pattern of veins.

It is often better to tape down thick stems rather than to rely entirely on glue; you can use strips of paper, adhesive tape or Scotch tape. Scotch tape is most convenient, but it will eventually dry up. This will not matter unless you wish to preserve your treasures for years. Woody stems, twigs, pine needles and evergreen branches with cones may have to be tied or sewn in position. The mounting paper has to be pretty strong to stand this kind of treatment.

It is very difficult to mount seaweeds and other soft plants, as well as those that have thick, fleshy stems or leaves, such as cactus. It is hardly worth while bothering with specimens of this kind.

Leaf prints generally last longer than pressed leaves and they are most decorative. Ordinary ink will not do for prints of this kind. Printer's ink and linoleum-block printing ink give excellent results; so do the oil colors used by artists. Put a small quantity of the ink or paint on a glass plate. A small rubber brayer, or roller, is generally used to spread the ink evenly over the glass plate. (A small glass bottle, rolled on its side, is sometimes used instead of a brayer.) Place the leaf, veined side up, on a flat piece of newspaper and ink the veins by rolling the brayer back

and forth over the leaf. Now you are ready to make the print.

Place the leaf, inky side down, on a piece of clean white paper and lay a sheet of clean newspaper over the leaf; then run the brayer firmly over the newspaper.

Good prints can be made by pressing the veined side of a leaf against a stamp pad such as is used for inking rubber stamps. Carbon paper and even paint that has just been brushed over a smooth piece of wood can also be employed.

Smoke prints are very effective. Rub candle wax over a sheet of smooth paper so as to form a thin layer. Hold the paper horizontally, waxed side down, and move it over a flame until it picks up a thin layer of soot. Use the soot deposit just as you would printer's ink or oil color.

To prepare spatter prints, use a thick-flowing ink like India ink; slightly diluted poster colors also give good results. The quickest way to make spatter prints is to place the leaf on a clean piece of paper, holding it down with pins or pebbles. Pour a small amount of ink in a saucer, and dip a toothbrush in it; shake off any surplus ink. Hold the toothbrush above the leaf and at an angle to it with the bristles up. Pull the bristles back toward you with a small stick; as they snap back, they throw a spray of colored drops on the leaf and the paper around it.

When you finish with the spattering and remove the leaf, you will have a white silhouette of the leaf against a background

of whatever color you used. Another method is to remove the top and bottom from a cigar box and cover the top with wire screening. Place this over your specimen and rub the inked brush over the top.

Excellent spatter prints can be made by using a spray gun or atomizer. Pour the ink into the spray gun or atomizer; pin the leaf to a sheet of white paper placed on a cardboard support. Now stand the cardboard on end and shoot a fine spray of ink at the leaf from the distance of a foot or two. Be careful not to inhale the spray.

Blueprinting, the method often used to reproduce architects' plans, provides very clear outline prints; so does photographic printing. In the latter case, use printing-out paper, the kind that turns dark when exposed to light. A short exposure will give an outline print; a long exposure to strong light will result in a photograph showing all the veins. Printing-out paper does not need to be developed. After removing the leaf, fix the print for five to ten minutes in regular photographer's hypo (sodium hyposulfite); wash the print for ten minutes and then dry.

You can produce a homemade leaf "fossil" that will resemble the fossils produced by nature. Get half a pound of artist's modeling clay (often sold under such names as "Plasteline" or "Plasticum"); also buy a few pounds of plaster of Paris. You will need an old table or a board on which to work and a dish in which to mix the plaster.

Spread out some of the modeling clay to make a surface a little larger than that of your specimen. Smooth the clay very carefully with a rubber roller or a glass bottle; moisten the roller with a little water if the clay sticks. Place the leaf or other specimen in position on the clay, lay a sheet of paper on top of it and rub the paper with your fingers. Rub hard enough to make a clear impression, especially near the edges.

Now remove the paper and the leaf. (This is the most ticklish part of the job.) Lift the leaf stem first, being careful not to pull away any clay. Your clay mold is now ready. You can engrave your name upon the mold, backward of course, since any writing on the mold will appear reversed in the finished product.

When the mold is ready, prepare the plaster of Paris. Pour water into a pottery or hard-rubber dish; then pour plaster of Paris into the dish until "cracks" begin to form. Mix the plaster and water with a stick or an old knife for a very short time until it becomes a thick, smooth cream. There should be no air bubbles or lumps in the mixture.

Before you pour the plaster into the clay mold, you will need a wall of some

You can produce photographic outline prints by placing your specimen on a sheet of printing-out paper, which is held in position between two sheets of glass.

kind around the mold to hold the plaster while it sets. A small cardboard or wood box will do; a tin box is even better. Pour a spoonful or two of the mixed plaster into the impression and blow on it to make sure that there are no air bubbles. Add enough plaster to fill the mold and the retaining wall. Then tap the table to make any air bubbles rise to the surface. If you wish to hang the finished product on a wall, insert a hoop of wire or string in the plaster near the top. The cast must not be removed until it is set and hard. If your fingernail does not leave a mark when you tap the cast gently, the cast is hard enough to remove. A coating of white shellac will give the cast a glossy appearance and protect it from soiling.

You can make fine casts not only of leaves but also of flowers, fruits, seeds and twigs. With sufficient ingenuity you can produce interesting nature book ends by the plaster-cast method. Striking effects can be obtained by coloring the water that is mixed with the plaster. The cast may also be painted, after it has set and dried, with show-card or poster colors. If the cast is too dry, you will have to immerse it in water for a few minutes before painting.

To use oil colors first apply a very light coat of white shellac. When this dries apply transparent oil colors (the kind used for painting photographs); you can also use colored lacquer or enamel or even fingernail enamel. Do not use too much coloring material in any case. It is best to have the original leaf or twig in front of you while you paint, so that you can imitate the natural colors.

A twig collection is easy to make; winter twigs are particularly suitable. The twigs can be mounted on the same sheet as the leaf or flowers of the plant from which they came, or else they can be kept in small boxes, properly labeled.

Some people like to collect seeds and wild fruits. Flat seeds and small hard seeds may be kept in cellophane envelopes; small glass or plastic bottles are much better containers for parachute seeds with fluffy hairs, such as those of dandelion or milkweed. Paste a narrow label with the name of the plant around each bottle.

Many plants have hard, dry fruits, which can be preserved in bottles. If the fruits are hard enough, they need no such protection; the label may be pasted directly upon them. Some fleshy fruits, such as rose hips, can be preserved for years.

If you want to keep the seeds for planting the next spring, you must be sure not to let them dry out completely. Some seeds, such as those of the bean family, can stand a good deal of drying; oak acorns and various other seeds will die if allowed to dry out. On the other hand, too much moisture may encourage mold. Many

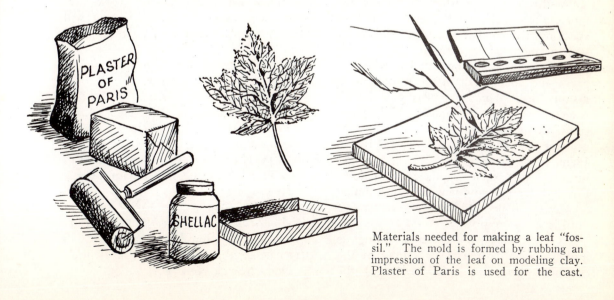

Materials needed for making a leaf "fossil." The mold is formed by rubbing an impression of the leaf on modeling clay. Plaster of Paris is used for the cast.

tree seeds keep best if placed in a box of sand outdoors. A good place for most northern-tree seeds is in a box in the refrigerator.

You can make an unusual home garden from the moss that carpets the soft ground in all seasons of the year. Take a trowel or a dull old table knife and cut out a piece six or seven inches square; this should include the soil or sand under the moss to the thickness of an inch or so. If you cut carefully, the moss will come away in one piece. Wrap this in waxed paper or newspaper and bring it home. Put the moss with the sand and any plants or seeds that came with it in an empty aquarium.

Cover the aquarium with a piece of glass, cellophane or transparent plastic. It should be kept in a place where it gets plenty of light but not too much heat. If you cut the moss in the wintertime, you will be amazed to see new plants appear as if by magic above the moss carpet; they come from seeds or roots that were sleeping through the winter. You can also make a dish garden by putting the moss in a deep saucer or other container and keeping the dish as cool as you can without letting the plants freeze. Moss is most beautiful when kept in a very moist atmosphere.

Certain wild flowers and plants that you pick up in your rambles can be raised in your own garden. Take some soil along with the roots and immediately wrap the soil and roots. If you have to go any distance, moisten the whole plant. Generally speaking, the smaller the plant, the better your chances of keeping it alive. Note carefully the conditions under which it grew; did you find it in the woods, or in a sunny field, or in a dry place or in a spot where it was cool and moist? Unless you can more or less duplicate these conditions at home, the plant will almost certainly die. Plant your specimen, as soon as you get home, to the same depth as in nature. Cover the soil around it with a thick mulch of leaves and be sure that it is kept moist until it starts to grow.

Growing wild plants from cuttings is interesting and often easy. Many of the common weeds and wild flowers of the roadside will thrive if you cut off the top foot or so of the plants and put the stems in a jar of water. Some of the plants will continue to grow; new flowers will appear and so will a tremendous mass of white roots. If this happens, you can plant the specimens in flowerpots or in your own garden.

Exquisite floral arrangements can be made with wild plants. Cut the stems of your specimens long enough to fit the vase or dish you intend to use. Don't take flowers whose petals fall off at a touch; don't take too many flowers; don't take rare plants. Keep your specimens moist as you carry them; wrap them, not too tightly, in newspaper or wrapping paper. Oiled paper is better and aluminum foil, which is more expensive, is better still. You can use the oiled paper and the aluminum foil a number of times if you are careful.

You can prepare an interesting exhibit by cutting slender stems, containing flower buds, from trees and shrubs; the stems should be two or three feet long. Keep the cut ends in containers of water. The buds will soon open indoors; you will have pussy willow blossoms, tiny yellow flowers from sassafras and spicebush, red and green blossoms from different kinds of maples and long catkins, like yellow-gray caterpillars, from the oak.

You will find the following works useful in identifying the plant life you will come upon in the course of your rambles:

MARGARET ARMSTRONG, *Field Book of Western Wild Flowers;* G. P. Putnam's Sons, New York, 1915.

C. H. COLLINGWOOD, *Knowing Your Trees;* American Forestry Association, Washington, 1946.

ETHEL H. HAUSMAN, *Beginner's Guide to Wild Flowers;* G. P. Putnam's Sons, New York, 1948.

F. SCHUYLER MATHEWS, *Field Book of American Wild Flowers;* G. P. Putnam's Sons, New York, 1955.

RUTHERFORD PLATT, *This Green World;* Dodd, Mead, New York, 1942.

THE MAKING OF MOUNTAINS

The Cycles of Building and Decay

THE poetic phrase "the eternal hills" is quite apt if we consider it in terms of the short span of human life. Viewed from the standpoint of geologic time, however, the oldest mountain range endures no longer than a single night's dream in the life of a man. From Pre-Cambrian times down to the present, the perpetual process of building and destroying mountains has continued. Massive cordilleras like the far-flung Andes may be the product of millions of years of sedimentary deposit and buckling of the earth's crust. The volcanic cone of Kilimanjaro, on the other hand, probably came into being with comparative abruptness, like the new volcano of Parícutin, Mexico, which was formed in 1943.

Geologists call mountain building "orogeny" (from two Greek roots meaning "the rise of mountains"). Three different kinds of processes are involved. In the volcanic process, isolated peaks are thrust up as the earth's internal heat pressure comes into play. Volcanic action occurs more often in ocean depths than on land, since the area of the sea is so much greater. Numerous submarine volcanoes are active in the sea's hidden recesses and may one day break through the surface. The second process is that of denudation and erosion by which high plateaus are gradually shaped into peaks and ridges by the denuding effect of the elements and the erosive action of rivers. A good example of an original plateau now worn into the form of mountains is the Catskill range in southern New York State. The Grand Canyon of the Colorado reveals the operation of erosion on the plateau above the Colorado River. In a few million years the entire area will have been formed into jagged peaks and clefts by the river.

The third way in which mountains arise is through the deposit of successive layers of sediment, either on the floor of a shallow sea or in a broad trough of sinking land known as a geosyncline. In the course of successive geological epochs, this sediment accumulates to such an extent that severe stress is created in the earth's crust. Other factors, such as the heat pressure in the interior of the earth and the presence of radioactive elements in the surrounding rock, have been suggested by geologists to explain the gradual upthrust of the layers of sedimentary deposit. The whole process is a very lengthy one and most probably alternates between extensive periods of slow rise and sudden thrusting up of sharp peaks.

The Appalachian mountains of the eastern United States were once a mass of geosynclinal sediments, such as we described above. More than half a million years ago, the present site of these mountains was occupied by a narrow trough (geosyncline), filled with the waters of the sea. Immediately to the east of the trough was an ancient landmass, to which the name Appalachia has been given by geologists. Present opinion holds that Appalachia was probably a series of islands, forming an arc off the eastern coast of North America. It is thought that Appalachia supplied most of the sediments to the sea that stretched between the island arc and the large continent to the west.

As the trough was filled with the debris eroded from the mountains and plains of Appalachia, its sediments turned into rocks. Following a few minor episodes of mountain building, these rocks were finally folded and uplifted into mountain belts, not once but several times, beginning

about 200 million years ago. Erosion brought these peaks low after each uplift. The present Appalachians are worn-down remnants of mountain chains that may once have rivaled the Himalayas in splendor.

Evidence for these mountain-making processes is conclusive. Fold mountains are composed primarily of bedded sedimentary rocks that often contain fossilized remains of sea animals and plants. After many fruitless attempts to explain these fossils in other ways, scientists have gradually come to accept them as proof of the origin of certain mountains (or of their remnants) from rocks formed under water. The mountains themselves need not have arisen from the depths of the sea, which may have vanished from the area before mountain building began in earnest.

Sediments may be regarded as the raw material of orogeny. They represent the rock fragments and soil weathered from already existing lands and mountains and carried by rivers into the sea, where they slowly accumulate layer upon layer. When several miles of sediments have gathered on top of each other in a mass hundreds of miles long, much of it already hardened into rock, the main mountain-making process starts, as described on the preceding page. It is intermittent at first, but finally reaches a grand climax of folding, faulting and upthrusting.

Whence has all this sediment come? To answer this question, let us consider present-day erosion processes. By way of example, the Ganges and Brahmaputra rivers of India and the Mississippi River of America together contribute nearly a billion tons of sediment to the oceans in one year. Increase this figure by the additional amount of sediment transported by the other large rivers of the world and multiply it by hundreds of millions of years. You would then have some idea of the staggering quantities of sands and muds involved.

Since mountains, including those derived from former sedimentary deposits, are themselves an important source of such material, it is not surprising that the supply of sediment appears to be almost limitless. Even today, the rocks of the Appalachian region are estimated to be still several miles thick in places. The ultimate origin of this sedimentary rock is the apparently inexhaustible reservoir of the earth's interior, which from time to time emits vast quantities of molten rock. The latter then solidifies and is later eroded.

Fold mountains themselves, however, do not give a real inkling of the tremendous masses of sediment that went into their creation. When sediments become rock, there is great shrinkage in their volume. Later these rocks are folded and compressed into a still smaller space. One must remember, also, that even existing mountains have undergone considerable erosion.

Geologists have attempted to reconstruct the original extent of the deposits making up some of the major mountain systems of the world. In extreme cases, the folding and faulting alone represent a "shortening" of the earth's crust measurable in miles. Yet even today we come upon ancient rocks that have scarcely been disturbed, proving that much sediment, including that derived from the same sources from which mountain-forming sediment came, have never been involved in orogenic processes. This reveals the superabundance of sediment available for geologic activities.

Not only have mountains originated from the bottom of vanished seas, but they have often been submerged long after their formation, and then re-elevated. The record of their submergence may be read in the deposits that settled on them while they were under water. These later deposits may lie at various angles to the original bedding of the mountains, since they were formed on slopes and ridges.

How can we explain or understand the powerful forces that folded and raised gigantic masses of rock into mountain ranges? Geologists have offered various theoretical explanations, some of which we shall discuss later in the article. Orogenic forces act very slowly and imperceptibly over long ages of geologic time. Fold mountains are not created in sudden upheavals.

Originally, when layers of sediment were deposited on the bottom of the sea, they must have been primarily flat and horizon-

tal. When we examine built-up mountain systems, such as the Rockies or the Andes, we find that the various strata, or layers, are anything but horizontal. They have generally been crumpled in such a way that they form a series of folds. In these, there are crests and troughs suggesting those of ocean waves. The crests, or archings, of the folds are called anticlines; the troughs, or downfoldings, are known as synclines.

A syncline is distinguished from a geosyncline by the fact that the latter is a vast downarching in the earth's crust measuring hundreds of miles in length. Synclines are generally much smaller, sometimes only a yard across. Corresponding to geosynclines there are tremendous uparchings of the crust known as geanticlines, which dwarf ordinary anticlines. Geosynclinal and geanticlinal structures are complex.

In some places, the strata have become fractured. Should the two sides of a rock crack become displaced in relation to each other, the crack is called a fault. Gigantic faults may extend for hundreds of miles; sudden movements along them often lead to severe earthquakes.

Anticlines, synclines and faults indicate significant distortions of the original arrangement of sedimentary layers. Such dislocations may be so extreme that beds which were once undermost are now uppermost. In many cases only the study of fossils and of other features in these beds may indicate their original sequence.

There is little to suggest that the stratified, or layered, rocks have been crumpled to form mountain ranges by forces acting directly in a vertical path. As a matter of fact, these distortions are of such a

Geologists examining a fault in sedimentary rock in Weldon County, California. A fault is a fracture in the earth's crust, accompanied by displacement of one side with respect to the other side.

Homer Page—Texaco

nature as to show that horizontal forces acted parallel to the rock beds. However, vertical forces have been responsible for a certain amount of folding and uplifting.

The drifting
land mass theory

Some geologists hold that vast land masses have shifted horizontally for long distances. In so doing they have collided with other land masses, causing the uplift of the earth's crust at the scene of the collision. According to this theory, the Alps and the other mountains of southern Europe were formed as the African continent moved northward and met the land mass to the north. The Rockies and the Andes resulted from the westward movement of the two Americas. The mountain chains of southern Asia were raised as the Asiatic continent drifted southward.

The supporters of the "continental drift" theory point to the fact that if, for example, we set the eastern part of South America against the western part of Africa, the margins of the continents would fit together surprisingly well. This proves, they say, that what is now South America broke off from what is now Africa and drifted away from it. But what forces caused huge continents to break apart in the first place? What forces caused them to be transported for thousands of miles? These questions have not yet been answered.

According to another theory, the great pressures deep within the earth have caused a steady increase in density and a corresponding decrease in volume. This means that the core of the earth has been constantly shrinking. The outer shell of the earth has collapsed as the earth's core has shrunk away from it; the result has been the deformation of the crust. This process has been compared to the wrinkling of the skin of an apple as the fruit gradually dries out and therefore shrinks.

The cooling-and-
shrinking theory

Still another theory is based on the idea that the earth's crust has been shrinking as its interior has been cooling and there-

fore contracting. This hypothesis was particularly popular when it was generally believed that our planet consisted of a thin crust enclosing a hot, molten interior. We now assume that in the main the earth's interior is solid; yet the cooling-and-shrinking theory still has a great many supporters. They maintain that even though the interior of the earth is not in a molten state, as scientists formerly believed, it is very hot; they also hold that it is gradually cooling, contracting and causing the crust of the earth to shrink and become deformed.

Supporters of the shrinking-crust theory believe that the existing deformations of the earth's crust give us some idea of the original area of our planet's surface. It has been estimated that the crumpled folds of the Alps represent a shrinkage of seventy-four miles in the earth's circumference, and that the crumpling of the Coast Ranges of California represents a shrinking of about ten miles.

The ingenious
theory of G. H. Darwin

The English astronomer George H. Darwin proposed an ingenious theory, at the turn of the present century, to account for the formation of mountain chains. He held that the earth was originally more flattened at the poles than it is now. In the course of time it became more spherical and, as it did so, it contracted particularly at the equator. It would seem logical that a shrinkage of this sort would cause lateral pressure to be applied in the region of the equator and would cause mountain chains to arise in that area. But how can we account for the fact that so many mountain ranges have an approximately north-and-south direction?

Darwin theorized that this was brought about by the influence of lunar tides and the rotation of the earth. These forces, acting together, would have a twisting effect on the earth's crust and would produce corrugations, or wrinkles, at right angles to the direction of greater pressure. "In the case of the earth," he wrote, "the wrinkles would run north and south at the equator . . . Any wrinkle when once formed would have a tendency to turn

The magnificent Alpine peak known as the Weisshorn rises 14,778 feet in the Swiss canton of Valais.

When rock strata are subjected to pressures beyond their elastic limits, they buckle, forming a series of alternating crests and troughs.   Above, we see a typical crest, which is known as an anticline.

slightly so as to become more nearly east and west than when it was first made."

This theory has few supporters at the present time. The tremendous forces that Darwin mentions could have acted effectively only in the youth of the world, before the formation of the world's mountain chains. Besides, the Darwin theory does not account for the evident relationship existing between the laying down of sediments and the formation of mountains.

Millions of years of sedimentation preceded the emergence of the Alps and the Carpathians from the sea. The same sequence of sedimentation followed by uplifting is evident in the mountain ranges of the North American continent, east and west. The American geologist James Dwight Dana observed that "the region over which sedimentary formations were in progress in order to make finally the Appalachian range reached from New York to Alabama, and had a breadth of 100 to 200 miles . . . The pile of horizontal beds along the middle was 40,000 feet in depth. The pile for the

Wasatch Mountains was 60,000 feet thick . . . The beds for the Appalachians were not laid down in a deep ocean, but in shallow waters, where gradual subsidence was in progress; and they at last, when ready for genesis [that is, for the actual mountain-raising process] lay in a trough 40,000 feet deep, filling the trough from brim to brim." The Laramie range, which extends from southeastern Wyoming into Colorado, is a curved spur of the great Rocky Mountain system; it was reared from sediment 50,000 feet deep.

Babbage's mountain-
building hypothesis

Whatever, then, the explanation of mountain chains may be, it has to account for their sedimentary beginnings. Various theories have been advanced to explain how mountains have arisen from sedimentary formations. An English geologist called Babbage offered an explanation that won considerable favor at one time. According to Babbage, the heaping up of sediment

THE MAKING OF MOUNTAINS 219

on the ocean floor must cause a rise in the temperature of the former floor, since the temperature of the earth increases with depth. A thousand feet of sediment deposited on the ocean bottom would cause the area that it covered to rise to about 20 degrees Fahrenheit. At the same time, the erosion of land surfaces by wind, running water, weathering and other factors would cause a lowering of temperature in other areas below the earth's surface, since they would not lie so deep as before.

Babbage held that the uneven heating of adjacent areas accounted for the formation of mountain systems. The areas where temperature had been raised as a result of sedimentation would become weakened and would be affected more than before by the lateral (sidewise) pressure exerted by the adjacent layers, whose temperatures would be lowered. Hence the pressure would cause the heated areas to be forced upward.

The English geologist T. Mellard Reade proposed a modification of Babbage's theory. He suggested that the sediment plastered on the floor of the sea would act like a strip of nonconducting material on the surface of a cooling ball of metal. It would retain and raise the heat of the part of the earth's surface that would be covered. In time, this sedimentary strip would be heated itself above the average temperature of the crust. The excess of heat would cause the sediment and the underlying rock to expand. Expansion laterally or downward would be restricted; hence the affected area would be forced upward, "as a cake expands upward on being baked."

Is mountain-building due to radioactivity?

Another geologist, John Joly, held that radioactive materials, accumulating in the earth's crust, brought about a rise in temperature that weakened the earth's crust in many places and caused the buckling that has brought about the formation of mountains. "Given a local source of heat [radioactivity] applied above, while the normal heat of the earth flows upward from

In this photo, we show the trough, or downfold, of a rock fold; it is called a syncline. At first, the anticlines form ridges; the synclines, valleys. Often the crests are leveled as a result of erosion.

beneath, and the area where these conditions exist must necessarily become the first place of yielding and flexure, as naturally as the rupture of the chain occurs at the weakest link."

Isostasy and
mountain building

It was quite generally held at one time that mountain building was due to isostasy (from two Greek words meaning "equal stability"). Isostasy is still a valid concept insofar as it refers to the maintaining of equilibrium in the earth's crust. This is brought about as large-scale earth movements in one area are counteracted by compensating movements in other areas. According to the concept of isostasy, segments, or blocks, of the outermost shell of our planet are more or less in balance with each other and weigh about the same. Uplands and mountains are underlain by rocks of a density less than that of the rocks beneath lowlands and the ocean bottom. The mountains and plains may be said to "float" in a layer of still denser rock under them. This deep layer has been compared to a liquid, although it is actually a plastic solid that "flows," or deforms, very slowly under high pressures.

The uplands resemble icebergs and the lowlands, ice floes, floating in water that is denser than they are. True, a berg in itself is larger and heavier than a floe. The former, therefore, floats deeper and has a large "root" of ice projecting down into the water and displacing it. The iceberg thus is supported by a "column" of water much shorter than the one holding up the ice floe.

In the earth's crust, isostatic adjustment by deep rock flow is a response to non-isostatic forces causing unbalance and strain in other rocks.

The older theory of the formation of mountains through isostasy was as follows. A sea bottom would be filling with sediments eroded from an adjacent mountain tract. As they would accumulate and press on the bottom, the latter would be down-warped into a trough, which would reach the crustal substratum, or flow zone. The substratum rocks would move toward the mountains, to compensate for the sinking trough and for the lightening of the mountains by erosion. The latter would rise, but less so with each successive uplift. There would be a limit as to how far the geosyncline would descend, also, and so the subcrustal flow would slacken. The transfer of vast amounts of sediment across the earth's surface was considered one of the prime movers in the building of mountains. This transfer plus the isostatic responses to it were supposed to have produced mountain ranges.

Isostasy is considered today as inadequate either to develop geosynclines or to cause orogeny. For example, certain very deep trenches in the ocean floor are underlain by rocks less dense than those of nearby mountainous lands. Obviously these rocks, here not supporting heavy loads of sediment as yet, were not pushed down so far by isostatic movements. Other forces, whose nature is still in dispute, must have been responsible for this situation.

Isostasy may, however, trigger off mountain-building forces. As the rocks of the geosyncline sink into the flow zone, the heat in this region softens and weakens them. The stronger rocks surrounding the geosynclinal layers at a somewhat higher level then fold and fault the latter by lateral (sidewise) pressure. Many of these layers thus become thickened; moreover, the lowermost ones are downfold farther into the zone of flow. These lower strata form a root of light material forcibly pushed downward into the denser part of the earth's crust. There is a limit as to how far this can go, however. Eventually the folded mass may tend to rise, or "float," higher. Also, continuing horizontal pressures may at last force the crumpled beds to "ride" or be bowed upward against or over the more resistant rocks around them. Molten rock material rising through the sedimentary layers probably helps raise them also.

Erosion of
mountain ranges

As soon as newly born mountains arose, the eroding effects of air and water began to carve them into peaks, now not half so

Above, we see a typical fault near Atoka, Oklahoma. A fault is a fracture in the earth's crust—a fracture along which slipping has occurred. It is most easily detected in a sedimentary rock formation.

high as they were originally. Wind and rain, frost and ice and snow and the mighty force of running water have been diligently at work for millions upon millions of years, and the wear and tear have been tremendous. Fifteen or twenty thousand feet have been removed from the ancient mountains of Wales. From the mountains in the Lake District of England and from part of the Appalachian range, in the eastern part of the United States, over twenty-five thousand feet — a little less than five miles — have been worn away. At one time there was a sedimentary layer fifty or sixty thousand feet deep above what is now the Simplon, an Alpine pass reaching an altitude of something like sixty-five hundred feet. The Laramie range in the Rocky Mountains would be about thirty-five thousand feet high today, on the average, if it had not been eroded to such a marked degree.

It is interesting to note that the original ridges, or anticlines, wear away much faster than the troughs, or valleys or synclines between them. The reason seems to be that anticlines are more exposed to erosive forces than synclines.

Anticlines are eroded so much more rapidly than synclines that in some cases the original relationship between these two types of folding has been reversed. The syncline has now become the mountain crest, and the anticline has become the valley. This reversal has taken place in the Appalachian Mountains, for example; the mountain summits of this range were originally synclines, the valleys anticlines.

The rate of wearing away of mountains and the shape to which they are worn depends on various factors. One of these is the direction followed by the strata that compose them; another is the material of which they are composed. Limestone is worn away quite rapidly and it generally assumes a curved pattern. In certain instances, it may take the shape "of ruined

masonry, suggesting crumbling battlements and tottering turrets." Although granite resists the action of the elements longer than limestone, it, too, is subject to denudation and is often worn into huge square blocks. Granite mountains rarely have sharp peaks; they are usually rounded and massive like Pikes Peak, the crown of which is naked granite. The lofty, jagged peaks of the European Alps, which constantly challenge the skill and courage of the mountain climber, are composed of gneiss and mica schist, hard crystalline rocks. These high, barren elevations are of more recent formation than the mountain chains of low rounded tops and uniform slopes like the Adirondacks.

The snow-covered crests of the Hindu Kush Mountains in central Asia, rising more than 24,000 feet above sea level in places, are of more recent origin than the more graduated Himalayas. Although a single peak of the Himalayas, Mount Everest, towers over 29,000 feet above sea level and is the grandest of all mountain tops, the Himalayan range is for the most part considerably lower than Everest.

The average height along the central axial line of the Himalayan peaks is not more than 20,000 feet above sea level. This mountain range is the result of a very long series of upheavals and depressions with a geological record going back to Pre-Cambrian times in the oldest beds. In this most ancient process the sharp upthrusting of Mount Everest is of comparatively recent origin.

This illustrates that within the history of a particular mountain chain the rate of uprising may vary considerably. Thus in the Himalayas there exist three plainly defined periods of development, beginning in the north and working south. It is probable that the initial process was a violent crumpling of the earth's crust along the southern margin of the great tableland of central Asia. The gradual character of subsequent changes is indicated by the undeviating courses of the Indus and Brahmaputra rivers, cutting deep gorges through the mountains.

This immense intrusive mass of solidified igneous rock was uncovered by the erosion of the overlying stratum.

U. S. Geol. Survey

Changes taking place in any given area may ultimately result in widespread effects over the whole mountain range. Thus the process of denudation — the stripping and weathering of mountain peaks by the elements — may be compensated by a gradual rise in the base elevation through faulting and folding of the earth's crust. The geologists who favor the theory of isostasy (which, as we saw previously, emphasizes the dynamic balance of forces) maintain that the effects of denudation (stripping) are offset by the elevation of the base. In Sweden, for instance, much of the land is gradually rising out of the sea. In some districts the pine forests of mountainous slopes have been elevated beyond the timber line into regions of perpetual snow, where the trees have been killed by the cold. The coasts of Scotland are notable for their rock terraces, rising one above the other to a height of seventy-five feet from the sea, illustrating an upthrusting of the land.

This increase in base elevation is often accompanied by the intrusion of great batholiths, igneous rock with a toughening core of granite, into the lower part of the mountain. Unlike extrusive rock, intrusive masses of igneous rock are prevented from reaching the surface of the earth but may act as a massive lever to elevate the surface strata. It is possible, however, that an intrusive mass lying near the surface may be in time uncovered by the action of the elements.

The interior heat
of the earth at work

Igneous rock is, as its name implies, molten rock from the interior of the earth. The earth's interior heat is constantly exercising a pressure against the upper strata of rock, creating folds and faults in the crust through which the igneous rock pushes. The original molten rock is cooled and solidified in the process of reaching the upper layers. It distributes itself in various forms such as the gold-bearing saddle reefs of South Australia or the domes and cupolas that are to be found in the tin regions of western Cornwall.

U. S. Geol. Survey

The pinnacled walls of a hogback mountain in southern California thrust sharply from tree-lined, sandy slopes.

In estimating the relative age of the mountains and the varying periods of their formation, certain yardsticks are employed by the geologist. Marine fossils have already been mentioned, and these are useful within definite limits. It seems evident, however, that the very extreme antiquity of the earth is hardly encompassed by the available marine fossils, highly complex forms obviously resulting from a long evolutionary process.

To supplement the fossils, the evidence of radioactive elements in the rocks of the earth is called on. All radioactive minerals found in rocks are a form of geologist's clock. There is a constant measurable rate of disintegration of the radioactive element that determines within close limits the age of the rocks. This wonderful self-operating clock reveals the earth to be several billion years old — much older than had once been supposed.

See also Vol. 10, p. 270: "Mountain-building Forces."

THE TWENTIETH CENTURY (1895-) X

BY JUSTUS SCHIFFERES

THE ROAD AHEAD IN SCIENTIFIC RESEARCH

THE scientists of one generation can never tell what developments the next generation will bring about. Certainly the physicists of the 1890's never dreamed that the apparently immutable law of gravitation laid down by Newton would be successfully challenged by Einstein. The chemists of the 1890's would have been appalled to learn that their neatly ordered system of indivisible atoms was a delusion; that the atom, far from being indivisible, is a miniature world consisting of many parts. The biologists of the same period did not have the slightest inkling that the study of genetics would be revolutionized by the discovery first of genes — the tiny bearers of hereditary traits — and the further disclosure that genes are in fact molecules, consisting of giant-size long chains of nucleoproteins.

It is clear that any attempt to point out the road ahead in science must be largely guesswork; we shall have to assume, too, that mankind will be too wise to blow itself up with H-bombs. Yet, with the reader's permission, we are going to risk some guesses — "predictions" is the more dignified word — about what science has in store for mankind. These guesses are based, as far as possible, on past achievements and present trends.

It seems altogether likely that in the future, as at present, important contributions will be made by organized scientific groups. Teams of scientists, trained in different disciplines, will pool their knowledge in order to attack major problems. They will be backed by the mighty resources of government agencies, private institutions and voluntary societies. Industrial-research laboratories will study many of the basic problems of science and technology. In all these joint undertakings, great numbers of obscure individuals will toil selflessly, each contributing his bit. They will advance the horizons of pure scientific research, conquer many human ills and create new industrial processes.

It is likely, however, that future scientific progress will not depend entirely upon such organized undertakings as we have mentioned. To quote the eminent American scientist, Irving Langmuir, a Nobel Prize winner in chemistry: "Only a small part of scientific progress has resulted from a planned search for specific objectives. A much more important part has been made possible by the freedom of the scientist to follow his own curiosity . . . It is not reasonable to expect that directors of laboratories or boards set up to direct scientific work are supermen who can foresee new knowledge before it exists."

The future of science will rest, then, to a considerable extent, with the individual scientist of genius, endowed with great ability, insatiable curiosity and infinite perseverance. "Genius flashes forth like a meteor, unproduced and unpredictable," wrote the American astronomer Forest Ray Moulton. "It is not limited to any race of people, or to any particular latitude or longitude. It has often come up from obscurity and has flourished under poverty and persecution as well as under the smiles of Fortune . . . At present we can only hope that it will come often."

Fortunately, genius has a way of asserting itself in every age. We may feel confident that there will be future Aristotles,

Bacons, Galileos, Newtons, Lavoisiers, Faradays, Pasteurs, Freuds and Einsteins to provide new insight into the eternal mystery of the universe.

There is every reason to believe, too, that earnest amateurs will make at least some contributions to the future development of science. Businessmen and factory workers and housewives will scan the heavens in search of hitherto unknown comets and satellites and radio signals; they will call the attention of biologists to new species of animals and plants; they will take part in statistical surveys. In other ways, too, they will make valuable forays into the realms of the unknown. Yet the sheer increase of the number of men and women devoting themselves to scientific research will add to the likelihood of the "happy accidents" of discovery chiefly befalling trained scientific minds.

Into what paths will these devoted professional and amateur scientists penetrate? It seems probable that the electron microscope, magnifying beyond 200,000 diameters, will open many a new vista, especially in the sciences of genetics and virology (the study of viruses and virus diseases). With the 200-inch Palomar Mountain telescope and other giant telescopes that are yet to be built, more and more of the heavens will be revealed to mankind. Rockets and satellites and space ships soaring hundreds, or thousands or millions of miles above the surface of the earth will help solve the mysteries of outer space.

The science of nucleonics, dealing with the phenomena of the atomic nucleus, will offer a fertile field. Through tagged atoms — radioactive isotopes — men will learn more about the mysterious borderland between the living and the dead, the organic and the inorganic worlds. Atomic energy will be harnessed more fully than it is now. The physical properties of matter under the bombardment of atomic bullets will be more fully analyzed. Today the nucleus of the atom is almost unknown territory. It will be fully explored and mapped out accurately in the years to come; it will also be exploited to a far greater extent than has hitherto been possible.

We still have much to learn about the process of aging — the subject matter of the new science of gerontology. Reputable scientists maintain that the average span of life of the human race can be increased to 150 years. They hold, too, that the diseases that now beset the aged will be conquered. Some day, they say, men will wonder at Shakespeare's famous description of old age (in As You Like It, Act II, Scene 7) as

". . . second childishness and mere oblivion, Sans [without] teeth, sans eyes, sans taste, sans everything."

The ideal antiseptic, the ideal anesthetic still remain to be found. We have much to learn about photosynthesis. Some future investigator, perhaps, will find a way to carry on artificial photosynthesis — that is, to manufacture food in sunlight, as plants do. Psychologists will look into the possibilities of mental telepathy. Emotional illnesses will be better understood and more readily cured. Mineral treasures will be extracted from the oceans. Progress in the seeding of clouds will bring abundant rainfall to crops.

Scientists are already working on the problem of travel in space; informed opinion holds that the first trip to the moon will take place between 1970 and 1975 and that the limits of the solar system will be explored by spacecraft before the year 2000. Some day, indeed, man's crust of earth may be so densely populated that interplanetary migration may be a grim necessity as well as a great adventure.

Radio astronomers have already set up a listening watch and are sending out signals to try to determine whether there is intelligent life on other planets within or beyond the solar system. The possibility of such a discovery, though it is infinitely small, is not zero.

World-wide communication by bouncing electromagnetic signals off earth-circling satellites is already well beyond the planning stage. In fact, radio waves have already been reflected from such satellites. In August 1960, the sound of the human voice was transmitted from California to New

Perkin-Elmer Corp.

BAKER-SCHMIDT TELESCOPE

Jersey by way of the United States satellite *Echo I* at the first try. We should see a well-established system of satellites sent into orbit for communication purposes within a decade or so.

Significant results may be confidently expected in the development of materials able to resist extraordinary heat and friction. The cermets—that is, ceramics bonded with metals — offer great promise in this field. Such new materials are urgently needed for spacecraft and also for the practical utilization of atomic energy.

Power plants based on atomic fission are already in operation; they provide electric energy for industrial and domestic use. We also use nuclear energy, released by atomic fission, to propel submarines and surface ships; it seems likely that we shall have nuclear-powered aircraft and spacecraft before long. Power by the process of atomic fusion is in the offing; it will involve the transformation of hydrogen to helium, releasing great amounts of energy. Once power from atomic fusion becomes a reality, the heavy hydrogen in the ocean will provide vast stores of energy.

At the present time, we are witnessing a "technological revolution" in which nineteenth- and twentieth-century develop-

ments in science and technology in the western world are being quickly adopted and exploited by the so-called "underdeveloped" countries. This revolution has already proceeded very rapidly indeed in Red China, and it is sweeping many countries of South America. It will probably be a reality in Africa within half a century.

"Life in a test tube" — the duplication of the chemical conditions under which life arises — already seems within our grasp; but this goal may be rather more elusive than it now seems.

The increasing application of scientific and technological methods to the convenience of working and living is inevitable. Electronic computers, or "electric brains" (which can never outthink man), point the way to performing quickly by machine a great number of tedious mental tasks, such as extensive astronomical calculations, compiling statistics for insurance companies and data-processing for inventory and production control. Computers have already served for translation and indexing through the application of the KWIC ("key word in context") system.

We shall shortly have drugs as powerful against virus infections as present antibiotics are against bacterial diseases. New

Brookhaven National Laboratory

**BROOKHAVEN NATIONAL LABORATORY
NUCLEAR REACTOR**

drugs will also be available for the alleviation of mental illness. The conquest of cancer and heart ailments — with an increasing life span for man — is coming through application of the all-important new concept of molecular disease. This concept considers disease at the infinitely small level of atoms within molecules. Do not scoff at these predictions of things to come; remember that a great many of the fantasies of yesterday have become the realities of today. Unquestionably there are limits to human achievement; but who knows what these limits are?

In the chapters of this group, we have given an outline of science as we can write it today. By following the map of the history of science, you can reach its outposts; beyond that, you are on your own. Some of you who read these lines of SCIENCE THROUGH THE AGES may pass beyond the "endless frontier" of present scientific knowledge and may help to write the history of science of the future.

FUTURE SPACE FLIGHT

"Science is adventure — man's great adventure with the universe," said the American botanist Edmond Ware Sinnott. If the annals of science are any criterion, there will never be a lack of scientific adventurers to face the unknown.

This is the last chapter of *Science through the Ages.*

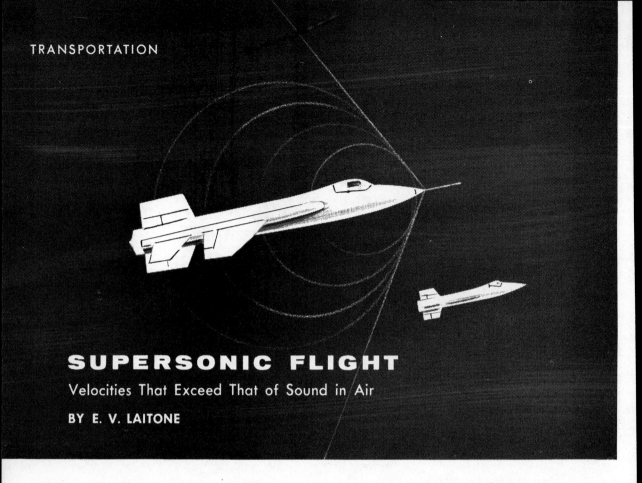

SUPERSONIC FLIGHT

Velocities That Exceed That of Sound in Air

BY E. V. LAITONE

THE term "supersonic" refers primarily to the flight or motion of any solid body through a gas at a velocity that exceeds the velocity of sound in that gas.* When we speak of sound in this connection, we have in mind the pressure variations that move outward in all directions, in the form of waves, from a "disturbance" such as the tooting of a horn or the roar of a lion.** The waves in question are usually very weak. When they strike our eardrums, they set up vibrations that are recorded in the brain so that we "hear" the disturbance that set off the waves. Of course, these pressure variations, or sound waves, as they are generally called, exist whether or not they strike our eardrums and result in the sensation of hearing.

Sound waves traveling through the atmosphere near the earth's surface have a velocity that decreases continually with alti-

tude. It ranges from 1,120 feet per second (762 miles per hour) at sea level, under standard conditions of temperature and pressure, to 970 feet per second (660 miles per hour) at an altitude of 36,000 feet. Then it remains constant to 82,000 feet altitude, after which it starts to increase.

Suppose that the velocity of sound in the atmosphere at a given altitude is 700 miles per hour. A plane traveling at 1,400 miles per hour is moving twice as fast as the velocity of sound; we would say that it has attained a supersonic velocity of twice the speed of sound. Supersonic velocities are not restricted to solids traveling through gases. Strong sound waves, such as those set up by an explosion, travel at a velocity greater than the very weak sound waves that we described above.

The speed of any supersonic flow is usually given in terms of the Mach number, named after the Austrian physicist Ernst Mach (1838–1916). The Mach number represents the ratio of the speed of a body to the speed of sound in the surrounding atmosphere. For example, the expression

* Editor's note: "Supersonic" is derived from the Latin words super: "above" or "more than" and sonum: "sound." The science that treats of speeds exceeding that of sound in air is called supersonics.
** Editor's note: The formation of these pressure variations is considered in detail in the article An Analysis of Sound, in Volume 5.

"Mach 2" applied to a supersonic aircraft means that its velocity relative to the atmosphere is twice the velocity of sound passing through the atmosphere.

The Mach number can also be applied to subsonic speeds — that is, speeds less than the speed of sound. In this case, also, it represents the ratio of the speed of a body to the speed of sound in the atmosphere. The Mach number, in the case of subsonic speeds, is always less than unity (that is, less than 1). For instance the Mach number .9 refers to flight at nine-tenths the speed of sound.

A plane traveling at subsonic speed is preceded by the sounds or pressure waves that are caused by its flight. But since a plane in supersonic flight travels faster than sound, it gives no advance warning of its coming. In other words, it is preceded by a "zone of silence." In World War II, the German jet-propelled device called the V-1,* traveling at the subsonic speed of some 300 miles per hour, was preceded by the sound waves caused by its passing, and it could therefore be heard before it arrived. But the terrible weapon called the V-2 traveled at supersonic speed. It could not be heard until after it passed by, and therefore it struck without warning.

At subsonic speeds, then, the sound or pressure waves travel faster than the body

* Editor's note: The "V" stood for *Vergeltungswaffe,* or "weapon of vengeance."

producing the waves. The waves spread out; they become closely spaced ahead of the moving body and they expand behind it, as shown in Figure 1. To a stationary observer, there are more waves per second ahead of the approaching body causing the waves; the frequency increases. There are fewer waves per second behind the body leaving the stationary observer, so the frequency is decreased. This is the familiar "Doppler effect" (see Index); it accounts for the fact that a train whistle has a higher frequency (that is, has a higher pitch) upon approaching than it does upon leaving.

At supersonic speeds, the sound source travels at a speed greater than the velocity of sound propagation and would tend to produce the wave pattern shown in Figure 2. Note that the sound waves would begin to be propagated *after* the object had passed by a given point. Since time would be consumed while the body traveled, the oldest of the waves would have the largest radius at any given moment, while the most recent wave would have an extremely small radius. In either case, the waves at any given moment would be limited by the zone of silence. They would form a cone called a Mach wave (also known as a Mach cone and Mach envelope), bounded by the zone of silence.

As the Mach number increases — that is, as the velocity of supersonic flight increases — the cone becomes progressively

1. At subsonic speeds, the pressure waves travel faster than the body producing them. They become closely spaced ahead of the moving body and expand behind it.

2. At supersonic speeds, the pressure waves are propagated after the body producing them passes by a given point. They form a cone that is called the Mach wave.

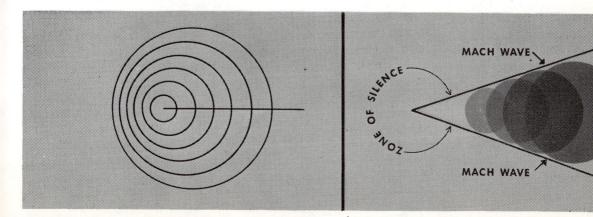

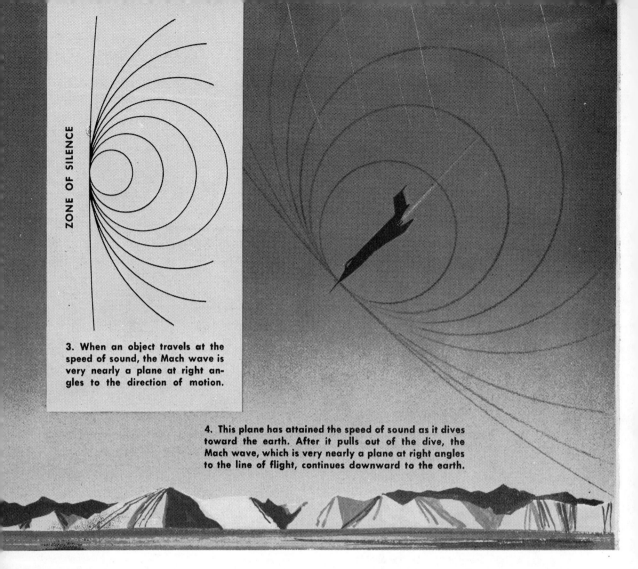

3. When an object travels at the speed of sound, the Mach wave is very nearly a plane at right angles to the direction of motion.

4. This plane has attained the speed of sound as it dives toward the earth. After it pulls out of the dive, the Mach wave, which is very nearly a plane at right angles to the line of flight, continues downward to the earth.

narrower; it becomes progressively wider as the Mach number decreases. Finally, when the Mach number is 1 — that is, when the object is traveling at the speed of sound, the Mach wave is no longer a cone but more nearly a plane at right angles to the direction of motion (Figure 3).

Suppose an airplane traveling at subsonic speed dives toward the earth. It may attain sonic speed during the dive pull-out. (Sonic speed is Mach 1, or the speed of sound.) The pressure disturbances can pile up at the Mach wave or envelope, which by this time resembles a plane at right angles to the line of flight (Figure 4). After the airplane has recovered from its dive, this envelope can continue downward until it reaches the ground and can make itself felt as a disturbance, called a sonic boom.

A plane traveling at supersonic speeds can bring about a supersonic boom even in steady, level flight. This cannot occur at subsonic speeds, since the increase in pressure produced as the plane passes through the air is spread over an unlimited area, and therefore results in a very small increase in pressure over the earth's surface. However, at supersonic speeds the pressure increase can be propagated only behind the envelope bounded by the zone of silence. It is this concentration of the pressure disturbance that can produce a supersonic boom. If the airplane is flying very low, the pressure concentration can be serious enough to damage an ordinary roof top.

Drag forces in subsonic and supersonic flight

An object moving forward through the air is retarded by it to a greater or lesser extent, since the air or any gas has friction. A plane in subsonic flight is preceded by

the pressure waves it creates as it makes its way through the air. These pressure waves push away the air in front of the plane and there is less drag than would otherwise be the case. But when the plane reaches sonic speed, or the speed of sound, the pressure waves no longer precede the plane. They no longer push away any of the air in front of the craft and the drag forces become much greater. The large drag rise as the plane approaches Mach 1, or the speed of sound, is generally referred to as the sonic barrier.

Even a conventional subsonic plane traveling at a speed below Mach 1 can encounter an extreme rise in drag. This is why. As the wing moves through the air, the pressure over the wing is decreased. This results from the increase in the speed of the air stream over the wing in accordance with the law of physics called Bernouilli's principle.* Because the pressure decreases, the temperature is also lowered. Now the increase in velocity of the airflow over the wing directly increases the local Mach number — that is, the speed at this particular place, while the decrease in temperature of the air flowing over the wing directly decreases the local speed of sound.** This leads to a still greater increase in the local Mach number, since this number indicates speed in relation to the speed of sound. Eventually, if the plane is going fast enough, the local Mach number will become supersonic, even though the flight Mach number remains subsonic — that is, even though the plane is still flying at a speed less than that of sound.

When this condition is reached, a shock wave arises and returns the flow over the wing back to subsonic conditions. The local shock wave on the upper surface of the wing reduces the lift. It can also cause the airflow to separate from the wing and can produce a severe buffeting of the rear tail surfaces. To avoid such buffeting, the rear tail surfaces are generally raised

quite high behind the wing of an airplane that travels at speeds approaching the speed of sound.

This high-tail position is not altogether effective. The airflow disturbance caused by the shock waves mentioned above lessens the so-called "downwash" on the tail and thereby increases the static stability of the airplane. By "static stability" we mean the tendency of a plane to point itself automatically in the wind, like a weathercock. This makes the craft more difficult to maneuver. In some cases it has been found impossible to pull an airplane out of a high-speed dive with the available elevator-control surface motion. This can lead to rather disastrous results.

A supersonic aircraft is confronted by much the same difficulties as it moves through the transonic range — that is, the range of speeds from slightly less than Mach 1 to slightly greater than Mach 1. Hence it generally tries to pass through this range as quickly as possible.

Supersonic aircraft are provided with swept-back wings as indicated in Figure 5 in order to minimize adverse effects on control and stability. Up to a certain speed, the Mach waves produced by each segment of the swept-back leading edge (the foremost edge) of the wing push back much of the air in front of the plane. The flow can then proceed smoothly about the

5. Supersonic aircraft are provided with swept-back wings in order to ensure maximum control and stability.

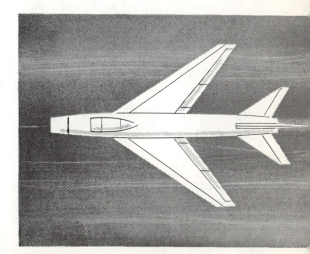

---

* *Editor's note:* Bernouilli's principle states that if there is an increase in speed, there is a decrease in the pressure for any fluid or gas flow, and vice versa.
** *Editor's note:* The speed of sound in a gas decreases as the temperature is lowered.

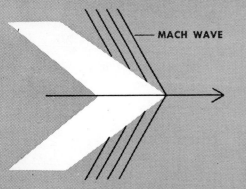

6. Up to a certain speed, the Mach waves push back much of the air in front of the plane; hence no shock waves are formed.

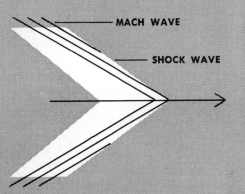

7. As the flight Mach number increases, the Mach waves become parallel to the leading edge of the wing; shock waves are formed.

8. The nose of a plane designed to travel at high supersonic speeds must be as sharply pointed as possible for maximum efficiency.

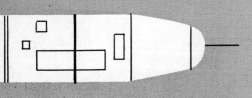

9. The intercontinental ballistic missile (ICBM) is provided with a blunt nose. The text explains why this design has been adopted.

remainder of the wing without forming a shock wave (Figure 6). As the flight Mach number increases, the Mach waves eventually become parallel to the fixed leading edge. By then shock waves have formed on the wing, as shown in Figure 7. Hence, the degree of sweepback on the wing is dictated by the flight Mach number desired. The higher the Mach number, the greater the degree of sweepback.

The leading edge of a swept-back wing actually performs best even at supersonic flight speeds if it is rounded, but only if the Mach waves lie ahead of the leading edge, as in Figure 6. When the leading edge lies ahead of the Mach waves, as in Figure 7, it must be razor sharp in order to decrease the shock-wave losses. The nose of such a plane must be as sharply pointed as possible (Figure 8).

Unlike the supersonic airplane, the nose cone of the intercontinental ballistic missile (ICBM) is provided with a blunt nose (Figure 9). The ICBM travels beyond the atmosphere and attains a speed of thousands of miles per hour. As the nose cone of the missile, freed from the other stages, re-enters the atmosphere, it has a velocity close to 5 miles per second or 18,000 miles per hour; it possesses a kinetic energy of 10,800,000 foot-pounds* per pound of nose cone. The major portion of this energy is converted into heat as the cone descends through the atmosphere. The blunt nose produces an extremely strong shock wave in front of it and, to a great extent, it is the atmosphere itself rather than the nose cone that is heated. Another effect of the blunt nose is that instead of minimizing the drag, as would a sharply pointed nose, it causes a much larger drag force. As a result, the nose cone is quickly decelerated and its velocity is soon reduced to nearly sonic speed. This reduces the effects of heating caused by friction between the nose cone and the molecules of the atmosphere.

Such high speeds as those characteristic of the re-entry nose cone are defined

---

* *Editor's note:* A foot-pound is equivalent to the work done in raising one pound avoirdupois against the force of gravity the height of one foot.

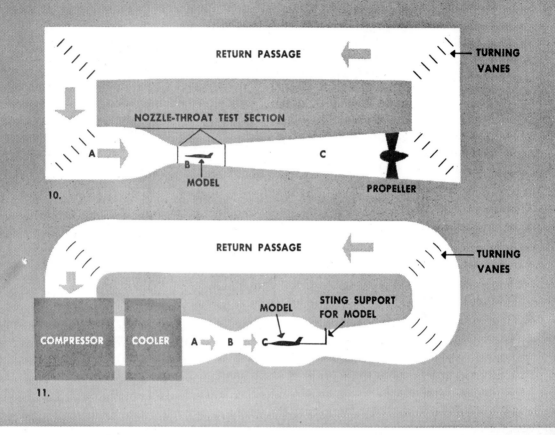

10. This wind tunnel is used to test aircraft performance at subsonic speeds, up to Mach 1. The test model is set at B; the higher the speed, the smaller the test section.

11. Wind tunnel designed to test the performance of aircraft flying at supersonic speeds. To counteract interference effects, the model is mounted on a sting, or boom.

as hypersonic; the Mach number for such speeds ranges from 7 to 20. The temperatures behind the shock wave of the nose cone are so high that some of the gas molecules in the atmosphere are broken down into atoms and some of the atoms can even become ionized.

Experimental tests on subsonic and supersonic flight

Much of our knowledge of the phenomena of subsonic, transonic and supersonic flight is derived from tests carried out in wind tunnels. The apparatus shown in Figure 10 can be used for subsonic wind-tunnel tests for speeds up to Mach 1. The airflow is nearly always maintained by means of a propeller downstream at C. The wind-tunnel model is placed in the nozzle throat (B), which is called the test section. The size of the nozzle throat varies, in different installations, depending upon the speed desired; the higher the speed to be

tested, the smaller the test section. For tests of speeds approaching Mach 1, the cross section of the nozzle throat is only a few square feet in area. At low, subsonic speeds, the cross section can be very large; for example, it is 40 feet by 80 feet in the full-scale wind tunnel operated by the National Aeronautics and Space Administration (NASA) at Moffett Field, California.

Sections A and C of the wind tunnel, in Figure 10, are generally connected by means of a return passage. This contains turning vanes at each corner in order to return the air supply smoothly from C to A. The velocity in a subsonic wind tunnel such as this can be increased by increasing the revolutions per minute (rpm) of the propeller. The highest Mach number in the nozzle throat is limited to unity (1).

To test aircraft flying at supersonic speeds, a wind tunnel such as that in Figure 11 is used. In this case, section C is the test section. Because interference effects

become greater as a plane attains super-sonic speed, the mounting of a model in a supersonic wind tunnel offers considerable difficulty. Generally the model is set on a long sting, or boom, which extends quite far downstream behind the model. The boom contains a series of gauges which measure electrically the stresses produced in the simulated supersonic flight.

If the area at C is decreased, the super-sonic Mach number is decreased and the re-quired operating pressure is higher. If the area at C is increased, the Mach number is also increased and the required operating pressure at C is lower. Hence supersonic wind tunnels that attempt to run tests at several Mach numbers must possess the equipment to vary the cross-section area at C as well as the operating pressure. This is generally done by increasing the pressure at A by means of air compressors, as shown in Figure 11, while the area at C is altered by having a flexible or movable section be-tween B and C. Great care must be used in making the necessary adjustment in cases such as these.

Supersonic wind tunnels require con-siderably greater horsepower for steady operation than do subsonic wind tunnels. The power requirements range from 1,000 horsepower for a 9-inch test-section diam-eter, to 60,000 horsepower for the 6-foot-by-6-foot test section of the supersonic wind tunnel at the Ames Aeronautical Laboratory of the NASA at Moffett Field, California.

Experimental tests on hypersonic flight

The speeds and the temperatures en-countered by the re-entry nose cone are so high that at present experimental tests can be carried out only on an extremely small scale. Most of these tests are performed in an apparatus called the shock tube (Fig-ure 12), which consists of a long pipe with a small diameter. A very small nose-cone model is mounted in the low-pressure end. This is temporarily shut off by a thin metal or plastic diaphragm from the high-pres-sure gas in the high-pressure chamber. The pressure ratios between the low-pressure and high-pressure parts of the pipe range from 1 to 100 to something like 1 to 10,000, in order to simulate Mach numbers from 7 to 20.

When the model nose cone is ready for testing, a trigger mechanism is set off and the diaphragm is punctured. A slug of high-pressure gas from the high-pressure chamber rushes past the model; the net effect is as if the model were traveling at hypersonic speeds.

12. Tests on re-entry nose cones are conducted in a shock tube, a long pipe of small diameter. The tube is blocked up by a diaphragm; when this is punctured, high-pressure gas rushes into the chamber that contains the model.

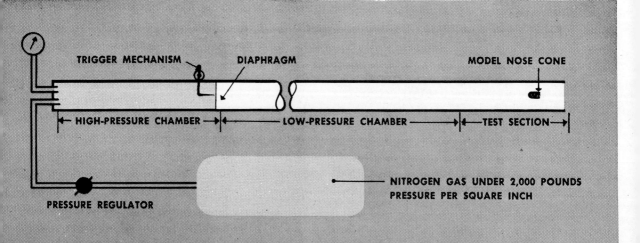

TRIGGER MECHANISM   DIAPHRAGM   MODEL NOSE CONE

|← HIGH-PRESSURE CHAMBER →|←——— LOW-PRESSURE CHAMBER ———→|←—TEST SECTION—→|

PRESSURE REGULATOR

NITROGEN GAS UNDER 2,000 POUNDS
PRESSURE PER SQUARE INCH

The automatic pumping station of an oil pipeline in Louisiana, seen from its control center.

result of the furnace's heating action. This result, the temperature, is constantly measured by the thermostat, compared to the desired result and fed back to the furnace to adjust its further heating action. In this case we have what is called a closed sequence — a circular chain of events — in which all the elements are interdependent. Most automatic controls are closed-sequence systems like this one.

Closed-sequence control systems can be used to regulate almost any process as long as three requirements are fulfilled. The controlled quantity must be measurable; there must be some way to regulate this quantity; measurement and regulation must be rapid enough for the job at hand.

Systems designed for very precise control must respond appreciably to tiny fluctuations. However, such highly sensitive systems tend to "hunt," or oscillate above and below the desired point, when a change occurs. In some cases, this oscillation is merely due to inertia. When the automatic fire control of a heavy antiaircraft gun calls for a five-degree rotation, a set of servomotors begins to move the gun. Once in motion, the momentum of the massive structure may carry it more than five degrees, and the servomotors will then move it in the opposite direction. The momentum may again carry it too far, and so on, resulting in a steady oscillation. This kind of overshooting is easily prevented by designing the regulator to take less cor-

rective action when the error is diminishing, and more when it is increasing.

Hydraulic, electronic and photoelectric instruments have been developed that can measure the smallest variations and amplify them almost without limit. These instruments lie at the very heart of our present accurate and flexible control systems. With such new tools, for example, the miniature motions of a flyweight pointer can precisely control the movement of an artillery weapon weighing hundreds of tons.

Automatic devices are now so common in our everyday lives that few people even take notice of them. Many public buildings have operatorless elevators; some of these even use tape-recorded messages to instruct passengers who thoughtlessly hold up their progress. Automatic volume controls on our radio and television sets continuously adjust to changes in reception. The automatic dial-telephone system that forms the backbone of modern communications is one vast feedback network.

The highest development of automatic control systems to date has been reached with electronic computing machines. In these assemblies of wires, relays, vacuum tubes, magnets and other elements, some of the simpler functions of the human brain are duplicated, but with many times more speed and efficiency. In processing data and performing calculations, these miraculous instruments require only min-

THE RISE OF AUTOMATION

The Industrial Revolution Takes a Step Forward

by EDWIN J. BROWN

A NEW word has appeared in the language of engineers, management executives, educators and social philosophers — "automation." This word is becoming more and more important, both to specialists and to ordinary people; for automation is now a major trend of twentieth-century civilization. The word was coined by management engineers as a less awkward form of an earlier word — "automatization." In its narrow sense, automation is merely the use of machines designed to regulate themselves without human operators. In a broader sense, automation is an economic pattern in which the principles of automatic control are applied to production on a large scale.

In the process of mechanization that has gone on since the eighteenth century, machines have improved on man's hands. With automation, machines are designed to judge and adjust their own operations, thus entirely replacing human operators.

Though automation seems a completely modern phenomenon, it had its beginnings at the time of the eighteenth-century Industrial Revolution. In 1788, James Watt designed a centrifugal governor to control the speed of his steam engine. The governor was geared to the engine by a belt and pulley, and consisted of a vertical shaft on which two arms were crisscrossed in scissors fashion. The arms were weighted at their lower ends; as the engine speed increased, the spinning arms were flung outward by centrifugal force, operating a linkage that reduced the engine's steam supply. When the engine slowed down, the reduced centrifugal force caused the arms to drop, thereby increasing the steam supply. In this way, the engine could be made to run automatically at a more or less constant speed. This type of governor, with minor modifications, is still used today.

The next major development of automatic control was Isambard K. Brunel's invention of a steering motor to turn the heavy rudders of ocean-going steamships. A device of this kind was installed on his ship, the Great Eastern, which was launched in 1858. An inlet valve, admitting steam to a cylinder, was opened by turning the helmsman's wheel. An ingenious "follow-up" linkage constantly compared the angle of the rudder to the angle of the wheel, and closed off the steam as the rudder swung around to the desired position. This early steering motor was the prototype of the modern servomotors — "enslaved" motors that use the principle of feedback to supply varying amounts of power according to the demands of a controlling mechanism.

By feedback we mean that the results of a regulator's actions are "fed back" to it — react upon it — causing it to modify its further behavior. We can illustrate this principle by looking at a familiar example — the thermostat in one of our automatic gas-heating systems. When the room temperature goes above a chosen thermometer setting, the thermostat decreases the flow of gas to the furnace, dropping the temperature to the right level. If the temperature falls below that setting, the thermostat increases the flow of gas, raising the temperature accordingly.

The operation of feedback in this system is clear. The room temperature is a

AUTOMATION
AT WORK

The name "automation" is given to the use of machines designed to regulate themselves, generally by means of automatic controls. In a broader sense, automation may be considered as an economic pattern in which automatic control is applied to large-scale production. Automated systems are already in wide use in industry and they have brought about an amazing increase in production.

In its modern application, automation consists of three main elements: (1) integrated machinery; (2) electronic computers; (3) feedback control.

INTEGRATION. In this phase of automation, a number of individual machines are joined together to form a single huge machine. The work piece is brought from one point of operation, or "work station," to another by means of automatic handling devices. A work unit of this type is known as a transfer machine, because in it the work is automatically transferred from one point to another. A given work piece enters the input end of the transfer machine in unfinished form and comes out from the output end as a completed product. As piece follows piece through the machine, production advances in a continuous flow.

A rough casting passes through the different stations of a transfer machine. From this, it will emerge as a finished cylinder block, ready to receive the many parts that will be fitted in it and to it.

The program is fed into the computer system from punched cards, punched paper tape, magnetic tape, or manually from a keyboard or a series of switches.

COMPUTER. The digital computer, which forms a basic part of automated systems, performs mathematical operations at very nearly the speed of light and can make choices or comparisons between two or more alternatives. It generally consists of five units. (1) In the input unit, the problem is fed to the machine by the programmer. (2) Information is stored in the storage, or memory, unit. (3) The arithmetic, or computing, unit does the necessary calculations. (4) The control unit acts as a timing device, making necessary circuit connections in the system. (5) The output unit records the results of the computations.

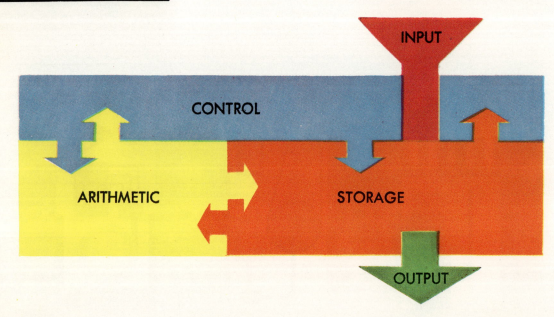

The simple type of windmill shown at the left represents one of the earliest examples of the feedback principle. The rudder of the windmill is mounted at right angles to the propeller. As the rudder is moved this way or that by the wind, it continually reduces the error in the direction of the propeller, so that the latter is kept heading directly into the wind.

WIND

WIND

FEEDBACK. In a fully automated operation, the so-called closed-loop system of feedback is employed. There are sensing, measuring and control units in such a system. The sensing unit keeps careful watch over the manufacturing process or the finished products. Any deviation from a predetermined standard is relayed immediately to the measuring unit (computer). The latter determines the amount of error involved, and it sends this data on to the control unit ef the machine. The control unit makes the necessary adjustments, so that the machine can again operate according to the "program" that was set for it.

FEEDBACK

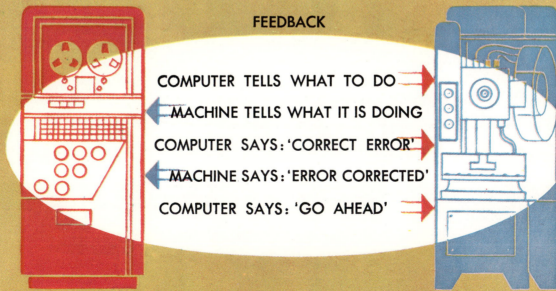

COMPUTER TELLS WHAT TO DO

MACHINE TELLS WHAT IT IS DOING

COMPUTER SAYS: 'CORRECT ERROR'

MACHINE SAYS: 'ERROR CORRECTED'

COMPUTER SAYS: 'GO AHEAD'

AUTOMATION IN AN OIL REFINERY

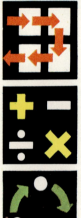

A fully automated polymerization unit has been set up at a Port Arthur (Texas) refinery. This unit converts various gases, produced when crude oil is "cracked," into high-octane gasoline. It accomplishes this by the process of polymerization, whereby molecules are "hooked together" to form larger molecules. The reaction in question takes place in beds of phosphoric acid, serving as a catalyst. An electronic computer in the polymerization unit measures pressures, gas flow and temperatures and calculates catalyst activity. Then it weighs these factors and decides what the processing unit should do to get maximum production for the least cost. It sets the controls to bring about desired changes in operation and it rechecks its figuring. Through an automatic typewriter, it writes a continuous detailed report as it works, explaining fully what it is doing.

CONTROL PANEL

AUTOMATIC TYPEWRITER

COMPUTER

utes or hours to carry out tasks that would take a team of expert mathematicians many weeks.

Electronic computing machines are widely used to solve a variety of mathematical problems. They are also playing an increasingly important part in the everyday work of the world. Three million accounts of one insurance company are now handled automatically by electronic machines; the constant revision of actuarial tables is accomplished in the same way. Researchers of the Bell Telephone Laboratories have developed a system that automatically times individual telephone calls, records billing data, assigns it to the correct subscriber and prints the appropriate billing forms.

Automatic controls have largely replaced men in various industries in which a break in the flow of production would ruin the product. Chemical and petroleum plants are now almost completely automatic, from the injection of crude materials, through the processing reactions to the final packaging for shipment. The chemical concentrations, heat and pressure throughout the processes are too extreme and require too much constant testing and adjustment for human control. Meters and feedback control systems have solved the problem.

A small group of engineers is still required to monitor the operation from a central control room. The end product is tested in a separate laboratory, and the results are sent back to the engineers for necessary corrections in the process. New methods of continuous end-product analysis, however, may soon be introduced to make these plants completely automatic.

In the United States, at least one fully automatic factory is already in existence. U. S. Industries, Inc., a company in Rockford, Illinois, now operates such a plant, making 155-millimeter artillery shells for the United States Government.

Automatic controls are indispensable in atomic-energy production; men cannot work too near the nuclear reactors because of the dangerous radiations that accompany the splitting of atoms. Automatic regula-

tion also avoids the possibility of a disastrous explosion caused by a slight error in human judgment or the slowness of human reactions.

The need for faster, cheaper production in modern mass industry has created the greatest demand for automation. Even the cutting of complicated high-precision parts is now done by self-regulating machines, in one smooth and rapid operation. The process no longer has to be interrupted to measure the work, compare it to specification, reject errors and make necessary adjustments; automatic controls perform all these tasks continuously.

The speed of these self-regulating machines is almost unbelievable. For example, in the Ford Motor Company's Cleveland plant, rough engine blocks go through 530 automatic operations in an assembly line, emerging as finished engine assemblies only 14.6 minutes after they enter.

Automation penetrates our lives more deeply every day; its effects have made themselves felt not only in science and industry but in politics, education and so-

Armour and Co.

Machines that automatically separate and peel frankfurters, and then drop them on a moving belt for packaging.

cial behavior as well. As people become more conscious of these effects, they are beginning to wonder what the ultimate consequence will be. Undoubtedly, there are both good and bad sides to automation, as there are to every technological advance.

Already the automation of industry has greatly increased its productive capacity, in relation to costs as well as in total volume. This productivity will help to satisfy the needs of our increasingly industrialized civilization; it will also make possible shorter work hours and smaller labor forces. Some labor leaders fear that the replacement of human workers by automatic factories will result in "technological" unemployment. While this danger cannot be ignored, automation has already led to the expansion of many industries and the development of some entirely new ones, providing additional employment.

For example, in the United States alone, over 1,000 companies now manufacture control systems and their various parts. In the future, automation may provide employment opportunities of which we do not now have the slightest idea.

Automation has led to the development of remote-control weapons of overwhelming destructiveness, such as the thermonuclear bomb and guided missiles, against which there is little or no defense. Such weapons are still in their infancy; it is not pleasant to contemplate what they will be-

come in the future when they are perfected. Yet some people think that the situation has its redeeming features. The possession of such terrible weapons by both sides in an international dispute may well serve as a deterrent to future wars.

Will all industries ultimately use automation? As far as we can see, the answer is "No." Since the cost of installing automatic control systems is great, they would probably not be worthwhile for small industries employing highly skilled labor; here the volume of production is not the important factor. Automation will also hold little attraction for industries whose products are subject to seasonal variations in demand or frequent changes in design. To be fully efficient, automatic production systems must be allowed to run continuously for long periods of time while making a single product.

Disputes over the value of automation will undoubtedly continue, but it is definitely here to stay. New developments and applications of automation are continually being found. The theory of feedback control systems has provided new tools and ideas for research in many fields, and promises to throw light on the functioning of man's brain and nerves. The release of atomic energy and the development of automation may well be ushering in a new era — a second Industrial Revolution even more significant than the first.

Ford Motor Co.

This gigantic device automatically machines newly cast cylinder blocks for V-8 automobile engines.

THE TAMING OF THE WILD

How Animals Have Become Man's Allies

FROM the forbidding plateaus of Tibet to the arid tablelands of Patagonia, man is dependent upon animal life. We do not have to go far afield to discover that this is so. A farmer in our own country may surround himself with all kinds of ingenious mechanical gadgets, but he will generally have to have many animals if he is to carry on his work. Cattle, sheep, pigs, dogs, chickens, ducks, geese — all these play an exceedingly important part on the farm or on the ranch. Horses have been replaced by mechanized vehicles to a considerable extent, yet they are still valuable co-workers on many ranches and on certain farms.

Some beasts and birds supply us with food or clothing, or both; we keep others to give us pleasure. Dogs and cats in big cities often serve no other purpose than to provide their owners with companionship or amusement. Certain birds, such as parrots, love birds and canaries, serve the same purpose; so do goldfish, tropical fish and such unconventional pets as hamsters and white mice.

In this chapter we shall deal with dogs and with certain animals providing us with food and clothing. There is a steady demand for the beef products, milk, butter and hides provided by cattle, for the lamb, mutton and wool that we obtain from sheep and for the eggs and flesh of poultry. Eliminate such products from the list of those that are available to man, and our civilization would be in a bad way.

The problem of finding suitable food for the great numbers of people in our large cities would become terribly difficult. A varied diet calls for more than the fruits and vegetables and cereals that we obtain from our fields and orchards. Deprived of the different food products supplied by the beasts and poultry of the farm, city people could hardly be properly fed. Many would have to depart from their homes and wander, nomadlike, in search of a more substantial diet.

The elimination of animal products would also greatly complicate the clothing problem. To be sure, a good deal of our clothing nowadays is made from plant products, and our chemical laboratories have developed certain effective substitutes for wool and leather. Yet we still use great amounts of wool for garments, and millions of people throughout the civilized world continue to wear shoes, boots and other articles that are made of leather.

The white men who first settled in New Zealand would probably never have won a foothold in that strange land if they had not brought domestic animals with them. For the islands of New Zealand were almost entirely lacking in animals that could be domesticated. There were only small primitive reptiles and no mammals except for two species of bats. Birds were the lords of the islands — birds that, unmenaced by foes, had lost the use of their wings and in some instances (as in the case of the giant moa) had developed great bulk. The Maoris, who had immigrated to New Zealand from the Polynesian Islands long before the coming of the white man, had added only one animal to those already existing on the islands — a dog that has now become extinct.

When the English landed in New Zealand in the nineteenth century, the animals that they brought with them — horses, cattle, sheep, pigs, dogs, poultry — were as essential for the settlement of the new land as the colonists themselves.

The first of the animals to be domesticated was the dog. While there is no way of knowing exactly how the long association between man and the dog started, there is enough evidence so that we can make some reasonable conjectures. Archaeologists digging in cave deposits and kitchen middens have found numerous bones obviously gnawed by dogs. It seems likely, then, that the domestication of dogs was the more or less direct consequence of early man's haphazard garbage-disposal methods.

We also know that man was a hunter for thousands of years before he turned to herding and farming. Therefore, the first use to which the dog was put was probably that of tracking and running down game. Perhaps a pack of half-tamed wild dogs or jackals ran ahead and brought some large animal or other to bay for the hunter to kill with club or spear. A piece of meat or perhaps the entrails of the victim would no doubt earn the dogs' loyalty and ensure their presence on the next hunt.

In time, man learned that through a combination of punishment and reward, dogs could be trained to perform an increasing number of tasks. Not only did the dog prove teachable, but it was found that through careful breeding, the animal could be adapted to a wide variety of needs.

Starting from a few basic types — the wild dog, the wolf and the jackal — man has produced an amazing variety of breeds. Ruins of the past indicate that the breeding of dogs, as distinct from the mere raising of these animals, began at the very dawn of civilization. The oldest breed we have today is the saluki, a greyhoundlike dog that is used for coursing game in open country. It differs in appearance from the greyhound chiefly in that its ears and tail are "feathered" — that is, covered with long, silky hair. Recent excavations in the area of the old Sumerian Empire, very roughly the region now occupied by Iraq, show pictures of a well defined saluki breed as early as 7,000 B.C. In Egypt, the tombs of the pharaohs indicate that the dog was known there by the third millennium B.C.

The greyhound also appears during this period. From the wall paintings of the time, it appears to have been used for sight hunting on the open plains of Egypt. The breed has been with us for such a long time that even the origin of the name is obscure. It may come from the Latin *Graius:* "Grecian," since it is known that the dog was highly valued by the Greeks. Another possibility is that the Old English *grech* or *greg,* meaning "dog," is the source of "greyhound." It may be, too, that the name comes from the fact that at one time the predominant color of the animal was gray.

Probably the first breeding was more or less accidental. Man may simply have retained, or at least made an effort to retain, the dog types that pleased him most — those that were the most successful in finding game for him.

Some breeds, such as the saluki and the greyhound that we mentioned before, seem so divergent from any naturally occurring stock that it is hard to conceive of their originating purely by chance. Apparently, the ancient Sumerians and Egyptians knew something about various techniques used in the breeding of animals. It is altogether unlikely, however, that they had any knowledge of the basic principles that were involved in this practice.

Today there are three main approaches to dog breeding, or for that matter, the breeding of any animals. The first is inbreeding — that is, animals are bred with their parents or with litter mates. Desirable traits are reinforced in this way, but unfortunately undesirable traits also occur more often, since relatives are more likely to have the same flaws as well as the same virtues. As a result, the inbreeder must constantly prune his stock to eliminate these faults. Of all breeding methods, inbreeding is perhaps the most difficult.

Outbreeding consists of mating nonrelated animals that are thought to possess favorable combinations of traits. Since most thoroughbred dog stocks in the United States come from a relatively small selection of animals imported from Europe, or in some cases from Asia, it is usually hard to find completely unrelated dogs. Hence it is often impossible to bring about true outbreeding in the case of dogs.

Evelyn M. Shafer

Mrs. William J. Worcester

Above: The sprightly little West Highland white terrier.

The fleet greyhound (left) is a popular sporting dog.

Mrs. Florence B. Ilch

The collie (above) was once bred exclusively in Scotland.

FOUR POPULAR
BREEDS OF DOGS

The cocker spaniel (right), a favorite long-haired breed.

Evelyn M. Shafer

The third and most commonly used method is line breeding, in which dogs are mated to distantly related animals. This method enables the breeder to preserve good traits, as does inbreeding, but it does not produce so many congenitally defective animals.

The lengths to which dog breeders will go to obtain the particular qualities desired is well illustrated by the history of the pointer. When it was first being developed about two centuries ago in England, its breeders tried crossing it with the greyhound to give it a little more speed. The dog that resulted was fast enough, but not quite so sturdy as might have been desired. It was hoped that crossing with the bulldog might strengthen the breed a bit, but the resulting creature was still not entirely satisfactory. A strain of foxhound was then added to the pointer's pedigree. The new breed was quite acceptable, except that it was wont to track by foot scent, rather than by body scent, and so the dog could not locate a bird if the latter remained motionless. In time, careful breeding brought back the habit of tracking by body scent, but by this time the animal had lost its old habit of pointing. After some years, careful breeding succeeded in bringing back the pointing habit without losing any of the other traits that had been so laboriously acquired. Eventually, the modern pointer, an excellent hunter, was evolved.

Almost any trait can be bred in or out

Breeders have found by now that almost any trait or combination of traits can be bred in or out, given sufficient time and effort. The wolfhound offers a fine example. By the early sixteenth century, the wolf had disappeared from England. Shortly thereafter, it seemed as if the wolfhound, a huge animal that stood nearly three feet tall at the shoulder, was also going to become extinct for lack of anyone to maintain the strain. An English breeder, G. A. Graham, decided to try to save the dying breed. There were so few wolfhounds left that in order to preserve the strain, he found it neccessary to introduce great Dane and deerhound stock. When the breeding population was again flourishing, he bred out the great Dane and deerhound characteristics and, after some twenty years of crossing, recovered the original wolfhound breed, which still exists.

Breeds that filled a need

Almost all modern breeds were developed to fill some definite need. The only exceptions seem to be dogs such as the pug and the Pekingese, toy specimens that have been developed by scaling down one or the other of the hunting or working breeds. Apart from dogs such as these, practically all the physical characteristics of a breed correspond to qualities that were highly desirable at one time. For example, the strong forepaws and round body of the terrier enabled it to make its way down the holes of burrowing animals.

Dogs whose thick fur serves as protection

The unusually heavy fur of the collie, originally a hunting animal, serves as a protection against the bitter winds of the Scottish highlands. Among the dogs found in northern regions, a double coat is common. There is a layer of fine woolly fur close to the skin and, outside of this, a longer, coarser outer covering. In breeds such as the Malemute and Eskimo dog, the coat offers such effective protection that the animals can sleep outdoors at temperatures of 60° F. below zero.

Some breeds have a distinctly odd appearance because of the particular requirement for which they were bred. The basset hound is an example. It resembles the beagle except that its legs are very short and almost deformed in appearance; for this reason, it is probably one of the slowest of dogs. The trait was maintained because the animal was used for hunting rabbits, and the hunters wanted a dog that would not outrun its master. The combination of lack of speed and fine tracking ability proved ideal in this case. When hunting is done on horseback, the beagle, which is much faster, was often used.

Bison were once the chief source of meat and clothing for the western Indians of the United States and Canada. Today their numbers are growing, and in time these noble beasts may serve again as a food animal.

Canadian National Railways

Even the comic dachshund was developed in Germany to serve a purpose. Its long body and short, sturdy legs with feet well suited for digging made it ideal for hunting the badger. Dachshunds were also employed in hunting wild boar and tracking wounded deer.

The mastiff, which was portrayed in ancient Babylonian monuments, is classed as a working dog rather than a hunter, though it was used for bull and bear baiting. In baiting a bull or bear, the dogs caught and securely held, or pinned, the animal by its ear or nose. The unfortunate beast was often tied or placed in an enclosure so that it could not escape and was torn to death for the amusement of spectators. Mastiffs are now used chiefly for protecting flocks and herds.

By crossing the English mastiff and the pug of southeast Asia, the bulldog was developed for the sport of baiting bulls. Its former occupation gone, the bulldog now makes a gentle pet and guardian for children. The great Dane, which may stand thirty inches at the shoulder, is also related to the mastiffs, for it was the product of crossbreeding the English mastiff with either the Irish wolfhound or the greyhound. Great Danes were developed in Germany to hunt boars. Another kin of the mastiff is the Saint Bernard, which can withstand the storms and rugged terrain of the Swiss Alps and is, consequently, used for rescuing travelers lost in this region. The terriers were originally developed for digging into burrows and putting to rout such animals as badgers, woodchucks, foxes, otters and weasels. The keen-sighted, agile and courageous Airedale terrier is linked to the hounds, since it represents a cross between the otterhound and a terrier of the Aire Valley of England. The bull terrier was a product of crossbreeding the now extinct white English terrier with the bulldog and, consequently, is related to the mastiffs. Terriers are still used for hunting and retrieving and as companions and watchdogs.

The story of domestic dogs is extremely interesting, for in tracing their ancestry we find that they evolved from only one or two basic wild-dog or wolf stocks. No matter how extravagantly unlike its ancestors, every modern breed of dog comes from a line of animals that once had a serious purpose in man's life.

The pig is another important animal taken from the wild to serve men. Wild pigs flourished in Eurasia, Africa and South America, and the modern barnyard pig is not much different from the wart hog of Africa and the swine found wild today in India and Malaya. The time and place where the pig was first tamed is uncertain, but some evidence shows that there were domesticated pigs in China around 2900 B.C. In Europe the pig was not domesticated until more than a thousand years later. Present-day breeds seem to have resulted from crossing Chinese swine with European swine.

We are all familiar with the old phrase "as dirty as a pig," which does these useful creatures a grave injustice. It is true that in hot weather pigs, like their relative the hippopotamus, often take mudbaths to cool off and to rid themselves of troublesome insects. In a wild state, however, they are not dirty creatures. The filth often found in pigsties is rather a commentary on the owners of the pigs than on the animals themselves.

The pig is one of man's most useful domestic animals

Pigs have long been among man's most useful domestic animals. A pig is one of the most economical meat-making "machines" that nature has ever produced. From it come pork, ham, bacon and lard. Almost nothing is wasted, for the pig's bristles, skin and bones are also used in various ways. Pigs are not fussy about their food and will eat either meat or vegetables. Perhaps the finest type of pigs are those that are fed on corn. In earlier days it was the custom to feed them only scraps and left-overs from the kitchen. The flesh of pigs can be preserved for long periods of time by salting or smoking.

Two main types of domestic pigs are found in both Europe and America — the lard type, which is bred for large hams and lard, and the bacon type, bred for the greatest amount of bacon.

There are many kinds of pigs and hogs

One of the true wild hogs, the red river hog, is an African bush pig that lives in low country. It ranges from south to central Africa, though its native habitat is in the marshy fringes of rivers and swamps. Africa also boasts one of the most repulsively ugly creatures in nature, the wart hog. As its name suggests, it has large warty outgrowths on the sides of its face. The eyeteeth of the upper jaw are thrust out to form huge tusks, curving upwards, while those of the lower jaw form similar but smaller tusks. Its body is round and shaped like a barrel. The eyes are high on the animal's head.

The strangest of all the relatives of the pig, however, is the babirusa, a name that it received from the Malays, meaning "pig-deer." In this pig the upper tusks protrude from the upper jaw near the middle line of the face. From there they curve backward until the points sometimes meet the animal's forehead. The lower tusks have a similar upward curve, but are not so thick and long. Many years ago this curious arrangement of tusks suggested to the natives of Celebes and the neighboring island of Buru a similarity to the antlers of the deer.

The wild pigs of the New World are called peccaries

The wild pigs that are native to the New World are called peccaries. There are only two species; one of these is occasionally found as far north as southern Texas and Arizona. Peccaries travel in large herds through the tropical forests. They will fight furiously when cornered, killing any animals that interfere with them. The two kinds of peccaries are the collared and the white-lipped.

Sheep were probably first tamed in Asia

Sheep, which are highly valuable to man, were probably first domesticated in Asia, where they lived on the high, bare plateaus and the mountainsides. While there is no definite proof as to their origin, it is more or less agreed that the domestic sheep of today are probably descended from the red sheep, an oriental breed. We know little about the ways in which earlier peoples made use of sheep, but probably they used their wool in some way, as well as their flesh.

Sheep are ruminants — animals that chew their cud. Grass and other vegetable food is swallowed before it is chewed; it goes directly to one of the sheep's several stomachs — the rumen. Later, when the animal is at rest, the food is regurgitated and thoroughly masticated and mixed with saliva. It then passes through the other stomachs and eventually into the intestines. Cows and goats are also ruminants.

It was not until the nineteenth century that sheep breeders mastered the secret of developing sheep that yielded superior wool and provided high-grade meat as well. The heavy, thick fleece of the modern sheep is the result only of very careful breeding and selection. Allowed to run wild, the animal shows a tendency to revert to its early hairy coat, which is not of any great commercial value.

Sheep are bred for many special purposes

Many breeds of sheep have been developed during the last century and a half. Some are, naturally, more suited to one country than to another. Some of the most famous kinds of sheep have been bred in Great Britain, Spain and France. Many American breeds came originally from these countries. The Merino, one of the most important wool-type sheep, was developed in Spain and later introduced into other countries. Sheep may be bred especially for mutton or for wool. Some types are particularly adapted to life on the mountainsides, others for life in the lowlands; some are bred for their long wool and others for their short or medium wool.

Australia raises more sheep than any other country

Australia produces more sheep than any other country; her annual clip is about 1,400,000,000 pounds. With sheep-raising her most important industry, Australia is responsible for some 29 per cent of all the wool produced throughout the world.

Wild sheep are still plentiful in Europe and in Asia northward from the outer range of the Himalayas, while the Punjab and Sind have their own types. In the United States the Rocky Mountain regions boast their famous bighorn.

The dividing line between sheep and goats is not always sharply defined. Two distinctions always hold true, however. No sheep, either domesticated or wild, is ever bearded, while most goats are. Male sheep lack the strong odor that characterizes the male goat. The goats as a rule inhabit hillier country than the average wild sheep. There is also an important difference in the feeding habits of the two kinds of animals. Sheep prefer to graze on the grass of pastures and hillsides. Owners of great estates often maintained large flocks of sheep to keep the grass of their wide lawns nibbled off. Goats are far from particular in their eating habits and are well-known for their catholic taste. They eat grass, the young shoots of trees, shrubs and even prickly plants. They can thrive where any other domesticated animal would starve. The goat is often the poor man's "cow" in countries or districts where good pasturage is lacking.

Goats are extremely destructive in their eating habits

In their eating habits goats are often very destructive and in some countries have an unenviable reputation. According to Karl Vogt, the famous Swiss naturalist, the goat does more harm in the forests than any other animal. "The old seats of civilization, namely, the countries round the Mediterranean, owe the destruction of their forests, the nakedness of their mountains, and the inevitable consequence of that condition, the dryness of the climate, to the devastation of these animals." It is inadvisable, therefore, to permit goats to run at large where any valuable green things are growing. They will eat even the bark of trees, as well as long-tended hedges and gardens.

The milk and skin of goats have commercial value

With all its faults, the goat has some commercial importance. Goat's milk is highly valued in many places and is often made into cheese. The skin is used in various ways and Eastern primitive peoples still use it to make their tents and some of their clothing.

The wild species include many magnificent animals. Among them are the tur — any one of several wild goats of the Caucasus — some Spanish species and the Rocky Mountain goat. There is no surer-footed or daring climber of giddy heights

IMPORTANT BREEDS OF SHEEP IN

For centuries man has kept sheep for the wool and the meat that they have provided. As he has learned more about animal husbandry, he has been able to crossbreed and improve the varieties of sheep. Today these useful animals are classified as to whether they are mutton or wool types, and as to the length and quality of their wool.

Union Pacific Railroad

A Rambouillet ewe and newborn lamb. This breed, very popular today, is a descendant of the Spanish Merino.

USDA

A handsome Merino ram strikes a dignified pose for the camera. The Merinos produce the world's finest wool.

Lincoln sheep are perhaps the heaviest in the world. The big ram seems unbothered by his straggling "curls."

The Romney is rugged and has short legs. A fashionable "pompadour" of tight "curls" is typical of this breed.

USDA

USDA

THE UNITED STATES AND CANADA

NWGA

NWGA

This Hampshire ram may well look suspicious and wary, for he belongs to a breed used almost wholly for mutton.

A yearling Suffolk ram. This breed, with black face, ears and legs, is primarily one of the mutton breeds.

This Columbia ram, looking down his long nose, is of a breed that can provide you with both wool and mutton.

A Targhee yearling ram. He belongs to a breed that was developed for good wool production and superior mutton.

USDA

NWGA

and precipitous rocks than that picturesque leaper, the wild mountain goat.

Following the order in which the animals were domesticated, we come next to the cattle, including the bison, the buffalo and other forms. Our domestic breeds of cattle are descended from the wild oxen of ancient Europe, Western Asia and North Africa. These oxen were of two chief kinds — a short-horned variety that probably gave rise to such familiar cows as the Jersey and the Guernsey; and a large, long-horned type, called the aurochs, or urus, that may have been partly ancestral to certain other European cattle.

Cattle have been of enormous value to mankind

Cattle have perhaps meant more to man throughout history than any other animal, with the exception of the horse. From his cattle man has obtained milk, butter, cheese and leather. These age-old servants of man have also carried his burdens and provided the motive power for his plows and vehicles.

Gradually, man learned to breed cattle for the characteristics that he most valued. The ancestral cattle were animals possessing enormous horns — sometimes with a span of fifty inches or more. Thanks to careful breeding, the shorthorn today is more numerous than all the other breeds of cattle combined.

European and other cattle differ in ancestry

The humped cattle of Africa and India have a different ancestry than the European cattle have. The cattle of India are probably in some cases descended from the banteng, a wild ox, of the Malay countries. The humped cattle of China and Madagascar may possibly have had an African origin.

The gaur, a magnificent and splendid wild ox of India, sometimes reaches a height of six feet at the shoulder. The gayal of India is only slightly smaller than the average gaur and is partially domesticated in Assam and elsewhere. It is said that sometimes herds of these animals, allowed to roam more or less at will, interbreed with the wild gaur.

Usage and habit have long accustomed us to accept the term "buffalo" for the mighty animal that once roamed our prairies. Actually, there is no true American buffalo. Our "buffalo" is the American bison, and these animals were the only wild cattle that were found in the New World. Vast hordes of them, numbering millions of animals, were ruthlessly destroyed by the white man as he pushed his civilization westward. The Indians killed the bison for their meat (pemmican — which they dried and pounded and stored in bags made of hide) and their skins. Ordinarily they did not kill wantonly or destroy whole herds. The white man, on the contrary, indulged in wholesale slaughter.

The bison are protected in the United States and Canada

The bones of the big animals littered the plains after the white man had passed by, and in time it was feared that they might become extinct. Today, however, there is no such danger. Herds of bison exist, under government protection, in both the United States and Canada. They owe their existence to the safety of the sanctuaries in both countries. A large herd, maintained by the Canadian Government, has its home in Buffalo National Park in Alberta. The largest herd in the United States is multiplying rapidly in Yellowstone National Park. Individual bison or small herds may be found in various zoos.

A huge male bison may weigh as much as one ton

The bison is a large animal, standing high at the shoulders. Sometimes a male may weigh as much as one ton, though the females usually weigh much less. Their heavy coats of fur (which looks almost like wool) are dark brown. The head is large in comparison to the body and has short horns curved like half-moons.

The true buffalo are most widely found in Asia and Africa, and they are only distant relatives of our American bison. The water buffalo is very common in India,

as well as in other parts of the East. In general, these animals are domesticated. The water buffalo are black, with great horns that are flattened and curved backward. In India and in the Malay countries, the natives have trained these animals to do much of their heavy work for them — hauling, pulling and carrying. The buffalo cows are very valuable for the milk they provide.

The African buffalo, which is wild, does not resemble the water buffalo. Seldom if ever tamed, it attacks with ferocity and with all its powerful strength. Hunters often argue as to whether the charge of this buffalo or that of the lion is the more

L. Green from Gendreau, N.Y.

A water buffalo performs his chores in the Philippines.

to be feared. The natives have a particularly well-founded terror of the mad charge of a wounded buffalo. The Cape buffalo is heavy, with curved, massive horns. West Africa and the Congo are the home of another kind of buffalo that is red and much smaller than the Cape buffalo. In south and east Africa we find the great black buffalo.

The European buffalo, or wisent, is an importation. It originated in the East Indies, and was taken to India and domesticated. It was also introduced into Egypt, Greece, Italy and other European countries. The wisent has been a beast of burden in Europe for the last fourteen centuries. During all this time it has pre-

served its ancient habit of wallowing in the mud, as its ancestors did in their native marshes.

The European buffalo is usually docile, although its temper is not always certain. It has been of the greatest use to man throughout the centuries. Powerful enough to do heavy work, it also yields abundant milk and its hide provides excellent leather. Its flesh, however, is inferior to that of the oxen.

The horse has always been man's good friend

In these days of automobiles, railroads and airplanes, it is easy to forget the enormous debt that man owes to his faithful friend and servant, the horse. Ever since the horse was "taken into the family of man," it has stood by its human master with loyalty and devotion. For thousands of years the horse has carried man on its broad back; it has pulled his wagons and chariots; it has hauled his plows through rough and uneven ground, so that man could plant his fields and make them bear.

The ancestor of the horse — no bigger than a fox

Through the evidence of fossilized bones that have survived through the ages, we have learned much of the ancestry and evolution of the horse. The animal evolved from *Eohippus* (the "Dawn Horse"), an animal no bigger than a fox, with four toes on its front feet and three on its hind feet. Several million years elapsed before our modern horse, as we know it today, developed from this ancestor. In this process, it lost all its toes but one, for the hoof of the modern horse was once a toe. This is true also of the close relatives of the horse — the donkey, the ass and the zebra. The small splint bones are all that remains of the other toes.

The horse and its relatives were probably all much alike in the early ages, but today they are very different. The little Shetland pony, the Palomino, the magnificent Arabians and the lumbering draft horses — it is hard to believe that they came from one ancestor.

The horse, undoubtedly, was more than a match for earliest man, whose crude weapons proved ineffectual against this speedy, agile and rugged wild animal. In time, however, man's weapons were improved, and he would occasionally bag a horse. He then began to hunt the animal extensively and to use its flesh as meat. The bones of young horses, deposited outside the cave of Solutré, near Lyons, France, prove that the men of the Old Stone Age were eaters of horseflesh. These bones were disjointed, and the long bones had been split to yield their marrow. The horse was depicted as a game animal, together with the bison, wild ox, reindeer, woolly elephant and wild boar, by cavemen artists. It was only several thousand years ago that the horse became tamed for man's use.

Domestic horses have descended from three wild-horse stocks

As far as we know, the domestic horses of today have descended from at least three different wild-horse stocks. The now-extinct tarpan, or a closely related horse, seems to have been the ancestor of the modern Arab horse — the domestic animal of North Africa. The tarpan was a light-boned, small animal, standing four feet at the shoulders; its forehead was broad and its mane stiff. It roamed widely, long ago, over Europe and Eurasia.

The ancestor of our draft horses was a stronger and larger animal inhabiting western Europe. The Mongolian pony, or Przewalski's horse, of central Asia, represented the third of the wild-horse stocks that gave rise to modern stocks. It is still found in Mongolia. It is about four and a half feet high, is light brown and has a blackish tail and a black, stiff mane.

Horses were domesticated in the early Bronze Age

Bronze Age deposits going back to about 2500 B.C. offer evidence, in the form of bridle bits and other items of harness, of the domestication of horses. A wall drawing in southern Sweden, almost 4,000 years old, is one of the oldest representations found of the domestic horse in Europe. Babylonian records indicate that domestic horses were known there in 2300 B.C. These tamed animals belonged to rather primitive nomadic tribes. The domestic horse, however, did not become common in Babylonia until after 2000 B.C. It was introduced into Africa probably by the Hyksos, or Shepherd kings of the Middle East, who conquered Lower Egypt in the seventeenth century B.C. Subsequently, tame horses were bred throughout Africa and across southern Asia to Celebes.

The first horses to be domesticated were trained to carry loads on their backs and to draw vehicles. They were not used as riding animals until a much later time; this practice probably originated with nomadic herdsmen in central Asia. Babylonians first tamed horses to draw war chariots; the horse did not serve as a mount until a thousand years later, in the twelfth century B.C. The Egyptians, too, harnessed chariots to their horses but rarely rode the animals and never had them pull plows or wagons.

The horse has aided man in war and peace

Wherever the horse has been pressed into man's service, it has altered his way of life. Cavalry units and war chariots drawn by horses changed the whole complexion of warfare. The horse-drawn plow simplified and broadened agricultural activities. Great amounts of cargo could be hauled long distances by draft horses; transportation by means of coach, carriage and wagon was made possible. Even today in the most modern countries, the horse has not lost its versatility on the farm and livestock ranch and as a sporting animal.

Another member of the horse family, the donkey, has proved its worth as a servant of man. This animal was derived from the African wild ass, which lived on the plains of northeastern Africa. Domesticated in ancient times, long before the horse, and distributed through the civilized world, the donkey has served admirably as a draft animal and mount where rough terrain and meager trails demand a hardy and sure-footed beast of burden.

ATOMIC FARMING

How Radioactivity Is Put to Work for Agriculture

by W. RALPH SINGLETON

"THE only thing constant in nature is change." This statement is as true today as when it was made by the Greek philosopher Heraclitus about 500 B.C. Change is all about us. Erosion and the growth and decay of vegetation constantly alter the face of the earth. Clouds and blue sky alternate overhead. All living things pass as individuals through the numerous stages of development that occur between youth and old age. Species go through long-sustained evolutionary changes and also meet sudden changes known as mutations. These sudden changes produce new characteristics that are passed on to coming generations. All animals and plants mutate, and scientific breeders have learned to select the best of various types from which to breed superior types. Cattle without horns, white turkeys, nectarines (from peaches) and seedless and pink grapefruit are the result of breeding from mutations.

For a long time breeders and scientists have tried to make new varieties of animals and plants appear with greater frequency than by nature's slow mutation rate. The most successful known method used to produce mutation is by radiation. H. J. Muller, of Indiana University, used X rays to speed up the production of mutations in *Drosophila* — the small fruit fly, or vinegar fly. L. J. Stadler, in Missouri, produced mutations in barley and in corn by X raying seeds. These two discoveries, in the late 1920's, opened the door to a new era in plant and animal breeding. It was no longer necessary to wait for nature, in her slow and uncertain way, to produce changes in animals and plants; we now had a tool for producing them ourselves.

Since these original discoveries, scientists have been trying to devise a scheme for exposing growing plants to continuous radiation. Radium, which is naturally radioactive, had been available as a source of gamma radiation for some time, but this element is scarce and expensive. Stadler proposed a portable X-ray machine, but it is difficult and expensive to maintain such a machine under continuous operation. The atomic-energy program brought the answer. Radioactive isotopes became available as a source of radiation.

Normal atoms can be made artificially radioactive by exposure in an atomic pile, or nuclear reactor. If cobalt metal is put in the pile, it soaks up neutrons and becomes radioactive; we then have the isotope cobalt 60, or cobalt with mass number 60 (see Index under Mass number). Cobalt 60 gives off energetic gamma rays, which are similar to X rays. It loses about half of its strength, or ability to produce gamma rays, in $5\frac{1}{3}$ years; we say that the isotope cobalt 60 has a half life of $5\frac{1}{3}$ years. This man-made radioactive cobalt is an excellent source of radiation for continuous exposure. It is cheap, compared to radium; it gives off powerful gamma rays; it loses only about 5 per cent of its strength in any summer growing season. Furthermore, it emits rays equally in all directions and not in a beam, like X rays.

For these reasons, cobalt 60 was selected for use in the experimental radiation field, or farm, at Brookhaven Laboratory. The cobalt 60 is installed in the center of a 6-acre field, and plants are grown in concentric circles around the ra-

dioactive material, which is referred to as the source. This is housed in a steel pipe that is set on top of a 2-ton lead cylinder, or "pig." The pipe containing the source can be raised or lowered into the cylinder by means of a windlass, some 460 feet away, connected to the pipe by an underground cable. The cylinder serves as a shield to shut off the radiation when workers enter the field.

The source used in 1952 was approximately 400 curies. (A curie is a unit of measurement representing the amount of radiation given off by one gram of radium.) In 1953, the source was increased to 2,000 curies. This amount gives off more gamma rays than all the refined radium in the world before the days of nuclear fission.

The source is a deadly instrument and must be handled with the greatest care. It gives off sufficient radiation to kill anyone remaining at the center of the field for even a few hours. Gamma rays (like X rays) are extremely penetrating. They pass through growing plants, through all animal tissues and through wooden structures. But the heavier elements, such as lead, are fairly effective in stopping them. Workers are protected by the lead shield, into which the source is always lowered when anyone enters the field.

How do we shield workers from danger when they are at the edge of the field and at the border of the laboratory grounds when the source is in operation? Fortunately, distance is the only shield that we need for the protection of these areas. The intensity of radiation at any distance from the source is proportional inversely (in reverse) to the square of the distance from the source. For instance, the radiation at a distance of 10 meters is only 1/100 as strong as at 1 meter, since 100 is the square of 10. It is possible to spend a few minutes at the control house where the windlass is located — 460 feet from the source — without any danger.

The injury to plants depends somewhat upon the total radiation received but more upon the rate at which it is applied. Corn plants were killed when grown in the inner circles of highest radiation from a 200-curie source. Corn seedlings were killed when they received 670 r (roentgens — a unit of measurement of X rays and gamma rays). They were badly stunted when they received 370 r and affected only mildly at 230 r per day. Although growth was almost normal at this latter rate, the yield was seriously reduced. Yield was little affected at rates less than 100 r per day. The lethal dose for most animals is less than 1,000 r; the corn plants that grew normally at 100 r per day received in 10 days enough radiation to kill a mouse or a man. Corn is much more resistant than animals, and certain plants are much more resistant than corn.

Mutations can be produced in abundance in corn plants growing in the "hot area." Colored kernels have changed to colorless, starchy kernels to sweet, purple to red and plump to shrunken. It should be just as possible to produce changes in plant characters such as more sturdy stalks, more disease resistance and higher yield. In fact, it seems probable that any change that would occur naturally over centuries of time can be made to occur in the period of a few plant generations.

In the radiation field we can also study changes in the cells of plants. These changes occur in the chromosomes, those parts of the cell nucleus that carry the hereditary factors — the genes. Radiation breaks chromosomes, and this results in abnormal cells and in reduced fertility. We can also study physiological changes. In tobacco plants, higher radiation doses noticeably decrease the vitamin content.

After exposure to radiation, have the plants themselves become radioactive? When the radioactive cobalt is shielded, neither the plants nor the soil have any radioactivity. To induce radioactivity, we must change the nucleus of the atom, and gamma rays cannot do this. Plants grown in the radiation field are just as safe to eat as those grown outside.

We now seem to have an efficient tool, in cobalt 60, for inducing mutations in growing plants and developing new and improved varieties. Thus atomic energy is being put to work for agriculture.

Ears of corn plants exposed to gamma rays. The ear shown at the left received the greatest dosage, the one at the right, the least.

Segment of gamma-ray field at Brookhaven National Laboratory. The signs indicate the number of meters from the radioactive source

Aerial view of gamma-ray field at Brookhaven National Laboratory. The concentric arrangement of plants around the source is revealed.

All photos, Brookhaven National Laboratory

Exploring the Animal World

How to Find and Study Our Animal Neighbors

by THOMAS GORDON LAWRENCE

ONE way to explore the animal world is to provide yourself with a formidable supply of armament, take passage to Africa and arrange for a safari with a professional hunter and a battalion of beaters. Another way is to set up a laboratory, complete with cages, aquarium, culture dishes and a compound microscope. A third way is simply to walk forth with a curious eye, on the lookout for whatever animals the region supports — bears in Yellowstone National Park, moose in the northern woods, pigeons and starlings in the streets of our great cities.

You may experience the thrill of discovery in the most unlikely places. One spring afternoon, as I was crossing a New York City street (where wildlife is about as scarce as it is anywhere in the world), I noticed that the sidewalk was black with tiny hurrying creatures. Many of them seemed burdened by their membranous wings, for they frequently bent their heads to nibble nervously at them. Thousands of others flew uncertainly, like poorly constructed helicopters, landing in great numbers on walls and lampposts and taking off again as if their motive power was a bit too weak for such craft. These creatures were winged male and female termites.

I discovered that the horde was streaming up from a basement where wood and coal were sold. It was the great moment in the life of these termites — their nuptial flight. Knowing that different colonies of termites are likely to have their marriage flights on the same day and even the same hour, I was not surprised to encounter another swarm three blocks away and a third a few streets to the north. On many walks in these streets in previous years I had never witnessed such a happening.

You can often observe a fascinating cross section of nature in your own back yard or even within your home. A good way to attract animals to your observation post is to offer food. Leave a banana peel

on a table for a few days; tiny red-eyed flies will appear upon it in time as if by magic. They are the famous fruit flies that scientists use in their experiments in order to find out the mysteries of inheritance. Put a bowl of syrup or water with sugar dissolved in it near some bushes or a clump of trees. Honeybees, bumblebees, ants and wasps will throng about it eagerly. The underside of a piece of soggy toast left on the ground for a few days becomes a small menagerie, housing "thousand leggers" (millepedes) and a host of jumpers and crawlers too small to be identified without a magnifying glass. A piece of half-rotten wood will serve as nourishment for many creatures and as a shelter for many others. Quite a few animals, especially birds, will be grateful for just plain water.

If you wish to do your animal exploration in an easy chair, set up a "bird's restaurant" — a feeding shelf outside a window. Perhaps you would prefer to prepare a feeding box on a post in the yard. The box should be about five feet from the ground; the post should be provided with a projecting metal guard to discourage cats and squirrels. (See Index, under Feeding devices.) If you wish, you can also set up "restaurants" for four-footed creatures, such as squirrels, rabbits, skunks, opossums and raccoons.

One of the best ways to attract animals to your back yard is to provide a natural food supply. A varied flower garden planted near a pool or stream will draw a great variety of insects, especially the most beautiful of all insects, the butterflies, together with their fantastic young, the caterpillars. A rich growth of plants will likewise attract birds; it will provide them with fruits and seeds and will support the insects upon which they also feed.

Exploring animal life
in vacant lots and city parks

A generous-sized vacant lot will often prove a bonanza to an ardent naturalist. It should be a lot where young trees are fighting their way up toward the light through a tangle of towering goldenrod and arches of blackberry — a lot that has

A fine way to attract animals to your back yard is to provide food for them.

Left to right: nature study in a park; migrating starlings; a young cottontail rabbit; a Canada goose nesting.

N. Y. Zool. Soc.

not been subjected to applications of 2,4-D and other weed sprays. If you keep your eyes open, you will see that this area is teeming with many kinds of animal life.

The birds and fur-bearing animals most likely to inhabit vacant lots and city parks must cope with extremely difficult living conditions. Yet squirrels, pigeons, sparrows, starlings and sometimes gulls manage to pick up a living in crowded cities where larger and wilder animals and birds cannot survive.

In many cities pigeons outnumber sparrows, starlings and all other birds. Since city pigeons have only a little more privacy than goldfish in a bowl, they will entertain you for hours at a time as you sit in comfort on a park bench. The strutting, coquetry, clownish ogling and amorous rebuffs that you will observe would be worth a long chapter in a book on birds — that is, if pigeons were rare and you had to spy upon them from a bird blind in a bone-chilling swamp. The English sparrows, too, are a fascinating lot. These stout-hearted outcasts, reviled by so many, have brightened our cities for generations. They gaily chirp their unmelodious call long after orioles and wood thrushes have departed for warmer climes. Look at these dime-a-dozen birds with an unprejudiced eye and observe their enterprise in hunting food, their courtship and the way they take care of their families.

If you see dogs or cats exploring on their own, watch them carefully. They may lead you to small game that you would never have located by yourself. An affable gray cat that lived where a big city began to fragment itself into suburbs used to go hunting every morning. Several times a week he would bring his discovery of the day — a snake, a lizard or a field mouse — to his mistress. She would have been quite unaware that such animals existed in the vicinity had it not been for this gifted feline collector.

Exploring animal life in the country

Of course the farther away you get from the confines of a city or town, the greater the variety of animal life you will encounter. That is why naturalists seek out, whenever they can, the areas least affected by man's activities. In meadows, woods, thickets and swamps, they spend many a rewarding hour looking for all kinds of animals, from scurrying ants to nonchalant skunks, in their native haunts.

Bird watching is a fascinating activity

The dawn hardly comes up like thunder in the United States and Canada, as Kipling claimed it did in Mandalay, but it is ushered in with a wonderful torrent of melodious sound wherever songbirds are numerous. Some of my most thrilling memories are of the period between dawn and full sunrise when the world seems like a great stage waiting for the curtain to go

U. S. Forest Service

N. Y. Zool. Soc.

up. Every sound, every slight change in the color of the sky increases the feeling of expectancy. Then comes the great moment when the bird chorus swells to a breathtaking level. This impromptu musical treat is one of the many delights that await the bird watcher.

You should rise early — 3 or 4 A.M. — when you set out on a bird-watching excursion, so that you may come upon the greatest possible variety of bird life. Be sure that you dress warmly enough and that you eat a good breakfast; it will spoil your fun if you are cold and hungry. Your shoes should be properly fitted and comfortable, since you are going to do a great deal of hiking, perhaps in rather rugged country.

If you are fortunate enough to know a confirmed bird watcher, take your first bird walk with him. You should provide yourself with a pocket field guide to the birds, such as the FIELD GUIDE TO THE BIRDS, by R. T. Peterson (Houghton Mifflin, Boston, 1947), the FIELD GUIDE TO WESTERN BIRDS, by R. T. Peterson (Houghton Mifflin, Boston, 1941), or BIRDS; A GUIDE TO THE MOST FAMILIAR AMERICAN BIRDS, by H. S. Zim and I. N. Gabrielson (Simon and Schuster, New York, 1949). Field glasses will add greatly to the pleasure of the trip.

As you walk through the country in the early hours of the day, birds that are rarely seen in full daylight will often sweep comparatively close; or you may see them silhouetted against the slowly brightening sky. You may also catch a glimpse of interesting four-footed creatures. Foxes, raccoons and skunks generally do their prowling at night; you may encounter them returning to their dens or burrows for a good day's sleep.

Plan your trip so that you will be walking west in the morning while observing, with the sun behind you. With the sun's full light on the birds, you can get an excellent view of them; if you walked east you would perceive only silhouettes against a bright sky. On late afternoon expeditions, plan to make most of your observations while heading east, so that the sun will not be in your face.

Once you arrive at the territory you plan to investigate, walk slowly, pause frequently and make as little noise as possible. Rapid, jerky movements are likely to alarm birds or other creatures. As soon as you see or hear a bird — or any unexplained sound or movement, such as the flickering of a leaf or branchlet — freeze. Most creatures, from insects to deer, tend to accept you as part of the environment (and not a very important part) if you remain quiet and motionless enough.

Birds are often inquisitive; hence you may be able to attract them by squeaking. To squeak, place your pursed lips against the back of your hand and draw in your breath with a long kiss. You can also learn to produce a variety of calls that will attract birds. Anyone who can whistle can

Top: woodpecker. Center: Swainson's hawk on nest. Below: a bird blind.

learn to imitate the simple repertory of such birds as phoebes, orioles and chickadees. With mechanical devices that you can purchase in sporting goods stores you can reproduce the calls of turkeys, ducks and geese.

Your field glasses will enable you to spot birds' nests in trees or other places. You may be fortunate enough to spy, high up in a tall tree, the big, loosely constructed nest of a large hawk or the cumbersome piles of material put together by crows. To find a nest in a tree, scan the tree from right to left at the top, from left to right at a somewhat lower level and so on.

Dead trees make ideal "apartment houses" for owls, woodpeckers, wrens and nuthatches. To find out who the occupants of a dead tree are, rap it with a stick; birds may fly out from openings that you had not noticed. (It may turn out, however, that the tenants are squirrels.) Nests on the ground and in low bushes may be revealed by the flight of the mother bird. Robins often favor cedar trees in suburban yards. They seem to sense that birds of prey avoid human dwellings and that cats cannot climb out on the flexible small branches through the spiky mass of red-cedar foliage.

Pigeons' nests are pretty skimpy structures, but they are quite amazing when you consider the difficulties that these birds have to overcome. In skyscraper districts, where nest-building materials are decidedly scanty, pigeons will construct nests on narrow ledges above a sheer drop of hundreds of feet. In these precarious homes they will raise their families with the greatest nonchalance.

You may consider yourself a dyed-in-the-wool bird watcher when you have constructed and successfully used a bird blind. This is any kind of structure in which you can hide while you observe birds. It may be erected close to their nests or in any other place where they carry on their activities. A frame for a blind can be made from wood or one-inch piping. Spread out a canvas cover over the framework, and cut out peepholes in the canvas. You can make a pretty good blind by setting a beach umbrella into the ground and draping cloth

from the top. Of course there will have to be peepholes in the cloth.

Your bird observations (and all your observations of wild life, for that matter) will be more valuable if you keep some sort of record of them. On a bird walk you can set down the name of each species in a small pocket notebook. Return to the same area a month later and find out how many of the same birds are still there, how many have disappeared and how many newcomers have arrived. Some nature lovers keep these records year after year.

You can make a list of birds seen on each trip, comparing different areas, such as forests, swamps, meadows and orchards. If you prefer, you can make your own census of a given locality month after month, recording the appearance and disappearance of various species. Or you can make your count on the same date each year. The National Audubon Society sponsors a Christmas bird count on one of the days of the Christmas-New Year holiday period.

As you get to know birds better, you will find that there are more and more things that you will want to know and see for yourself. When do migrants put in their appearance? Do males and females arrive together? If not, which come first? What happens in courtship? Are some birds unable to find mates? Can you connect the songs and different types of calls with the birds that produce them? Do some birds use a variety of calls? When and where is the singing done? Do the females sing? How is the nest constructed? Who does the work — the male, female or both? Do both parents feed the young?

How to observe mammals in the wilds

The hardest animals to observe are the mammals — except for a few species, such as rabbits, red and gray squirrels and chipmunks. Foxes, opossums and most other fur bearers keep out of man's way as if their life depended on it — and indeed such is often the case. Many mammals are difficult to observe because they sleep during the day.

Moving cautiously and freezing at every suspicious sound or movement, you may surprise rabbits, chipmunks and once in a while a skunk (who will probably frighten you more than you frighten him). Several times I have flushed a baby rabbit while my very energetic dog continued his investigations, oblivious of the newly discovered game. The rabbit and I would look at one another, each wondering what the other's next move would be. The dog would not become aware of the rabbit's presence until the little animal was bounding off through the underbrush.

The antics of the lively squirrels

Squirrels often make an astonishing commotion as they drop acorns and hickory nuts from high branches and chase one another in wild acrobatics from tree to tree. They are the most active of the rodents; like the starlings among birds, they seem to have boundless energy. Woodchucks, also called ground hogs, are large, short-tailed relatives of the squirrel; they live in holes they dig in the ground. You will have to be on the alert if you wish to see these animals, since they move very cautiously above ground. If you conceal yourself in the vicinity of a woodchuck's burrow and remain still, you may be able to see the animal's nose sniff at the entrance to the burrow; you may even see the woodchuck hesitatingly emerge from its home.

The chances of your seeing deer are good in many areas, even quite near cities. Because of the extermination or near extermination of wolves and various other beasts of prey and also because of stringent game laws, white-tailed deer have become so abundant in some places that their number must be reduced from time to time. Otherwise they would eat up all the available vegetation and would starve.

To help you identify the mammals you will see, you will find Ivan T. Sanderson's HOW TO KNOW THE AMERICAN MAMMALS (Little, Brown, Boston, 1951) very useful. Field glasses and a powerful flashlight will be very helpful in seeking out the animals. Remember that magnification is not the

only important feature of binoculars. If mammals are your quarry, be sure that the lenses have good light-gathering qualities. Otherwise the magnification is wasted, since you will not receive enough light in the forest aisles or thickets inhabited by the animals. A five-cell, focused-beam flashlight is excellent to help spot animals; even an ordinary two-cell lamp is helpful. A flashlight attached to your head or cap leaves your hands free.

Look for the animals' homes as well as for the animals themselves. Many creatures reside in burrows — among these are woodchucks, prairie dogs, foxes, coyotes and various kinds of mice. Natural caverns are the homes of bears, bobcats, porcupines and gray foxes. Opossums and raccoons frequently set up their "apartments" in hollow trees. Squirrels (including the beautiful and elusive flying squirrels) often nest in small cavities in trees. Squirrels also construct nests of twigs and leaves; so do wood mice. Mounds and ridges indicate the tunnels of moles; these tunnels serve not only as dwellings but also as hunting places. North American rabbits are satisfied with very simple homes, merely bedding down in depressions in the ground. (European rabbits dig holes.) Deer bed down in thickets.

You must become something of a detective if you would be a skillful tracker of animals. If you see leaves and flower stems flattened against the ground, you may reasonably assume that some animal spent the night in the spot and may be in the vicinity. Chewed cones, gnawed bark, cut twigs, stores of nuts or other seeds, claw marks on trees — these signs all indicate that some animal has passed that way. Bones and feathers and droppings tell the expert just what wild creatures are about. You can also deduce from runways what beasts inhabit or visit a given area. Meadow mice, muskrats, deer (and in their native countries, tigers and elephants) make their own trails.

Recent tracks are important in locating animals, especially the larger ones, such as deer or moose. Tracks on snow and in muddy ground are most conspicuous. Hardened ones in mud may indicate that an animal went by days or weeks before, as when a dry spell has followed rains. The dinosaur tracks in the Connecticut Valley are mementos of huge beasts that strolled or ran over clay or mud in that region many millions of years ago.

You should learn to recognize the tracks of animals that are found in your neighborhood. The type of track is determined by the structure of the animal's foot and by its manner of walking, running or jumping. Fresh tracks have sharp edges. Walk at the side of the track, not in it; keep looking ahead as much as possible, because good fresh tracks form a trail that can often be made out for a distance. If you think you are close to your quarry,

A mallard nest, with a baker's dozen of eggs, at the base of a dead tree.

Telltale signs of an animal builder — tracks of a beaver in fresh snow.

U. S. Fish and Wildlife Service

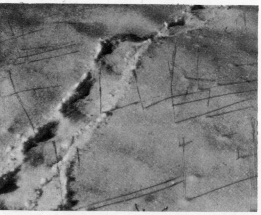

slacken your pace, and above all, be quiet. A noisy tracker is no tracker at all. Make use of rocks, trees, stumps or thick shrubby growths for concealment. Sometimes you may flush an animal by arousing its curiosity. Antelopes and some kinds of deer are so inquisitive that if you wave a handkerchief on a stick above your head, they may approach quite close.

Reptile and amphibian life

I have been prowling through forests, meadows and swamps most of my life, but I still cannot help starting when I unexpectedly come upon a snake. An instant later I recall that there is very slight danger of being bitten. When I have made certain that the reptile is not poisonous, my mind is at ease and, if possible, I try to watch the animal as it goes about its activities.

Since most snakes are rather furtive creatures, you will have to be very alert to spy upon them. Still, it can be done. I have watched a good-sized black snake devouring a large bullfrog, and a milk snake pursuing a field mouse right down into the little animal's burrow. If you are particularly fortunate, you may come upon a completely harmless hog-nosed snake, which will try to drive you away by a fantastic performance. It will swell up to twice its normal size, hissing loudly and striking repeatedly with its open mouth; and yet it will not have the slightest inten-

tion of doing you bodily harm. As a last resort, if all these dramatics have not scared you away, the poor creature will play dead.

You are more likely to come upon the reptile that we call the box tortoise, with its high arched shell, for it loves to wander through open woodlands, meadows, pastures and thickets, and it cannot dart away from you as a snake can. When the box tortoise is startled, it does not indulge in the dramatics of the hog-nosed snake. It simply pulls its head, legs and tail into its tight-fitting armor and defies you to do your worst. The upper and nether shells fit together so tightly when the animal has closed them that you would not be able to slide a piece of paper between the shells.

You are almost sure to come upon certain amphibians, such as frogs and salamanders, in the course of your rambles. Green frogs along the margin of a pond will leap into the water with an outcry as you approach. You will see leopard frogs and wood frogs hunting worms, bugs and

Baby (left) and adult box tortoises. They belong to the genus *Terrapene*.

A young woodchuck. Woodchucks generally move cautiously above ground.

beetles in shady woods and meadows half a mile from the nearest pond or swamp. Sometimes when you explore a swampy lowland or a damp bare area under trees near water, you will walk into what seems a veritable rain of dark little frogs that look like grasshoppers. These are usually the tiny cricket frogs or the still smaller least swamp frogs, which can sit with room to spare on a penny.

The insect world
is abundant and varied

The most abundant and varied of all the creatures you will find in your walks are the insects. As you stride through meadows or along dusty roads in the country, you will stir up swarms of grasshoppers. In early summer they are mostly small, weak-looking creatures with large heads and tremendous eyes. Later, these animals make their last molt and blossom out with long wings. Where the grass is short enough, they turn around as they alight, so as to watch as you come closer. Some advertise their presence as they fly by, unfurling bright, black-barred, yellow or red wings and making a whirring noise. Once they settle down, all is silence and you may have trouble distinguishing them from the vegetation.

The grasshoppers you see in dry meadows and along roads are usually the short-horned variety, so-called because they have comparatively short antennae, or feelers. In rich grass, and especially in wet places where plants are lush and sappy, you are more likely to find long-horned grasshoppers, with elongated and thread-like antennae. Female long-horned grasshoppers have a conspicuous ovipositor, or egg-laying tool, at the tip of the abdomen. In some species it is quite short, in others very long.

Among the most interesting insects you are likely to see in your rambles is the praying mantis, with its turretlike head, huge eyes and forelegs raised as if in supplication. This creature is one of man's chief allies in the insect world, for it eagerly devours mosquitoes, flies and a thousand other pests (including plant lice, when it is small enough to be interested in such game). The small native species of mantis cannot stand the winter north of southern New Jersey. The large Chinese praying mantis, which has established itself in the eastern part of North America, can endure the cold winters of the north.

The egg cases of mantes are tough and made of a bubbly substance chemically similar to silk. If you find any, do not bring them inside the house. The indoor heat will cause the eggs to hatch prematurely and all the young will starve, since their natural prey will not be available. Leave the egg case where you found it. Make a note of the place, and return there daily as the spring sun grows warmer. One fine day you may find a cascade of wrapped up mummies squirming from the case, each attached by a thin thread to the slit from which it emerged. In time each mummy skin splits. Out struggles a skeleton-thin devilkin with long legs, long neck, big eyes and swiveling head.

The mantis is a finicky eater for all its voracious appetite. Watch how daintily it nibbles its way into a protesting fly or moth; how it holds up one leg of the victim when it has separated it from the body and how it devours whatever is toothsome in the joint.

You will also probably see a great many caterpillars. Some of them have what look like numerous white bags adhering to their skins. If you follow one of these caterpillars long enough (or put it in a container with its favorite food plant) you will see it move more and more feebly. The bags are the cocoons of tiny parasites that have eaten away its insides, leaving it little more than a shell. Eventually a gleaming, parasitic wasp will emerge from each cocoon. It will fly nimbly away to mate. The female will then lay its eggs in other caterpillars, which will also be slowly devoured in time.

You will find other insect species galore: bees gathering nectar for the hive, swarms of ants, lovely butterflies, beetles large and small, darting dragonflies, fragile May flies and many, many others. To help identify them, consult such books as the

FIELD BOOK OF INSECTS, by F. E. Lutz (G. P. Putnam's Sons, New York, 1948), the INSECT GUIDE, by R. B. Swain (Doubleday, New York, 1948), and INSECTS; A GUIDE TO FAMILIAR AMERICAN INSECTS, by H. S. Zim and Clarence Cottam (Simon and Schuster, New York, 1951).

A hand lens is as valuable in observing insects (and many other small creatures) as binoculars are in studying birds. Of course hand lenses are much cheaper than binoculars. You can buy a hand lens (also called a pocket magnifier) magnifying two, four or five diameters for about a dollar; a magnifier enlarging ten diameters will cost perhaps $1.75. Prices go up to about $12.00 for the best ten-diameter lenses. My pupils get fine results with $1.75 lenses; they use them to observe ants and smaller water creatures less than a tenth of an inch long. With such a magnifier you can watch an ant wash its face, clean its antennae, nibble at its feet, "milk" plump aphids and exchange signals with sister ants. (All of the ants you see ordinarily are workers — females that will never have any young.) You can watch clumsy aphids dig their long beaks into plant stems.

The best places to find animal life

Edwin Way Teale

You can find interesting animals, large and small (more often small) wherever there is sufficient vegetation to support them. It may seem odd to think of carnivores, such as lions and pumas, as dependent upon vegetation. The fact is that all animals require certain basic food elements that only green plants can manufacture. Animals obtain these elements either by feeding on vegetation or else by devouring vegetation-eating animals.

There are certain places that will yield particularly worthwhile harvests to those who seek animal life. One of the likeliest areas to explore is the margin of a wood, where a wall of trees fronts a meadow and where wild roses, blackberries, sumac, young locust trees and tall herbs form a vivid border between wood and field. Here animals find a varied bill of fare.

Above photo: dragonfly at rest.
Below: the nest of a skimmer.

U. S. Fish and Wildlife Service

With a simple, homemade waterscope, you can have a remarkably clear view of animals living in ponds or streams.

Bears sometimes come berrying in such favored places. Rabbits hop about and nibble happily, protected by a thicket of stems. Birds find a richer diet of insects, seeds and wild fruits than is available in either grassland or dense forest. The greatest variety of insect life is to be found here, since so many different types of plants grow close together and provide food for myriads of insects.

My favorite hunting ground, however, is a sunny swamp, its margin rising to higher ground, with groves of trees here and there and a winding stream, widening in places to form still ponds. Such a swampy area offers something to attract most kinds of animal life. The larger animals come down to the pond to drink; raccoons moisten their food in its water. Frogs and salamanders mate and lay their eggs in the pond. You will find these eggs in the early spring, and you can take them home to your aquarium.

In summer the place is alive with the iridescent wings of dragonflies and their delicate cousins, the damsel flies. Turtles take sun baths on floating logs, while frogs ride serenely on water-lily pads, keeping their big eyes open for any insects they can gobble up. Water striders race about on the surface of the water. They are always on the lookout for prey — small insects dropping into the water — and also for their enemies, such as fish, which can lunge up from below and devour them. Here is your chance to study the family life of wild ducks, as well as the comings and goings of sunfish and crayfish. Sometimes you may espy a fearsome apparition — a snapping turtle rising from the bottom mud to seize a fish or young duck.

How to make a simple waterscope

Water creatures appear dim and distorted because of light reflected from the surface of the water. You can easily make a waterscope (a device for seeing under water) that will give you some of the advantages of a glass-bottomed boat. A very simple waterscope consists simply of a deep flat-bottomed glass dish. Push this into the water, bottom part down, and then look into it. You can make a much better waterscope from a piece of stove pipe two feet long, with a round piece of plate glass in the end that is to be inserted in the water. Rivet metal handles near the other, or viewing, end, for ease in handling. Also put a thick padding of adhesive tape around the upper edge to avoid cutting yourself as you look through the waterscope.

In addition to the titles we have already suggested, you will find the following books extremely useful as you continue your exploration of the animal world:

WILLIAM HILLCOURT, *Field Book of Nature Activities;* G. P. Putnam's Sons, New York, 1950.

ANN HAVEN MORGAN, *Field Book of Ponds and Streams;* G. P. Putnam's Sons, New York, 1930.

J. A. PARTRIDGE, *Natural Science through the Seasons;* Macmillan, New York, 1946.

TED S. PETTIT, *The Book of Nature Activities;* Didier, New York, 1947.

SELECTED READINGS
IN SCIENCE

SELECTED READINGS IN SCIENCE

by JACK E. BROWN; reviewed by HILARY J. DEASON

This bibliography is intended for readers who wish to investigate more fully any of the topics discussed in *The Book of Popular Science*. The majority of the books selected are written at the same level of comprehension as *The Book of Popular Science* itself, and require little or no scientific training. To meet the needs of more advanced readers, other titles have been included, presupposing a background knowledge of physics, chemistry and mathematics. The annotation given for each work indicates how advanced it is. In every case titles have been selected on the basis of scientific accuracy, up-to-dateness and readability.

The titles are divided into fourteen broad subject groups, corresponding to the arrangement of subject matter in *The Book of Popular Science*. Within each group there is, in almost every case, a further breakdown of titles under an alphabetical listing of more specific topics. For example, books on television are found under Television in the Communication group.

"Selected Readings in Science" is continuously revised in order to keep it up-to-date. Hilary J. Deason, Ph.D., director of the Science Library Program of the American Association for the Advancement of Science, collaborates in these revisions.

GENERAL WORKS ON SCIENCE

ASIMOV, ISAAC, *The Intelligent Man's Guide to Science*. N.Y., Basic Books, 2 vols., 1960; 853 pp. — Extensive, well-illustrated history and exposition of many fields of science. Vol. 1: The Physical Sciences; Vol. 2: The Biological Sciences.

BLUEMLE, ANDREW (ed.). *Saturday Science*. N.Y., Dutton, 1960; 333 p. — Excellent introduction to scientific investigation. Requires elementary knowledge of mathematics.

BRONOWSKI, J., *The Common Sense of Science*. Cambridge, Harvard Univ. Press, 1953; 154 pp. — Sets forth relationship of science to art and literature and its place in present-day knowledge.

CONANT, JAMES B., *Science and Common Sense*. New Haven, Yale Univ. Press, 1951; 371 pp. — Techniques and methods of experimental science.

FRANK, PHILIPP G., *Modern Science and Its Philosophy*. N.Y., Braziller, 1955; 324 pp. — Discusses scientific controversies of past and gives contemporary point of view.

FREEDMAN, PAUL, *The Principles of Scientific Research*. N.Y., Pergamon, 2nd ed., 1960; 227 pp. — Clear presentation of scientific research; how it is planned, organized and conducted.

HOGBEN, LANCELOT T., *Science for the Citizen*. N.Y., Norton, rev. ed., 1957; 1,162 pp. — Clear and interest-holding review of scientific knowledge.

MOULTON, FOREST R. and J. J. SCHIFFERES, eds., *Autobiography of Science*. N.Y., Garden City, 2nd ed., 1960; 748 pp. — Highlights of scientific progress told through judicious selection of key writings by great scientists.

NEWMAN, JAMES R., ed., *What Is Science?* N.Y., Simon & Schuster, 1955; 493 pp. — Twelve famous scientists trace development and achievements of various branches of science.

POLLACK, PHILIP, *Careers and Opportunities in Science*. N.Y., Dutton, rev. ed., 1960; 194 pp. — Activities, opportunities and compensation.

SARTON, GEORGE, *The Life of Science*. Bloomington, Ind., Indiana Univ. Pr., 1960; 170 pp. — Outstanding historian of science describes scope, purpose and methods of science history.

SHAPLEY, H., S. RÀPPORT and H. WRIGHT, *A Treasury of Science*. N.Y., Harper, 4th ed., 1957; 776 pp. — Selections from writings of scientists, arranged to give over-all view of science.

THE UNIVERSE

GENERAL WORKS

ALTER, DINSMORE and C. H. CLEMINSHAW, *Pictorial Astronomy*. N.Y., Crowell, 1956; 296 pp. — Numerous illustrations; well suited to laymen.

BAKER, ROBERT H., *Astronomy*. Princeton, N.J., Van Nostrand, 7th ed., 1959; 547 pp. — Good introductory work at college level.

BOEKE, KEES, *Cosmic View: the Universe in 40 Jumps*. N.Y., Day, 1957; 48 pp. — Series of drawings ranging from atom's nucleus to galaxies, each picture representing a ten-fold increase in size over preceding one.

BONDI, HERMANN, The *Universe at Large*. N.Y., Doubleday, 1960; 154 pp. — Outstanding contribution to understanding of numerous important theories, including receding-galaxies hypothesis.

FATH, EDWARD A., *The Elements of Astronomy*. N.Y., McGraw-Hill, 5th ed., 1955; 369 pp. — Nonmathematical treatment for college students and general readers.

GAMOW, GEORGE, *The Creation of the Universe*. N.Y., Viking Press, rev. ed., 1960; 147 pp. — Popularization of advanced theory on origin of galaxies, stars and planets.

HOYLE, FRED, *Frontiers of Astronomy*. N.Y., Harper, 1955; 360 pp. — Interesting account of present state of our knowledge of astronomy.

LEE, OLIVER J., *Measuring Our Universe*; from the inner atom to outer space. N.Y., Ronald Press, 1950; 170 pp. — How astronomers measure infinitely great distances of universe.

LOVELL, A. C. B., *The Individual and the Universe.* N.Y., Mentor, 1961; 126 pp. — Clear and succinct account of modern theories concerning origin of universe and solar system.

MATTERSDORF, LEO, *Insight into Astronomy.* N.Y., Lantern Press, 1952; 223 pp. — Elementary work; gives beginner good idea of astronomy.

MOORE, PATRICK, *Suns, Myths and Men.* London, Muller, 1954; 192 pp. — Growth of astronomical knowledge from ancient to modern times.

PAYNE-GAPOSCHKIN, CECILIA, *Introduction to Astronomy.* N.Y., Prentice-Hall, 1954; 508 pp. — Somewhat more advanced than other introductions, but excellent survey for interested laymen.

Scientific American: the Universe. N.Y., Simon & Schuster, 1957; 160 pp. — Recent developments in astronomy as described by experts in the field and written for the educated layman.

STOKLEY, JAMES, *Atoms to Galaxies.* N.Y., Ronald Press, 1961; 361 pp. — Simple and well-written account of latest developments in astronomy.

CALENDAR

ACHELIS, ELISABETH, *Of Time and the Calendar.* N.Y., Nelson, 1955; 132 pp. — Traces development of modern calendar and stresses need for calendar reform.

WATKINS, HAROLD, *Time Counts.* London, Spearman, 1954; 274 pp. — Deals primarily with calendar reform, but includes good history of calendar.

COMETS

LYTTLETON, RAYMOND A., *Comets and Their Origin.* Cambridge, Cambridge Univ. Press, 1953; 173 pp. — Advanced and mathematical treatment; preliminary chapters are recommended for lay readers.

WATSON, FLETCHER G., *Between the Planets.* Cambridge, Mass., Harvard Univ. Press, rev. ed., 1956; 188 pp. — Contains authoritative and interesting account of comets.

See also GENERAL WORKS

CONSTELLATIONS. See STARS AND CONSTELLATIONS

ECLIPSES

LEWIS, ISABEL M., *A Handbook of Solar Eclipses.* N.Y., Duffield, 1924; 118 pp. — Readable account of causes of eclipses and methods of observation.

MITCHELL, SAMUEL A., *Eclipses of the Sun.* N.Y., Columbia Univ. Press, 5th ed., 1951; 445 pp. — Reliable survey of theory, history and techniques of observing eclipses.

See also GENERAL WORKS

INSTRUMENTS OF ASTRONOMY

KING, HENRY C., *History of the Telescope.* London, Griffin, 1955; 456 pp. — Evolution of telescope from its invention.

PENDRAY, G. E., *Men, Mirrors and Stars.* N.Y., Harper, rev. ed., 1946; 335 pp. — Story of telescopes and other astronomical instruments.

SIDGWICK, JOHN B., *Observational Astronomy for Amateurs.* London, Faber & Faber, 1955; 358 pp. — Astronomical instruments and observational techniques interestingly described.

METEORITES AND METEORS

LAPAZ, LINCOLN and JEAN LAPAZ, *Space Nomads.* N.Y., Holiday, 1961; 187 pp. — Discusses origins and characteristics of meteorites.

NININGER, H. H., *Arizona's Meteorite Crater.* Sedona, Ariz., American Meteorite Museum, 1957; 232 pp. — Investigation of key meteoritic phenomena by distinguished authority in field.

MILKY WAY

BOK, BART J. and PRISCILLA F. BOK, *The Milky Way.* Cambridge, Harvard Univ. Pr., 3rd ed., 1957; 269 pp. — Semipopular description of Milky Way.

PLASKETT, JOHN S., *The Dimensions and Structure of the Galaxy.* Oxford, Clarendon Press, 1935; 30 pp. — Short and readable account.

See also STARS AND CONSTELLATIONS

MOON

BRANLEY, FRANKLYN M., *The Moon, Earth's Natural Satellite.* N.Y., Crowell, 1960; 114 pp. — Simply written; tells what man will find on reaching moon.

GAMOW, GEORGE, *The Moon.* N.Y., Abelard-Schuman, 1959; 120 pp. — Contains most recent data on moon, including account of "moon shots." Profusely illustrated.

WILKINS, H. P. and PATRICK MOORE, *The Moon.* N.Y., Macmillan, 1955; 388 pp. — Illustrated discussion of geography of earth's satellite.

OBSERVATORIES

MOYER, CLAIRE I., *Silver Domes*; a directory of the observatories of the world. Denver, Mountain Press, 1955; 174 pp. — History, location and description of equipment.

WOODBURY, DAVID O., *The Glass Giant of Palomar.* N.Y., Dodd, Mead, 1954; 385 pp. — Describes great telescopes of world and observatories in which they are used. Devotes particular attention to world's largest telescope — Palomar Observatory's 200-inch.

See also INSTRUMENTS OF ASTRONOMY

PLANETS

MOORE, PATRICK, *A Guide to Mars.* N.Y., Macmillan, 1958; 124 pp. — Authoritative and well-written summary of what we know about Mars; can be readily understood by nonspecialist.

———, *A Guide to the Planets.* N.Y., Norton, rev. ed., 1960; 222 pp. — Good presentation of what science knows or theorizes regarding planets.

STRUGHOLD, HUBERTUS, *The Green and Red Planet.* Albuquerque, N. Mexico, University of New Mexico Press, 1953; 107 pp. — Physiologist's views on possibility of life on Mars or other planets.

WHIPPLE, FRED L., *Earth, Moon and Planets.* N.Y., Grosset, 1958; 293 pp. — Basic information, well presented, by distinguished astronomer. Excellent for laymen.

RADIO ASTRONOMY

HAWKINS, GERALD S., *Splendor in the Sky.* N.Y., Harper, 1961; 292 pp. — Among other things, has excellent description of radio astronomy.

PFEIFFER, JOHN, *The Changing Universe.* N.Y., Random House, 1956; 243 pp. — Traces development of radio astronomy and gives some idea of its findings.

SOLAR SYSTEM

MARSHALL, ROY K., *Sun, Moon and Planets.* N.Y., Holt, 1952; 129 pp. — Readable and concise description of structure and motions of solar system.

WATSON, FLETCHER G., *Between the Planets.* Cambridge, Harvard Univ. Pr., rev. ed., 1956; 188 pp. — Description of planets, comets and meteors.

See also GENERAL WORKS

STARS AND CONSTELLATIONS

BAKER ROBERT H., *Introducing the Constellations.* N.Y., Viking Press, rev. ed., 1957; 209 pp. — Interesting information concerning constellations.

KRUSE, W. and W. DIECKVOSS, *The Stars.* Ann Arbor, Mich., Univ. of Michigan Press, 1957; 202 pp. — Survey of stars and galaxies.

LYTTLETON, RAYMOND A., *The Modern Universe.* N.Y., Harper, 1957; 207 pp. — Begins with earth and goes outward through space. Up-to-date views on moon, planets, comets, stars and our galaxy.

PICKERING, JAMES S., *The Stars Are Yours.* N.Y., Macmillan, rev. ed., 1953; 298 pp. — Brief descriptions of major heavenly bodies; charts show star positions at different times of year.

REY, H. A., *The Stars;* a new way to see them. Boston, Houghton Mifflin, 2nd ed., 1961; 143 pp. — Basic astronomical principles clarified by imaginative and unusual charts and diagrams.

SUN

ELLISON, M. A., *The Sun and Its Influence.* London, Routledge, 1955; 235 pp. — What science knows regarding sun's activity and its influence on earth.

GAMOW, GEORGE, *The Birth and Death of the Sun.* N.Y., Mentor, 1959; 219 pp. — Discusses evolution of universe with particular reference to sun.

KIEPENHEUER, KARL, *The Sun.* Ann Arbor, Univ. of Michigan Press, 1959; 160 pp. — Lucid explanation of the structure of sun and various solar phenomena.

MENZEL, DONALD H., *Our Sun.* Cambridge, Mass., Harvard Univ. Pr., rev. ed., 1959, 350 pp. — Interesting examination of many aspects of solar research, including recent information about solar prominences.

TIME, MEASUREMENT OF

COWAN, HARRISON J., *Time and Its Measurement.* N.Y., World Pub., 1958; 159 pp. — Traces development of time-recording methods and devices from 3000 B.C. to modern times.

CUSS, T. P. C., *The Story of Watches.* N.Y., Philosophical Lib., 1952; 172 pp. — Includes history of time-telling devices.

HARRISON, LUCIA C., *Sun, Earth, Time and Man.* Chicago, Rand McNally, 1960; 287 pp. — Describes time in relation to sun and calendar construction.

HOOD, PETER, *How Time Is Measured.* London, Oxford Univ. Press, 1955; 64 pp. — History of calendars and clocks; how time is determined; structure and operation of time-keeping devices.

THE EARTH

GENERAL WORKS

CRONEIS, C. and W. C. KRUMBEIN, *Down to Earth.* Chicago, Univ. of Chicago Press, 1936; 501 pp. — Interesting and finely illustrated book for beginners.

EMMONS, WILLIAM H. and others, *Geology; principles and processes.* N.Y., McGraw-Hill, 5th ed., 1960; 491 pp. — Attractive and well-presented introduction to earth science.

GAMOW, GEORGE, *Biography of the Earth.* N.Y., Viking Press, rev. ed., 1959; 242 pp. — Story of evolution of earth.

KUMMEL, BERNHARD, *History of the Earth.* San Francisco, Freeman, 1961; 610 pp. — Profusely illustrated text for advanced student.

LEET, DON and SHELDON JUDSON, *Physical Geology.* Englewood Cliffs, N.J., Prentice-Hall, 2nd ed., 1958; 512 pp. — Up-to-date presentation.

LONGWELL, CHESTER R. and R. F. FLINT, *Introduction to Physical Geology.* N.Y., Wiley, 2nd ed., 1962; 504 pp. — Authoritative and readable work of value to laymen.

MOORE, RUTH, *The Earth We Live on; the Story of Geological Discovery.* N.Y., Knopf, 1956; 416 pp. — Absorbing account for general reader.

REINFELD, FRED, *Treasures of the Earth.* N.Y., Sterling, 1954; 156 pp. — Origin of earth; formation of mountains, glaciers, deserts and mineral deposits.

STUMPFF, KARL, *Planet Earth.* Ann Arbor, Mich., Univ. of Michigan Pr., 1959; 191 pp. — Fascinating account of earth as part of universe. Requires elementary background in mathematics and physics.

SULLIVAN, WALTER, *Assault on the Unknown.* N.Y., McGraw-Hill, 1961; 460 pp. — Complete account of International Geophysical Year.

SWINNERTON, H. H., *The Earth beneath Us.* London, Muller, 1955; 320 pp. — Introductory geology for layman.

ATMOSPHERE

COOK, J. GORDON, *Our Astonishing Atmosphere.* N.Y., Dial Press, 1957; 200 pp. — Readable summary of present-day knowledge concerning atmosphere of the earth.

NEWELL, HOMER E., *High Altitude Rocket Research.* N.Y., Academic Press, 1953; 298 pp. — Techniques of investigating upper atmosphere; more technical than Vaeth book.

ORR, CLYDE, JR., *Between Earth and Space.* N.Y., Macmillan, 1959; 253 pp. — Deals with origin and nature of atmosphere and the part it plays in everyday life.

VAETH, J. G., *200 Miles Up.* N.Y., Ronald Press, 2nd ed., 1955; 261 pp. — Facts about composition of stratosphere and ionosphere as obtained through use of rockets and high altitude balloons.

See also WEATHER AND CLIMATE

CAVES

CASTERET, NORBERT, *The Darkness under the Earth.* N.Y., Holt, 1955; 174 pp. — Famous explorer of caves describes his adventures.

CULLINGFORD, C. H. D., ed., *British Caving.* London, Routledge, 1953; 468 pp. — Collection of previously scattered information about scientific study of caves.

FOLSOM, FRANKLIN, *Exploring American Caves.* N.Y., Crown, 1956; 280 pp. — What interior of cave is like; how caves came to exist; history of cave discovery.

MOHR, CHARLES E. and HOWARD N. SLOANE, eds., *Celebrated American Caves*. New Brunswick, N.J., Rutgers Univ. Pr., 1955; 339 pp. — Description and stories of famous and little-known caves.

CLIMATE. See WEATHER AND CLIMATE

EARTHQUAKES

EIBY, G. A., *About Earthquakes*. N.Y., Harper, 1957; 168 pp. — Short popular account of what causes earthquakes and how they are recorded and studied.

HEWITT, R., *From Earthquake, Fire and Flood*. N.Y., Scribner, 1957; 215 pp. — Dramatic and scientifically accurate account of physical agents of disaster; written for layman.

LEET, LEWIS D., *Causes of Catastrophe*; earthquakes, volcanoes, tidal waves and hurricanes. N.Y., McGraw-Hill, 1948; 232 pp. — Fascinating work for laymen.

FOSSILS

ANDREWS, ROY C., *All about Dinosaurs*. N.Y., Random House, 1953; 146 pp. — Elementary and fascinating account of prehistoric animals by famous naturalist.

COLBERT, EDWIN H., *Evolution of the Vertebrates*. N.Y., Wiley, 1955; 479 pp. — Development of backboned animals as revealed by fossil record.

EPSTEIN, SAM and BERYL EPSTEIN, *Prehistoric Animals*. N.Y., Watts, 1956; 210 pp. — Account of fossil traces that led to paleontologist's knowledge of ancient animals.

FENTON, CARROLL L. and M. A. FENTON, *Fossil Book*. N.Y., Doubleday, 1958; 482 pp. — Story of life during past two billion years, written for layman; profusely illustrated.

LIBBY, WILLARD F., *Radiocarbon Dating*. Chicago, Univ. of Chicago Press, 2nd ed., 1955; 175 pp. — Techniques for estimating ages of organic materials, including fossil remains, by measuring their radioactive-carbon content.

SIMPSON, GEORGE G., *Life of the Past*. New Haven, Yale Univ. Press, 1953; 198 pp. — Clear and readable book dealing with study of fossil remains.

GEYSERS. See VOLCANOES AND GEYSERS

GLACIERS AND ICEBERGS

FLINT, RICHARD F., *Glacial and Pleistocene Geology*. N.Y., Wiley, 1957; 553 pp. — Standard account of Ice Ages for advanced students.

VIAL, A. E. L., *Alpine Glaciers*. London, Batchworth, 1952; 126 pp. — Primarily for mountain climbers but contains good descriptions of origin and nature of glaciers; excellent photographs.

See also GENERAL WORKS

MINERALS

BATEMAN, ALAN M., *The Formation of Mineral Deposits*. N.Y., Wiley, 1951; 371 pp. — Clear account of origin of mineral deposits and their economic importance.

HURLBUT, CORNELIUS S., Jr., *Dana's Manual of Mineralogy*. N.Y., Wiley, 16th ed., 1957; 530 pp. — Source book of mineralogy for advanced student.

VOSKUIL, WALTER H., *Minerals in World Industry*. N.Y., McGraw-Hill, 1955; 324 pp. — Reviews sources, properties and uses of major minerals.

ZIM, HERBERT S. and PAUL R. SHAFFER. *Rocks and Minerals*. N.Y., Simon and Schuster, 1957; 160 pp. — Colorfully illustrated presentation of various specimens and means of identification.

MOUNTAIN-BUILDING FORCES

LANE, FERDINAND C., *The Story of Mountains*. N.Y., Doubleday, 1950; 488 pp. — Miscellany of interesting information concerning formation of mountains and their relationship to man.

LOBECK, A. K., *Things Maps Don't Tell Us*. N.Y., Macmillan, 1956; 159 pp. — Explains formation, changes and deterioration of geographical features. Greatly aids in map interpretation.

See also GENERAL WORKS

OCEANOGRAPHY

CARSON, RACHEL L., *The Sea Around Us*. N.Y., Oxford Univ. Press, rev. ed., 1961; 237 pp. — Readable and accurate account of ocean.

CLARKE, ARTHUR C., *The Challenge of the Sea*. N.Y., Holt, Rinehart and Winston, 1960; 168 pp. — For secondary school; discusses resources drawn from sea and methods of exploration.

COKER, R. E., *This Great and Wide Sea*. Chapel Hill, Univ. of No. Carolina Press, rev. ed., 1949; 325 pp. — Readable discussion of such topics as formation of oceans, physical properties of sea water, tides, waves and ocean life.

DE LATIL, PIERRE and JEAN RIVOIRE, *Man and the Underwater World*. N.Y., Putnam's, 1956; 400 pp. — Anecdotal history of man's efforts to explore the underwater world.

SHEPARD, FRANCIS P., *The Earth Beneath the Sea*. Baltimore, Johns Hopkins Press, 1959; 275 pp. — Book on submarine geology for laymen.

SVERDRUP, HAROLD U., R. H. FLEMING, and MARTIN W. JOHNSON, *The Oceans*; their physics, chemistry and general biology. N.Y., Prentice-Hall, 1942; 1087 pp. — Classic work; comprehensive treatment for advanced student.

PALEONTOLOGY. See FOSSILS

ROCK STRUCTURE

FENTON, CARROLL L., *The Rock Book*. N.Y., Doubleday, 1940; 357 pp. — Describes various types of rocks and how they originated.

KEMP, JAMES F., *A Handbook of Rocks*. N.Y., Van Nostrand, 6th ed., 1940; 300 pp. — How to recognize various rocks without use of optical equipment.

SPOCK, LESLIE E., *Guide to the Study of Rocks*. N.Y., Harper, 2nd ed., 1962; 256 pp. — Authoritative work for students and interested laymen.

SCULPTURE OF LAND

LOBECK, ARMIN K., *Geomorphology*. N.Y., McGraw-Hill, 1939; 731 pp. — Explains how various types of landscapes have been produced; profusely illustrated.

SHIMER, JOHN A., *This Sculptured Earth*. N.Y., Columbia Univ. Press, 1959; 255 pp. — Well-presented description of forces that have produced American landscape features.

SHULER, ELLIS W., *Rocks and Rivers of America*. N.Y., Ronald Press, 1945; 300 pp. — How moving water modifies landscape structure.

STAMP, L. DUDLEY, *The Earth's Crust.* London, Harrap, 1951; 120 pp. — Color photographs of geological models illustrate this description of landscape patterns and their formation.

THORNBURY, WILLIAM D., *Principles of Geomorphology.* N.Y., Wiley, 1954; 618 pp. — Descriptions and interpretation of earth's major relief features.

VOLCANOES AND GEYSERS

BAUER, CLYDE M., *The Story of Yellowstone Geysers.* Saint Paul, Minn., Haynes, 1937; 125 pp. — Includes material on cause and nature of geysers.

COLEMAN, SATIS N., *Volcanoes New and Old.* N.Y., Day, 1946; 222 pp. — Describes earth's great volcanoes, and gives eye-witness account of birth of volcano Paricutin.

COTTON, C. A., *Volcanoes as Landscape Forms.* N.Y., Wiley, 1952; 416 pp. — Emphasizes results of volcanic activity rather than theories of volcanism.

JAGGAR, THOMAS A., *Volcanoes Declare War.* Honolulu, Paradise of the Pacific,.1945; 166 pp. — Vivid descriptions and photographs of volcanic activity in Pacific Ocean area.

POUGH, FREDERICK H., *All about Volcanoes and Earthquakes.* N.Y., Random House, 1953; 150 pp. — Elementary treatment of subject.

TAZIEFF, HAROUN, *Craters of Fire.* N.Y., Harper, 1952; 239 pp. — Nature and geophysics of volcanoes, with first-hand descriptions of volcanic eruptions.

WEATHER AND CLIMATE

BLAIR, THOMAS A., *Weather Elements.* Englewood Cliffs, N.J., Prentice-Hall, 4th ed., 1960; 414 pp. — Good introductory work; nonmathematical treatment.

FISHER, ROBERT M., *How about the Weather?* N.Y., Harper, rev. ed., 1958; 172 pp. — Contains good description of weather-forecasting techniques.

HAYNES, BENARTHUR C., *Techniques of Observing the Weather.* N.Y., Wiley, 1947; 272 pp. — Describes instruments and methods used in observing and recording weather data.

KIMBLE, GEORGE H. T., *Our American Weather.* N.Y., McGraw-Hill, 1955; 322 pp. — An unusual book on American climatology by well-known meteorologist.

KRICK, IRVING P. and ROSCOE FLEMING, *Sun, Sea and Sky.* Phila., Lippincott, 1954; 248 pp. — Lucid and well-organized account of how and why of weather.

SHAPLEY, HARLOW, ed., *Climatic Change.* Harvard Univ. Press, 1954; 318 pp. — Twenty-two scientists have contributed to discussion of why climate changes and what its changes do to earth and living things.

TANNEHILL, IVAN R., *The Hurricane Hunters.* N.Y., Dodd, Mead, 1955; 271 pp. — Tells of experiences of those who have delved by air and sea into internal mysteries of hurricanes.

———, *Weather around the World.* Princeton, Princeton Univ. Press, 2nd ed., 1952; 212 pp. — Handy compilation of information concerning weather in various parts of world.

LIFE

GENERAL WORKS

AMERICAN MUSEUM OF NATURAL HISTORY, *Illustrated Library of the Natural Sciences.* N.Y., Simon & Schuster, 4 vols., 1958; 3042 pp. — Outstanding collection of articles by distinguished authorities.

BARNETT, LINCOLN, ed., *The World We Live In.* N.Y., Simon & Schuster, 1955; 304 pp. — Covers entire field of natural history; clearly written and lavishly illustrated.

BEEBE, WILLIAM, *Adventuring with Beebe.* N.Y., Duell Sloan & Pearce, 1955; 283 pp. — Selections from Beebe's earlier works; covers whole field of natural history and makes enjoyable reading.

BOREK, ERNEST, *The Atoms Within Us.* N.Y., Columbia Univ. Press, 1961; 272 pp. — Fine introduction to procedures and accomplishments of biochemistry.

COMSTOCK, ANNA B., *Handbook of Nature Study.* Ithaca, N.Y., Cornell Univ. Press, 24th ed., 1957; 937 pp. — Classic work that has long been a favorite.

DARLINGTON, C. D., *Facts of Life.* N.Y., Macmillan, 1955; 467 pp. — Famous geneticist discusses heredity, evolution, race and other biological topics.

MARTIN, ALEXANDER C. and HERBERT S. ZIM, *American Wildlife and Plants.* N.Y., Dover, 1961; 500 pp. — Prepared under direction of U.S. Fish and Wildlife Service.

NORDENSKIÖLD, ERIK, *The History of Biology*; a survey. N.Y., Tudor, 1960; 629 pp. — For advanced students; remarkably comprehensive survey of influence of biology on Western culture.

SHIPPEN, KATHERINE B., *Men, Microscopes and Living Things.* N.Y., Viking, 1955; 192 pp. — History of biological sciences, told largely through contributions of individual scientists.

SINGER, CHARLES J., *History of Biology.* N.Y., Abelard-Schuman, rev. ed., 1959; 579 pp. — Comprehensive study by famous historian.

SMITH, ELLA T., *Exploring Biology.* N.Y., Harcourt, Brace, 5th ed., 1959; 731 pp. — Attractive and highly successful text at college level.

THOMPSON, D'ARCY W., *On Growth and Form,* abridged by J. T. Bonner. Cambridge, Eng., Cambridge Univ. Press, 1961; 346 pp. — On mathematics of biology; abridged from 1,000-page original. Should be read by all serious students of biology.

CELL AS BASIS OF LIFE

BONNER, JOHN T., *Cells and Societies.* Princeton, N.J., Princeton Univ. Press, 1955; 234 pp. — Comparisons of representative animals, stressing basic similarity of all life.

DOWNES, HELEN R., *Chemistry of Living Cells.* N.Y., Harper, 1955; 549 pp. — Concise and readable survey of biochemistry for undergraduates.

SWANSON, CARL P., *The Cell.* Englewood Cliffs, N.J., Prentice-Hall, 1960; 114 pp. — For use in advanced high-school biology classes.

CLASSIFICATION OF PLANTS AND ANIMALS. See GENERAL WORKS

ECOLOGY (relations between living things and environment)

ODUM, EUGENE P., *Fundamentals of Ecology.* Phila., Saunders, 2nd ed., 1959; 546 pp. — Lively style makes this text suitable for interested laymen.

STORER, JOHN H., *The Web of Life.* N.Y., Devin-Adair, 1953; 144 pp. — Very readable study of interrelationships of living things.

TEALE, EDWIN W., *Circle of the Seasons*. N.Y., Dodd, 1953 ; 306 pp. — Collection of essays showing relationship between living things and environment.

WATTS, MAY T., *Reading the Landscape*. N.Y., Macmillan, 1957 ; 230 pp. — Informal and readable introduction to scope and applications of ecology.

WOODBURY, ANGUS M., *Principles of General Ecology*. N.Y., Blakiston, 1954 ; 503 pp. — College text but useful for laymen ; includes good bibliography.

EVOLUTION

BATES, MARSTON and P. S. HUMPHREY (eds.), *The Darwin Reader*. N.Y., *Scribner,* 1956 ; 470 pp. — Well-edited selection of significant works of Darwin.

ROMER, ALFRED S., *The Vertebrate Story*. Chicago, Univ. of Chicago Press, 4th ed., 1959 ; 437 pp. — Evolution and ways of life of backboned animals.

SHULL, AARON F., *Evolution*. N.Y., McGraw-Hill, 2nd ed., 1951 ; 332 pp. — For college students and general reading.

SIMPSON, GEORGE G., *The Meaning of Evolution,* New Haven, Yale Univ. Press, 1960 ; 364 pp. — Excellent introduction to subject of evolution by distinguished authority.

GENETICS

DOBZHANSKY, THEODOSIUS, *Evolution, Genetics and Man*. N.Y., Wiley, 1955 ; 398 pp. — Authoritative treatment at college level.

DUNN, L. C. and T. DOBZHANSKY, *Heredity, Race and Society*. N.Y., New American Lib. (Mentor Book), rev. ed., 1952. — Interesting introduction for laymen by two distinguished authorities.

GOLDSCHMIDT, RICHARD B., *Understanding Heredity*. N.Y., Wiley, 1952 ; 228 pp. — Introduction to the subject by eminent authority.

GOLDSTEIN, PHILIP, *Genetics Is Easy*. N.Y., Lantern Press, 2nd ed., 1955 ; 238 pp. — Easy-to-read explanation of basic facts.

HUTCHINS, CARLEEN M., *Life's Key—DNA*. N.Y., Coward-McCann, 1962 ; 64 pp. — Interesting account of vital genetic development for young students.

SCHEINFELD, AMRAM, *The Human Heredity Handbook*. Philadelphia, Lippincott, 1956 ; 276 pp. — Concise manual of information about heredity in man ; excellent for quick reference.

SINNOTT, EDMUND W., et al, *Principles of Genetics*. N.Y., McGraw-Hill, 1958 ; 459 pp. — Well-developed text for serious student ; includes sections on microorganisms and biometrics.

HEREDITY. See GENETICS

REPRODUCTION

BERRILL, NORMAN J., *Sex and the Nature of Things*. N.Y., Dodd, Mead, 1953 ; 256 pp. — Part played by sex in evolution and development of living world.

ETS, MARIE H., *The Story of a Baby*. N.Y., Viking, 1939 ; 63 pp. — For young people ; has remarkably fine drawings of actual embryos.

KERMACK, W. O. and P. EGGLETON, *The Stuff We're Made Of*. N.Y., St. Martin's Press, 2nd ed., 1948 ; 354 pp. — Contains clear explanation of reproduction.

LANGDON-DAVIES, JOHN, *Seeds of Life*. N.Y., Devin-Adair, 1955 ; 172 pp. — Readable study of various methods of sexual and asexual propagation.

Miracle of Growth. (Publication of Chicago Museum of Science and Industry.) Urbana, Ill., Univ. of Illinois Press, 1950 ; 73 pp. — Condensed yet comprehensive explanation of physical aspects of human reproduction.

PLANT LIFE

GENERAL WORKS

ANDERSON, EDGAR, *Plants, Man and Life*. Boston, Little, Brown, 1952 ; 245 pp. — Rambling but fascinating account of origin of cultivated plants.

CHRISTENSEN, CLYDE M., *The Molds and Man*. Minneapolis, Univ. of Minnesota Press, rev. ed., 1961 ; 238 pp. — General account of fungi ; includes little-known aspects of subject.

FULLER, HARRY J. and OSWALD TIPPO, *College Botany*. N.Y., Holt, rev. ed., 1954 ; 993 pp. — Comprehensive treatment at college level.

HYLANDER, CLARENCE J., *The World of Plant Life*. N.Y., Macmillan, 2nd ed., 1956 ; 653 pp. — Comprehensive survey of plant life of America.

PLATT, RUTHERFORD, *This Green World*. N.Y., Dodd, Mead, 1942 ; 219 pp. — Book of interesting facts.

ROBBINS, WILFRED W. and T. E. WEIER, *Botany*. N.Y., Wiley, 2nd ed., 1957 ; 578 pp. — Comprehensive account of phenomena of plant life.

Scientific American: Plant Life. N.Y., Simon & Schuster, 1957 ; 256 pp. — Recent progress in botany as written for educated laymen by experts in the field.

SINNOTT, EDMUND W. and KATHERINE S. WILSON, *Botany*. N.Y., McGraw-Hill, 5th ed., 1955 ; 528 pp. — Attractive format and excellent illustrations are important features of this introductory text.

AGRICULTURE

BENEKE, RAYMOND R., *Managing the Farm Business*. N.Y., Wiley, 1955 ; 464 pp. — Introductory text on basic principles of farm management and operation.

HARDING, THOMAS S., *Two Blades of Grass*. Norman, Univ. of Oklahoma Press, 1947 ; 352 pp. — Interesting account of U.S. Department of Agriculture's search for better and disease-free plants and animals.

JACOBS, HERBERT A., *Practical Guide for the Beginning Farmer*. N.Y., Harper, 1951 ; 237 pp. — Ranges in scope from choosing of farm land to raising crops and livestock.

JOHNSON, SHERMAN E. and others, *Managing a Farm*. N.Y., Van Nostrand, 1946 ; 365 pp. — Farm economics and management for beginning farmers.

PEARSON, HAYDN S., *Successful Part-Time Farming*. N.Y., McGraw-Hill, 1947 ; 322 pp. — Practical and elementary manual for operators of small farms.

DISEASES OF PLANTS

DODGE, B. OGILVIE and HAROLD W. RECKETT, *Diseases and Pests of Ornamental Plants*. N.Y., Ronald Press, 1948 ; 638 pp. — Describes appearance, cause and control of plant diseases and pests.

RIES, VICTOR H., *The Gardener's Trouble Shooter*. N.Y., Sheridan House, 1952 ; 320 pp. — Control of diseases and pests ; for amateur gardener.

WESTCOTT, CYNTHIA, *Gardener's Bug Book*. N.Y.,

Doubleday, 2nd ed., 1956; 579 pp. — Convenient and practical guide to various methods of controlling garden pests.

ECOLOGY, PLANT (relation of plants to environment)

McDOUGALL, W. B., *Plant Ecology*. Phila., Lea, 4th ed., 1949; 234 pp. — Introductory study of interrelationship between plants and environment.

NEWBIGIN, MARION I., *Plant and Animal Geography*. N.Y., Dutton, 2nd ed., 1948; 298 pp. — Influence of natural conditions on distribution and characteristics of plants and animals.

OOSTING, HENRY J., *The Study of Plant Communities*. San Francisco, Freeman, 2nd ed., 1956; 389 pp. — Introduction to ecology for college students.

WATTS, MAY T., *Reading the Landscape; an Adventure in Ecology*. N.Y., Macmillan, 1957; 230 pp. — Stimulating introduction to the subject.

FLOWERS

FOLEY, DANIEL J., *Garden Flowers in Color*. N.Y., Macmillan, 1943; 319 pp. — Brief descriptions of major flower garden plants and directions for cultivation.

JAEGER, PAUL, *The Wonderful Life of Flowers*. N.Y., Dutton, 1961; 196 pp. — Beautifully illustrated, with some pictures in color; will be valued by amateur botanist or anyone who likes flowers.

KIERAN, JOHN, *Introduction to Wild Flowers*. N.Y., Hanover House, 1952; 77 pp. — Skilled writer and talented illustrator have collaborated on this inviting book.

MOLDENKE, HAROLD N., *American Wild Flowers*. N.Y., Doubleday, 1952; 453 pp. — Fine guide to identification, geography and botany of 2,000 varieties of wild flowers.

TAYLOR, NORMAN, *The Everblooming Garden*. N.Y., Van Nostrand, 1954; 104 pp. — Selection and cultivation of plants that will give year-round show of color.

FRUITS

BARKER, RALPH E., *Small Fruits*. N.Y., Rinehart, 1954; 90 pp. — Explicit instructions for planting and care of bush fruits and grapes.

HEDRICK, ULYSSES P., *Fruits for the Home Garden*. N.Y., Oxford Univ. Press, 1944; 171 pp. — Written for inexperienced gardener.

MELADY, JOHN H., *Better Fruits for Your Home Garden*. N.Y., Grosset & Dunlap, 1952; 156 pp. — Concise instructions for amateur gardener.

TAYLOR, NORMAN, *Fruit in the Garden*. N.Y., Van Nostrand, 1954; 134 pp. — Selection and cultivation of fruits in small garden.

INSECTS AND PLANTS

CHEESMAN, LUCY E., *Insects; their secret world*. N.Y., Apollo, 1961; 246 pp. — Includes chapter on relationship of insects and plants.

CURRAN, C. H., *Insects in Your Life*. N.Y., Sheridan House, 1951; 316 pp. — Deals particularly with insects that affect our lives.

MEEUSE, B. J. D., *The Story of Pollination*. N.Y., Ronald, 1961, 243 pp. — Comprehensive account; gives a good many examples of pollination; principally by insects, but also by birds and bats.

METCALF, C. L. and others, *Destructive and Useful Insects*. N.Y., McGraw-Hill, 3rd ed., 1951; 1,071 pp. — Comprehensive book on habits and control of insect pests.

STEFFERUD, ALFRED, ed., *Insects; the Yearbook of Agriculture,* 1952. Washington, D.C., U.S. Govt. Printing Office, 1952; 780 pp. — Series of articles by experts on useful and harmful insects and their importance in agriculture.

PHYSIOLOGY OF PLANTS

BONNER, JAMES and ARTHUR W. GALSTON, *Principles of Plant Physiology*. San Francisco, Freeman, 1952; 499 pp. — Simply presented but requires elementary knowledge of chemistry and botany.

MILLER, ERSTON V., *Within the Living Plant*. N.Y., Blakiston, 1953; 325 pp. — Stresses practical applications of knowledge of plant physiology.

NORTHEN, HENRY T., *The Secret of the Green Thumb*. N.Y., Ronald Press, 1954; 431 pp. — Plant structure, chemical composition and metabolism, for amateur gardeners.

YOCUM, LAWSON E., *Plant Growth*. N.Y., Ronald Press, 1945; 203 pp. — Comprehensive and well-illustrated explanation of nature of plant growth.

PLANT BREEDING

BEATY, JOHN Y., *Plant Breeding for Everyone*. Boston, Branford, 1954; 102 pp. — Practical advice on home propagation of plants.

BUSH-BROWN, LOUISE and JAMES BUSH-BROWN, *America's Garden Book*. N.Y., Scribner, rev. ed., 1958; 1,242 pp. — Comprehensive and practical coverage of all aspects of plant cultivation.

FREE, MONTAGU, *Plant Propagation in Pictures*. N.Y., Doubleday, 1957; 249 pp. — Describes simple methods for propagating house and garden plants.

HAWKES, ALEX D., *Orchids: Their Beauty and Culture*. N.Y., Harper, 1960; 297 pp. — Classification guide and manual on care and propagation.

KING, E. J., *Plant Propagation*. N.Y., Farrar, Straus, 1952; 264 pp. — Methods of propagating major garden plants.

SOIL

DOWNEY, EARL F., *Improving Your Garden through Soil Management*. N.Y., Crown, 1955; 250 pp. — Essential ingredients of good soils, and requirements of various plants.

GUSTAFSON, AXEL F., *Using and Managing Soils*. N.Y., McGraw-Hill, 1948; 420 pp. — Simple presentation of methods for preparing, improving and conserving farm and garden soils.

HYAMS, EDWARD S., *Soil and Civilization*. London, Thames & Hudson, 1952; 312 pp. — Stimulating book for serious student.

JOFFE, JACOB S., *ABC of Soils*. New Brunswick, N.J., Pedology Publications, 1949; 383 pp. — Elementary text by soil research specialist at Rutgers University.

KELLOGG, CHARLES E., *Our Garden Soils*. N.Y., Macmillan, 1952; 232 pp. — Emphasis on methods of improving and managing poor garden soils.

LYON, T. L., *Nature and Properties of Soils*. N.Y., Macmillan, 5th ed., 1952; 591 pp. — Primarily for students, but suitable for general reader.

TREES

GRIMM, WILLIAM CAREY, *The Book of Trees*. Harrisburg, Stackpole, 1962; 487 pp. — Illustrated guide for identification of and important facts concerning trees of United States.

HYLANDER, CLARENCE, *Trees and Trails*. N.Y., Macmillan, 1952; 237 pp. — Photographs and drawings supplement this description of trees of North America.

LANE, FERDINAND C., *Story of Trees*. N.Y., Doubleday, 1952; 384 pp. — Readable miscellany of facts regarding history, development and uses of trees.

PEATTIE, DONALD C., *Natural History of Western Trees*. Boston, Houghton Mifflin, 1953; 751 pp. — Lore and romance of forests, and guide to identification of more than 200 varieties of trees.

STEFFERUD, ALFRED, ed., *Trees; the Yearbook of Agriculture*, 1949. Washington, D.C., U.S. Govt. Printing Office, 1949; 944 pp. — Series of articles by experts in field.

WYMAN, DONALD, *Trees for American Gardens*. N.Y., Macmillan, 1951; 376 pp. — Describes 745 species of trees on basis of their landscaping qualities.

VEGETABLE GARDEN PLANTS

FOLEY, DANIEL J. and CATHERINE E. MEIKLE, *Vegetable Gardening*, in color. N.Y., Macmillan, 1942; 255 pp. — Cultural directions for major vegetable crops.

KNOTT, JAMES E., *Vegetable Growing*. Phila., Lea, 5th ed., 1955; 358 pp. — Planting, growth, care and harvesting of commercial vegetables.

MELADY, JOHN H., *Better Vegetables for Your Home Garden*. N.Y., Grosset & Dunlap, 1952; 159 pp. — Elementary treatment for amateur gardener.

SWARTOUT, JACK M., *Vegetables*. N.Y., Rinehart, 1954; 92 pp. — Growing vegetables in small garden.

ANIMAL LIFE

GENERAL WORKS

BURTON, MAURICE and others, *The Story of Animal Life*. London, Elsevier Press, 1949; 2 vols., 390, 430 pp. — Very readable text supplemented by numerous high-quality photographs.

DEVOE, ALAN, *This Fascinating Animal World*. N.Y., McGraw-Hill, 1951; 303 pp. — Answers hundreds of questions about animal life and behavior.

DRIMMER, FREDERICK, editor-in-chief, *The Animal Kingdom*. N.Y., Garden City, 1954; 3 vols., 2062 pp. — Interesting and authentic work about wildlife by seven distinguished naturalists.

GRAY, JAMES, *How Animals Move*. Cambridge, Cambridge Univ. Press, rev. ed., 1959; 143 pp. — Simplified but accurate presentation of way in which animals move about in water, land and air.

HEGNER, ROBERT W. and KARL A. STYLES, *College Zoology*. N.Y., Macmillan, 7th ed., 1959; 726 pp. — Clear presentation of field.

HICKMAN, CLEVELAND P., *Integrated Principles of Zoology*. St. Louis, Mosby, 1961; 972 pp. — Complete zoology textbook for advanced students.

LORENZ, KONRAD Z., *King Solomon's Ring*. N.Y., Crowell, 1952; 202 pp. — Informative and entertaining account of birds, fishes and other animals.

MILNE, LORUS and MARGERY MILNE, *Animal Life*. Englewood Cliffs, N.J., Prentice-Hall, 1959; 367 pp. — Revision and enlargement of zoology section of previous book by these authors; concise, accurate.

PETERSON, ROGER T., *Wildlife in Color*. Boston, Houghton Mifflin, 1951; 191 pp. — Scientifically accurate pictures of animal and plant life of North America.

ROMER, ALFRED S., *The Vertebrate Story*. Chicago, Univ. of Chicago Press, 1959, 422 pp. — Evolution and fossil history of backboned animals, including man. Complete revision of earlier book by author.

STORER, T. I. and R. L. USINGER, *General Zoology*. N.Y., McGraw-Hill, 3rd ed., 1957; 664 pp. — Revised edition of well-known college text.

AMPHIBIANS AND REPTILES

CONANT, R. and I. H. CONANT, *A Field Guide to Amphibians and Reptiles*. Boston, Houghton Mifflin, 1958; 366 pp. — Useful guide to identification of familiar species.

HAUSMAN, LEON A., *Beginner's Guide to Freshwater Life*. N.Y., Putnam, 1950; 128 pp. — Deals with 250 common forms of animal life, including frogs and turtles.

NOBLE, G. KINGSLEY, *The Biology of the Amphibia*. N.Y., Dover Publ., 1954; 577 pp. — Comprehensive study of frogs, salamanders and caecilians for the advanced student.

OLIVER, JAMES A., *The Natural History of North American Amphibians and Reptiles*. Princeton, Van Nostrand, 1955; 359 pp. — Interesting account by well-known authority.

POPE, CLIFFORD H., *Snakes Alive and How They Live*. N.Y., Viking Press, 1952; 238 pp. — Packed with interesting information concerning the habits of snakes.

———, *The Reptile World*. N.Y., Knopf, 1955; 380 pp. — Comprehensive natural history of snakes, lizards, turtles and crocodilians.

STEBBINS, ROBERT C., *Amphibians and Reptiles of Western North America*. N.Y., McGraw-Hill, 1954; 528 pp. — Identification of salamanders, frogs, toads, turtles, lizards and snakes.

WRIGHT, ALBERT H. and ANNA WRIGHT, *Handbook of Frogs and Toads of the United States and Canada*. Ithaca, N.Y., Comstock, 3rd ed., 1949; 640 pp. — Brief descriptions and methods of identification.

ZIM, HERBERT S. and HOBART M. SMITH, *Reptiles and Amphibians*. N.Y., Simon & Schuster, 1953; 157 pp. — How to study and identify turtles, lizards, snakes, frogs, alligators and salamanders.

BIRDS

ALLEN, ARTHUR A., *Stalking Birds with Color Camera*. Washington, Nat. Geog. Soc., 1951; 328 pp. — Contains wealth of natural color photographs.

FORD, ALICE (ed.), *The Bird Biographies of John James Audubon*. N.Y., Macmillan, 1957; 282 pp. — Collection of Audubon's descriptions of North American birds, with color reproductions.

GILLIARD, E. T., *Living Birds of the World*. N.Y., Doubleday, 1958; 400 pp. — Readable survey of world's birds. 400 photographs, 200 in color.

LEMMON, ROBERT S., *Our Amazing Birds*. N.Y., Doubleday, 1952; 239 pp. — Habitat, range, intel-

ligence and unusual characteristics of well-known and rare species.

MURPHY, ROBERT C. and DEAN AMADON, *Land Birds of America.* N.Y., McGraw-Hill, 1953; 240 pp. — Readable text prepared by two leading ornithologists and supplemented by natural habitat color photographs.

PETERSON, ROGER T., *How to Know the Birds.* Boston, Houghton Mifflin, 1949; 144 pp. — Beginner's guide to identification of over 200 common species.

WALLACE, GEORGE J., *Introduction to Ornithology.* N.Y., Macmillan, 1955; 443 pp. — College text covering evolution, anatomy, biology, behavior, conservation and management.

CRUSTACEANS. See INVERTEBRATES

ECOLOGY, ANIMAL (relation of animals to environment)

ALLEE, W. C. and KARL P. SCHMIDT, *Ecological Animal Geography.* N.Y., Wiley, 2nd ed., 1951; 715 pp. — Comprehensive and readable.

REID, LESLIE, *Earth's Company.* London, Murray, 1958; 221 pp. — Describes life of animals in relation to each other and to environment.

STORER, JOHN H., *The Web of Life.* N.Y., Devin-Adair, 1953; 144 pp. — Outstanding study of ecology; interesting material on conservation.

FISHES

Book of Fishes. (Publication of National Geographic Society.) Washington, D.C., Nat. Geog. Soc., 1952; 339 pp. — Noteworthy for excellent illustrations.

HERALD, EARL, *Living Fishes of the World.* N.Y., Doubleday, 1961; 304 pp. — Unusually beautiful volume with 145 color plates, accompanied by interesting and authoritative text.

LEDANOIS, EDOUARD, *Fishes of the World.* Woodstock, Vermont, Countryman Press, 1957; 190 pp. — Interesting and well-illustrated account.

NORMAN, J. R., *A History of Fishes.* N.Y., Hill & Wang, 1958; 463 pp. — Summary of our knowledge about fishes, their habits and evolutionary development.

INSECTS

BARKER, WILL, *Familiar Insects of America.* N.Y., Harper, 1960; 236 pp. — Exceptionally well-written and informative description of selected members of insect class.

BASTIN, HAROLD, *Insect Communities.* N.Y., Roy, 1957; 142 pp. — Habits and histories of ants, bees and wasps.

BORROR, DONALD J. and DWIGHT M. DELONG, *An Introduction to the Study of Insects.* N.Y., Rinehart, 1954; 1030 pp. — Guide to and description of insects found in United States; for serious students.

CLAUSEN, LUCY W., *Insect Fact and Folklore.* N.Y., Macmillan, 1954; 194 pp. — Unusual facts concerning insect life.

GAUL, ALBRO T., *The Wonderful World of Insects.* N.Y., Rinehart, 1953; 290 pp. — Insect habits and how they affect our lives.

KLOTS, ALEXANDER B., *The World of Butterflies and Moths.* N.Y., McGraw-Hill, 1958; 207 pp. — Comprehensive account by distinguished American authority; profusely illustrated.

LUTZ, FRANK E., *Field Book of Insects.* N.Y., Putnam, 1948; 510 pp. — Standard pocket field guide; includes most of the commonly observed insects in United States and Canada.

MICHENER, CHARLES D. and MARY H. MICHENER, *American Social Insects.* N.Y., Van Nostrand, 1951; 267 pp. — Life and habits of bees, wasps, ants and termites.

MORLEY, DEREK W., *The Evolution of an Insect Society.* N.Y., Scribner, 1954; 215 pp. — Deals with evolution of social mode of life among ants.

PESSON, PAUL, *World of Insects.* London, Harrap, 1959; 204 pp. — Bird's-eye view of evolution, physiology and behavior of insects. Fine illustrations.

VON FRISCH, KARL, *The Dancing Bees.* N.Y., Harcourt, Brace, 1955; 183 pp. — Life story of honey bees and discussion of their senses.

INVERTEBRATES

BERRILL, N. J., *The Living Tide.* N.Y., Fawcett, 1956; 239 pp. — Interesting account of marine life inhabiting Atlantic coast.

BUCHSBAUM, RALPH M., *Animals without Backbones.* Chicago, Univ. of Chicago Press, rev. ed., 1948; 405 pp. — Zoology of amebas, sponges, jellyfishes, starfishes, etc.

CARTER, G. S., *General Zoology of the Invertebrates.* London, Sidgwick & Jackson, 1948; 509 pp. — Introduction for college students.

HAUSMAN, LEON A., *Beginner's Guide to Seashore Life.* N.Y., Putnam, 1949, 128 pp. — Information on crustaceans, mollusks, sponges and corals.

MINER, ROY W., *Field Book of Seashore Life.* N.Y., Putnam, 1950; 888 pp. — Aid to rapid identification of invertebrates found off Atlantic coast of North America.

RAMSAY, J. A., *A Physiological Approach to the Lower Animals.* Cambridge, Cambridge Univ. Press, 1952; 148 pp. — Well-written general study of physiology of invertebrates.

ROGERS, JULIA ELLEN, *The Shell Book.* Newton Centre, Mass., Branford, 1951; 503 pp. — Authoritative guide for identification of shells.

MAMMALS

BOURLIÈRE, FRANCOIS, *The Natural History of Mammals.* N.Y., Knopf, 1956; 364 pp. — Interestingly presented story of mammalian locomotion, feeding habits, territory, reproduction and so on.

BURT, WILLIAM H., *Field Guide to the Mammals.* Boston, Houghton Mifflin, 1952; 200 pp. — Identifies and describes all species found north of the Mexican border.

MOORE, CLIFFORD B., *Ways of Mammals.* N.Y., Ronald Press, 1953; 273 pp. — Examines various superstitions and legends regarding animal behavior.

PALMER, RALPH S., *Mammal Guide.* N.Y., Doubleday, 1954; 384 pp. — Detailed descriptions of various families, from shrews to whales.

SANDERSON, IVAN T., *Living Mammals of the World.* N.Y., Garden City, 1955; 303 pp. — Comprehensive and readable; excellent photographs.

ZIM, HERBERT S. and DONALD F. HOFFMEISTER, *Mammals*; a guide to familiar American species. N.Y., Simon & Schuster, 1955; 160 pp. — Good for rapid identification.

MOLLUSKS. See INVERTEBRATES

ONE-CELLED ANIMALS

DUNCAN, WINIFRED, *Private Life of the Protozoa.* N.Y., Ronald Press, 1950; 141 pp. — Life and habits of various one-celled animals.

HALL, R. P., *Protozoology.* N.Y., Prentice Hall, 1953; 682 pp. — Covers major aspects of protozoology in scholarly but readable manner.

JAHN, THEODORE L. and FRANCES F. JAHN, *How to Know the Protozoa.* Dubuque, Iowa, Brown, 1949; 234 pp. — Student's guide, with pictured key for identifying common fresh-water, marine and parasitic protozoa.

REPTILES. See AMPHIBIANS AND REPTILES

SANCTUARIES, GAME AND BIRD

BAKER, JOHN HOPKINSON, ed., *Audubon Guide to Attracting Birds.* N.Y., Doubleday, 1941; 268 pp. — Includes material on managing sanctuary.

BLACK, JOHN D., *Biological Conservation.* N.Y., Blakiston, 1954; 328 pp. — Introduction to problems of wildlife conservation; excellent bibliography.

GABRIELSON, IRA N., *Wildlife Management.* N.Y., Macmillan, 1951; 274 pp. — Study of present-day problems in management and conservation of wildlife population.

McELROY, THOMAS P., *New Handbook of Attracting Birds.* N.Y., Knopf, rev. ed., 1960; 262 pp. — Advice on planting trees and shrubs for birds, building bird houses and starting sanctuary.

TILDEN, FREEMAN, *The National Parks.* N.Y., Knopf, rev. ed., 1954; 417 pp. — What national parks offer people of United States; fine photographs.

SPIDERS

DUNCAN, WINIFRED, *Webs in the Wind.* N.Y., Ronald Press, 1949; 387 pp. — Entertaining account of life history and behavior of spiders.

GERTSCH, WILLIS J., *American Spiders.* N.Y., Van Nostrand, 1949; 285 pp. — Comprehensive study of life and habits of spiders.

KASTON, B. J. and ELIZABETH KASTON, *How to Know the Spiders.* Dubuque, Iowa, Brown, 1953; 220 pp. — Consists primarily of series of keys for identification purposes; also contains much information.

LAMBURN, JOHN B. C., *Life of the Spider.* Boston, Houghton Mifflin, 1951; 254 pp. — Stresses unusual skills and accomplishments of spiders.

WORMS. See INVERTEBRATES

ZOOS

BENCHLEY, BELLE, *My Life in a Man-made Jungle.* Boston, Little, Brown, 1940; 293 pp. — Habits, care and selection of zoo inmates.

BLAIR, WILLIAM R., *In the Zoo.* N.Y., Scribner, 1929; 195 pp. — Varied and interesting information concerning behavior of animals in captivity.

BRIDGES, WILLIAM, *Big Zoo.* N.Y., Viking Press, 1952; 160 pp. — Behind-the-scene activities at New York Zoological Park told largely through pictures.

CANSDALE, GEORGE, *George Cansdale's Zoo Book.* London, Phoenix House, 1954; 64 pp. — Author's experiences as superintendent of the London Zoo; excellent photographs.

MAN

GENERAL WORKS

BARNETT, ANTHONY, *The Human Species.* Baltimore, Penguin, 1961; 354 pp. — How biology contributes to understanding of racial, population and food-production problems.

BOREK, ERNEST, *Man, the Chemical Machine.* N.Y., Columbia Univ. Press, 1952; 219 pp. — Chemical make-up and mechanism of human body.

CARREL, ALEXIS, *Man, the Unknown.* N.Y., Harper, 1939; 346 pp. — Survey of science's contribution to our knowledge of man and his functions.

HENSILL, JOHN S., *Biology of Man.* N.Y., Blakiston, 1954; 440 pp. — Principles of animal biology as applied to man.

MARTIN, PHYLLIS C. and ELIZABETH LEE VINCENT, *Human Development.* N.Y., Ronald Press, 1960; 542 pp. — Interestingly written introduction to human biology for advanced high-school biology classes.

RAVIELLI, ANTHONY, *Wonders of the Human Body.* N.Y., Viking, 1954; 125 pp. — Nontechnical introduction for laymen.

SPROUL, EDITH E., *The Science Book of the Human Body.* N.Y., Watts, 1955; 232 pp. — Nontechnical and skillfully illustrated presentation.

ANATOMY

CATES, H. A., *Primary Anatomy.* Baltimore, Williams & Wilkins, 4th ed., 1960; 360 pp. — Text for nonmedical students.

FROHSE, FRANZ ET AL, *Atlas of Human Anatomy.* N.Y., Barnes & Noble, 1961; 180 pp. — Excellent anatomical charts, supplemented by good test for advanced high-school students.

KIMBER, DIANA C. and C. E. GRAY, *Textbook of Anatomy and Physiology.* N.Y., Macmillan, 14th ed., 1961; 779 pp. — Elementary treatment of subject.

MARSHALL, CLYDE, *An Introduction to Human Anatomy.* Phila., Saunders, 4th ed., 1955; 420 pp. — General anatomy for students and laymen.

PHYSIOLOGY

ASIMOV, ISAAC, *The Living River.* N.Y., Abelard-Schuman, 1959; 232 pp. — Comprehensive description of human blood stream and related systems.

BEST, CHARLES H. and N. B. TAYLOR, *The Human Body; Its Anatomy and Physiology.* N.Y., Holt, 3rd ed., 1956; 783 pp. — Clear and simple account, particularly suited to lay readers.

CARLSON, ANTON J. and VICTOR JOHNSON, *The Machinery of the Body.* Chicago, Univ. of Chicago Press, 5th ed., 1961; 752 pp. — Good introduction to physiology at college level.

CLENDENING, LOGAN, *The Human Body.* N.Y., Knopf, 4th ed., 1945; 443 pp. — Popular introductory work.

STACKPOLE, CAROLINE E. and LUTIE C. LEAVELL, *Textbook of Physiology.* N.Y., Macmillan, 1953; 418 pp. — Good introduction at college level.

YOUMANS, W. B., *Human Physiology.* N.Y., Macmillan, 1954; 481 pp. — Elementary text for beginning students and laymen.

PSYCHOLOGY

Carmichael, Leonard, *Basic Psychology.* N.Y., Random House, 1957; 340 pp. — Nontechnical introduction to psychology of normal adults.

Engle, T. L., *Psychology: Its Principles and Applications.* N.Y., Harcourt, Brace, World, 3rd ed., 1957; 657 pp. — Modern approach to human behavior.

Munn, Norman L., *The Evolution and Growth of Human Behavior.* Boston, Houghton Mifflin, 1955; 525 pp. — Environment, inheritance and human association in development of human mind.

Murphy, Gardiner, *Historical Introduction to Modern Psychology.* N.Y., Harcourt, Brace, 2nd ed., 1949; 466 pp. — One of most readable accounts of origin and development of psychology.

Strecker, Edward A. and Kenneth E. Appel, *Discovering Ourselves,* 3rd ed., 1958; 303 pp. — Elementary and readable information about human behavior and moving forces in human nature and in society.

HEALTH

GENERAL WORKS

Diehl, Harold S., *Textbook of Healthful Living.* N.Y., McGraw-Hill, 5th ed., 1955; 802 pp. — Comprehensive guide to personal hygiene.

Meredith, Florence L., *The Science of Health.* N.Y., Blakiston, 3rd ed., 1957; 492 pp. — Introduction to fundamentals of physical and mental health.

Rossman, I. J. and D. R. Schwartz, *Family Handbook of Home Nursing and Medical Care.* N.Y., Doubleday, 1958; 403 pp. — Sound information concerning illness and nursing procedures.

Smiley, Dean F. and Adrian G. Gould, *Your Health.* N.Y., Macmillan, 1951; 555 pp. — How to develop sensible habits of living.

AIR POLLUTION

Meetham, A. R., *Atmospheric Pollution: Its Origins and Prevention.* London, Pergamon Press, 2nd ed., 1956; 302 pp. — Stresses preventive measures.

Mills, C. A., *Air Pollution and Community Health.* Boston, Christopher Pub. House, 1954; 180 pp. — Interesting account for layman by expert.

World Health Organization, *Air Pollution.* N.Y., Columbia Univ. Press, 1961; 442 pp. — Advanced and comprehensive study of effects of pollution on plants and humans; considers preventive measures.

ALCOHOL, EFFECTS OF

Blakeslee, Alton L., *Alcoholism;* a sickness that can be beaten. N.Y., Public Affairs Committee, 1952; 32 pp. — Facts about alcoholism.

Lovell, Harold W., *Hope and Help for the Alcoholic.* N.Y., Doubleday, 1951; 218 pp. — Excellent presentation of problems of alcoholism and current methods of treating victims.

McCarthy, Raymond G., ed., *Drinking and Intoxication.* N.Y., Free Press, 1959; 455 pp. — Series of selected readings, giving historical background of alcoholic beverages.

McCarthy, Raymond G. and Edgar M. Douglass, *Alcohol and Social Responsibility.* N.Y., Crowell, 1949; 304 pp. — Problems associated with the use of alcoholic beverages in our society.

DIETETICS

Barach, Joseph H., *Food and Facts for the Diabetic.* N.Y., Oxford Univ. Press, 1949; 113 pp. — Includes valuable material on proper diets for sufferers from diabetes.

Field, Richard M., *The Complete Book of Diets.* N.Y., Doubleday, 1942; 272 pp. — Layman's guide to role of correct diet in preventive medicine.

Gerard, Ralph W., ed., *Food for Life.* Chicago, Univ. of Chicago Press, 1952; 306 pp. — Explanation of body's processes and requirements as aid to intelligent selection of food.

Macy, Icie G. and Harold H. Williams, *Hidden Hunger.* N.Y., Ronald Press, 1945; 286 pp. — Part played by proper diet in life of individual and nation.

Sherman, Henry C., *Chemistry of Food and Nutrition.* N.Y., Macmillan, 8th ed., 1952; 721 pp. — Standard and useful guide to relationship of nutrition, health and efficiency.

————, *Food and Health.* N.Y., Macmillan, 1947; 290 pp. — Selection of foods and diets to obtain an optimum level of health.

EXERCISE

Drew, Lillian C., *Individual Gymnastics.* Phila., Lea & Febiger, 5th ed., 1945; 253 pp. — Practical book of instruction with many diagrams.

Gawer, Herman and Herbert Michelman, *Body Control;* how to build up, reduce or strengthen any part of your body. N.Y., Crown, 1950; 134 pp. — Title gives good idea of book.

Lane, Janet, *Your Carriage, Madam!* N.Y., Wiley, 2nd ed., 1947; 160 pp. — Suggestions for maintaining good posture.

Mensendreck, Bess M., *Look Better, Feel Better.* N.Y., Harper, 1954; 276 pp. — System of exercises that has proved successful in correcting body weaknesses and faulty posture.

GERIATRICS (branch of medicine dealing with old age and its diseases)

Gilbert, Jeanne G., *Understanding Old Age.* N.Y., Ronald Press, 1952; 422 pp. — Physiological, pathological and sociological aspects of aging.

Johnson, Wingate M., *The Years after Fifty.* N.Y., McGraw-Hill, 1947; 153 pp. — Clear discussion of bodily changes which may occur in person over 50.

Shock, Nathan W., *Trends in Gerontology.* Stanford, Cal., Stanford Univ. Press, rev. ed., 1957; 214 pp. — Problem of aging American population and what is being done about it.

Stieglitz, Edward J., *The Second Forty Years.* Phila., Lippincott, rev. ed., 1952; 317 pp. — Simple account of aging process and how to maintain good mental and physical health in old age.

HEATING AND VENTILATION

Adlam, Thomas N., *Radiant Heating.* N.Y., Industrial Press, 2nd ed., 1949; 504 pp. — Comprehensive manual for architects and heating engineers.

Graham, Frank D., *Audels House Heating Guide.* N.Y., Audel, 1948; 966 pp. — Clear and practical guide to basic principles, methods of installation and servicing.

Holmes, Richard E., *Air Conditioning in Summer*

and Winter. N.Y., McGraw-Hill, 2nd ed., 1951; 352 pp. — Elementary and practical treatment of basic principles and equipment.

SHANK, J. L., *Modern Methods of Home Heating.* N.Y., Simmons-Boardman, 1948; 64 pp. — Background information for home builders.

STOUT, G. J., *Home Air Conditioning.* Princeton, N.J., Van Nostrand, 1956; 276 pp. — Cost, design, performance and selection of room conditioners and central systems.

MEDICINE, PROGRESS OF

CAMERON, CHARLES S., *The Truth about Cancer.* Englewood Cliffs, N.J., Prentice-Hall, 1956; 268 pp. — Survey of known facts; good introduction to subject for laymen.

GARLAND, JOSEPH, *Story of Medicine.* Boston, Houghton Mifflin, 1949; 258 pp. — Major advances in knowledge of human body, its diseases and their cure.

GOFMAN, JOHN W., *What We Do Know about Heart Attacks.* N.Y., Putnam, 1958; 180 pp. — Clear and objective treatment of latest facts.

HAGGARD, HOWARD W., *Mystery, Magic and Medicine.* N.Y., Doubleday, 1933; 192 pp. — Development of medical science from earliest beginnings to close of 19th century.

WRIGHT, HELEN and SAMUEL RAPPORT, *The Amazing World of Medicine.* N.Y., Harper, 1961; 302 pp. — Account of great pioneering discoveries in medicine.

REINFELD, FRED, *Miracle Drugs and the New Age of Medicine.* N.Y., Sterling, rev. ed., 1959; 115 pp. — Development and production of modern drugs from antibiotics to tranquilizers. Beautifully illustrated.

SPENCER, STEVEN M., *Wonders of Modern Medicine.* N.Y., McGraw-Hill, 1953; 276 pp. — Informative account of outstanding medical advances of recent times.

See also PUBLIC HEALTH MOVEMENT

NARCOTICS

DEUTSCH, ALBERT, *What Can We Do about the Drug Menace?* N.Y., Public Affairs Committee, 1952; 32 pp. — Study of drug addiction.

MAURER, DAVID W. and VICTOR H. VOGEL, *Narcotics and Narcotic Addiction.* Springfield, Ill., Thomas, 1954; 303 pp. — Describes various drugs of addiction and their physiological and psychological effects.

WESTON, PAUL B., ed., *Narcotics, U.S.A.* N.Y., Greenberg, 1952; 319 pp. — Panel of experts deals with drug addiction in United States.

YOST, ORIN R., *The Bane of Drug Addiction.* N.Y., Macmillan, 1954; 155 pp. — Professional psychiatrist and social worker points out necessity for united attack against drug addiction.

PSYCHIATRY

BLUEMEL, C. S., *Psychiatry and Common Sense.* N.Y., Macmillan, 1954; 259 pp. — Introductory treatment for layman.

EIDELBERG, LUDWIG, *Take Off Your Mask.* N.Y., International Universities Press, 1948; 230 pp. — Principles and methods of psychiatry presented in form of condensed case histories.

HUGHES, MARGARET M., ed., *The People in Your*

Life. N.Y., Knopf, 1951; 278 pp. — Provides layman with understanding of himself and his relations with other people.

MENNINGER, WILLIAM C. and MUNRO LEAF, *You and Psychiatry.* N.Y., Scribner, 1948; 175 pp. — Workings of human mind and how normal behavior can become abnormal.

MORGAN, JOHN J. B., *How to Keep a Sound Mind.* N.Y., Macmillan, 1946; 404 pp. — Evidences of mental ill-health and methods of developing good mental habits.

RAY, MARIE B., *Doctors of the Mind.* Boston, Little, Brown, 1946; 356 pp. — Readable account of major techniques employed in psychiatry.

STRECKER, EDWIN A., *Basic Psychiatry.* N.Y., Random House, 1952; 473 pp. — Simplified account of human problems that require psychiatric attention.

PUBLIC HEALTH MOVEMENT

BROCKINGTON, FRASER, *World Health.* Baltimore, Penguin, 1958; 405 pp. — Discusses public-health approach to modern social problems.

DUBLIN, LOUIS I., *The Facts of Life from Birth to Death.* N.Y., Macmillan, 1951; 461 pp. — Interesting data regarding population, birth, marriage, causes of illness and death, incidence of specific diseases, etc.

GOODMAN, NEVILLE M., *International Health Organizations and Their Work.* N.Y., Blakiston, 1952; 327 pp. — Detailed account for serious reader.

MCNEIL, DONALD R., *Fight for Fluoridation.* N.Y., Oxford Univ. Pr., 1957; 241 pp. — Absorbing history of a controversial subject.

SCHUBERT, JACK and RALPH E. LAPP, *Radiation; what it is and how it affects you.* N.Y., Viking Press, 1957; 314 pp. — Present and future menace of uncontrolled radiation.

SMILEY, DEAN F. and A. G. GOULD, *Your Community's Health.* N.Y., Macmillan, 1952; 454 pp. — Review of community health practices for professional worker and interested layman.

WINSLOW, CHARLES E. A., *Man and Epidemics.* Princeton, N.J., Princeton Univ. Press, 1952; 246 pp. — Narrative account of public health movement and its achievements.

SLEEP

BENDER, JAMES, *How to Sleep.* N.Y., Coward-McCann, 1949; 243 pp. — Physiological and psychological facts about sleep.

ROSENTEUR, PHYLLIS, *Morpheus and Me; the Complete Book of Sleep.* N.Y., Funk, 1957; 344 pp. — Amusing and informative work.

TOBACCO, EFFECTS OF

LIEB, CLARENCE W., *Safer Smoking.* N.Y., Exposition Press, 1953; 106 pp. — Facts regarding the relationship between smoking and health; excellent bibliography.

OSTROW, ALBERT A., *Why Stop Smoking?* N.Y., Dutton, 1955; 94 pp. — Plea for moderation in smoking.

WYNDER, ERNEST L., ed., *The Biologic Effects of Tobacco.* Boston, Little, Brown, 1955; 215 pp. — Discusses cause and effect relations between tobacco and disease.

VENTILATION. See HEATING AND VENTILATION

WATER SUPPLY

BAKER, MOSES N., *The Quest for Pure Water*. N.Y., American Water Works Association, 1948; 527 pp. — Comprehensive history of water purification methods.

GAINEY, P. L. and THOMAS H. LORD, *Microbiology of Water and Sewage*. Englewood Cliffs, N.J., Prentice-Hall, 1952; 432 pp. — Basic principles underlying supply of water and disposal of sewage.

MATHEMATICS

ADLER, IRVING, *The New Mathematics*, N.Y., Day, 1958; 187 pp. — Gives lay reader idea of new developments in secondary-school and college courses.

BAKST, AARON, *Mathematical Puzzles and Pastimes*. Princeton, N.J., Van Nostrand, 1954; 206 pp. — Diverting examples of lighter moments with mathematics.

BELL, ERIC TEMPLE, *Mathematics, Queen and Servant of the Sciences*. N.Y., McGraw-Hill, 1951; 437 pp. — Panorama of mathematics; written so that reader may avoid difficult or uninteresting parts.

BERKELEY, EDMUND C. and LAWRENCE WAINWRIGHT, *Computers: Their Operation and Applications*. N.Y., Reinhold, 1956; 366 pp. — Presents basic information about digital, analog and miniature computers.

HOGBEN, LANCELOT, *Mathematics for the Million*. N.Y., Norton, 3rd ed., 1951; 695 pp. — Exciting introduction for serious student.

————, *Mathematics in the Making*. N.Y., Doubleday, 1961; 320 pp. — Outstanding illustrated history of mathematics with general appeal.

KASNER, EDWARD, and JAMES NEWMAN, *Mathematics and the Imagination*. N.Y., Simon and Schuster, 1940; 381 pp. — Classical work; stimulating discussion for intermediate student.

KRAMER, EDNA E., *The Main Stream of Mathematics*. N.Y., Oxford Univ. Pr., 1951; 321 pp. — Historical development of mathematics for serious student.

TITCHMARSH, E. C., *Mathematics for the General Reader*. N.Y., Doubleday, 1959; 197 pp. — Well-written introduction for beginner.

MATTER AND ENERGY

A: Chemistry

GENERAL WORKS

FINDLAY, ALEXANDER, *Hundred Years of Chemistry*. N.Y., Macmillan, 2nd ed., 1948; 318 pp. — Condensed and readable history of modern chemistry.

JAFFE, BERNARD, *Crucibles: the Story of Chemistry from Ancient Alchemy to Nuclear Fission*. N.Y., Fawcett, rev. ed., 1960; 480 pp. — Simple and dramatic account of growth of chemical knowledge.

PAULING, LINUS, *College Chemistry*. San Francisco, Freeman, 2nd ed., 1955; 685 pp. — Outstanding introduction to subject for college students.

POSIN, DANIEL Q., *Chemistry for the Space Age*. Phila., Lippincott, 1961; 680 pp. — Well-illustrated and up-to-date high school chemistry text.

SNELL, CORNELIA and F. S. SNELL, *Chemistry Made Easy*. N.Y., Chemical Pub., 1959; 704 pp. — Inorganic and organic chemistry for nonscientists.

TAYLOR, MODDIE D., *First Principles of Chemistry*. Princeton, N.J., Van Nostrand, 1960; 688 pp. — Novel combination of necessary mathematics and physics with detailed, orderly presentation of chemistry.

WEAVER, ELBERT C. and LAURENCE S. FOSTER, *Chemistry for Our Times*. N.Y., McGraw-Hill, 2nd ed., 1954; 666 pp. — Attractive and well-written text at high-school level.

ANALYTICAL CHEMISTRY (books listed here offer good introduction to subject; they presuppose knowledge of elementary chemistry)

HOGNESS, THORFIN R. and WARREN C. JOHNSON, *An Introduction to Qualitative Analysis*. N.Y., Holt, 1957; 376 pp.

VAN PEURSEM, RALPH L., *Elementary Quantitative Analysis*. N.Y., McGraw-Hill, 1953; 383 pp.

ATOM, STRUCTURE OF. See PHYSICS — ATOMIC ENERGY

COLLOIDS

McBAIN, JAMES W., *Colloid Science*. N.Y., Reinhold, 1950; 450 pp. — Introduction to colloid phenomena and its practical applications.

MYSELS, K. J., *Introduction to Colloid Chemistry*. N.Y., Interscience, 1959; 475 pp. — General discussion of colloids, colloidal dispersion and related topics.

See GENERAL WORKS for more elementary treatment of subject

CRYSTALS

HOLDEN, ALAN and PHYLLIS SINGER, *Crystals and Crystal Growing*. N.Y., Doubleday, 1960; 320 pp. — Basic explanation of theory and practice of modern crystallography, including home experiments.

WAHLSTROM, ERNEST E., *Optical Crystallography*. N.Y., Wiley, 3rd ed., 1960; 356 pp. — Outlines fundamental concepts and describes techniques and instruments involved.

ELECTROCHEMISTRY

BLUM, WILLIAM, *Principles of Electroplating and Electroforming*. N.Y., McGraw-Hill, 3rd ed., 1949; 455 pp. — Describes techniques of electroplating; emphasizes basic principles and chemical reactions.

SANDERS, A. H., *Electroplating*. Scranton, Pa., International Textbook Co., 1950; 118 pp. — Briefly describes basic principles and techniques; for amateur worker.

ELEMENTS

ASIMOV, ISAAC, *Building Blocks of the Universe*. N.Y., Abelard-Schuman, rev. ed., 1961; 280 pp. — For beginners. Tells who discovered elements; how they were discovered; how they got names; their uses.

DAVIS, HELEN A. M., *The Chemical Elements*; with revisions by Glenn T. Seaborg. Washington, Science Service, 2nd ed. rev., 1959; 198 pp. — Basic facts concerning discovery and properties of elements.

SEABORG, GLENN T. and E. G. VALENS, *Elements of the Universe*. N.Y., Dutton, 1958; 253 pp. — Up-to-date and clear presentation of development of chemistry from the alchemists to the most recently discovered elements.

WEEKS, MARY E., *Discovery of the Elements*. Easton, Pa., Journal of Chemical Education, 1956;

910 pp. — Tells story of scientists who played major role in discovery of chemical elements.

INDUSTRIAL APPLICATIONS

FINDLAY, ALEXANDER, *Chemistry in the Service of Man*. London, Longmans, 8th ed., 1957; 326 pp. — An account of what chemistry has accomplished in improving man's well-being.

HOLMES, HARRY N., *Out of the Test Tube*. N.Y., Emerson, 5th ed., 1956; 313 pp. — Importance of chemistry in our daily life.

PYKE, MAGNUS, *About Chemistry*. N.Y., Macmillan, 1960; 219 pp. — Outline of industrial uses of chemistry, with stress laid on applications of synthetics. Written particularly for layman.

TAYLOR, F. SHERWOOD, *A History of Industrial Chemistry*. N.Y., Abelard-Schuman, 1957; 467 pp. — Shows how chemical knowledge and craftsman's skill are fused to produce modern chemical industry.

INORGANIC CHEMISTRY

EMELEUS, H. J. and J. S. ANDERSON, *Modern Aspects of Inorganic Chemistry*. N.Y., Van Nostrand, 3rd ed., 1960; 611 pp. — Good introduction to subject at college level.

PARKES, G. D., *Mellor's Modern Inorganic Chemistry*. N.Y., Longmans, rev. ed., 1961; 1,048 pp. — Detailed text on chemical and physical change, including exhaustive description of elements.

See also GENERAL WORKS

ORGANIC CHEMISTRY

ASIMOV, ISAAC, *The World of Carbon*. N.Y., Abelard-Schuman, 1958; 178 pp. — Describes relation of organic chemistry to daily living; excellent introduction for laymen.

FIESER, LOUIS F. and MARY FIESER, *Introduction to Organic Chemistry*. Boston, Heath, 1957; 613 pp. — Comprehensive text for one-year course, with additional section on "applications to research," for superior students.

MACY, RUDOLPH, *Organic Chemistry Simplified*. N.Y., Chemical Pub. Co., 2nd ed., 1955; 611 pp. — Textbook suitable for home study; stresses industrial applications.

READ, J. and F. D. GUNSTONE, *Textbook of Organic Chemistry*. London, Bell, 4th ed., 1958; 610 pp. — Clear and lucid treatment for beginners.

B: Physics

GENERAL WORKS

KNAUSS, HAROLD P., *Discovering Physics*. Cambridge, Addison-Wesley, 1951; 443 pp. — Introductory text at high school level.

MARBURGER, W. G. and C. W. HOFFMAN, *Physics for Our Times*. N.Y., McGraw-Hill, 2nd ed., 1958; 602 pp. — Readable style and attractive format make this volume well-suited for beginning student.

POLLACK, PHILIP, *Careers and Opportunities in Physics*. N.Y., Dutton, rev. ed., 1961; 159 pp. — Useful outline of field.

RESNICK, ROBERT and DAVID HALLIDAY, *Physics: for Students of Science and Engineering*. N.Y., Wiley, 1960; 1075 pp. — Emphasis placed on problem-solving, particularly in mechanics, heat and sound.

ROGERS, ERIC M., *Physics for the Inquiring Mind*. Princeton, N.J., Princeton Univ. Press, 1960; 778 pp. — For serious layman; no mere survey course, but requires active study and thought.

SEARS, F. W. and M. W. ZEMANSKY, *College Physics*. Cambridge, Mass., Addison-Wesley, 3rd ed., 1960; 1024 pp. — Vivid presentation of subject; many graphic illustrations.

SLATER, JOHN C., *Modern Physics*. N.Y., McGraw-Hill, 1955; 322 pp. — A substantial but not too difficult treatment for general reader.

WHITE, HARVEY E., *Modern College Physics*. Princeton, Van Nostrand, 3rd ed., 1956; 824 pp. — Outstanding text, covering all basic fields of physics, including modern atomic physics.

ATOMIC ENERGY

FRISCH, OTTO R., *Atomic Physics Today*. N.Y., Basic Books, 1961; 254 pp. — Gives good idea of great unsolved problems of physics, particularly those involving fundamental particles of matter.

GAMOW, GEORGE, *The Atom and Its Nucleus*. Englewood Cliffs, N.J., Prentice-Hall, 1961; 153 pp. — Basic principles of atomic structure and interaction of particles; for laymen.

GLASSTONE, SAMUEL, *Sourcebook on Atomic Energy*. Princeton, N.J., Van Nostrand, 2nd ed., 1958; 641 pp. — Comprehensive survey for serious students.

HECHT, SELIG, *Explaining the Atom*. N.Y., Viking Press, rev. ed., 1954; 237 pp. — Explains difficult subject in terms layman can understand.

LAURENCE, WILLIAM L., *Men and Atoms*. N.Y., Simon & Schuster, 1959; 312 pp. — Account of atomic age from its beginnings to the present time by distinguished science reporter.

STOKLEY, JAMES, *The New World of the Atom*, N.Y., Ives Washburn, 1957; 288 pp. — Noted science writer tells story of atomic energy, its present uses in war and peace and what lies ahead.

WOODBURY, DAVID O., *Atoms for Peace*. N.Y., Dodd, Mead, 1955; 259 pp. — How nuclear energy is being used for benefit of mankind.

COLOR

BIRREN, FABER, *New Horizons in Color*. N.Y., Reinhold, 1955; 200 pp. — Nature of light and color, and survey of applications of light and color in business and industry.

CREWDSON, FREDERICK M., *Color in Decoration and Design*. Wilmette, Ill., Drake, 1953; 232 pp. — Gives material on general theory of color.

HARTRIDGE, H., *Colours and How We See Them*. London, Bell, 1949; 158 pp. — Authoritative and readable explanation of how colors are produced and seen.

MINNAERT, MARCELLUS, *Nature of Light and Color in the Open Air*. N.Y., Dover, 1954; 362 pp. — Interesting work for serious student.

MURRAY, HUMPHREY D., *Colour in Theory and Practice*. London, Chapman & Hall, 1952; 360 pp. — Comprehensive survey of color science.

COSMIC RAYS

AUGER, PIERRE, *What Are Cosmic Rays?* Chicago, Univ. of Chicago Press, 1945; 128 pp. — One of first discussions of subject for educated laymen.

LEPRINCE-RINGUET, LOUIS, *Cosmic Rays.* N.Y., Prentice-Hall, 1950; 290 pp. — Authoritative and readable presentation of highly technical subject.

ELECTRICITY

CORNETET, WENDELL H., *Principles of Electricity.* Bloomington, Ill., McKnight, 1952; 341 pp. — Stresses practical application of electrical principles and theory.

DUNSHEATH, PERRY, *Electricity: How It Works.* N.Y., Crowell, 1960; 248 pp. — For high school students; contains instructions for experiments.

EATON, J. R., *Beginning Electricity.* N.Y., Macmillan, 1952; 365 pp. — Written especially for reader lacking mathematical training beyond high school level.

GRAHAM, KENNARD C. (ed.), *Fundamentals of Electricity.* Chicago, Amer. Tech. Soc., 1960; 342 pp. — Introduction to electricity, containing abundant diagrams and complete dictionary of terms.

MCDOUGAL, W. and others, *Fundamentals of Electricity.* Chicago, Amer. Tech. Soc., 4th ed., 1960; 342 pp. — Good introduction; many fine diagrams.

MORGAN, BRYAN, *Men and Discoveries in Electricity.* London, Murray, 1952; 188 pp. — History of electricity told by its discoverers.

ELECTRONICS

BUKSTEIN, EDWARD J., *Magic of Electronics.* N.Y., Ungar, 1954; 256 pp. — Brief nontechnical descriptions of basic principles and methods of operation of electronic devices.

HICKEY, HENRY V. and WILLIAM M. VILLINES, *Elements of Electronics.* N.Y., McGraw-Hill, 2nd ed., 1961; 560 pp. — Basic text for beginners.

LEWELLEN, JOHN, *Understanding Electronics from Vacuum Tube to Thinking Machine.* N.Y., Crowell, 1957; 213 pp. — Lucid introduction to subject for either juveniles or adults.

OLDFIELD, R. L., *Radio-Television and Basic Electronics.* Chicago, Amer. Tech. Soc., 2nd ed., 1960; 400 pp. — Good introduction; useful for beginners and advanced students.

PIERCE, JOHN R., *Electrons, Waves and Messages.* N.Y., Doubleday, 1956; 318 pp. — Science of electronics and electronics of communication. Excellent collateral reading for physics course.

UPTON, MONROE, *Electronics for Everyone.* N.Y., Devin-Adair, 2nd rev. ed., 1959; 386 pp. — Evolution of electronics and latest developments described in simple terms.

HEAT

CROFT, TERRELL W., *Practical Heat.* N.Y., McGraw-Hill, 2nd ed., 1939; 726 pp. — Stresses practical applications; includes simplified explanations of fundamental theory.

DEAN, F. E., *Engines for Power and Speed.* London, Temple Press, 1952; 81 pp. — Operation and uses of steam and gas turbines, internal-combustion engines and jet engines.

MACDONALD, D. K. C., *Near Zero.* N.Y., Doubleday, 1961; 116 pp. — Interesting study of behavior of materials at very low temperatures.

RANSHAW, G. S., *Great Engines and Their Inventors.* London, Burke, 1950; 212 pp. — Basic principles of operation of various types of engines utilizing heat as source of power.

SOLBERG, HARRY L., *Elementary Heat Power.* N.Y., Wiley, 2nd ed., 1952; 624 pp. — Principles and operation of heat-power machinery.

LIGHT AND ILLUMINATION

ADLER, IRVING, *Secret of Light.* N.Y., International Pub. Co., 1952; 96 pp. — Basic principles and properties of light.

COLLIS, JOHN STEWARD, *The World of Light.* N.Y., Horizon, 1960; 180 pp. — Introduction to nature of light and its role in our civilization; well-written work for beginners.

COOK, JAMES GORDON, *We Live by the Sun.* London, Harrap, 1957; 183 pp. — Interesting work; covers wide range of phenomena associated with production and use of light.

DOGIGLI, JOHANNES, *The Magic of Rays.* N.Y., Knopf, 1961; 264 pp. — Complete coverage of light and other forms of radiation at high-school level.

RUCHLIS, HY, *The Wonder of Light.* N.Y., Harper, 1960; 154 pp. — Well-written and abundantly illustrated presentation for general reader.

RUECHARDT, EDUARD, *Light, Visible and Invisible.* Ann Arbor, Univ. of Michigan Press, 1958; 201 pp. — Introduction to nature and behavior of light, for the general reader.

MAGNETISM

DAUNT, J. G., *Electrons in Action.* London, Sigma Books, 1946; 151 pp. — Nonmathematical outline of basic principles of electricity and magnetism.

LEMON, HARVEY B., *What We Know and Don't Know about Magnetism.* Chicago, Museum of Science & Industry, 1946; 58 pp. — Clear and concise presentation for nonscientist.

See also ELECTRICITY

MUSIC, PHYSICAL BASIS OF

BARTHOLOMEW, WILMER T., *Acoustics of Music.* N.Y., Prentice-Hall, 1942; 242 pp. — Comprehensive treatment of subject; has long been regarded as an outstanding presentation.

BENADE, ARTHUR H., *Horns, Strings and Harmony.* N.Y., Doubleday, 1960; 271 pp. — Discussion of physical basis of music and musical instruments for high-school students.

CULVER, CHARLES A., *Musical Acoustics.* Phila., Blakiston, 4th ed., 1956; 305 pp. — Elementary text on physics of musical sounds.

See also SOUND

RADIOACTIVITY. See ATOMIC ENERGY

SOUND

BUNTAINE, ROBERT R., *A Story of Sound.* Chicago, Burgess-Manning, 1945; 34 pp. — Brief and elementary explanation of phenomena of sound.

HOLTON, GERALD J., *Story of Sound.* N.Y., Harcourt, Brace, 1948; 74 pp. — Includes material on musical sounds and musical instruments.

PIERCE, JOHN R. and E. E. David, *Man's World of Sound.* N.Y., Doubleday, 1958; 287 pp. — Principles of speech and hearing.

MILLER, DAYTON C., *Anecdotal History of the Science of Sound to the Beginning of the 20th Century.* N.Y., Macmillan, 1935; 114 pp. — Principal events in progress of science of sound.

X RAYS

CLARK, GEORGE L., *Applied X Rays.* N.Y., McGraw-Hill, 4th ed., 1955; 843 pp. — Sufficiently nontechnical to be of value to laymen.

GLASSER, OTTO, *Physical Foundations of Radiology.* N.Y., Hoeber, 2nd ed., 1952; 181 pp. — Nonmathematical discussion of production, properties and uses of X rays; intended primarily for medical students.

WEYL, CHARLES and S. R. WARREN, *Radiologic Physics.* Springfield, Ill., C. C. Thomas, 2nd ed., 1951; 491 pp. — Standard text on physical principles of X rays; requires some knowledge of mathematics and physics.

INDUSTRY

GENERAL WORKS

BRADY, GEORGE S., *Materials Handbook.* N.Y., McGraw-Hill, 8th ed., 1956; 1,022 pp. — Encyclopedic treatment of many materials of all kinds used in civilized world, arranged by commonly known names.

CROWTHER, J. G., *Discoveries and Inventions of the 20th Century.* London, Routledge, 4th ed., 1955; 432 pp. — Comprehensive review of recent developments in fields of power, metallurgy, communication, transportation, etc.

DERRY, T. K. and TREVOR I. WILLIAMS, *A Short History of Technology.* N.Y., Oxford Press, 1961; 782 pp. — From early Egyptian times to nineteenth century.

FORBES, R. J., *Man the Maker.* N.Y., Abelard-Schuman, rev. ed., 1958; 365 pp. — Comprehensive review of development of tools and techniques.

LEYSON, BURR W., *Marvels of Industrial Science.* N.Y., Dutton, 1955; 189 pp. — Describes manufacture of synthetic fibers, cellulose derivatives, glass silicones and other scientific marvels.

OLIVER, JOHN W., *History of American Technology.* N.Y., Ronald, 1956; 676 pp. — Nontechnical historical survey of development of applied science in the United States and its effect on culture.

PRINGLE, PATRICK, *How It's Made.* London, Ward, 1951; 239 pp. — Manufacture of such common things as soap, coinage, pottery, carpets, tin cans, razor blades, etc.

ROSS, FRANK, JR., *Automation: Servant to Man.* N.Y., Lothrop, 1958; 216 pp. — Aimed at junior-high-school student; stress on electronic computers.

WILSON, MITCHELL, *American Science and Invention.* N.Y., Simon & Schuster, 1954; 437 pp. — Readable and profusely illustrated account of progress of American industrial science.

WOODBURY, DAVID, *Let ERMA Do It.* N.Y., Harcourt, 1956; 305 pp. — What automation is, how it is applied and how it will affect our lives.

CERAMICS

HOME, RUTH M., *Ceramics for the Potter.* Peoria, Ill., Bennett, 1953; 299 pp. — Blend of historical, scientific and technical information regarding pottery manufacture.

HYMAN, N. R., *The Ceramics Handbook.* N.Y., Arco, 1959; 144 pp. — Methods of mold-making, glazing and other ceramic processes.

KENNY, JOHN B., *The Complete Book of Pottery Making.* N.Y., Greenberg, 1949; 252 pp. — Practical guide to pottery making for beginner and advanced craftsman.

CHEMURGY

BORTH, CHRISTY, *Pioneers of Plenty.* Indianapolis, Bobbs-Merrill, 1942; 410 pp. — How agricultural products are being utilized in industrial chemistry.

McMILLEN, WHEELER, *New Riches from the Soil.* N.Y., Van Nostrand, 1946; 397 pp. — History, practical developments and social importance of chemurgy.

ROSIN, JACOB and MAX EASTMAN, *The Road to Abundance.* N.Y., McGraw-Hill, 1953; 166 pp. — Shows contributions of chemical industry to production of food and clothing.

COAL

MOORE, ELWOOD S., *Coal, Its Properties, Analysis, Classification, Geology, Extraction, Uses and Distribution.* N.Y., Wiley, 2nd ed., 1940; 473 pp. — Comprehensive; but reduces technical detail to minimum.

PERRY, JOSEPHINE, *The Coal Industry.* N.Y., Longmans, Green, 1944; 128 pp. — Elementary account of formation of coal, its production and economic importance.

ROWLANDS, DOROTHY H., *Coal and All about It.* London, Harrap, 1945; 236 pp. — Interesting presentation for general reader.

CONSTRUCTION

Buildings for Industry: an Architectural Record Book of F. W. Dodge Corporation. N.Y., 1957; 309 pp. — Analysis of 74 industrial showplaces in United States and various other countries.

COWDREY, IRVING H. and EDWARD L. BARTHOLOMEW, *Introductory Engineering Materials.* N.Y., McGraw-Hill, 1953; 424 pp. — Brief review of properties, methods of fabrication and uses of major building materials.

DALZELL, J. RALPH, *Simplified Masonry Planning and Building.* N.Y., McGraw-Hill, 1955; 362 pp. — Step-by-step explanations for young mechanic or apprentice.

GIEDION, SIGFRIED, *Space, Time and Architecture.* Cambridge, Harvard Univ. Press, 1954; 778 pp. — Tells of growth of architectural traditions and of men who led important movements.

HOLMES, BURTON H., ed., *Materials and Methods in Architecture.* N.Y., Reinhold, 1954; 412 pp. — Describes important developments in architectural engineering techniques.

KIRBY, RICHARD S. and others, *Engineering in History.* N.Y., McGraw-Hill, 1956; 530 pp. — Emphasizes engineering achievements that have had greatest influence on civilization.

ELECTRICAL INDUSTRY

HAMMOND, JOHN W., *Men and Volts;* the story of General Electric. Phila., Lippincott, 1941; 436 pp. — Popularized account of origin and growth of a pioneering organization.

NEILL, HUMPHREY B., *Forty-Eight Million Horses.* Phila., Lippincott, 1940; 241 pp. — Story of part played by electricity in everyday life.

PERRY, JOSEPHINE, *The Electrical Industry.* N.Y., Longmans, Green, 1945; 128 pp. — Overall picture of importance of electrical industry in modern life.

SHACKLETON, SAMUEL P., *Opportunities in Electrical Engineering.* N.Y., Vocational Guidance Manuals, 1953; 128 pp. — Designed to aid in selection of career in this field.

FISHERIES

MORGAN, ROBERT, *World Sea Fisheries.* London, Methuen, 1956; 307 pp. — Survey of fish distribution, fishing techniques and fishing craft.

ROUNSEFELL, GEORGE A. and W. H. EVERHART, *Fishery Science,* its methods and applications. N.Y., Wiley, 1953; 444 pp. — Describes techniques for obtaining maximum fishery products.

SMITH, F. G. W. and H. CHAPIN, *Sun, the Sea and Tomorrow.* N.Y., Scribners, 1954; 210 pp. — Role of sea as provider of food and mineral wealth.

FUELS. See POWER

FURS

ASHBROOK, FRANK G., *Fur Farming for Profit.* N.Y., Judd, 1948; 429 pp. — Essentials of feeding, breeding, housing and handling fur animals.

————, *Furs Glamorous and Practical.* N.Y., Van Nostrand, 1954; 88 pp. — Processing and identification of modern furs; guide for consumer.

BACHRACH, MAX, *Fur.* N.Y., Prentice-Hall, 3rd ed., 1953; 660 pp. — Detailed account of source, processing and qualities of modern furs.

SAMET, ARTHUR, *Pictorial Encyclopedia of Furs.* N.Y., Samet, 1950; 474 pp. — Describes source, production and characteristics of commercial furs; profusely illustrated.

GLASS

DIAMOND, FREDA, *The Story of Glass.* N.Y., Harcourt, Brace, 1953; 246 pp. — Manufacture, properties and uses of increasingly important commodity.

DICKSON, J. H., *Glass*; a handbook for students and technicians. N.Y., Chemical Pub. Co., 1951; 300 pp. — Review of physical structure, properties, methods of manufacture and uses of glass.

PHILLIPS, C. J., *Get Acquainted with Glass.* N.Y., Pitman, 1950; 235 pp. — Simplified explanation of glass technology with emphasis on applications.

LEATHER

CLAIR, COLIN, *Leather.* London, Bruce, 1954; 64 pp. — How hides and skins are processed for manufacture of leather products.

GREENWOOD, EILEEN C. M., *Leathercraft.* London, Spon, 1949; 2 vols., 174 pp. each. — Detailed instructions for making a wide variety of leather articles.

KATES, H. G., *A Luggage and Leather Goods Manual.* N.Y., Luggage & Leather Goods Manufacturers. 1948; 235 pp. — Nontechnical description of manufacture, properties and uses of leather.

LUMBER

CARHART, ARTHUR H., *Timber in Your Life.* Phila., Lippincott, 1955; 317 pp. — Primarily plea for conservation of timber resources.

HORN, STANLEY F., *This Fascinating Lumber Business.* Indianapolis, Bobbs-Merrill, 1951; 313 pp. — Production, transportation and marketing of lumber in United States.

WALL, GERTRUDE W., *Gifts from the Forest.* N.Y., Scribner, rev. ed., 1958; 96 pp. — Story of lumber industry; excellent photographs.

MACHINE TOOLS

HALL, HERBERT D. and H. E. LINSLEY, *Machine tools; what they are and how they work.* N.Y., Industrial Pr., 1957; 426 pp. — For students and for the general reader.

HERB, CHARLES O., *Machine Tools at Work.* N.Y., Industrial Press, 2nd ed., 1953; 584 pp. — Describes specific operations performed on wide variety of machine tools.

MIX, FLOYD, ed., *All about Power Tools.* Chicago, Goodheart-Willcox, 1954; 192 pp. — Simple instructions, supplemented by numerous illustrations.

METALLURGY

DEARDEN, JOHN, *Iron and Steel Today.* London, Oxford Univ. Pr., 2nd ed., 1956; 271 pp. — Making and shaping of iron and steel.

HIBBEN, THOMAS, *The Sons of Vulcan.* Phila., Lippincott, 1940; 259 pp. — Describes discovery and early uses of metals and alloys.

JOHNSON, CARL G. and WILLIAM R. WEEKS, *Metallurgy.* Chicago, American Technical Soc., 4th ed., 1956; 454 pp. — Introduction to manfacture, properties and behavior of metals and their alloys.

ROGERS, BRUCE A., *The Nature of Metals.* Cleveland, Ohio, American Soc. for Metals, 1951; 248 pp. —Explains physical structure of metals and their behavior during various metallurgical operations.

STREET, ARTHUR, *Metals in the Service of Man.* N.Y., Penguin Books, 1944; 192 pp. — Nontechnical account of how metals are obtained, processed and used.

SULLIVAN, JOHN W. W., *The Story of Metals.* Ames, Iowa, Iowa State College Press, 1951; 290 pp. — History of discovery, refinement and use of metals. Interesting presentation for beginners.

MINING

BROWN, MAURICE R., *Mining Explained in Simple Terms.* Toronto, Northern Miner Press, 1955; 162 pp. — Clear description of typical mining operations.

FITZHUGH, EDWARD F., *Treasures in the Earth.* Caldwell, Idaho, Caxton Printers, 1936; 130 pp. — Fundamentals of mining geology.

LANGFORD, G. B., *Out of the Earth.* Toronto, Univ. of Toronto Press, 1954; 125 pp. — Nature of mineral deposits and skills required to exploit them.

NININGER, ROBERT D., *Minerals for Atomic Energy*; a guide to exploration for uranium, thorium and beryllium. Princeton, N.J., Van Nostrand, 2nd ed., 1956: 399 pp. — Comprehensive treatment for both professional and amateur prospectors.

RICKARD, T. A., *The Romance of Mining.* Toronto, Macmillan, 1944, 450 pp. — Tells stories behind discovery of famous mineral deposits.

PAPER

HUNTER, DARD, *Papermaking.* N.Y., Knopf, 2nd

ed., 1947; 611 pp. — Comprehensive treatment for general reader.

PERRY, JOSEPHINE, *The Paper Industry.* N.Y., Longmans, Green, 1946; 128 pp. — Outlines highlights in history and manufacture of paper.

SUTERMEISTER, EDWIN, *The Story of Papermaking.* Boston, Warren, 1954; 209 pp. — Excellent nontechnical account of various papermaking processes.

PETROLEUM

LEVEN, DAVID D., *Done in Oil.* N.Y., Ranger Press, 1941; 1084 pp. — Covers all phases of petroleum industry, from geological origin of petroleum to its marketing and use.

MILLER, MAX, *Speak to the Earth.* N.Y., Appleton-Century-Crofts, 1955; 310 pp. — Intensely interesting story of discovery, history and development of petroleum.

SCHACKNE, STEWART and N. D'ARCY DRAKE, *Oil for the World.* N.Y., Harper, 2nd rev. ed., 1960; 128 pp. — Well-illustrated elementary account of origin, production and utilization of petroleum.

PLASTICS

DEARLE, DENIS A., *Opportunities in Plastics.* N.Y., Vocational Guidance Manuals, 1953; 128 pp. — Besides job descriptions, includes material on properties and uses of plastic materials.

MELVILLE, HARRY, *Big Molecules.* N.Y. Macmillan, 1958; 180 pp. — Deals with one of the most interesting fields of chemistry — high polymers; includes plastics and rubber (natural and synthetic).

Modern Plastics Encyclopedia. N.Y., Breskin, 1963; 1,196 pp. — Introduction contains excellent account of sources of plastics and of processing.

WALTON, HARRY, *Plastics for the Home Craftsman.* N.Y., McGraw-Hill, 1951; 191 pp. — Techniques of working with plastics and instructions for making variety of articles.

POTTERY. See CERAMICS

POWER

AYRES, EUGENE, *Energy Sources — the Wealth of the World.* N.Y., McGraw-Hill, 1952; 344 pp. — Excellent picture of the world's energy sources, reserves and rate of consumption.

BOUMPHREY, GEOFFREY, *Engines and How They Work.* N.Y., Watts, 1960; 255 pp. — Covers engines from windmill to rocket engine; contains numerous diagrams and simplified descriptions.

MARCUS, ABRAHAM and R. B. MARCUS, *Power Unlimited.* Englewood Cliffs, N.J., Prentice-Hall, 1959; 152 pp. — Elementary description of major types of machines used to produce power.

TAYLOR, FRANK S., *Power Today and Tomorrow.* London, Muller, 1954; 192 pp. — Various sources of power and how they are utilized to do man's work.

WENDT, GERALD, *Prospects of Nuclear Power and Technology.* Princeton, N.J., Van Nostrand, 1957; 348 pp. — Simple discussion of technical aspects of producing nuclear power.

RUBBER

FISHER, HARRY L., *Rubber and Its Uses.* Brooklyn, N.Y., Chemical Pub. Co., 1941; 128 pp. — Clear picture of nature, history, manufacture and use of rubber.

HOWARD, FRANK A., *Buna Rubber.* N.Y., Van Nostrand, 1947; 307 pp. — Story of synthetic rubber industry.

TUDOR, R. J., *The Story of Rubber.* London, Burke, 1947; 96 pp. — Includes numerous photographs of rubber processing and manufacture of rubber products.

WILSON, CHARLES M., *Trees and Test Tubes.* N.Y., Holt, 1943; 352 pp. — Development of rubber industry and its contributions to modern civilization.

SALT

ESKEW, GARNETT L., *Salt, the Fifth Element.* Chicago, Ferguson, 1948; 239 pp. — Based largely on records of Morton Salt Company.

Salt; Historic, Romantic and Essential to Life. Scranton, Pa., International Salt Co., 1939. — Includes excellent photographs showing mining and processing of salt.

STANDARDS OF INDUSTRY

MELNITSKY, BENJAMIN, *Profiting from Industrial Standardization.* N.Y., Conover-Mast, 1953; 381 pp. — Clear and practical account of why and how standards are developed and used.

PERRY, JOHN, *Story of Standards.* N.Y., Funk, 1955; 271 pp. — Importance of standards in science and everyday life.

STEEL INDUSTRY. See METALLURGY

TEXTILES

BENDURE, ZELMA and GLADYS PFEIFFER, *America's Fabrics.* N.Y., Macmillan, 1946; 688 pp. — Profusely illustrated with views of machinery, manufacturing operations and fabrics.

HOLLEN, NORMA, *Modern Textiles.* Minneapolis, Burgess, 1952; 138 pp. — Basic information about fibers and fabric construction for consumer.

MONCRIEFF, R. W., *Artificial Fibres.* N.Y., Wiley, 2nd ed., 1954; 455 pp. — Manufacture, properties and uses of artificial fibers.

WINGATE, ISABEL B., *Textile Fabrics and Their Selection.* Englewood Cliffs, N.J., Prentice-Hall, 4th ed., 1955; 703 pp. — Guide to manufacture, properties and uses of natural and synthetic fabrics.

TRANSPORTATION

GENERAL WORKS

CARLISLE, NORMAN V., *Your Career in Transportation.* N.Y., Dutton, 1942; 188 pp. — Vocation guidance for young people.

GOODWIN, ASTLEY J. H., *Communication Has Been Established.* London, Methuen, 1937; 267 pp. — Deals primarily with methods of transportation in early times.

HAWKS, ELLISON, *The Romance of Transport.* N.Y., Crowell, 1931; 333 pp. — Popular history of land, sea and air transportation.

ST. CLAIR, LABERT, *Transportation.* N.Y., Dodd, Mead, 1942; 349 pp. — Development of various means of transportation from ancient to modern times.

THROM, EDWARD L., ed., *Popular Mechanics' Picture History of American Transportation*. N.Y., Simon & Schuster, 1952; 312 pp. — Panorama of American vehicles from the stage coach to the jet plane.

AUTOMOBILES

CLYMER, FLOYD, *Those Wonderful Old Automobiles*. N.Y., McGraw-Hill, 1953; 214 pp. — Photographs and description of early American automobiles.

GRAHAM, FRANK D., *Audels New Automobile Guide for Mechanics*. N.Y., Audel, 1954; 1664 pp. — Elementary and practical guide to theory, construction, operation and repair.

HYDE, MARGARET O., *Driving Today and Tomorrow*. N.Y., Whittlesey House, 1954; 143 pp. — Problems confronting driver of automobile.

LENT, HENRY B., *O.K. for Drive-away*. N.Y., Macmillan, 1951; 152 pp. — How cars are designed, constructed and tested.

VENK, ERNEST A. and WALTER E. BILLIET, *Automotive Fundamentals*. Chicago, Amer. Tech. Soc., 1961; 520 pp. — Explains operation thoroughly and simply.

AVIATION

AHNSTROM, D. N., *The Complete Book of Helicopters*. Cleveland, World Pub. Co., 1954; 160 pp. — Development of helicopter, how it flies and present-day uses.

ALEXANDER, HOLMES, *Tomorrow's Air Age*. N.Y., Rinehart, 1953; 248 pp. — Recent developments that have made commercial flight faster and safer.

BERNARDO, JAMES V., *Aviation in the Modern World*. N.Y., Dutton, 1960; 352 pp. — Explains basic principles of flight and air navigation.

BLACKNER, ROBERT D., *Basic Aeronautical Science and Principles of Flight*. Chicago, Amer. Tech. Soc., 1958; 242 pp. — Excellent introduction for layman.

Flight Handbook; the theory and practice of aeronautics. London, Iliffe, 5th ed., 1954; 782 pp. — Comprehensive review of basic information on airplanes and related topics.

GIBBS-SMITH, C. H., *A History of Flying*. London, Batsford, 1953; 304 pp. — Reliable and readable history of aviation.

HYDE, MARGARET O., *Flight Today and Tomorrow*. N.Y., Whittlesey House, 1953; 140 pp. — How aviators use the airways.

MORRIS, LLOYD R. and KENDALL SMITH, *Ceiling Unlimited*. N.Y., Macmillan, 1953; 417 pp. — Story of famous aviators and their machines.

BRIDGES

BILLINGS, HENRY, *Bridges*. N.Y., Viking, 1956; 159 pp. — Traces progress of bridge construction in United States; effective presentation at junior-high level.

SMITH, H. SHIRLEY, *The World's Great Bridges*. N.Y., Harper, 1954; 180 pp. — Concise and readable history of bridge-building from ancient to modern times.

STEINMAN, D. B., *Famous Bridges of the World*. N.Y., Random House, 1953; 99 pp. — Leading engineer's account of development of bridges from prehistoric to modern times.

CANALS

ADAMS, SAMUEL H., *The Erie Canal*. N.Y., Random House, 1953; 182 pp. — Construction and early operation of Erie Canal.

BRIDGES, T. C., *Great Canals*. London, Nelson, 1936; 91 pp. — Historical background and construction of Panama, Suez, Kiel, Manchester and other famous canals.

DU VAL, MILES P., *And the Mountains Will Move*. Stanford, Cal., Stanford Univ. Press, 1947; 374 pp. — Narrative account of construction of Panama Canal.

FLYING SAUCERS

KEYHOE, DONALD E., *The Flying Saucer Conspiracy*. N.Y., Holt, 1955; 315 pp. — Deals with what author says is deliberate suppression of evidence.

MENZEL, DONALD H., *Flying Saucers*. Cambridge, Harvard Univ. Press, 1953; 319 pp. — Famous astronomer offers his explanations of what flying saucers really are.

TACKER, LAWRENCE J., *Flying Saucers and the United States Air Force*. Princeton, N.J., Van Nostrand, 1960; 164 pp. — Up-to-date presentation of controversial subject; United States Air Force presents its side of flying-saucer dispute.

RAILROADS

ALLEN, G. F., *Railways the World Over*. London, Allan, 1952; 128 pp. — Covers most aspects of railroad operation; well illustrated.

BEEBE, LUCIUS and C. M. CLEGG, *Hear the Train Blow*; a pictorial epic of America in the railroad age. N.Y., Dutton, 1952; 407 pp. — Interestingly written; 860 illustrations.

FARRINGTON, S. K., *Railroading around the World*. N.Y., Coward-McCann, 1955; 230 pp. — Excellent photographs and descriptions of railroads in various parts of world.

HOLBROOK, STEWART H., *The Story of American Railroads*. N.Y., Crown, 1947; 468 pp. — Birth and development of railroads in United States.

VAN METRE, THURMAN W., *Trains, Tracks and Travel*. N.Y., Simmons-Boardman, 9th ed., rev., 1960; 503 pp. — Popular account of history, rolling equipment and operation of American railroads.

ROADS

ALLHANDS, J. L., *Tools of the Earth Mover*. Huntsville, Texas, Sam Houston College Press, 1951; 362 pp. — Development of machinery used in moving of rocks and earth.

BILLINGS, HENRY, *Construction Ahead*. N.Y., Viking Press, 1951; 158 pp. — Methods of designing and constructing American roads.

BOARDMAN, FON W., JR., *Roads*. N.Y., Walck, 1958; 139 pp. — Quite comprehensive history of road building from earliest times; written for junior-high student.

HART, VAL, *The Story of American Roads*. N.Y., Sloane, 1950; 243 pp. — Origin of early American roads; how and where they were built.

LANKS, HERBERT C., *Highway to Alaska*. N.Y., Appleton-Century, 1944; 200 pp. — Construction problems and wonders of Alaskan highway.

SHIPPING

BLOCK, IRVIN, *Real Book about Ships.* N.Y., Garden City, 1953; 190 pp. — Excellent account for beginners.

DURANT, JOHN and ALICE DURANT, *Pictorial History of American Ships.* N.Y., Barnes, 1953; 312 pp. — Informal and comprehensive account of American maritime history from Indian canoe to modern liner.

GIBSON, CHARLES E., *Story of the Ship.* N.Y., Schuman, 1948; 272 pp. — History and romance of ships from primitive devices to modern vessels.

HARNACK, EDWIN P., ed., *All about Ships and Shipping.* London, Faber, 9th ed., 1952; 707 pp. — Contains wide variety of information on history, construction and operation of merchant and naval ships.

LA DAGE, JOHN H., *Merchant Ships; a Pictorial Study.* Cambridge, Md., Cornell Maritime Pr., 1955; 481 pp. — Lavishly illustrated work.

LEWELLEN, JOHN B., *Atomic Submarine.* N.Y., Crowell, 1954; 134 pp. — Fine work for laymen; describes conventional and atomic submarines.

RUSH, C. W., *Complete Book of Submarines.* Cleveland, World Pub., 1958; 156 pp. — Well-illustrated history of submarines, covering structure, propulsion, weapons and operations.

SPACE TRAVEL

ADAMS, C. C., *Space Flight.* N.Y., McGraw-Hill, 1958; 373 pp. — Informative account of present, past and future of space travel.

CAIDIN, MARTIN, *Countdown for Tomorrow.* N.Y., Dutton, 1958; 288 pp. — Rockets and missiles and the race between American and Soviet science.

HANRAHAN, JAMES S., and DAVID BUSHNELL, *Space Biology: the Human Factors in Space Flight.* N.Y., Basic Books, 1960; 236 pp. — Describes hazards of space travel: weightlessness, cosmic rays, etc.

LEY, WILLY, *Rockets, Missiles and Space Travel.* N.Y., Viking Press, 2nd rev. ed., 1961; 556 pp. — Pioneer in field tells about rockets and rocket power.

MULLER, WOLFGANG, *Man among the Stars.* N.Y., Criterion, 1957; 307 pp. — One of most readable and "down-to-earth" accounts of development and problems of space flight.

SHTERNFELD, ARI, *Soviet Space Science.* N.Y., Basic Books, 2nd rev. ed., 1959; 361 pp. — Authoritative treatment of Soviet artificial-satellite program; translated from Russian.

TUNNELS

BOARDMAN, FON W., JR., *Tunnels.* N.Y., Walck, 1960; 144 pp. — Describes recent advances in structural engineering as applied to tunnel construction.

STEVENS, F. L., *Under London.* London, Dent, 1939; 204 pp. — Stories behind the many tunnels that serve London.

WHITE, EDWARD and MURIEL WHITE, *Famous Subways and Tunnels of the World.* N.Y., Random House, 1953; 97 pp. — Emphasizes difficulties and hazards involved.

COMMUNICATION

GENERAL WORKS

DOSS, M. P., ed., *Information Processing Equipment.* N.Y., Reinhold, 1955; 270 pp. — Describes machines used in recording, reproducing and interpreting of information — tape recorders, typewriters, microfilm readers, etc.

DUNLAP, ORRIN E., JR., *Communications in Space.* N.Y., Harper, 1962; 175 pp. — Records development of space-communication technology from wireless radio to satellite relay.

FLOHERTY, JOHN J., *Men against Distance.* Phila., Lippincott, 1954; 148 pp. — Enthusiastic review of wonders of telephone, telegraphy, radio and television.

HOGBEN, LANCELOT T., *From Cave Painting to Comic Strip.* N.Y., Chanticleer Press, 1949; 286 pp. — Popular history of methods of visual communication from ancient to modern times.

McSPADDEN, J. W., *How They Sent the News.* London, Harrap, 1937; 219 pp. — Useful for its account of communication systems prior to invention of telegraph.

STILL, ALFRED, *Communication through the Ages.* N.Y., Rinehart, 1946; 201 pp. — How communication techniques have kept pace with man's social progress.

ELECTRONIC PATHFINDERS AND DETECTORS

HORNUNG, J. L., *Radar Primer.* N.Y., McGraw-Hill, 1948; 218 pp. — Nontechnical explanation of how radar works.

LARSEN, EGON, *Radar Works Like This.* London, Phoenix House, 1952; 64 pp. — Highly simplified account.

ROSS, FRANK, *Radar and Other Electronic Inventions.* N.Y., Lothrop, 1954; 244 pp. — Describes basic principles of radar and other electronic detecting devices.

SMITH, R. A., *Radio Aids to Navigation.* N.Y., Macmillan, 1948; 114 pp. — Operating principles of radar, loran, shoran and other navigational systems using radio techniques.

LANGUAGE

BLOOMFIELD, LEONARD, *Language.* N.Y., Henry Holt, 1933; 564 pp. — Comprehensive account by great American philologist.

BODMER, FREDERICK, *Loom of Language.* N.Y., Norton, 1944; 692 pp. — Origin and growth of modern languages.

LAIRD, CHARLTON G., *Miracle of Language.* N.Y., World Pub. Co., 1953; 308 pp. — Readable treatise on evolution of language, particularly English.

PEI, MARIO, *All about Language.* Phila., Lippincott, 1954; 186 pp. — Origin, structure and growth of languages and their relationship to each other.

MOTION PICTURES

BATTISON, JOHN H., *Movies for TV.* N.Y., McGraw-Hill, 1950; 376 pp. — Techniques of making and using motion pictures in television.

BRODBECK, EMIL E., *Handbook of Basic Motion-picture Techniques.* N.Y., McGraw-Hill, 1950; 311 pp. — Good introduction to subject.

How to Make Good Movies. Rochester, N.Y., Eastman Kodak Co., 1948; 232 pp. — Emphasis on black-and-white movies.

ROTHA, PAUL and RICHARD GRIFFITH, *Film till Now; a survey of world cinema.* N.Y., Funk & Wag-

nalls, rev. ed., 1950; 755 pp. — Interesting account; 175 illustrations.

TAYLOR, DEEMS, *Pictorial History of the Movies.* N.Y., Simon & Schuster, 1950; 376 pp. — Limited to evolution of moving pictures in United States.

PHOTOENGRAVING

BIGGS, JOHN R., *Illustration and Reproduction.* N.Y., Pellegrini & Cudahy, 1952; 240 pp. — On photoengraving techniques; for advanced students.

GAMBLE, CHARLES W., *Modern Illustration Processes.* N.Y., Pitman, 3rd ed., 1953; 474 pp. — Practical information on various photographic processes.

HORGAN, STEPHEN H., *Photoengraving in Black and Color.* Boston, American Photographic Pub. Co., 2nd ed., 1938; 112 pp. — Step-by-step explanations of photoengraving processes.

MARINACCIO, ANTHONY, *Exploring the Graphic Arts.* Princeton, N.J., Van Nostrand, 2nd ed., 1959; 297 pp. — Excellent introduction to subject; explains such processes as letterpress, relief cuts, silk screens, planography, etc.

PHOTOGRAPHY

ABBOTT, BERENICE, *New Guide to Better Photography.* N.Y., Crown, 1953; 180 pp. — Comprehensive treatment of subject for beginners.

BOUCHER, PAUL E., *Fundamentals of Photography.* N.Y., Van Nostrand, 3rd ed., 1956; 526 pp. — Although designed as college text, has found wide use among amateur photographers.

FEININGER, ANDREAS, *The Creative Photographer.* N.Y., Prentice-Hall, 1955; 329 pp. — Famous photographer outlines philosophy and basic principles of photography.

How to Make Good Pictures. Rochester, N.Y., Eastman Kodak Co., 1951; 224 pp. — Essential directions for taking, developing and printing pictures.

SUSSMAN, AARON, *Amateur Photographers Handbook.* N.Y., Crowell, 5th ed., 1958; 400 pp. — Guide to obtaining successful photographs.

WALLS, H. J., *How Photography Works.* N.Y., Macmillan, 1959; 352 pp. — Nontechnical explanation of chemical and optical principles of photography; film-processing techniques are omitted.

PRINTING

ALLEN, AGNES, *Story of the Book.* N.Y., Macmillan, 1953; 224 pp. — History of printing and bookmaking.

BIGGS, JOHN R., *Use of Type.* N.Y., Pitman, 1954; 220 pp. — Practical and well-illustrated account of practice of typography.

CLEETON, GLEN U. and C. W. PITKIN, *General Printing.* Bloomington, Ill., McKnight, 1958; 195 pp. — Useful for students and teachers of printing trade.

DENMAN, FRANK, *The Shaping of Our Alphabet.* N.Y., Knopf, 1955; 228 pp. — Surveys development of typography; each chapter set in type face representative of period discussed.

POLK, RALPH W., *Practice of Printing.* Peoria, Ill., Manual Arts Press, 1945; 300 pp. — Clearly written and fully illustrated.

RYDER, JOHN, *Printing for Pleasure.* Boston, Branford, 1955; 142 pp. — Practical guide for amateur printer.

RADIO BROADCASTING

ANDERSON, EDWIN P., *Audels Radiomans Guide.* N.Y., Audel, 1952; 1040 pp. — Particularly valuable for radio amateurs and apprentice servicemen.

COLLINS, ARCHIE F., *Radio Amateurs Handbook.* N.Y., Crowell, 10th ed., 1957; 352 pp. — Simple and practical approach for beginner.

HENNEY, KEITH and GLEN A. RICHARDSON, *Principles of Radio.* N.Y., Wiley, 6th ed., 1952; 655 pp. — Designed for home study use.

MARCUS, ABRAHAM and WILLIAM MARCUS, *Elements of Radio.* Englewood Cliffs, N.J., Prentice-Hall, 4th ed., 1959; 667 pp. — Requires no previous knowledge of mathematics and physics.

RECK, FRANKLIN M., *Radio from Start to Finish.* N.Y., Crowell, 1942; 160 pp. — Interesting and concise history of radio.

SOUND RECORDING

BEGUN, S. J., *Magnetic Recording.* N.Y., Holt, Rinehart, Winston, 1949; 242 pp. — Account of history and techniques of recording on tape.

CANBY, EDWARD T., *Home Music Systems.* N.Y., Harper, 1955; 300 pp. — Useful guide to purchasing units of home musical equipment.

GELATT, ROLAND, *The Fabulous Phonograph.* Phila., Lippincott, 1955; 320 pp. — Events and personalities behind invention and development of phonograph.

KING, GORDON J., *The Practical Hi-Fi Handbook.* N.Y., Macmillan, 1959; 224 pp. — Presents summary of output hi-fi systems with clear diagrams; mathematical aspects of field are minimized.

READ, OLIVER, *The Recording and Reproduction of Sound.* Indianapolis, Sams, 2nd ed., 1952; 790 pp. — Semitechnical treatment of theory, construction and characteristics of sound-recording and -reproducing apparatus.

TELEGRAPHY AND TELEPHONY

GARNHAM, S. A., and ROBERT L. HADFIELD, *The Submarine Cable.* London, Low, 1934; 241 pp. — Story behind the making, laying and use of Atlantic cable.

RANDELL, WILFRID L., *Messengers for Mankind.* London, Hutchinson, 1940; 240 pp. — History of communication systems, with emphasis on telegraph and telephone.

SCHNEIDER, HERMAN and NINA SCHNEIDER, *Your Telephone and How It Works.* N.Y., Whittlesey House, 1952; 96 pp. — Well-illustrated account for young people.

TALLEY, DAVID, *Basic Carrier Telephony.* N.Y., Rider, 1960; 176 pp. — Schematic presentation of operation of telephone system, written for layman.

See also GENERAL WORKS

TELEVISION

ANDERSON, EDWIN P., *Audels Television Service Manual.* N.Y., Audel, 1956; 434 pp. — Elementary home-study book for students and apprentice servicemen.

BENEDICK, JEANNE and ROBERT BENEDICK, *Television Works Like This.* N.Y., McGraw-Hill, 3rd ed., 1959; 64 pp. — Layman's first book on subject.

DERBY, JOHN, *Fix-it-yourself Television Manual.* N.Y., Popular Mechanics Press, 1955 ; 164 pp. — Explains television principles, how to choose a receiver, how to select and erect antennas, etc.

KIVER, MILTON S., *Television Simplified.* N.Y., Van Nostrand, 5th ed., 1955 ; 541 pp. — Introductory text for students and apprentice servicemen.

TYPEWRITERS

BLIVEN, BRUCE, *Wonderful Writing Machine.* N.Y., Random House, 1954 ; 236 pp. — Development of typewriter ; how it affected communications and opened new careers.

CURRENT, RICHARD N., *The Typewriter and the Men Who Made It.* Urbana, Ill., Univ. of Illinois Press, 1954 ; 149 pp. — Story of invention of typewriter.

PEPE, PHILIP S., *Personal Typing in 24 Hours.* N.Y., McGraw-Hill, 3rd ed., 1960 ; 64 pp. — Effective self-instruction book.

SCIENCE THROUGH THE AGES

GENERAL HISTORIES OF SCIENCE

HULL, L. W. H., *History and Philosophy.* London, Longmans, 1959 ; 340 pp. — Fine introduction, stressing development of scientific ideas in relation to cultural progress.

JAFFE, BERNARD, *Men of Science in America.* N.Y., Simon & Schuster, 1959 ; 715 pp. — Compact and readable summary for general reader.

MCKENZIE, A. E. E., *The Major Achievements of Science.* N.Y., Cambridge Univ. Press, 2 vols., 1960 ; 563 pp. — How main generalizations of science developed and their influence on Western thought.

MASON, STEPHEN F., *Main Currents of Scientific Thought.* N.Y., Abelard-Schuman, 1954 ; 520 pp. — Survey of physical and biological sciences from Bronze Age to modern times.

SINGER, CHARLES, *A Short History of Science to the Nineteenth Century.* Oxford, Clarendon Press, 1941 ; 399 pp. — Outstanding introduction to subject by distinguished science historian.

TAYLOR, F. S., *An Illustrated History of Science.* N.Y., Praeger, 1955 ; 178 pp. — Interesting and lavishly illustrated treatment.

WIENER, PHILIP P. and AARON NOLAND (eds.), *Roots of Scientific Thought : a Cultural Perspective.* N.Y., Basic Books, 1957 ; 677 pp. — Panorama of twenty-five centuries of scientific thought and method.

SCIENCE IN ANTIQUITY AND MIDDLE AGES

CROMBIE, A. C., *Augustine to Galileo.* London, Falcon Press, 1952 ; 436 pp. — Comprehensive survey of medieval science.

FARRINGTON, BENJAMIN, *Science in Antiquity.* London, Butterworth, 1936 ; 256 pp. — Devoted mainly to history of Greek science from 6th century B.C. to 5th century A.D.

SARTON, GEORGE, *Ancient Science and Modern Civilization.* Lincoln, Univ. of Nebraska Press, 1954 ; 111 pp. — Early Greek science and scientists and their influence on modern science and technology.

———, *A History of Science.* Cambridge, Harvard Univ. Press, 2 vols., 1952, 1959 ; 615, 624 pp. — Account of ancient science from beginnings to approximately first century A.D. For serious reader.

MODERN SCIENCE (1450–   )

BUTTERFIELD, H., *The Origins of Modern Science, 1300–1800.* London, Bell, 2nd ed., 1957 ; 242 pp. — Readable history by eminent historian.

CROWTHER, J. G., *Sciences of Energy* ; a commentary for the general reader on recent advances in astronomy, physics and chemistry. London, Muller, 1954 ; 271 pp. — Fine summary.

DAMPIER, WILLIAM C., *History of Science.* London, Cambridge Univ. Press, 4th ed., 1948 ; 527 pp. — Emphasizes developments during 19th century.

DINGLE, HERBERT, ed., *A Century of Science, 1851–1951.* London, Hutchinson, 1951 ; 338 pp. — Group of experts trace progress of scientific thought.

HARVEY-GIBSON, R. J., *Two Thousand Years of Science.* London, Black, 2nd ed., 1931 ; 508 pp. — Deals primarily with developments since 16th century.

HEATH, A. E., ed., *Scientific Thought in the Twentieth Century.* London, Watts, 1951 ; 387 pp. — Collection of essays by eminent scientists writing in their respective fields.

PLEDGE, H. T., *Science since 1500.* London, H. M. Stationery Office, 1939 ; 357 pp. — Reliable and useful coverage of era.

WOLF, ABRAHAM, *A History of Science, Technology and Philosophy in the 16th and 17th Centuries.* N.Y., Macmillan, 2nd ed. (revised by D. McKie), 1951 ; 692 pp. — Admirable work for advanced students ; contains much of interest to less advanced readers.

———, *A History of Science, Technology and Philosophy in the Eighteenth Century.* N.Y., Harper, 2nd ed. (revised by D. McKie), 1961 ; 798 pp. — See comment on preceding work.

HISTORY OF INDIVIDUAL SCIENCES. See GENERAL WORKS under I. UNIVERSE, II. THE EARTH, etc.

PROJECTS AND EXPERIMENTS

GENERAL WORKS

BEELER, NELSON F. and FRANKLYN M. BRANLEY, *Experiments with a Microscope.* N.Y., Crowell, 1957 ; 154 pp. — For beginners ; excellent introduction to use of microscope.

BROWN, VINSON, *How to Make a Home Nature Museum.* Boston, Little, Brown, 1954 ; 214 pp. — Interesting discussion of how to collect items and arrange and display collections.

GOLDSTEIN, PHILIP, *How to Do an Experiment.* N.Y., Harcourt, Brace, 1957 ; 192 pp. — For senior high-school student ; specific suggestions for various student experiments are given throughout.

JORDAN, EMIL L., *Hammond's Guide to Nature Hobbies.* N.Y., Hammond, 1953 ; 64 pp. — Covers collecting of minerals, shells, butterflies and so on ; good introduction.

KINGERY, ROBERT E., *How-to-do-it Books* ; a selected guide. N.Y., Bowker, 2nd ed., 1954 ; 262 pp. — Annotated guide to books on wide variety of topics.

LYNDE, CARLETON J., *Science Experiences with Inexpensive Equipment.* Scranton, Pa., International Textbook Co., 2nd ed., 1950 ; 266 pp. — How to perform 200 simple experiments ; illustrated.

Seven Hundred Science Experiments for Everyone, compiled by Unesco. N.Y., Doubleday, 1958; 223 pp. — Simple experiments; entertaining and instructive.

STONG, C. L., *The Scientific American Book of Projects for the Amateur Scientist.* N.Y., Simon & Schuster, 1960; 584 pp. — Presents significant projects in every major field of science.

SWEZEY, KENNETH M., *After-Dinner Science.* N.Y., McGraw-Hill, rev. ed., 1961; 182 pp. — Simple experiments performed with equipment found around home.

ASTRONOMY FOR AMATEURS

BARTON, SAMUEL G. and WILLIAM H. BARTON, *A Guide to the Constellations.* N.Y., McGraw-Hill, 3rd ed., 1943; 80 pp. — Beginners' guide to star observations without aid of instruments.

BARTON, WILLIAM H., *Starcraft.* N.Y., McGraw-Hill, 2nd ed., 1946; 250 pp. — Fundamental facts about solar system for older boys and girls and interested adults.

MOORE, PATRICK, *The Amateur Astronomer.* N.Y., Norton, 1957; 337 pp. — Aimed at needs of beginner, who must work with limited equipment.

OLCOTT, W. T., *Field Book of the Skies.* N.Y., Putnam, 4th ed., 1954; 482 pp. — Primarily guide to star observations without aid of instruments.

ZIM, HERBERT S., *Stars*; a guide to the constellations, sun, moon, planets and other features of the heavens. N.Y., Golden Press, 1951; 157 pp. — Handy pocket guide for amateur astronomer.

CHEMISTRY, EXPERIMENTS IN

BEELER, NELSON F. and F. M. BRANLEY, *Experiments in Chemistry.* N.Y., Crowell, 1952; 152 pp. — Employs inexpensive equipment and materials.

FREEMAN, MAE and IRA FREEMAN, *Fun with Chemistry.* N.Y., Random House, 1944; 58 pp. — Simple experiments that can be performed at home.

HORNING, JOHN L. and G. C. McGINNIS, *An Open Door to Chemistry.* N.Y., Appleton-Century, 1946; 86 pp. — Describes simple experiments that can be performed at home.

SWEZEY, KENNETH M., *Chemistry Magic.* N.Y., McGraw-Hill, 1956; 180 pp. — Many photographs supplement explanatory text.

INSECT COLLECTIONS

BEIRNE, BRYAN P., *Collecting, Preparing and Preserving Insects.* Ottawa, Canada, Dept. of Agriculture, Entomology Division, 1955; 133 pp. — For both amateurs and professionals.

SWAIN, RALPH B., *The Insect Guide.* N.Y., Doubleday, 1948; 261 pp. — How to identify, capture and preserve various kinds of insects; a first-rate introduction for beginners.

TEALE, EDWIN WAY, *The Junior Book of Insects.* N.Y., Dutton, 1953; 249 pp. — Facts about lives and habits of common insects. Simple instructions for collecting, rearing and studying are included.

URQUHART, FREDERICK, *Introducing the Insect.* N.Y., Holt, 1949; 287 pp. — General descriptions and hints on collecting.

MINERAL AND ROCK COLLECTIONS

ENGLISH, GEORGE L. and DAVID E. JENSEN, *Getting Acquainted with Minerals.* N.Y., McGraw-Hill, 1958; 362 pp. — For hobbyist, amateur collector or beginning student of mineralogy.

JENSEN, DAVID E., *Mineral Collectors Guide.* Rochester, N.Y., Ward's Natural Science Establishment, 1953; 36 pp. — Interesting and useful book for novice collector.

PEARL, RICHARD M., *How to Know the Minerals and Rocks.* N.Y., McGraw-Hill, 1955; 192 pp. — Field guide for identifying more than 125 of the more important minerals and rocks.

POUGH, FREDERICK H., *A Field Guide to Rocks and Minerals.* Boston, Houghton Mifflin, 1953; 333 pp. — Practical and simplified guide to identification of common minerals.

ZIM, HERBERT S. and PAUL R. SHAFFER, *Rocks and Minerals.* N.Y., Simon & Schuster, 1957; 160 pp. — Presents, with illustrations, over 400 specimens of minerals and rocks; shows how to identify them.

PETS, CARE OF

ASHBROOK, FRANK G., *Raising Small Animals for Pleasure and Profit.* N.Y., Van Nostrand, 1951; 260 pp. — Care and feeding of rabbits, hamsters, goats, poultry, mink, game birds, etc.

BRYANT, DORIS, *Care and Handling of Cats.* N.Y., Washburn, 1949; 226 pp. — Thorough treatment of subject.

MEEK, STERNER ST. P., *So You're Going to Get a Puppy.* N.Y., Knopf, 1950; 148 pp. — Practical guide to selecting, owning and training dogs.

MOORE, CLIFFORD B., *The Book of Wild Pets.* Newton Centre, Mass., Branford, 1954; 553 pp. — Care and feeding of native wildlife in captivity.

POE, BERNARD (pseudonym of L. A. HAUSMAN), *Care and Training of Home Cage Birds.* N.Y., Putnam, 1953; 120 pp. — How to train and breed birds and how to take care of sick birds.

SHERMAN, JANE, *The Real Book about Dogs.* N.Y., Garden City, 1956; 192 pp. — Contains useful information on feeding and training.

WHITNEY, L. F., *Complete Book of Home Pet Care.* N.Y., Garden City, 1950; 552 pp. — Care and handling of common household pets.

PHYSICS, EXPERIMENTS IN

BEELER, NELSON F., *Experiments with Electricity.* N.Y., Crowell, 1949; 145 pp. — Requires use of very simple equipment.

BEELER, NELSON F. and FRANKLYN M. BRANLEY, *Experiments in Optical Illusion.* N.Y., Crowell, 1951; 114 pp. — Simply performed optical illusions, with explanations of why they occur.

KADESCH, ROBERT R., *The Crazy Cantilever and Other Science Experiments.* N.Y., Harper, 1961; 175 pp. — Forty experiments in physics for young amateur.

MORGAN, ALFRED P., *The Boy Electrician.* N.Y., Lothrop, 1948; 407 pp. — Basic principles of electricity and instructions for making simple electrical machines.

YATES, RAYMOND F., *Atomic Experiments for Boys.* N.Y., Harper, 1952; 132 pp. — Simple experiments illustrate basic principles of atomic energy.

ROCK COLLECTIONS. See MINERAL AND ROCK COLLECTIONS

SHELL COLLECTIONS

ABBOTT, R. T., *American Seashells.* N.Y., Van Nostrand, 1954 ; 541 pp. — Unusually complete guide to shells of Atlantic and Pacific shores.

ROGERS, JULIA, *Shell Book.* Boston, Branford, 1951 ; 503 pp. — How to identify various types of shells.

SMITH, MAXWELL, *World-wide Sea Shells.* Lantana, Fla., Tropical Photographic Laboratory, 1940 ; 139 pp. — Photographs and line drawings illustrate brief descriptive text.

VERRILL, ALPHEUS H., *Shell Collector's Handbook.* N.Y., Putnam, 1950 ; 228 pp. — How shells are formed, where found, their uses and value.

TELESCOPE CONSTRUCTION

HENSON, TRUMAN, *Binoculars, Telescopes and Telescopic Sights* ; how they work, how to select them and how to design and build your own. N.Y., Greenberg, 1955 ; 515 pp. — Detailed work for amateur.

HOWARD, N. E., *Standard Handbook for Telescope Making.* N.Y., Crowell, 1959 ; 326 pp. — Complete amateur's guide to telescope making with diagrams ; from grinding of lenses to mounting.

INGALLS, ALBERT G., ed., *Amateur Telescope Making.* N.Y., Scientific American Pub. Co., rev. ed., 1955 ; 497 pp. — This and next two books cover all phases of amateur telescope making.

————, *Amateur Telescope Making; Advanced.* N.Y., Scientific American Pub. Co., rev. ed., 1954 ; 650 pp.

————, *Amateur Telescope Making: Book Three.* N. Y., Scientific American Pub. Co., rev. ed., 1956 ; 646 pp.

WEATHER OBSERVATION

LAIRD, CHARLES and RUTH LAIRD, *Weathercasting.* Englewood Cliffs, N.J., Prentice-Hall, 1955 ; 163 pp. — How to make and use weather maps and basic meteorological instruments.

SLOANE, ERIC, *Eric Sloane's Weather Book.* Boston, Little, Brown, 1952 ; 90 pp. — Numerous drawings and charts supplement this simplified introduction to elements of meteorology.

SPILHAUS, ATHELSTAN F., *Weathercraft.* N.Y., Viking Press, 1951 ; 64 pp. — Building and using home weather station.

YATES, RAYMOND F., *The Weather for a Hobby.* N.Y., Dodd, Mead, 1946 ; 172 pp. — Construction details for weather instruments.

SCIENTIFIC FACTS
AND FIGURES

SCIENTIFIC FACTS AND FIGURES

LIST OF CHEMICAL ELEMENTS*

Elements	Symbol	Atomic No.	Atomic Weight	Elements	Symbol	Atomic No.	Atomic Weight
Actinium	Ac	89	227(?)	Molybdenum	Mo	42	95.94
Aluminum	Al	13	26.9815	Neodymium	Nd	60	144.24
Americium	Am	95	243(?)	Neon	Ne	10	20.183
Antimony	Sb	51	121.75	Neptunium	Np	93	237(?)
Argon	Ar	18	39.948	Nickel	Ni	28	58.71
Arsenic	As	33	74.9216	Niobium	Nb	41	92.906
Astatine	At	85	210(?)	Nitrogen	N	7	14.0067
Barium	Ba	56	137.34	Nobelium	No	102	254(?)
Berkelium	Bk	97	249(?)	Osmium	Os	76	190.2
Beryllium	Be	4	9.0122	Oxygen	O	8	15.9994
Bismuth	Bi	83	208.980	Palladium	Pd	46	106.4
Boron	B	5	10.811	Phosphorus	P	15	30.9738
Bromine	Br	35	79.909	Platinum	Pt	78	195.09
Cadmium	Cd	48	112.40	Plutonium	Pu	94	242(?)
Calcium	Ca	20	40.08	Polonium	Po	84	210(?)
Californium	Cf	98	251(?)	Potassium	K	19	39.102
Carbon	C	6	12.01115	Praseodymium	Pr	59	140.907
Cerium	Ce	58	140.12	Promethium	Pm	61	147(?)
Cesium	Cs	55	132.905	Protactinium	Pa	91	231(?)
Chlorine	Cl	17	35.453	Radium	Ra	88	226(?)
Chromium	Cr	24	51.996	Radon	Rn	86	222(?)
Cobalt	Co	27	58.9332	Rhenium	Re	75	186.2
Copper	Cu	29	63.54	Rhodium	Rh	45	102.905
Curium	Cm	96	247(?)	Rubidium	Rb	37	85.47
Dysprosium	Dy	66	162.50	Ruthenium	Ru	44	101.07
Einsteinium	Es	99	254(?)	Samarium	Sm	62	150.35
Erbium	Er	68	167.26	Scandium	Sc	21	44.956
Europium	Eu	63	151.96	Selenium	Se	34	78.96
Fermium	Fm	100	253(?)	Silicon	Si	14	28.086
Fluorine	F	9	18.9984	Silver	Ag	47	107.870
Francium	Fr	87	223(?)	Sodium	Na	11	22.9898
Gadolinium	Gd	64	157.25	Strontium	Sr	38	87.62
Gallium	Ga	31	69.72	Sulfur	S	16	32.064
Germanium	Ge	32	72.59	Tantalum	Ta	73	180.948
Gold	Au	79	196.967	Technetium	Tc	43	99(?)
Hafnium	Hf	72	178.49	Tellurium	Te	52	127.60
Helium	He	2	4.0026	Terbium	Tb	65	158.924
Holmium	Ho	67	164.930	Thallium	Tl	81	204.37
Hydrogen	H	1	1.00797	Thorium	Th	90	232.038
Indium	In	49	114.82	Thulium	Tm	69	168.934
Iodine	I	53	126.9044	Tin	Sn	50	118.69
Iridium	Ir	77	192.2	Titanium	Ti	22	47.90
Iron	Fe	26	55.847	Tungsten			
Krypton	Kr	36	83.80	(Wolfram)	W	74	183.85
Lanthanum	La	57	138.91	Uranium	U	92	238.03
Lawrencium	Lw	103	257(?)	Vanadium	V	23	50.942
Lead	Pb	82	207.19	Wolfram, see			
Lithium	Li	3	6.939	Tungsten			
Lutetium	Lu	71	174.97	Xenon	Xe	54	131.30
Magnesium	Mg	12	24.312	Ytterbium	Yb	70	173.04
Manganese	Mn	25	54.9380	Yttrium	Y	39	88.905
Mendelevium	Md	101	256(?)	Zinc	Zn	30	65.37
Mercury	Hg	80	200.59	Zirconium	Zr	40	91.22

* Figures based on table of atomic weights released by the International Union of Pure and Applied Chemistry in 1961. For more information about different elements, see appropriate Index entries.

MATHEMATICAL DATA

A. Some Familiar Symbols

π (Greek letter, pronounced "pi," with "i" as in "dine") = ratio of circumference of circle to diameter = 3.1415926536+

$>$ = is greater than
Example: 10$>$5

$<$ = is less than
Example: 5$<$10

∞ = infinity
Example: the sum of all the odd integers =
1 + 3 + 5 + 7 + ... ∞

$i = \sqrt{-1}$

Σ (Greek letter, pronounced "sigma") = sum of all the quantities of a given collection

Example $\displaystyle\sum_{n=1}^{4} n$ = sum of all the integers from
1 through 4 = 1 + 2 + 3 + 4 = 10

$n!$ (called factorial n) = product of all the integers up to and including n, n being any given integer
Example: 4!, or factorial 4 = 1 X 2 X 3 X 4 = 24

e = 1 + sum of reciprocals* of all the factorials
$= 1 + \dfrac{1}{1!} + \dfrac{1}{2!} + \dfrac{1}{3!} + \dots \dfrac{1}{n!}$
= approximately 2.71828

*The reciprocal of a number is one divided by that number.

B. Lengths, Areas and Volumes

Area of triangle with base b and altitude h
$= \dfrac{hb^*}{2}$

Perimeter of square with side a
$= 4a$

Perimeter of any other parallelogram with sides a and b
$= 2(a + b)$

Area of rectangle with sides a and b of unequal length
$= ab$

Area of square with side a
$= a^2$

Area of any parallelogram with side b and with h as perpendicular distance from b to side parallel to b
$= bh$

Area of rhombus with diagonals c and d
$= \dfrac{cd}{2}$

Area of trapezoid with parallel sides a and b and altitude h
$= \dfrac{h(a + b)}{2}$

*hb = h X b

Circumference of circle with radius r
$= 2\pi r$
Area of circle with radius r and diameter d (2r)
$= \pi r^2 = \frac{1}{4}\,\pi d^2 = .7854d^2$

Area of ellipse with major axis a and minor axis b
$= \dfrac{\pi ab}{4}$

Volume of regular prism with a as area of base and h as altitude
$= ah$

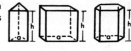

Volume of regular pyramid with a as area of base and h as altitude
$= \dfrac{ah}{3}$

Surface of sphere with radius r and diameter d (2r)
$= 4\pi r^2 = \pi d^2 = 12.57r^2$

Volume of sphere with radius r and diameter d (2r)
$= \dfrac{4}{3}\,\pi r^3 = \dfrac{1}{6}\,\pi d^3 = 4.189r^3$

Volume of right cylinder with r as radius of base and with h as altitude
$= \pi r^2 h$

Volume of right cone with r as radius of base and with h as altitude
$= \dfrac{\pi}{3}\,r^2 h = 1.047r^2 h$

Atmosphere (conventional unit of pressure per unit of area): 14.697 pounds per square inch.

Acceleration due to gravity at sea level, 45° latitude: 980.665 centimeters per second per second or 32.172 feet per second per second.

Dyne: fundamental unit of force in centimeter-gram-second system of units; the force applied to a mass of one gram that gives it an acceleration of one centimeter per second per second.

Megadyne: 1,000,000 dynes.

Erg: fundamental unit of work in centimeter-gram-second system of units. One erg of work is done on a body when a force of one dyne is exerted upon it through a distance of one centimeter.

Joule: unit of work equal to 10,000,000 ergs.

Foot-pound: unit of work, equal to work done in raising one pound avoirdupois against the force of gravity the height of one foot; equivalent to 1.3549 joules.

Horse-power: unit of power, equal to a rate of 33,000 foot-pounds of work per minute.

Small calorie: amount of heat required at a pressure of one atmosphere to raise the temperature of one gram of water one degree centigrade.

Large calorie: amount of heat required at a pressure of one atmosphere to raise the temperature of one kilogram of water one degree centigrade.

British thermal unit (B.T.U.): quantity of heat necessary to raise the temperature of one pound of water one degree Fahrenheit at its point of maximum density. Equal to 252.00 calories (small).

Mean density of earth: 5.522 grams per cubic centimeter.

Density of mercury at 0° C.: 13.59559 grams per cubic centimeter.

Density of water at 3.98° C.: 0.999973 grams per cubic centimeter.

Density of dry air at 0° C. and at a pressure of one atmosphere: .001293 grams per cubic centimeter.

Velocity of light: 186,281 miles per second.

Velocity of sound in dry air at 0° C.: 1,087 feet, or 33,136 centimeters, per second.

TABLES OF WEIGHTS AND MEASURES

Linear Measure

12 inches	=	1 foot
3 feet	=	1 yard
5½ yards	=	1 rod
40 rods	=	1 furlong
8 furlongs	=	1 mile
5,280 feet	=	1 mile
3 miles	=	1 league

Square Measure (Area)

144 square inches	=	1 square foot
9 square feet	=	1 square yard
30¼ square yards	=	1 square rod
160 square rods	=	1 acre
43,560 square feet	=	1 acre
640 acres	=	1 square mile

Cubic Measure (Volume)

1,728 cubic inches	=	1 cubic foot
27 cubic feet	=	1 cubic yard
(measure for cordwood)		
16 cubic feet	=	1 cord foot (4'x4'x1')
8 cord feet or 128 cubic feet	=	1 cord (4'x4'x8')

Dry Measure

2 pints	= 1 quart	=	67.20 cubic inches
8 quarts	= 1 peck	=	537.61 cubic inches
4 pecks	= 1 bushel	=	2,150.42 cubic inches

Liquid Measure

4 gills	= 1 pint	=	28.885 cubic inches
2 pints	= 1 quart	=	57.75 cubic inches
4 quarts	= 1 gallon	=	231.0 cubic inches

Avoirdupois Weight

16 drams	=	1 ounce
16 ounces	=	1 pound
100 pounds	=	1 quintal
2,000 pounds	=	1 short ton
2,240 pounds	=	1 long ton

Apothecaries' Weight

20 grains	=	1 scruple
3 scruples	=	1 dram
8 drams	=	1 ounce
12 ounces	=	1 pound

Troy Weight

3.086 grains	=	1 carat
24 grains	=	1 pennyweight
20 pennyweights	=	1 ounce
12 ounces	=	1 pound

Time Measure

60 seconds	=	1 minute
60 minutes	=	1 hour
24 hours	=	1 day
7 days	=	1 week
365 days or 12 months	=	1 year
366 days	=	1 leap year
100 years	=	1 century

Circular Measure

60 seconds	=	1 minute
60 minutes	=	1 degree
60 degrees	=	1 sextant
90 degrees	=	1 quadrant
360 degrees	=	1 circumference

Nautical Measure

6 feet	=	1 fathom
1 cable's length	=	100 fathoms, ordinary; 608 feet, Brit.; 720 feet, U. S. Navy
1 nautical mile	=	6,080 feet, Brit.; 6,080.20 feet, U. S. Navy
1 knot	=	unit of speed, equal to 1 nautical mile per hour

Agate	= a size of type used in printing (5½ points)
Carat	= Unit of weight for precious stones, equal to 3.086 grains. Also means twenty-fourth part when used to indicate the proportion of gold in a gold alloy. Thus 10 carats fine means 10 parts gold and 14 parts alloy.
Gross	= 12 dozen
Hand	= 4 inches (used in measuring the height of a horse)
Pica	= a size of type used in printing (1/6 of an inch)
Point	= a unit of measurement used in printing (1/72 of an inch or 1/12 of a pica)
Quire of paper	= 24 or 25 sheets
Ream of paper	= usually 20 quires

THE METRIC SYSTEM

The metric system was established in France in 1793, has been adopted in many countries and is used to some extent in the United States and Great Britain. It is a decimal system based on the meter as a fundamental unit. Originally, the measurement of one ten-millionth of the earth's quadrant was taken as the length of the meter. For more accurate computation, the meter is now determined by the International Prototype Meter, a platinum-iridium bar, which is kept at the International Bureau of Weights and Measures in Sèvres, France, near Paris.

Linear Measure

10 millimeters	= 1 centimeter
10 centimeters	= 1 decimeter
10 decimeters	= 1 meter
10 meters	= 1 decameter
10 decameters	= 1 hectometer
10 hectometers	= 1 kilometer
10 kilometers	= 1 myriameter

Measure of Capacity

10 milliliters	= 1 centiliter
10 centiliters	= 1 deciliter
10 deciliters	= 1 liter
10 liters	= 1 decaliter
10 decaliters	= 1 hectoliter
10 hectoliters	= 1 kiloliter

Square Measure (Area)

100 square millimeters	= 1 square centimeter
100 square centimeters	= 1 square decimeter
100 square decimeters	= 1 square meter
100 square meters	= 1 square decameter (are)
100 square decameters	= 1 square hectometer
100 square hectometers	= 1 square kilometer
10,000 square meters	= 1 hectare

Weights

10 milligrams	= 1 centigram
10 centigrams	= 1 decigram
10 decigrams	= 1 gram
10 grams	= 1 decagram
10 decagrams	= 1 hectogram
10 hectograms	= 1 kilogram or kilo
10 kilograms	= 1 myriagram
10 myriagrams	= 1 quintal
10 quintals or 1,000 kilos	= 1 metric ton

Cubic Measure (Volume)

1,000 cubic millimeters	= 1 cubic centimeter
1,000 cubic centimeters	= 1 cubic decimeter
1,000 cubic decimeters	= 1 cubic meter (stere)

CONVERSION TABLE FOR WEIGHTS AND MEASURES

1 acre	= 0.4047 hectares
1 foot	= 0.3048 meters
1 foot, cubic	= 0.0283 cubic meters
1 foot, square	= 0.0929 square meters
1 inch	= 2.54 centimeters
1 inch	= 0.0254 meters
1 mile	= 1.6093 kilometers
1 ounce	= 28.3495 grams (avdp.)
1 pint, dry	= 0.5506 liters
1 pint, liquid	= 0.4732 liters
1 pound (avdp.)	= 0.4536 kilograms
1 rod	= 5.0292 meters
1 yard	= 0.9144 meters
1 yard, cubic	= 0.7646 cubic meters
1 yard, square	= 0.8361 square meters

1 centimeter	= 0.3937 inches
1 gram	= 0.0353 ounces (avdp.)
1 hectare	= 2.4710 acres
1 kilogram	= 2.2046 pounds (avdp.)
1 kilometer	= 0.6214 miles
1 liter	= 1.8162 dry pints
1 liter	= 2.1134 liquid pints
1 meter	= 3.2808 feet
1 meter	= 39.37 inches
1 meter	= 0.1988 rods
1 meter	= 1.0936 yards
1 meter, cubic	= 35.3144 cubic feet
1 meter, cubic	= 1.3079 cubic yards
1 meter, square	= 10.7639 square feet
1 meter, square	= 1.1960 square yards

Sir Francis Beaufort (1774-1857), a rear admiral in the English navy, devised a method in 1805 for gauging the apparent strength of the wind. The Beaufort scale was accepted by the British Admiralty and adaptations of it are still used by navigators and by the Weather Bureau in its forecasts. The Beaufort scale classifies the winds in thirteen groups, ranging from 0 to 12, as follows:

Scale Number	Miles per hour	Description of wind	Indications on Land
0	0 to 1	Calm	Smoke goes straight up
1	1 to 3	Light air	Smoke drifts
2	4 to 7	Slight breeze	Leaves rustle
3	8 to 12	Gentle breeze	Leaves and small twigs are in motion
4	13 to 18	Moderate breeze	Small branches move; dust and paper fly
5	19 to 24	Fresh breeze	Ripples on water; small trees sway
6	25 to 31	Strong breeze	Large branches move
7	32 to 38	High wind	The trunks of trees bend; walking is difficult
8	39 to 46	Gale	Twigs are broken off
9	47 to 54	Strong gale	Chimneys and shingles are carried away
10	55 to 63	Whole gale	Trees may be uprooted
11	64 to 75	Storm	Damage is widespread
12	Over 75	Hurricane	Any disaster may be expected

COMPARISON OF THERMOMETER SCALES

(F. = Fahrenheit; C. = Centigrade; R. = Réaumur)

	F.	C.	R.		F.	C.	R.
				(Freezing point: water)	41	5	4
					32	0	0
(Boiling point: water)	212°	100°	80°		23	—5	—4
	194	90	72		14	—10	—8
	185	85	68		5	—15	—12
(Boiling point: alcohol)	167	75	60		0	—17.8	—14.2
	158	70	56		—13	—25	—20
	140	60	48		—22	—30	—24
	131	55	44		—31	—35	—28
	122	50	40		—40	—40	—32
	104	40	32	(Centigrade $\times$ %) + 32° = Fahrenheit			
(Temperature of blood)	98	36.7	29.3	(Fahrenheit — 32°) $\times$ 5⁄9 = Centigrade			
	86	30	24	Réaumur $\times$ 5⁄4 = Centigrade			
	77	25	20	Centigrade $\times$ 4⁄5 = Réaumur			
	68	20	16	(Fahrenheit — 32°) $\times$ 4⁄9 = Réaumur			
	50	10	8	(Réaumur $\times$ 9⁄4) + 32° = Fahrenheit			

ASTRONOMICAL CONSTANTS

Light-year: 5,880,000,000,000 miles.

Parsec: approximately 3.26 light-years or 19.2 trillion miles.

Velocity of light: 186,281 miles per second.

Astronomical unit (mean distance from sun to earth): 92,900,000 miles.

Mean distance from earth to moon: 238,854 miles.

Equatorial radius of the earth: 3,963.34 statute miles.

Polar radius of the earth: 3,949.99 statute miles.

Earth's mean radius: 3,958.89 statute miles.

Meridional circumference of earth: 24,860 miles.

Equatorial circumference of earth: 24,902 miles.

Sun's diameter: 864,000 miles.

Sidereal year (year measured with units that depend upon the apparent diurnal movement of the stars): 365.2564 days.

Tropical year (time elapsing between two passages in succession of the sun through the same equinox): 365.2422 days.

Sidereal month (month measured with units that depend upon the apparent diurnal movement of the stars): 27.3217 days.

Synodic month (time elapsing between two suc-

cessive passages of the moon between the earth and the sun) : 29.5306 days.

Sidereal day (day measured with units that depend upon the apparent diurnal movements of the stars) : 23 hours 56 minutes 4.091 seconds of mean solar time.

Mean solar day: 24 hours 3 minutes 56.555 seconds of sidereal time.

THE SUN, MOON AND PLANETS

Name	Diameter in miles	Mass (compared to that of earth)	Density (compared to that of earth)	Mean distance from sun in miles	Period of revolution around sun	Period of rotation
Sun	865,600	333,420	0.25			about 4 weeks
Mercury	3,008 *	0.04	0.69	36,000,000	88 days	88 days
Venus	7,575 *	0.82	0.89	67,200,000	225 days	several weeks
Earth	7,927 *	1.00	1.00	93,003,000	365.25 days	23 h. 56 m.
Mars	4,216 *	0.11	0.70	141,700,000	687 days	24 h. 37 m.
Jupiter	88,700 *	318.3	0.24	483,900,000	11.86 yrs.	9 h. 50 m.
Saturn	75,000 *	95.3	0.13	887,200,000	29.46 yrs.	10.2 h.
Uranus	30,900 *	14.7	0.23	1,783,800,000	84.01 yrs.	10.8 h.
Neptune	27,700 *	17.3	0.29	2,795,700,000	164.79 yrs.	15.8 h.
Pluto	3,600 *	1.0 ?	?	3,675,500,000	248.43 yrs.	?
Moon	2,160	0.012	0.61	Mean distance from earth: 238,857 miles	Period of revolution around earth: 29 d., 12 h., 44.05 m.**	Same as period of revolution

* Diameter at equator.
** Period between two identical phases, as new moon to new moon.

THE SIGNS OF THE ZODIAC

The celestial orbit described by the sun in its annual path among the stars is called the ecliptic. The zodiac is a theoretical division of the firmament, 16° in width, extending 8° on each side of the ecliptic. It begins at the point of the ecliptic that marks the position of the sun at the vernal equinox and proceeds toward the east. The zodiac is divided into twelve parts or signs of 30° each; they are named for the twelve constellations with which they corresponded at the time of Hipparchus (second century B.C.). The precession of the equinoxes in the two thousand years that have elapsed since that time has moved the signs 30° toward the west. The signs of the zodiac are:

♈ Aries (the Ram)

♉ Taurus (the Bull)

♊ Gemini (the Twins)

♋ Cancer (the Crab)

♌ Leo (the Lion)

♍ Virgo (the Virgin)

♎ Libra (the Balance)

♏ Scorpio (the Scorpion)

♐ Sagittarius (the Archer)

♑ Capricornus (the Goat)

♒ Aquarius (the Water-Bearer)

♓ Pisces (the Fishes)

In the second century B.C., the Greek astronomer Hipparchus arranged the stars in six grades or classes, of brightness, or apparent magnitude. (As applied to a star, the word "magnitude" has to do with brightness and not with size.) The brightest stars were put in the first grade, the next brightest stars in the second grade and so on. Hipparchus' classification was adopted and improved by Ptolemy of Alexandria in the second century A.D. Our present system of apparent magnitudes is based on the work of these men, though the light values assigned to the different magnitudes have been greatly refined. In the case of the heavenly bodies that are brighter than the stars of the first magnitude, each increasing stage of brightness above 1 is indicated by the appropriate numeral (0, 1, 2, 3 and so on) preceded by a minus sign.

Sun	—26.7		Aldebaran	1.1
Moon	—12.5 at brightest		Antares	1.2
Venus	—4.3 at brightest		Spica	1.2
Mars	—2.8 at brightest		Pollux	1.2
Sirius A	—1.5		Fomalhaut	1.3
Jupiter	—1.3		Deneb	1.3
Canopus	—0.9		Regulus	1.3
Alpha Centauri A	0.33		Castor	1.6
Vega	0.1		Bellatrix	1.7
Capella	0.2		Mira Ceti	2.2 (variable)
Arcturus	0.2		Shedir	2.3
Rigel	0.3		Polaris	2.3
Procyon A	0.5		Mizar	2.4
Betelgeuse	0.9 (variable)		Alcyone	3.
Altair	0.9		Alcor	4.
Saturn	1.		Uranus	6.
Mercury	1.			

NOBEL PRIZE WINNERS IN SCIENCE

Alfred Bernard Nobel (1833-96), the Swedish engineer who invented dynamite, left $9,000,000 in a fund to provide yearly awards for men and women whose work has benefited mankind. There are five Nobel Prizes—in physics, chemistry, medicine or physiology, literature and for the promotion of peace. The physics and chemistry prizes are awarded by the Royal Academy of Science in Stockholm; the medicine prizes by the Caroline Medical-Chirurgical Institute in Stockholm; the literature prizes by the Swedish Academy in Stockholm; the peace prizes by the Swedish Parliament. The names of candidates are submitted by persons qualified in the various fields. Although the winners are generally announced earlier in the year, the actual ceremony of awarding the prizes takes place annually on the anniversary of Nobel's death, December 10. A gold medal and a diploma accompany the money. The value of the prize varies; it was about $50,000 in 1915 and is now about $31,000.

Following are the Nobel Prize winners in physics, chemistry and medicine or physiology from the year 1901, when the prizes were first awarded, to the present time. We give the specific contributions for which prizes were granted.

Year	Physics	Chemistry	Medicine or Physiology
1901	*Wilhelm K. Roentgen* (Germany): discovery of Roentgen rays, or X rays.	*Jacobus H. van't Hoff* (Netherlands): discovery of laws of chemical dynamics and osmotic pressure.	*Emil A. von Behring* (Germany): research on use of serums against diphtheria.
1902	*Hendrik A. Lorentz* (Netherlands) and *Pieter Zeeman* (Netherlands): research on influence of magetism upon radiation.	*Emil Fischer* (Germany): experiments in sugar and purin groups.	*Ronald Ross* (England): work on malaria.

Year	Physics	Chemistry	Medicine or Physiology
1903	*Antoine-Henri Becquerel* (France) : research on spontaneous radioactivity. *Pierre Curie* (France) and *Marie Curie* (France; born in Poland) : series of outstanding discoveries in the field of radiation.	*Svante A. Arrhenius* (Sweden) : theory of electrolytic dissociation.	*Niels R. Finsen* (Denmark) : treatment of lupus vulgaris with light-rays.
1904	*John Strutt* (Lord Rayleigh) (England) : discovery of argon.	*Sir William Ramsay* (England) : work on inert gases.	*Ivan P. Pavlov* (Russia) : research on physiology of digestion.
1905	*Philipp Lenard* (Germany; born in Hungary) : work on cathode rays.	*Adolph von Baeyer* (Germany): research on organic dyes and aromatic hydrocarbons.	*Robert Koch* (Germany) : work on tuberculosis.
1906	*Joseph J. Thomson* (England): research on passage of electricity through gases.	*Henry Moissan* (France) : isolation of fluorine; development of electric furnace.	*Camillo Golgi* (Italy) and *Santiago Ramón y Cajal* (Spain) : research on structure of nervous system.
1907	*Albert A. Michelson* (U.S.) : research on spectroscopy and metrology.	*Eduard Buchner* (Germany) : discovery of cell-less fermentation; researches in biological chemistry.	*Charles L. A. Laveran* (France): research on role of protozoa in disease.
1908	*Gabriel Lippmann* (France) : work on reproduction of colors by photography.	*Ernest Rutherford* (England): research on disintegration of elements and chemistry of radioactive substances.	*Paul Ehrlich* (Germany) and *Elie Metchnikoff* (Russia) : work on immunity.
1909	*Guglielmo Marconi* (Italy) and *Karl Ferdinand Braun* (Germany) : development of wireless.	*Wilhelm Ostwald* (Germany) : research on catalysis, chemical equilibrium and rate of chemical reaction.	*Emil Theodor Kocher* (Switzerland) : work on thyroid gland.
1910	*Johannes D. van der Waals* (Netherlands) : theory of equation of state for gases and liquids.	*Otto Wallach* (Germany) : work on alicyclic compounds.	*Albrecht Kossel* (Germany) : research on chemistry of the cell.
1911	*Wilhelm Wien* (Germany) : laws of radiation of heat.	*Marie Curie* (France; born in Poland) : discovery of radium and polonium.	*Allvar Gullstrand* (Sweden) : work on dioptrics.
1912	*Gustaf Dalén* (Sweden) : invention of automatic regulators for lighting lighthouses and light buoys.	*Victor Grignard* (France): discovery of Grignard reagent. *Paul Sabatier* (France) : work on hydrogenation of organic compounds.	*Alexis Carrel* (U. S.; born in France) : work on ligature and grafting of blood vessels and organs.
1913	*H. Kamerlingh-Onnes* (Netherlands) : research paving way for production of liquid helium.	*Alfred Werner* (Switzerland): work on linking up atoms within the molecule.	*Charles Richet* (France) : research on anaphylaxy.
1914	*Max von Laue* (Germany) : discovery of diffraction of X rays passing through crystals.	*Theodore W. Richards* (U. S.): determining atomic weight of many elements.	*Robert Bárány* (Austria) : research on physiology and pathology of vestibular system.

Year	Physics	Chemistry	Medicine or Physiology
1915	*W. H. Bragg* (England) and *W. L. Bragg* (England): analysis of crystal structure by use of X Rays.	*Richard Willstaetter* (Germany): work on nature of chlorophyll and other coloring matter of plants.	No award.
1916	No award.	No award.	No award.
1917	*Charles G. Barkla* (England): discovery of Roentgen radiation of the elements.	No award.	No award.
1918	*Max Planck* (Germany): work on quantum theory.	*Fritz Haber* (Germany): synthetic production of ammonia.	No award.
1919	*Johannes Stark* (Germany): decomposition of spectrum lines by electric fields; discovery of Doppler effect in canal rays.	No award.	*Jules Bordet* (Belgium): research on immunity.
1920	*Charles E. Guillaume* (Switzerland): research on nickel-steel alloys.	*Walther Nernst* (Germany): work on thermochemistry.	*Schack August Krogh* (Denmark): research on motor mechanism of capillaries.
1921	*Albert Einstein* (Germany): law of photoelectric effect.	*Frederick Soddy* (England): work on isotopes.	No award.
1922	*Niels Bohr* (Denmark): research on structure of atoms and radiations from atoms.	*Francis W. Aston* (England): discovery of isotopes in non-radioactive elements.	*Archibald V. Hill* (England): work on heat production in muscles. *Otto Meyerhof* (Germany): discovery of correlation between consumption of oxygen and production of lactic acid in the muscles.
1923	*Robert A. Millikan* (U. S.): research on photoelectric phenomena and charge on electron.	*Fritz Pregl* (Austria): microanalysis of organic substances.	*Frederick G. Banting* (Canada) and *John J. R. McLeod* (Canada; born in Scotland): discovery of insulin.
1924	*Karl M. G. Siegbahn* (Sweden): work on X-ray spectroscopy.	No award.	*Willem Einthoven* (Netherlands): discovery of mechanism of electrocardiogram.
1925	*James Franck* (Germany) and *Gustav Hertz* (Germany): discovery of laws governing impact of electrons upon atoms.	*Richard Zsigmondy* (Germany; born in Austria): work on colloid solutions.	No award.
1926	*Jean-Baptiste Perrin* (France): work on discontinuous structure of matter; discovery of equilibrium of sedimentation.	*Theodor Svedberg* (Sweden): work on dispersion systems.	*Johannes Fibiger* (Denmark): researches on cancer.
1927	*Arthur H. Compton* (U. S.): discovery of Compton phenomenon. *Charles T. R. Wilson* (England): paths taken by electrically charged particles.	*Heinrich Wieland* (Germany): work on bile acids and similar substances.	*Julius Wagner-Jauregg* (Austria): use of malaria inoculation in treating dementia paralytica.

Wide World

Enrico Fermi (1901–54), below, won the Nobel Prize in physics in 1938 for outstanding work on radioactive elements and on the effect of slow neutrons on nuclei.

Wide World

Arthur H. Compton (1892–1962), above, won the Nobel Prize in physics in 1927 for the researches in which he analyzed the changes in the wave length of X rays.

Harold C. Urey (1893–   ), below, received the Nobel Prize in chemistry in 1934 for his discovery of heavy hydrogen (deuterium). It is present in heavy water.

Acme

U. S. Atomic Energy Commission

Glenn T. Seaborg (1912–   ), above, and E. M. McMillan were given the Nobel Prize in chemistry in 1951 for their discovery of the chemical element plutonium.

PRIZE WINNERS

Arthur Kornberg (1918–   ), below, and Severo Ochoa won the Nobel Prize in physiology in 1959 for their researches on compounds playing a vital role in heredity.

Stanford University

Willard F. Libby (1908–   ), below, won the Nobel chemistry award in 1960 for developing the radiocarbon method of dating objects by measuring their radioactivity.

Jules LeBaron, University of California

J. B. Atkinson

Sir Edward V. Appleton (1892–   ), above, won the Nobel Prize in physics in 1947 for discovering the layer that reflects radio short waves in the ionosphere.

General Electric

Irving Langmuir (1881–1957), above, received the Nobel Prize in chemistry in 1932 for his discoveries in surface chemistry. He was also a pioneer in cloud seeding.

Year	Physics	Chemistry	Medicine or Physiology
1928	Owen W. Richardson (England): work on thermionics: discovery of Richardson Law.	Adolph Windaus (Germany): work on constitution of sterols and their connection with vitamins.	Charles Nicolle (France): work on typhus exanthematicus.
1929	Prince Louis-Victor de Broglie (France): discovery of wave character of electrons.	Arthur Harden (England) and Hans K. A. S. von Euler-Chelpin (Sweden): work on fermentation of sugars.	Sir Frederick G. Hopkins (England): discovery of growth-promoting vitamins of different kinds. Christiaan Eijkman (Netherlands): discovery of antineuritic vitamins.
1930	Sir Chandrasekhara V. Raman (India): work on diffusion of light; discovery of Raman effect.	Hans Fischer (Germany): work on coloring matter of blood and leaves; synthesis of hemin.	Karl Landsteiner (U. S.; born in Austria): discovery of human blood groups.
1931	No award.	Friedrich Bergius (Germany) and Karl Bosch (Germany): development of chemical high-pressure methods.	Otto Warburg (Germany): work on respiratory ferment.
1932	Werner Heisenberg (Germany): development of quantum mechanics.	Irving Langmuir (U. S.): work on surface chemistry.	Sir Charles S. Sherrington (England) and Edgar D. Adrian (England): discovery of functions of neuron.
1933	Paul A. M. Dirac (England) and Erwin Schroedinger (Austria): discovery of various new forms of the atomic theory.	No award.	Thomas H. Morgan (U. S.): research on hereditary function of chromosomes.
1934	No award.	Harold C. Urey (U. S.): discovery of heavy hydrogen.	George R. Minot (U. S.), William P. Murphy (U. S.) and George H. Whipple (U. S.): discovery of liver therapy in treatment of anemia.
1935	James Chadwick (England): discovery of neutron.	Frédéric and Irène Joliot-Curie (France): synthesis of new radioactive elements.	Hans Spemann (Germany): discovery of organizer effect in embryonic development.
1936	Victor F. Hess (Austria): discovery of cosmic radiation. Carl D. Anderson (U. S.): discovery of positron.	Peter J. W. Debye (Germany; born in Netherlands): work on dipole moments and diffraction of X rays and electrons in gases.	Sir Henry H. Dale (England) and Otto Loewi (Austria): work on chemical transmission of nerve impulses.
1937	Clinton J. Davisson (U. S.) and George P. Thomson (England): discovery of diffraction of electrons by crystals.	Walter N. Haworth (England): research on carbohydrates and vitamin C. Paul Karrer (Switzerland): work on carotenoids, flavins and vitamins A and B.	Albert Szent-Györgyi von Nagyrapolt (Hungary): research on biological combustion.
1938	Enrico Fermi (Italy): identification of new radioactive elements; nuclear reactions effected by slow neutrons.	Richard Kuhn (Germany; declined the award): study of carotenoids; research on vitamins.	Corneille Heymans (Belgium): research on importance of sinus and aorta mechanisms in regulation of respiration.

Year	Physics	Chemistry	Medicine or Physiology
1939	*Ernest O. Lawrence* (U. S.): development of cyclotron.	*Adolph F. Butenandt* (Germany; declined the award): work on sexual hormones. *Leopold Ruzicka* (Switzerland): research on the polymethylenes.	*Gerhard Domagk* (Germany; declined the award): discovery of antibacterial effect of prontocilate.
1940	No award.	No award.	No award.
1941	No award.	No award.	No award.
1942	No award.	No award.	No award.
1943	*Otto Stern* (U. S.; born in Germany): detection of magnetic momentum of protons.	*Georg von Hevesy* (Hungary): work on use of isotopes as chemical indicators.	*Edward A. Doisy* (U. S.) and *Henrik Dam* (Denmark): discovery of the chemical nature of vitamin K.
1944	*Isidor Isaac Rabi* (U. S.): work on magnetic movements of atomic particles.	*Otto Hahn* (Germany): work on atomic fission.	*Joseph Erlanger* (U. S.) and *Herbert S. Gasser* (U. S.): research on functions of nerve threads.
1945	*Wolfgang Pauli* (Austria): work on atomic fission.	*Artturi Virtanen* (Finland): research in field of fodder conservation.	*Sir Alexander Fleming* (England), *Ernst Boris Chain* (Germany) an l *Sir Howard Walter Florey* (England): discovery of penicillin, derived from the mold *Penicillium notatum*.
1946	*Percy W. Bridgman* (U. S.): work on high-pressure physics.	*James B. Sumner* (U. S.): crystallizing of enzymes. *John H. Northrop* (U. S.) and *Wendell M. Stanley* (U. S.): preparation of enzymes and virus proteins in pure form.	*Herman J. Muller* (U. S.): research on hereditary effects of X rays on genes.
1947	*Sir Edward Appleton* (England): discovery of layer reflecting radio short waves in ionosphere.	*Sir Robert Robinson* (England): work on plant substances.	*Carl F. and Gerty T. Cori* (U. S.; born in Czechoslovakia): work on animal-starch metabolism. *Bernardo Houssay* (Argentina): hormone study of pituitary gland.
1948	*Patrick M. S. Blackett* (England): improvement on Wilson cloud chambers; series of outstanding discoveries in cosmic radiation.	*Arne Tiselius* (Sweden): biochemical discoveries; isolation of mouse-paralysis virus.	*Paul Mueller* (Switzerland): discovery of insecticidal properties of DDT.
1949	*Hideki Yukawa* (Japan): for mathematically predicting existence of meson.	*William F. Giauque* (U. S.; born in Canada): research in field of thermodynamics.	*Walter R. Hess* (Switzerland): work on brains of dogs and cats; discovery of how parts of brain control different parts of body. *Antonio Caetano de Abreu Freire Egas Moniz* (Portugal): development of brain operations for treatment of mental illness.

Year	Physics	Chemistry	Medicine or Physiology
1950	*Cecil Frank Powell* (England): development of simple photographic method for studying atomic nucleus; work on mesons.	*Otto Diels* (Germany) and *Kurt Adler* (Germany): developing Dien synthesis by which odors and complicated compounds are made artificially.	*Philip S. Hench* (U. S.), *Edward C. Kendall* (U. S.) and *Tadeus Reichstein* (Switzerland; born in Poland): discoveries regarding hormones of adrenal cortex, their structure and their biological effect.
1951	*Sir John Cockcroft* (England) and *E. T. S. Walton* (Ireland): experiments in splitting atomic nuclei with artificially propelled "bullets."	*Glenn T. Seaborg* (U. S.) and *Edward M. McMillan* (U. S.): discovery of plutonium.	*Max Theiler* (South Africa): discovering effective vaccines protecting human beings against yellow fever.
1952	*Felix Bloch* (U. S.) and *Edward M. Purcell* (U. S.): development of new method of measuring magnetic fields in atomic nuclei.	*Archer Martin* (England) and *Richard Synge* (Scotland): development of paper partition chromatography.	*Selman A. Waksman* (U. S.): discovery of streptomycin, first effective antibiotic against tuberculosis.
1953	*Fritz Zernike* (Netherlands): development of microscope for study of living cells colored by light waves.	*Hermann Staudinger* (Germany): work on synthesizing of fiber.	*Fritz A. Lipmann* (U. S.) and *Hans A. Krebs* (England): research on basic life processes carried on in human cells.
1954	*Max Born* (Germany): for fundamental work in quantum mechanics. *Walther Bothe* (Germany): for development of coincidence method in the study of cosmic radiation.	*Linus Pauling* (U. S.): for his work on the nature of chemical bonds, especially as applied to the structure of complicated substances.	*John F. Enders* (U. S.), *Thomas H. Weller* (U. S.) and *Frederick C. Robbins* (U. S.): for discovery that the poliomyelitis virus is capable of growing in cultures of different tissues.
1955	*Willis E. Lamb* (U. S.): for work on the hydrogen spectrum. *Polykarp Kusch* (U. S.): for precision measurement of the magnetic moment of the electron.	*Vincent du Vigneaud* (U. S.): for identification and synthesis of two hormones — oxytocin and vasopressin.	*Hugo Theorell* (Sweden): for work on the nature and action of oxidation enzymes.
1956	*William B. Shockley* (U. S.), *Walter H. Brattain* (U. S.) and *John Bardeen* (U. S.): development of the electronic transistor.	*Sir Cyril N. Hinshelwood* (England) and *Nikolai N. Semenov* (U. S. S. R.): independent but parallel research on chemical kinetics leading to the improvement of the internal combustion engine and the development of modern plastics.	*Dickinson W. Richards, Jr.* (U. S.), *Andre Cournand* (U. S.) and *Werner Forssman* (West Germany): developed a new technique of diagnosis and treatment of heart disease.
1957	*Tsung Dao Lee* (U. S.) and *Chen Ning Yang* (U. S.): atomic research disproving the principle of "conservation of parity."	*Sir Alexander Todd* (England): research on nucleotides and nucleotide enzymes, chemical compounds known to be factors in heredity.	*Daniel Bovet* (Italy): development of antihistamines and drugs based on *curare* — a South American Indian arrow-tip poison — to desensitize and relax muscles subjected to prolonged surgery.

Year	Physics	Chemistry	Medicine or Physiology
1958	*Pavel A. Cherenkov* (Russia), *Ilya M. Frank* (Russia) and *Igor E. Tamm* (Russia): work with high-speed subatomic particles.	*Frederick Sanger* (England): research on the structure of insulin.	*Joshua Lederberg* (U. S.), *Edward L. Tatum* (U. S.) and *George W. Beadle* (U. S.): work on the genes (genetic units).
1959	*Emilio Segre* (U. S.) and *Owen Chamberlain* (U. S.): proof of existence of antiproton, negative counterpart of proton.	*Jaroslav Heyrovsky* (Czechoslovakia): development of electrolytic method of chemical analysis.	*Arthur Kornberg* (U. S.) and *Severo Ochoa* (U. S.): work on RNA (ribonucleic acid) and DNA (deoxyribonucleic acid).
1960	*Donald A. Glaser* (U. S.): for discovery of "bubble chamber," used in measuring energy of atoms accelerated in atom smashers.	*Willard F. Libby* (U. S.): for development of radiocarbon-dating technique.*	*Peter B. Medawar* (England) and *Macfarlane Burnet* (Australia): for breaking "immunity barrier" that (with few exceptions) had prevented permanent transplants of different body parts from one animal to another.
1961	*Robert Hofstadter* (U. S.) and *Rudolf Moessbauer* (Germany): Hofstadter for work on core of atom; Moessbauer for gamma-ray research.	*Melvin Calvin* (U. S.): for research on carbon-dioxide assimilation in plants.	*Georg von Bekesy* (U. S.): for work on mechanics of hearing.
1962	*Lev Davidovich Landau* (Russia): for researches in field of cryogenics (very-low-temperature physics).	*John C. Kendrew* (England) and *Max F. Perutz* (England): for their use of X rays to determine position of atoms in two protein molecules—myoglobin and hemoglobin.	*Francis H. C. Crick* (England), *James D. Watson* (U.S.) and *Maurice H. F. Wilkins* (England): for their work on DNA, the nucleic acid that transmits hereditary patterns.

* Dr. Libby describes the technique in his article Radiocarbon Dating, in this volume.

FULL-COLOR PICTURES IN
THE BOOK OF POPULAR SCIENCE

FULL-COLOR PICTURES IN
THE BOOK OF POPULAR SCIENCE

VOLUME 1

pp. 92a-d
INDUSTRY AND SCIENCE

High energy fuel .... p. 92a
Jet engine pods .... p. 92b
Aluminum forgings .... p. 92b
Processing of corn .... p. 92c
Printing cotton cloth .... p. 92c
Underground coal cutter .... p. 92d

pp. 148a-h
IMPORTANT
SYSTEMS IN MAN

Skeletal system .... p. 148b
Muscular system .... p. 148c
Digestive system .... p. 148d
Respiratory system .... p. 148e
Excretory system .... p. 148e
Circulatory system .... p. 148f
Lymphatic system .... p. 148g
Endocrine system .... p. 148g
Nervous system .... p. 148h

pp. 204a-d
FOUR-COLOR LITHOGRAPHY

Old hand-operated lithographic press .... p. 204a
Modern lithographic press .... pp. 204a-b
Weighing inks .... p. 204b
Diagram of 4-color lithographic printing .... pp. 204b-c
Distributing ink and moisture on the plate .... p. 204c
Printed sheet coming off press .... p. 204c
Developing film .... p. 204d
Working on negatives .... p. 204d
Placing negatives in master form sheets .... p. 204d
Applying emulsion to surface of plate .... p. 204d

pp. 348a-d
VERSATILE STEEL

Tapping open-hearth furnace .... p. 348a
Flow chart showing steelmaking processes .... pp. 348b-d

VOLUME 2

pp. 12a-d
THE CELL

Plastic model of cell .... pp. 12a, c-d
Electron photomicrographs of cell .... pp. 12b, d

pp. 412a-d
INSECT FARMERS,
SIGNALERS AND
BUILDERS

Ants "milking" their aphid herd .... p. 412b
Leaf-cutting ants at work .... p. 412b
Signaling activities of honey bees .... p. 412c
Papermaking wasps at work .... p. 412d
Vertical mud tubes of pipe-organ wasp .... p. 412d
Potter wasp constructing pot-shaped nest .... p. 412d

VOLUME 3

pp. 42a-d
PHOTOSYNTHESIS

Cross section of leaf .... p. 42b
Close-up of palisade cell .... p. 42c
Chloroplast .... p. 42c
Daytime and nighttime in plant life .... p. 42c
Photosynthesis in higher and lower plants .... p. 42d

pp. 202a-d
BUTTERFLIES AND MOTHS

Caterpillar of spicebush swallowtail butterfly .... p. 202a
Adult spicebush swallowtail butterfly .... p. 202a
Chrysiridia ripheus .... pp. 202b-c
Imperial swallowtail .... p. 202c
Lola giant silkworm moth .... p. 202d
Pantherodes pardalaria .... p. 202d
Regal hairstreak .... p. 202d
Catagramma cynosura .... p. 202d

pp. 298a-d
ROADS

New York State Thruway .... p. 298a
Excavating and grading a highway .... p. 298b
Paving a highway .... p. 298c
Landscaping and marking .... p. 298c
Finished asphalt and concrete highways in cross section .... p. 298d

pp. 314a-d
GLASS

Hand processing of glass .... p. 314a
Plate glass .... pp. 314b-c
Machine-blown glass .... pp. 314b-c
Machine-drawn glass .... pp. 314b-c
Machine-pressed glass .... pp. 314b-c
Properties of glass .... p. 314d

VOLUME 4

pp. 114a-d
ATOMIC-POWERED SHIPS FOR WAR AND PEACE

The nuclear submarine *Nautilus* .... p. 114a
The aircraft carrier *Enterprise* .... p. 114a
The Russian icebreaker *Lenin* .... p. 114a
The nuclear ship *Savannah* and her power plant .... pp. 114b-c
The revolutionary nuclear submarine .... p. 114d
Island superstructures of aircraft carriers .... p. 114d

pp. 146a-d
THE PETROLEUM INDUSTRY

Derrick floor of drilling rig .... p. 146a
Portable drilling rig .... p. 146a
Flow chart tracing crude oil from well to finished product ... pp. 146b-c
Quality-control laboratory of a processing tower .... p. 146d
Baton Rouge refinery .... p. 146d

pp. 342a-d
MODERN RESEARCH PROJECTS

Wear-tests for automobile parts .... p. 342a
General Motors research headquarters .... p. 342b
Federal Telecommunication Laboratories .... p. 342b
Erecting a giant atom smasher .... pp. 342b-c
Firing a rocket-propelled research missile .... p. 342c
Testing the first atomic submarine engine .... p. 342d
Growing molds that produce antibiotics .... p. 342d

pp. 374a-d
**PAPERMAKING METHODS
AND PRODUCTS**

Growing southern pine seedlings .... p. 374a
Unloading pulp wood .... p. 374a
Wet end of paper machine .... p. 374a
Press section of paper machine .... p. 374a
Flow chart showing pulp and papermaking processes ...... pp. 374b-c
Traveling crane carrying roll of paper .... p. 374d
Paper products .... p. 374d

VOLUME 5

pp. 58a-d
CAVES AND CAVE DEPOSITS

Saracen's Tent, Luray Caverns .... p. 58a
Totem Pole, Carlsbad Caverns .... p. 58a
Ballroom, Luray Caverns .... pp. 58b-c
Helictites .... p. 58c
Gypsum flowers .... p. 58c
Bone Yard, Carlsbad Caverns .... p. 58c
Billing Doves, Carlsbad Caverns .... p. 58d
Titania's Veil, Luray Caverns .... p. 58d
Liberty Column, Luray Caverns .... p. 58d

pp. 98a-d
NATURAL GAS

Drilling .... p. 98a
Gas-well Christmas tree .... p. 98a
Transmission of natural gas .... p. 98b
Underground storage .... pp. 98b-c
Natural-gas pipeline .... pp. 98b-c
Regulator station .... p. 98c
How natural gas serves a community .... p. 98d

pp. 354a-d
**HOW SNAKES
MOVE ABOUT**

Horizontal undulatory movement of snakes .... p. 354a
Caterpillar crawl of snakes .... p. 354b
Sidewinder traveling over loose sand .... p. 354b
Flying snake soaring .... p. 354c
Pelamis platurus, a sea snake .... p. 354c
Cook's tree boa climbing up tree trunk .... p. 354d
Cook's tree boa moving along branches .... p. 354d
North American corn snake climbing up tree .... p. 354d

pp. 418a-h
**COURTSHIP, MIGRATIONS
AND NESTING HABITS
OF BIRDS**

Courtship of hawks .... p. 418a
Male marsh hawk courting female .... p. 418b
Prairie chickens in mating season .... p. 418b
Male shrike serenading female .... p. 418b
Female crossbill receiving food offering .... p. 418c
Courtship display of great bird of paradise .... p. 418c
Male common tern presenting food offering .... p. 418c
Aluminum bird band .... p. 418d
The nonmigratory bobwhite .... p. 418d
The golden plover and its travels .... p. 418d
The four major North American flyways .... pp. 418d-e
Migration of Canadian geese .... p. 418e
Night-traveling sparrows .... p. 418e
Day-traveling swallows .... p. 418e
Hanging nest of Baltimore oriole .... p. 418f
Flamingo colony and mud nests .... p. 418f
Nest of great horned owl .... p. 418g
Tailorbird and its stitched nest .... p. 418g

Nest of burrowing owl .... p. 418g
"Community house" of social weavers .... p. 418h
Insect sentinels guarding cacique nests .... p. 418h

VOLUME 6

pp. 26a-d   Clare Booth Luce with trapped squirrelfish .... p. 26a
SCUBA DIVING   Aqualung diver's equipment .... p. 26b
                     Typical open-water scuba dive .... p. 26c
                     Scuba divers wrapping wooden piling .... p. 26d
                     Scuba-equipped gold miner .... p. 26d
                     "Headlight" used in scuba diving .... p. 26d
                     Scuba diver recovering murder weapon .... p. 26d
                     Underwater geologist .... p. 26d
                     Diver preparing to photograph ocean bottom .... p. 26d

pp. 74a-d   Cross section of bathyscaphe .... p. 74b
THE BATHYSCAPHE   How the bathyscaphe works .... p. 74c
                     Some of the tasks of the bathyscaphe .... p. 74d

pp. 218a-d   Migration of slime mold .... p. 218a
PLANT MOVEMENTS   Movements of morning-glory tendril .... p. 218b
                     Phototropism—turning toward light .... p. 218c
                     Geotropism—bending in response to gravity .... p. 218c
                     Hydrotropism—movement in response to water .... p. 218c
                     Venus's-flytrap catching insect prey .... p. 218d

pp. 298a-d   The UNIVAC .... pp. 298a, b
APPLICATIONS OF   Tiny gas-filled electron tube .... p. 298b
ELECTRONICS   Huge amplifier tube .... pp. 298b-c
                     Color cameras focusing on a model .... p. 298c
                     Ship's radar screen .... p. 298c
                     Manufacture of klystrons (high-frequency electron tubes) ... p. 298d
                     Wiring selenium rectifier units used in television receivers ... p. 298d

VOLUME 7

pp. 124a-d   Steel skeleton construction .... pp. 124a-b
ERECTING A SKYSCRAPER Four types of foundation .... p. 124b
                     Jumping the derrick .... p. 124c
                     Fireproofing columns .... p. 124c
                     Fitting outer wall in place .... p. 124c
                     Details of construction .... p. 124d

pp. 284a-d   Spectrum of incandescent light produced by diffraction
THE WORLD OF COLOR   grating .... p. 284a
                     A group of spectra .... p. 284a
                     Additive combinations of colors .... p. 284b
                     Subtractive mixtures of colors .... p. 284b
                     Different degrees of intensity in colors .... p. 284b
                     Colors used in the printing process .... p. 284b
                     Bolt viewed in polarized light .... p. 284c
                     Color effects on revolving phonograph record .... p. 284c
                     Colors produced as light strikes cut-glass carvings .... p. 284c
                     Colors from an oil slick .... p. 284c

Testing color perception .... p. 284d
The effect of color contrast .... p. 284d
A striking optical illusion .... p. 284d

VOLUME 8

pp. 156a-h
A CELESTIAL COLOR
DISPLAY

Ring Nebula in Lyra .... p. 156a
Veil Nebula in Cygnus .... pp. 156b-c
Great Galaxy in Andromeda .... p. 156c
Crab Nebula in Taurus .... pp. 156d-e
Great Nebula in Orion .... pp. 156f-g
North American Nebula .... p. 156h

pp. 220a-d
PLASTICS

Colored pellets of Tenite Polyethylene .... p. 220a
Compression molding .... p. 220b
Injection molding .... p. 220b
Extrusion molding .... p. 220b
Objects made of styrene .... p. 220c
Red Tenite Polyethylene washers .... p. 220d
Colored sheets of Tenite Butyrate .... p. 220d
Bow housing for boats made of Tenite Butyrate .... p. 220d

pp. 300a-d
GEYSERS AND VOLCANOES

Old Faithful, a Yellowstone National Park geyser .... p. 300a
Izalco, an active volcano in El Salvador .... p. 300a
Whakarewarewa, a New Zealand geyser .... p. 300b
Parícutin, a Mexican volcano formed in 1943 .... pp. 300b-c
Eruption of Hawaiian volcano of Puna .... p. 300c
Lava gushing from Halemaumau, in crater of Kilauea,
    Hawaii .... p. 300c
Daisy Geyser, Yellowstone National Park .... p. 300d
Popocatepetl, dormant Mexican volcano .... p. 300d

pp. 316a-d
DAMS — A PICTORIAL SURVEY

Shasta Dam, California .... p. 316a
Kamishiiba Dam, Japan .... p. 316b
Hoover Dam, Arizona-Nevada .... p. 316b
Dam No. 8, Ohio River .... p. 316c
Yale Dam, north of Portland, Oregon .... p. 316c
Bliss hydroelectric development, near Gooding, Idaho ...... p. 316d
Ross Dam, Washington .... p. 316d

VOLUME 9

pp. 138a-b
ATOMIC ENERGY FOR
RESEARCH

Nuclear reactor .... p. 138a
Swimming pool reactor .... p. 138b

pp. 234a-d
GENERATION, TRANSMIS-
SION AND DISTRIBUTION
OF ELECTRICITY

Steam station for generation of electricity .... p. 234a
Hydroelectric development .... p. 234a
Power plant with diesel engine .... p. 234a
Giant step-up transformer .... p. 234b
Tower for transmission line ... . p. 234b
Circuit breakers at switching station .... p. 234c
Substation .... p. 234c
Pole with step-down transformer .... p. 234c
How electricity serves man .... p. 234d

pp. 400a-b
COLOR PHOTOGRAPHY

Reproducing colors by a reversal color film .... p. 400a
Cross section of Kodachrome film .... p. 400b
Yellow, cyan and magenta filters .... p. 400b

VOLUME 10

pp. 130a-d
IMPORTANT ANTIBIOTICS

The mold *Penicillium* .... p. 130a
Growing soil organisms in Petri dishes .... p. 130a
Molds in a microscopic "jungle" .... pp. 130b-c
Examining a culture of antibiotic-producing organisms ..... p. 130c
The "cup-plate" method of testing antibiotics .... p. 130d
How antibiotics affect bacteria .... p. 130d

pp. 234a-d
AUTOMATION AT WORK

Integration .... p. 234a
Electronic computer .... p. 234b
Feedback .... p. 234c
Automation in an oil refinery .... p. 234d

GENERAL OUTLINE

GENERAL OUTLINE

THE UNIVERSE

	VOL.	PAGE
THE STUDY OF THE UNIVERSE — How Astronomy Contributes to Man's Progress	1	16
THE FACE OF THE SKY — Shifting Patterns Formed by Heavenly Bodies	1	255
THE CONSTELLATIONS — Star Patterns in the Heavens	1	322
MAN-MADE SKIES — The Story of the Zeiss Planetarium	2	396
THE SUN, OUR STAR — Its Disk, Atmosphere and Other Features	3	99
SHADOWS IN THE HEAVENS — Eclipses of the Sun and of the Moon	3	130
THE FAMILY OF THE SUN — A Survey of the Vast Solar System	3	157
COMPANIONS OF THE SUN — Mercury and Venus — Planets inside Earth's Orbit	4	25
THE PLANET EARTH — Facts and Theories Concerning Our Home in Space	4	42
THE MOON — Interesting Facts about Earth's Satellite	4	277
MARS AND THE MINOR PLANETS — Diminutive Members of the Solar System	4	415
A GIANT AMONG PLANETS — The Story of Jupiter, Fifth Planet from the Sun	5	20
SATURN THE MAGNIFICENT — A Big Planet Less Dense Than Water	5	107
THE OUTERMOST PLANETS — Huge Uranus and Neptune and Tiny Pluto	5	289
ROVING MEMBERS OF THE SUN'S FAMILY — The Origin, Nature and Destruction of Comets	5	390
METEORITES AND METEORS — An Introduction to the Science of Meteoritics	6	87
THE STARS — Luminous Bodies That Shine by Their Own Light	6	255
VARIABLE STARS — Eclipsing Binaries, Novae and Supernovae	7	45
THE MOTIONS OF THE STARS — Apparent and Real Movement in Space	7	223
THE GALAXIES — Island Universes in the Heavens	8	47
ASTRONOMICAL OBSERVATORIES — An Account of the Astronomer's Headquarters	8	55
THE MILKY WAY — A Modern Interpretation of This "Band of Light"	8	151
REFLECTING TELESCOPES — A Footnote on Progress in Telescopy	9	153
RADIO ASTRONOMY — The Study of Radio Waves from Outer Space	9	206
THE ASTRONOMER EXPLORES SPACE — Materials Scattered between the Stars	9	359
RECORDING THE FLEETING DAYS — The Development of the Calendar	10	171

THE EARTH

	VOL.	PAGE
THE STUDY OF THE EARTH — An Introduction to Geology	1	27
EARTH'S AIRY ENVELOPE — How the Atmosphere Affects Our Planet	1	230
THE WEATHER PROBLEM — Forecasting Storm and Fair Weather	1	241
WHEN LIGHTNING STRIKES — Fathoming the Mysteries of Nature's Fireworks	1	398
AIR IN MOTION — The Origin and Nature of the Earth's Winds	2	89
PROBLEMS OF CLOUDLAND — The Formation and Patterns of Clouds	2	212
TRANSFORMATIONS OF WATER VAPOR — Rain, Snow and Other Forms of Precipitation	2	346
JET STREAMS — Swift Currents of Air High in the Atmosphere	2	358
CLIMATES OF THE PAST — Methods of Analysis and Results	3	177
THE CRUST OF OUR PLANET — The Basic Structure of Earth's Overlying Rocks	3	419
THE ISLANDS OF THE MAIN — Their Formation and Their Structure	4	133
THE INTERIOR OF THE EARTH — Little-known Nether Regions of Our Planet	4	169
IN THE DEPTHS OF THE EARTH — The Wonders of Caves and Cave Deposits	5	50
CRYSTALS IN THE EARTH — A Brief Survey of the Minerals	5	248
THE SEA — Broad Highway and Rich Storehouse	6	27
THE DEPTHS OF THE SEA — What the Study of the Ocean Bottom Reveals	6	69
EARTH'S FLATTENED AREAS — A Survey of Plateaus and Deserts	6	109
THE TIDES — The Ceaseless Ebb and Flow of Ocean Waters	6	201
THE CIRCULATION OF THE SEA — Tracing the Patterns Formed by Ocean Currents	6	229
THE WAVES OF THE SEA — Why Ocean Waters Are Never Still	6	361
THE GEOLOGICAL TIME SCALE — Earth's History Recorded in Rock	6	369

	VOL.	PAGE
THE RETURN OF THE WATERS — The Great River Systems of the World	6	409
INLAND WATER RESERVES — The Formation of the Earth's Lakes and Marshes	7	55
THE IMPORTANCE OF DUST — Numberless Particles That Fill the Atmosphere	7	137
THE WINDS AT WORK — How Wind-blown Sand and Dust Erode the Land	7	318
VOLCANIC CATASTROPHES — Historic Eruptions in Many Lands	7	334
THE WORK OF RUNNING WATER — How Streams and Rivers Carve the Land	8	9
GEYSERS AND VOLCANOES — How Earth's Internal Heat Bursts Forth	8	288
WATER IN THE GROUND — A Vast Reserve Stored Up in Soil and Rock	8	321
CHANGING SHORELINES — Beaches, Coasts and Shore Processes	8	348
THE TREMBLING OF THE EARTH — What We Know about Earthquakes	9	105
THE WORK OF GLACIERS — Huge Ice Masses That Mold the Land	9	162
FLOATING ICE ISLANDS — The Birth and Journeyings of Icebergs	9	333
MOUNTAIN STOREHOUSES — Ranges and Peaks That Hold Water Reserves	10	18
THE MAKING OF MOUNTAINS — The Cycles of Building and Decay	10	213

LIFE

	VOL.	PAGE
WHAT IS LIFE? — Unsolved Problem of the Universe	1	37
THE ROLL CALL OF LIVING THINGS — How Animals and Plants Are Classified	1	287
BASIC UNITS OF LIFE — The Structure and Functions of Living Cells	2	1
LIVING LIGHT — The Amazing Phenomenon of Bioluminescence	2	182
HOW AND WHY CELLS DIVIDE — The Story of Bodily Growth	2	287
LIVING ELECTRIC BATTERIES — An Introduction to Bioelectricity	2	421
THE STRUGGLE FOR LIFE — Adaptations That Serve in the War for Survival	3	235
THE CHANGING SEASONS AND LIFE — How Living Things React to Cold and Heat	5	408
A MODERN THEORY OF EVOLUTION — How Living Things Have Diverged	6	269
LAND AND SEA HABITATS — The Natural Abodes of Animals and Plants	10	135
PLANT AND ANIMAL COMMUNITIES — How Living Things of a Region Dwell Together	10	181

PLANT LIFE

	VOL.	PAGE
THE LIFE OF PLANTS — An Introduction to the Science of Botany	1	45
THE SOIL — The Thin Surface Layer That Supports Plant Life	2	15
THE FERTILITY OF THE SOIL — The Scientific Cultivation of the Land	2	163
EARTH'S INVISIBLE ARMY — Small Organisms in the Soil	2	203
PLANTS AS STOREHOUSES — The Accumulation of Reserve Materials	2	415
THE FUNGI — Molds, Yeasts, Mushrooms and Their Kin	3	22
THE VITAL PROCESSES OF PLANTS — Food Manufacture, and Other Phenomena	3	43
THE BACTERIA — Microscopic Enemies and Allies of Man	3	63
MOSSES, FERNS AND THEIR ALLIES — Plants with Unlike Alternating Generations	3	186
THE ALGAE — Primitive and Infinitely Varied Plants	3	214
THE SEED PLANTS — Dominant Forms of the Earth's Vegetation	3	397
ROOTS, STEMS AND LEAVES — Essential Structures of All Seed Plants	4	62
FLOWERS, FRUITS AND SEEDS — How Flowering Plants Reproduce Their Kind	4	119
VEGETABLE FIBERS — Important Raw Materials for Industry	4	177
SEED AND FRUIT DISPERSAL — Some Interesting Adaptations of Seed Plants	5	1
THE WATER OF THE SOIL — Problems of Moisture Control	5	25
FROM SEED TO SEEDLING — The Vital Process of Germination	5	61
THE TREES OF THE FOREST — American Forests and Their Management	5	257
AUTUMN'S STORAGE OF LIFE — How Plants Prepare for Winter and Spring	6	52
HOW THE SOIL WAS FORMED — A Thin Film upon Which Life Depends	6	136
A PLANT'S FIGHT FOR LIFE — How Plants Adapt to Their Environment	6	218
THE DEFENSES OF PLANTS — How Plants Ward Off Their Animal Enemies	7	75
PLANT SCOURGES — Weeds — a Standing Menace to Our Fields	7	111
PLANTS AND THEIR PARTNERS — The Pollination of Flowers by Insects	7	239
SOILLESS AGRICULTURE — A Weapon in the War against Hunger	8	34
DISEASES OF GARDEN PLANTS — Methods of Prevention and Eradication	8	369

PROPAGATION OF PLANTS — Artificial Reproduction by Various Methods 9   7
INSECT ENEMIES OF FRUIT CROPS — A Survey of Approved Methods of Defense 9   185
THE TREATMENT OF PLANTS — The Use of Surgery in the Garden 10   143

ANIMAL LIFE

THE LIFE OF ANIMALS — A Foreword to the Study of Zoology 1   51
LIVING MACHINES — Pumps, Floats and Levers in Animal Bodies 1   277
THE ANNALS OF ANIMAL LIFE — The Story Told by Fossils in the Rocks 1   383
ANIMAL INTELLIGENCE ON DISPLAY — A Pictorial Record 2   26
THE PROTOZOANS — Microscopic Organisms with Varied Ways of Life 2   58
SPONGES, JELLYFISH AND SEA STARS — Familiar Marine Animals without Backbones 2   146
THE WORMS — Dreaded Enemies and Humble Benefactors of Man 2   153
THE MOLLUSKS — Soft-bodied Creatures of Land and Sea 2   192
THE CRUSTACEANS — Lobsters, Crabs, Crayfish and Their Kin 2   236
SPIDERS AND THEIR KIN — Widely Distributed Little Creatures 2   258
THE MIGHTY INSECT — A Small, Six-legged Competitor of Man 2   402
GRASSHOPPERS AND THEIR KIN — The Orthopteroids, a Varied Group of Insects 3   138
BUTTERFLIES AND MOTHS — Graceful Scale-winged Insects 3   193
THE TRUE BUGS — Stinkbugs, Chinch Bugs and Other Hemiptera 3   252
FLIES AND MOSQUITOES — Two-winged Members of the Vast Insect Group 3   283
WING-SHEATH HORDES — The Beetles, Most Numerous of the Insects 3   335
ANTS, BEES AND WASPS — Social Organization in the Insect World 3   357
THE PRIMITIVE CHORDATES — Unique Relatives of the Backboned Animals 4   1
THE FISHES — A Survey of the Largest Vertebrate Group 4   93
A FOSSIL COMES TO LIFE — The Discovery of the "Extinct" Coelacanth 4   196
WARRIORS OF THE OCEAN — The Story of Sharks, Rays and Their Kin 4   285
THE SEA FISH WE EAT — Boundless Reserves of Food for Man 4   311
HOW VERTEBRATES HEAR — Development of the Ear in Backboned Animals 4   379
THE AMPHIBIANS — Life Cycles of Frogs, Salamanders and Their Kin 5   152
THE LIZARDS — A Widely Distributed Reptile Group 5   196
THE SNAKE TRIBE — Reptiles with a Varied Way of Life 5   351
ANIMALS IN ARMOR CLAD — Picturesque Survivals of Past Ages 5   380
THE LIFE OF BIRDS — Highlights of Structure and Behavior 5   414
OUR COMMON BIRDS I — Thrushes, Chickadees, Nuthatches and Others 6   37
OUR COMMON BIRDS II — Warblers, Vireos, Waxwings and Swallows 6   60
OUR COMMON BIRDS III — Flycatchers, Crows, Blackbirds and Others 6   99
OUR COMMON BIRDS IV — Vultures, Hawks, Eagles and Owls 6   152
OUR COMMON BIRDS V — Woodpeckers, Hummingbirds, Swifts and Others 6   209
OUR COMMON BIRDS VI — Doves, Pigeons, Cuckoos and Kingfishers 6   304
OUR COMMON BIRDS VII — Quail, Grouse, Turkeys and Pheasants 6   331
OUR COMMON BIRDS VIII — Loons, Grebes, Gulls and Other Water Birds 6   394
THE LIFE OF MAMMALS — Their History, Structure and Habits 7   1
FIN-FOOTED CARNIVORES — Seals, Walruses and Sea Elephants 7   84
THE INSECT EATERS — Animals That Maintain the Balance of Nature 7   94
LIFE WITHOUT GERMS — The Answer to a Great Scientist's Question 7   151
MAMMALS IN THE WATER — Fishlike Creatures That Suckle Their Young 7   181
THE BEAR AND HIS COUSINS — Bears, Pandas, Raccoons and Others 7   307
SOME ANIMAL HELPERS OF MAN — Beasts of Burden in Many Lands 7   327
THE ASTONISHING GIANTS — Elephant, Hippopotamus, Rhinoceros, Giraffe 7   408
THE POUCHED MAMMALS — Kangaroos, Opossums and Other Marsupials 7   418
THE DOG FAMILY — Wolves, Coyotes, Jackals, Foxes and Others 8   132
THE GNAWING ANIMALS — The Rodents, Competitors of Man 8   160
THE WILY WEASEL FAMILY — Small Flesh Eaters of the North Temperate Zone 8   171
THE CATS — Lions, Leopards, Jaguars, Pumas and Lynxes 8   202
THE DEER FAMILY — The Story of the Widespread Antlered Herd 8   234
CIVETS, MONGOOSES AND HYENAS — Carnivores of the Old World Tropics 8   244

	VOL.	PAGE
THE ANTELOPE FAMILY — A Varied Group of Hoofed Mammals	8	376
ANIMAL HOME BUILDERS — Engineering Feats of Beavers and Other Rodents	9	1
APES, MONKEYS AND THEIR KIN — Interesting Members of the Order of Primates	9	250
GAME AND BIRD SANCTUARIES — Measures Taken to Preserve Wild Life	9	266
ANIMAL MIGRATIONS — Remarkable Journeys of Birds, Fishes and Others	9	415
THE ANIMALS OF THE ZOO — Sidelights on Modern Zoological Collections	10	154
THE TAMING OF THE WILD — How Animals Have Become Man's Allies	10	239

MAN

MAN — AN INTRODUCTION — How We Resemble and Differ from Other Living Things	1	57
THE BASIC UNITS OF THE BODY — How the Parts of the Body Are Linked Together	1	143
THE COVERING OF THE BODY — Fact and Fancy about the Skin, Hair and Nails	2	173
THE BONES OF THE BODY — Living Tissues That Serve Many Purposes	3	73
THE MUSCULAR SYSTEM OF MAN — What Muscles Are and How They Work	3	203
POPULATION PROBLEMS — The Mighty Surge and Ebb of Human Tides	3	225
THE LIFE STREAM — What Blood Is and What It Does	3	325
THE CIRCULATORY SYSTEM — How Blood Is Transported through the Body	3	381
THE RESPIRATORY SYSTEM — The Why and Wherefore of Breathing	4	200
THE DIGESTIVE TRACT — How Food Is Transformed in the Body	4	321
INTERNAL LABORATORIES — The Glands of the Human Body	5	8
THE TEETH — What They Are and How to Care for Them	5	129
THE NERVOUS SYSTEM — A Vital Network of the Human Body	6	317
THE SENSES — An Analysis of the World of Sensation	7	291
THE DEFENSES OF THE BODY — Structures and Processes That Guard Us	7	346
A BABY IS BORN — The Process of Reproduction in Man	8	19
THE SAGA OF HUMAN LIFE — The Annals of Growth, Development and Decline	8	90
THE RACES OF MANKIND — A Modern Approach to Their Classification	8	213
HEREDITY IN MAN — How Successive Generations Are Molded	8	333
PROBLEMS OF PSYCHOLOGY — How the Scientist Studies Human Nature	9	310
EXERCISE AND REST — How the Body Expends and Renews Energy Stores	10	85

HEALTH

THE HEALTHY MAN — How to Make Good Use of the Body's Resources	1	67
HEATING AND VENTILATION — Closely Linked Systems Affecting Our Comfort	2	244
THE WATER SUPPLY — How It Is Collected, Processed and Distributed	2	270
AIR POLLUTION — What Causes It and How We Can Combat It	3	349
THE VIRUSES — Tiny Disease Agents in Life's Twilight Zone	3	451
BASIC FOOD ELEMENTS — Proteins, Carbohydrates, Fats and Other Factors	4	51
STARCHES AND SUGARS — Carbohydrates Essential for Health and Growth	4	76
FOOD PRESERVATION — How Our Food and Drink Are Safeguarded	4	153
THE ALLERGIES — What They Are and What to Do about Them	4	257
OF ALCOHOLIC BEVERAGES — How Ethyl Alcohol Affects the Human Body	4	405
THE VITAMINS — Accessory Factors Essential for Health	5	38
THE REGULATION OF DIET — How to Achieve Health through Proper Food	5	267
THE DISPOSAL OF WASTES — How Communities Deal with an Age-old Problem	5	326
THE TOBACCO PROBLEM — The Effects of Smoking upon the Human Body	5	343
THE RISE OF TRANQUILIZERS — "Wonder Drugs" for the Mentally Ill — and Others	5	377
THE NARCOTIC-DRUG EVIL — A Problem of Our Modern Civilization	5	400
ACCIDENT PREVENTION IN THE HOME — Safety Rules for All Members of the Family	6	1
PROBLEMS OF SLEEP — An Analysis of "Nature's Second Course"	6	143
PENICILLIN AND STREPTOMYCIN — Two Wonder-working Germ Killers	7	52
ACCIDENT PREVENTION IN THE HOME — Safety Rules for All Members of the Family	7	190
ON GROWING OLD — Science of Geriatrics	8	78
THE CANCERS — A Survey of Malignant Growths in Man	8	265
THE TRUE PARASITES — Organisms within or on Other Organisms	8	360

	VOL.	PAGE
ON THE MICROBE'S TRACK — The Lifework of Louis Pasteur	9	71
THE GRIM WHITE PLAGUE — The Story of Man's War against Tuberculosis	9	175
THE HEALING OF SICK MINDS — Advances in the Science of Psychiatry	9	197
A FIRST-AID PRIMER — What to Do While Waiting for the Doctor	10	5
MAN AND THE MOSQUITO — The War against Malaria	10	30
A HOME-NURSING PRIMER — How to Care for the Sick or Injured at Home	10	55
KEEPING FIT — How to Care for the Body in Health	10	75
ATOMIC MEDICINES — Battling Disease with Radioactive Isotopes	10	98
PROGRESS IN MEDICINE — Important Landmarks of Modern Research	10	127

MATHEMATICS

THE SCOPE OF MATHEMATICS — The Study of the "Queen and Servant of the Sciences"	1	73
OF ARITHMETIC — Computation with the Numbers of the Decimal System	1	149
AN INTRODUCTION TO ALGEBRA — The Mathematics of "Any Numbers" or "Variables"	2	67
FROM POINTS TO SOLIDS — Plane and Solid Geometry and Trigonometry	3	427
A GLIMPSE INTO HIGHER MATHEMATICS — Analytic Geometry, Calculus and Other Fields	4	423
LIGHTER MOMENTS WITH MATHEMATICS — An Introduction to Mathematical Recreations	4	443
THE ELECTRONIC COMPUTER — A Fantastically Rapid and Accurate Calculator	9	143

MATTER AND ENERGY

THE WORLD OF MATTER AND ENERGY — What Chemistry and Physics Reveal to Us	1	79
HOW MOLECULES BEHAVE — The Why and Wherefore of Gases, Liquids and Solids	1	162
PLASMAS — A Brief Account of the "Fourth State of Matter"	1	173
INSIDE THE ATOM — Man's Fateful Discovery of a Miniature World	1	307
NATURAL FORCES THAT WORK FOR MAN — Harnessing Pressures in Liquids and Gases	2	30
HOW THINGS MOVE — An Account of the Different Types of Motion	2	118
CHEMICAL REACTIONS — How the Chemist Transforms His Materials	2	223
CRYSTALS AT WORK FOR MAN — Piezoelectricity and Electrostriction	2	293
THE FORCE OF GRAVITATION — How All Things Attract One Another	2	315
IMPORTANT METALS — Valuable Resources in the Earth's Crust	3	33
SIMPLE MACHINES — Basic Tools That Make Us More Powerful	3	56
THE FIXATION OF NITROGEN — Putting to Work an Abundant Atmospheric Gas	3	126
SUPERACTIVE ELEMENTS — The Alkali and Alkaline-Earth Metals	3	165
HOW ATOMS COMBINE — The Nature of Valence	3	245
NONMETALLIC ELEMENTS — From Cleansing Oxygen to Versatile Carbon	3	317
WHAT IS HEAT? — An Analysis of a Common Form of Energy	3	407
HEAT TRANSMISSION — Conduction, Convection and Radiation	4	9
HEAT ENGINES — How Heat Energy Is Made to Perform Work	4	80
THE THEORY OF RELATIVITY — Milestone in the History of Scientific Thought	4	210
THE NATURE OF SOLUTIONS — Mixtures Found in Living and Nonliving Things	4	296
THE PERIODIC TABLE — How the Chemical Elements Are Classified	4	304
ACIDS, BASES AND SALTS — Vital Interlinked Chemical Substances	4	336
OF ELECTROCHEMISTRY — Chemical Reactions Based on Electric Energy	5	87
AN ANALYSIS OF SOUND — How Pressure Changes Create a World of Sensation	5	114
THE INTERNATIONAL GEOPHYSICAL YEAR — A Scientific Co-Operative Effort	5	186
A GLIMPSE AT CRYOGENICS — The Science of Very Low Temperatures	5	207
MUSICAL SOUNDS — The Scientific Basis of the Musician's Art	5	211
BETWIXT-AND-BETWEEN PARTICLES — The Importance of Colloids in Today's World	5	294
A ROTATING STEAM ENGINE — The Development of the Turbine	5	305
SYMMETRY UNLIMITED — The Fascinating World of Crystals	5	337
PROPERTIES OF MATTER — An Analysis of Viscosity and Other Phenomena	5	369
PRINTED CIRCUITS — How Flat Metal Ribbons Replace Mazes of Wires	6	49
THE NATURE OF ELECTRICITY — Moving Electrons That Have Transformed Man's Life	6	119
THE SNAP GENERATOR — A Device That Produces Heat Directly from Atomic Energy	6	172
AN INTRODUCTION TO ELECTRONICS—How Controlled Electric Particles Serve Man	6	295
DATING BY THERMOLUMINESCENCE — How Age Is Determined by the Application of Heat	6	375

	VOL.	PAGE
THE SOLAR BATTERY — How Sunlight Is Used to Generate Electricity	7	103
THE LAW OF PARITY — New Discoveries in the World of Atomic Particles	7	107
THE WONDER-WORKING X RAYS — Radiations That Have Opened New Paths	7	143
MAGNETS LARGE AND SMALL — What We Know about Magnetism	7	162
ELECTROMAGNETIC RADIATION — Waves of Energy That Fill the Universe	7	199
AN INTRODUCTION TO OPTICS — Some Striking Effects of Light	7	249
ORGANIC CHEMISTRY — The Study of the Countless Compounds of Carbon	7	263
THE WORLD OF COLOR — Effects of Different Wave Lengths of Light	7	277
PROGRESS IN ACOUSTICS — Some Recent Advances in the Study of Sound	8	38
A BIT OF ELECTRONIC HISTORY — The Development of the Revolutionary Audion	8	84
THE STRANGE WORLD OF "SILENT" SOUND — Ultrasonics, a New Tool for Man	8	103
THE LAND THEORY OF COLOR VISION — A Revolutionary Mid-Century Development	8	178
THE CHEMIST AS CREATOR — How Man Produces New Materials	8	181
THE COSMIC RAYS — High-powered Missiles from Outer Space	8	393
SEEING THE HITHERTO INVISIBLE — How the Microscope Has Revealed New Worlds	9	81
ATOMIC ENERGY — Boundless Power from the Core of the Atom	9	120
ATOM SMASHERS — Devices for Speeding Up Charged Particles	9	241
THE GEIGER-MUELLER COUNTER — An Indispensable Tool of Modern Science	9	340
ELECTROLUMINESCENCE — What It Is and How It Has Been Put to Work	9	344
PERILS OF THE ATOMIC AGE — Atomic Energy: Boon or Menace to Mankind?	9	348
IF A NUCLEAR WEAPON STRIKES — Protective Measures That May Save Lives	9	391
RADIOCARBON DATING — How the Relics of the Past Reveal Their Age	10	92
THE MIGHTY MIDGET OF ELECTRONICS — The Transistor — What It Is and Can Do	10	102
PRESERVING FOOD BY ATOMIC RADIATION — Using Gamma Rays to Sterilize Foodstuffs	10	114
ELECTRONICS — Its Effect on Daily Living	10	168
ATOMIC FARMING — How Radioactivity Is Put to Work for Agriculture	10	251

INDUSTRY

INDUSTRY ON THE MARCH — Industrial Progress through Research	1	87
MODERN ENGINEERING — How the Discoveries of Science Are Put to Practical Use	1	215
THE STORY OF STEEL — A Basic Metal of the Modern World	1	338
AN INTRODUCTION TO METALLURGY — How Metals Are Made Available to Man	1	369
EARTH'S DARK TREASURE — The Story of the Coal Industry	1	405
TREASURES OF THE QUARRY — The Wonderful Uses of Stone	2	81
THE FOREST INDUSTRIES — How Man Uses a Precious Resource	2	105
SCIENCE DEVELOPMENTS — Science Pushes Forward Its Frontiers	2	232
FROM CAVE TO SKYSCRAPER — How the Builder Triumphs over Space and Matter	3	113
THE STORY OF GLASS — A Basic Material of Modern Civilization	3	307
OUR LIQUID GOLD — A Survey of the Far-Flung Petroleum Industry	4	140
POWER OVER DARKNESS — The Wonder of Modern Illumination	4	232
THE SYMBOLS OF WEALTH — Searching for Nature's Buried Treasure	4	242
THE BUILDING OF THE HOME — Problems of Planning and Decoration	4	265
MAN-MADE DIAMONDS — An Exciting Achievement of the Present Century	4	273
THE ART OF PAPERMAKING — A Brief Account of a Key Industry	4	364
NATURAL GAS — A Valuable Underground Resource of Man	5	97
THE MEAT-PACKING INDUSTRY — The Processing of Animals for Food and By-Products	5	163
THE SILK INDUSTRIES — Moth Larvae That Yield Costly Materials	5	173
WHERE SALT COMES FROM — The Story of a Vital Industry	5	313
CONSERVATION — Guarding the Natural Resources of Mankind	6	1
THE HARVEST OF THE SEA — The Development of the Fishing Industry	6	15
ON ENDLESS BANDS OF RUBBER — A Brief Account of the Conveyer Belt	6	168
THE STORY OF RUBBER — A Key Industrial Material with Many Uses	6	350
PROGRESS IN CHEMURGY — New Riches down on the Farm	7	35
THE BUILDER'S MATERIALS — A Survey of Substances Used in Every Age	7	115
HOW BUTTONS ARE MADE — A Survey of a Flourishing Industry	7	208
THE FASHIONING OF LEATHER AND FURS — From Animal Pelts to Industrial Materials	7	230

	VOL.	PAGE
MODERN METHODS OF PROSPECTING — How Hidden Ore and Oil Deposits Are Located	7	355
FROM CLAY TO POTTERY — The Story of One of the Oldest Industries	7	393
IRRIGATION AT WORK — How Man Brings Water to His Farm Lands	8	191
THE GROWING WORLD OF PLASTICS — Moldable Materials That Serve Man in Countless Ways	8	221
A MIGHTY FORCE — How High Explosives Are Used	8	273
THE STORY OF DAMS — Structures That Hold Back, Store or Divert Water	8	305
GLASS HOUSES — New Windows on the World	8	388
THE RADIATION THICKNESS GAUGE — A Revolutionary Device Based on Atomic Energy	9	43
THE POWER OF THE AIR — How Compressed Air Serves Mankind	9	58
ELECTRICITY FOR MAN — How It Is Generated, Transmitted and Distributed	9	226
THE BAKING INDUSTRY — Modern Methods of Preparing the "Staff of Life"	9	293
POWER-DRIVEN TOOLS — Machines by Which Men Build Other Machines	10	105
INDUSTRIAL DESIGN — A Striking Twentieth-Century Development	10	117
THE RISE OF AUTOMATION — The Industrial Revolution Takes a Step Forward	10	235

TRANSPORTATION

PRIMITIVE LAND TRANSPORTATION — An Interesting Chapter in the Story of Man's Progress	1	98
THE STORY OF THE RAILROAD — A Basic Form of Land Transportation	1	179
TUNNELING THE EARTH — How Man Burrows through and under Rock	2	43
THE AUTOMOBILE — The Universal Vehicle of Modern Times	2	129
THE STORY OF BRIDGES — Vital Links in Land Transportation	2	332
ROADS AND ROAD MAKING — Avenues of Travel and Trade in Many Lands	3	293
THE HYDROFOIL — A Striking Modern Development in Marine Engineering	4	5
CONQUERING THE OCEAN — The Fascinating Story of Man's Ships	4	106
THE WORLD'S GREAT CANALS—The Development of Artificial Waterways	4	183
THE SUBMARINE — Sleek Terror of the Seas	5	31
FLOATING TRAFFIC SIGNS — How Buoys Guide the Mariner	5	68
THE CONQUEST OF THE AIR — The Inspiring Saga of Airships and Airplanes	6	176
JET-PROPULSION PROGRESS — A New Era in the History of Aviation	7	67
GUIDANCE IN SPACE — Controlling the Flight of Missiles and Space Vehicles	8	125
THOSE MYSTERIOUS FLYING SAUCERS — Optical Illusions or Visitors from Outer Space?	9	16
THE STORY OF ROCKETS — Swift Travelers in Air and Space	10	1
SPACE TRAVEL — Man's Future Journeying beyond Our Atmosphere	10	40
SUPERSONIC FLIGHT — Velocities That Exceed That of Sound in Air	10	228

COMMUNICATION

BASIS OF HUMAN COMMUNICATION — An Account of the Development of Language	1	107
THE ART OF PRINTING — A Survey of a Vital Means of Communication	1	196
THE TYPEWRITER — The Machine That Revolutionized Business	1	265
TELEGRAPH AND TELEPHONE — Two Vital Means of Communication	2	377
AN INTRODUCTION TO RADIO — Bringing Voices and Music from Distant Places	3	85
PRACTICAL TELEVISION — Transmission and Reception of Moving Images	5	276
MACHINES THAT TALK — The Phonograph and the Tape Recorder	7	362
FACSIMILE MAGIC — How Pictures Are Transmitted by Wire	7	390
RADAR TODAY — A Pictorial Record	9	387
THE VERSATILE ART OF PHOTOGRAPHY — How Images Are Produced and Fixed	9	397
MICROFILMING—First Aid to Crowded Archives	10	68
PHOTOGRAPHY AT WORK — A Pictorial Record of Recent Developments	10	163

SCIENCE THROUGH THE AGES

ANTIQUITY (TO 450 A.D.) I 1   122
    The Beginnings
    Early Greek Scientists
    The Pythagorean Brotherhood
    The Golden Age of Greek Philosophy

	VOL.	PAGE
ANTIQUITY (TO 450 A.D.) II	1	354
The Alexandrian School		
Roman Contributions		
Medicine Men and Rational Physicians		
The Decline of Ancient Science		
THE MIDDLE AGES (450–1450)	2	295
The Early Period		
Arab Standard-Bearers of Scientific Learning		
The Flowering of Medieval Thought		
A Daring Friar of Oxford		
Science Wedded to Tradition		
Progress in the Practical Arts		
RENAISSANCE (1450–1600)	2	361
The New Learning		
The Age of Discovery		
First Fruits of the New Science		
The Revolution in Astronomy		
The Rediscovery of Anatomy		
SCIENCE GROWS UP (1600–1765) I	3	1
The First of the Moderns		
Two Theorists of the New Science		
The Circulation of the Blood		
Mechanical Explanations of the Human Body		
"Philosophical Instruments"		
Mathematics Becomes Practical		
SCIENCE GROWS UP (1600–1765) II	3	265
Invisible Colleges and Scientific Societies		
The Beginnings of True Chemical Science		
The Microscope Reveals a New World		
On the Nature of Light		
Newton and the Falling Apple		
SCIENCE GROWS UP (1600–1765) III	3	373
The Plant and Animal Kingdoms		
SCIENCE IN REVOLUTION (1765–1815) I	4	32
An Age of Revolution		
The Industrial Revolution		
SCIENCE IN REVOLUTION (1765–1815) II	4	353
The Revolution in Chemistry		
The Beginnings of Electrical Research		
SCIENCE IN REVOLUTION (1765–1815) III	4	386
Fossils Come to Life		
The Structure of the Earth		
The Nature and Origin of the Universe		
The Rise of Preventive Medicine		
The Haunting Problem of Overpopulation		
SCIENCE AND PROGRESS (1815–95) I	5	72
The Spirit of Progress		
Chemistry Comes of Age		
The Classification of the Chemical Elements		
SCIENCE AND PROGRESS (1815–95) II	5	231
Lawgivers of Electrical Science		
Electricity Goes into Action		
SCIENCE AND PROGRESS (1815–95) III	6	239
Light and Other Electromagnetic Waves		
The Conservation of Energy		

	VOL.	PAGE
SCIENCE AND PROGRESS (1815–95) IV	6	377
Industry Takes Root in the Nineteenth Century		
New Knowledge of the Heavenly Bodies		
SCIENCE AND PROGRESS (1815–95) V	7	27
New Voyages of Discovery		
SCIENCE AND PROGRESS (1815–95) VI	7	156
The Cells of Animals and Plants		
SCIENCE AND PROGRESS (1815–95) VII	7	370
New Directions in Medical Research		
A Memorable Victory over Pain		
The Germ Theory of Disease		
Surgical Operations Become Safer		
"The Quality of Mercy Is Not Strain'd"		
SCIENCE AND PROGRESS (1815–95) VIII	8	251
Students of the World's Fauna and Flora		
The Bombshell — Evolution		
THE TWENTIETH CENTURY (1895–) I	8	400
The Achievements of the Miracle Decade		
The Road to Modern Alchemy		
THE TWENTIETH CENTURY (1895–) II	9	21
The New Science of Man		
Modern Triumphs of Medicine		
The Public-Health Movement		
THE TWENTIETH CENTURY (1895–) III	9	47
The Study of the Human Mind		
THE TWENTIETH CENTURY (1895–) IV	9	96
Probing Human Personality		
THE TWENTIETH CENTURY (1895–) V	9	211
Science and Technology in World War I		
The Coming of the Air Age		
Exploring the Depths and the Heights		
THE TWENTIETH CENTURY (1895–) VI	9	279
From Relativity to Uncertainty		
The Rise of a New Science — Electronics		
Agriculture Becomes Scientific		
THE TWENTIETH CENTURY (1895–) VII	9	323
Science and Technology in World War II		
The Dawn of the Atomic Age		
THE TWENTIETH CENTURY (1895–) VIII	9	375
The Race for Space		
THE TWENTIETH CENTURY (1895–) IX	10	191
The Making of a Scientist		
Careers in Science — A Bird's-Eye View		
THE TWENTIETH CENTURY (1895–) X	10	224
The Road Ahead in Scientific Research		

PROJECTS AND EXPERIMENTS

PROJECTS AND EXPERIMENTS — Learning about Science by Doing	1	139
THE AMATEUR WEATHERMAN — How to Set up Your Own Weather Station	1	315
SHELL COLLECTING — A Fascinating Hobby Based on the Mollusk Group	2	99
EXPERIMENTS WITH AIR — Remarkable Properties of Our Gaseous Ocean	2	323
COLLECTING INSECTS — A Brief Account of Equipment and Methods	3	153
KEEPING AN ANT COLONY — How to Spy upon the Private Lives of Ants	3	393
EXPERIMENTS WITH HEAT — The Surprising Effects of Molecules in Motion	4	17
THE HOME CHEMIST I — How to Build and Use a Home Laboratory	4	221
THE HOME CHEMIST II — Experiments with Water, Hydrogen and Oxygen	4	343

	VOL.	PAGE
HOW TO RECOGNIZE TREES — Suggestions and Hints for the Amateur Naturalist	5	138
EXPERIMENTS WITH SOUND — Interesting Effects with Common Materials	5	221
HOME TERRARIUMS — How to Create Wee Forests, Deserts and Swamps	5	365
OBSERVING THE HEAVENS — Useful Hints for the Amateur Astronomer	6	78
EXPERIMENTS WITH ELECTRICITY — Following the Trail of Mobile Electrons	6	286
PHOTOGRAPHING NATURE — Hunting with a Camera Instead of a Gun	6	311
HOW TO ATTRACT BIRDS — Food and Lodging for Our Feathered Friends	6	341
UNUSUAL PETS — How to Collect and Keep Wild Creatures	7	17
THE HOME CHEMIST III — Experiments That Entertain and Instruct	7	129
THE IDIOTIC CHEMIST — A Topsy-turvy Chemical-Magic Session	7	173
EXPERIMENTS IN MECHANICS — Moving, Lifting and Holding Things	7	214
EXPERIMENTS WITH WATER — The Most Familiar of All Chemical Compounds	8	1
COMPETITIONS FOR YOUNG SCIENTISTS — A Survey of Projects and Awards	8	67
HOME AQUARIUMS — Fish Pets and How to Care for Them	8	112
EXPERIMENTS WITH LIGHT — How It Is Given Off and How It Travels	8	117
EXPERIMENTS WITH MAGNETISM — A Mysterious Force Serving Man in Many Ways	8	142
COLLECTING MINERALS AND ROCKS — An Outdoor Hobby for Young and Old	9	300
MAKING A REFLECTING TELESCOPE — Suggestions and Hints for Beginners	9	365
EXPLORING THE PLANT WORLD — Interesting Finds and How to Preserve Them	10	203
EXPLORING THE ANIMAL WORLD — How to Find and Study Our Animal Neighbors	10	254

ALPHABETICAL INDEX

ALPHABETICAL INDEX

MAIN entries are given in bold face; subentries in light face. Illustrated articles, indicated by an asterisk, are given first under each entry. A bold-face number refers to the volume; a light-face number to the page. When two pages are separated by a dash, the references extend from one to the other. For example:

Acorn worms. *with illus.,* 4-178-79

indicates that information concerning acorn worms will be found in Volume 4, pages 178 to 179, inclusive, together with illustrative material. The alphabetization is by first word and not "straight through;" thus **Acid soils** precedes **Acids.** Hyphenated words are considered two separate words.

A

A battery, in radio. 3-97

A horizon, in soils. 2-17, 18, 22, *illus.,* 17, 25

Aardvarks. *illus.,* 7-16

Aardwolves. 8-249, 250, *illus.,* 248

Abaca, Manila hemp.
Plant and fiber, *with illus.,* 4-181

Abaci, calculating devices. *with illus.,* 9-144

Abalones. 2-201
Shell of, *illus.,* 2-100

Abbe, Ernst, German physicist. 9-82, 92

Abdomen.
Ants use abdomen for food storage, 3-364
Blood vessels of, *illus.,* 1-148f
Breathing, role of abdominal muscles in, 3-209, *diagram,* 211
Insects, 2-404, 406, *illus.,* 403
Muscles of, *illus.,* 1-148c
Spiders, 2-259, *with illus.,* 261

Abdominal organs. *illus.,* 1-148d-e

Abducens nerve. 6-328

Aberration, of earth.
Location of stars affected by, 7-224-25

Abiotic (nonliving) substances, in ecosystems. 10-184

Abnormal psychology. 9-321

Abomasum, chamber of cow's stomach. *illus.,* 7-10

Aborigines, native peoples. See **Anthropology**

Abrasion. Streams wear away rocks by, 8-13, 14

Abrasives.
Paper, abrasive, 4-377
Sandpaper, industrial research on, 1-88

Abscesses, accumulation of pus. 3-328; 7-348

Abscissas, X-axis distances in analytic geometry. *with diagrams,* 4-425-31

Abscission layer, of leaves. 4-73-74
Leaf fall due to, 6-54-55

Absolute magnitude. *with table,* 6-261-62; 8-49

Absolute scale (Kelvin scale), of temperature. *with diagram,* 1-164

Absolute zero. *with diagram,* 1-164; 3-416
Phenomena at temperatures near, *with illus.,* 5-208-10

Absorption.
Light, 7-250, 253
Photography, color absorption in, 9-413, 414
Plant processes of, 3-44
Sound, 5-122, 128

Absorption, heat. *with illus.,* 3-413-14; 4-16

Absorption, selective, of wave lengths of light. 7-283-85, *illus.,* 287

Absorption lines, in solar spectrum. 3-108

Absorption spectra. 7-280, *illus.,* 284a

Absorption system, of refrigeration. *with illus.,* 4-159

Absorptometry, X-ray. 7-147

Abutments, bridge supports. 2-334

Abysses, great oceanic deeps. 6-71, 74, 75
See also **Deeps, oceanic; Trenches, oceanic**

Académie des Sciences. *with illus.,* 3-268

Academy of Experiments. *with illus.,* 3-265-66

Academy of Sciences (French). *with illus.,* 3-268

Academy of Sciences (German). 3-268-69

Academy of the Secrets of Nature. 3-265

Acadian Disturbance, time of mountain making. 1-389; 6-372

Acadian owls. 6-165

Acanthocephala, phylum of worms. 1-293

Acanthodesmia, genus of protozoa. *illus.,* 6-33

Accademia del Cimento. *with illus.,* 3-265-66

Acceleration. *with illus.,* 2-118, 119-21
Gravitation as, 2-318; 4-218-19
Gravity as, *with table,* 2-318
Space and air vehicles, factor in motion of, 8-130, *diagram,* 131
Space-travel problem, 10-48

Accelerator nerves. Heartbeat, effect on, 3-387

Accelerometers, inertial-guidance devices. Space vehicles and missiles use, 8-130, *diagram,* 131

Accessories, automobiles. 2-145
Typewriters, 1-275

Accessory fruits. *with illus.,* 4-129

Accident prevention. *7-190-98
Home laboratory precautions, *with illus.,* 4-228-29

Accidents.
*First aid, 10-5-17
Nitroglycerine causes, 8-276

Accretion, inorganic growth. 1-38

Acetabulum, part of hip bone. 3-82

Acetaldehyde.
Ethyl alcohol converted into, 4-407

Acetic acid.
Acetaldehyde broken down into, 4-407
Solution of, *with diagram,* 4-298
See also **Vinegar**

Acetobacter, genus of bacteria. Nucleic acid synthesized by aid of, 9-386

Acetone.
Production in World War I, 9-212
Schlieren photograph of vapor, *illus.,* 10-165
Solvent action of, 4-346
Structural formula, 7-273

Acetylcholine. Produced by nerve tissue, 2-426

Acetylene, unsaturated hydrocarbon. 7-270

Achenes, dry fruits. *with illus.,* 4-130

Achernar, star in Eridanus. 1-337

Achilles and tortoise. See **Zeno's paradox**

Achilles' tendon, in foot. 3-210, *illus.,* 205

Achlorhydric anemia, anemia due to lack of stomach acid. 3-330

Achromatic lenses. 7-260
Development of, 7-158

Acid dyes. Development of, 8-186

Acid poisoning. First aid for, 10-10

Acid soils. 2-22, 24
Effects and correction of, with illus., 2-168-70

Acidophilus milk, fermented milk. 4-167

Acids.
*Acids, bases and salts, 4-336-42
Dyes, acid, 8-186
Electrical conductivity of, testing, with illus., 4-345
Electrolytes, 2-423
Food preservers. 4-164, 167
Minerals tested with, with illus., 9-305
Photoengraving, acids used in, 1-205-06
Poisoning by acids, first aid for, 10-10
Printing, acids used in, 1-212
Reactions of, with illus., 4-231
Soil, 2-16, 22, 24
Voltaic cells, use of acids in, 5-95-96
See also **Lactic acid; Organic acids; Sulfuric acid**

Acne. 10-83-84

Aconcagua, peak of the Andes. Highest mountain of Western Hemisphere, 10-24

Acorn barnacles. 2-242

Acorn worms. illus., 1-297; with illus., 4-2-3

Acorns. illus., 4-131
Dispersed by rodents, illus., 5-7
Woodpeckers' use of, 6-211

Acoustical engineering. 5-128, illus., 127

Acoustical tiles. 5-122

Acoustics.
*Musical sounds, 5-211-20
*Noise meters, 8-38-46
*Sound, 5-114-28

Acromegaly, disease caused by overactive pituitary gland. 5-17

Acromion process, of shoulder blade. 3-80

Acrylic resins, plastics. with illus., 8-226
Teeth fillings made of, 5-137

Acrylonitrile, nitrogen chemical.
Synthetic rubber, use in, 6-358

ACTH, hormone. 5-169; 10-133-34, illus., 132

Actinides, group of chemical elements. 4-308
Periodic series, position in, 4-310, tables, 307, 309

Actinium (Ac), chemical element. Atomic number, 89 atomic weight, 227(?). Discovered by Debierne in 1899. Name derived from Greek aktis (genitive, aktinos): "ray." Radioactive; minute amounts are present in all uranium minerals. Has half life of 27.7 years; when it decomposes, it gives rise to series of elements known as actinium series.

Actinopterygii, major subdivision of true fishes. 4-95, 196

Actinosphaerium eichhorni, a protozoan. illus., 2-63

Activated carbon.
Water purified by, 2-279

Activated sludge. Treatment of sewage, with illus., 5-332

Active immunity. 7-351

Acute angles. with illus., 3-431

Adams, John Couch, English astronomer. 6-392
Neptune, role in discovery of, 2-317; 5-290-91

Adam's apple. See **Larynx; Thyroid cartilage**

Adam's laburnum. 9-10-12

Adaptations. *3-235-44
Definition of, 7-75
Marsupials, 7-422
Plants, with illus., 6-218-28
Seed and fruit dispersal, with illus., 5-1-7
Rodents, 8-162
Snakes, 5-351-52
See also **Natural selection**

Adaptive radiation, lines of evolutionary development. 4-317; with diagram, 6-281-83; 7-422

Addaxes, antelopes. 8-383, 384

Addiction.
*Alcoholic beverages, 4-405-10
*Narcotic drugs, 5-400-07

Adding machines. with illus., 1-276
See also **Electronic computers**

Addison's disease. Cortisone used to treat, 10-134

Addition, arithmetical operation. 1-157

Additive color combinations. illus., 7-284b

Additive color photographs. 9-413

Additive mixtures, of colored lights. 7-286

Additive principle, applied to number systems. 1-150

Adenosinetriphosphate (ATP), protein-building compound. 9-385
Firefly light activated by, 2-189

Adhesion, attraction between molecules of different substances. 5-371, 374; with illus., 8-3-4

Adirondack Forest Preserve, United States. 9-276

Adirondack Mountains, New York State. 10-222
Ausable Chasm, illus., 8-13

ADL-Collins Helium Liquefier. with illus., 5-208

Adler, Alfred, Austrian psychiatrist. 9-102

Adler Planetarium, Chicago. 2-398

Administration, as function of engineers. 1-227

Adolescence.
Critical period in human development, 8-98-100
See also **Psychology**

Adonis, asteroid. Earth, close approach to, 6-92

Adrenal glands. illus., 1-148g; 5-18, illus., 16-17
Hormones of, 10-133

Adrenaline (adrenalin), a hormone. 5-15, 18, 19
Cholesterol level raised by, 10-134
Relationship to psychological states, 9-52

Adsorption. 5-299, 303-04, 374
Catalytic reactions, 8-190
Soils exhibit, 2-18, 24

Advection. Cloud formation by, 2-214

Adventitious buds. 4-67; 9-7-8

Adventitious roots. 4-65; 9-7-8

Advertising. Package design a factor in, 10-124

Aeolipile, ancestor of steam engine. 1-359; with illus., 4-80; 5-305

Aequorea aequorea, luminous jellyfish. illus., 2-184

Aeration, water purification. 2-278, with illus., 282
Aquarium, aeration installation for, with illus., 8-113
Treatment of sewage, with illus., 5-331-32

Aerial-ground system, in radio. with illus., 3-93-94

Aerial organisms. 10-137-40, illus., 141

Aerial photography. Early, 9-403

Aerial reconnaissance. Geological surveying and prospecting by, 7-357

Aerial roots. 4-65

Aerobic respiration, carried on in presence of oxygen. 2-12; 3-48
Bacteria engage in, 3-65-66

Aerodrome No. 5, early experimental airplane. 9-216

Aerodynamics. See **Aeronautics**

Aerolites, meteorites composed chiefly of stone. 6-93, 98

Aeronautical engineering. 1-219, 220

Aeronautics. *6-176-200
*Flying saucers, 9-16-20
*Jet planes, 7-67-74
*Space travel, 10-40-54
*Supersonics, 10-228-34
Airplane-wing lift, with illus., 2-39, 329
First sustained flight by powered model plane, 8-403, illus., 402

Aeronautics (continued)
  Health hazards caused by airplane transportation, 9-40
  History of, with illus., 9-215-20
  Ice patrol, aircraft used in, 9-338, illus., 333, 338
  Insecticide-dusting planes, 9-185, illus., 186
  Jet engines, illus., 1-92b
  Jet plane take-off, 6-frontispiece
  Link jet trainer, illus., 2-235
  Radar, use of, illus., 9-387
  Rocket research, illus., 4-342c
  Sound-proof airplane cabins, 8-43
  Telecasting, planes used in, illus., 5-287
  Transportation of animals for zoos, planes used in, illus., 10-156
  Weather observations, airplane used in, 1-252, 253
  World War II planes, 9-326
  X-ray picture of plane crankcase, illus., 7-150
Aerosol sprays.
  Insects controlled by, 9-186
  Painting by, illus., 9-63
Aerovanes, wind gauges. 1-249
Aesculapius, god of healing. 1-364, illus., 365
Afferent (sensory) nerves and fibers.
  Definition and functions of, 6-318, illus., 322
  See also **Sensory nerves and fibers**
Africa.
  Explorations of, in nineteenth century, 7-31
  Mount Kenya, 10-26, illus., 23
  Mountain systems of, 10-24, 26
  Petroleum production and reserves, 4-151
  Plateaus of, 6-110
African civets. 8-245, illus., 244
African geographical race. with illus., 8-216
African sleeping sickness. See **Trypanosomiasis**
African snails. 2-200
Afterburners, devices for increasing thrust of jet engines. 7-71
Afterdamp, carbon-monoxide gas in coal mines. 1-413
Aftershocks, minor quakes. 9-108
Agamids (Agamidae), family of lizards. 5-202, 205
Agar-agar, or agar, gelatinous substance made from algae. illus., 2-207; with illus., 3-224
  Antibiotic molds grown on, illus., 4-342
  Cultivating bacteria in medium of, with illus., 3-72
Agassiz, Jean Louis Rodolphe, Swiss-American naturalist, geologist and teacher (1807–73). The son of a Swiss pastor, he studied at various German universities. He made notable contributions to the study of fossil fishes and other fossil forms. In his Studies on Glaciers (1840) he showed that Switzerland was covered at a geologically recent period by a vast ice sheet; he concluded that great sheets of ice once covered all countries in which boulder drift is found. He came to the United States in 1846 to lecture. He joined the faculty of Harvard University, where he founded the Museum of Comparative Zoology.
  Study of glaciers, 4-396-97
  Viesch Glacier, drawing of, illus., 9-162
Agassiz Lake. 7-62
Age.
  Guessing person's age: mathematical recreation, with diagram, 4-448-49
  Tuberculosis, age factor in, 9-179
Age of animals. See **Longevity of animals**
Age of Reptiles (Mesozoic era), time in earth's history. 1-391-95
  Temperature variations in, 3-181-82
Age of Steel. 1-340
Ages, in earth's history.
  *Geological time scale of earth's history, 6-369-74

Ages in man's history. 9-24
Agglutination of blood cells (clumping). 3-332-34
Agglutinins, antibodies. 3-333-34; 7-349, 350
Agglutinogens, blood antigens. 3-333-34
Aggradation, building up of earth's surface by deposition. 1-34, illus., 35
  See also **Sedimentary rock**
Aggregate culture. Soilless-agriculture method, 8-35-36
Aggregate fruits. with illus., 4-129
Aggregates, soil. with illus., 2-19
Aging.
  *Geriatrics, 8-78-83
  Gerontology, science of, 10-225
  Human beings, 8-100-01
  Skin, effect of aging on, illus., 2-175
Agitators. Gold mine, illus., 4-247
Agnatha, major group of fishes. with illus., 4-93-94
Agoutis. 8-168
Agranulocytosis, deficiency in white blood cells. 3-331
Agrichemistry, chemistry applied to agriculture. 9-290-91
  See also **Chemurgy**
Agricola, Georgius (Georg Bauer), German mineralogist and scholar. with illus., 2-368-69
Agricultural chemistry.
  *Soil fertility, 2-163-72
  Beginnings of, 5-80
Agricultural machinery. See **Farm machinery**
Agriculture.
  *Atomic farming, 10-251-53
  *Chemurgy, 7-35-44
  *Insect enemies of fruit crops, 9-185-96
  *Irrigation, 8-191-201
  *Soil fertility, 2-163-72
  *Soilless agriculture, 8-34-37
  *Vegetable fibers, 4-177-82
  *Water of soil, 5-25-30
  *Weeds, 7-111-14
  Antibiotics used in, 10-129
  Calendar of ancient Egypt related to, 10-171-72
  Gas, agricultural uses of, 5-106
  Industrial research, 1-89, illus., 91, 92
  Machinery used for, 9-291-92
  Progress in eighteenth century, 3-380
  Scientific development of, with illus., 9-290-92
  Synthetic products affecting, 8-183-85
  See also **Fruits; Grain; Irrigation; Parasites; Seeds; Soil; Spraying**
Agulhas Current, oceanic current. 6-237, map, 6-232-33
Ahmes Papyrus, Egyptian scroll. 2-68
Ahnighito meteorite, from Greenland. 6-90
Aiken, H. H., American physicist.
  Electronic computers developed by, 9-144
Ailanthus moths. 3-200
Ailanthus trees. with illus., 5-149-50
Ailerons, movable parts of airplane-wing edges. 6-188-89
Ainu local race. 8-219
Air.
  *Atmosphere, 1-230-40
  *Breathing, 4-200-09
  *Compressed air, 9-58-70
  *Dust, 7-137-42
  *Experiments with air, 2-323-31
  *Heating and ventilation, 2-244-57
  *Lightning, 1-398-404
  *Pollution, 3-349-56
  *Winds, 2-89-98
  Balloons inflated with heated air, 6-177, illus., 176
  Boyle's experiments, with illus., 3-271

Air (continued)
Currents, schlieren photograph of, illus., 10-165
Dust in, 2-213, 216
Gravitational force affected by, 2-318
Habitat of plants and animals, 10-137-40, illus., 141
Heat transfer and insulation by, 4-10-14, 16, illus., 11, 15
Liquid air, 8-224
Malaria once attributed to bad air, 10-31
Molecules, numbers and sizes of, 1-172
Plastics and plastic products, used in manufacture of, 8-224, with diagrams, 231, 232
Pressure, with illus., 2-36-40
  Experiments with, with illus., 7-220-22
  Explosions bring about, 8-274
  Isobaric lines indicate atmospheric pressures, 9-223
  Water animals show changes in, with illus. and diagrams, 1-280-81
Seed dispersal by air currents and wind, 3-240; with illus., 5-2-4
Sewage treated with, with illus., 5-331-32
Soil air, 2-25
Sound, speed in air, 5-119; 10-228
Water vapor of, 2-213, 347
Weather due to atmospheric movements, with diagrams, 1-241-44
Weight of, 1-233
See also **Aeronautics; Atmosphere; Breathing; Cyclones; Oxygen; Sound; Supersonics; Tornadoes; Winds**
Air bladder. Bony fish have, 4-313
Fish use as floating and swimming mechanism, with illus. and diagram, 1-280-81
Air brakes. 9-68
Invention of, 6-380
Railroad trains, with illus., 1-189
Air cells, electric batteries. 5-95
Air cleaning. Grains separated from dust and straw by, 9-295, diagram, 294
Air compressors. See **Compressors, air**
Air conditioning. with illus., 2-256-57
Mechanical engineering and, 1-224
See also **Ventilation**
Air-lift pumps. with illus., 2-275
Air liners. with illus., 6-189-93
Air passages.
First aid for foreign bodies in, 10-15
Air pollution. *3-349-56
Cancer may be caused by, 8-268
Air pressure.
Atmospheric movements and, with diagrams, 1-242-44
Boiling and, 1-168, diagram, 169
Experiments with, with illus., 2-324-29; with illus., 7-220-22
Isobaric lines indicate atmospheric pressures, 9-223
Measuring and recording atmospheric pressure, 1-318-19, with diagrams, 247, 249, 254, diagrams, 316, 320; with illus., 3-16-17
Water animals use changes in, with illus. and diagrams, 1-280-81
See also **Atmospheric pressure; Pneumatic tools**
Air pumps. with illus., 2-40
Development in seventeenth century, with illus., 3-17-18
Air raids.
*Nuclear-bomb precautions, 9-391-96
World War II, 9-326
Air sacs, bird. with illus., 5-420-21
Air tanks, used in scuba diving. with illus., 6-26b
Airbrushes, 9-70

Aircraft. See **Aeronautics; Airplanes; Lighter-than-air flight**
Aircraft carriers.
Atomic-powered, with illus., 4-114d
Enterprise, nuclear-powered carrier of United States Navy, 4-118, with illus., 114a
Airflow, term used in aeronautics. 6-186-88; 10-231
Airglow, weak glow in night sky. 1-238
Airgraph, British system of microfilmed mail. 10-74, illus., 73
Airplanes. *6-181-200
*Supersonic airplanes, 10-228-34
Geological surveying and prospecting by, 7-357
History of, with illus., 9-215-20
  World War I, with illus., 9-214
  World War II, 9-218
Pressurized cabins in, 1-234-35
Weather study by means of, 1-252, 253
Weightlessness produced in, 10-49-50
See also **Aeronautics**
Airports. with illus., 6-196-200
Airships. See **Aeronautics**
Airspeed indicators. 6-192
Airy, Sir George Biddell, English astronomer. 5-290; 6-392; 7-32
Akademie der Wissenschaften. 3-268-69
Alamogordo Air Base, New Mexico.
First atomic explosion at, 9-348
Alanine, amino acid.
Molecular structure, diagram, 7-275
Alaska.
Earthquake in, illus., 9-119
Fisheries, 6-21
Fur seals, with illus., 7-89
Glaciers of, illus., 9-163, 166-67, 172
Muir Glacier, illus., 9-334
Alaska Current, oceanic current. 6-238, map, 232-33
Alaska Highway. 3-303
Alaska Range, mountain range of central Alaska. 10-23
Al-Battani, Arab astronomer. 2-299
Albedo, reflecting power of heavenly bodies. 4-277
Jupiter, 5-21
Alberta, Canada.
Irrigation in, 8-200, illus., 199
Petroleum industry and reserves, 4-143, 147
Albertus Magnus, German scholastic philosopher and scientist. 2-304, 309-10
Albinism, inheritable defects in pigmentation of skin, eyes and hair. with illus., 8-344
Albinos. See **Albinism**
Albumin. See **Proteins**
Alchemical reactions, of chemical elements. 9-123, 125, 126, 128, 131-32, 140
Alchemical symbols. illus., 5-76
Alchemy.
Contributions to chemistry, 8-181
History
  Beginnings of, in Alexandria, 1-360
  Arab devotees of, 2-299-300
  Later Middle Ages, 2-311, illus., 310
  Sixteenth century, 2-368
Alcmaeon of Croton, Greek physician.
Work in anatomical dissection, 1-365
Alcoa Building, Pittsburgh, Pa. illus., 7-126
Alcock, John. Transatlantic flight, first nonstop, 6-184; 9-217
Alcohol.
*Beverages, alcoholic, 4-405-14
Anaerobic respiration produces, 3-48
Content in fermented wines, 4-168

Alcohol (continued)
Ethers derived from, 7-273
Experiments and tricks with, *with diagram*, 7-179
Glycerol, 7-275
Methyl (wood) alcohol, synthesis of, 8-190
Solvent action of, 4-346
Thermometers, used in, 3-410
See also **Alcoholic fermentation; Fermentation**
Alcohol lamps. Home laboratory, *with illus.*, 4-224
Alcoholic anesthesia. 4-409
Alcoholic fermentation. 9-73-75
See also **Alcohol**
Alcoholics Anonymous (AA), fellowship made up of former alcoholics. 4-414; 9-200
Alcoholism. Psychopathic personality due to, 9-200
Alcoholism, chronic. *with illus.*, 4-409-14
Alcoholism clinics. 4-414
Aldebaran, star in Taurus. 1-335
Aldehydes. 7-273
Luciferin contains, 2-188
Alder trees. 5-145, *illus.*, 144
Aletsch Glacier, Switzerland. *illus.*, 7-56
Aleurone grains, protein in plants. 2-418
Aleutian Islands. Shishaldin, Mount, *illus.*, 8-295
Alexander, Jerome, American chemist.
Quotation from, 8-264
Alexandria, Egypt.
Center of ancient culture, *with illus.*, 1-354-60
Alfalfa.
Harvesting crop of, *illus.*, 2-210
Water required by, 5-25
Alfonso the Wise, King of Castile. 2-309
Algae. *3-214-24
Adaptations of marine algae, *with illus.*, 6-224-25
Aquariums, growth in, 8-113
Connecting link between plants and animals, 2-59
Diatoms, *illus.*, 1-41
Fossil algae, *illus.*, 6-370
Fungi, partnership with, 10-187, *illus.*, 188
Green algae, *illus.*, 1-45
Lichens formed by combination of fungi and, *with illus.*, 3-32
Marine diatom deposits, *with illus.*, 6-32-33
Meteorites containing fossils of?, 6-94-95
Red, 6-221
Reef-building organisms, 4-134
Similarities with bacteria, 3-63
Water supply, problem in, 2-276-77
Algalike fungi. *with illus.*, 3-25-26
Algebra. *2-67-80
Recreation, algebraic, 4-445
Algebraic sequences. *with illus.*, 2-77-80
Algol, eclipsing binary. 1-334; 7-46
Alhazen, Arab physicist. 2-300-01
Alimentary system. *4-321-35
First aid for foreign bodies in, 10-15
Fishes, 4-103
Man's, *illus.*, 1-148d
See also **Carbohydrates; Diet; Digestive system; Fats; Meat; Proteins; Vegetables**
Alizarin, dye. Synthesis of, 5-80-81; 8-183
Alkali. See **Bases**
Alkali flats. 2-23
Alkali metals. 3-165-70
Distinguished from other metals, 3-33-34
Alkali poisoning. First aid for, 10-10
Alkaline-earth metals. 3-170-76
Distinguished from other metals, 3-33-34
Alkaline soils. 2-22, 24
Alkalinity, degree of antiacidity. Water supply and, 2-279, 280

Alkanes, methane hydrocarbons. 7-267-69
Al-Kwarizmi, Mohammed ibn Musa, Persian mathematician. 2-68-69, 298
Alkyd resins, plastics. 8-226
Alkyl halides, derivatives from paraffin hydrocarbons. 7-271
Alkylation, molecular synthesis. Petroleum refining uses, 4-148
All-American Canal. *with illus.*, 8-199
All-or-none principle, of nerve stimulation. 6-321
Allen's rule, concerning size of limbs. 8-219
Allergens, allergy-producing substances. 4-259-61, *illus.*, 258-61
Allergic Index, used in diagnosis of allergy. 4-262
Allergies. *4-257-64
Mushrooms causing, 3-32
Allfrey, V. G., American biologist. Nucleoprotein research of, 9-385
Alligator fleas, true bugs. 3-263
Alligators. 5-383-84, *illus.*, 380, 385
Pets, 7-23-24
Skeleton compared with those of other vertebrates, *illus.*, 1-57
Allosaurs (genus **Allosaurus**), carnivorous dinosaurs. 1-393, *illus.*, 392
Allosaurus. See **Allosaurs**
Allotropes (allotropic forms). 3-320-24
Carbon, 4-273
Alloy steels. Manufacture and uses of, 1-353
See also **Steel**
Alloying elements, in steel. 1-346, 353, *table*, 352
Alloys. 1-81-82
*Steel, basic modern alloy, 1-338-53
Distinguished from pure metals, 3-33
Gold, 4-250
Metallic alloys, 1-382; 3-34, 36-37, 40-42
Photoengraving plates, metals used in, 1-205
Printing plates, alloys used in making of, 1-207-08, 211
Quench-hardened steels, 7-166
Superconductive, 5-210
Type-casting alloy, 1-200-01, 207-08
Alluvial aprons, stream deposits. 8-16
Alluvial fans, stream deposits. 8-16
Allylic resins, plastics. *with illus.*, 8-226
Aloes, plants.
Desert-terrarium plants, use as, 5-365
Leaves of, 7-80, *illus.*, 79
Alpacas. 7-331-32
Alpha Centauri, double star in the constellation Centaurus. 1-337; 3-157
Distance from earth, 6-390
Alpha Orionis, star. 7-228
Alpha particles (rays). 9-349
Detection by Geiger-Mueller counter, *with illus.*, 9-342-43
Primary cosmic rays made up of, 8-397
Radioactive elements sources of, 8-416; 9-126-28
Alphabet.
Origin and development of alphabetic writing, 1-115
Phonetic, 1-110
Alphard, star in Hydra. 1-332
Alpheratz, star in Pegasus and Andromeda. 1-334
Alpine local race. 8-218
Alps. 10-21
History of, 10-216, 218, 221, 222
Matterhorn, *illus.*, 10-18
Tunnels in, 2-44-45
See also **Switzerland**
Altair, star in Aquila. 1-333; 7-228

Altamira, Spain.
  Prehistoric cave paintings at, *with illus.,* 9-29-30
Altazimuth mounts, for telescopes. *with diagram,* 9-373
Alternate leaves. *with illus.,* 5-140
Alternating current, electrical. 6-129, *illus.,* 128; 9-228
  Electronics, uses in, 6-296-99, 301-02
  High-frequency, in electronics, *with illus.,* 3-86-88; *with illus.,* 6-297-300
  Waves emitted from, 7-202, *diagram,* 200
Alternating gradient accelerators, atom smashers. 9-249, *illus.,* facing 249
Alternation of generations, plant and animal reproduction.
  Animals
    Coelenterates, 2-150
    Insects, 2-406
  Plants
    Algae, 3-217, 220, 224
    Ferns, club mosses and horsetails, 3-190-92
    Liverworts, 3-190
    Mosses, 3-187
Altimeters. 6-192
Altiplano, plateau of Bolivia. 6-110
Altitude, star.
  Determination of, *with diagram,* 1-261; *with diagram,* 6-80
Altitude, terrestrial.
  Blood, effect on, 3-326-27
  Breathing, effect on, 4-209, *illus.,* 208
  Mammals, effects on blood of, 7-8
  Space vehicles and artificial satellites, altitudes of, 8-127, 128, 131
Altocumulus clouds. *diagram,* 1-317; 2-222, *illus.,* 212
Altostratus clouds. *diagram,* 1-317; 2-222, *illus.,* 216
Alum.
  Coagulant for purifying water, 2-278
  Crystals of, formed from saturated solution, *with diagram,* 4-299
  Experiment with ammonia water, 4-230-31
Alumina, aluminum oxide. 3-40
  Smelting of, *with diagram,* 1-381; 5-93-94, *illus.,* 92
Aluminizing, of optical glass reflectors. 9-372
Aluminum (Al), chemical element. Atomic number, 13; atomic weight, 26.9815; melting point, 659.7° C.; boiling point, 2,057° C.; specific gravity, 2.699. Light metal; good conductor of heat and electricity. First isolated in 1825; name derived from Latin *alumen:* "alum." Never occurs free in nature; compounds found in almost all rocks, animals and plants. Extracted from bauxite. Widely used, often alloyed with other metals, for planes, automobiles, kitchenware, furniture, roofs, high-tension power lines and so on. See also 3-40
  Alloys, 1-382
  Building material, 7-128, *illus.,* 126
  Cans made of, 4-155
  Crystalline structure, 5-340, *diagram,* 339
  Electrolytic production of, 5-93-94, *illus.,* 92
  Fire-fighting suit, *illus.,* 2-235
  Forging, *illus.,* 1-92b
  Goldschmidt process, used in, 3-317
  Hall-Héroult process for production of, *with diagram,* 1-381; 6-385
  Production of, in World War II, 9-324
  Sound, speed of, in aluminum, 5-119
  Steelmaking, use in, 1-347, 352
  Telescope mirrors coated with, 9-159
Aluminum sulfate.
  Coagulant for purifying water, 2-271, 278
Alva B. Adams Tunnel, irrigation tunnel. 8-195

Alvarez, Luis W., American physicist.
  Linear accelerator, development of, 9-246
Alveoli, air cavities of the lungs. 4-204, 206, *illus.,* 202
Amalgamation. Gold-recovery process, 1-375; 4-248, 250
Amalgams, mercury alloys. 3-42
Amateurs, scientific. 10-225
  Comets discovered by, 5-398-99
Amazon ants, slave makers. 3-365
Amazon River. 8-12
  Discharge of, 6-415
Ambergris. 7-188
Ambler, Ernest, atomic scientist.
  Parity law of physics tested by, 7-110
Ambrosia beetles, weevils. 3-348
Ambursen dams. 8-314
Ameba proteus, protozoan. *illus.,* 2-58
Amebas. *illus.,* 1-292; 2-63-65, *illus.,* 62-63
  Movements of, 2-12, *illus.,* 10
  Reproductive rate of, 3-225
  Respiration of, 4-200, *illus.,* 201
  Slime molds resemble, *with illus.,* 3-24-25
  Structure of, *illus.,* 1-42
  White blood cells may resemble, 3-328-29
  See also **Cells; Sarcodina**
Amebic dysentery. 4-333-34
  Entamoeba histolytica causes, 2-64, *illus.,* 62
Ameboid movement, protoplasmic movement. 2-12, *illus.,* 10
  White blood cells may display, 3-328-29
Amendments, soil additives. *with illus.,* 2-167-72
America.
  Colonial America, petroleum used in, 4-141
  Discovery of, 2-364-65
  Indian writings, *with illus.,* 1-112
  See also **Alaska; Andes Mountains; Canada; Columbus, Christopher; Mexico; North America; South America; United States; under names of cities, etc.**
American Association for the Advancement of Science.
  Conservation urged by, 6-2
American basswood trees. 5-146
American Bison Society. 9-270
American brants, geese. 6-400
American buckeye trees. 5-147
American Cancer Society. 8-270, 272
  Lung cancer, investigation of, 5-348-49, *diagrams,* 347, 348
American Chemical Society. Awards to young scientists by, 8-72
American cockroaches. 3-148
American elm trees. 5-145
American Indian-Central local race. 8-219
American Indian-Marginal local race. 8-219
American Indians. Petroleum, use of, 4-141
  Writing of, *with illus.,* 1-112
American Meat Institute. 5-169, 172
American Meat Institute Foundation. 5-172
American Meteorological Society, in the United States.
  Hobbyists may join, 1-322
American National Foundation for Infantile Paralysis.
  Tests of Salk antipolio vaccine, 10-131
American Psychological Association. 9-322
American Red Cross. See **Red Cross**
American Revolution. 4-33, *illus.,* 32
American Society for Industrial Designers. 10-126
American Society for Microbiology. Awards to young scientists by, 8-72

American Standards Association. Film-speed index, **9-409**

American Telephone and Telegraph Company. **2-388**

Americium (Am), chemical element. Atomic number, 95; atomic weight, 243(?). Discovered in 1944 at the University of Chicago by Seaborg, James, Morgan and Ghiorso through intense neutron bombardment of plutonium. Named after America. First isolated in compound form by Cunningham in 1945. A member of the actinium series of elements.

Americus, Georgia. Solar-battery project at, **7-106**

Amerindian geographical race. *with illus.,* **8-217**

Ames, Adelaide, American astronomer.
Galaxies catalogued photographically by, **8-49**

Ames Aeronautical Laboratory. **10-234**

Amino acids. **9-383, 386**
Components of proteins, **2-3, 10, 11; 4-53-54; 7-275**
Laboratory production of, **8-190**
Nitrogen in, **3-318**
Viruses, amino acids of, **3-455**

Amino resins, plastics. **8-226-27**

Aminotriazole. Cranberry crop contaminated by, **8-268-69**

Ammeters. *with illus.,* **6-132-33**
Photoelectric exposure meters contain, *with illus.,* **9-409**

Ammonia.
Bacteria that transform organic compounds into, **3-68**
Chlorine combined with, for water purification, **2-280**
Coal, ammonia indirectly derived from coking of, *with illus.,* **1-419**
Experiments with ammonia water, *with illus.,* **4-230-31**
Formation of, **3-250,** *illus.,* **251**
Haber process for producing, *with diagram,* **2-230-31; 3-127,** *illus.,* **128-29; 9-211-12**
Jupiter's atmosphere contains, **5-20, 22**
Molecule of, **3-245,** *illus.,* **246**
Refrigeration, use in, **4-159,** *illus.,* **158, 159**
Uses of, **3-318**

Ammoniated toothpastes. **10-78**

Ammoniates, nitrogen compounds. Soil fertilizers, **2-171**

Ammonites, prehistoric cephalopods. *with illus.,* **1-389**

Ammonium bichromate. Photosensitive material, **1-205**

Ammonium cyanate. Urea produced from, **7-264**

Ammonium picrate, explosive. **8-282**

Ammonium sulfate, fertilizer. **2-171**
Coal as primary source of, *with illus.,* **1-419**

Ammonius the Porter, Alexandrian Christian philosopher. Founder of Neoplatonic school, **1-368**

Ammunition. See **Explosives; Warfare**

Amnesia, loss of memory.
Alcoholism may bring about, **4-411**

Amnion, membrane surrounding embryo. **8-23, 32,** *illus.,* **22**

Amoebas. See **Amebas**

Amor, asteroid. Earth, close approach to, **6-92**

Amorphous solids. **1-170-71; 5-337, 374**

Amperage. **9-235**

Ampère, André-Marie, French physicist. **5-233, 235**
Magnetic needle deflection experiments, **2-379**

Amperes, units of electric current. **6-130**

Amphibians. **5-152-62**
Adaptations for survival, *with illus.,* **3-241-42**
Cave-dwelling species, *with illus.,* **5-59**
Classification of, **1-298**
Ears of, *with illus.,* **1-282; 4-381, 383**
Evolution of, **4-196-97,** *diagram,* **199**
Field study of, **10-261-62**
Fossil amphibians, *illus.,* **6-372, 373**
Heart of, *with illus.,* **1-277-78**

Amphibians *(continued)*
Lungs used as float mechanism, *with illus.,* **1-280**
Migrations of, **9-415, 428-29**
Pets, *with illus.,* **7-25-26**
Prehistoric, **1-390**
Seasonal changes affect, **5-411, 412**

Amphineurans, mollusks. **2-201**

Amphioxi (plural of amphioxus). See **Lancelets**

Amphisbaenians (Amphisbaenidae), lizards. **5-199-200, 203**

Amphiuma, genus of amphibians. *illus.,* **5-157**

Amplification. **3-95**
Audion of De Forest, **8-88**
Electron tubes bring about, **6-299**
Noise meter, **8-38**
Transistors bring about, *with illus.,* **10-102-04**

Amplitude.
Pendulum, **2-121**
Sound waves, **5-117, 124,** *illus.,* **117**

Amplitude modulation (AM). *with illus.,* **3-89; 6-297-98**

Amundsen, Roald, Norwegian explorer. **7-34**

Amylase, digestive enzyme. **3-47**

Amylopectin, in starch-grain envelope. **4-76**

Amylose corn. *illus.,* **7-39**
Chemurgic development of, **7-40**

Anabaena, blue-green algae. **3-215**

Anabolism. **3-43**

Anacondas, snakes. **5-357**

Anaerobic decomposition. Sludge left by sewage, **5-332**

Anaerobic respiration, carried on in absence of oxygen. **2-12; 3-48**
Bacteria engage in, **3-66**

Anal canal. **4-330-31,** *illus.,* **331**

Anal fin, of fishes. *with illus.,* **4-96**

Anal sphincters, ringlike muscles. **4-330-31,** *illus.,* **331**

Analysis.
Electrochemical, **5-91**
Fertilizers, **2-171**
Ores, **1-376**
Soils, **2-172,** *illus.,* **165, 171**

Analytic (analytical) geometry. *with diagrams,* **4-423-31**
Invention of, **3-20-21**

Anaphase, stage of cell division. **2-14,** *illus.,* **13**

Anastigmatic lenses. Cameras containing, **9-406**

Anatomy.
*Adaptations of animals and plants, **3-235-44**
*Basic units of body, **1-143-48**
*Blood, **3-325-34**
*Body defenses, **7-346-53**
*Bones, **3-73-84**
*Circulatory system, **3-381-92**
*Digestive system, **4-321-35**
*Glands, **5-8-19**
*Mechanisms, animal, **1-277-86**
*Muscles of the human body, **3-203-13**
*Nervous system, **6-317-30**
*Respiratory system, **4-200-09**
*Sense organs, **4-379-85; 7-291-306**
*Skin, hair and nails, **2-173-81**
*Systems of human body, **1-148a-h**
*Teeth, **5-129-37**
Animals
Birds, **5-416, 419-23,** *diagram,* **421**
Crustaceans, **2-237-38,** *illus.,* **239**
Fish, **4-196-99, 285-86**
Insects, *with illus.,* **2-402-06**
Beetles, *with illus.,* **3-335-36**
Butterflies and moths, **3-193-95, 196**

Anatomy, Insects *(continued)*
 Flies and mosquitoes, 3-283, 284-86, *illus.,* 285, 287
 Orthopterous insects, *illus.,* 3-141
 Man's, a survey of, *with illus.,* 1-58-62
 Mollusks, 2-193-94, 196, *illus.,* 197
 Snakes, 5-351-52
 Spiders, 2-259, *with illus.,* 261
 Worms, 2-154, 159-60
 Gum of newborn baby in cross section, *illus.,* 10-164
 History
 Early discoveries by Greeks, 1-365-66
 Sixteenth century, *with illus.,* 2-374-76
 1600–1765, *with illus.,* 3-273-74
 Development of comparative anatomy, *with illus.,* 4-390-92
 Plant, 1-45-46
 See also **Blood; Body; Brain; Circulatory System; Man; Skeleton; etc.**
Anaxagoras, Greek philosopher. 1-135
Anaximander, Greek philosopher. 1-130-31
Anaximenes, Greek philosopher. 1-131
Anchorages, elements of suspension bridges. *with illus.,* 2-338
Anchovies. 4-314
 Migration of, 9-427
Ancient times.
 *Science, history of, 1-230-46, 354-68
 Astronomical observatories, 8-63-64
 Breadmaking in, 9-293-94
 Coal, use of, 1-408
 Irrigation in, *with illus.,* 8-192-93
 Navigation in, 4-106-07
 Sea, beliefs about, 6-27
 Transportation on land during, 1-100-01, *with illus.,* 98-99, 102-04, *illus.,* 105
 Waste disposal in, 5-326
 Water supply in, 2-271
 See also **Primitive peoples**
Andean wild dogs. *illus.,* 8-139
Andersen, Karsten, Arctic explorer. 5-172
Anderson, Carl David, American physicist (born 1905). Educated at the California Institute of Technology, he joined its faculty and was made full professor in 1939. In 1932 Anderson discovered the positron, for which he was awarded the 1936 Nobel Prize in physics. (He shared the prize with V. F. Hess.) Further research in cosmic radiation (with S. H. Neddermeyer) led him to the discovery of mesons—particles having greater ability to penetrate matter than electrons.
 Positron, discovery of, 8-396
Anderson, Clinton P., American administrator.
 Quotation from, 9-290
Anderson, Orville A., American explorer of stratosphere. 1-235; 6-179
Andes Mountains. 10-24, 213, 215
 Hummingbirds, 6-212
 Inca Lake, *illus.,* 10-27
 Roots of, 5-189
Andesite, igneous rock. 3-423
Andrée, Salomon August, Swedish aeronaut.
 Balloon flight over North Pole attempted, *with illus.,* 6-178
Andromeda, constellation. 1-334
 Spiral galaxy in, *illus.,* 1-259; *illus.,* 8-156c; 9-363
 Distance from earth, 8-51
Andromedids (Bielids), meteor shower. *table,* 6-97
Androscoggin River, Maine. Natural barrier to plant and animal communities, 10-182
Anemia, pernicious.
 Treated with liver extract, 9-35

Anemias, diseases due to lack of hemoglobin. 3-330-31
 Bone-marrow damage may cause, 3-74
 Cancer as cause of, 8-267
 Caused by folic-acid deficiency, 5-44
 Diagnosis of, with radioisotopes, 10-99
 Sickle-cell anemia, cause of, 9-386
Anemometers, wind gauges. 1-249, 320, *illus.,* 248, *diagram,* 321
Anemones, sea. See **Sea anemones**
Aneroid barometers. 1-318-19, *with diagrams,* 247, 249
Anesthesia, alcoholic. 4-409
Anesthetics.
 Cocaine and procaine, 5-401-02
 Dentistry, use in, *with illus.,* 5-136
 Nineteenth-century developments in use of, *with illus.,* 7-375-78
 Sleep, relation to, 6-150
Angel, destroying, poisonous mushroom. *with illus.,* 3-31-32
Angelfish, tropical fish. 4-290, *illus.,* 291; 8-115, *illus.,* 116
Angell, James Rowland, American psychologist and educator, 9-51
Angina pectoris. 3-390
 Alcoholic beverages supposed to provide relief for, 4-408
Angiosperms, seed plants. 3-399-400, 403-06, *illus.,* 398, 402-05; *with illus.,* 4-119-32
 *Food storage in seed plants, 2-415-20
 *Fruit and seed dispersal, 5-1-7
 *Germination, 5-61-67
 Classification of, 1-302-05
 See also **Seed plants**
Anglers, luminous fish. *illus.,* 2-191
Angles, in geometry. *with illus.,* 3-430-31
 Sums of angles in various triangles, *with diagrams,* 4-440-41
Angles of rotation. *with illus.,* 3-449-50
Anglo-Saxon. See **Old English**
Angstrom unit. Explanation of, 7-145, 278, 284a
Anguids (Anguidae), family of lizards, 5-200
Aniline. Dyes from, 8-186, 187
 Rocket fuel, use as, 10-45
Animal ammoniates, nitrogenous materials.
 Soil fertilizers, 2-171
Animal behavior. *Intelligence in animals, 2-26-29
 Development of study of, *with illus.,* 9-51-54
 See also **Behavior**
Animal husbandry. Antibiotics used in, 10-129
 See also **Domestication of animals**
Animal kingdom. See **Animals; Zoology**
Animal (farm) manures. 2-163, *with diagram,* 165-67
Animal psychology. 9-320-21
 *Intelligence in animals, 2-26-29
 Development of study of, *with illus.,* 9-51-54
Animal skins.
 *Leather and furs, 7-230-38
Animal starch. See **Glycogen**
Animalcules. Relation of, to higher organisms, *with illus.,* 7-157-58
Animals.
 *Adaptations, 3-235-44
 *Amphibians, 5-152-62
 *Antelope family, 8-376-87
 *Ants, keeping colony of, 3-393-96
 *Apes, monkeys and kin, 9-250-65
 *Bears and kin, 7-307-17
 *Beavers and others, 9-1-6
 *Beetles, 3-335-48
 *Bioluminescence, 2-182-91

Animals (*continued*)

*Birds, 5-415-26; 6-37-48, 60-68, 99-108, 152-66, 209-18, 304-10, 331-40, 341-49, 394-408

*Cats, 8-202-12

*Cells, 2-1-14

*Civets, mongooses and hyenas, 8-244-50

*Classification, 1-287-300

*Coelacanths, 4-196-99

*Coelenterates, 2-148-51

*Communities, 10-181-90

*Crocodilians, 5-380-85

*Crustaceans, 2-236-43

*Deer family, 8-234-43

*Dog family, 8-132-41

*Domestic animals, 7-327-33; 10-239-50

*Echinoderms, 2-151-52

*Exploring animal world, 10-254-64

*Fishes, 4-93-105, 285-95, 311-20; 8-112-16

*Germ-free animals, 7-151-55

*Giant land mammals, 7-408-17

*Habitats, 10-135-42

*Hearing of, 4-379-85

*History of animal life, 1-383-97

*Human biology, 1-57-66

*Insect collecting, 3-153-56

*Insect eaters, 7-94-102

*Insects, 2-402-14; 3-138-52, 193-202, 252-64, 283-92, 335-48, 357-72; 9-185-96; 10-30-39

*Intelligence in animals, 2-26-29

*Introduction to study of animals, 1-51-56

*Lizards, 5-196-206

*Mammals, 7-1-16

*Marine mammals, 7-181-89

*Marsupials, 7-418-28

*Mechanisms, animal, 1-277-86

*Migrations of, 9-415-32

*Mollusks, 2-192-202

*Muscles of the human body, 3-203-13

*Primitive chordates, 4-1-4

*Protozoans, 2-58-66

*Rodents, 8-160-70; 9-1-6

*Sanctuaries, bird and game, 9-266-78

*Seals and kin, 7-84-93

*Seasonal changes that affect animals, 5-409-13

*Senses, human, 7-291-306

*Snakes, 5-351-64

*Spiders and kin, 2-258-69

*Sponges, 2-146-52

*Systems of human body, 1-148a-h

*Turtles, 5-386-89

*Weasel family, 8-171-77

*Wild animals as pets, 7-17-26

*Worms, 2-153-62

*Zoo animals, 10-154-62

Allergic reactions to, 4-260

Animal psychology, development of study of, *with illus.*, 9-51-54

Backbone important for classification of, 3-74

Beast book of the Middle Ages, excerpt from, *illus.*, 2-309

Cancer in, 8-268, 272

Cave-dwelling species, *with illus.*, 5-58-60

Classification of

Cuvier, 4-392, *illus.*, 391

Lamarck, 4-389-90, *illus.*, 388

Linnaeus, 3-376

Fossils, *with illus.*, 4-386-94; *with illus.*, 6-370, 371, 372, 373, 374

Harmful to man, 1-56

Hearing in, 8-104-05

Machines, animals as: doctrine of Descartes, 3-13

Animals (*continued*)

Manure and remains of animals fertilize soil, 2-163, 171, *with diagram*, 165-67

Marine animals, study of, 6-29, 32-33, 35-36, *with illus.*, 74d, *illus.*, 33-34

Organic compounds derived from, 7-263

Parasitic worms of, *with illus.*, 2-153-59, *illus.*, 160-61

Photography of, *with illus.*, 6-311-13

Plants, comparison with, 1-40-42; 3-43

Poisonous plants avoided by, 7-78

Radiation affects, 10-252

Seeds and fruits dispersed by, 3-240-41; *with illus.*, 5-5-6, *illus.*, 4

Soil organisms, *with illus.*, 2-203-04

Struggle for existence among, 3-225-26

Transportation, use in, 1-98, *with illus.*, 99-106

Useful to man, 1-55-56

Virus diseases of, 3-452, 453, *illus.*, 454

See also **Biology; Birds; Evolution; Fish; Insects; Mollusks; Reptiles;** etc.

Anions, negatively charged electrified atoms. Salt water, removal from, 2-284

Anis, cuckoo family. 6-306

Ankle joints. *with illus.*, 1-283

Ankles. Bones of, 3-83, *illus.*, 74-75, 82-83

Tendons and ligaments of, *illus.*, 3-212, 213

Annealing. Glassmaking, 3-311-12, *illus.*, 312

Heat-treatment process for steel, 1-353

Plastics products, 8-233

Annelida (Annelids), phylum of worms. 1-294

Annelids, segmented worms. *with illus.*, 2-159-62, *illus.*, 153, 158

Annual meteor showers. 6-97

Annual rings, of trees. *with illus.*, 4-69-70

Climatic variations indicated by, 3-180

Solar activity affects annual rings, 3-107

Annuals, plants. 2-420; 6-57

Annular eclipses. 3-134-35; 6-83

Anodes, positive electric poles. *with illus.*, 5-89-93

Copper anodes in copper refining, *with diagram*, 1-378

Name introduced by Faraday, 5-236

"Plates" of electron tubes, *with illus.*, 6-295-302

Anoles, lizards. 5-201

Anomalops, East Indian fish. 2-186

Anopheles mosquitoes. *illus.*, 10-30, 32-33

Life cycle, *illus.*, 3-286-87

Malaria carried by, 2-66; 8-405, *illus.*, 404; 10-33, 34

Anoplura, order of insects. 2-413

"Ant eggs," cocoons. 3-358, *illus.*, 359

Ant gardens. 3-362, 364

Ant lions, insect larvae. See **Neuroptera**

Antarctic.

Atmospheric circulation and phenomena over, 1-238

Continental glacier of, 9-165-66

Exploration of, 7-34; 9-221

Icebergs of, *with illus.*, 9-339

IGY investigations of, 5-187, 190-91

IGY mapping of, *with diagram*, 5-190-91

Weather stations in, 6-175

Antarctic Drift, oceanic current. See **West Wind Drift**

Antares, star in Scorpius. 1-332

Anteaters. *with illus.*, 3-236; *with illus.*, 7-14, *illus.*, 12

Adaptations for feeding, 7-11

Antelopes. *8-376-87

Pronghorned, 8-235; 9-270, *illus.*, 272-73

Zoo, *illus.*, 10-154

Antennae, of animals.

Crustaceans, 2-237, *illus.*, 239

Insects, 2-402-03, 406, *illus.*, 403, 404

Antennae, Insects (continued)
  Beetles, 3-335, illus., 336
  Butterflies and moths, 3-196; illus., 9-191
  Flies, 3-284, illus., 285, 287
  Orthopterous insects, 3-139, 140, illus., 141
Antennas, radar. 9-387, illus., 388
Antennas, radio. 3-93, with illus., 90
  Parabolic, illus., 4-342b; 9-224
Antennas, radio-telescope. 9-207, illus., 208, 209
Antennas, television. illus., 5-283
Antheridia, sperm-producing structure of plants.
  Mosses, 3-187
Anthers, flower parts. with illus., 4-121
Anthocyanins, plant pigments. 4-73, 74; 6-55
Anthodites, calcium carbonate deposits in caves. 5-56
Anthracene. Alizarin synthesized from, 8-183
  Coal tar yields, with illus., 1-419
Anthracite, hard coal. 1-408, 418-19
Anthrax, bacterial disease of animals.
  Bacilli, illus., 3-66
  Germs of, carried by flies, 7-382
  Pasteur's and Koch's studies of, 7-380; 9-77, 79-80
Anthropology.
  *Language development, 1-107-21
  *Population problems, 3-225-34
  *Races of mankind, 8-213-20
  Development of study of, with illus., 9-21-30
  Human evolution, 1-65-66
  Races and heredity, 8-346
  Wundt's work in, 9-48-49
Anthropometry, science of measurement of human body
    and its parts.
  Galton's contributions to, 8-264
Anti-A, agglutinin in blood serum. 3-333
Anti-B, agglutinin in blood serum. 3-333
Anti-Rh factor, blood agglutinin, 3-334
Antianemic factor. 3-330
Antibiotics. with illus., 10-127-29, illus., 130a-d
  Allergic reactions to, 4-260
  Bacteria that produce antibiotics. 3-70; illus., 4-342d
  Dentistry, use in, 5-136
  Development of, 9-33-34
  Food preservation, used in, 4-164
  Germ-free animals not affected by, 7-154
  Ineffective against viruses, 3-457-58
  Tuberculosis treated by, 9-183
Antibodies. 4-259
  Absence of, in germ-free animals, 7-154
  Bacterial vaccines cause production of, 3-70
  Body's defenses, antibodies in, 7-349, 350-51
  Defense against tuberculosis, 9-177
  Formation of, 8-366
  Gamma globulins in blood, 3-326
  Virus vaccines cause production of, 3-458
Anticlines, upfolds of rocks. 10-215, 221, illus., 218
  Petroleum in, with diagram, 4-143, diagram, 142
Anticoincidence counters, radiation detectors. 9-343
Anticyclones, high-pressure wind systems. with dia-
    gram, 1-244; 2-95-96
  Glacial, 9-170
Antidiuretic hormone. 5-345
Antidotes, for use in treating poisons. 10-10
Antielectrons. See **Positrons**
Antifouling paint. 2-243
Antifreezes.
  Freezing point of solution lowered by, 4-301
Antigens, substances that stimulate antibody produc-
    tion. 3-333-34; 7-351
Antihistamines, in allergy control. 4-264
Antilles Current, oceanic current. 6-237, map, 232-33

Antimetabolites, chemicals that keep living organisms
    from growing. 9-291
Antimony (Sb), chemical element. Atomic number, 51;
  atomic weight, 121.75; melting point, 630.5° C.; boiling
  point, 1,380° C.; specific gravity, 6.691. Very brittle,
  blue-white metal, with flaky, crystalline texture and
  metallic luster. Recognized by ancients in compounds;
  known as a metal by about beginning of seventeenth
  century. Name derived from Latin antimonium; chemical symbol (Sb), from Latin stibium: "mark." Occurs
  sometimes as pure element but chiefly as sulfide. Obtained from sulfide by heating and reduction. Widely
  used in alloys to increase hardness and mechanical
  strength. Compounds, such as chlorides, oxides and
  sulfides, serve many industrial purposes.
Antimony trichloride. Test for vitamin A, with illus.,
    7-136
Antineutrinos, subatomic particles of low mass. 7-109,
    110
Antinoise measures. 8-43-44
Antiparticles, subatomic. 1-313, table, 314
Antiperistalsis, in digestive tract. 4-327
Antipolio vaccines. illus., 7-350-51; with illus., 10-
    131, 133
Antiprotons. Atomic nuclear antiparticles: that is,
  negative counterparts to the positive particles called
  protons. The antiproton has the same mass as the
  proton (about 1,837 times the mass of an electron),
  but it has an opposite charge; it is negative instead
  of positive. When a proton and antiproton collide,
  they annihilate each other, producing photons and
  mesons.
Antiquity. See **Ancient times**
Antiseptics.
  Nineteenth-century developments in use of, with
    illus., 7-374-75, 385-87
  Surface tension should be low, 5-373
Antisubmarine measures. 5-33
  World War I, 9-215
Antitoxins, antibodies. 7-349-51
Antitrade winds. 1-244; 2-93
Antlers, deer. Growth and shedding of, 8-235-36
Ants. *3-357-65
  *Keeping colony of, 3-393-96
  Aphids and, with illus., 2-412b
  Field study of, 10-263
  Leaf-cutting ants, with illus., 2-412b
  Parasitic tendencies among, 8-361-62
  Seeds dispersed by, 5-6
  Soil development aided by, 2-203-04
  Trees protected from other insects by, 7-81
Anura, order of amphibians. See **Frogs**
Anvil (incus), bone of ear. with illus., 4-380; 7-299,
    illus., 298
Anxiety. Tranquilizers used as relief from, 5-379
Anxiety neuroses. Mental illnesses, 9-202
Aorta, great artery. illus., 1-148e-f; with illus., 3-384
  Circulation, difference between mammals and birds
    in, 1-278
Apatite. illus., 5-250
Apes. 9-251-54, 260-64, illus., 250, 252-53
  Adapted for tree-dwelling, 7-9
  Brain, compared with that of man, illus., 1-63
  Hands of, illus., 2-176
  Mental life of, with illus., 9-52-54
Aphasia, brain disorder. 6-326
Aphelion. Earth's, 3-185
Aphid destroyers, true bugs. 3-261
Aphids.
  Ants and, with illus., 2-412b

Aphids (continued)
Ants milk secretion from, **3-361**
Life cycle of, **9-432**
Woolly aphids, **9-192-93**, *illus.,* **192**
Apiculture. See **Beekeeping**
Apogee, farthest orbital point. **8-127, 128, 131,** *diagram,* **126**
Apoidea, superfamily of bees. *with illus.,* **3-367-72**
Apollo, asteroid. Earth, close approach to, **6-92**
Apollo, sun god. God of healing, **1-364**
Apollo, Project. See **Project Apollo**
Apoplexy. 6-330
First aid for, **10-14**
Apothecaries' weights. *table,* **10-295**
Appalachia, ancient American landmass. **10-213**
Appalachian Mountains. 10-24
History of, **10-213-14, 218, 221**
Uplifts of, **8-18**
Appalachian Revolution, time of mountain making. **1-391; 6-372, 373**
Apparatus.
Alchemical, **1-360; 2-311,** *illus.,* **310**
Nucleonics and electronics, use of, *illus.,* **10-200-01**
Pictures sent by wire and radio uses, *with illus.,* **7-390-92**
Apparent images. See **Virtual images**
Apparent magnitude. 8-49
Pogson's scale of apparent magnitude of stars, **6-389**
Stars and other heavenly bodies, *with table,* **6-260-62;** *table,* **10-209**
Appendages, insect. Abdominal, **2-404, 406,** *illus.,* **405**
Appendicitis. 4-334
Appendicular bones. *with illus.,* **3-74, 79-84**
Appendix. See **Vermiform appendix**
Appert, Nicolas, French pioneer in canning. **4-155**
Appetite.
Alcoholic beverages as stimulants to, **4-407**
Hunger distinguished from, **4-331**
Appian Way. 3-296, *illus.,* **294, 297**
Apple trees.
Flowers of, *illus.,* **4-122**
Fruits, *illus.,* **4-129**
Retaining fruit till ripe, *illus.,* **10-149**
Apples.
Brown-rot disease of, **3-28**
San José scale on, *illus.,* **8-367**
Scab disease of, *illus.,* **8-375**
Syrup from cull apples, **7-39**
Appleton, Sir Edward Victor, English physicist (born in 1892). Did extensive research in the field of electricity, particularly wireless telegraphy. Received the Nobel Prize in physics in 1947 for his discovery of the layer (Appleton layer) reflecting short radio waves in the ionosphere. Sir Edward contributed to the development of radar. He is the principal and vice-chancellor of the University of Edinburgh.
Sun's radio storms studied by, **9-209**
Appliances, gas. 5-106
Applied art. See **Design of products**
Applied potential, electrical. Prospecting with, *with diagram,* **7-360-61**
Applied science. See **Engineering; Technology**
Aptitude tests. Older workers, tests for, **8-83**
Aqua regia, oxidizing agent. **3-320**
Gold dissolved by, **4-245**
Aqualung, device used in free diving. *with illus.,* **6-26a-d**
Ocean explorers use, *illus.,* **6-76**
Aquarids, meteor showers. **6-96,** *table,* **97**
Aquariums. *****8-112-16**
Aquarius (Water Carrier), constellation. **1-334-35**

Aquatic mammals.
Environmental factors affecting, **7-7-8**
Aquatic organisms. *with illus.,* **10-140-42**
Aqueducts.
Roman, *illus.,* **1-364**
Tunnels that carry water, **2-48,** *illus.,* **47, 49**
Water transported by, **2-275-76,** *illus.,* **276-77**
Aqueous humor, of eye. **7-294,** *illus.,* **292**
Aquifers, water-bearing rock strata. **2-274**
Aquila (Eagle), constellation. **1-333,** *illus.,* **322**
Aquinas, St. Thomas, Italian scholastic philosopher. **2-304-05**
Arabia.
Deserts of, **6-118**
Sea water converted into fresh water in, **2-283**
See also **Saudi Arabia**
Arabic, language. Scientific words derived from, **2-303-04**
Arabic numerals. 1-153-54, *illus.,* **154-55**
Derivation of, **2-298**
Arabs.
Astronomical observatories in Middle Ages, **8-64**
Bedouin, *illus.,* **6-116**
Papermaking, contributions to, **4-364**
Scientific contributions in the Middle Ages, *with illus.,* **2-298-304**
Arachne, mythical princess. Story of, **2-259**
Arachnids. *****2-258-69**
Arachnoid, one of the meninges membranes. *with illus.,* **6-327-28**
Arago, Dominique-François-Jean, French physicist. **5-232-33, 235**
Daguerreotype process promoted by, **9-399**
Aral Lake, U.S.S.R., 7-61
Aralac, synthetic fiber. **8-189**
Aralen, antimalarial drug. Preparation of, *illus.,* **8-183**
Aratus of Soli, ancient Greek authority on weather. **1-245**
Araucaria, genus of pine tree.
Layering used to propagate, *illus.,* **9-15**
Arboreal habitats. 10-136, *illus.,* **138, 140**
Arc, degrees of, sky distances. **1-259**
Arc lamps. 4-239; 9-344
Photography, use in, **9-408**
Arc welding. Electronic equipment, **10-170**
Arcas, mythological figure linked with legends of constellations. **1-325**
Arcella, genus of one-celled animals. **2-64-65**
Arch bridges. 2-344, *with illus.,* **336-38**
Arch dams. 8-314-15, *illus.,* **311, 314, 316b, 316d**
History of, **8-308**
Arch-gravity dams. 8-315
Arch of aorta, great artery. *illus.,* **1-148f**
Archaeocyathids, extinct spongelike animals. **1-387**
Archaeology.
*****Radiocarbon dating, **10-92-97**
Astronomy, relation to, **1-24**
Breadmaking, prehistoric and ancient, **9-293-94**
Calendar development, *with illus.,* **10-171-76**
Development of study of, *with illus.,* **9-21-30**
Petroleum used in ancient times, **4-140**
Ships and boats of ancient times, **4-106-07**
Archaeopteryx, extinct bird. **1-393,** *illus.,* **394; 5-415-16;** *illus.,* **6-373; 8-262,** *illus.,* **261**
Archaeornis, extinct bird. **5-415-16,** *illus.,* **417**
Archegonia, egg-producing structure of plants.
Mosses, **3-187**
Archeozoic era. See **Pre-Cambrian era**
Archer, Frederick Scott, English photographer. **6-387**
Photographic images, development, **9-402-03**

Arches. Building construction, 7-119

Arches, of feet. 3-83-84

Arches, in rocks. See **Anticlines; Synclines**

Archimedean screw. *with illus.,* 1-357-58; *with illus.,* 8-193

Archimedes, Greek mathematician, physicist and inventor. *with illus.,* 1-357-58
  Buoyancy, principle discovered by, 2-33-34
  Calculus used by, *with diagrams,* 4-434-35
  Engineering accomplishments of, 1-216

Archimedes' principle of buoyancy. 2-34; 8-8

Architecture.
  *Builder's materials, 7-115-28
  *Concrete structures, 3-113-25
  *Glass houses, 8-388-92
  *Modern houses, 4-265-72
  Acoustics in, 5-128, *illus.,* 127
  Animal architecture, *with diagrams,* 1-286
  Cloister of the Cathedral of Saint Trophime, Arles, France, *illus.,* 2-296
  Granite fountain in Washington, D.C., *illus.,* 2-83
  Mayan pyramid, *illus.,* 9-29
  Modern concrete apartment house, *illus.,* 3-125
  Rome, ancient, 1-363, *illus.,* 364
  Stone as building material, 2-81
  Twentieth-century developments, 10-119, 123
  See also **Archaeology; Housebuilding**

Archosaurians, extinct reptiles. 5-415

Arctic.
  All-meat diet in, 5-172
  Atmospheric circulation and phenomena over, 1-237, 238
  Exploration of, 7-34
  Icebergs and ice islands of, 9-334-39, *map,* 336-37
  Weather stations in, *with illus.,* 6-174-75
  See also **North Pole**

Arctic foxes. 8-141
  Temperature affects, 7-7

Arctic hares. 8-170

Arctic Ocean.
  Ice islands of, 9-338-39, *map,* 336-37
  Salinity of, 6-31

Arctic sharks. 4-290

Arctic terns. *illus.,* 9-418
  Migration of, 9-420, *diagram,* 419

Arcturus, star in Boötes. 1-331

Areas. Calculus to determine areas, *with diagrams,* 4-434-35

Arêtes, land forms due to glacial erosion. 9-168, *diagram,* 164-65

Argand burner, eighteenth-century lamp. 4-232

Argelander, Friedrich Wilhelm August, Prussian astronomer. 6-389

Argentina. Industrial research, 1-96

Argentine Farm Chemurgic Council. 1-96

Argo Navis (Ship Argo), formerly a constellation. 1-337

Argon (Ar), chemical element. Atomic number, 18; atomic weight, 39.948; melting point, —189.2° C.; boiling point, —185.7° C.; specific gravity (air = 1), 1.3796. Best recognized by characteristic lines in red end of spectrum. First seen by Rayleigh and Ramsey with aid of the spectroscope in 1894; name derived from Greek word *argon,* meaning "inactive." Makes up about 0.94 per cent of the air; prepared by fractionation of liquid air. Used in electric light bulbs and fluorescent tubes.
  Color of, when electrically excited, 8-118
  Electron tubes containing, 6-300-01
  Incandescent-lamp bulbs filled with, 4-239

Argonne National Laboratory.
  Heavy-water reactor, *illus.,* 1-94

Argus pheasants. 6-340

Argyrol. Removing silver from, *with illus.,* 7-134

Arid (dry) regions. Soils of, 2-19, 21-23
  Water erosion and deposition in, 8-10-12, 16

Arietids, meteor shower. *table,* 6-97

Aristarchus of Samos, Greek astronomer. 1-356-57
  Forerunner of Copernicus, 2-372

Aristolochia sipho, woody plant. *illus.,* 4-69

Aristotle, Greek philosopher. 1-133, 137-38, *illus.,* 135-37
  Classification of living things, 1-287
  Composition of matter, idea of, 1-307
  Doctrines of, disproved by Galileo, 3-2-3
  Evolutionary views, 8-258
  Fossils, work with, 4-387
  Influence on medieval thought, 2-304-05
  Marine biology, work in, 6-29
  Mind, definition of, 9-47-48
  Study of man, 9-21, 25

Arithmetic. *1-149-61
  Algebra differs from, 2-67-68
  Recreations, arithmetical, 4-443-45, 453-54

Arithmetic progressions. Malthusian theory, 3-229

Arithmetic series. 2-77

Arkansas. Bauxite mine in, *illus.,* 3-38

Arkwright, Richard, English inventor. 4-37

Arlandes, Marquis d'.
  Pioneer balloon flight, 6-177, *illus.,* 176

Arlberg Tunnel, Austria. 2-44-45

Armadillos. 7-14, *illus.,* 11
  Defense mechanisms, 7-11
  Pets, 7-22

Armati, Salvino degli, Italian spectacle-maker. 9-82

Armpits. Taking temperature by, 10-58

Arms.
  Blood vessels of, *illus.,* 1-148f
  Bones of, *illus.,* 1-148b; *with illus.,* 3-80-81, *illus.,* 74-75
  Development in unborn human young, 8-29
  Levers, human arms as, *with illus.,* 1-283
  Muscles of, *illus.,* 1-148c; 3-210-11, *with illus.,* 208-09, *illus.,* 204, 205, 206, 207

Armstrong, Edwin H., American inventor. 9-288

Army. See **Civil War; Warfare; World War I; World War II; etc.**

Army (driver) ants. 3-364-65

Army worms. 3-198, 202

Arnold, Kenneth, American businessman.
  "Flying saucers" sighted by, 9-17

Aromatic hydrocarbons. 7-274-75

Aromatic (organic) compounds.
  Discovery of structure of, *with illus.,* 5-79-80

Arrhenius, Svante August, Swedish chemist and physicist (1859–1927). He taught at the University of Stockholm and later became director of the Nobel Institute for Physical Chemistry. In 1903 he received the Nobel Prize in chemistry for his theory of electrolytic dissociation. Arrhenius suggested that molecules of electrolytes are dissociated into electrically charged particles (ions); furthermore, electrolytic action need not be limited to specific chemical reactions but may exist in atmospheric phenomena. Arrhenius originated the theory that light exerts pressure. See also 5-83.

Arrow worms. *illus.,* 1-293

Arsenates. Minerals in the form of, 9-306

Arsenic (As), chemical element. Atomic number, 33; atomic weight, 74.9216; melting point, 814° C. at 36 atmospheres; sublimes; boiling point, 615° C.; specific gravity, 5.73. Dark gray, semimetallic solid; not

Arsenic (As) (continued)
ductile or malleable; no tensile strength. Albertus Magnus probably obtained the element in 1250; name derived from Greek (by way of Latin) *arsenikon:* "yellow orpiment." Found native in sulfides realgar and orpiment and in other compounds, such as arsenate. Obtained in compounds by roasting copper, lead and other ores, by reduction and by oxidizing white arsenic. Compounds useful as insecticides, in bronzing, fireworks and war gases.

   Solar battery, function in, *with illus.,* **7-103-06**
Arrowroot, plant. Starch from, **4-78**
Art.
   *Ceramics, **7-393-407**
   *Industrial design, **10-117-26**
   Oil paintings by X ray, analysis of, **7-147**
   Photoengraving of art work, *with illus.,* **1-204-06**
   Stone Age painting, *illus.,* **1-110-11;** *with illus.,* **9-29-30**
   Stone Age sculpture and engraving, *illus.,* **9-25**
   See also **Archaeology**
Arteries. *illus.,* **1-148e-f; 3-381,** 382, 383, 384, 386, *diagrams,* 381, 382, 384, 385
   Aging, affected by, **8-80-81**
   Bleeding from arteries, control of, *with illus.,* **10-5-7**
   Diseases of, *with diagram,* **3-390-92**
   Hardening of, **5-14**
   Kidney, *diagram,* **5-12**
Arterioles, small arteries. **3-384,** *illus.,* 385
Arteriosclerosis. **3-390,** 391, 392, *diagram,* 391
   Cerebral, **6-330; 9-201**
Artesian wells. **8-329,** *illus.,* 329-30
Arthritis.
   Treatment with adrenal hormones, **10-133-34**
Arthrodires, extinct sharklike fishes. **1-389**
Arthropods.
   *Crustaceans, **2-236-43**
   *Insects, **2-402-14; 3-193-202,** 283-92, 335-48, 357-72; **9-185-96; 10-30-39**
   *Spiders and kin, **2-258-69**
   Cave-dwelling species, **5-60**
   Classification of, **1-295-97**
   See also **Insects**
Artifacts. Early man studied with aid of, **9-23-24**
Artificial immunity. *with illus.,* **7-350-51**
   See also **Jenner, Edward; Vaccines**
Artificial-lightning generators. **1-401,** *illus.,* 400
Artificial pneumothorax. **9-182**
Artificial respiration. *with illus.,* **4-205-06**
   Childbirth, applied in, **8-33**
   How to apply, *with illus.,* **10-8-10**
Artificial satellites. See **Satellites, artificial**
Artificial teeth. **5-134-35**
Artillery. Rocket artillery, *illus.,* **9-379**
Artiodactyla, order of mammals. *with illus.,* **7-16**
Arts and Crafts Movement, in nineteenth century. **10-119**
Aruba, island in Caribbean. Sea water converted into fresh water in, **2-283**
Asbestos.
   Crystalline structure, **5-338**
   Insulating material, **7-124**
   Uses of, in home chemistry laboratory, **4-221-22,** 227
Asbestos cement. Sewer pipes made of, **5-328**
Aschelminthes, phylum of wormlike animals. **1-293**
Asci, spore sacs of fungi. **3-26**
Ascorbic acid, vitamin C. **5-45-46**
   Daily requirement and sources of, *table,* **4-55-57**
   Food preservative, **4-164**
   Test for, **7-136**
Ascospores, sexual reproductive spores of fungi. **3-28**

Ash trees. **5-150,** *illus.,* 151
   Fruits, *illus.,* **4-130;** *illus.,* **5-141**
Ashlar, cut stone. **7-118**
Asia.
   Deserts of, **6-118**
   Petroleum production and reserves, **4-151**
   Plains and plateaus, **6-109-10**
   Rainfall statistics, **2-347**
   Silk industry in Far East, *with illus.,* **5-176,** 184, *illus.,* 178-79, 181, 183, 185
   See also **China; Himalayas; India; Japan**
Asiatic geographical race. **8-216,** *illus.,* 217
Askja, volcano of Iceland. **8-290**
Aspen trees. **5-144**
   Winter buds, *illlus.,* **6-58**
Aspergillus, mold. *illus.,* **10-130b-c**
Asphalt. **4-142,** 148, 150
   Building material, **7-128**
   Road surfaces of, **3-301,** *illus.,* 298c-d
   See also **Concrete; Roads**
Asphaltum varnish, acid proof coating. **4-221-22**
Asphyxiation, suspended breathing. Causes of, **10-8**
   Gas appliances may cause, **7-197**
Aspirators. Collecting small insects with, **3-154**
Aspirin. Production of, **5-81**
Assassin bugs. *with illus.,* **3-259**
Assays, analyses of substances. Ores, **1-376**
Assembly lines. Automobile manufacture, **2-145**
   Meat-packing technique, **5-164,** 166
Asses. See **Donkeys**
Assimilation, conversion or incorporation of nutritive material into body substance.
   Carbohydrates, **4-52**
   Cells, **2-11**
   Fats, **4-53**
   Plants, **3-49**
   Proteins, **4-54**
Associated Press.
   Facsimile transmission, **7-392,** *illus.,* 390
Association areas, of cerebral cortex. **6-325-26**
Association of American Railroads. **1-195**
Associative laws of addition and multiplication. **2-69**
Assuan Dam. See **Aswan Dam**
Assyria. Pottery of, **7-396**
Astatine (At), chemical element. Atomic number, 85; atomic weight, 210(?). Halogen; only one without stable isotope. Synthesized in 1940 at the University of California by Corson, MacKenzie and Segré through bombarding bismuth with alpha particles. Reportedly concentrated in thyroid of guinea pigs in a manner similar to iodine, which it resembles in many chemical properties.
Asterisms. See **Astronomy; Constellations; Stars**
Asteroids (planetoids). **3-159; 4-419-22**
   Collide possibly with earth, **6-92**
   Discovery of, **6-393**
   Jupiter's satellites VIII—XII may be, **5-24**
   Origin of, **4-422**
Asters, plants. **10-205**
Asters, protoplasmic radiations. **2-14,** 290, *illus.,* 291
Asthma. Allergy as cause of, **4-260**
Astigmatism, of eyes. **7-296**
   Lenses and mirrors, **7-260,** 262
Aston, Francis W., English physicist. **8-418**
Astor, John Jacob, German-American fur trader. **7-236**
Astrolabes, astronomical instruments. *illus.,* **2-300**
Astrology.
   Antiquity, **1-126**
   Middle Ages, **2-309**
Astronautics (space travel). *9-375-83; *10-40-54**
   See also **Supersonics**

Astronomers. See **Astronomy**; also names of as-
tronomers
Astronomers, amateur.
Comets discovered by, 5-398-99
Astronomical constants. 10-297-98
Astronomical tables.
Alfonsine Tables, 2-309
Prussian Tables, 3-5
Rudolphine Tables, 3-5-6
Astronomical unit (A.U.) 4-49
Astronomy.
*Amateur astronomy, 6-78-86
*Telescope making, 9-365-74
*Calendars, 10-171-80
*Comets, 5-390-99
*Constellations, 1-323-37
*Earth as planet, 4-42-50
*Eclipses, 3-130-37
*Face of sky, 1-255-64
*Galaxies, 8-47-54
*Interstellar materials, 9-359-64
*Meteorites and meteors, 6-87-98
*Milky Way, 8-151-59
*Moon, 4-277-84
*Motions of stars, 7-223-29
*Observatories, 8-55-66
*Planetaria, 2-396-401
*Planets, 4-25-31, 415-22; 5-20-24, 107-13, 289-93
*Radio astronomy, 9-206-10
*Relativity theory, 4-210-20
*Solar system, 3-157-64
*Stars (introduction), 6-255-68
*Study of astronomy, 1-16-26
*Sun, 3-99-112
*Telescopes, 9-153-61
*Variable stars, 7-45-51
Constants, 10-297-98
History
Antiquity, 1-126, 129-30, 134, 137, 356-59, illus.,
360
Arabic contributions to, 2-298-99, illus., 300-01
Sixteenth century, with illus., 2-371-74
1600–1765, 3-278, 281-82
Seventeenth century, with illus., 3-2-4
Eighteenth century, with illus., 4-398-400
Nineteenth century, with illus., 6-385-93
Twentieth century, 9-223-25, illus., 222
Mathematics and, 1-78
Observatories, list of, 8-66
Planets, theories of formation, with illus., 1-27-30
Zodiac, signs of, 10-298
See also **Astronautics; Comets; Constellations; Earth;
Eclipses; Mars; Nebulae; Observatories; Planets;
Radio astronomy; Radio telescopes; Stars; Sun;
Universe; Venus; etc.**
Astrophysics. See **Astronomy; Physics**
Aswan Dam. 8-193, 306, illus., 200
Atacama Desert, Chile. 6-118
Athabasca tar sands, in Canada. 4-143
Athens, Greece.
Center of learning in antiquity, 1-135
Atherosclerosis, form of arteriosclerosis. 10-134
Athlete's foot, disease. Fungi cause, 3-32
Athletics. See **Exercise**
Atkinson, Robert d'E., British scientist. 9-224
Atlanta, Georgia.
Heat from city incinerator used, 5-335
Atlantic, steamship. 4-110
Atlantic flyway, bird migration route. illus., 5-418e
Atlantic Ocean. Airplane crossings, 6-184; 9-217
Bed of, in profile, diagram, 6-73

Atlantic Ocean (continued)
Bottom features of, 6-74
Currents in, with illus., 5-191-92
Eel migrations, 3-243-44
Ship crossings and service, with illus., 4-108-11, 115-
18
Steamship crossing, first, 6-378
See also **Ocean**
Atlantic Ridge. 6-74, diagram, 73
Atlantic Telegraph Company. 2-384
Atlas, first neck bone. with illus., 3-76
Atlas moths. 3-200
Atlas Mountains. 10-24
Atlas rockets. illus., 10-40-41
Atmosphere, *1-230-40
*Air pollution, 3-349-56
*Clouds, 2-212-22
*Dust, 7-137-42
*Lightning, 1-398-404
*Meteorology for amateurs, 1-315-22
*Past climates, 3-177-85
*Weather forecasting, 1-241-54
*Winds, 2-89-98
Definition of, 1-33
Density calculations, electronic computers used for,
9-151
Dust in, 2-214, 216
IGY studies of upper, 5-194-95
Jupiter, 5-20, 21-22
Layers of, 4-45
Mars, 4-417
Meteorites and meteors affected by, 6-87-88, 89,
95-97
Molecules, numbers and sizes of, 1-172
Moon has no, 4-279, 284
Radio waves that penetrate, with illus., 9-206-07
Research into upper atmosphere with rockets, with
illus., 10-1
Saturn, 5-109
Seed dispersal by air currents and wind, 3-240
Solar, with illus., 3-100-02
Sound, speed in air, 10-228
Space travel in, 10-41, 45
Twentieth-century study of, 9-220, 223; illus., 221
Water vapor in, 2-347
See also **Aeronautics; Breathing; Exosphere; Iono-
sphere; Respiration; Sound; Stratosphere; Super-
sonics; Troposphere**
Atmosphere, unit of atmospheric pressure. 1-249;
4-275
Atmospheric pressure. with diagrams, 1-242-44; with
illus., 2-36-40
Boiling and, 1-168, diagram, 169
Experiments with, with illus., 1-141; with illus.,
2-324-29; with illus., 7-220
High-altitude planes, pressure in, 6-191
Measuring and recording, 1-318-19, with diagrams,
247, 249, 254, diagrams, 316, 320
Vegetable growth experiments under low, illus., 8-
37
Atmospheric temperature.
Measuring and recording, 1-247, with diagrams,
316, 317-18, illus., 246, 250
Atmospheric tides. 1-319
Atolls, coral islands. 4-135-39; 6-75, 77, illus., 77
Atom bombs. See **Nuclear bombs**
Atom smashers. *9-241-49, 330, with illus., 129-32,
illus., 138a-b; illus., 1-309; illus., 10-200
Producing cosmic and X rays with, 7-203, 206
See also **Cosmotron; Cyclotrons; Electrostatic
generators**

Atomic Age.
  *Perils of Atomic Age, 9-348-58
  Dawn of, *with illus.,* 9-328-32
"Atomic bomb disease," 9-351
Atomic clocks. *illus.,* 2-234
Atomic energy. *9-120-42
  *Atom smashers, 9-241-49
  *Atomic farming, 10-251-53
  *Atomic medicines, 10-98-101
  *Food preservation, 10-114-16
  *Geiger-Mueller counter, 9-340-43
  *Nuclear-bomb precautions, 9-391-96
  *Perils of Atomic Age, 9-348-58
  *Radiation thickness gauges, 9-43-46
  *Radioisotope-fueled thermoelectric generators,
    6-172-75
  *Structure of atoms, 1-307-14
  Astronomy contributes to knowledge of, 1-19
  Automation in production of atomic energy, 10-237,
    238
  History of man's use of, 8-410-20; 9-328-32
  Jet aviation, application to, 7-74
  Nuclear power for generating electricity, 6-7; 9-229,
    231
  Peacetime uses of, 9-331-32
  Petroleum released by nuclear blasting, 4-143
  Research in, 1-90, 93, 96, 97, *illus.,* 94
  Rockets driven by, 9-381-82; 10-4
  Ships driven by, 4-118, *with illus.,* 114a-d
  Space travel, possibilities for, 10-54
  Submarine power plants, *illus.,* 4-342d; 5-35-37
  Sun's energy a form of atomic (nuclear) reaction, 9-
    224
Atomic farming. *10-251-53
Atomic fission. 9-330-32, 351, 352
Atomic fusion. 9-139-41, 142
Atomic medicines. *10-98-101
Atomic numbers. 1-310-11, *diagrams,* 312; 9-124-26;
    table, 10-293
  Moseley introduces concept of, 8-417
Atomic piles. See Nuclear Reactors
Atomic ships. 4-118, *with illus.,* 114a-d
Atomic submarines.
  Arctic explored by, 5-37, 190
  Nautilus, *with illus.,* 5-35-37
  Testing power plant, *illus.,* 4-342d
Atomic theory.
  Nineteenth century, *with illus.,* 5-74-76
  See also **Atoms** and other entries such as **Atom
    smashers, Atomic energy,** etc.
Atomic theory of matter. Proposed by Democritus,
    1-131
Atomic warfare. *with illus.,* 9-351-58
  Nuclear tests, 9-352-54
Atomic weights. 1-308, 309-10, 311, *with diagrams,*
    312, *diagrams,* 313; 2-227, 231; 9-124-26; *table,*
    10-293
  Calculation of, 8-419
  Classified by means of, *with illus.,* 5-83-85
  Development of idea of, 5-74
"Atomized" coal. See Powdered coal.
Atomizers. 2-39, *illus.,* 38
  Experiment with, *with illus.,* 2-328-29
Atoms.
  *Atomic energy, 9-120-42
  *Chemical reactions involving, 2-223-31
  *Structure of atom, 1-307-14
  *Valence, 3-245-51
  Atomic structure of acids and bases, 4-337-40
  Audibility of, 8-45

Atoms *(continued)*
  Carbohydrate molecules, constitution of, 4-76, 77,
    78-79
  Crystals made of, 5-340, *diagram,* 339
  Electrical charges in atoms, 6-120-21; 9-227, *illus.,* 228
  Gas atoms, in electron tubes, 6-301-02
  Interstellar space, atoms in, 9-359-64
  Plastics molecules, atoms in, *with diagram,* 8-222
  Quantum and wave-mechanics theories of, 7-205
  Structure of, 2-422; 8-416-17
  X rays, source of, 7-144-46, 148
  See also **Atomic energy; Chemistry; Electrons; Energy;
    Matter; Molecules; Nuclei, atomic; Parity law;
    Physics**
ATP. See Adenosinetriphosphate
Atrophy, breaking down of tissues.
  Sign of aging, 8-80
Attar of roses, perfume.
  Synthesis of, 8-188-89
Attila the Hun, early conqueror. *illus.,* 3-232
Attitude, airplane position. 6-188, 193, *illus.,* 191
Attraction, intermolecular. *with diagram,* 1-166-68
Auction markets, for supply of livestock. 5-166
Audio-frequency current. 3-88-89
Audiometers, for hearing tests. *with illus.,* 10-80
Audion tubes. 9-287
  *Development of, 8-84-89
Auditory canal. *with illus.,* 7-298
Auditory nerves. *with illus.,* 4-380; 6-328
Auditory ossicles. See Ossicles of ear
Auditory placode, ear pit in embryo. *with illus.,* 4-385
Audubon, John James, American naturalist and artist.
    with illus., 8-252-54
Auger mining, for coal. *with illus.,* 1-410
August. Origin of name for month, 10-175
Augustus, Roman emperor. Calendar reform, 10-175
Auks. Extinction of great auk, 9-268
Aurcoloid, colloidal radiogold. Medical uses of, 10-100
Aureomycin, 10-128
  Fish diseases treated with, 8-116
  Food preservation, used in, 4-164
Auricles (pinnae), of the ear. 4-385, *with illus.,* 380;
    with illus., 7-298
Auricles of heart. *with illus.,* 1-277-78, *illus.,* 148f;
    3-383, 386, *illus.,* 382, 383
Auricular fibrillation, a heart disease. 3-391
Auriculo-temporal nerve. *illus.,* 1-148h
Auriculo-ventricular node, tissue associated with heart-
    beat. *with diagram,* 3-386
Auriga (Charioteer), constellation. 1-336
Aurochs, European bison. 10-248
Aurora australis.
  Cause, *with diagram,* 7-172
Aurora borealis, northern lights. *illus.,* 1-236, 258
  Cause, *with diagram,* 7-172
Aurora polaris. See Auroras
Auroras (polar lights). 1-240, *illus.,* 236, 258; *with il-
    lus.,* 3-106
  IGY studies of, 5-195
  Venus, theory auroras on, 4-29
Ausable Chasm, in New York. *illus.,* 8-13
Auscultation. Diagnosis of tuberculosis uses, 9-179
Austin, Texas. Reservoir at, 2-273
Australia.
  Deserts of, 6-118
  Great Barrier Reef, *illus.,* 4-137
  Marsupial mammals of, 7-421
  Sheep of, 10-245
Australian cockroaches. 3-148
Australian geographical race. 8-217, *illus.,* 216
Australopithecus, manlike primate. 1-397

Austria. Stelvio Road, *illus.,* 10-25

Autochrome, color-photography process. 9-413

Autoclaves. *illus.,* 9-79

Autogiros. 6-193; 9-220

Automatic control systems.
 *Automation, 10-235-38
 *Guidance of missiles and space vehicles, 8-125-31
 *Radiation thickness gauges, 9-43-46
 Gas appliances automatically operated, 5-106
 Gyropilots, ships', 4-117

Automatic fire-control systems. Heavy guns, 10-236

Automatic machines.
 *Automation, 10-235-38
 *Electronic computers, 9-143-52
 *Radiation thickness gauges, 9-43-46
 Coal extracted by robot miners, *with illus.,* 1-409
 Natural-gas supply and use regulated automatically, 5-104, *with illus.,* 105-06

Automatic Message Accounting, in telephony. 2-391

Automatic regulation. See **Automatic control systems**

Automatic train identification (Identra). 1-193

Automation. *10-235-38
 *Electronic computers, 9-143-52
 *Printed circuits, 6-49-51
 *Radiation thickness gauges, 9-43-46
 Coal extracted by robot miners, *with illus.,* 1-409
 Natural-gas supply and use regulated automatically, 5-104, *with illus.,* 105-06
 Soviet industry and, 1-96
 Weather study, automatic devices in, *illus.,* 1-252, 253

Automobile engines. *with illus.,* 4-86-89

Automobiles. *2-129-45
 Automatic production of automobile engines, *with illus.,* 10-237-38
 Garbage-collection trucks, 5-335, *illus.,* 334
 General Motors research center, *illus.,* 4-342b
 Nineteenth century, *with illus.,* 6-380-81
 Simple machines, combination of, 3-61-62
 Testing parts, *illus.,* 4-342a
 Trucks, first use of, 8-407

Autonomic nervous system.
 Nature and functions of, 6-329
 Nicotine's effects on, 5-345
 See also **Nervous system**

Autopilots, flight steering devices. Space vehicles and missiles use, 8-129-30, *diagram,* 130

Autoselection. 4-410

Autotrophic plants, capable of manufacturing food from simple inorganic substances. Bacteria, 3-65

Autumn.
 *Storage period, 6-52-59
 Exploring plant world in, 10-206

Autumn constellations, seen from middle northern latitudes. *map,* 1-328

Auxiliary languages. 1-119-21

Auxins, plant growth hormones. 3-50, 53; 9-8

Available water, soil water that can be used by plants. *with illus.,* 5-27

Avalanche Lake, Glacier National Park. *illus.,* 6-415

Averages, norms. Use in psychology, 9-313

Averroës, Spanish-Arabian physician and philosopher. 2-302

Avery, Amos G., American chemist. 9-291

Aves. See **Birds**

Aviaries. Zoo, *illus.,* 10-161

Aviation. See **Aeronautics**

Avicenna, Arab physician and philosopher. 2-301

Avidin, substance contained in raw eggs. 5-44

Avocets. 6-405

Avogadro, Amedeo, Italian chemist and physicist. 5-76
 Molecular calculations of, 1-172

Avogadro's law. 1-172; 5-76

Avogadro's number. 1-172; 5-76

Avoirdupois weights. *table,* 10-295

Avro Jetliners, Canadian jet planes. *illus.,* 6-194

Awards. Nobel prize winners in science, 10-299-307
 Science awards for youth, 8-67, 72-74

Axel Heiberg Island, in the Canadian Arctic. Radioisotope-fueled thermoelectric generator in weather station on, *with illus.,* 6-174-75

Axes, geometric. *with diagrams,* 4-425-31
 Ellipses, 8-126-27
 Graphs, use in, *with illus.,* 2-70

Axial bones. *with illus.,* 3-74-79

Axial fans. 2-255

Axillary nodes, lymphatics in armpit. *illus.,* 1-148g

Axis, second neck bone. *with illus.,* 3-76

Axis, earth's. Inclination of, 3-182-83, 185

Axis deer. 8-239, *illus.,* 241

Axolotls. Pets, 7-26

Axons, nerve-cell processes.
 Nature and functions of, *with illus.,* 6-317-18
 See also **Nerve fibers**

Aye-aye, lemur. 9-265

Azacyclonol hydrochloride, synthetic tranquilizer. 5-379

Azimuth, arc of horizon. 1-261
 Determining azimuth of a star, *with diagram,* 6-80

Azo dyes. Development of, 8-186

Aztecs. Calendar, 10-173, *illus.,* 174

B

B-29 airplanes. 6-185, *illus.,* 186

B-36 bombers. *illus.,* 6-186

B battery, in radio. 3-97

B horizon, in soils. 2-17, 18, 22, *illus.,* 17, 25

B.T.U. See **British thermal units**

B-Y, species of bacteria. 9-212

Baade, Walter, German-American astronomer. Stars classified by, 8-50

Babbage, Charles, British mathematician. Calculating devices of, *with illus.,* 9-144

Babbage's hypothesis, of mountain formation. 10-218

Babcock, C. D., American inventor. Development of electron tube, 8-85, 86, 87

Babesia bigemina, sporozoan parasite. Texas cattle fever caused by, 2-66

Babies.
 Balanced diets for, *with table,* 5-273-74
 Gums of newborn, *illus.,* 10-164
 Hair of, 2-178
 Lung test on dead infants, 4-204
 Physical growth, *with illus.,* 8-90-98
 See also **Children**

Babirusas, wild pigs. 10-244

Baboons. 9-258, 260-64, *illus.,* 259

Baby teeth. See **Deciduous teeth**

Babylonia, ancient civilization.
 Algebra, contributions to, 2-68
 Cuneiform writing of, 1-115, *illus.,* 114
 Irrigation in, 8-192
 Mathematics, contributions to, 3-427
 Number system of, 1-150, *illus.,* 151
 Pottery of, 7-396
 Science in, *with illus.,* 1-126-27
 Tile, development of, 7-119

Bacillary dysentery. 4-333

Bacilli, bacteria. *illus.,* 1-301; 3-64, *illus.,* 63
 Bone tuberculosis caused by, 3-84
 See also **Bacteria**

Bacillus typhosus. See **Eberthella typhi**
Bacitracin. 10-128
Back, human. Muscles of, *illus.*, 3-205
Back rest. Bedridden patient, *with illus.*, 10-61
Backbone (vertebral column). *illus.*, 1-148b; *with illus.*, 3-74-77
  Supporting function of, *with diagrams*, 1-286
Backshores, of beaches. *with diagram*, 8-352
Backwash, return motion of ocean waves. 8-349, 351
Backwash ripples. *with illus.*, 8-352-53
Backwashing, method of cleaning rapid sand filters. 2-280
Bacon, Sir Francis, English philosopher and writer. *with illus.*, 3-6-8
Bacon, Roger, English scientist and philosopher. *with illus.*, 2-305-08
  Human flight, proposal for, 6-181
  Lenses, ideas on, 9-82
Bacon. Preparation of, *illus.*, 5-167
Bacteria. *3-63-72
  *Germ-free animals, 7-151-55
  *Pasteur's contribution to bacteriology, 9-71-80
  Acetone produced by, 9-212
  Adaptations of, 6-225
  Agar as culture medium for, *illus.*, 2-207
  Antibiotics used against, 10-127-29
  Bacteriology, founding of, 7-378-85
  Body's defenses against, 7-347-51, *illus.*, 348, 349, *diagrams*, 748, 749
  Carbon bacteria, 2-209
  Chemicals used against, 10-151
  Coliform bacterium, present in water, 2-276
  Commercial value and products of, 1-50
  Cowpeas, partnership with, *illus.*, 10-189
  Dental caries, 5-131
  Fermentation caused by lactic acid bacteria, 4-167; 7-135
  Fish diseases caused by, 8-116
  Food preservation as means of curbing, *with illus.*, 4-153-68
  Forms of, *illus.*, 2-205
  Luminous, 2-183, 185-87
  Mineral bacteria, 2-208
  Nervous diseases caused by, 6-330
  Nitrate bacteria, 2-211
  Nitrogen cycle, bacteria in, 3-318
  Nitrogen fixation by, *with illus.*, 2-209-11
  Nucleic acids synthesized by aid of, 9-386
  Nursing precautions against germs, 10-55-57, 65-66
  Petroleum formation, role in, 4-142
  Rickettsiae and psittacosislike organisms resemble, 3-458
  Seeds attacked by, 5-65, 67
  Sewage purified by, *with illus.*, 5-331-32, 334
  Soil bacteria, 2-16, 23-24, 166-67, 205-11; 10-137
  Streptomycin used against, 7-52, *illus.*, 54; 10-128
  Sulfa drugs used against, 10-127
  Tuberculosis bacteria, *with illus.*, 9-175-78
  Viruses, distinguished from, 1-40; 3-452
  White blood cells defend against, 3-328
  See also **Anthrax; Contagious diseases; Microbes; Tuberculosis;** etc.
Bacterial vaccines. 3-70
Bacteriology. See **Bacteria**
Bacteriolysins, antibodies. 7-349
Bacteriophages, viruses. 3-453, 458, *illus.*, 454
Bactrian camels. 7-331
Bacubirito meteorite, from Mexico. 6-90
Badgers. 8-176-77, *illus.*, 173
  Fur, 7-238
Badlands. 8-11

Baekeland, Leo, Belgian-American chemist (1863–1944). 8-223-24
Baer, Karl Ernst von, Estonian naturalist and embryologist. *with illus.*, 7-161
Baeyer, Adolf von, German organic chemist (1835–1917). From 1875 he was professor of chemistry at Munich, where he founded the New Chemical Institute for the training of organic chemists. He is famous for his work on the synthetic production of the dye indigo. Baeyer received the 1905 Nobel Prize in chemistry for his researches in organic dyes and aromatic hydrocarbons. See also 5-81
  Indigo synthesized by, 8-183
  Phenolic resins studied by, 8-223
Bagasse, sugar-cane fibers. Industrial products from, 7-39
Baggage cars, of railroad trains. 1-186
Bagworms. 3-202
Baikal seals. 7-91
Bailey bridges, portable bridges. *with illus.*, 9-327
Baily, Francis, English astronomer (1774–1844). One of the founders of the Royal Astronomical Society, he revised several star catalogues. Baily first described fully the bright spots (Baily's Beads) seen along the moon's rim immediately before the sun is totally eclipsed. This phenomenon is caused by the light of the disappearing sun shining through the valleys and depressions of the moon's edge. Baily correctly explained this effect as due to irradiation and diffraction.
Baily's beads. 3-135
Bainbridge, Kenneth T., American physicist. 8-420
Bakelite, synthetic resin. 8-223-24
  Buttons made from, 7-210, *illus.*, 211
Baker, Samuel, English explorer. 7-31
Baker, Mount, Washington. Glacial effect on bedrock, *illus.*, 6-138
Baker-Schmidt telescope. *illus.*, 10-226
Bakeries. See **Baking**
Baker's yeast. 3-27
Baking. *Bread, 9-293-99
Baking soda. Experiments and tricks with, *with diagram*, 7-173-74
Baku, U.S.S.R. Oil fields, 4-140-41
Balance, equilibrium. *with illus.*, 7-305-06
  Ear as balancing organ, 4-380-82, 384
  Cerebellum controls, 6-326
  Water animals' hydrostatic organs, *with illus. and diagram*, 1-280-81
Balance, in chemical equations. 2-226-27, 230-31, *diagram*, 226-27
Balance, in physics.
  Parity law of physics and, *with illus.*, 7-108
Balance of nature.
  Man disturbs, 10-190
Balances, weighing devices.
  Equal-arm balances, how to make, *with illus.*, 7-216
  Home laboratory, *with illus.*, 4-227
Balances, torsion.
  Earth's mass determined by, 4-44
  Prospecting with, 7-358-59
Balboa, Vasco Nuñez de, Spanish explorer. 2-365
Bald cypress trees. 4-65; 5-143, *illus.*, 142
Bald eagles. *with illus.*, 6-156
  Flight of, *illus.*, 5-418
Bald-faced hornets. *illus.*, 3-361
Baldness, loss of hair. *with illus.*, 2-180
Baleen whales. 7-186-87
  Feeding methods of, 7-10
Balinese craftsman and dancers. *illus.*, 9-28
Ball-and-socket joints. 3-80, 82, *illus.*, 81

Ball bearings.
Homemade version of, *with illus.,* 7-219
Ball mills, in ore dressing. *with diagram,* 1-372
Ballast, for railway tracks. 1-192
Ballistite, explosive. 8-280
Ballooning. By spiders, 2-263, *illus.,* 262
Balloons. 6-177-81, *illus.,* 176, 178-81
Air-current study, use in, 2-92
Cosmic-ray research, *illus.,* 8-396-97, 399
Helium used in, 3-319
Hydrogen used in, 3-319
Lifting force, 2-41-42
Polyethylene balloon, *illus.,* 2-235
Stratosphere ascents and weather observations, balloons for, 1-235
Telescopes and cameras carried aloft by, *illus.,* 1-21
Weather-observation balloons, 1-251-52; *illus.,* 9-221
World War I, 9-214
Balls. Curved flight of, 2-39
Balsam firs. *illus.,* 1-302
Self-protection, 7-82
Baltic Sea. Salinity of, 6-31
Baltimore orioles. *with illus.,* 6-105
Nesting activities of, *with illus.,* 5-418f
Baluchitherium, genus of prehistoric rhinoceroses. 7-408
Bananas.
Leaves of, *illus.,* 4-72
Vegetative reproduction, 5-62
Band-tailed pigeons. 6-305
Band wheels, of engines. Well drilling, use in, *diagram,* 4-144
Bandages. First aid, 10-15-16, *illus.,* 16-17
Bandai-san, Japanese volcano. 7-338-39
Banded anteaters, marsupials. 7-427
Banded robins. 6-39-40
Bandicoots, marsupials. 7-426
Banding of birds. See Bird banding
Banff National Park, Alberta, Canada.
Rocky Mountain sheep in, *illus.,* 9-275
Bank-and-turn indicators. 6-193, *diagram,* 191
Bank checks. Typewriters used for, 1-275
Bank swallows. *with illus.,* 6-68
Bankfull stage, of streams. 8-12
Banking, aeronautical term. 6-189, *diagram,* 191
Banking, of curve in road. 2-126
Banks, Sir Joseph, English naturalist (1743–1820). He led a scientific expedition to Newfoundland and Labrador in 1766 and accompanied Captain Cook on his first expedition. In the course of Bank's travels he collected numberless specimens of plants and insects, which passed to the British Museum at his death. He was president of the Royal Society from 1778 to 1820.
Banks, ocean. *with illus.,* 6-71
Banshees, U. S. naval jet planes. *illus.,* 9-217
Banting, Sir Frederick Grant, Canadian physiologist (1891–1941). In 1922, with several associates at the University of Toronto, he succeeded in extracting insulin, an internal secretion of the pancreas. It proved to be effective in the treatment of diabetes. In 1923 Banting and J. J. R. McLeod received the Nobel Prize in medicine for the discovery of insulin. Banting was professor of medical research at the University of Toronto from 1923 until his death. See also *illus.,* 9-34-35
Bantu local race. 8-218
Banyan trees. 4-65
Bar, unit of atmospheric pressure. 1-249
Bar graphs. *with illus.,* 2-71
Bar magnets. *with illus.,* 7-164-65; *with illus.,* 8-142-43
Barbaro, Daniello, Venetian nobleman. Camera obscura constructed by, 9-398
Barbary apes. 9-257

Barberries. Leaves and fruits of, *illus.,* 7-77
Rust, wheat-barberry, 3-29
Barbiturates, sedatives. 5-405; 8-408
Alcoholism treated with, 4-409
Barchans, dunes. 7-321-22, *illus.,* 322-23
Barite, mineral. 5-256
Barium (Ba), chemical element. Atomic number, 56; atomic weight, 137.34; melting point, 850° C.; boiling point, 1,140° C.; specific gravity, 3.5. Alkaline-earth metal; soft, silvery white, highly reactive. Discovered by Davy in 1808; name derived from Greek *barys:* "heavy." Found chiefly in the mineral barite, never in its pure state. Prepared by electrolysis of the chloride. Useful in removing oxygen from electron tubes and, alloyed with nickel, in tube filaments; also used in compounds in white paint, rat poison and fireworks. See also 3-174, *illus.,* 175
Uranium, produced by fission from, 9-133, 330
Barium sulfate. X-ray diagnosis, use in, 3-174, *illus.,* 175
Barium titanate. Piezoelectric effects in crystals of, 2-294
Bark, of mature woody stems. 4-69
Trees can be recognized by, *with illus.,* 5-140
Bark beetles, weevils. 3-348
Barkers, devices for removing bark from logs. *illus.,* 4-374b
Barking drums, devices for removing bark from logs. 4-366
Barn-door skates. 4-292
Barn owls. *with illus.,* 6-165-66
Barn swallows. *illus.,* 5-414; *illus.,* 6-67
Barnacles. *with illus.,* 2-242-43
Degenerate forms, 6-284
Barnard, Edward E., American astronomer (1857–1923). He served as astronomer at the Lick and Yerkes observatories and taught practical astronomy at Chicago University. He discovered the 5th, 6th, 7th, 8th and 9th satellites of Jupiter and sixteen comets. Barnard also discovered a star (Barnard's Star) relatively near the earth and made thousands of photographs of the Milky Way, comets and nebulae.
Barnard's star discovered by, 7-225
Comets discovered by, 5-399
Jupiter's satellite V, discovery of, 5-24
Barnard's star. Proper motion of, *with illus.,* 7-224-25
Barographs, recording barometers. 1-249, *illus.,* 247
Barometers. 1-318-19, *with illus.,* 234, *with diagrams,* 247, 249, *diagrams,* 320
Invention and development of, in seventeenth century, *with illus.,* 3-16-17
Principle of, 2-37
See also Climate; Weather
Baroque pearls. 2-202
Barouches, horse-drawn vehicles. *illus.,* 1-105
Barrage balloons. *with illus.,* 6-181
Barred owls. 6-164
Barrier islands. *with illus.,* 8-358
Barrier reefs. 4-135; 6-72, 75, 77, *illus.,* 77; 8-359
Bars, stream deposits of sand and gravel. 8-17
Beaches, *with diagrams,* 8-352
Stream deposits, 8-16
Bars, compound. *with illus.,* 3-415
Bars, steel. Manufacture and uses of, 1-349
Barton, O., American inventor. 2-191
Basal metabolic rate. 10-85-86, 91
Basalt, igneous rock. 2-82; 3-423, *illus.,* 422; *with illus.,* 4-394-96; 9-308
Bascule bridges. 2-340-41, *illus.,* 339
Base, mathematical term. 1-150, 154-57; 2-75, 76
Base-five system, of calculation. 1-155

Base-ten system, of calculation. See **Decimal system**
Base-twelve system, of calculation. See **Duodecimal system**
Base-twenty system, of calculation. 1-156
Base-two system, of calculation. See **Binary system**
Basements. Safety precautions for, 7-190-91, 193
Bases.
  *Acids, bases and salts, 4-336-42
  Acidity of soils neutralized by basic elements, **2** 168-69
  Alkali metals, 3-165
  Dyes, basic, 8-186
  Electrolytes, 2-423
  Reactions of, *with illus.,* 4-231
  Testing ability of, to conduct electricity, *with illus.,* 4-345
Basic components, of alloys. 1-382
Basic English. 1-120
Basidia, spore-producing organs of fungi. *with illus.,* 3-29
Basilar membranes, of ears. 5-122-23; *with illus.,* 7-300
Basilisks, lizards. *with illus.,* 5-201
Basin irrigation. 8-196
Baskers, lizards that bask in the sun. 5-203
Basketball. *illus.,* 10-90
Basking sharks. 4-289
Basophils, white blood cells. 3-328, *illus.,* 329
  See also **White blood cells**
Bass, fish. Sea bass, 4-314, 320
Bassets, dogs. 10-242
Bassoons. Sound production in, 5-218
Basswood. Stem of, *illus.,* 10-164
Bast, strong, woody fiber. *with illus.,* 5-263
Bastille. Storming of, *illus.,* 4-34
Batea, Spanish prospecting implement. 1-370
Bates, Henry W., English naturalist. 8-252
Bathing.
  Dangerous in thunderstorm, 1-404
  Person ill in bed, *with illus.,* 10-61-62, *illus.,* 63
  Safety precautions in bathrooms, 7-194
Bathing beaches. Ruined because of water pollution, 5-328
Batholiths, geologic formations. *with illus.,* 3-421-22
Bathyscaphes (Bathyscaphs), for exploration of ocean depths. *6-74a-d; 9-222-23
  Fishes observed from, 4-99
Bathyspheres, for exploration of ocean depths. 2-191
Bating bath, solution used in processing leather. 7-232
Batok, volcano of Java. *illus.,* 8-297
Bats. *illus.,* 1-300; *with illus.,* 7-14
  Adaptations for feeding, 7-9, 11
  Caves as dwelling places of, *with illus.,* 5-58-59
  Environment, adaption to, 10-139-40
  Hibernation, 5-411
  Humidity affects, 7-7
  Migration of, 9-422, *illus.,* 422-23
  Obstacles in the dark, avoidance of, 1-283; 8-104-05
  Pets, 7-21
"Batswing burners" ("Fishtail burners"). 4-234
Battelle Memorial Institute. 1-88, *illus.,* 89
Batteries, electric. See **Voltaic cells**
Batteries, storage. *with illus.,* 5-95-96; 6-127
  *Solar battery, 7-103-06
  Radio receivers that use, 3-97
  Source of power for dirigibles, 6-178
Batteries of cameras, used in astronomical observation. *illus.,* 1-20
Battery jars. Home laboratory, 4-227, *illus.,* 226
Battleships. See **Submarines**

Bauersfeld, Walter, German optical expert. 2-397-98
Bauhaus (House of Architecture), Dessau, Germany. 8-390; 10-119
Bauhin, Casper, Swiss biologist. 3-375
Baum, William A., American astronomer.
  Galactic velocities measured by, 8-54
Bauxite, ore of aluminum. Smelting of, *with diagram,* 1-381
Bay of Fundy. See **Fundy, Bay of**
Bayer, Johann, German astronomer.
  Contribution to the cataloguing and naming of stars, 6-260
Bayeux tapestry. Halley's comet depicted on, *with illus.,* 5-394
Bayonne (Kill van Kull) Bridge, New York City. *with illus.,* 2-337
Bazookas, antitank weapons. *with illus.,* 9-327, 378
Beach cusps. *with illus.,* 8-353
Beaches.
  *Shoreline changes, 8-348-59
Beaded lizards. See **Helodermatids**
Beadle, George W., American biologist. Bread-mold heredity studied by, 9-385
Beagle, British ship. 7-31, *illus.,* 30
Beagles. 10-242
Beaks, of birds. 5-420
  Adaptations for obtaining food, *with illus.,* 3-236-37
  Parrot's, *with illus.,* 1-285
Beam bridges. 2-334-35
Beam trawls, devices used in sea fishing. 6-16
Beams, construction elements. 2-334
Beams. See **Levers; Walking beams**
Bean mosaic virus. Crystals of, *illus.,* 3-456
Beans.
  Anthracnose of, 8-372, *illus.,* 373
  Diseases of, 8-372
  Geotropism of, *illus.,* 6-218c
  Germination of, *illus.,* 1-38; *with illus.,* 5-66-67
  Hydrotropism of, *illus.,* 6-218c
  Industrial products from various, 7-42-43, 44, *diagram and illus.,* 40-41, 42
  Phototropism of, *illus.,* 6-218c
Bear, research vessel. *illus.,* 6-36
Bear cats. See **Binturongs**
Bearings.
  Ball bearings, homemade version of, *with illus.,* 7-219
Bears. *7-307-17
  Antisocial, 7-12
  Hibernation, 5-411; 7-7
  National parks as sanctuaries for, 9-276
Beating, process of preparing wood fibers for paper-making. *with illus.,* 4-368-69
Beating sheets. Collecting insects with, *with illus.,* 3-154
Beats, sound. 5-126
Beaufort, Sir Francis, British naval officer. 10-297
Beaufort scale. 2-92-93
  Gauging apparent strength of wind, 10-297
Beaumont, William, American surgeon. *with illus.,* 7-372-73
Beauperthuy, Louis-Daniel, French medical researcher. 10-32
Beauty. Mathematics as search for, 1-75
Beavers. *illus.,* 1-300; *with illus.,* 9-1-5
  Family groups, 7-12
  Fur, 7-238
  Tracks in fresh snow, *illus.,* 10-260
Becher, Johann Joachim, German physician and chemist. 3-271-72
Beckman differential thermometers. 3-411

Becquerel, Antoine-César, French physicist (1788–1878). He studied at the Polytechnic School in Paris, served in the army engineer corps and later became a professor of physics at the Museum of Natural History in Paris. Becquerel was one of the founders of electrochemistry. He also carried on researches in atmospheric electricity and the electric conductivity of metals.

Becquerel, Antoine-Henri, French physicist (1852–1908). Like his grandfather Antoine-César Becquerel, Antoine-Henri taught physics at the Museum of Natural History in Paris. For his discovery of radioactivity and his work with uranium and other radioactive substances he shared (with Madame and Pierre Curie) the 1903 Nobel Prize in physics. "Becquerel rays" was the name first given to the rays emitted by a radioactive substance. See also 8-412-13, illus., 403
   Radioactivity of uranium discovered by, 8-403; 9-349

Bedbugs. with illus., 3-260

Bedding planes, surfaces between rock layers. 5-52, illus., 52-53

Bedford oölite. See **Salem limestone**

Bedlam. Origin of term, 9-197

Bedouin Arabs. illus., 6-116

Bedpans. Use of, 10-62-63

Bedrock, rock substratum under soil.
   Bridges, foundation for, 2-342-43
   See also **Outcrops; Rocks**

Beds. Care and comfort of person ill in bed, with illus., 10-59-63, 65, 66, illus., 64, 67

Bee flies. 3-240

Bee hummingbirds. 6-212

Bee larkspurs, plants. 7-242

Bee smokers, devices for calming honeybees. illus., 3-369

Bee veils, protective headgear. 3-370, illus., 369

Beebe, Charles William, American naturalist.
   Bathysphere developed by, 2-191; 9-222

Beech trees. with illus., 5-147
   Buds, illus., 5-140
   Winter buds, illus., 6-58

Beef. Cuts of, with illus., 5-170-71

Beef tapeworms. 2-154

Beehive, cluster of stars in Cancer. 1-332

Beehives. 3-370, 372, illus., 368-69

Beekeeping. 3-370, 372, illus., 368-69, 371

Beers, Clifford W., American reformer. 9-103

Beers. 4-405, 407, with illus., 406

Bees. illus., 1-296; illus., 2-404, 405, 410; *3-367-72, illus., 366
   Bumblebee pollinating hibiscus, 8-frontispiece
   Flies resembling, 3-240
   Lady-slipper orchids, pollination of, illus., 4-127
   Pollen carried by, 7-243, 245-47, illus., 246, 247
   Signaling activities of, with illus., 2-412c

Beeswax. 3-368, 372, illus., 371

Beet sugar. See **Sucrose**

Beetles. illus., 1-296; *3-335-48
   Bombardier beetles, 3-239
   Japanese beetles, 9-196
   Luminous, 2-183

Beets. Diseases of, 8-374

Behavior. *Adaptations of structure and behavior in living things, 3-235-44
 *Animal intelligence, 2-26-29
 *Insect societies, 3-357-72
   Animals
     Ants, 3-359-60, with illus., 393-96
     Birds, with illus., 5-423-25
     Hummingbird moths, illus., 3-201
   Human growth, development in, 8-98-100

Behavior (continued)
   Race, relation to, 8-220
   See also **Mind; Psychology**

Behavior, of minerals. with illus., 5-255-56

Behaviorism. Rise of psychological theory of, 9-52

Beijerinck (Beigerinck), M. W., Dutch scientist. Work on tobacco mosaic disease, 3-451-52

Beisa oryxes, antelopes. 8-383, 384, illus., 381

Beisas, African antelopes. illus., 8-385

Belgium.
   Contributions to science, 1600–1765, 3-270
   Smog damage at Liége (1930), 3-352-53

Bell, Alexander Graham, Scottish-American inventor. with illus., 5-242-44; 9-216
   Graphophone of, 7-365
   Hydrofoil boat of, 4-6
   Telephone, invention of, with illus., 2-386-88

Bell, Sir Charles, Scottish anatomist (1774–1842), who discovered the distinction between sensory and motor nerves. He held the chair of anatomy and surgery in the London College of Surgeons from 1824 to 1836; from 1836 until his death he was professor of surgery in the University of Edinburgh. See also 9-48

Bell, Eric T., American mathematician. 4-428

Bell, Lawrence D., American aeronautical designer.
   X-series experimental rocket planes, 9-219

Bell buoys. 5-71, illus., 69

Bell Telephone Company. Founding of, 2-388

Bell Telephone Laboratories.
   Electronic computers built by, 9-145
   Radio-command guidance system of, 8-128-30, 131, illus., 125, 129
   Solar battery development, 7-103, illus., 105

Bellows. Ancient use ot, 9-60
   Chest and lungs compared with, 4-205, illus., 204

Bellows cameras. 9-404-05, illus., 404

Bells. Sound production in, 5-218-19

Belly. See **Abdomen**

Belostomatids, family of true bugs. with illus., 3-263-64

Belted kingfishers. with illus., 6-310

Belts, in machinery.
   Homemade verisions of, with illus., 7-218-19

Belts of Jupiter. with illus., 5-22-23

Beltsville, Maryland. Meat research project at, 5-169

Bendix-Friez aerovanes. See **Aerovanes**

"Bends." See **Caisson disease**

Benedict, Aaron, American businessman. 7-209

Benedict, Ruth, American anthropologist. 9-27

Bengal system of hydroponics. 8-36

Benguela Current, oceanic current. 6-236, map, 232-33

Benham disks. with illus., 7-289-90

Benign tumors. 8-265

Bennett, James Gordon, American editor. 7-31

Benthonic organisms. 6-35, illus., 34

Benthoscopes, for exploration of ocean depths. 2-191

Bentley, Wilson, American meteorologist, 2-354

Bentonite, sedimentary rock. 7-326

Benz, Karl, German inventor. Automobile of, 2-130

Benzedrine, stimulant. 5-403

Benzene.
   Coal tar yields, with illus., 1-419
   Discovery of structure of, with illus., 5-79-80
   Molecule of, illus., 3-246; 7-274

Benzol, chemical mixture.
   Bone marrow poisoned by, 3-74
   See also **Benzene**

Berenice, mythological figure linked with constellation legend. 1-331-32

Berger, Hans, German psychiatrist. 9-103

Bergius hydrogenation process. *with illus.,* 1-418

Bergman, Tobern Olof, Swedish chemist. Early steel research, 1-339

Bergmann's rule, concerning body size. 8-219

Bergschrunds, deep crevasses in glaciers. 9-168

Beriberi, vitamin-deficiency disease. 5-39, 41

Berkelium (Bk), chemical element. Atomic number, 97; atomic weight, 249(?). Actinide metal with properties similar to terbium. Discovered in 1950 by Seaborg, Thompson and Ghiorso at the University of California, Berkeley, California; named after Berkeley. Produced by irradiation of americium-241 with helium ions in the Berkeley 60-inch cyclotron; half life, 4.8 hours.

Berliner, Emile. Born in Hanover, Germany, 1851; died 1929. Educated in Germany, he came to the United States in 1870. His invention of the microphone and other devices vastly improved telephone transmission. He also invented the gramophone, an apparatus for reproducing sound, which is the basis of all disc-playing phonographs.

Berms, backshores of beaches. *with diagrams,* 8-352

Bernard, Claude, French physiologist. 7-373

Bernoulli, Daniel, Swiss physicist. 6-248

Bernoulli's principle. *with illus.,* 2-35-36, *illus.,* 39; 10-231

Beroë rufescens, luminous ctenophore. *illus.,* 2-184

Berries, fleshy fruits. 4-129, *illus.,* 130

Berthelot, Pierre-Eugène-Marcelin, French chemist and statesman (1827–1907). A professor of organic chemistry at the College of France, he also served as senator, inspector general of higher education and minister of public instruction and foreign affairs. He investigated heat phenomena and is considered the founder of the science of thermochemistry. He also conducted researches in explosives and dyestuffs. See also 5-83

Berthollet, Claude-Louis, French chemist (1748–1822). He was one of the founders of the Polytechnic School in Paris and taught chemistry there. Principally known as the inventor of a process for the bleaching of vegetable substances by means of chlorine, he is also credited as a founder of the theory of chemical affinity. With Lavoisier, he devised a system of chemical nomenclature.

Beryllium (Be), chemical element. Atomic number, 4; atomic weight, 9.0122; melting point, about 1,278° C.; boiling point, 2,970° C.; specific gravity, 1.8. Hard alkaline-earth metal; alloys strong, light and corrosion-resistant. First isolated in 1828; name derived from Latin *beryllus:* "beryl"; found in many minerals, most of them rare, with beryl the chief source. Prepared by electrolysis of the double fluoride. Use of pure metal confined largely to X-ray tube windows and as source of neutrons; generally used in alloys with common metals, especially copper. See also *with illus.,* 3-170-71

Berzelius, Joens Jakob, Swedish chemist. *with illus.,* 5-77-78; 7-264

Bessel, Friedrich Wilhelm, Prussian astronomer. 6-389

Bessemer, Sir Henry. Born in Hertfordshire, England, 1813; died in London, 1898. During his early youth he received an excellent mechanical training in his father's type foundry. The most important of his many inventions is the Bessemer process for making steel. The process was discovered during the course of the inventor's experiments to improve the quality of iron for projectiles. The invention increased the output of cheap steel tremendously. See also 6-384

Bessemer converters. Steel manufacture, *with illus.,* 1-344, *diagram,* 348c; *with illus.,* 6-384

Bessemer process, of steelmaking. 1-340, *with illus.,* 344, *diagram,* 348c; *with illus.,* 6-384

Best, Charles H., Canadian physiologist and physician (born 1899). He taught at the University of Toronto and became the head of its medical research laboratories. In 1922 he isolated (with F. G. Banting) the internal secretion known as insulin, which proved to be invaluable in the treatment of diabetes. During World War II he helped inaugurate the project of providing dried human serum for military use. See also *with illus.,* 9-34-35

Best Friend of Charleston, early locomotive. *with illus.,* 1-181; 6-379

Bestiaries, medieval books on animals. *with illus.,* 2-309

Beta particles (rays). 9-349

Geiger-Mueller counter, use in detecting, *with illus.,* 9-343

Mass measurements of, 4-216

Medical uses of, 10-98

Parity law of physics violated by, 7-110

Positrons in, 1-313

Preserving food by, *with illus.,* 4-168

Radiation thickness gauges use beta particles, *with illus.,* 9-43

Radioactive elements that yield, 8-416; 9-128

Beta-Taurids, meteor shower. *table,* 6-97

Betatrons, X-ray machines. *with diagram,* 7-148, 149

Betatrons, atom smashers. 9-247

Relativistic speed of particles in beams of, 4-216-17

Betelgeuse, star in Orion. 1-335

Bethe, Hans A., German-born American physicist. 9-224

Bevatron, atom smasher. 9-249, *illus.,* facing 248

Beverages. *Alcoholic beverages, 4-405-14

Bewick's wrens. 6-45

Bible.

Gutenberg Bible, 1-197

Petroleum ("pitch") mentioned, 4-140

Water supply referred to in, 2-271

Bible paper. 4-378

Biceps brachii, upper-arm muscle. 3-208-09, *illus.,* 204, 206

Biceps femoris, thigh muscle. *illus.,* 3-205, 213

Biceps muscles. *illus.,* 1-148c; 3-203, 208-09, *illus.,* 204, 205, 206, 213

Bichat, Marie François, French anatomist and physiologist (1771–1802); founder of histology, the science of minute anatomy. He studied medicine in Lyons and Paris and became a successful lecturer on anatomy, experimental physiology and surgery. In 1800 he was appointed physician of the Hôtel-Dieu in Paris and began his work in pathology and therapeutics. His principal published works are his *General Anatomy* and his *Descriptive Anatomy,* finished after his death. See also 7-387

Bichirs, fishes. 4-95

Bicuspid valve of heart. 3-383

Bicuspids (premolars), teeth. 5-129, *table,* 130, *illus.,* 132

Bicycles. Invention and development of, 6-380

Biela's comet. 5-393; 6-96

Bielids (Andromedids), meteor shower. *table,* 6-97

Biennials, plants. 2-420; 6-57

"Big Bertha" cameras. 9-406

Big Dipper, group of stars in Ursa Major. 1-324, 325

Distances in heavens estimated by using Big Dipper as standard, *with diagram,* 6-79

Big Inch, pipeline. 4-147

Big Springs, Nebraska. Tornado near, *illus.,* 2-97

Bighorns. See Rocky Mountain sheep

Bikini Atoll, Marshall Islands.

Drilling exploration in, 6-77

Bikini Atoll (continued)
Nuclear tests at, 9-352, 353
Bilateral symmetry. Flowers, 4-122, illus., 123
Bile, liver secretion. 4-328
Production of, 5-13-15
Bile duct, common. illus., 1-148d
Pancreas, position relative to, illus., 5-13
Bile pigments. See Bilirubin; Biliverdin
Bile salts. 5-14
Bilirubin, bile pigment. 5-13, 14
Biliverdin, bile pigment. 5-13, 14
Billet mills. 1-348-49, diagram, 348d
Billets. Rolled steel shapes, 1-347-49, diagrams, 348d
Bills, bird. See Beaks
Bimetallic thermometers. 3-415
Bimetallic thermostats. with illus., 2-253
Binaries, double stars. 7-45-46
Binary system, of calculation. 1-155-56; with diagram, 9-146-47
Mathematical recreations involving, with diagrams, 4-448-49
Binding, of books. See **Bookbinding**
Binet, Alfred, French psychologist. 9-54-55
Intelligence tests, 9-198
Binet-Simon intelligence test. 9-54-55, 198
Binocular microscopes. 9-88, 91, illus., 89
Binocular vision. Man, 7-296
Binoculars. Observing the sky with, 6-79
Binomial nomenclature, two-term naming of living things. 1-288
Binomial series. 2-79-80, illus., 78, 79
Binturongs (bear cats). with illus., 8-246
Biochemical-oxygen demand, sanitary engineer's measure of wastes. 5-329, 330, 332
Biochemistry.
*Blood, 3-325-34
*Carbohydrates in nutrition, 4-76-79
*Glands, functioning of, 5-8-19
*Soil fertility, 2-163-72
Breathing processes, 4-200-01, 206, illus., 201-02
Cancer research, 8-272
Life, chemical nature and origin of, with diagram, 9-383-86
Metabolic processes duplicated in the laboratory, 8-190
Muscular exercise, chemistry of, 3-205-07
Photosynthesis and plant respiration, 3-45-48, illus., 42a-d
Protoplasm, chemical composition and activities of, 2-3-7, 10-13
Bioelectricity. *2-421-28
Biogenetic law. 8-262
Biogeography, geographic study of plant and animal populations. See **Ecology; Environment**
Biological purification, of sewage. 5-331-32, illus., 331, 332, 334
Biological warfare. Insects, used against, 2-411
Biologists. See **Biology; Botany; Zoology;** also names of individual biologists
Biology.
*Adaptations of plants and animals, 3-235-44
*Bioelectricity, 2-421-28
*Bioluminescence, 2-182-91
*Cells, 2-1-14, 287-92
*Classification of animals and plants, 1-287-306
*Communities of plants and animals, 10-181-90
*Evolution, 6-269-85
*Habitats of animals and plants, 10-135-42
*Nature of life, 1-37-44
*Seasonal changes and life, 5-408-13
*Senses, human, 7-291-306

Biology (continued)
*Time scale of evolutionary history, 6-369-74
Cells of animals and plants, with illus., 7-156-61
Colloids in living matter, 5-301
Development
Antiquity, 1-138, illus., 136
Nineteenth century, with illus., 8-251-64
Fossil study, with illus., 4-386-94
Marine biology, 6-29, 32-33, 35-36, illus., 33-34
Mathematics and, 1-78
Oldest things living, 2-110
Origin of life, research and theory concerning, with diagrams, 9-383-86
Petroleum formed from dead sea organisms, 4-142
Sex, see Reproduction
See also **Animals; Evolution; Fossils; Heredity; Life; Old age; Paleontology; Plants**
Bioluminescence. *2-182-91
Fishes, 4-103
See also **Luminescence.**
Biometry. Galton's contributions to, 8-264
Bionics. The study of the brain, nerves and senses and of memory, instinct and communication in animals, and the application of such research to the design of electronic and electrical equipment. Bionics deals specifically with (1) the study of the animals themselves; (2) the construction and use of instruments designed to aid in this research; and (3) the development of man-made devices based on the principles underlying the observed animal behavior. Devices such as radar, sonar, computers and sensing instruments have been improved as a result of researches in bionics.
Bionomics. See **Ecology**
Biophysics, physics of living things. *Animal mechanisms, 1-277-86
*Muscles of the human body, 3-203-13
Breathing mechanisms, 4-205-06, illus., 204
Biopsy, surgical diagnostic technique. Cancer, 8-270
Biot, Jean-Baptiste, French mathematician, physicist and astronomer (1774–1862). He was a professor of physics at the College of France. He demonstrated that meteorites were bodies coming from outer space. He investigated the properties of polarized light and is known as the founder of saccharimetry (the science of sugar analysis by means of polarized light).
Work on optical activity of substances, 9-71
Biotin, B vitamin. 5-43-44
Bipolar cells, of eye. 7-293, illus., 292
Birch trees. with illus., 5-144-45
Bark, illus., 5-140
Bird banding. with illus., 5-418d; 9-418, 420, illus., 278, 421
Bird baths. Birds attracted by, with illus., 6-346
Bird blinds. with illus., 10-258-59
Bird calls.
Hummingbirds, 6-214
Use of, for bird watching, 10-257-58
Bird flight. with illus., 5-416-19
Bird houses. Birds attracted by, 6-346, 348-49
Bird migration. 5-423-24; with illus., 9-415-21
Theory of, in Middle Ages, 2-310
Bird watching. with illus., 10-256-59
Bird-wing butterflies. 3-198
Birds. *5-414-26
*Allies of man, 6-341-49
*Attracting birds to house and garden, 6-341-49
*Common birds, 6-37-48, 60-68, 98-108, 152-66, 209-18, 304-10, 331-40, 394-408
*Adaptation to environment, 10-136, 137, 138-39, illus., 141

Birds (*continued*)
  Adaptations, for survival, 3-242, *with illus.*, 236-37, *illus.*, 239, 242-43
  Banding. See **Bird banding**
  Cave-dwelling species, 5-59
  Classification of, 1-298-99; 5-425-26
  Ear and jaw structure. *with illus.*, 4-381
  Fossil birds, *illus.*, 6-373, 374
  Heart of, *with illus.*, 1-278
  Jaws of, *with illus.*, 1-285
  Legs, *with illus.*, 1-284
  Malaria, birds subject to, 10-33
  Migrations of, *with illus.*, 9-415-21
    See also **Bird migration**
  Muscles, *with illus.*, 1-284-85; 10-138-39
  Perching effected by leg tendon, *with illus.*, 1-284
  Pets, 7-17-18, 23, *illus.*, 22
  Photography of, 6-313
  Seasonal changes affect, *with illus.*, 5-413
  Seeds dispersed by, 5-5
  Voice, production of, *with illus.*, 1-282-83
  Whooping cranes, *illus.*, 9-266
  Wings, *with illus.*, 1-284-85
  Wings suggested means of human flight, 6-181
  Zoo aviary, *illus.*, 10-161
  See also names of birds
Bird's-nest fungi. 3-30, *illus.*, 31
Birds of paradise.
  Courtship behavior of, *with illus.*, 5-418c
Birds of prey. *6-152-66
Birdseye, Clarence, pioneer of food-freezing industry. 4-162
Biremes, ships. *illus.*, 6-28
Birth. Human growth before and after, 8-93-94
Biscuit guns. For signaling planes, 6-198
Bismuth (Bi), chemical element. Atomic number, 83; atomic weight, 208.980; melting point, 271.3° C.; boiling point, 1,560° C.; specific gravity, 9.747. White, brittle, crystalline metal, most diamagnetic substance known. Distinguished from lead by Claude Geoffroy in 1753; name derived from German *weisse Masse*: "white mass," later *Wismuth*. It is found in uncombined form. Common ore is bismuthinite, a sulfide, from which it is extracted by melting out the free metal; also recovered as a by-product in lead smelting. Produces low-melting alloys, used for fuses and automatic sprinkler systems. Also employed in X-ray examinations, as a wound dressing and in the treatment of syphilis.
Bison. 9-268-69, *illus.*, 271; **10**-248, *illus.*, 243
  Conservation of, 9-270
  Domestication, attempted, 9-270
  Migrations of, 9-422
Bisque ware. 7-402
Bissextile years. 10-174
Bits, cutting tools. Well drilling, use in, 4-145, *diagram*, 144
Bitterns, birds. 6-398
Bitumen. Reaction to light, 9-399
Bituminous coal, soft coal. 1-408
  See also **Coal**
Bituminous materials. Road surfaces of, 3-301, *illus.*, 298c-d
Bituminous Research, Inc. 1-89
Biuret reaction, test for protein. 7-136
Bivalves. See **Lamellibranchs**
Bjerknes, Jakob Aall Bonnevie, Norwegian meteorologist (1897–   ). 9-223
Black. 7-284
  Printing color, 1-213
Black, Davidson, Canadian anatomist. 9-23

Black, Joseph, Scottish scientist. Research on carbon dioxide, *with illus.*, 4-353-54
Black-and-white warblers, birds. *illus.*, 6-60
Black apes. 9-257-58
Black bears. 7-308, 313, 315, *illus.*, 314
Black-bellied plovers. *with illus.*, 6-408
Black-billed cuckoos. 6-306, 308
Black birch trees. 5-145
Black brants, geese. 6-400
  Migration route of, *illus.*, 5-418d
Black bread mold. 3-27, *with illus.*, 26, *illus.*, 23
Black-bulb thermometers, solar-heat instruments. 1-247
Black-capped chickadees. *illus.*, 6-40
Black cherry trees. 5-149
Black Death. See **Plague**
Black ducks. 6-402
"Black earth." See **Chernozem soils**
Black earwigs. 3-152
Black flies. 3-287, 289
Black gum trees. 5-146; *illus.*, 10-182
Black honey ants. 3-364
"Black liquor," liquid removed from cooked wood pulp. 4-367
Black locust trees. 5-148
  Leaves of, *illus.*, 4-72
Black oak trees. *with illus.*, 5-147
Black powder, explosive. Manufacture of, *illus.*, 8-283
Black raspberries. Runners of, *illus.*, 4-67
Black rhinoceroses. 7-414, *illus.*, 415
Black River, New York State. *illus.*, 6-414
Black salamanders, amphibians. 5-161
Black skimmers. 6-397
Black snakes, venomous Australian snakes. 5-363, *illus.*, 354
Black tegus (tejus), lizards. 5-199
Black widow spiders. 2-265-66, *illus.*, 267
Blackberries. *illus.*, 4-129
Blackbirds. *with illus.*, 6-104-05
Blackbucks, antelopes. 8-387
Blackett, Patrick M. S., English physicist. Earth's magnetic field, explanation of, 4-176
Blackleg, disease of potato. 8-371
Blackouts, communication. Radio, 1-240
Bladder, air or swim. See **Air bladder**
Bladder, gall. See **Gall bladder**
Bladder, urinary. *illus.*, 1-148d-e
Bladder ferns. *illus.*, 3-188
Bladder wracks, marine algae. *illus.*, 6-225
Blades. Reaction turbines, 5-307
Blakeslee, Albert F., American chemist. 9-291
Blanching.
  Foodstuffs blanched before canning, 4-157
  Foodstuffs blanched before freezing, 4-162
Blankets. Dynel fiber, *illus.*, 2-233
Blankets, in printing. *with diagram*, 1-211-12
Blast cells, cells that give rise to specialized tissues. 8-31
Blast effects, of nuclear bombs. 9-392-93
Blast furnaces.
  Iron-ore smelting, *with illus.*, 1-341-43, *diagram*, 348c
  Nonferrous smelting, 1-377, *with diagram*, 379
Blasting. *8-273-87
  Coal mining, 1-412
  Explosives used in, 8-276
  Granite requires, 2-84
  Marble quarried by, 2-87
Blasting caps, explosives. Filling of, *illus.*, 8-278
Blasting gelatin. 8-276, 278
Blastula, stage in animal development. *illus.*, 2-13
Blattaria, order of insects. 2-412; *with illus.*, 3-147-49

Bleaching.
  Silk, 5-184
  Wood fibers for papermaking, bleaching of, 4-368
Bleeders' disease. See **Hemophilia**
Bleeding. 3-392
  First aid for, *with illus.,* 10-5-7
  Internal, studied with radioisotopes, 10-99
  Urine volume lessened after, 5-12
Bleeding-heart doves. 6-304
Blenders, used in breadmaking. *with illus.,* 9-295-96
Blepharisma, genus of protozoans. 2-66
Blériot, Louis, French aviator. 9-216-18
  Early flying machine of, 6-183, *illus.,* 184
Blights.
  Chestnut blight, 5-147
  Plants attacked by, 3-25
  Potato crop, 8-370
Blimps, nonrigid dirigibles. 6-179, 181
  World War I, 9-214, 215
Blimps, underwater, type of camera. *illus.,* 10-167
Blind plane landings. 6-198, 200
Blind snakes. *with illus.,* 5-356-57
Blind spot, in field of vision. *with illus.,* 7-293-94
Blindfishes. 5-59
Blindness.
  Deep-sea animals, 10-142
  Reading aid for blind, *illus.,* 10-168
  Ultrasonic walking cane for the blind, 8-109-10
Blinds, places of concealment.
  Animal photography, 6-312
  Bird blinds, *with illus.,* 10-258-59
Bliss Dam. *illus.,* 8-316d
Blister beetles. 3-348
Blister copper, impure molten copper. *with diagram,* 1-378
Blizzards. 2-355
Block and tackle. Combination of pulleys, *with illus.,* 3-62; 7-217
  Well drilling, use in, *diagram,* 4-144
Block pavements. *with illus.,* 3-302
Block signal systems. 1-192
Blocklike (nutlike) subsoils. *with illus.,* 2-19
Blood. *3-325-34
  *Circulation, 3-381-92
  Body's defenses, blood as part of, 7-348-49, 350-51
  Bone and, 3-73-74, 84
  Calcium, regulation of, 5-18
  Circulation
    Discovery of, *with illus.,* 3-10-12
    Increased during muscular exercise, 10-87
  Clotting due to colloids, 5-301
  Distribution of, altered during sleep, 6-147
  Filtered by liver, 5-15
  Insect blood and circulation, 2-405
  Kidneys regulate composition and volume of, 5-11
  Muscular exercise, role in, 3-206, 207
  Pumping of, *with illus.,* 1-277-79
  Respiration, function in, 4-200-01, 204, 206-07, *illus.,* 202
  Skin supply, 2-176
  Spleen as blood-forming organ, 5-10
  Transfusion, storage and breakdown of, 9-35-36
Blood banks. 3-334
Blood cells. *with illus.,* 3-326-29, 330-34
  Body's defenses, blood cells as part of, *with illus.,* 7-348
  Glands as source of, 5-10
  See also **Red blood cells; White blood cells**
Blood clotting (coagulation). 3-332, *with illus.,* 329-30
  Body's defenses, role in, 7-348

Blood clotting (Coagulation) *(continued)*
  Colloidal phenomenon, 5-301
  Role of vitamin K in, 5-48-49
Blood counts.
  Platelet count, 3-329
  Red-cell count, *with illus.,* 3-327
  White-cell count, 3-328, 329
Blood diseases. *with illus.,* 3-330-32
Blood fractioning. Development of, 9-36
Blood groups. *with table,* 3-332-34
  Race, importance in study of, 8-214
Blood plasma. 3-325-26, 334
Blood platelets. 3-331-32, *with illus.,* 329
Blood poisoning. Bacteria that cause, *illus.,* 9-73
  Pyemia due to clots in blood vessels, 3-332
Blood pressure. *with illus.,* 3-387-88
  Development in human being, 8-95-96
  Hypertension and hypotension, 3-392
  Lowered during sleep, *chart,* 6-146, 147
  Pituitary gland affects, 5-17
Blood rains and snows. 7-139
Blood serum.
  Defense against disease, 8-365
Blood transfusions. *with illus.,* 3-332-34
  Blood volume determined with radioisotopes, 10-99
  Development of use of, 9-35-36
Blood types. Discovery of, 9-35
  See also **Blood groups**
Blood vessels.
  Clots obstructing, 3-332, *illus.,* 331
  Diseases of, effect on nervous system, 6-330
  Man's, *illus.,* 1-148e-f
  Respiration, role in, 4-204, 206-07, *illus.,* 202
Blood volume (quantity in body).
  Kidneys help control, 5-11-12
  Measured with radioisotopes, 10-99
Bloodworms, midge larvae. 3-289
Blooming mills. 1-347-49, *diagram,* 348d
Blooms. Rolled steel shapes, 1-347-49, *diagram,* 348d
Blow molding. Plastics, *with diagram,* 8-231
Blower fans. 2-255
Blowflies. 3-292, *illus.,* 283
  Head, *illus.,* 2-404
Blowing, glass. See **Glass blowing**
Blowouts, depressions blown out by wind. 7-323, *illus.,* 324
"Blue babies." 8-33
Blue crabs. 2-240, *illus.,* 236
  Migration of, 9-430
Blue gas, fuel. *with illus.,* 1-418
Blue geese. 6-400
Blue-gray gnatcatchers. 6-44
Blue-green algae. 3-214-15, *illus.,* 215-16
  Lichens formed by combination of fungi and, *with illus.,* 3-32
Blue Grotto, sea cave at Capri. *with illus.,* 5-57
Blue ground, diamond-bearing soil. 4-253, *illus.,* 252
Blue grouse. 6-337
Blue-headed vireos. 6-64
Blue heat hazes. 3-356
Blue herons. *illus.,* 6-398
Blue jays. *illus.,* 6-102
Blue molds. *with illus.,* 3-27
"Blue powder" (zinc dust). 1-380
Blue sharks. 4-288
Blue whales. *illus.,* 7-184
  Migration of, 9-424
  Size, 7-1
Bluebells. Adaptations for seed dispersal, 5-2
Blueberries. *illus.,* 1-305
Bluebirds. 6-38, *illus.,* 39

Bluefish. 4-320, illus., 94
    Migration of, 9-427
Blueprints. Microfilming, 10-74
Bluets. Flowers of, illus., 7-241
Blumenbach, Johann Friedrich, German scientist.
    Classification of races, 8-213
Boas, Franz, American anthropologist. with illus.,
    9-26-27
Boas, snakes. 5-357, illus., 356
    Adaptation for obtaining food, 3-237
    Cook's tree boa, with illus., 5-354d
Boats. *4-106-18
    Collisions as result of decreased water pressure, with
        illus., 2-36
    Dories, 6-23
    Hydrofoils, with illus., 4-5-8
    "Mosquito boats," illus., 9-69
    See also Ships
Bobcats. 8-212
Bobolinks. 6-105
Bobwhites, birds. with illus., 5-418d; 6-333, illus., 338
Boccaccio, Giovanni, Italian writer. 2-361
Bode, Johann Elert, German astronomer. 3-158, with
    illus., 159
Bode's law. with table, 3-158
Bodies, automobile. 2-144
Bodo, genus of one-celled animals. 2-63
Body.
    *Alcoholic beverages and their effects on body,
        4-405-14
    *Allergies, 4-257-64
    *Basic units, 1-143-48
    *Bones, 3-73-84
    *Defenses of, 7-346-53
    *Glands, 5-8-19
    *Growth, development and decline, 8-90-102
    *Keeping fit, 10-75-84
    *Muscles, 3-203-13
    *Reproduction, human, 8-19-33
    *Respiratory system, 4-200-09
    *Senses, 4-379-85; 7-291-306
    *Skin, hair and nails, 2-173-81
    *Smoking and its effects on the body, 5-343-50
    *Systems, 1-148a-h
    Acceleration affects, 10-48
    Atmosphere's effects on, 1-231, 232, 234-35
    Movements during sleep, with diagram, 6-145-46
    See also Anatomy; Exercise; Glands; Life; Nutrition;
        Physiology; Posture of the body; Senses
Body, of stomach. 4-324
Body wall. Development in unborn human young, 8-28
Boehi system, for preserving food. 4-164-65
Boehler, Lorenz, Austrian physician. 9-31
Boeing Bomarc, U.S. Air Force pilotless interceptor. 7-72
Boeing Company.
    Hydrofoil development, 4-8
    Jet-plane development, 7-73-74
Boeing 707, United States jet liner. 7-73-74; 9-219
Boerhaave, Hermann, Dutch physician. Work in physi-
    ology, 3-379
Bogoslof Island, islet produced by volcanic action. 8-303
Bogs.
    Coal formed from ancient peat bogs, with illus.,
        1-406-07
    Distribution of, 7-66
    Peat bogs laid down in Carboniferous period, illus.,
        3-180
    Soil development in swamps and bogs, 2-20, 23
Bohemian waxwings, birds. 6-65; 9-421
Bohr, Niels, Danish physicist (born 1885). He was pro-
    fessor of theoretical physics at the University of Copen-

Bohr, Niels (continued)
hagen and helped establish the Institute of Theoretical
Physics at Copenhagen, becoming its first head. Bohr
adapted Planck's quantum theory to the problem of
atomic structure. For this work, which became the basis
of modern nuclear physics, he received the 1922 Nobel
Prize in physics.
    Atom theory, 8-417
    Atomic fission, work on, 9-330
    Quantum theory, development of, 7-205
Boilers, for heating systems. 4-13, diagrams, 12
Boilers, for steam engines. with illus., 4-82-83
    High-pressure, in modern steam turbines, 5-308
    Locomotives, 1-186, illus., 185
    Ships, 4-111, 114
Boiling points. 3-418
    Molecular behavior at, with diagrams, 1-168-69
    Petroleum refining and, 4-147-48
    Solutions, 4-301
Boils.
    Bacteria that cause, illus., 3-71
    Bodily reaction to infection, 7-348
Bolides, meteors. illus., 6-87
Bolitophila luminosa, luminous larva. 2-183
Bolivia. Lake Titicaca, illus., 6-115
Boll weevils. See Weevils
Bologna stone, mineral. 5-256
Bolometers, electrical thermometers.
    Invented by Langley, to detect infrared rays, 7-201
Bolton, J. G., Australian physicist. 9-210
Bolton, Werner von, Russian chemist.
    Electric-lighting, experiments, 4-238
Bolus, ball of food that enters stomach. with illus.,
    4-323
Bolyai, János, Hungarian mathematician (1802-60). 9-
    282
    Geometry of, with diagrams, 4-439-41
Bomb (combustion) calorimeters. with illus., 3-414
Bombardier beetles. 3-239, 337
Bombers, planes. with illus., 6-185-86
    See also World War I; World War II
Bombs.
    *Nuclear-bomb precautions, 9-391-96
    Atomic, illus., 9-122
    Atomic and hydrogen, with illus., 9-132-39
    Digester gas used in, 5-333
Bombycillidae, family of birds. 6-65-66
Bombyx mori, silkworm moth. with illus., 5-173-76, 179
Bond, George P., American astronomer. 6-387
Bond paper. 4-378
Bonding, of atoms. Carbon, with illus., 4-274
Bone buttons. 7-213
Bone marrow. Blood cells formed in, 3-74, 84, 326,
    327, 329, 331
Bones. *3-73-84
    Aging, effect on, 8-80, 82
    Dislocations of bones, first aid for, 10-11-12
    Ear, 5-122, 123, illus., 123
    Fossil remains, 1-384
    Fractures
        First aid for, with illus., 10-11
        Healing of, illus., 7-352
    Human growth or aging, effect on, 8-96, 100
    Man's skeleton, illus., 1-148b
    Muscles and ligaments hold bones together, 3-210,
        211-12
    Tumors caused by strontium 90, 9-355
    Vertebrate skulls and skeletons, with illus. and dia-
        grams, 1-285-86
    X-ray photographs show, 7-143, illus., 144
    See also Muscles; Skeleton

Bongos, antelopes. 8-379

Bonitos, fish. 4-315

Bonner Durchmusterung (Bonn Catalogue), catalogue of stars. 6-389

Bonnethead sharks. illus., 4-289

Bonneville, Lake, Utah. 7-64

Bonney, Thomas George, English geologist. Description of river sources, 10-27

Bonpland, Aimé-Jacques-Alexandre, French naturalist. 7-30; 8-252

Bony fishes. See Osteichthyes

Book lungs. In arachnids, 2-261

Book of Hours, medieval manuscript. February depicted, illus., 10-177

Book of the Dead. illus., 1-127

Book paper. 4-378

Bookbinding. 1-214

Bookkeeping. Machines for, 9-144

Boomslangs, snakes. 5-361

Booster rockets. illus., 10-52-53

Boötes (Herdsman), constellation. 1-331, 332

Bora, a wind of the Adriatic. 2-94

Boranes, chemical compounds. 10-4

Borazon, a synthetic compound of boron and nitrogen. 4-273

Bordeaux mixture.
    Plant diseases treated with, 3-25-26; 8-370, 374-75

Borden, Gail, originator of condensed milk. 4-167

Border-strip irrigation. 8-196

Bordered plant bugs. 3-259

Borelli, Giovanni Alfonso, Italian physiologist, physicist and astronomer. 3-13-14, 265

Borers, insects.
    Cane-borers, illus., 9-196
    Peach-tree borers, illus., 9-195
    Raspberry cane-borers, 9-196

Bores, tidal currents. 6-205

Boring, tooling operation. with illus., 10-109-10
    See also Drilling

Boron (B), chemical element. Atomic number, 5; atomic weight, 10.811; melting point, 2,300° C.; boiling point, sublimes at 2,550° C.; specific gravity, crystals: 2.34, amorphous: 2.37. A nonmetal; acts as both acid and base. Discovered in 1808 by Davy and by Gay-Lussac and Thenard. Name derived from Persian burah. Never occurs free in nature, but is found as orthoboric acid, usually in volcanic spring waters, and as borates in borax and colemanite. Obtained by heating the trioxide with magnesium powder. Pure element has little commercial value, but certain compounds are widely used. Boric acid is mild antiseptic; borax serves as water softener and as cleansing flux in welding.
    Electron arrangement, with illus., 3-247
    Fuel, use as, illus., 1-92a
    Occurrence of boron in the sea, 6-31
    Solar battery, use in, with illus., 7-103-06

Boron carbide. Rods of, used in nuclear reactors, illus., 9-138b

Boss, Lewis, American astronomer. 7-228

Boston, Massachusetts. Fish pier at, illus., 6-15
    Water supply of, 2-275

Bosumtwi, Lake, in Ghana, Africa. Meteorite crater? 6-92

Botanists. See Biology; Botany; also names of biologists

Botany. *1-45-50
    *Adaptations, 3-235-44; 6-219-28
    *Algae, 3-214-24
    *Amateur botany, 10-203-12
    *Bacteria, 3-63-72
    *Bioluminescence, 2-182-91

Botany (continued)
    *Cells, 2-1-14
    *Classification of plants, 1-287-91, 300-05
    *Communities, 10-181-90
    *Defenses of plants, 7-75-83
    *Diseases of plants, 8-369-75
    *Fibers, vegetable, 4-177-82
    *Flowers, fruits and seeds, 4-119-32
    *Food storage in plants, 2-415-20; 6-52-59
    *Fungi, 3-22-32
    *Germination, 5-61-67
    *Habitats of plants, 10-135-42
    *Insect enemies of plants, 9-185-96
    *Mosses, liverworts, club mosses, horsetails and ferns, 3-186-92
    *Movements of plants, 6-218a-d
    *Photosynthesis, 3-42a-d
    *Physiology of plants, 3-43-55
    *Pollination of plants by insects, 7-239-48
    *Propagation, 9-7-15
    *Roots, stems and leaves, 4-62-75
    *Seed and fruit dispersal, 5-1-7
    *Seed plants, 3-397-406
    *Soil, 2-15-25
    *Soil fertility, 2-163-72
    *Soilless agriculture, 8-34-37
    *Terrariums, 5-365-68
    *Treatment of plants, 10-143-53
    *Trees, 5-257-66
        *How to recognize trees, 5-138-51
    *Weeds, 7-111-14
    Animals and plants, difference between, 1-40-42
    Cell theory, development of, with illus., 7-160-61
    Classification of plants by Linnaeus, 3 375-76
    Fossil plants, with illus., 6-370, 371, 372
    History
        Antiquity, 1-128, 138
        Nineteenth century, with illus., 8-251-56
    Nitrogen cycle traced by Liebig, 5-80
    Plants' foothold in rocks, 6-139
    Science and agriculture, 9-290-92
        Chemurgy developments, with illus., 7-35-44
        Industrial and chemurgic research on agricultural products, 1-89, illus., 91, 92
    Seasonal changes affect plants, 5-409, illus., 408
    Stem cross section, illus., 10-164
    Subdivisions of, 1-49
    See also Biology; Evolution; Fertilizers; Flowers; Mendel, Gregor Johann; Reproduction; Seeds

Botflies. 3-287-88, 291

Böttger, John, German potter. 7-401, with illus., 399

Bottle-making machines. with illus., 3-310

Bottle-nosed chimaeras. 4-295

Bottlenose dolphins. illus., 7-189

Bottlenose whales. illus., 7-185

Bottles. Manufacture, with illus., 3-310

Botulism, food poisoning. 4-153, 156, 163

Bouchardat, Gustave, French chemist. 6-357

Boucher de Crèvecoeur de Perthes, Jacques, French archaeologist. 9-23

Bouguer, Pierre, French mathematician. Mass of earth estimated by, with illus., 4-43-44

Boulder Dam. See Hoover Dam

Boulder ferns. illus., 3-189

Boulders. Streams carry and deposit, 8-13

Boulton, Matthew, English manufacturer. 4-35-36, 41

Bourdon-element thermostats. with illus., 2-253

Bourdon spring gauges, devices for measuring high pressures. 2-42

Bourseul, Charles, French inventor. 2-386

Boussingault, Jean, French chemist.   Plant-nutrient experiments by, 8-34-35
Bouvard, Alexis, French astronomer.
   Neptune, predicted existence of, 5-290
Bovine tuberculosis. 9-176
Bowditch, Nathaniel, American mathematician, navigator and astronomer (1773–1838).   Self-educated in mathematics, languages and astronomy, he was a leading authority in mathematics and a pioneer in the art of navigation by the stars.   His *New American Practical Navigator,* based on an earlier publication, became the standard navigation authority of the U.S. Navy Department.
Bowels.
   Elimination habits, 10-83
   See also **Constipation; Digestive systems**
Bowman's capsules, structures in kidneys.   *with diagram,* 5-12
Box cameras. 9-403, 405, *illus.,* 404, 405
Box elder bugs. 3-258
Box elder trees. 5-150
Box turtles. 5-388-89, *illus.,* 387; *with illus.,* 10-261
Boxcars, freight cars.   *with illus.,* 1-190
Boyle, Robert, English chemist.   *with illus.,* 3-270-71
   Chemical elements, theory of, 1-308
Boyle's law, of gases.   *with diagram,* 1-165; 3-416
Boys, Sir Charles Vernon.   Developed special camera for study of lightning, 1-402
Boys.
   Puberty in, 8-99
   See also **Children**
Boys camera. 1-402
Brachial plexus.   *illus.,* 1-148h; 6-329, *illus.,* 319
Brachiopoda (brachiopods), phylum of shellfish. 1-293, 387, *illus.,* 386
   Fossil brachiopods, *illus.,* 6-371
Brachiopods.   See **Brachiopoda**
Brachioradialis, forearm muscle.   *illus.,* 1-148c
Brachiosaurus, herbivorous dinosaur. 1-393; *illus.,* 6-373
Bracken ferns. 3-191-92; *illus.,* 189
Bracket (leather) fungi.   *with illus.,* 3-30
Bracts, floral parts. 4-123, *illus.,* 124
Brady, Mathew B., American photographer. 9-403
Bragg, Sir William H.   Work on crystals and X rays, 7-144-45
Bragg, Sir William L.   Work on crystals and X rays, 7-144-45
Brahe, Tycho, Danish astronomer. 2-373-74
Brahmaputra River, India. 10-222
   Sediment carried by, 10-214
Braid, James, English surgeon. 9-99
Braille, Louis.   Born in Coupvray, France, 1809; died in Paris, 1852.   Blind from the age of three years, he studied at the Institute for the Blind in Paris and later became a teacher there.   He created a new system of writing for the blind, using raised points, which can be written as well as printed.   It is admirably suited to musical notation.   His system has been widely adopted.
Braille, system of printing for the blind.
   Typewriter that prints, 1-275
Brain.
   *Nervous system, 6-317-30
   Alcoholic beverages affect, 4-407
   Baby, development in, 8-97
   Birds, *with illus.,* 5-421-22
   Body's defenses, role in, 7-346-47, 353
   Cerebral arteriosclerosis, 9-201
   Insect nervous system, *with illus.,* 2-406
   Man's, compared with those of other vertebrates, *illus.,* 1-63

Brain *(continued)*
   Muscular activity, role in, 3-208, *illus.,* 206
   Operations by means of high-frequency sound, 8-110
   Primates, development in, 1-64-65
   Recording electrical waves generated by cerebral cortex, *with illus.,* 2-426-28
   Waves, interpretation of, 6-241
   Weight of, 6-323
   See also **Cerebellum; Cerebrum; Mind; Nervous system; Psychology;** etc.
Brain box, of skull.   *illus.,* 3-77, 78
   Evolution of, *illus.,* 7-3
Brain case.   See **Brain box**
Brain-center theory of sleep. 6-148
Brain stem. 6-323-24
   See also **Brain; Nervous system**
Brain waves.   Recording of, *with illus.,* 2-426-28
Brakes.
   Automobile, *with illus.,* 2-143-44
   Operated by compressed air, 9-68
   Railroad trains, *with illus.,* 1-189
Brambles.   Stems, *illus.,* 6-220
Bran, indigestible covering of wheat seed.   *illus.,* 2-416
Branca, Giovanni, Italian architect.   Impulse turbine of, 5-305
Branchiopods, crustaceans.   *with illus.,* 2-243
Brandon, steamship. 4-111
Branly, Edouard, French physicist. 6-245
Brants, geese. 6-400, *illus.,* 399
   Migration route of, *illus.,* 5-418d
Brass. 3-36
   Building material, 7-122
   Buttons made of, 7-209, 213
Brass instruments (musical).   Sound production in, 5-219, *illus.,* 218
Braun, Wernher von, German-American rocket expert. 9-377-78
   Space station proposed by, *illus.,* 10-51
Brazil.
   Diamond searchers, *illus.,* 4-251
   Industrial research, 1-96
Brazil Current, oceanic current. 6-237, *map,* 232-33
Brazil nuts.   Seed coat of, 5-63
   Seeds, *illus.,* 5-62
Brazil rubber trees.
   Flowers and seeds, *illus.,* 5-65
   Viability of, 5-65
Bread.   *9-293-99
   Black bread mold, *illus.,* 1-37; 3-27, *with illus.,* 26, *illus.,* 23
   Pink bread mold, hereditary studies of, 9-385
Breadmaking.   See **Bread**
"Break-even point," beyond which action is unprofitable.
   Ore dressing, 1-375-76
Breakers, preparation plants for anthracite coal.   *with illus.,* 1-415-16
Breakers, waves breaking into foam. 8-349
Breakfast cereals.
   Corn breakfast food, manufacture of, *illus.,* 1-92c
Breast feeding.   Diet for mother, before and during, *with table,* 5-272-73
Breast muscles. 3-209, *illus.,* 204, 207
Breast rolls, Fourdrinier paper machines.   *illus.,* 4-374b
Breastbone.   See **Sternum**
Breasted, James Henry.   Comment on ancient Egyptian calendar, 10-117-27
Breasts (mammary glands). 8-20-21
Breathing.   *4-200-09
   Artificial respiration for stopped breathing, *with illus.,* 10-8-10
   Baby, human. 8-94

Breathing (continued)
  Bones that are involved in, **3-77, 79**
  Changes in, during sleep, **6-147**
  Combustion, form of, **1-231**
  Diaphragm plays part in, **3-209**, diagram, **211**
  Estivating animals, breathing of, **5-412**
  Fish, with illus., **1-279**
  Hibernating animals, breathing of, **5-410, 411**
  Human, how to measure, **10-58-59**
  Insects, **2-405**
  Mammals, mechanism of, with diagram, **1-279**
  Mechanics of breathing, demonstration of, **2-331**, illus., **330**
  Muscular exercise, breathing in, **10-87-90**
  See also **Air; Lungs; Respiration; Respiratory systems; Ventilation**
Breccia, sedimentary rock. **3-424**
Breech presentation, type of delivery. **8-32**
Breeder reactors. 9-138
Breeding.
  Dogs, **10-240, 242**
  Frogs, **5-158-59**
  Livestock improved by, **5-165-66**
  Salamanders, **5-160-61**
  See also **Heredity; Hybrids; Reproduction**
Bréguet, Louis-Charles, French aeronautical engineer. **9-220**
Bremsstrahlung, radiation resulting in slowing down of electrons. **8-396**
Breuer, Josef, Austrian physician. **9-100-01**
  Revelation of subconscious mind, **8-403**
Brewer's yeast. 3-27
Bricks.
  Building material, with illus., **7-118-19**
  Heat-resistant, illus., **7-407**
Brickwedde, Ferdinand G., American scientist. Discovery of heavy hydrogen, **8-418**
Bridalveil Falls, Yosemite National Park. illus., **10-29**
Bridge dams. 8-315
Bridges. *2-332-45
  Bailey bridge, with illus., **9-327**
  Cuscatlán, El Salvador, illus., **3-302**
  Hilo, Hawaii, illus., **9-109**
  List of, **2-345**
  Railway, **1-192**, illus., **183**
  Skeleton and muscles of backboned land animals resemble, with diagram, **1-286**
Bridges, dental. 5-134-35
Bridges, natural, geologic formations. Formation of, with illus., **8-15**
Bridges, ship. Normandie, steamship, **4-115, 117**
Bridgman, Percy W., American physicist. Quotation from, **9-280**
  Diamond-synthesis experiments by, **4-275**
Briggs, Henry, English mathematician. **3-20**
Bright-line spectra. 7-280
  Sodium, illus., **7-284a**
  Spectrum analysis, laws of, **5-86**
Brightness, color quality. **7-287**
Brightness of celestial bodies.
  Comets, **5-398**
  Stars, **1-255; 6-256-57, 260-62,** table, **262**
  Apparent magnitudes, scale of, **6-389**
Brine.
  Electrolysis of, **5-92-93**
  Processing of brine for salt, **5-98**, with illus., **320-24**
Brine shrimp.
  Fish in aquariums fed with, with illus., **8-115**
Brine wells. See **Wells, salt**
Bristletails, insects. See **Thysanura**
Bristol Britannia, British turboprop jet plane. **7-73**

British Columbia.
  Stony Creek Bridge, illus., **1-183**
British Commonwealth. See **Australia; Canada; Great Britain;** and other countries of Commonwealth.
British Overseas Airways Corporation (BOAC). 7-73
British thermal units (B.T.U.). 3-412; 4-160
Brittle bones, in aged and sick. **3-84**
Brittle stars. 2-152
Brittleness. 5-376
Broaches, planing tools. **10-110-11**, illus., **109**
Broaching, tooling operation. **10-110-11**
Broad-leaved evergreens, plants. **6-57**
Broad-leaved trees. with illus., **5-144-51**
Broad-winged hawks. 6-156
Broadcasting. See **Radio**
Broadcasting studios. 3-88
Broadleaf maple trees. 5-150
Broadtail sheep. Fur, **7-238**
Brockets, deer. **8-243**
Broglie, Louis-Victor de, French physicist. **9-283**
  Theory of wave mechanics, **7-205**
Bromides. Photography, use in, **9-403**
Bromine (Br), chemical element. Atomic number, 35; atomic weight, 79.909; melting point, —7.2° C.; boiling point, 58.78° C.; specific gravity, liquid: 3.12. The only liquid nonmetallic element; a member of the halogen group. Heavy, mobile, deep-red; volatilizes readily at room temperature to red vapor with bad odor. Discovered by Balard in 1826. Name derived from Greek bromos: "stench." Found chiefly as bromides in brines, salt deposits and sea water. Obtained by displacement with chlorine or electrolysis. Compounds useful in photography, medicine, coal tar derivatives and antiknock gasoline.
  Occurrence in the sea, with chart, **6-31**
Bromo, volcano of Java. illus., **8-297**
Bronchi (plural of **bronchus**). See **Bronchial tubes**
Bronchial rami (plural of **ramus**). illus., **1-148e; 4-204,** illus., **202**
Bronchial tubes (bronchi). illus., **1-148e; 4-204,** illus., **202**
Bronchioles, subdivision of bronchial tube. **4-204,** illus., **202**
Brontosaurus, herbivorous dinosaur. **1-393**
Bronze. 3-36-37
  Building material, **7-121**
Bronze, Age of. Spearheads, illus., **1-125**
Bronzed cuckoos. 6-306
Brookhaven National Laboratory.
  Cosmotron, illus., **4-342b-c; 9-249,** illus., facing **249**
  Experimental radiation farm, with illus., **10-251-53**
Brooklyn-Battery Tunnel, New York City. **2-57**
Brooklyn Bridge, New York City. **2-340**
Brooks, W. R., American astronomer. Comets discovered by, **5-399**
Brooks' comet. illus., **1-258**
Brown, Arthur. Transatlantic flight, first nonstop, **6-184; 9-217**
Brown, Robert, Scottish botanist. **1-164; 7-159**
Brown algae. with illus., **3-219-21**
Brown bears. 7-308, with illus., **310-12**
Brown coal, variety of lignite. **1-408**
Brown-headed nuthatches. 6-42
Brown hyenas. 8-250
Brown rot, plant disease. **3-28**
Brown snakes. Pets, **7-25**
Brown soils, soil type. **2-22**
Brown thrashers. 6-48, illus., **47**
Brownian movement. 1-164
  Colloidal suspension, **5-299-300**
Bruangs. See **Malayan sun bears.**

Bruce, Sir David, British physician and bacteriologist. 7-382, 384
  Work with African sleeping sickness, **6-151**
Bruises. Bone, **3-84**
  Muscular, **3-213**
Brunel, Isambard K., English engineer and inventor.
  Automatic steering motor for steamships. **10-235**
  Shield invented by, **2-52**
Bruno, Giordano, Italian monk and scientist. **2-374**
Brush, Charles Francis, American scientist. **5-246**
Brush-footed butterflies. **3-199,** illus., **198-99**
Bryant, Gridley, American industrialist.
  Railroad built by, **1-180-81**
Bryce Canyon, Utah. illus., **8-15**
Bryophytes, mosses and liverworts. **3-187-90,** illus., **186**
  Classification of, **1-301**
Bryozoa, phylum of mosslike animals. **1-293**
Bryum, genus of mosses. **3-188**
Bubbles. Boiling produces, **1-168,** diagram, **169**
Bubonic plague. See **Plague**
Buchanan, J. Y., oceanographer. **7-33-34**
Bucherer, A. H., German physicist.
  Mass measurements of beta particles, **4-216**
Buckeye trees. **5-147**
  Leaves, illus., **5-139**
Bucking, process of cutting trees into logs. **2-112**
Buckland, William, English divine and geologist. **7-409**
Buckwheat. Growth of seedlings in darkness, illus., **3-50**
Bud-grafting. See **Budding** (method of plant propagation)
Budd, William, English physician. **9-175**
Budding, method of animal reproduction.
  Sea squirts, **4-3**
  Sponges, **2-147,** illus., **146**
Budding (bud-grafting), method of plant propagation. **9-8, 10-11, 14,** illus., **10-11**
  Rubber-tree cultivation, with illus., **6-353-54**
Buds. with illus., **4-66-67; 6-53,** illus., **55, 58**
  Flowers that develop from, with illus., **4-120**
  Growth experimentally studied, **8-71-72**
  Trees can be recognized by, with illus., **5-140**
Buerg, Joost, Swiss mathematician. **3-20**
Buerger's disease. Smoking aggravates symptoms of, **5-345**
Buffalo, New York.
  Railroad yards at, illus., **1-194**
Buffalo gnats. **3-289**
Buffaloes. with illus., **10-248-49**
  Domestication of, **7-328-29**
  See also **Bison**
Buffers.
  Controlling acidic and alkaline solutions, **2-424**
  Human body, buffers in, **3-326; 4-341**
Buffeting, pounding of aircraft by shock waves. **10-231**
Buffon, Count de (Georges Louis Leclerc), French naturalist. **3-377-79,** illus., **376-77**
  Earth, theory of origin and structure of, **4-393**
  Fossils, work with, **4-387-88**
  Solar system, theory of, **1-27, 29**
Bufo, genus of toads. **5-155**
Buggies, horse-drawn vehicles. illus., **1-105**
Bugles. Sound production in, **5-219**
Buhl Planetarium, Pittsburgh. **2-398**
Building.
  *Canals, **4-183-95**
  *Concrete construction, **3-113-25**
  *Glass as construction material, **8-388-92**
  *Homes, **4-265-72**
  *Materials, **7-115-28**
  *Roads and highways, **3-293-306**
  *Tunnels, **2-43-57**

Building (continued)
  Insulation and heating of, **4-11-14, 16,** illus., **11-15**
  Stone used in, **2-82,** with illus., **83**
  See also **Archaeology; Bridges; Concrete; Skyscrapers**
Building boards. **4-378**
Building paper. **4-378**
Bulbs, underground stems. with illus., **4-68; 6-58**
  Food storage in, **2-420**
  Plant reproduction by, illus., **9-15**
Bulbs, electric light. See **Electric lighting**
Bulk-plant operators, petroleum distributors. **4-152**
Bull snakes. **5-359**
  Pets, **7-25**
Bull wheels, of engines. Well drilling, use in, diagram, **4-144**
Bullard, Sir Edward, geophysicist. Earth's magnetic field, possible explanation of, **4-176**
Bullbaiting. **10-243**
Bulldogs. **10-243**
Bulldozers. illus., **8-309**
Bullen, Keith E., Australian geophysicist. Earth's density, internal pressure and rigidity calculated by, **4-173-74**
Bullet-resistant glass. **3-313**
Bullfrogs. **5-155, 159, 161, 162,** illus., **155, 158-59**
Bullock's orioles. **6-105**
Bumblebees. illus., **2-410; 3-372**
  See also **Bees**
Buna rubbers. **6-358**
Bunker Hill. Battle of, illus., **4-32**
Bunsen, Robert Wilhelm, German chemist (1811–99). Serving as professor of chemistry at Heidelberg, he was a pioneer in the field of spectroscopic analysis; by this method he discovered (with Kirchhoff) the chemical elements cesium and rubidium. With Kirchhoff he formulated the laws of spectrum analysis. He invented many pieces of laboratory equipment, including the carbon-zinc electric cell and ice colorimeter and he perfected the device called the Bunsen burner. See also **5-86**
  Astrophysics, founding of science of, **6-390-91**
  Cesium and rubidium, discovery of, **3-169**
  Geysers, explanation of eruption of, **8-326**
Bunsen burners.
  Home laboratory use, with illus., **4-223-24**
Buoyancy.
  Animals' use of, with illus. and diagram, **1-280-81**
  Liquids and gases, **2-32-33, 41-42**
  Principle of, and experiments concerning, with illus., **8-7-8**
  Seed dispersal, factor in, with illus., **5-3-5**
Buoys. *5-68-71
  Lighted, illus., **4-238**
  Radioisotope-fueled thermoelectric generators for buoys, with illus., **6-175**
Burdocks.
  Distribution of seeds, **3-240-41**
  Fruit of, **5-5,** illus., **4**
Bureau of Reclamation, U. S. Department of Interior. **8-199**
Burgess Pass, British Columbia.
  Invertebrate fossils found near, **1-387**
Burglar alarms. Electron tubes (thyratrons) in, **6-301**
Burma. Elephants used as beasts of burden in, illus., **7-413**
Burned lime (quicklime). Soil fertilizer, use as, **2-168**
Burnelli, Vincent. Development of Flying Wing, **6-193,** illus., **192**
Burners, gas. **4-234**
Burney, Leroy S., American physician. **9-104**
Burning. See **Combustion**

Burns.
First aid for, *with illus.*, **10-12**
Nuclear-bomb explosion causes, 9-351, 393
Prevention of, in home, 7-196
Burroughs, John, American naturalist. **8-254**
Burroughs, William Seward, American inventor.
Bookkeeping machine developed by, 9-144
Burroughs adding machines. *illus.*, **9-145**
Burrowing mammals, 7-8
Burrowing owls. 6-165
Nesting activities of, *with illus.*, 5-418g
Burrs, barbed seeds and fruits. 3-240-41; 5-5, 6, *illus.*,
4, 5
Bursae, bags of connective tissue. **3-211**
Bursitis. Cause of, 3-211
Burt, William, American inventor.
Typewriter developed by, 1-266
Burying beetles. 3-339
Bus bars. See Buses
Busch, H., German physicist. 9-289
Buses, electric-current carrying conductors. 9-235, 237,
illus., 236, 238
Bush, Vannevar, American physicist.
Analog computers developed by, 9-144
Bushbucks, antelopes. 8-382-83, *illus.*, 380
Bushman local race. 8-218
Bushmasters, snakes. 5-364
Bushnell, David, American inventor. Early submarine
(*Turtle*) of, *with illus.*, 5-31
Business.
Electronic computers used in, 9-152
Microfilming in, *with illus.*, 10-71-72
Typewriter's influence on, 1-265-66, 269
Business machines.
*Electronic computers, 9-143-52
*Typewriters, 1-265-76
Bookkeeping, 9-144
Butadiene, product of petroleum cracking.
n-butane source of, 7-268
Synthetic rubber made from, 6-358
Butadiene-styrene rubber. *with illus.*, 6-358-59
Butane, a methane hydrocarbon. 7-268
"Butcher birds." 6-66
Butler Creek, Montana.
Civilian Conservation Corps project near, *illus.*, 6-3
Buttercups. Fruits, *illus.*, 4-130
Butterflies. *illus.*, 2-404, 408-10; *3-193-202
Dead-leaf butterflies, 3-240
Migration of, 9-415-16, 430-31
Pollen carriers, 7-247
Butterfly rays, fish. 4-295
Buttermilk, fermented milk. 4-167
Buttes, land erosion remnants. *illus.*, 8-10
Buttocks. Muscles of, *illus.*, 3-205
Buttons. *7-208-13
Lead alloys with precious metals, 1-376
Buttress dams. 8-314, *illus.*, 311
History of, 8-309
Butyl rubber. 6-359
Buys Ballot's Law. 2-96
Buzzers, electric signaling devices.
Homemade, *with illus.*, 8-146-47
By-product coke ovens. 1-342, *with illus.*, 417, 419
By-products.
Coal tar, 8-183-84, 186, 187
Coke manufacture, 1-342, *with illus.*, 419-20
Leather manufacture, 7-235
Meat-animal by-products, 5-168-69
Metallurgical, 1-382
Byssus, attachment filaments of bivalves. **2-199**

Byzantine Empire. Perpetuation of Greek thought in
Middle Ages, 2-297-98

C

C battery, in radio. 3-97
C horizon, in soils. 2-17-18, 22, *illus.*, 17, 25
C.I.T. Financial Corporation Building, New York City.
illus., 2-84
C. J. Strike project, Idaho.
Spillway dam of, 8-313-14
Cabbage.
Red cabbage juice as acid-base indicator, 4-231
Cabbage butterflies. 3-199
Cabbage webworms. 3-198
Cabinets. Home-chemical laboratory, *with illus.*, 4-221
Cable-tool well drilling. Oil wells, 4-145, *diagram*,
144
Water wells, *with illus.*, 2-274
Cables.
Earthquakes disable submarine cables, 6-74
Siphon recorder, 2-384
Submarine, 2-384, *illus.*, 385; *with illus.*, 5-241-42
Telephone cable, transoceanic, *with illus.*, 8-226
Underground, for telephones, 2-389, 394
Cabooses, cars attached to freight trains. *with illus.*,
1-190
Cabot, John (Giovanni Caboto), Italian navigator.
2-365
Cabs, locomotive. 1-182
Caciques (tropical orioles), birds.
Nesting habits of, *with illus.*, 5-418h
Cacomistles. See Ring-tailed cats
Cacti. *illus.*, 1-305; *with illus.*, 6-226-28; *illus.*, 10-182
Adaptation to desert life, 3-238; 10-182
Flower and spines of, *illus.*, 7-79
Fruit cactus, *illus.*, 3-49
Cactus wrens. 6-343-44
Caddis flies. See Trichoptera
Cadmium (Cd), chemical element. Atomic number, 48;
atomic weight, 112.40; melting point, 320.9° C.; boiling
point, 767° C.; specific gravity, 8.65. Soft, bluish-white
metal; tarnishes in air and forms oxide when heated.
Discovered in 1817; name derived from Greek *kadmia*:
"earth." Never found uncombined in nature; present
in small quantities in some zinc deposits. In preparation
of zinc, it comes off first; it condenses as a brown oxide
and can then be reduced with carbon. Widely used in
electroplating and other industrial processes; forms low-
melting and bearing alloys. Cadmium barriers serve
to control atomic fission. See also 3-42
Caecilians, limbless amphibians. 5-157
Caecum, part of the large intestine. *with illus.*, 4-329,
illus., 322
Caen, France. Devastated in World War II, *illus.*,
9-325
Caesar, Augustus. See Augustus
Caesar, Julius. *illus.*, 1-361
Calendar reform, 1-361; 10-173-76, *illus.*, 172
Caesarian section, operation sometimes performed in
childbirth. 8-32
Caesar's amanita, edible mushroom. *with illus.*, 3-31,
illus., 29
Cages. Wild animals kept as pets in, *with illus.*, 7-18-19
Zoo animals' cages, 10-160-62, *illus.*, 154, 160-61
Cages, underground mine elevators. 1-410
Caiman lizards. Mollusks devoured by, 5-204
Caisson disease. 2-52; *with illus.*, 4-206-07
Caissons, used for construction work under water. 2-
343
Calcaneus. See Heel bones

Calcination, heating of substances. Ores, 1-376

Calcite, mineral. 5-256, *with illus.,* 250; *illus.,* 9-304
  Cave deposits of, *with illus.,* 5-55-56
  Test for, with acids, 9-305

Calcium (Ca), chemical element. Atomic number, 20; atomic weight, 40.08; melting point, about 842° C.; boiling point, 1,240° C.; specific gravity, 1.55. Alkaline-earth metal; tough, crystalline, harder than lead, ductile and malleable. Discovered by Davy and by Berzelius and Pontin independently in 1808; name derived from the Latin *calx:* "lime." Fifth most abundant element in nature, found in earth's crust, leaves, bones, teeth and shells; never occurs uncombined. Prepared by electrolysis of the fused chloride. Used widely in compounds, as with quicklime, mortar, plaster, cement. Highly useful as deoxidizer for metals like nickel. See also 3-173-74
  Blood, calcium in, 5-18
  Blood clotting, calcium necessary for, 3-330
  Body's use of, 8-82
  Bone, calcium stored in, 3-73
  Bread, 9-299
  Diet, calcium essential to, 4-58-59; 5-272, 273, 274
  Interstellar space contains, 9-363
  Nutritional requirement and food sources of, *table,* 4-55-57
  Protoplasm, function of calcium ions in, 2-6
  Radioactive isotopes of, used in dentistry, 5-137
  Salts of, in the sea, *with chart,* 6-31
  Soil and plant life, role in, 2-167-70
  Soil calcium available to plants, 2-24
  Water hardened by calcium compounds, 2-280-81

Calcium carbonate.
  Caves, reactions involving calcium carbonate in the formation of, *with illus.,* 5-51-56
  Distribution of, 3-324
  Precipitation of, 4-231, *illus.,* 230
  Soil fertilizer, use in, 2-168
  Uses, 3-174

Calcium chloride.
  Water absorbed by, *with illus.,* 4-343

Calcium hydroxide.
  Experiment with, 4-231, *illus.,* 230
  Soil fertilizer, use as, 2-168
  Solubility of, 4-299

Calcium oxide.
  Lighting, use in, 4-236
  Soil fertilizer, use as, 2-168

Calcium pectate, plant cement. 2-169

Calculating machines.
  *Electronic computers, 9-143-52
  Development of, 9-144
    Seventeenth century, 3-20
  Electronic, *illus.,* 7-110; 9-289

Calculation.
  *Arithmetic, 1-149-61
  *Electronic computers, 9-143-52

Calculus, branch of mathematics. *with diagrams,* 4-433-39
  Development, 3-21, 279-80

Calderas, shallow volcanic craters. 8-298

Caledonian Disturbance, time of mountain making. 1-388

Caledonian Orogeny, time of mountain making. 6-371

Calendars. *10-171-80
  Ancient peoples, 1-17, 125-26
  Julius Caesar, reforms under, 1-361
  Roger Bacon's studies of, 2-307-08

Calenders, devices for pressing paper and other materials.

Calenders *(continued)*
  Papermaking, used in, *with illus.,* 4-372-73, *illus.,* 374c
  Plastic films by means of, *with diagram,* 8-232

Calends, Roman dates. 10-173

Calf wheels, of engines. Well drilling, use in, *diagram,* 4-144

Calibration, determining or rectifying the markings of instruments.
  Weather instruments, 1-317, 319, 320

Calico bugs. See **Harlequin bugs**

California.
  Alluvial fans in Mojave Desert, *illus.,* 8-16
  Giant trees of, 2-108, 110
  Rain-eroded orchard, *illus.,* 2-353
  Sand dunes in, 7-320, *illus.,* 322-23
  See also **Los Angeles**

California Current, oceanic current, 6-238, *map,* 232-33

California gulls. *illus.,* 6-396

California Institute of Technology, Pasadena.
  Construction of 200-inch telescope, 9-159
  Report of radio star by, 9-208

California job cases, in printing. 1-199

California laurel trees. 5-148

California quail. 6-333-34, *illus.,* 337

California (stovepipe) drilling. 2-274

Californium (Cf), chemical element. Atomic number, 98; atomic weight, 251(?). Radioactive actinide metal, emitting alpha particles with a half life of only 45 minutes. Discovered in 1950 by Seaborg, Ghiorso, Thompson and Street at the University of California; named in honor of the school and state where it was first identified. Produced by bombarding curium-242 with alpha particles in the 60-inch cyclotron at Berkeley, California.

Calla lilies. 7-244

"Calling card," portraiture technique. 9-403

Callisto, mythological figure linked with legends of constellations. 1-325

Callisto, satellite IV of Jupiter. 5-24

Calls, bird.
  Blackbirds, 6-104
  Coots, 6-404
  Doves, 6-304
  Gallinules, 6-404
  Goatsuckers, 6-216
  Herons, 6-397
  Hummingbirds, 6-214
  Kingfishers, 6-309, 310
  Kinglets, 6-42, 43
  Loons, 6-394
  Mockingbirds, 6-46
  Nuthatches, 6-42
  Owls, 6-165
  Pigeons, 6-304
  Shrikes, 6-66
  Sparrows, 6-106
  Swans, 6-399
  Tanagers, 6-108
  Thrashers, 6-48
  Titmice, 6-40-41
  Vireos, 6-63, 64-65
  Warblers, 6-62
  Waxwings, 6-65
  Woodpeckers, 6-210
  Wrens, 6-44, 45, 46

Callus, plant tissue. 10-143

Caloric, supposed heat fluid. 3-408

Calories, heat units. 3-412-13
  Aging, factor in, 8-82
  Diet requirements and sources of, *table,* 4-55-57

Calories (continued)
Diets, balanced, **5**-268-69, 270, 271, 272
Foods provide, **4**-51
Calories, mean. **3**-413
Calorimeters, bomb (combustion). with illus., **3**-414
Calorimeters, continuous-flow. with illus., **3**-414
Calotypes, early photographs. **9**-402, illus., 401
Calyxes, flower parts. **3**-405; **4**-120
Cambium, plant tissue. **3**-50, 399; **4**-64, 68, 70, illus.,
64, 69, 70
Budding and grafting, role in, **9**-12, 14
Cambrai, Battle of. Tanks successfully used in World
War I, **9**-214
Cambrian period, time in earth's history. **1**-386-87;
6-371
Camel-back turtles. illus., **5**-387
Camel crickets. with illus., **3**-145
Camels. with illus., **7**-329-31
Adaptation to environment, **10**-135, illus., 139
Transportation, use in, **1**-101, illus., 102
Camera obscura. **9**-397-98, illus., 398
Cameras. **7**-260-61
*Nature photography, **6**-311-16
*Photography, **9**-397-414; **10**-163-67
Color television cameras, illus., **6**-298c
Design improved by Walter Teague, **10**-120
Eyes compared with, **7**-294-95
Markowitz moon camera, with illus., **5**-187-88
Meteor photography, **6**-95-96
Microfilming with, with diagrams, **10**-69-70, illus., 74
Television, illus., **5**-276
Underwater, with illus., **6**-26b
Cameras, pinhole. Experiments with, with illus., **8**-120
Camouflage. Insect adaptations for, **2**-409-10, illus.,
410-11; with illus., **3**-240
Camphor. Synthesis, **8**-184-85
Cams, of automobile engines. with illus., **2**-133
Camshafts, of engines.
Automobile engines, **2**-133
Gasoline engines, with illus., **4**-88-89
Can buoys. **5**-70, illus., 69
Canada.
Animal refuges, **9**-278
Forest conservation, **2**-105
Forests of, **2**-108, 110
Frank, landslide at, **2**-353
Glaciers in Canadian Rockies, illus., **9**-162
Gold-bearing ore en route to mill, illus., **4**-246
Industrial research, **1**-92-93
Irrigation in, with illus., **8**-199-200
Mining operations in, illus., **3**-35
Mount Rundle and Vermillion Lake, illus., **10**-21
Petroleum industry and reserves, **4**-143, 147, 150
Photographed from air. illus., **10**-163
Population density of, **3**-227, 232
Railroads of, **1**-184, illus., 183, 188
Salmon cannery, illus., **6**-24-25
Sheep, breed of, illus., **10**-246-47
Welland Canal, with illus., **4**-187-89
Canada geese. **6**-399; illus., **9**-268-69; illus., **10**-257
Migration of, illus., **5**-418e; **9**-420, illus., 416-17
Canada thistles. **7**-113
Canadian, crack train, illus., **1**-183, 188
Canadian meteoric procession of 1913. **6**-94
Canadian Pacific Railway.
Canadian, crack train, illus., **1**-183, 188
Canal locks. **4**-185
Canals. *4-183-95
Irrigation water carried by means of, **5**-30; **8**-195,
illus., 198

Canals (continued)
Mars (planet), canals on, **6**-392
Tidal currents in Cape Cod Canal, **6**-206-07
Canals, beaver. **9**-2, 5
Canals, ear. with illus., **1**-282
Canaries Current, oceanic current. **6**-238, map, 232-33
Cancellous bone. **3**-74
Cancer. *8-265-72
Alcoholism may have bearing on, **4**-412
Bone, cancer of, **3**-84
Gastrointestinal tract, cancer of, **4**-335
Lymph system spreads, **3**-390
Radiation exposure as cause, **9**-349
Radioactivity used to combat, illus., **10**-132
Radioisotopes, used in diagnosis and treatment,
10-98, 99-100, illus., 101
Radium used in treatment of, with illus., **3**-176
Strontium 90 may cause, **9**-356
Virus-caused cancers, **3**-453
X-ray treatment of, with illus., **7**-149-50; illus., **10**-132
X rays used to diagnose, **8**-270
Cancer (Crab), constellation of zodiac. **1**-332
Candid photography. **9**-406
Candles. Ancient use of, **4**-232
Experiments and tricks with, with diagrams, **7**-177-78
Candling, food-inspection method. illus., **4**-319
Candolle, Alphonse-Louis-Pierre-Pyrame de, Swiss natu-
ralist. **8**-254
Candolle, Anne-Casimir-Pyrame de, Swiss naturalist.
8-254
Candolle, Augustin-Pyrame de, Swiss naturalist. **8**-254
Cane-borers. illus., **9**-196
Cane sugar. See **Sucrose**
Canine teeth. **5**-129-30, table, 130, illus., 132
Carnivores', **3**-235, illus., 236
Canis dirus, extinct wolf. **1**-397
Canis Minor (Lesser Dog), constellation. **1**-337
Canker sores. **5**-132
Cankerworms. **3**-197-98, 202
Canned foods. See **Canning**
Canneries, salmon. with illus., **6**-24-26
Cannibals. See **Primitive peoples**
Canning.
Meat processing, **5**-167, illus., 168
Precautions to be taken in opening cans, **7**-198
Preservation of food by, with illus., **4**-154-58
Cannizzaro, Stanislao, Italian chemist (1826–1910). He
held professorships of chemistry in Alessandria, Genoa,
Palermo and Rome. By clearly defining the distinction
between molecular and atomic weights, he established
the validity of Avogadro's hypothesis. He discovered
the Cannizzaro reaction (the decomposition of aromatic
aldehydes by potassium hydroxide into aromatic alcohols), and he developed methods of deducing atomic
weights. See also **5**-76
Cannon, Annie Jump, American astronomer (1863–
1941). She served as astronomer and curator of astronomical photographs in the Harvard College Observatory. Noted for her monumental catalogue of
stellar spectra, she also compiled a voluminous bibliography of variable stars. She discovered 300 variable
stars, five new stars and one spectroscopic binary (two
stars so close together that they cannot be distinguished
by other than spectroscopic means).
Cannon, Walter B., American physiologist. **9**-52, 320
Cannon. Medieval, **1**-217
Canoe birch trees. Bark, illus., **5**-140
Canopus, bright star in Carina. **1**-337
Cantilever bridges. **2**-343-44, with illus., **2**-336
Cantor, Georg, German mathematician (1845–1918).
Sets, theory of, with diagrams, **4**-441-42

Canvasback ducks. 6-403, *illus.,* 402

Canyon Diablo meteorite crater, Arizona. 6-91, 92, *illus.,* 91

Canyon wrens. 6-46

Canyons.
    Erosion as cause of, 8-11, 12, 13
    Submarine, 6-72-74

Canyons, submarine. *illus.,* 6-76

Caoutchouc, rubber (French name derived from Indian word). 6-351

Cap rock, dense rock layer trapping oil or gas. *with diagram,* 4-142-43; 5-98

Capacitors (condensers). 3-86, 87, *illus.,* 94

Capacity, measures of.
    Metric system, *table,* 10-296

Cape Canaveral, Florida, rocket-research center. 9-381
    Atlas launching, *illus.,* 10-40-41
    Rocket launching, *illus.,* 8-125

Cape Cod Canal. Tidal currents in, 6-206-07

Cape hunting dogs. 8-140, *illus.,* 139

Capella (She-goat), star in Auriga. 1-336

Capella's kids, group of stars in Auriga. 1-336

Capillaries. *illus.,* 1-148f; 3-381, 384-85, 386, *diagram,* 385
    Development in unborn human young, 8-26
    Respiration, role in, 4-204, 206, *illus.,* 202

Capillarity. *with illus.,* 5-371-72
    Principle of, and experiments with, *with illus.,* 8-4-5
    Sap, rise of, 4-71
    Soil water influenced by, 5-25-26

Capillary water, water held by soil. 2-24-25, *diagram,* 25; 5-25-26

Capricornus (Sea Goat), constellation. 1-333-34

Caps, bone. 3-73

Capsules, dry fruits. 4-130, *illus.,* 131

Capsules, space. See **Space travel**

Capuchin monkeys. 9-259

Capybaras. 8-168

Caracals, cats. 8-212

Carats, units expressing fineness of gold alloys. 3-34

Caravels, early European sailing ships. 4-108

Carbohydrates.
    *Starches and sugars, 4-76-79
    Aging, effect on, 8-82
    Balanced diet, carbohydrates in, 5-268, 269, 271-72
    Chemical elements in, 7-276
    Digestion and assimilation of, 2-10-11
    Essential food elements, *with illus.,* 4-51-52, *table,* 55-57
    Plants manufacture, 3-45-46
    Protoplasm, carbohydrate content of, 1-43; 2-5
    Water content, testing for, *with illus.,* 4-344
    See also **Photosynthesis; Starches; Sugars**

Carbolic acid.
    Lister's use of, as antiseptic, *with illus.,* 7-385-87

Carbon (C), chemical element. Atomic number, 6; atomic weight, 12.01115; melting point, sublimes above 3,500° C.; boiling point, 4,200° C.; specific gravity, amorphous: 1.88; graphite: 2.25; diamond: 3.51. A constituent of all organic matter; unreactive at ordinary temperatures. Known in prehistoric times; name derived from Latin *carbo:* "coal." Occurs free as diamond and graphite, and in combination with many elements. Forms an almost infinite variety of compounds, used for industrial, medical and agricultural purposes.
    *Diamond synthesis, 4-273-76
    *Organic chemistry, 7-263-76
    *Radiocarbon dating, 10-92-97
    *Synthetic organic compounds, 8-181-90
    Activated carbon, 2-277, 279; 5-303-04
    Arc lamp, carbon rods in, 4-239

Carbon (C) *(continued)*
    Archaeological dating, radiocarbon as aid in, 9-30
    Atom of, *with diagram,* 7-266; *diagram,* 8-415; *diagram,* 9-125
    Diamond, a form of, 4-251; *with diagram,* 5-338
    Graphite, a form of, *with diagram,* 5-338
    Interstellar space contains, 9-363
    Meteorites containing carbon compounds, 6-94
    Muscular energy furnished by high-carbon foods, 3-205-06
    Plastics contain, 8-224, 225, *with diagram,* 222
    Properties and role in nature, 3-322-24
    Rings of, in turbines, 5-310
    Sea water, carbon compounds in, *with chart,* 6-31
    Steelmaking, uses in, 1-339-41, 344, 353
    Sun contains, 3-109; 9-140

Carbon black. 3-324; 4-150, 273

Carbon-cycle theory.
    Solar energy explained by, *with illus.,* 3-110-11; 9-224

Carbon dioxide.
    Aquariums, getting rid of carbon dioxide in, 8-113
    Atmosphere contains, 1-231, 237; 5-193
    Bread dough contains, 9-296-97, 298
    Breathing and, 4-200-01, 206, 207-09, *illus.,* 201-02
    Calcium carbonate precipated by use of, 4-231, *illus.,* 230
    Carbon for living things supplied by, 10-93-94
    Carbonated water, vapor pressure of, *with illus.,* 4-300-01
    Cell processes, role in, 2-11, 12
    Climatic determinant, 3-184
    Coal mines, carbon-dioxide gas in, 1-413
    Crystalline structure of solid (dry ice), 5-337-38
    Diffusion of, into capillary network, 3-385
    Discovery of, 4-353-54
    Dissolving agent in formation of limestone caves, 5-51
    Experiments with, *with illus.,* 7-129-32
    Fire-extinguishing uses of, 4-352
    Food preservation, used in, 4-164-65
    Occurrence and uses of, 3-324
    Plants accumulate, use and release carbon dioxide, 3-44-45, 47-49
    Production by hydrocarbon combustion, 7-269
    Rain contains, 2-350
    Respiration, fish, 4-100
    Sea-water content of, 6-32
    Soil formation and chemistry, factor in, 2-16, 25
    Sublimation of solid (dry ice), 1-171; 3-418
    Water treated with, 2-280, *illus.,* 283
    See also **Dry ice; Fermentation**

Carbon monoxide.
    Coal mines, carbon-monoxide gas in, 1-413
    Production by hydrocarbon combustion, 7-269
    Tobacco smoke, contained in, 5-346

Carbon tetrachloride.
    Fire-extinguishing uses of, 4-351-52
    Formation of, 3-250, *illus.,* 251
    Solvent action of, 4-346

Carbon tissues, in printing. 1-212

Carbonates.
    Fossil carbonates analyzed for oxygen-isotope content, 3-181-82
    Minerals in form of, *with illus.,* 5-250; 9-306
    Water hardness due to calcium and magnesium carbonate, 2-280-82

Carbonation.
    Soil formation, 2-16

Carbonic acid.
    Solvent in soil solution, 2-16, 24

Carboniferous period, time in earth's history. **3**-324; **6**-372
  Coal formation during, *with illus.,* **1**-406-07
  Peat bogs laid down during, *illus.,* **3**-180
  Vegetation during, *illus.,* **3**-177
Carborundum. See **Silicon carbide**
Carborundum Company. **4**-275
Carbro color photographs. **9**-413
Carbureted water gas, fuel. *with illus.,* **1**-418
Carburetors.
  Automobile engines, carburetors of, *with illus.,* **2**-134
  Gasoline engines, carburetors of, **4**-87, *illus.,* 86, 89
Carburizing, casehardening process for steel. **1**-353
Carcajous, wolverines. *with illus.,* **8**-172
Carcinomas, cancers of the skin and membranes lining the internal and glandular organs. **8**-266
Cardiac cycle. **2**-428
Cardiac muscle. **3**-204
  Tissue structure, **1**-145
Cardiac sphincter, ringlike muscle. **4**-323
Cardio-vascular system. Definition, **8**-25
Careers in science. *10-191-202
  Psychology, **9**-322
Caribou. **7**-333; **8**-243; **9**-270, *illus.,* 424
  Food chain involving, **10**-187
  Migration of, **9**-422
Caries, dental. **5**-130-31, 133-34, *illus.,* 135; **10**-77
Carina (Keel), constellation. **1**-337
Carlisle, Sir Anthony, English scientist.
  Electrolysis, discovery of, **4**-363
Carlsbad Caverns, New Mexico. **5**-53, *illus.,* 58, 58a, 58c-d
Carmel Bay, in California. Submarine canyon in, **6**-73
Carnassial teeth, shearing teeth of carnivores. **7**-10; **8**-202
Carnegie Institution. IGY studies by, **5**-188
Carnivora, order of mammals. *with illus.,* **7**-15
Carnivores.
  *Bears and kin, **7**-307-17
  *Cats, **8**-202-12
  *Civets, mongooses and hyenas, **8**-244-50
  *Dog family, **8**-132-41
  *Seals and kin, **7**-84-93
  *Weasel family, **8**-171-77
  Raccoons, *with illus.,* **7**-316-17
  Teeth, *with illus.,* **3**-235-36
  See also **Animals; Bears; Lions; Tigers**
Carnivorous plants. **3**-238; *with illus.,* **4**-74
  Venus's-flytrap, *illus.,* **6**-218d
Carnot, Nicholas-Léonard-Sadi, French physicist. **6**-254
Carob beans. Mucilage from, **7**-44
Carolina mantids. **3**-151
Carolina wrens. **6**-45
Caroline Mars, flying boat. *illus.,* **6**-196
Carotene, plant pigment. **4**-73, 74; **6**-55
Carotenoids, complex lipids. **2**-5
Carp.
  Air bladder of, *with illus.,* **1**-280-81
  Taste organs of, **4**-101
Carpaccio, Italy. Malaria epidemics in, **10**-33
Carpal bones, in wrist. *with illus.,* **3**-81, *illus.,* 74, 80
Carpels, seed-bearing parts of pistils. **4**-121-22
Carpenter ants. **3**-362, *illus.,* 359
Carpenter bees. **3**-367
Carpenterian local race. **8**-219
Carpus. See **Carpal bones**
Carracks, early European sailing ships. **4**-108
Carrara, Italy. Marble quarries, **2**-86
Carrel, Alexis, French-born biologist and surgeon (1873–1944). In 1905 he came to the United States and joined the staff of the Rockefeller Institute for

Carrel, Alexis *(continued)*
Medical Research, on which he served until 1939. Carrel made many notable contributions to the study of living tissue and he created a number of new surgical techniques. In the year 1912 he received the Nobel Prize in physiology and medicine for his work on the ligature and grafting of blood vessels and on the transplanting of organs.
  Heart tissue from chick embryo, experiment with, **8**-80
Carriages, vehicles. *with illus.,* **1**-104-05
Carriages, typewriter. **1**-270
Carrier, Willis H., American engineer.
  Air-conditioning system of, **2**-256
Carrier current. **3**-88, 89; **9**-239
Carrier telephony. **2**-394-95
Carrier waves. Radio broadcasting, **6**-297
Carriers, soil-fertilizer compounds. **2**-171
Carriers, disease. Viruses spread by, **3**-457
Carrion beetles. *with illus.,* **3**-339
Carroll, James, American physician. **10**-38
Carrots.
  Food stored in roots of, **2**-420
  Fruit of wild carrot, **5**-5
Cars. See **Automobiles; Railroads**
Carso, district in Yugoslavia. "Swallow holes" in, **2**-351
Cartesian co-ordinates, axes defining space. **4**-212-13, *with diagrams,* 424-31; **7**-109
Cartesian divers. *with illus.,* **1**-281; *with illus.,* **7**-221-22
Cartier, Jacques, French explorer. **2**-366
Cartilage. **1**-60
  Transformation into bone, in human baby, **8**-29-30, 96
  See also **Bones**
Cartilaginous fish. *4-285-95
Cartography, making of maps.
  Ancient world, Erathosthenes' map of, *illus.,* **1**-359
  History
    Antiquity, **1**-131, *with illus.,* 359, *illus.,* 130
    Sixteenth century, **2**-366-67, *illus.,* 365
  Saracen empire, map of, *illus.,* **2**-299
  See also **Maps**
Carts. See **Wagons**
Cartwright, Edmund, English clergyman and inventor. *with illus.,* **4**-37-38
Carty, John Joseph, American electrical engineer. **5**-244
Carvel ship hulls. **4**-107, 108
Carver, George Washington, American scientist. *with illus.,* **10**-191-202
Cascade process, for producing ionization in a gas. **1**-173
Cascade Range, mountain range of western North America. **10**-23
Cascade Tunnel. **1**-192
Cascadian Revolution, time of mountain making. **6**-374
Case-study methods. Psychological analysis, **9**-314
Casehardening. Steel, treatment of, **1**-353
Casein, protein occurring in milk.
  Fiber synthesized from, **8**-189
  Paper, used in coating of, **4**-374
Casein plastics. **8**-223, 227
Cases, in printing. *with illus.,* **1**-199
Casing, lengths of pipe. Well drilling, use of, *illus.,* **2**-275; **4**-146, *diagram,* 144
Caspian Sea. *with illus.,* **7**-62-63
Caspian seals. **7**-91
Caspian terns. *illus.,* **6**-397
Cassava, tapioca plant. Starch from, **4**-78

Cassegrain, N., French telescope designer. 9-153-54
Cassegrainian telescopes. 8-58-59
Cassini, Jean-Dominique (Italian form **Giovanni Domenico**), noted Italian-born French astronomer (1625–1712). Cassini won fame as an astronomy professor at Bologna and in 1671 became the first director of the Paris observatory. He discovered four of Saturn's satellites and determined the laws of the moon's motion, the time of Jupiter's complete revolution and the eccentricity of the earth's orbit. He described the structure and division of Saturn's rings and made systematic observations of zodiacal light.
    Saturn's rings, described by, **5**-110
    Venus' period of rotation, theory of, **4**-30
Cassiopeia, constellation. 1-330
Cassiopeia, mythological figure linked with legends of constellations. 1-335
Cassiopeia A, radio star. 9-210
Cassiterite, mineral. 5-254
Cast iron. 1-339-40
    Piping made of, **2**-276
Castes (classes), among insects. See **Social insects**
Casting.
    Glass products shaped by, *with illus.,* **3**-311, *illus.,* 314a
    Plastic products shaped by, **8**-232
    Steel products shaped by, **1**-351-52
    Type casting in printing, *with illus.,* **1**-200-02
Castles, ship deck structures. Medieval ships, **4**-108
Castor beans. Industrial oil from, **7**-43, *illus.,* 42
Castor-oil plants. Seeds of, *illus.,* **4**-131
Casts.
    Plant-specimen casts, preparation of, *with illus.,* **10**-210-11
"Cat whisker," in radio. 3-96
Catabolism. 3-43
Cataclysmic evolution. 9-291
Catagramma cynosura, butterfly. *illus.,* 3-202d
Catalogues, celestial. See **Celestial catalogues**
Catalpa trees. *with illus.,* 5-150
    Fruits, *illus.,* **5**-141
Catalysts, substances speeding chemical reactions. 2-229, 231
    Action of, **8**-189-90
    Defined by Berzelius, **5**-77
    Diamond synthesis, **4**-276
    Petroleum refining uses, **4**-148
    Plastic manufacture uses, **8**-225
Catalytic cracking, molecular breakdown. Petroleum refining uses, **4**-148
Cataracts, of eye. 7-294
Catbirds. 6-48, *illus.,* 47
Caterpillar crawl, movement used by snakes. *with illus.,* **5**-354b
Caterpillar tractors. *illus.,* 2-168
Caterpillars, larvae of butterflies and moths. *illus.,* **2**-408; **3**-195, 197-98, *illus.,* 194, 197, 200
    Field study of, **10**-262
Catfish.
    Sea catfish, *illus.,* **4**-104
    Taste organs of, **4**-101
Catgut, product made from animal intestines. 5-169
Cathedrals.
    Rheims, France, Gothic cathedral at, *illus.,* **3**-116
    Saint Trophime's Cathedral, Arles, France, *illus.,* **2**-296
    Windows of Gothic cathedrals, *with illus.,* **8**-389
Cathode-ray oscillographs. *illus.,* 10-201
    Brain waves recorded by, **2**-428
Cathode-ray tubes. 6-302; 7-145-46, 148
    Discovery of, **8**-411

Cathode-ray tubes *(continued)*
    Television, use in, **5**-283-84
Cathodes. *with illus.,* 5-89-90, 92-93
    Audion tube, cathode in development of, **8**-85-87, 89
    Electron-tube elements, *with illus.,* **6**-295-302
    Faraday introduced name, **5**-236
Cations, positively charged electrified atoms. Salt water, removal from, **2**-284
Catkins, flower clusters. 4-123, *illus.,* 124; *with illus.,* **5**-144
Cats. *8-202-12
    Claws of, *with illus.,* **1**-284
    Dimetrodon, compared with, *illus.,* **7**-2
    Evolution of, **1**-396
    Experiments with cats to show neurotic basis of alcoholism, **4**-410
    Eye glow, **2**-187
    Intelligence, *illus.,* **2**-26
Catskill Mountains, New York State. 10-213
Cattail. *illus.,* 1-302
Cattell, James McKeen, American psychologist. 9-49
Cattell, Raymond B., American psychologist.
    Primary personality traits, list of. **9**-319
Cattle.
    Domestication of, *with illus.,* **10**-248-49
    Domestication of oxen, **7**-328
    Fever ticks attack, **8**-368
    Parasitic-worm infestation, **2**-154, 159
    Processing of cattle for food, **5**-166
    Texas fever in, **7**-383-84
    Transportation, use in, **1**-100
    Tuberculosis in, **9**-176
Caucasoid subspecies of man.
    Blood groups in Caucasian (white) race, **3**-334, *with table,* 333
    Hair of Caucasians, *illus.,* **2**-178
Caudal fin, of fishes. 4-98, *with illus.,* 96
Caustic soda. See **Sodium hydroxide**
Cavalry. Ancient, 1-103, *illus.,* 104
Cave crickets. 3-145
Cave-ins. Coal mines, precautions against collapse of, **1**-414
Cave men. Drawings made by, *illus.,* 1-110-11
Cave of the Winds, Niagara Falls. 5-56-57
Cave pearls, calcium carbonate deposits in caves *with illus.,* **5**-55
Cavendish, Henry, English scientist (1731–1810). *with illus.,* 4-354
    Electricity, work on, **4**-361
    Gravitation, experiment testing law of, **2**-317, *illus.,* 316
Caves. *5-50-60
    House caves in loess deposits, *illus.,* **7**-140
    Streams may form, **8**-15
Cavies. 8-168
Cavitation, low-pressure phenomenon. 4-8
Cayley, Sir George.
    Heavier-than-air craft, contributions to, **6**-181, *illus.,* 182
Cecropia moths. *illus.,* 2-405; 3-200, *illus.,* 194-95
Cedar trees. *with illus.,* 5-143
    Fruits, *illus.,* **5**-141
    Leaves of, *illus.,* **4**-72
Cedar waxwings. 9-421
Ceiling, altitude of cloud base. Measuring and recording, **1**-251
Ceilometers, ceiling-measuring instruments. 1-251
Celestial catalogues, counts and classifications of astronomical bodies.
    Galaxies, nebulae and star clusters, **8**-49

Celestial equator. *with diagram,* 1-260
  Reproduction of, in planetarium, 2-401, *illus.,* 400
  Star position, determination of, *with diagram,*
    6-80-81
Celestial eyes, tropical fish. *illus.,* 8-116
Celestial mechanics, laws of motion in space. Missiles,
  vehicles and artificial satellites, 8-126-28
Celestial meridian. Reproduction of, in planetarium,
  2-401
Celestial navigation. Observation of heavens as basis
  of, 1-18, *illus.,* 19
  Space travel, 8-128-31
Celestial poles. 1-260, *diagram,* 259
Celestial sphere. *with diagram,* 1-259-60; *with illus.,*
  3-446
  Celestial objects, determining position of, *with dia-*
    grams, 6-79-81
Cell division. 2-13-14, *illus.,* 13
  Plants, 3-50
  See also **Mitosis**
Cell sap, in plant vacuoles. 2-9
Cell theory. Development of, *with illus.,* 7-156-61
Cell walls, biological. 2-1-2, 7, *illus.,* 2, 4
  Animal and plant cell walls, differences between, 1-41
  Bacteria, 3-64
Cellini, Benvenuto, Italian goldsmith and sculptor.
  with illus., 2-363
Cells, biological units. *2-1-14; 3-368
  *Growth, role in, 2-287-92
  *Protozoans, 2-58-66
  Bipolar, of eye, 7-293, *illus.,* 292
  Blood cells, *with illus.,* 3-326-29, 330-34
  Cancer cultures, *illus.,* 8-272
  Cancerous, 8-266, *illus.,* 265
  Cell theory, development of, *with illus.,* 7-156-61
  Chemical constituents of, *with diagram,* 9-383-86
  Choanocytes, 2-146
  Colloids in, 5-301
  Ganglion, of eye, 7-293, *illus.,* 292
  Glandular, 5-8-10, 12, 18-19
  Hair cells of ear, *with illus.,* 7-300
  High-frequency sound affects, 8-110
  Human body cells, *with illus.,* 1-143-45, 147
  Living things formed by, 1-41, 42-44
  Low-temperature chemical reactions of, 2-188
  Luminous, 2-186
  Meristematic cells of plants, 3-50, *illus.,* 46
  Meteorites containing fossils of?, 6-94-95
  Model of, *illus.,* 2-12a-d
  Multiplication in human growth, 8-92
  Muscle cells, *with illus.,* 3-204-05
  Nematocysts, 2-148-49
  Osmotic effects on, 4-302-03
  Plant, 1-45-46
  Respiration and, 4-200-01, 206, *illus.,* 201-02
  Sex cells, role in heredity, *with illus.,* 8-334-37
  Skin cells, 2-173, 174, 179, 181, *illus.,* 174, 177, 179
  Structures of, 2-425
  Virus infections of, 3-453, 456-57
  See also **Amebas; Blood cells; Germ cells; Protozoans;**
    Nerve cells; Reproduction
Cells, in printing. 1-199, 212, 213, *diagram,* 198
Cells, of bees' and wasps' nests. *with illus.,* 3-366, 367,
  illus., 363-65
Cells, dry. See **Dry cells**
Cells, flotation. *with diagram,* 1-374
Cells, photoelectric. See **Photoelectric cells**
Celluloid.
  Buttons made from, 7-210
  Development of, 8-223, *illus.,* 224; 9-292
  Photographic film, 9-403, 408

Cellulose.
  Bacteria aid animals in digestion of, 3-69
  Fibers, source of synthetic, *with illus.,* 8-189
  Plant cells, found in, 2-5
  Plastics from cellulose derivatives, 8-222, 223, *with*
    illus., 227, *illus.,* 224
  Polysaccharide, 7-276
  Rayon from, *with illus.,* 5-303
Cellulose acetate, plastic. *with illus.,* 8-227
  Buttons made from, 7-210
Cellulose acetate butyrate, plastic. 8-227
Cellulose nitrate plastics. 8-223, *illus.,* 224
Celsius, Anders, Swedish astronomer (1701–44). He
was professor of astronomy at Upsala University and
director of the observatory which was built under his
supervision. His most notable achievement was the
development of the centigrade thermometer. See also
3-19
  Centigrade thermometer scale, contributions to de-
    velopment of, 3-410
Celsus, Roman medical writer. 1-366
Cement. See **Concrete; Portland cement**
Cementum, tooth tissue. 5-129, *illus.,* 134
Cenozoic era, time in earth's history. 1-395-97; 6-374
Centaurus, constellation, see **Alpha Centauri**
Center-exhaust tunnels, devices for dehydrating food.
  with illus., 4-166
Center of gravity. Space flight and, 8-127
Centigrade scale. *with diagram,* 1-164; 3-410, *illus.,*
  411
  Compared with Fahrenheit and Réaumur scales,
    3-411; 10-297
  Development of, 3-19
Centipedes. *illus.,* 1-295; *with illus.,* 2-269
Central deafness. 5-125
Central flyway, bird migration route. *illus.,* 5-418e
Central nervous system. 3-323-29
  See also **Brain; Nervous system; Spinal cord**
Centralized traffic control (CTC), for railroads. 1-193
Centrifugal fans. 2-255
Centrifugal force, *with illus.,* 2-125-26
  Gravity simulated by, in space research, 10-48, 52, 53
Centrifugal pumps. 2-274-75, 285, *illus.,* 284
Centrifuges, machines using centrifugal force to sepa-
  rate materials of different densities. *with illus.,*
  2-126; 4-371
  Honey, extraction of, 3-372, *illus.,* 371
Centrioles, cell structures. 2-9, 14, 290, *illus.,* 4, 9,
  12b-d, 289, 291
Centripetal force. 2-125
Centrosomes, cell bodies. 2-9, 290, *illus.,* 4, 9, 12b-d
Centuries. Leap years in century years, 10-176
Cephalic index. 9-24
Cephalization, location of sense organs in or near the
  head. 4-379
Cephalochordates, class of chordates. *with illus.,*
  4-2, 4
Cephalopods, squidlike animals. *with illus.,* 2-192-96
  Fossil cephalopods, *illus.,* 6-371
  Shell collecting, 2-100, *illus.,* 101
Cephalothorax.
  Crustaceans, 2-237, *illus.,* 239
  Spiders, 2-259, *illus.,* 261
Cepheids, variable stars. 7-51, 52-53
Cepheus, constellation. 1-330
Cepheus, mythological figure linked with legends of
  constellations. 1-335
Ceramics. *7-393-407
  Colloidal phenomena in, *with illus.,* 5-302-03
  Dating ceramics by thermoluminescence, *with illus.,*
    6-375, 376

Cereals. Weeds, damage caused to cereals by, **7**-111
  See also **Corn; Rice; Wheat**
Cerebellum. **6**-326, illus., 325
  See also **Hindbrain**
Cerebral arteriosclerosis. **6**-330; **9**-201
Cerebral cortex. **2**-426-27; with illus., **6**-324-26, 330
  Evolution of, **7**-3
Cerebral palsy. **6**-330
  Tranquilizers used in treatment of, **5**-379
Cerebral thrombosis. **6**-330
Cerebrospinal fluid. **6**-323, 328
Cerebrospinal nervous system.
  Nature and functions of, **6**-317-18, 328-29
  See also **Central nervous system**
Cerebrum. with illus., **6**-323-26
  Development of, in higher primates, **1**-64
  See also **Forebrain**
Ceres, asteroid. Discovery of, **3**-159; **4**-420-21; **6**-393
Cerium (Ce), chemical element. Atomic number, 58;
  atomic weight, 140.12; melting point, 804° C.; boiling
  point, 1,400° C.; specific gravity, 3.92. Rare-earth
  metal, steel-gray and lustrous. Discovered in 1803 and
  first prepared in 1875; name derived from the asteroid
  Ceres, which was discovered only two years before the
  element. Most abundant of the rare earths; found in a
  number of minerals, such as orthite, cerite and samarskite. Prepared by the electrolysis of the chloride.
  The oxide is used in incandescent gas mantles; its
  sulfate, as an oxidizing agent in quantitative analysis.
    Radioisotope-fueled thermoelectric generators, cerium
    as fuel for, **6**-174
Cermets, ceramics bonded with metals. **10**-226
Certainty, in science. **9**-284-85
Cerumen, earwax. **5**-11
Cervical nerves. **6**-329, illus., 328
Cervical plexus, group of nerves. illus., **1**-148h; **6**-329,
  illus., 319
Cervical vertebrae, neck bones. with illus., **3**-75, 76
Cervix. Cancer of, illus., **8**-265
Cesium (Cs), chemical element. Atomic number, 55;
  atomic weight, 132.905; melting point, 28.5° C.; boiling
  point, 670° C.; specific gravity, 1.873. Discovered by
  Bunsen and Kirchhoff in 1860. Alkali metal; found in
  pollucite and lepidolite and in the water of various
  mineral springs. Prepared by heating cesium chloride
  with calcium. Used in electron tubes to remove last
  traces of oxygen; also in electron tubes and photoelectric cells as heat-sensitive or light-sensitive emitter
  of electrons. See also **3**-169
    Radioisotope-fueled thermoelectric generators, use in,
    6-174
    Rockets powered by cesium ions, **9**-382; **10**-4
    Television, use in, **5**-279-80
Cesium chloride.
    Structure of crystal, **5**-340, diagram, 339
Cestodes, tapeworms. **2**-154-55, illus., 153
Cestriacont sharks, prehistoric sharks. **1**-390
Cetacea, order of mammals. with illus., **7**-15
Cetaceans. **7**-181, with illus., 183-89
Cetus (Whale), constellation. **1**-334, 335
Cetus, mythological figure linked with legends of con-
  stellations. **1**-335
Ceylon moss, red algae. **3**-224
Chadwick, Sir Edwin, English sanitary reformer. **9**-37
Chadwick, James, English physicist.
  Neutrons discovered by, **8**-419
Chaemeras. illus., **3**-223
Chaetognatha, phylum of worms. **1**-294
Chaff, metallic foil used to spoil radar reception. **9**-390
Chagas' disease, South American sleeping sickness.
  2-63

Chagas' disease (continued)
  Triatoma transmits, **3**-260
Chain fall, combination of pulleys. **7**-217
Chain reaction, in atomic fission. **9**-135-36, 330-31, 351
Chairs. Plywood chair, illus., **10**-118
  Transportation, use in, **1**-98, illus., 99-100
Challenger expedition. with illus., **6**-29-30; with illus.,
  7-32-34
Chamaeleonids (Chamaeleonidae), family of lizards.
  5-202, 203-04
Chamberlin, Thomas Chrowder, American geologist and
  educator (1843–1928). He taught at Beloit College
  and Chicago University, was president of the Univer-
  sity of Wisconsin and served with the U.S. Geological
  Survey. From studies of glacial deposits he noted evi-
  dences of climatic conditions in past ages. He proposed the theory that life originated in the soil; with
  F. R. Moulton, he formulated the planetesimal theory
  of the earth's origin. Chamberlin founded the Journal
  of Geology.
    Planetesimal hypothesis of, **1**-29, illus., 28; **9**-225
Chameleons. with illus., **5**-202, 203-04
Chamois, goat antelopes. with illus., **8**-378-79
Chamois leather. Making of, **7**-234
Change of state, in matter. **1**-171, with illus., 162-63,
    with diagram and illus., 166-69; with illus., **3**-416-18
    Chemical and physical changes distinguished, with
    diagrams, **2**-223-24
Changes, chemical.
    Physical changes distinguished from, with illus., **1**-81
Channels. *Buoys, **5**-68-71
Channels, stream. **8**-12, 14, 17
Chanute, Octave, aviation pioneer. **9**-216
    Gliders, work on, **6**-182
Chaos, giant ameba. **2**-64, illus., 62
Chapel Hill, North Carolina, site of astronomical ob-
  servatory. **8**-64
Chapman, Frank M., American ornithologist and au-
  thor of many books on bird life (1864–1945). He has
  been called the most influential ornithologist since
  Audubon. Chapman was the originator of the habitat
  bird groups and seasonal bird exhibits at the Ameri-
  can Museum of Natural History, where he was curator
  of ornithology from 1908 to 1942 and then curator
  emeritus.
Chappe, Claude, French engineer.
    Semaphore telegraph developed by, **2**-378; **5**-239
Chappe, Ignace-Urbain, French engineer.
    Semaphore telegraph developed by, **2**-378; **5**-239
Characteristic, part of logarithm. **2**-76
    See also **Mantissa**
Charcoal. **3**-324; **4**-273
Charcot, Jean-Martin, French neurologist. with illus.,
  9-99-101
Charges, electrical. **6**-119-21
    Atomic particles may have, **1**-309, 310, with diagram,
    313, diagram, 312, table, 314
    Experiments showing effects of, with illus., **6**-286-88
Chariots, ancient vehicles. **1**-102-03, illus., 104
Charlemagne, Frankish emperor (742–814).
    Educational reforms of, **2**-297
    Empire of, **2**-295
Charles, Jacques-Alexandre-César, French mathemati-
  cian and physicist (1746–1823).
    Hydrogen-inflated balloons, experiments with, **6**-177
Charles' law, of gases. **1**-165-66; **2**-72; **3**-416
"Charley horse," muscle fatigue. **3**-213
Charlotte Dundas, steamboat. with illus., **4**-109;
  6-377-78
Charts.
    Earth's magnetic field, with illus., **7**-169-71

Charts (continued)
Harbor, illus., 5-70
Home medical records, with table, 10-66
Weather charts, 1-253-54
Chases, frames for holding printing material. 1-207, illus., 206
Chassis, automobile. 2-142
Chauliodus sloani, fish. illus., 10-142
Checks, against population growth. 3-225-26, 228-30
Checks, irrigation devices. 8-196
Cheeks, human. Cell, illus., 2-1
Cheeses. Fungi used in manufacture of, 3-27
Cheetahs. 8-212, illus., 211
Fastest mammals, 7-10
Chelicerae, jaws of spiders. with illus., 2-261
Chemical analysis.
Fertilizers, 2-171
Soils, 2-172, illus., 165, 171
Chemical burns. First aid for, 10-13
Chemical changes. *2-223-31; 3-245
Example of, with mercuric oxide, 4-230-31
Physical changes distinguished from, with illus., 1-81
See also **Reactions, chemical**
Chemical elements. See **Elements, chemical**
Chemical energy. 1-83
Transformation of, 6-247, illus., 248-49
Chemical engineering. 1-219, 220-21
See also **Chemistry**
Chemical fertilizers. with illus., 2-167-72
Chemical industries. illus., 1-92a; *8-181-90
Automatic production in, 10-237
Rise of, in nineteenth century, 6-385
Chemical laws.
Formulation of, in nineteenth century, 5-74, 76
Chemical Revolution. 4-33
Chemical symbols. See **Symbols for chemical elements**
Chemical warfare.
World War I, with illus., 9-212-13
Chemical weathering. with illus., 3-179
Chemicals.
*Amateur chemistry, 4-221-31, 343-52; 7-129-36
Animal light stimulated by, 2-187
Carbon compounds, 7-263-76
Coal, chemicals derived from, with illus., 1-418-20
Food preservatives, with illus., 4-163-65
Cancer may be caused by, 8-268-69
Low-temperature reactions, 2-188
Minerals identified by testing with, 9-305
Nineteenth century industry, demand for chemicals in, 6-385
Plants treated by, 10-151, 153
Rain, contained in, 2-350
Rubber manufacture, 6-355-56
Salt (NaCl) used in manufacture of, 5-325
Sewage purified by use of, 5-330-31
Soil fertilizers, with illus., 2-167-72
Weed-killers, 7-114
Cancer may be caused by, 8-268-69
Wood distillation as source of, 2-105-06
X rays affect, 7-146, 148
X rays measure quantity of a material in a compound, 7-147
Chemiluminescence. 2-188-89
Chemistry.
*Acids, bases and salts, 4-336-42
*Amateur chemistry, 4-221-31, 343-52; 7-129-36
*Atomic structure, 1-307-14
*Carbohydrates in nutrition, 4-76-79
*Chemurgy, 7-35-44
*Colloids, 5-294-304
*Crystals, 5-337-42

Chemistry (continued)
*Diamond synthesis, 4-273-76
*Electrochemistry, 5-87-96
*Elements, periodic law of, 4-304-10
*Explosives, 8-273-87
*Magic chemical tricks, 7-173-80
*Matter and energy, 1-79-86
*Metallurgy, 1-369-82
*Metals, survey of, 3-33-42, 165-76
*Molecules, 1-162-72
*Nitrogen, fixation of, 3-126-29
*Nonmetallic elements, 3-317-24
*Organic chemistry, 7-263-76; 8-181-90
*Periodic table of elements, 4-304-10
*Plastics, 8-221-33
*Reactions of chemical elements, 2-223-31
*Soil and fertilizers, 2-163-72
*Soilless agriculture, 8-34-37
*Solutions, 4-296-303
*Valence, 3-245-51
Atmosphere, 1-231-32
Atomic structure and the formation of ions, with diagrams, 2-422-24
Body, effect of aging on chemical balance of, 8-80-82
Breadmaking, applications in, 9-294, 295, with diagrams, 296-97, 299
Breathing processes, 4-200-01, 206, illus., 201-02
Brine, extraction of chemicals from, 5-315
Cancer research, 8-272
Carbon compounds, 7-263-76
Elements, list of, 10-293
History
Antiquity, theory of elements in, 1-132, 137
Alchemists' contributions, 2-311
Modern chemistry, beginnings of, 3-269-72
1765–1815, 4-353-57
Nineteenth century, 5-74-86
Twentieth century, 9-32-35, 211-13
Inorganic: definition, 7-263
Job opportunities in, 10-201
Life, chemical nature and origin of, with diagram, 9-383-86
Mathematics and, 1-77-78
Meat-packing industry, chemical research in, 5-169
Microwaves used in research, 7-206
Muscular exercise, chemistry of, 3-205-07
Nobel Prize winners in, 10-299-307
Petroleum, chemical treatment of, with illus., 4-147-52
Petroleum, origin of, with illus., 4-142-43
Prospecting, chemical, 7-355
Protoplasm, chemical composition and activities of, 2-3-7, 10-13
Soil, 2-16-18, 21-24
See also names of elements and compounds; also **Assays; Atoms; Dyes; Electrolysis; Electroplating; Metallurgy;** etc.
Chemists. See **Chemistry;** also names of chemists
Chemosynthesis, synthesis of organic compounds by energy derived from chemical reactions.
Bacterial, 3-65
Chemotherapy.
Advancement of, in twentieth century, with illus., 9-32-35
Development of, 8-188
Paracelsus' contributions to, 2-368
Plants treated by, 10-151, 153
Chemurgy, scientific industrial use of plant and agricultural products. *7-35-44
Development of, 9-292
Industrial research, contributions to, 1-89, illus., 91, 92

Chemurgic Council. See **Council for Agricultural and Chemurgic Research**
Chernozem soils, soil type. **2**-22, map, 20-21
Cherrapunji, India. Rainfall statistics, **2**-347
Cherries. illus., **4**-129, 130
  Brown rot of, **8**-375, illus., 373, 374
  Stump sprout of black-cherry tree, illus., **10**-144
Cherry fruit flies. 9-194
Cherry trees. 5-149, illus., 148
  Fruit flies attack, **9**-194
  Fruits, illus., **5**-141
Chest. Bones of, illus., **1**-148b; illus., **3**-74-75
  Muscles of, illus., **1**-148c; **3**-209, illus., 204, 207
Chest cavity.
  Blood vessels of, illus., **1**-148f
  Breathing, role in, with diagram, **1**-279; with illus., **4**-204-06
  Factor in breathing, with diagram, **1**-279
  Lymphatic nodes, illus., **1**-148g
  Organs of, illus., **1**-148d-e
Chest muscles. illus., **1**-148c
Chest respirators. with illus., **4**-205-06
Chestnut blight, fungus that attacks chestnut trees. **3**-28; **5**-147
Chestnut-sided warblers, birds. illus., **6**-60
Chestnut soils. See **Brown soils**
Chestnut trees. with illus., **5**-147
  Blight of, **3**-28
  Bur of, illus., **3**-404
  Fruits, illus., **5**-141
Chevalier, Charles-Louis, French optician. **7**-158, illus., 159
Chevrotains, deerlike ruminants. **8**-243
Chi Cygni, variable star. **7**-50
Chicago, University of. Meat-research projects at, **5**-169, 172
Chickadees. 6-40-41, illus., 40, 43
Chicken cholera. Pasteur's work with, **9**-78
Chicken snakes. Pets, **7**-25
Chickens. Eggs, illus., **1**-43
  Heart tissue of chick embryo, experiment on, **8**-80
  Virus diseases of, illus., **3**-454
  Voice, production of, **1**-283, illus., 282
Chickweeds. Terrarium plants, **5**-368
Chiggers. 2-268
Chigoes, insects. See **Siphonaptera**
Child Development Clinic, Yale Medical School. **9**-56-57, illus., 55-56
Child-guidance clinics. 9-204
Child psychology. 9-320
  Behavioristic psychology, rise of, **9**-52
Childbirth. Diet of mother before and after, with table, **5**-272-73
Childbirth fever. See **Puerperal fever**
Children.
  Allergic symptoms in, **4**-258, 264
  Diets, balanced, for children, with tables, **5**-273-75
  Diseases that attack children, **8**-79
  Experiences of, as clue to adult behavior, **9**-98
  Health indexes in, **10**-76-77
  Houses, accommodation of children in, **4**-269
  Intelligence testing, development of, with illus., **9**-54-56
  Mental growth, studies of, **9**-56-57, illus., 55-56
  Mental illness, prevention of, **9**-204
  Physical growth, with illus., **8**-90-100
  Psychological testing of, illus., **9**-310
  Rickets in, **3**-84
  Zoo exhibits for, with illus., **10**-162
Chile. Atacama Desert, **6**-118
  Nitrates of, **3**-166, 425, illus., 167

Chile saltpeter. See **Sodium nitrate**
Chimaeras, fish. **4**-285-87, 295, illus., 293
  Reproduction, **4**-104
"Chimney swallows." 6-214
Chimney swifts. 6-214, illus., 215
  Migration of, **9**-420
Chimneys.
  Convection currents through, with illus., **4**-13-14
Chimpanzees. 9-252, 260-63, illus., 250; illus., **10**-136
  Mental life, studies of, with illus., **9**-52-54
  See also **Monkeys; Primates**
China.
  Balloons, invention of, **6**-177
  Caves dug out from loess, illus., **7**-140
  Compass, invention of, **7**-167
  Earthquake recorder, ancient, illus., **3**-293
  Fertilizer derived from human wastes, **5**-327
  Grand Canal of, **4**-183
  Industrial development of, **1**-97
  Irrigation in ancient, **8**-192
  Irrigation in modern, **8**-200-01
  Loess deposits in, **6**-142
  Natural gas, early use of, **5**-98
  Number system in ancient, with illus., **1**-152-53
  Opium den, illus., **5**-403
  Papermaking, development of, **4**-364
  Porcelain of, **7**-396, 398
  Printing, development of, **1**-197
  Silk industry, **5**-173, illus., 183
  Writing, development of, **1**-111-12, 113, 114
Chinch bugs. with illus., **3**-258, illus., 254
Chinchillas. 8-168, illus., 165; **9**-6
  Fur, **7**-238
  Home building, **9**-6
Chinese language.
  Typewriters printing Chinese characters, **1**-274-75
Chinese mantids. 3-150, illus., 151
Chinese primroses, flowering plants.
  Flower of, illus., **4**-126
Chinese water deer. illus., **8**-242
Chinook, a warm, dry wind. **2**-94; **10**-28
Chipmunks, rodents. **8**-163, illus., 160
  Acorns dispersed by, illus., **5**-7
  Antisocial, **7**-12
  Pets, **7**-21, illus., 22
Chippers, devices for reducing logs to chips. with illus., **4**-366
Chipping sparrows. 6-108
Chiroptera, order of mammals. with illus., **7**-14
Chirus, goat antelopes. **8**-379
Chisels. Cold chisel used in collecting minerals, **9**-302, illus., 304
Chitals, medium-sized deer. **8**-239
Chitin, horny substance forming outer covering of some invertebrates. **2**-237
Chitons, mollusks. **2**-100, 201
Chladni figures, vibration patterns. **5**-218
Chlamydomonas, genus of green algae. **2**-62; with illus., **3**-216-17
Chloride ions. Protoplasm, **2**-6
Chlorides. Compounds with chlorine, **3**-319
Chlorination, water purification. **2**-278, 280, illus., 278
Chlorine (Cl), chemical element. Atomic number, 17; atomic weight, 35.453; melting point, about —103° C.; boiling point, —34.6° C.; specific gravity, 1.56. One of the halogens. Greenish-yellow gas, combining readily with most elements. Discovered in 1774 by Scheele; name derived from Greek *chloros*: "light green." Always found combined in nature, chiefly with sodium. Obtained from chlorides by oxidizing agents or electrolysis. Was used as war gas in World

Chlorine (Cl) *(continued)*
War I. Serves as oxidizing agent, as germicide in drinking water and in the manufacture of bleaching powder, chloroform and various industrial compounds. See also 3-319-20
  Diet requires, 4-59
  Electroluminescent devices, use in, 9-345
  Electron arrangement of, 3-249, *illus.,* 248
  Molecule, formation of, *with illus.,* 3-250
  Plastics often contain, 8-222
  Reduction of, 5-88-90
  Salt (NaCl), derived from, 5-325; 7-134
  Salt crystals, chlorine ions in, *with diagrams,* 5-338-40
  Salt electrolysis produces, 5-89
  Sewage sterilized by, 5-332
  Water purified by, 2-278, 280, *illus.,* 278
  World War I, used as gas in, 9-212
Chlorine fluoride. Formation of, *with illus.,* 3-250
Chlorobenzene, structural formula. 7-274
Chlorodifluoromethane, refrigerant. 4-310
Chloroform, anesthetic. 7-377-78
Chloromycetin. 10-128
Chlorophyll, green plant pigment. 2-9, 11; 4-73, 74
  Fungi lack, 3-23
  Magnesium as constituent of, 3-172
  Photosynthesis, role in, 3-45
  Seasonal changes in, 6-55
Chlorophyta, phylum of algae. 1-300; *with illus.,* 3-216-19
Chloroplasts, cell structures. *with illus.,* 2-9; 3-45, *illus.,* 42c
Chlorosis, plant disease. Chemical treatment of, 10-153
Chlorpromazine, synthetic tranquilizer. 5-379; 9-104
Choanichthyes, major subdivision of true fishes. 4-95, 196-97
Choanocytes, specialized cells. 2-146
Chofu, Tokyo, Japan. Hydroponic farming in, 8-36, *illus.,* 35
Choke resistance. Fluorescent lamps, 4-240
Chokeberries. Fruits of, *illus.,* 5-7
Chokecherry trees. 5-149
Chokedamp, carbon-dioxide gas in coal mines. 1-413
Chokes, for automobiles. 2-135, *illus.,* 134
Cholera.
  Pasteur's work on chicken cholera, 7-380
Cholesterol, white fatty alcohol found in bile. 5-14; 10-134
Cholinesterase, enzyme in nerve cells. 6-318
Cholla, variety of cactus. *illus.,* 10-182
Chondrichthyes, major group of fishes. *with illus.,* 4-94-95
Chope, Henry Roy.
  Co-inventor of radiation thickness gauges, 9-46
Chope, Wilbert.
  Co-inventor of radiation thickness gauges, 9-46
Chordates (Chordata).
  Classification of, 1-291, 297-300
  Heart, evolution of, *with illus.,* 1-277-79
  See also **Animals**
Chorion, covering of mass of cells developing from egg. 8-22, *illus.,* 23
Choroid coat, of eye. 7-293, *illus.,* 292
Chousinghas, four-horned antelopes. 8-383
Christianity.
  Rise of, *with illus.,* 1-368
Christmas ferns. 3-192, *illus.,* 188-89
"Christmas tree," valves controlling oil or gas flow from well. 5-101, *illus.,* 98a
Christmas trees. Danger of fire, 7-193

Chromates, minerals. 5-250
Chromatic aberration. 7-260; 9-91
  Overcoming of, in microscopes, 7-158
Chromatids, chromosome parts. 2-14
Chromatin, substance of cell's nucleus. 2-9, 14, 290, *illus.,* 4, 13, 289, 291
Chromatography. Technique used to separate complex mixtures into their components. In column chromatography a solution containing the mixture to be analyzed is poured through a "column"—a glass tube packed with adsorbing material. (See Index, under Adsorption.) Clear solvent is then poured down the column. Each component in the mixture has a characteristic affinity for the solvent and for the adsorbent; hence it will occupy a definite position on the column. For example, substances most strongly attracted to the adsorbent and most weakly held in solution will adhere to the topmost part of the column. The separated substances will form a succession of distinct colored bands; hence the name "chromatography" ("analysis by color," in Greek). The separated components are extracted and analyzed. In paper chromatography filter paper is used instead of adsorbing material.
Chromatophores, chlorophyll-containing structures in protozoans. 2-61, 62
Chromium (Cr), chemical element. Atomic number, 24; atomic weight, 51.996; melting point, 1,890° C.; boiling point, 2,480° C.; specific gravity, 7.1. Hard, gray metal. Discovered in 1797 by Vauquelin, who prepared it the next year; name derived from Greek *chroma:* "color." Found chiefly in chrome iron ore; prepared by reduction of the oxide with aluminum. Serves in hardening steel, manufacturing stainless steel and plating; used widely as a catalyst.
  Alloy steels, containing, 1-352-53
  Medical uses of radiochromium, 10-99
  Tanning leather, chromium used in, 7-233-34
Chromoplasts, cell structures. 2-9
Chromosome doubling. 9-291
Chromosomes. *illus.,* 2-12b-d
  Cell division, part played in, 2-14, *with illus.,* 290-92, *illus.,* 13
  Evolution, factor in, 6-270, 271
  Gamma radiation's effect on, 10-252
  Heredity, role in, 8-91-92, 334-44
  Human chromosomes, 1-143-44
  Molecular nature of, 9-385
  See also **Cells; Heredity**
Chromosphere, layer of sun's atmosphere. *with illus.,* 3-101-02
Chromulina, genus of one-celled animals. 2-61, *illus.,* 60
Chronology.
  *Geological time scale of earth's history, 6-369-74
  Archaeological studies, dating methods in, 9-29-30
  Meteorites and meteorite craters, ages of, 6-91, 95
  See also **Geochronology**
Chrysalises. See **Pupae**
Chrysiridia ripheus, moth. *illus.,* 3-202b, 202c
Chrysler Building, New York City. 3-114, *illus.,* 117
Chrysophyta, phylum of algae. 1-301; *with illus.,* 3-221, 224
Chuck-will's-widows, birds. 6-218
Chyme, semifluid food mass. 4-326
Chymotrypsin, digestive enzyme. 4-328
Cicadas. Life history of, 9-431
Cierva, Juan de la, inventor of the Autogiro. 6-193; 9-220
Cigarette paper.
  Flax straw used for, 7-39, *with illus.,* 38

Cigarettes.
Radiation thickness gauges used in manufacture of, 9-46
See also **Smoking, tobacco**
Cigars. See **Smoking, tobacco**
Cilia, external hairlike processes of some cells. 1-145; 2-66
Nasal cilia aid in body's defenses, 7-348
Respiration, role of cilia in, 4-201, 203, 204
Ciliary movement. 2-12
Ciliated cells. 2-12
Ciliates. See **Ciliophora**
Ciliophora, class of protozoans. 2-66, illus., 64, 65
Cimicids, family of true bugs. with illus., 3-260
Cincinnati, United States. Meat-processing center, 5-164
Cinerarias. illus., 4-123
Cinnamon ferns. 3-192, illus., 188
Circle graphs. with illus., 2-71
Circle of confusion, photographic phenomenon. with diagrams, 9-407
Circles, plane figures. with illus., 3-435-39
Analytic geometry, equations in, 4-427, diagrams, 428
Degrees, division into, 1-259
Orbits in space may be nearly circular, 8-126-27, 128, 131
Circles of latitude. 3-444, illus., 445
Circles of longitude. 3-444, illus., 445
Circlet (Western Fish), group of stars in Pisces. 1-334
Circuit breakers. 6-134, illus., 135
Power transmission, used in, illus., 9-234c
Short circuits prevented by, 9-235, 237, 238, illus., 236, 238
Circuits, electrical. with illus., 6-132-36
*Printed circuits, 6-49-51
Homemade circuits, with illus., 6-288-94
See also **Electrical circuits; Electricity; Electronics**
Circuits, short. See **Short circuits**
Circular measures. table, 10-295
Circular turns, in bandaging. 10-16, illus., 17
Circular velocity, for space rockets. 10-44
Circulating matrices. 1-200
Circulation, atmospheric. with diagrams, 1-241-44; *2-89-98
See also **Winds**
Circulation of blood. *3-325-34; 381-92
Development in unborn human young, 8-26, illus., 32
Discovery, with illus., 3-10-12
Growth and aging, circulation in, 8-80-81, 95-96, 101
Heart's role in, with illus., 1-277-79
Muscular exercise, role in, 3-206, 207; 10-87
Pulse rate, 10-76, 87
Respiration, role in, 4-204, 206-07, illus., 202
See also **Blood; Capillaries; Heart**
Circulatory systems.
Animal
Birds, with illus., 5-421
Fishes, with illus., 4-100-01
Insects, 2-405
Lancelets, 4-4
Lobsters, illus., 2-239
Man, illus., 1-148f; with illus., 3-325-34
See also **Circulation of blood**
Circumpolar circulation, atmospheric. 1-238
Circumpolar stars. 1-262, illus., 261
Circuses. Elephants in, 7-410-11
Photographing animals at, 6-313
Cirques, land forms due to glacial erosion. 9-168-69, diagram, 164-65

Cirrhosis of liver, liver disease.
Alcohol indirectly responsible for, 4-411
Cirri, bristle-like processes on some protozoans. 2-66
Cirripeds, crustaceans. with illus., 2-242-43
Cirrocumulus clouds. diagram, 1-317; 2-222, illus., 217
Cirrostratus clouds. diagram, 1-317; 2-222, illus., 216, 217
Cirrus clouds. diagram, 1-317; 2-222, illus., 217
Cities.
*Air pollution, 3-349-56
*Waste disposal, 5-326-36
Animals found in, 10-256
Destruction of, in World War II, illus., 9-325
Location of, 3-227-28
Water pumping systems, 2-34
Citric acid.
Experiment with, with illus., 4-231
Food preservative, 4-164
Citric-acid cycle, metabolic process. 2-12
Civet, type of fur. 7-238
Civets. with illus., 8-244-47
Civil defense. *Nuclear-bomb precautions, 9-391-96
Civil engineering. 1-221-23
Civil War, United States. Balloons used in, 6-177
Meat-processing advanced during, 5-164
Civilian Conservation Corps (CCC). 6-4, illus., 3
Civilization.
*Language development, 1-107-21
*Population, 3-225-34
Communication advances, effects of, 6-382-83
Domestication of animals, effects of, 7-327, 332; 10-250
Nuclear warfare's effects on, 9-356, 358
Spirit of progress in nineteenth century, 5-73-74
Stone used for building by various peoples, 2-81
Transportation advances, effects of, 6-382
Winds, effect of, 2-89
See also **Archaeology; Education; Inventions; Man; Races**
Cladophora, species of green algae. 3-218
Clairvoyance. Study of, 9-57
Clams. 2-196, 198-99, illus., 193
Shell of, illus., 2-101
Clamworms. 2-162, illus., 160-61
Clarinets. Sound production in, 5-217-18
Clark, William, American explorer. 7-28
Classes, groups in classification of living things. 1-289
Classes (castes), among insects. See **Social insects**
Classification.
*Elements, periodic law of chemical, 4-304-10
*Living things, 1-287-306
Birds, orders of, 5-425-26
Cuvier's, 4-392, illus., 391
Insectivores, families of, 7-96
Insects, orders of, 2-412-24
Lamarck's, 4-389-90, illus., 388
Linnaeus' binomial system of nomenclature, 3-376-77
Chemical elements, nineteenth century classification of, 5-83-86
Color, 7-286-88
Languages, 1-117-19
Clastic rocks, sedimentary rocks. 3-424
Clausewitz, Karl von, Prussian army officer. 9-211
Clausius, Rudolf Julius Emanuel, German mathematical physicist (1822—88). He taught in the universities of Zurich, Würzburg and Bonn. His researches led to the formulation of the second law of thermodynamics (heat cannot of itself pass from a colder to a hotter body). He contributed to the kinetic theory of gases

Clausius, Rudolf Julius Emanuel (continued)
and paved the way for Arrhenius' electrolytic-dissocia-
tion theory. See also 6-254
Clavicles, collarbones, in shoulder. illus., 1-148b; 3-
78-80, illus., 74, 207
Clavius, Christopher, Bavarian astronomer and mathe-
matician.
Calendar reform, 10-176
Claw hammers. with illus., 7-215-16
Claws, animal. Cats', action of, with illus., 1-284
Clay, Jacob, Dutch scientist.
Cosmic-ray investigations, 8-394
Clay.
  *Pottery made from clay, 7-393-407
  Colloidal state of, 5-302-03
  Feldspar changes to, with illus., 3-179
  Fertility of soil maintained by, 2-172
  Limestone caves containing residue of, 5-54
  Sewer pipes made of, 5-328
  Soil texture, 2-18, 19, illus., 19
  Streams carry and deposit, 8-13
Clay, red, marine deposit. 6-34
"Clean" atom bombs. 9-141
Cleaning.
  Coal from mine, cleaning of, 1-415
  Detergents, testing of, illus., 2-232
  High-frequency sound used for, 8-110, illus., 109
  House design, factor affecting, 4-267
  Nursing, role in, 10-56, 58, 61-63, 65-66, illus., 56,
    62-63
  Volcanic dust used in cleaning powders, 7-140
Cleaning fluids. Safety procedures in using, 7-192
Cleanliness.
  Health, effect on, 10-81-84
  Zoos, cleanliness in, 10-157-58
Clear-wing moths. 3-202
Cleavage, splitting of crystals along structural lines.
  5-340, illus., 337
  Minerals identified by cleavage patterns, 5-255; 9-
    303
Cleft palate, abnormal condition of palate. 4-332;
  8-29
Clement IV (Guy de Foulques), Pope. 2-306-07
Clermont, steamboat. with illus., 4-109-10; 6-378, illus.,
  379
Click beetles. 3-341, illus., 340
Cliff dwellers. Irrigation systems of, 8-192
Cliff swallows. 6-68, illus., 67
Climate.
  *Atmosphere, 1-230-40
  *Clouds, 2-212-22
  *Meteorology for amateurs, 1-315-22
  *Past climates, 3-177-85
  *Precipitation, 2-346-57
  *Seasonal changes and life, 5-408-13
  *Weather forecasting, 1-241-54
  *Winds, 2-89-98
  Changes in climate through geologic time, 6-370,
    371, 372, 373, 374
  Cold, 3-179-80
  Desert, 3-178-79
  IGY studies of, 5-192-94
  Oceanic currents have effect on, 6-238, illus., 237
  Soil development influenced by, 2-21-23
  Warm-moist, 3-179
  See also Rain; Weather
Climatius, extinct fish. illus., 4-94
Climax stage. 6-224, illus., 222; 10-188
  Forest climaxes of the United States, 5-257-60
Climbing perch, fish. 4-99
Clinical psychology. 9-321

Clinical thermometers. with illus., 3-411; with illus.,
  10-57-58
Clinics, alcoholism. 4-414
Clinker ship hulls. 4-107, 108
Clippers, sailing ships. 4-108-09
Cloaca, discharge chamber.
  Man's—embryonic structure, 8-28
  Primitive animals', 7-4, 6
Clock-radio. Electronic device, illus., 10-168
Clocks. Atomic clock, illus., 2-234
  Development of, in seventeenth century, 3-19
  Frequency regulated by electrostriction crystals,
    2-294
  Medieval, illus., 2-313
Closed-sequence systems.
  Type of automatic control, 10-235-36
Clostridium botulinum, organism that causes botulism.
  4-153
Cloth. See Fabrics
Clothes moths. with illus., 3-202
Clothing.
  *Buttons, 7-208-13
  *Furs, 7-235-38
  Coal-miner's clothing, 1-414
  Function of, 2-245
  Heat, insulating effect of, 4-11
  Mildewing of, 3-27
Clotting, blood. See Blood clotting
Cloud chambers, devices that show paths of atomic
  particles, with illus., 9-127
Cloud classification. 2-220, 222
Clouded leopards. 8-210
Clouds. *2-212-22
  Dust as framework of, 7-142
  Experiment in cloud formation, with illus., 2-330
  Explanation of, 1-245
  Formation of, 2-89
  Jupiter's cloud belts, with illus., 5-22-23
  Lightning and, 1-398-99
  Photography of, illus., 1-241; with illus., 6-316; 9-223
  Types of clouds, table, 2-222
  Weather indicated by clouds, with diagram, 1-315-16,
    diagram, 317
Club fungi. with illus., 3-29-32
Club mosses. illus., 1-302; 3-192, illus., 190
  Unchanged for millions of years, 6-283
Clubs. Aged persons', 8-83
Clumping of blood cells (agglutination). 3-332-34
Clutches, for automobiles. with illus., 2-138-40
Coaches, horse-drawn. with illus., 1-104-05
Coaches, railway. with illus., 1-186-87
  Development of, 1-182
Coagulants.
  Sewage purified by, 5-330-31
  Water purified by, 2-279, with illus., 278
Coagulation of blood. See Blood clotting
Coal. *1-405-20
  Ammonia derived from, 3-126
  Coking coal for iron smelting, 1-341-42
  Conveyer belts carry, 6-170, illus., 171
  Dust explosions, 2-229; 8-273
  Formation of, 3-424
  Kerosene from, 4-141
  Liquid and gas fuels from, 1-89
  Locomotives and, 1-89, 416, diagram, 90
  Origin and nature of, 3-324, 407
  Plastics, used in manufacture of, 8-224
  Vegetation of Carboniferous period, 3-192
  See also Coke; Lignite
Coal gas. Lighting, used for, 4-233

Coal mining. *1-405-20
  Explosives used in, 8-286-87
  Machinery, *illus.*, 1-92d
Coal oil. See Kerosene
Coal Sack, dark area near Southern Cross. 1-337;
  8-153, 155, *illus.*, 152; 9-361
Coal tars.
  Aromatic hydrocarbons distilled from, 7-274
  Chemicals and other products from, *with illus.*,
    1-419-20; 8-183-84, 185
  Dye stuffs from, 8-183-84, 186, 187
  Organic compounds synthesized by use of, *with illus.*,
    5-80-81
  See also **Dyes**
Coalinga, California. Brackish water converted into
  fresh water in, 2-284
Coast Guard. See **United States Coast Guard**
Coast Mountains, mountain range of western North
  America. 10-23
Coast Ranges, mountain system of western North
  America, 10-24, 216
Coastal crabs. Migration of, 9-430
Coasting orbit techniques, for placing artificial satellites.
  with diagram, 8-131
Coasts. Types of, *with illus.*, 8-354-58
Coating, process for providing smooth surface for paper.
  4-374-75, *illus.*, 375-76
Coatis. 7-317
Coaxial cables. 2-383, 395
  Television, use in, 5-288
Cobalt (Co), chemical element. Atomic number, 27;
  atomic weight, 58.9332; melting point, 1,495° C.; boiling point, 2,900° C.; specific gravity, 8.9. Metal; hard,
  brittle, highly magnetic, gray with reddish tinge. Discovered by Brandt in 1735; name derived from German
  kobold: "goblin" or "evil spirit." Occurs in certain
  ores, usually sulfide or arsenide, in small amounts. Prepared by reducing the oxide with aluminum. The alloy
  Stellite consists of 75 to 90 per cent cobalt and 10 to
  25 per cent chromium, sometimes with small amounts of
  other metals; it is used for machine tools, surgical instruments, dies and so on. Cobalt salts have been employed to produce permanent blue colors in porcelain,
  glass and enamel.
  Radioactive cobalt
    Atomic farming with, 10-251-52
    Food preservation with, 10-116, *illus.*, 114, 116
    Radium substitute, 9-332
    Tumor treatment, use in, 10-100, *illus.*, 101
    Steelmaking, use in, 1-352
Cobalt bombs. 9-141
Cobras. *with illus.*, 5-361-62
Cobwebs. 2-263
Coca leaves. Cocaine yielded by, 5-401, *illus.*, 400
Cocaine. 5-401-02, *illus.*, 400; 8-188
Cocci, bacteria. 3-64, *illus.*, 63
  Pneumococci, *illus.*, 8-363
  See also **Bacteria**
Coccygeal nerves. 6-329, *illus.*, 328
Coccyx, lower end of backbone. 3-77, *illus.*, 75
Cochlea, of ear. 4-381, *with illus.*, 380; 5-122-23;
  7-299-300, *illus.*, 298
Cockcroft, John Douglas, English physicist. 8-419
  Voltage multiplier, development of, 9-242
Cockleburs. Fruits of, 5-5, *illus.*, 4
Cockles, bivalves. Shell of, *illus.*, 2-101
Cockroaches. *with illus.*, 3-147-49
  Close-up view, *illus.*, 2-frontispiece.
  Fossil cockroaches, *illus.*, 6-372
  Legs of, *with illus.*, 1-283-84
  Prehistoric, 1-390

Coconut palms. *illus.*, 1-303
Coconuts. Water as a dispersal agent of, 3-240, *illus.*,
  241; 5-4-5, 7
Cocoons, insect-larva wrappings. 2-407; 3-196, 358,
  368, *illus.*, 359; *with illus.*, 5-174-75, 178-81
  Moths and butterflies, 3-196, *illus.*, 195, 197
  Silk prepared from silkworm cocoons, 5-178-80, *illus.*,
    175, 178-81, 183
  Silkworm, *with illus.*, 5-174-75, 178-80, *illus.*, 181
Cod. 4-320, *illus.*, 316
  Migration of, 9-427
Codes. Biological cellular code in protein formation,
  9-386
  Space and missile flights guided by coded signals,
    8-128
Codling moths. *with illus.*, 9-192
Codosiga, genus of one-celled animals. 2-63
Coefficient of cubical expansion. 3-415
Coefficient of linear expansion. 3-414-15
Coelacanths, primitive fish. *4-196-99
Coelenterates, *2-148-51
  Classification of, 1-292
  See also **Corals; Sea anemones**
Coesite, form of silica. Meteorites, evidence of, 6-92
Coffee trees. *with illus.*, 5-148
  Leaves, *illus.*, 5-139
Cofferdams. Bridge construction, 2-343, *illus.*, 342
  Dam construction, 8-320
Coherers.
  Wireless telegraphy, use in, 6-245
Cohesion, attraction between molecules of the same
  substance. 5-370, 371
  Water molecules, 8-2-4
Cohn, Edwin J., American biochemist.
  Blood-plasma fractionation, research in, 3-326; 9-36
Coincidence counters, radiation detectors. 9-340-41
Coins. Antiquity, use in, 4-244
Coke.
  Coal, manufacture of coke and by-products from,
    with illus., 1-417, 419-20
  Iron smelting, 1-341-43
  Ovens, 1-341-42
  Petroleum coke, 4-150
  Plastics, used in manufacture of, 8-224, 225
Colbert, Jean-Baptiste, French statesman.
  Academy of Science proposed by, 3-268
Colchicine, alkaloid derived from roots of autumn cro-
  cus.
  Chromosome doubling caused by, 9-291
Cold.
  Animals affected by, 5-413, *with illus.*, **409-12**
  Atmosphere of earth moderates, 1-232
  Cryogenics, science of very low temperatures, *with
    illus.*, 5-207-10
  Food preservation by, 4-159-63. *illus.*, 158, 159, 162-63
  Plants affected by, *illus.*, 5-408, 409
  Treatments by, 10-67
  See also **Heat**
Cold, sense of. *with illus.*, 7-304-05
Cold climate. 3-179-80
Cold-drawing, steel-shaping process. 1-349, 351
Cold forging. Plastics, 8-228
Cold fronts. See **Fronts**
"Cold" light. Examples of, 8-118
Cold (wet) manures, soil fertilizers. 2-165
Cold-reduction, steel-shaping process. 1-349-50
Cold-rolling, metal-shaping process.
  Steel applied to, 1-349-50, *illus.*, 338
Cold-type (photographic) machines, for typesetting.
  with illus., 1-202-03
Colds. Vaccination against, 7-351

Colebrookdale Iron Works. Rails built by, 1-180
Coleoptera, order of insects. 2-414; *3-335-48
  See also **Beetles**
Coleuses, plants.
  Meristematic tissue of, *illus.,* 3-46
  Terrariums, use in, 5-367
Coliform bacteria. 2-276
Collagen. Bone contains, 3-73
Collagenous fibers. Skin contains, 2-174
Collapsing of lungs. Tuberculosis treated by, 9-182
Collar cells. See **Choanocytes**
Collarbones. See **Clavicles**
Collared lizards. *illus.,* 5-201
Collation, in bookbinding. 1-214
Collections, scientific. See **Projects and experiments**
Collective pitch, of helicopter. 6-194
Collembola, order of insects. 2-412
Collenchyma, tissue of living cells. 5-263-64
Collies, dogs. *illus.,* 10-241
Collimators, of spectroscopes. 7-279, *illus.,* 280
Collisions.
  Boats may collide because of decreased water pressure, *with illus.,* 2-36
Collodion.
  Photography, use in, 9-402-03, *illus.,* 402
  Uses of, 8-276
Colloidal science. Definition and scope, 5-296
Colloids. *5-294-304
  Protoplasm contains, 2-6, 11
  Radioactive colloids used in medicine, 10-100
Colombia. Panama secedes from, 4-192
Colon, part of large intestine. 4-329-30, *illus.,* 322, 330
Colonies of microorganisms. *illus.,* 10-130a
Colonization. Overpopulation solved by, 3-233
Color. *7-277-90
  *Land theory of color vision, 8-178-80
  Bioluminescence, 2-189
  Birds' feathers, 5-419
  Clouds, colors of, 2-220
  Colloidal particles scatter light and cause, 5-300-01
  Dust as cause of colors in sky, 7-142
  Dyes, 8-186
  Experiments with, *with illus.,* 8-122-23
  Film (photographic) and, 9-408, 412-14
  Heat reflected or absorbed by, 4-16
  Insects, 2-404-05, 408-10
    Moths and butterflies, 3-194-95
    True bugs, 3-254
  Interior decoration, element in, 4-269-71
  Leaves, causes of color, 6-55
    Changes in color of, 4-73-74
  Meaning of, 4-470-71
  Minerals identified by, 5-254
  Photography, separation of color in, *illus.,* 9-400a-b
  Rivers, color of, 6-417
  Scattering of light produces, 5-300-01
  Skin and hair color, 2-175-76, 179
  Sky colors, causes of, 1-232
  Solutions, experiments with colored, 7-179, *with diagrams,* 176-77
  Stars, color of, 7-45; 8-57, 60
  Study of, 1600-1765, 3-275-78
  Triangle of complementary colors, *with diagram,* 9-412
  See also **Protective coloration**
Color blindness. 7-289
  Inheritance of, 8-342-43
Color changes, in animals.
  Amphibians, 5-156
  Lizards, 5-203-04

Color-corrected photographic plates. *illus.,* 9-408
Color filter glass. 3-315
Color lithography. *illus.,* 1-204a-d
Color mixing. 7-285-86
  Land theory of, *with illus.,* 8-178-80
Color perception.
  *Land theory, 8-178-80
  Psychology of, 7-290
Color photography. 9-412-14
  Separation of colors for, *illus.,* 9-400a-b
Color printing. *with diagram,* 1-213-14, *illus.,* 204a-d
  Principle of, 7-286
Color-printing presses. 1-214, *diagram,* 213
Color television. 5-288; *illus.,* 6-298c
Color triangle. *with diagram,* 9-412
Color vision. *with diagram,* 7-288-90, *illus.,* 287
  *Land theory, 8-178-80
  Birds, 5-422-23
Color wheels, for analysis of color. 7-285-86, *illus.,* 287
Colorado.
  Zinc mine in, *illus.,* 3-39
Colorado Plateau. 6-109; 8-11
Colorado River, western United States.
  Dammed up by Hoover Dam, *illus.,* 8-316b
  Grand Canyon of, *with illus.,* 8-11
Colorado river toads. *illus.,* 5-152
Colorants. Plastics, used in manufacture of, 8-225
Coloration, protective. See **Natural selection; Protective coloration**
Colorimeters, devices for measuring color properties. 7-288
Colubridae, family of Old and New World harmless snakes. 5-358-60
Columbia, breed of sheep. *illus.,* 10-247
Columbia Broadcasting System (CBS).
  Color-television system, 5-288
Columbia Plateau. 6-109
Columbines. Seeds, *illus.,* 5-63
Columbus, Christopher, Italian sea captain.
  America, discovered by, 2-364-65
Columella, auditory ossicle in birds, mammals and amphibians. 4-383, *with illus.,* 381
Columns, calcium carbonate deposits in caves. *with illus.,* 5-55
Coma. Alcoholic anesthesia, 4-409
Coma, nebulous portion of comet's head. 5-391-92
Coma Berenices (Hair of Berenice), constellation. 1-331-32
Coma cluster, group of galaxies. 8-53
Combs, cellular nests of bees and wasps. *with illus.,* 3-366-68, 372, *illus.,* 363, 364, 365, 370
Combustion.
  Breathing, relation to, 4-200-01, 207-08, *illus.,* 202
  Essential needed for, 4-351
  Gases that play a part in, 1-231
  Muscular energy furnished by "burning" of foods in body, 3-205-06
  Rocket and jet fuels, 10-41-42, 45, 54, *illus.,* 43
  Spontaneous combustion, 7-193
Combustion, heat of. *with illus.,* 3-414
Combustion (bomb) calorimeters. *with illus.,* 3-414
Combustion knocking. Combustion knock is a rattling sound in an engine. It is caused by vibration due to the uncontrolled explosion of compressed gas in the cylinders. The reaction that takes place is as follows: When the spark from the spark plug is set off in the combustion chamber, it meets with already vaporized gas; this gas ignites and burns rapidly. If, however, the gas burns and expands too rapidly, it compresses and superheats the gas that remains in front of the flame. The temperature of the remaining gas is then higher

Combustion knocking *(continued)*
than necessary for ignition and when it fires, it does so with an explosive force called detonation. This reaction causes pressure waves to move back and forth across the combustion chamber at the speed of about 700 miles an hour. The pressure waves in turn set up reciprocal motion in the cylinder head and walls, resulting in a knocking or rattling sound. Combustion of this kind is, of course, undesirable because it causes wear and tear on certain parts of the engine and also a wasteful consumption of fuel.

Comet, de Havilland. *illus.,* 6-195

Comets. *5-390-99
  Brooks' comet, *illus.,* 1-258
  Jupiter's family of, 5-24
  Meteor showers associated with, 6-97
  Nineteenth century study of, 6-393, *illus.,* 392
  Observations of, 6-85
  Radar used to track, 9-207
  Search for, in solar eclipses, 3-137
  Solar system, comets as part of, 3-159-60, 161
  See also **Astronomy; Halley, Edmund**

Comité Spécial de l'Année Géophysique Internationale (CSAGI). See **Special Committee of the International Geophysical Year**

Commensalism. 8-361

Commercial fertilizers. 2-170-71

Common bile duct. *illus.,* 1-148d

Common iliac artery and vein, in abdomen. *illus.,* 1-148f

Common-impression cylinder presses, in printing. 1-214, *diagram,* 213

Common logarithms, logarithms to the base 10. 2-75-76

Common mushrooms. 3-31, *illus.,* 23

Common space motion, of stars. 7-228

Communicable diseases. See **Infectious diseases**

Communication.
  *Facsimile transmission, 7-390-92
  *Language, 1-107-21
  *Microfilming, 10-68-74
  *Phonograph, 7-362-69
  *Photography, 9-397-414; 10-163-67
    *Nature photography, 6-311-16
  *Printing and engraving, 1-196-214
  *Radar, 9-387-90
  *Radio, 3-85-98
  *Telegraph, 2-377-85
  *Telephone, 2-386-95
  *Television, 5-276-88
  *Typewriter, 1-265-76
  Development of, in nineteenth century, *with illus.,* 6-381-82
  Electrical devices, *with illus.,* 5-238-46; 9-239
  Ionosphere affects radio, 1-240
  Nervous system as communication network, 6-317, *illus.,* 319
  Pneumatic tubes used for, 9-66-67
  Radio waves, uses in communication, 7-202, 207, *illus.,* 200, 207
  Train, 1-193-94
  Weather-data communication, *with illus.,* 1-252-54
  See also **Electronics; Radio; Telegraph; Telephone; Television**

Communication, animal.
  Antelopes, 8-387
  Bears, 7-311
  Birds, 5-424-25
  Honeybees, 3-370
  Primates, 1-66; 9-262

Communication satellites. 10-47

Communities.
  *Human populations, 3-225-34
  *Insects, 3-357-72
  *Plant and animal communities, 10-181-90
  *Waste disposal, 5-326-36
  Gas, community uses of, 5-105-06
  Insects, *with illus.,* 2-412a-d

"Community houses," nests built by social weavers. *with illus.,* 5-418h

Commutative laws of addition and multiplication. 2-69

Commutators.
  Electric generators', *with illus.,* 6-129-31

Como, Lake, Italy. *illus.,* 7-59

Compact bone. 3-73-74

Comparative anatomy. See **Anatomy**

Compartments, Pullman sleeping cars. 1-187-88

Compasses.
  Electric current effects, 5-231, *illus.,* 232
  Gyroscopic. 6-193
  Homemade, *with illus.,* 8-143

Complementary colors.
  Light, 9-412-13, *diagram,* 412, *illus.,* 400a-b

Complete fertilizers. 2-171

Complete flowers. 4-122

Complete metamorphosis, of insects. 2-407-08, 414

Complex numbers (imaginary numbers). *with illus.,* 1-161

Composite family, large plant group.
  Flowers, *with illus.,* 4-123-24

Composting, of wastes. 5-336

Composition, chemical. 1-85

Compositional formulas. 7-266

Compositors, typesetters. *with illus.,* 1-199

Compound bars. *with illus.,* 3-415

Compound eyes. Insects, 2-403, *illus.,* 403, 404; 7-262

Compound fractures. 3-84
  First aid for, *with illus.,* 10-11

Compound leaves. *with illus.,* 5-139

Compound (expansion) steam engines. Ships, use in, 4-111

Compounds, chemical. *with illus.,* 1-80-81
  Carbon compounds, 7-263-76
  See also **Chemistry; Elements, chemical**

Compressed air. *9-58-70
  Breathing air under pressure, effects of, *with illus.,* 4-206-07
  Experiments with, *with illus.,* 2-324-25; *with illus.,* 7-220-21

Compressed-air sickness. See **Caisson disease**

Compression.
  Sound waves, *with illus.,* 5-116, 117

Compression molding. Plastics, 7-210, *illus.,* 211; *with diagram,* 8-230, *illus.,* 220b

Compression system, of refrigeration, 4-159, *illus.,* 158

Compression waves. Earthquakes show, 9-107, 114-15

Compressive strain. 5-375

Compressor plants, compressed-air suppliers. 9-66

Compressor stations, for pumping natural gas. 5-103-04, *illus.,* 98b

Compressors, air. 9-60-65
  Penicillin, used in manufacture of, *illus.,* 7-53
  Portable compressors for refilling divers' air tanks, *with illus.,* 6-26b
  Wind-tunnel air compressors, 10-234, *diagram,* 233

Compton, Arthur Holly, American physicist (1892-1962); director of plutonium research for the atomic-bomb project. His scientific work has been with X rays, photons and gamma rays. He discovered the change in wave length occurring with scattered X rays, known as the Compton effect, for which he received the Nobel Prize in physics in 1927, jointly with C. T. R. Wilson.

Compton, Arthur Holly (continued)
Compton has also directed a world-wide survey on the nature of cosmic rays. He became Chancellor of Washington University in 1945. illus., **10-303**
  Cosmic-ray investigations, **8-395**
Compton, Karl, American scientist. Research investment and stock values, **1-88**
Computers.
  Space and missile flights guided by, **8-128, 130,** diagram, **129**
  Superconductive elements used in, **5-210**
Computing machines. See **Automation; Digital computers; Electronic computers**
Comstock Lode, vein of gold- and silver-bearing ore. **4-243**
Concentrated fertilizers. 2-171
Concentrating, in ore dressing. with diagrams, **1-371-75**
Concentrating (or shaking) tables, in ore dressing. with diagram, **1-373**
Concentration, method of preserving beverages. **4-167**
Concentrations, chemical. Ions in acid and base solutions, **4-340-42**
  Reactions affected by, **2-228-29, 230**
Conceptus, product of conception. **8-22**
Concertina method, of snake locomotion. with illus., **5-354d**
Conchae. See **Turbinate bones**
Conchoidal break, type of fracture characteristic of certain minerals. **5-255**
Conchs. 2-201
Concrete.
  *Construction, concrete, **3-113-25**
  Building material, illus., **7-127**
  Chemical formation, rate of, with diagram, **2-227-28**
  Dam construction, **8-313**
  Gamma rays absorbed by, **9-351**
  Highway construction, **3-301-02,** illus., **298c-d**
  Piping made of, **2-276**
  Reinforced concrete, **7-123-24**
  Sewer pipes made of, **5-328**
  See also **Reinforced concrete**
Condensation.
  Molecular behavior in, with illus., **1-167-68**
  Water vapor, **1-245,** with illus., **2-347-48**
Condensation trails, of airplanes. **2-214**
Condensers. 6-122
  Making Liebig condenser for home laboratory, with illus., **4-225-26**
  See also **Capacitors**
Condensers, steam-engine. Ships, **4-111**
Conditioned reflexes. See **Reflexes**
Conditioning. Alcoholism treated by, **4-413**
Condors. 6-155, 156
Conduction.
  Electricity, **9-227,** illus., **228**
  Heat transferred by, **4-10-13, 19-20,** illus., **9-11, 21**
  Sound, in various materials, with illus., **5-222-25**
Conduction, of nerve impulses. **6-318,** with illus., **320-21, 323**
Conduction testers. Testing electrical properties of solutions with, with illus., **4-345**
Conductors, electrical. 6-121, 129; 9-227, illus., **228**
  Metals as, **6-302**
  Prospecting with, with diagram, **7-359-61**
Conductors, heat. 4-10-13, 19-20, illus., **9-11**
Condyles, processes of femur. with illus., **3-82**
Cone-bearing plants. with illus., **3-399-403**
  *Germination, **5-61-67**
Cone crushers, in ore dressing. with diagram, **1-372**
Cones, common solids. with illus., **3-443**

Cones, of retina. See **Rods and cones of eye**
Cones, crater. See **Crater cones**
Cones of eye. See **Rods and cones of eye**
Conestoga wagons. with illus., **1-106**
Coney Island, New York.
  Chemicals used to purify bathing water, **5-330-31**
Confinement, of plasmas. **1-175-78**
Conglomerate, sedimentary rock. **3-424; 9-308**
Congo eels, salamanders. with illus., **5-157**
Congo floor maggots. 3-287
Conic sections. with illus., **3-438-40**
  Cometary orbits depicted as, **5-394-95,** illus., **396**
Conidia, asexual reproductive spores of fungi. **3-22, 28,** with illus., **27**
Conies, animals. Fur, **7-238**
Coniferales, order of gymnosperms. **3-402-03,** illus., **400**
Coniferous forests. United States, **5-257-60**
Conifers, plants. **3-402-03,** illus., **400; 6-57**
  How to recognize, with illus., **5-141-43**
  Seed dispersal in, **5-1,** illus., **3**
Conjunction, orbital. Jupiter, **5-21**
Connecting rods.
  Automobile engines, with illus., **2-132, 133**
Connective tissues.
  Human body, **1-144-45, 147**
  Human muscles, relation to, **3-203, 204**
Connector neurons (nerves). Body's defenses, role in, diagram, **7-347**
Conquest.
  Overpopulation solved by, **3-233**
Consciousness.
  Cerebral cortex and, **6-324**
  See also **Mind; Nervous system; Psychology**
Conservation of energy. 1-84-85
Conservation of matter. 1-84-85
  Chemical reactions and, **2-226**
  Lavoisier's statement, **4-356-57**
Conservation of natural resources. *6-1-14
  Forests, illus., **5-265**
  See also **Coal; Minerals; Oil; Wastes; Water power**
Conservation of parity, law in physics. *7-107-10
Conservation of wildlife. *9-266-78
  International agencies devoted to marine-life conservation, **6-36**
  Methods of marine-fish conservation, **4-311-12**
  Necessity for, **6-8, 10**
Consonance, of musical tones. **5-213-14**
Constant speed. 2-118
Constantine, Roman emperor.
  Baptism, illus., **1-368**
  Calendar reforms, **10-175-76**
Constants.
  Astronomical, **10-297-98**
  Physical, **10-295**
Constellations. *1-323-37
  How to observe, with diagrams, **6-79-81**
  See also **Astronomy; Stars; Universe**
Constipation. 4-332-33
  Nature of, and dietary remedies, **5-275**
Constitution of Massachusetts Commonwealth.
  Promotion of science, **4-34**
Constitution, United States.
  Promotion of science, **4-34**
  See also **Government; United States**
Construction.
  *Bridges, **2-332-45**
  *Canals, **4-183-95**
  *Concrete construction, **3-113-25**
  *Dams, **8-305-20**
  *Glass as construction material, **8-388-92**

Construction (continued)
*Homes, 4-265-72
*Materials, 7-115-28
*Roads and highways, 3-293-306
*Shipbuilding history, 4-106-18
*Tunnels, 2-43-57
Engineers engaged in, 1-227
Pipelines for natural gas, 5-101-03
Pneumatic caissons used in, 9-67-68
Stone used in, 2-82, with illus., 83
Constructive interference, optical phenomenon. with illus., 7-281-82
Consultation, as function of engineers. 1-227
Consumers, in ecosystems. 10-184-86
Consumption. See Tuberculosis
Contact allergies. 4-260
Detection of, 4-263
Contact, chemical. Reactions influenced by degree of, 2-228-29
Contact prints, photographic. 9-410
Contacts, in solar eclipses. 3-137
Contagious diseases. See Diseases; Health; Tuberculosis
Containers, food, 4-155-56
Continental code. 2-381, diagram, 380
Continental drift, movement of continents.
Ice ages accounted for by, 3-184
Mountain building explained by, 10-216
Ocean ridges as evidence of?, 6-74
Continental glaciers, ice sheets. 9-165-66, 170-73
Land forms produced by, with illus., 9-171-73
Continental islands. 4-133
Continental shelves. 6-70-72, diagram, 72-73
Continental slopes. 6-70-71, 72-74, diagram, 73
Continents. See Continental drift; Geological time
Continuous emission spectra. illus., 7-284a
Laws of spectrum analysis, 5-86
Continuous-flow calorimeters. with illus., 3-414
Continuous miner, in coal. 1-412
Continuous-process distillation. Petroleum refining uses, 4-147
Continuum. See Four-dimensional continuum
Contour ditches, used in flood irrigation. 8-196
Contour farming. illus., 5-265; 6-5
Contraction. Cooling causes, 3-414, 415
Contraction, muscular. 3-205, 206-08
Contraction theory of sun's energy. 3-109
Contrast, with color. illus., 7-284d
Contrasts, color. 7-290
Control of air pollution. with illus., 3-354-56
Control systems, automatic. See Automatic control systems
Control towers.
Airports, with illus., 6-198-200
Convair, American turbojet plane. 7-74
Convair YB-60, U.S. Air Force plane. illus., 9-218
Convection, heat transfer by currents. 4-12-16, 20, illus., 4-12-13, 21; 9-106
Atmospheric currents example of, with diagrams, 1-242-44
Cloud formation by, 2-213-14
Experiments with, 4-20, illus., 21
Heating, part played in, 2-245
Conventions, scientific. Young scientists at, 8-72
Convergence, optical illusion. Meteor showers exhibit, 6-96
Convergence, phenomenon in biologic evolution. 7-422
Conversion table. Weights and measures, 10-296
Conversions, energy. with illus., 9-226-34
Converters, copper. with diagram, 1-378

Conveyer belts. *6-168-71
Breadmaking, with diagrams, 9-297-98, diagram, 299
Conveyers. Gold mines, illus., 4-247
Convolutions, of cerebral cortex. with illus., 6-324
See also **Cerebral cortex; Cerebrum**
Cooking.
High-frequency sound, illus., 8-107
Safety precautions in, 7-191, 196, 197, 198
Cook's tree boas, snakes. with illus., 5-354d
Coolidge, William D., American physical chemist.
Tungsten electric-light filament, 4-239
Cooling. Beehives cooled by worker bees, 3-370, illus., 366
Heat pumps can provide, 2-251-52
See also **Refrigeration**
Cooling systems, of air compressors. 9-62-63
Cooling systems, of engines.
Automobile engines, with illus., 2-136
Gasoline engines, 4-89
Cooper, Edward, American iron and steel manufacture. 6-384
Cooper, Peter, American ironmaster.
Locomotive built by, 1-181
Co-operation.
*Insects, 3-357-72
Industrial scientific research, 1-88-89, 93-94
See also **Social life, animal; Symbiosis**
Co-operatives, farmers'. Meat-packing plants, 5-166
Cooper's hawks. 6-157, illus., 158
Cooper's tanagers. 6-108
Co-ordinates. See Cartesian co-ordinates
Co-ordination of muscular movements.
Cerebellum as center for, 6-326
Development in human baby, 8-97
Coots, birds. 6-403-04
Copenhagen Observatory. 5-395
Copepods, crustaceans. 2-243
Intermediate hosts of Guinea worms. 2-158
Copernicus, Nicolaus, Polish astronomer. with illus., 2-371-73
Theory of universe, 3-162
Upheld by Galileo, 3-2-4
Copernicus, crater on moon. illus., 4-283
Copolymers, chains of molecules. 8-222
Synthetic rubber made from, 6-358
Copper (Cu), chemical element. Atomic number, 29; atomic weight, 63.54; melting point, 1,083° C.; boiling point, 2,336° C.; specific gravity, 8.93-8.95. Bright, malleable metal; good conductor of heat and electricity. Discovered in prehistoric days; name derived from Latin cuprum, after the island of Cyprus. Found pure and in many minerals; obtained from compounds by smelting, leaching or electrolysis. Used widely for kitchen utensils and in the electrical and building industries. Its alloys, particularly brass and bronze, are very important. The sulfate, blue vitriol, is an effective agricultural poison. See also 3-36-37
Alloys, 1-382
Building material, 7-121
Diet, copper essential in, 4-59
Electroluminescent devices, use in, 9-345
Heat conductivity of, 4-10
Living cells contain, 2-6
Oxidation of, 5-89-90
Printed circuits, use of copper in, with illus., 6-50-51
Printing plates made electrolytically from, 1-207, diagram, 208
Smelting and refining, with diagrams, 1-377-78
Sound, speed of, in copper, 5-119
Steelmaking, uses in, 1-352
Copper chloride. Electrolysis of, with illus., 5-89-90

Copper converters. *with diagram,* 1-378
Copper sulfate.
  Algae in water supply destroyed by, 2-277
  Experiments and tricks with, 7-176-77
  Testing for protein, use in, 7-136
Copperheads, snakes. 5-364, *illus.,* 362
Coptos, Egypt. Buttons found in tomb, 7-209
Coquina, sedimentary rock. *illus.,* 3-424
Coracoid process, of shoulder blade. 3-80
Coral. *illus.,* 1-41
  Beach sands consist of, in tropics, 8-352
  Growth of reefs, *with illus.,* 4-134-39
Coral fungi. *with illus.,* 3-30
Coral reefs. 6-71-72, 75, 77; 8-358-59
Coral snakes. 5-363, *illus.,* 360
Corals. 2-151, *illus.,* 148-49
  Drawings by Cuvier, *illus.,* 4-391
  Fixed animals, 1-41
  Fossil forms, 1-389
  Growth of reefs, 6-75, 77, *illus.,* 77
  Reef-building polyps, 4-134-35
Cordite.
  Manufacture of, 8-280
  World War I, used in, 9-212
  See also **Explosives**
Cordoba, Spain. Great Mosque, façade, *illus.,* 7-119
Cords, imperfections in glass. 3-312
Cordylobia anthropophaga, fly. 8-368
Core, earth's. 4-171, 173, *illus.,* 170, 172
Coreids, family of true bugs. *with illus.,* 3-258
Corey, Robert B., American chemist. Protein structure investigated by, 9-386
Corixids, family of true bugs. *with illus.,* 3-264
Corizids, family of true bugs. 3-258
Cork. Cells of, 2-1-2, *illus.,* 2
  Insulating material, 7-125
Cork cambium, plant tissue. 4-64, 68, *illus.,* 69
Cork cells, of plants. *illus.,* 1-42; 4-64, 73
Corms, underground stems. 4-68; 6-58, *illus.,* 59
Corn.
  Breakfast-cereal manufacture, *illus.,* 1-92c
  Cell of, *illus.,* 2-9
  Hybrid, 9-291
  Industrial materials from, 7-36, 38-39, 40, *diagram,* 36-37
  Radiation effect on corn, 10-252, *illus.,* 253
  Seed and seedling of, *illus.,* 5-61
  Seeds, *illus.,* 5-63
  Smuts attack, 3-29
  Starch from, 4-78
  Water required by, 5-25
Corn snakes. *with illus.,* 5-354d, *illus.,* 359
  Pets, 7-25
Cornea, of the eye. 7-293
Cornell, Ezra, American financier. 5-240
Cornets. Sound production in, 5-219
Corning Glass Works. 9-159
Corns, on feet. 10-82
Cornwall, England. Kaolin pits, *illus.,* 7-395
Corolla, flower structure. 3-405; 4-120
Corona Borealis (Northern Crown), constellation. 1-332
Corona, luminous envelope surrounding sun. 3-102, 106, *with illus.,* 136, *illus.,* 101
Coronagraphs, instruments for viewing sun's corona in sunlight. 3-105
Coronary disease. 3-390
Coronary thrombosis. *with diagram,* 3-391
Corporations, business. Designers help improve, 10-123
Corps, France. Cloud formation near, *illus.,* 6-411
Corpuscles of blood. See **Blood cells**

Corpuscular theory of light. 6-239; 7-199, 205, 249, 250, 251, *illus.,* 250; 8-119
Correction, of flight paths. Space vehicles and missiles, corrective maneuvers of, 8-128-31
Correlation, statistical method. Psychological problems, application to, 9-313
Correlation, of sedimentary rocks. See **Sedimentary rocks.**
Correspondence, in mathematical sets. 4-442
Corrodentia, order of insects. 2-413
Corrosion. Electrochemistry of, 5-96
Corrugated paper. 4-378
Cort, Henry, English ironmaster. 6-383
Cortes, Hernando, Spanish conquistador. Rubber, early use observed by, 6-350
Cortex, plant tissue. 4-63, 68, 69, 70, *illus.,* 64, 69
Cortex cerebri. See **Brain**
Corti, organ of. *with illus.,* 7-300
Cortisone, hormone. 5-18; 10-133-34
  Allergies controlled by, 4-264
Corundum, mineral. 5-256, *illus.,* 249
Corvus (Crow), constellation. 1-331
Corymbs, flower clusters. *illus.,* 4-124
Cosigüina (Consegüina), volcano in Nicaragua. 8-302
Cosine, trigonometric function. *with illus.,* 3-447
Cosmetics. Use of, 10-84
Cosmic rays. *8-393-99
  Atmosphere affected by, 1-236-38
  Effect of, on gases in atmosphere, 10-93
  Properties as electromagnetic radiations, 7-203, 205-06, *diagram,* 201
  Relativity theory applied to study of, 4-215
  Space-travel hazard, 10-50
Cosmic years. 6-263
Cosmochemistry, chemical study of extraterrestrial matter.
  Meteorites, 6-92-95
Cosmology, science dealing with the astronomical universe.
  *Stars and galaxies, 8-47-54
  Radio cosmology, 9-210
  See also **Astronomy; Island universes; Universe**
Cosmoses, flowers. *illus.,* 3-402
Cosmotron, atom smasher. *illus.,* 4-342b-c; 9-249, *illus.,* facing 249
Cost of living. See **Economics**
Cotangent, trigonometric function. *with illus.,* 3-447
Cotopaxi, volcano of Peru. 8-303
Cotton.
  Cloth, research on, *illus.,* 1-92
  Fabric printing, *illus.,* 1-92c
  Paper made from, 4-370
  Plants and fiber, *illus.,* 1-49; *with illus.,* 4-177-79
  See also **Guncotton**
Cotton gins. Invention of, *with illus.,* 4-38-39
Cotton stainers, true bugs. *with illus.,* 3-259
Cottontail rabbits. 8-170; *illus.,* 10-257
Cottonwood trees. 5-144
Cottrell electrical precipitator. *with diagram,* 5-304
Cotyledons, seed leaves. 2-415, 419; *with illus.,* 4-131-32; 5-62, 67, *illus.,* 62, 66
Cotylosaurs, primitive reptile group. 7-1-2
Couch rolls, in Fourdrinier paper machines. *illus.,* 4-374b
Coudé spectrographs. 8-59
Cougars. See **Pumas**
Coughing.
  Allergy as cause of, 4-261
  Tuberculosis spread by, 9-176
Coulomb, Charles-Augustin, French scientist. Electricity, work on, 4-361-62

Coulombs, units of electric charge. 6-130
Council for Agricultural and Chemurgic Research (Chemurgic Council). 7-37
Council of Scientific and Industrial Research, India. 1-96
Counter-current tunnels, devices for dehydrating food. with illus., 4-166
Counters, radiation. See Geiger counters; Radiation detectors; Scintillometers
Counting.
    Development of systems of, with illus., 1-149-54
Couplers, for railroad trains. with illus., 1-189
Courant, E., American physicist. 9-249
Courtship behavior, animal.
    Birds, 5-424, with illus., 418a-c, illus., 422
    Snakes, 5-354-55, 357
    Whales, 7-136, 188
Cousteau, J. Y., French naval officer.
    Aqualung developed by, 6-26a
Covalence, bond in which atoms share electrons. with illus., 3-250-51
Covered buttons. 7-213
Covered wagons. with illus., 1-106
Cow manure, as soil fertilizer. 2-165
Cow-nosed rays, fish. 4-295
Cow sharks.
    Unchanged for millions of years, 6-283
Cowbirds. 6-104-05
Cowpeas, plants.
    Bacteria, partnership with, illus., 10-189
Cowpox. Immunization against smallpox with, 7-350
Cowries, gastropods.
    Shells of, illus., 2-100
Cows.
    Domestication of, 10-248
    Milking machine, illus., 9-62
    Stomach of, illus., 7-10
    See also Milk
Coyotes. 8-137, illus., 135
Coypus (nutrias), aquatic rodents, with illus., 8-167
CR tubes, television tubes. 5-283-84
Crab Nebula. illus., 8-156d-e; 9-210
    Origin of, 7-47
Crabs. 2-240-42, illus., 236, 240-41
    Beach sand markings produced by, 8-354
    Migration of, 9-430, illus., 428
    Prepare soil of coral islands, 4-136
Cracking, molecular breakdown. Petroleum refining uses, 4-148
Craftsmen. Design of products, role in, 10-118
Cramer, Stewart W., American engineer.
    Air-conditioning system of, 2-256
Cramps, muscle. 3-213; 6-150
Cranberries. Aminotriazole causes contamination of, 8-268-69
Crane flies. with illus., 3-288-89
Cranial flexure. 1-65, illus., 64
    Man and other mammals, 6-278
Cranial nerves. 6-328
    See also Optic nerve; Vagus nerves; etc.
Cranium. Development in human being, 8-96, 98, illus., 99
    See also Skull
Crankshafts, of engines.
    Automobile engines, 2-133
    Gasoline engines, 4-87-88, illus., 86-88
    Steam engines, 4-110, 111, with illus., 84
"Crater cones," structures on surface of moon, 4-280
Crater Lake, Oregon. 7-57; illus., 8-299
    Charcoal dated from vicinity, 10-97

Craters.
    Galileo's observations of lunar craters, 4-279
    Meteorite, 6-90, 91-92, 94, diagrams and illus., 90, 91, table, 90
    Moon's craters, 4-279-80
    Theories of the moon's craters, 4-280, 282
Craters of volcanoes. with illus., 8-293-98
Crayfish. 2-239-40
Creation. See Evolution; Natural selection; Nebular hypothesis; Origin of species; Solar system; Universe
Creepers. 6-44
    Brown, illlus., 6-43
Creodonts, extinct carnivores. 7-307
Crepe, form of rubber. 6-355
Crepe silk. 5-182, 184
Creped paper. 4-378
Cresol. Coal tar yields, with illus., 1-419
Crests, of ocean waves. with illus., 6-362; 8-348, with illus., 349
Cretaceous period, time in earth's history. 1-293-95; 6-374
    Temperature variations in, 3-181-82
Cretinism. 5-18
Crevasses of glaciers. 9-168, 169, 171, illus., 163, 168
Crick, F. H. C., English chemist. Nucleic-acid model of, 9-386, diagram, 385
Cricket frogs. 10-262
Crickets. with illus., 3-145-47
    Terrarium insects, 5-366
Crime. Illumination as deterrent to, 4-233
Crimean War. Medical care in, 7-388-89
Crinoids, sea lilies. 1-388
    Fossil, illus., 1-387; illus., 6-372
    See also Sea lilies
Criteria of race. 8-214
Critical angle. 7-255
Critical mass, atomic explosion of. 9-135-36
Critical temperatures, of liquids and gases. with diagram, 1-168-69
Crocodiles. 5-383, 384-85, illus., 383
    Zick-zack plovers and, 6-408
Crocodilians. *5-380-85
Crompton, Samuel. Born in Lancashire, England, 1753; died 1827. A spinner himself, he worked to improve existing methods. His mule, which combined Hargreave's spinning jenny and Arkwright's spinning frame with the additional principle of the spindle carriage, made it possible to spin fine cotton yarn. See also, 4-337 (with illus.)
Croninger, A. B., American medical researcher.
    Cancer, investigation of, 5-350
Crookes, Sir William, English physicist and chemist. with illus., 8-410-11
    X rays, near discovery of, 7-143
Crookes tube. Description, 7-143
    Experiments with, 8-411-12
Crop dusting. with illus., 9-185-89
Crops.
    *Chemurgy, 7-35-44
    *Insect enemies, 9-185-96
    *Irrigation, 8-191-201
    *Soil fertility, 2-163-72
    *Vegetable fibers, 4-177-82
    *Weeds, 7-111-14
    Hailstorm damage, 2-357
    Insects harming, 2-410-12, 414
    Plant diseases, losses due to, 8-369
    See also Agriculture; Corn; Cotton; Fertilizers; Plant diseases; Plants; Soil; Wheat
Cross-bedding. 3-178, illus., 179

Cross-pollination. *with illus.*, 4-125-27
  Insects aid in, 7-239-48
Crossbar systems, in telephony. 2-389, 391
Crossbills, birds. 6-108
  Courtship behavior of, *with illus.*, 5-418c
Crossing over, phenomenon in germ-cell division. *with illus.*, 6-273; 8-335
Crossopterygians, primitive fish. 1-389-90; 4-197
  Amphibians derived from, 5-153
Crossopterygii. See **Crossopterygians**
Crossties, for railway tracks. *with illus.*, 1-191, 192
Croton bugs. See **German cockroaches**
Crowbars. Used as levers, 3-57-58, *illus.*, 56
Crowd psychology. Le Bon's theory of, 9-56
Crown blocks. See **Block and tackle**
Crows. 6-102-03, *illus.*, 101
  Pets, 7-23, *illus.*, 22
Cruciate crural ligaments, in feet. *illus.*, 3-212, 213
Crude oils. See **Petroleum**
Crusades.
  Arabic learning, spread of contributed to, 2-304, *illus.*, 303
  Shipbuilding influenced by, 4-108
Crushing, in ore dressing. *with diagram*, 1-371-72
Crushing rolls, in ore dressing. *with diagram*, 1-372
Crust, earth's. 4-173, *illus.*, 172
  *Earthquakes, 9-105-19
  *Mountain building, 10-213-23
  *Time scale of earth's history, 6-369-74
  Chemical elements of, 1-80
  Density, variations in, 2-318-19, 320
  Electrical currents in, 7-360
  Expanding crust, theories of, 5-189-90
  Mountain roots in, 5-188-89
Crustaceans, jointed shellfish. *2-236-43
  Trilobites (extinct crustaceans), *illus.*, 6-371
Crux (Southern Cross), constellation. 1-337
Cryogenics, science of very low temperatures. *5-207-10
Cryolite, sodium-aluminum-fluoride mineral.
  Aluminum smelting, role in, *with diagram*, 1-381; 5-93-94, *illus.*, 92
Cryotrons, superconductive elements for computers. 5-210
Cryptocoryne, aquatic plant. *illus.*, 8-114
Cryptodira, group of turtles, 5-388
Cryptomonas, genus of one-celled animals. 2-61
Crystal diffraction, Law of. 7-145
Crystal habit, individual forms of crystals. **5-252**
Crystal lattice. See **Lattice, crystal**
Crystal Palace, London. 8-390, *illus.*, 388-89
Crystallography. See **Crystals**
Crystalloluminescence. 2-188
Crystals. *5-337-42
  *Electric effects in, 2-293-94
  *Minerals, crystals of, 5-248-56
  Diamond, structure of, *with illus.*, 4-273-74, 276
  Experiments and tricks with, *with diagram*, 7-175-76
  Germanium, in transistors, 10-103-04
  Graphite, structure of, *with illus.*, 4-273-74, 276
  High-frequency sound produced using, 8-107-10, *illus.*, 106, 109
  Interstellar solids, 9-364
  Meteorite features due to crystallization?, 6-94-95
  Minerals in the form of, 9-303, *illus.*, 304
  Molecular structure and behavior of, *with diagrams*, 1-169-70, 171
  Production of, from saturated solutions, 4-298-99
  Protoplasm, crystalline nature of 2-6
  Radio detectors, crystals used as, 3-95-96
  Radio transmission, use in, 3-88

Crystals *(continued)*
  Refraction method of identification, 7-255
  Salt and rock-candy crystals, homemade, *with illus.*, 4-347
  Snow, *with illus.*, 2-354
  Sodium chloride lattice, *illus.*, 5-89
  Viruses isolated in the form of, 3-453, *with illus.*, 456
  X-ray crystallography, 7-144-45, 147, 206; 9-151
Ctenophores.
  Classification of, 1-292
  Luminescent, *illus.*, 2-184
Cubes, of numbers. *with diagram*, 4-424
Cubic measures.
  Metric system, *table*, 10-296
  United States, *table*, 10-295
Cubic system.
  External crystal structure, 5-341-42, *diagram*, 340
Cubical expansion, coefficient of. 3-415
Cuckoos. 6-306, 308-09, *illus.*, 307
Cucumbers.
  Flowers of, *illus.*, 4-122
Cud-chewing. *with illus.*, 7-10
Cugnot, Nicolas-Joseph.
  Steam-driven vehicle built by, 2-129
Culebra Cut. See **Gaillard Cut**
Cullinan Diamond. 4-256
Cultivation.
  *Soil fertility, 2-163-72
  Mushroom cultivation, 3-32
  Weeds kept in check by, 7-114
Culture.
  *Language development, 1-107-21
  *Population problems, 3-225-34
  *Prehistoric and primitive societies, *with illus.*, 9-25-30
  Beginnings of, 1-66, *illus.*, 64-65
  See also **Education; Man; Races**
Culture of microorganisms. *illus.*, 10-130a
  Bacteria, *with illus.*, 3-72
Culture pearls. 2-202
Cumulonimbus clouds. 2-222, *illus.*, 221, *diagram*, 317
Cumulus clouds. *diagram*, 1-317; 2-222, *illus.*, 215, 216
Cunard Company, steamship line. Origin of, 4-110
Cuneiform writing. 1-115, 125, *illus.*, 114
  Numbers expressed in, 1-150, *illus.*, 151
Cup anemometers, wind gauges. 1-249, *with illus.*, 103, *illus.*, 248
Cup-plate method, of testing antibiotics. *illus.*, 10-130d
Cupellation. See **Cupels**
Cupels, containers for separating precious metals from lead. 1-376
Cupro-nickel, alloy of copper and nickel. 1-382
Cups, force, plumber's suction devices. *with illus.*, 7-220
Curculios, weevils. 3-348
  Plum curculios, *with illus.*, 9-194
Curdling. Milk, 5-302
Cures. See **Health**
Curie, Jacques, French chemist.
  Piezoelectricity, discovery of, 2-293
Curie, Marie, Polish-born French chemist. 8-413-15, *illus.*, 412; 9-349
  Atom as source of energy, theory of, 9-329
Curie, Pierre, French chemist. 8-413-15, *illus.*, 412; 9-349
  Atom as source of energy, theory of, 9-329
  Piezoelectricity, discovery of, 2-293
Curie point. 7-165
Curing.
  Meat and fish, curing of, 4-163-64; *with illus.*, 5-167
  Plastics, *with diagram*, 8-223

Curium (Cm), chemical element. Atomic number, 96; atomic weight, 247(?). Metallic member of the actinide series. Discovered in 1944 by Seaborg, James, Morgan and Ghiorso at the University of Chicago; produced by bombarding plutonium with high-energy helium ions. Named after Pierre and Marie Curie. A pure compound containing curium was isolated in 1947 by Werner and Perlman.

Curliness of hair. 2-178

Curly-grass ferns. 3-192

Currency paper. 4-378

Current electricity. 6-124-36; 9-227-28, 235, *illus.*, 228
  *Electrochemistry, 5-87-96
  *Telegraph and telephone, 2-377-95
  Alternating, *with illus.*, 3-86-88
  Electronics, 6-295
  Experiments with, *with illus.*, 6-288-94
  Prospecting with, *with diagram*, 7-359-61
  Research on, 1765–1815, 4-362-63, *illus.*, 360-61; 4-363

Current meters. 6-229-30, *illus.*, 234
  Galvanometer, homemade, *with illus.*, 8-147

Current ripples. 8-353, *illus.*, 352

Currents, air. 1-236-38, 240, *with diagrams*, 242-44

Currents, oceanic. *6-229-38
  Fish distribution influenced by, 4-97
  IGY investigations of, *with illus.*, 5-191-92
  Submarine, 6-73-74, 75, *with illus.*, 74d
  Tide-caused currents, 6-206-07

Curtain walls, nonsupporting walls. *illus.*, 7-124c; 8-391

Curtains. Interior decoration, 4-271

Curtis, C. G., American inventor. Steam turbine of, 5-307

Curtis, Heber D., American astronomer.
  Galaxies studied by, 8-49

Curve-billed thrashers, birds. 6-48

Curved-plate glass. *with illus.*, 3-314

Curvilinear motion. 2-118

Cuscatlán. El Salvador. Bridge at, *illus.*, 3-302

Cuscuses, marsupials belonging to phalanger group. 7-425

Cushing, Harvey, American surgeon. 7-387; 9-31

Cuspids, canine teeth. 5-129-30, *table*, 130, illus., 132

Cusps (horns), of moon. 4-278

Customs. See Primitive peoples

Cut-off walls, in dams. 2-272

Cuticle. Hair and nails, 2-179, *illus.*, 181
  See also Pellicle

Cuts, meat. *illus.*, 5-170-71

Cuts, sections of photoengraved plates. 1-206

Cuts, railway. 1-192

Cuts and scratches. Prevention of in home, 7-197-98
  Treatment of, 10-7

Cutting frames.
  Glass bottles, cut in, 4-227, *illus.*, 226

Cutting machines, in coal mining. *with illus.*, 1-411-12

Cutting tools. *with illus.*, 10-108-09

Cuttings, method of plant propagation. 9-7-8, *illus.*, 9, 15

Cuttlebone. 2-195

Cuttlefish. 2-195
  Defense mechanism, 3-239-40

Cutworms. 3-198, 202

Cuvier, Baron Georges, French naturalist. *with illus.*, 4-388-92

Cyan. Printing color, 1-213
  Vision experiments with, 8-180

Cyanamide process, for fixing nitrogen. 3-127

Cyanidation, gold recovery process. 1-375; 4-250

Cyaniding, casehardening process for steel. 1-353

Cyanocobalamin, vitamin B$_{12}$. 5-44-45
  Anemia (pernicious), role in, 3-330

Cyanogen. Interstellar space contains, 9-363

Cyanophyta, phylum of algae. 1-300; 3-214-15, *illus.*, 215-16

Cybernetics. A science dealing with the comparison of the human brain and the electronic "brain" (computer). It also considers the application of electronic computers to many of the mental tasks now performed by human beings. An outstanding example of this sort of application is the use of giant electronic computers in the field of astronomy, where the positions in space of various celestial bodies must be calculated by a long and arduous process of mathematical computation.

Cycadales, order of gymnosperms. *with illus.*, 3-401

Cycads, gymnosperms. *with illus.*, 3-401

Cycles, sound-wave. *with illus.*, 5-117

Cycles, stream and valley. 8-17-18

Cyclic changes. Atmosphere, upper, 1-237-38, 240
  Jupiter's belts, cycles in, 5-22
  See also Sunspots

Cyclic pitch, of helicopter. 6-194

Cyclobutane. 7-269

Cyclohexane. 7-269

Cyclone chambers. Smoke particles trapped by, 3-355

Cyclones, low-pressure wind systems. *with diagram*, 1-244; *with diagrams*, 2-95-98

Cycloparaffins. 7-269

Cyclopentane. 7-269

Cyclopropane. Structural formula, 7-269

Cyclosis, protoplasmic movement. 2-12

Cyclotrons. Atom-smashers, 8-420, *illus.*, 419; 9-131-32, 330, *with illus.*, 244-46, *illus.*, 130
  Relativistic speed of particles in beams of, 4-216-17

Cygni, 61. Calculation of distance from earth, 6-390
  Orbital motion of, *illus.*, 7-229

Cygnus (Swan), constellation. 1-333
  Nebula in, *illus.*, 8-157

Cygnus A, radio star. 9-208

Cylinder heads, of automobile engines. *with illus.*, 2-132

Cylinder machines, for papermaking. 4-373, *illus.*, 374

Cylinder presses, in printing. *with diagram*, 1-209-10

Cylinders, common solids. *with illus.*, 3-442-43

Cylinders, of automobile engines. *with illus.*, 2-132, 133, 134

Cylinders, of printing presses. *with diagrams*, 1-208-10, 211-12, 213

Cylinders, steam. Ship engines, early, 4-110, 111

Cymes, flower clusters. 4-123, *illus.*, 124

Cynodictis, primitive dog. 8-133

Cynognathus, genus of extinct mammallike reptiles. *illus.*, 6-373

Cypress swamps. *with illus.*, 7-66

Cypress trees. *illus.*, 1-48; 4-65; *illus.*, 7-66
  Bald cyprus trees, 5-143, *illus.*, 142

Cypridina, crustacean. 2-188, 189

Cyrus the Great, Persian king (600?–529 B.C.). Signal system of, 2-377

Cysts. Protozoans form, 2-61

Cytology, science dealing with cells.
  *Cells, structure and function of, 2-1-14
  Blood cells, *with illus.*, 3-326-29, 330-34
  Cell theory, development of the, *with illus.*, 7-156-61
  Human body, cells of, 1-147, *with illus.*, 143-45
  Muscle cells, *with illus.*, 3-204-05
  See also Cells

Cytoplasm. 2-8-9, 14, *illus.*, 4, 10, 13
  Cells of human body, *with illus.*, 1-143-44
  See also Cells

D

D layer, ionized atmospheric region. 1-238, *diagram,* 239

d-lysergic acid, drug. 9-104

Dachshunds. 10-243

Dacron, polyester fiber. 8-228

Daddy longlegs. 2-268, *illus.,* 258

Dagron, René, early French photographer. Microfilming invented by, 10-68, *illus.,* 69

Daguerre, Louis-Jacques-Mandé, French inventor and painter. 6-382; *with illus.,* 9-399

Daguerreotype process. 6-382; 9-399-401

Daguerreotypes, early photographs. *illus.,* 9-399, 400

Dahana, desert area of Arabia. 6-118

Daimler, Gottlieb, German inventor. 6-380
Internal-combustion engine of, 2-130

Daisies. *illus.,* 1-305

Daisy Geyser, Yellowstone National Park. *illus.,* 8-300d

Dalton, John, English chemist and physicist. *with illus.,* 5-74-75, 77
Atomic theory of, *with illus.,* 1-308

Daly, Reginald A., American geologist.
Coral-reef-formation theory, 4-139; 6-75, 77

Dam, Henrik, Danish scientist. Vitamin K_1 discovered by, 5-48

Damodar Valley, India. Tilaiya Dam, *illus.,* 8-201

Dampier, William, English buccaneer and navigator. 2-366; 6-28

Dams. *8-305-20
Construction, *illus.,* 2-30
Hydroelectric stations associated with, 9-233, 234
Irrigation water collected by, 5-30; *with illus.,* 8-194-95
Water supply, 2-272-73, *illus.,* 270-71, 272, 281, 282-83
See also **Waterways**

Dams, beaver. 9-3-5

Damsel flies. See **Odonata**

Dana, James Dwight, American mineralogist, geologist and zoologist (1813–95). He studied under Benjamin Silliman at Yale and taught geology and mineralogy there. After serving as geologist on a U. S. exploring expedition (led by Charles Wilkes) in the southern Pacific, he published books and papers on the material collected. He also investigated the formation of continents, mountains and volcanoes. See also 10-218

Dancing, of honeybees. 3-370

Dandelions. Fruits and seeds of, *illus.,* 5-3
Kok-sagyz, which yields rubber, 7-44
Seed dispersal of, 3-240

Dandruff, hair disease. 2-180

Dandy rolls, in Fourdrinier paper machines. *illus.,* 4-374b

Danjon astrolabe, device fixing latitude and longitude by means of astronomical sightings. 5-188

Daphnia, genus of crustaceans. *with illus.,* 2-243
Fish in aquariums fed with, *with illus.,* 8-115

Dark-line spectra. In laws of spectrum analysis, 5-86

Dark nebulae. 8-155

"Dark period," in virus infections. 3-457

"Darkening experiments," with light-sensitive chemicals. 9-398-99

Darkling beetles. 3-344

Darkrooms, photographic. *illus.,* 9-402, 410-11

Darwin, Charles Robert, English naturalist. *with illus.,* 8-256-60
Coral islands, theory of, 4-137-38; 6-75, 77, *diagram,* 77
Earthworms, observations on, 2-160
See also **Evolution; Natural selection**

Darwin, Erasmus, English physiologist and poet. 8-258

Darwin, George H., English astronomer and physicist.
Mountain-building forces, theory of, 10-216, 218

Darwinian theory. See **Darwin, Charles Robert**

Darwin's finches. *illus.,* 10-183
Evolution of, *with illus.,* 6-282

Dates. *Calendars, 10-171-80
*Geologic time scale of earth's history, 6-369-74

Dates, fruit. *illus.,* 4-130
Food crop of the Sahara, 6-117

Dating, of objects.
*Radiocarbon dating, 10-92-97
*Thermoluminescence, dating by, 6-375-76
Meteorites and meteorite craters, 6-91, 95
See also **Chronology; Geochronology; Time**

David Dunlap Observatory, Canada. 8-64, *illus.,* 60

Davy, Sir Humphry, English chemist (1778–1829). He was chemistry professor at London's Royal Institution and the teacher of Michael Faraday. He investigated the character of nitrous oxide (laughing gas) and isolated, by electrochemical means, potassium, sodium and calcium. Davy showed chlorine to be an element, suggested that hydrogen is responsible for the nature of acids and believed chemical affinity to be an electrical phenomenon. He did important work in agricultural chemistry; he also invented the miner's safety lamp. See also 5-83, *with illus.,* 76
"Electric flame", 5-246
Heat experiment of, 6-250
Light produced by passing electricity through metal filaments, 4-234
Magnesium, calcium, strontium and barium, first isolated by, 3-171-72
Miner's safety lamp invented by, 1-413-14
Tutor and friend to Faraday, *with illus.,* 5-234

Dawson, Charles. Alleged dawn or piltdown man, discovered by, 9-23

Dawson, Sir John William, Canadian geologist and educator (1820–99). He was principal and natural-history professor at McGill College, Montreal. With Sir Charles Lyell he made a geological study of Nova Scotia. He became an authority on the natural history and geology of Nova Scotia and New Brunswick.

Day tanks, used in glassmaking. 3-310

Daylight walls, glass walls. 8-391

Days.
*Calendar, 10-171-80
Length changes with seasons, 1-263

Dayton, Ohio. Dams for flood control built by, 8-307

Daytona Beach, Florida. Beach sands of, 8-352

DDT, insecticide. 1-88, 92
Codling moths controlled by, 9-192
Insect-borne diseases controlled by, *illus.,* 5-265; 9-40
Insects acquire immunity to, 9-189.
Mosquito control by use of, *illus.,* 10-36, 37

Dead-leaf butterflies. 3-240

Dead Sea. 7-64, *illus.,* 65

Deafness.
Hearing aids, *illus.,* 5-125
Kinds of, 5-125
See also **Ears; Hearing**

Deaminization, protein breakdown. 5-14

Dean, William, American soldier. 10-38

Death.
Biological explanation, 8-102
Feigned-death defense mechanism, 3-240

Death "adders." 5-363

Deathwatch beetles. 3-342, 344

De Beers Diamond Syndicate. 4-276

Debris. Dams that hold back, 8-307

Decay, of dead organic matter. Bacteria's role in, 3-68
　Fungi bring about, 3-23
　Manures decay and fertilize soil, 2-163, 165, 166-67
　Peat due to partial decay of plants, *with illus.,*
　　1-406-07
　Petroleum formation, role in, 4-142
　Soil formed and enriched by, 2-16-17, 20-23
Decay, of sounds. 5-213
Decay, dental. See **Caries, dental**
Decay, radioactive. See **Radioactivity**
Deceleration. 2-118, 119
　Space and air vehicles, factor in motion of, 8-130,
　　diagram, 131
De Chéseaux's comet. *illus.,* 5-397
Decibels, sound units. 5-212, *illus.,* 214; *with diagram,*
　8-39-41
Decidua, tissue that develops from mucous membrane
　of uterus. 8-22-23
Deciduous (milk) teeth. 5-129-31, *illus.,* 131-32, *table,*
　130
Decimal system. 9-146
　Antiquity, 1-127
　Mathematical recreations involving, 4-443-45
　Meaning of, 1-154
　Metric system, based on, 10-296
Deck bridges. *with illus.,* 2-334
Declination, position of a star. *with diagram,* 1-260
　Star maps, indicated on, 1-324, *maps,* 325-30
　Star position, determination of, 6-81, *diagram,* 80
Declination axis, of telescopes. 8-57
Declination of the compass. *with diagram,* 7-168-69
Decoders. Space vehicles and missiles carry, 8-128,
　129, *diagram,* 129
Decomposers, in ecosystems. 10-186
Decomposition. Sewage and other wastes purified by
　bacterial action, 5-328, 331, 332, 336, *illus.,* 331,
　332, 334
Decompression chambers. *with illus.,* 4-207
Decontamination, removal of radioactive material.
　9-396
Decoration.
　Design of products, element in, 10-118
　House, *with illus.,* 4-269-72
　Primitive pottery, 7-394, 396
Deep pelvic nodes, lymphatics in hip. *illus.,* 1-148g
Deep scattering layer, layer of animal life found in
　oceans. *with illus.,* 6-74d
Deep sound channels. 6-74d
Deeps, oceanic. 6-74
Deer. *8-234-43
　Field study of, 10-259
　See also **Reindeer**
Dees, electrodes of cyclotrons. *with illus.,* 9-244-45
Defectives, mental. 9-198-99
Defense.
　*Human body, defenses of, 7-346-53
　　Skin a factor in, 2-176
　*Plants, defenses of, 7-75-83
　　Amphibians, 5-162
　　Animal and plant, adaptations for, *with illus.,* 3-238-
　　　40
　　　Luminescence, 2-190-91
　　Hosts, defenses of, 8-365
　　Insect adaptations for, 2-409-10, *illus.,* 410-11
　　Lizards, 5-206
　　Mammalian adaptations for, 7-11
　　Turtles' adaptations for, 5-386
Deficiency diseases.
　Kwashiorkor, 4-54
　See also **Diseases; Vitamins**
Definite proportions, law of. 1-80; 5-74

Deflection anemometers, wind gauges. 1-249, 320,
　diagram, 321
De Forest, Lee, American inventor. 9-287; 10-196
　*Audion development, history of, 8-84-89
Deforestation. Effect on rainfall, 2-349, 350
Degeneration, among animals and plants. *with illus.,*
　6-284
Degradation, wearing down of earth's surface. 1-33-
　34, *illus.,* 35
　See also **Erosion**
Degree-day. 1-318
De Havilland Comets, British turbojet planes. *illus.,*
　6-195; 7-73
Dehiscent fruits. *with illus.,* 4-130, *illus.,* 130-31
Dehydration of foods. *with illus.,* 4-165-67
　Water content of dehydrated foods, testing of, 4-344
Dehydrofreezing, method of food preservation. 4-167
De-icers. Airplane, 6-191
De Kay's snakes. 5-359
Delambre, Jean-Baptiste-Joseph, French astronomer.
　Uranus' orbit, tables of, 5-290
DeLaval, Gustaf Patrik, Swedish engineer and inventor.
　5-306-07
DeLaval steam turbine. *with illus.,* 5-306-07
Delavan's comet. 5-397
Delaware and Hudson Canal Company Railroad,
　pioneer American railroad. 1-181
Delaware Aqueduct Tunnel, for New York City water
　supply.
　Construction, *illus.,* 2-47
Delaware River Aqueduct. 2-50
Delirium tremens, condition resulting from withdrawal
　of alcohol. 4-412
Delphi, Oracle of, near gas seep in ancient Greece.
　5-98
Delphinoidea. 7-189
Delphinus (Dolphin), constellation. 1-334
Delta-Aquarids, meteor shower. *table,* 6-97
Delta Cephei, variable star. 7-50
Delta plains, stream deposits. 8-17, *diagram,* 16
Deltas, stream deposits. 8-17, *diagram and map,* 16
　Building of, 8-355-56
　Formation, 5-301-02; 6-415
Deltoid (deltoideus), upper-arm and shoulder muscle.
　illus., 1-148c; 3-209, *illus.,* 204
Demerol, sedative. 5-404
Demersal fish. 4-311
Democritus, Greek philosopher. 1-131
　Atomic nature of matter suggested by, 1-307
Demonstrations. Definition of, 1-141
Dendrites, nerve cell processes.
　Nature and functions of, *with illus.,* 6-317-18
Dendy, A., British biologist. 7-421-22
Deneb, star in Cygnus. 1-333
Denebola, star in Leo. 1-332
Denison, hydrofoil ship. *illus.,* 4-5
Denmark.
　Fisheries, 6-20
　Mountain of Heaven, *illus.,* 10-20
　Scientific contributions, 1600–1765, 3-278
Density. 2-31-33
　Atmospheric layers, varying density and pressure of,
　　1-233-40, *with diagrams,* 242-44
　Earth, 4-44
　Earth's crust, variations in density of, 2-318-19, 320;
　　with diagrams, 7-357-59
　Earth's interior, variations in density of, 4-173-74
　Heat (convection) currents and, *with illus.,* 4-12-14
　Minerals identified by, 5-254
　Planets, *table,* 10-298
　Radiation thickness gauges measure density, 9-45

Density (continued)
Sea water, 6-34-35
Sound, speed of, and density of medium, 5-119
Density distribution currents, oceanic currents.
6-235-36
Density of population. with map, 3-230-33
Densmore, James, businessman. Typewriting invention financed by, 1-267
Dental arches. 5-129-30, illus., 132
Dental caries. 5-130-31, 133-34, illus., 135; 10-77
Dental drills. 5-137
Dentine, tooth tissue. 5-129, 131, illus., 134-35
Dentistry.
*Teeth, 5-129-37
Caries, 10-77
X rays, use of, 7-148, illus., 150
Dentures. See Plates, dental
Deodorants. 10-84
Deoxyribonucleic acid (DNA). with diagram, 9-383-86
Hereditary patterns established by, 8-339
Depanning, breadmaking operation. 9-298, diagram, 299
Department of Scientific and Industrial Research, Great Britain. 1-93-94
Department of the Interior, United States.
Conservation work, 9-276
Depilatories. 10-84
Deposition terraces, of streams. 8-16
Deposits.
Coal deposits and reserves of the world, 1-420
Formation of mineral and rock deposits through geologic time, 6-371, 372, 373, 374
Glacial, 3-179-80
Gypsum, 3-178
Mineral, caused by evaporation, 3-178
Ocean-bottom deposits, 6-32-34, 73-74, 75
Red soil, 3-178-79
Salt, 3-178
Soil, 2-16
Stream deposits, 8-12-13, 16-17
See also Sedimentary rocks
Depressants, drugs. 5-401, 403-05, illus., 400
Depression of 1930's.
Railroads of United States affected by, 1-183-84
Depth finding, in the ocean. See Echo sounding; Sounding
Depth gauges, used in scuba diving. with illus., 6-26b
Depth of field. Photography, 9-407
Dermaptera, order of insects. 2-412; with illus., 3-151-52
Dermatology, science treating of skin. See Skin
Dermis, inner layer of skin. with illus., 2-174-75
Dermoptera, order of mammals. with illus., 7-13
Derricks.
Building construction, illus., 3-120, 121
Oil-well derricks, 4-145, diagrams, 144
Skyscraper construction, illus., 7-124c
Desalting, of water. 2-283-84; 6-6-7, diagram, 5
De Sazilly, French engineer. 8-308
Descartes, René, French philosopher and scientist. with illus., 3-8-10, 13, 19
Algebra, contributions to, 2-68
Animal intelligence, views on, 2-26
Cartesian co-ordinates, 4-212-13, with diagrams, 424-31
Formation of the earth, theory of, 4-393
Light, theory of, 3-277
Desert. Land habitat, 10-139
Desert soils, soil types. 2-22-23, map, 20-21
Desert terrariums. with illus., 5-365-66
Desert tortoises. illus., 5-387

Desert-type climates. Geologic evidence of, with illus., 3-178-79
Deserts. with illus., 6-113, 116-18
*Irrigation, 8-191-201
Climate in, 3-178-79
Dust storms in, 7-325
Land habitats, 10-135
Mojave Desert, illus., 8-16
Plants, adaptation of, 3-238
Sahara, 6-116
Saudi Arabia, illus., 6-113
Design.
Geometric figures used in, with illus., 3-440
Design of products. *10-117-26
Engineers who take part in, 1-227, illus., 299
Desk-Fax, facsimile machine. 7-392, illus., 390
Desmans, water moles. 7-98
Desmarest, Nicholas, French geologist. 4-395
Desmids, green algae. 3-219
Des Moines, Iowa. Water supply furnished by ground water, 2-274
Destaticizers, compounds that overcome static electricity.
Plastics, used in manufacture of, 8-225
Destroying angel, poisonous mushroom. with illus., 3-31-32
Destructive distillation. Oil shale, applied to, 4-143
Destructive interference, optical phenomenon. with illus., 7-281-82
Detector circuit, in radio. with illus., 3-95-96
Detectors, electron tubes.
Audion tubes as, 8-85-88
Diodes used as, in radio receivers, 6-298, 303
Detergents.
Testing, illus., 2-232
Wetting agents, with illus., 8-3-4, 6
Detergents, synthetic.
Action of, in hard water, 4-348
Surface tension reduced by, 5-372-73
See also Detergents
Determinatives, in writing. 1-114
Determiners of hereditary characters. See Chromosomes; Genes
Deuterium, isotope of hydrogen. 1-312, diagram, 313; 3-319
Fuel for atomic fusion, 1-174
Deuterons, nuclei of heavy isotope of hydrogen. 9-132
Developers, photographic. 9-409
Developing, in photography. 9-399, 400, 401, 402, 403-04, 408, 409, diagrams, 410-11
Development, as function of engineers. 1-227
Devil Postpile National Monument, California. illus., 3-422
Devil rays, fish. 4-295
Devilfish. 4-295
Devils Tower, Wyoming. 8-11
Devitrification, crystallizing of glass. 1-171
Devonian period, time in earth's history. 1-388-90; 6-372
De Vries, Hugo, Dutch botanist (1848–1935). Educated in several German universities, he later taught at the University of Amsterdam in the Netherlands. De Vries studied inheritance in plants and advanced the theory that new species arise suddenly by major changes known as mutations. According to him, evolution proceeded mainly because of these mutations rather than gradually by means of natural selection, as stated by the English naturalist Charles Darwin. In 1900, together with several other men, De Vries rediscovered the experiments of Gregor Mendel (a Catholic priest in Austria), who in the 1860's had established the laws of heredity and whose findings had been

De Vries, Hugo (*continued*
ignored by the scientific world. See also **Darwin, Charles; Evolution; Mendel; Mutations**
Dew. Formation of, 2-222
DEW line. See **Distant Early Warning (DEW) line**
Dew point. 2-213, 354
Dewar, Sir James, Scottish chemist and physicist (1842–1923). Famous as a lecturer at Cambridge and at London's Royal Institution, he studied the properties of matter at low temperatures and he liquefied various gases. He studied the physiological effects of light on the eye, invented (with Frederick Abel) cordite and devised the Dewar flask, or vacuum bottle. See also 5-207
Dewey, John, American psychologist and philosopher. 9-51
Dextrin, carbohydrate. 4-77
Dholes, wild dogs of India. 8-140
Diabetes.
  Cause and treatment of, 5-19
  Inherited, 8-91-92
  Insulin, discovery of, *with illus.,* 9-34-35
  Race, relation to, 8-220
Diabolic magic squares. See **Perfect magic squares**
Diagnosis, medical.
  Cancer, 8-270
  Radioisotopes used in, *with illus.,* 10-98, 99-100
Diagonal, element of reflecting telescope. 9-366, 370, 371-72, *diagram,* 367, 372
Dial-operated telephones. 2-389, 391, *illus.,* 390
Dialectics. Socrates developed, 1-136
Dialects. English, 1-117
Diallyl phthalate, allylic plastic. *with illus.,* 8-226
Dialysis, filtering of solutions through membranes.
  Water desalted by electrodialysis, 2-284
Diamagnetic materials. *with diagram,* 7-165
  Faraday identified, 5-236
  Rock, diamagnetic materials in, 7-357
  Superconductors, 5-210
Diamond cutting. 4-256
Diamonds. *4-251-56; *illus.,* 5-249, 254
  *Synthetic diamonds, 4-273-76
  Crystal structure of, 5-338, 374, *illus.,* 337-38, 375
  Properties and uses of, 3-324
  Specific gravity of, 5-254
  Synthetic diamonds, 4-251, 253
Diaphragm, human.
  Breathing, function in, *with diagram,* 1-279; 3-77, 209, *diagram,* 211; 4-205, *illus.,* 204
  Evolution of, 7-3
  Liver, relation to, *illus.,* 5-14
Diaphragms.
  Camera, 9-411
  Loud-speakers, 3-96, *illus.,* 97
  Microphones, 3-88
  Shock-tube diaphragms, *with diagram,* 10-234
Diarrhea. 4-333
  Dietary remedies for, 5-275
Diastole, phase in pumping action of heart. 3-383
Diastrophism, movements of parts of earth's crust with respect to one another. 1-34, *illus.,* 35
Diatom ooze, marine deposit. 6-32-33
Diatomaceous earth. 3-224; 7-124
Diatomin, algal pigment. 3-221
Diatoms. *illus.,* 1-41; *with illus.,* 3-221, 224; 4-312; 9-85
  Marine diatom deposits, *with illus.,* 6-32-33
Diatonic scales, musical. *with table,* 5-214-15
Dibatags, antelopes. 8-387
Dichlorethyl sulfide. See **Mustard gas**
Dichlorodifluoromethane (CCl_2F_2), Freon refrigerating fluid. 4-310

Dicotyledons, flowering plants. 2-415; 3-403-04
  Classification of, 1-303-05
Didinium, genus of one-celled animals. 2-66, *illus.,* 64-65
Dieldrin, insecticide. 9-189
Dielectric. 3-86
Dielectric heating. 9-239
Diesel, Rudolph. Born in Paris, 1858, of German parents, he was educated in Paris and Germany. Working to find a more efficient prime mover than the steam engine, Diesel invented the internal-combustion engine that bears his name. Many improvements were made upon his first model, patented in 1892. Diesel was drowned while crossing the English Channel in 1913. See also 6-254
Diesel-electric locomotives. See **Locomotives, diesel-electric**
Diesel-electric power.
  Locomotives using, 4-92
Diesel engines. *with illus.,* 4-89-92
  Electricity generated by use of, 9-231, *illus.,* 230
  Invention of, 6-254
  Road rollers, *illus.,* 3-300
  Ships, 4-114
  Submarines, 5-34, 36
  Tractors, *illus.,* 2-168
Diesel oil. 4-149
  Gasoline as fuel, compared with, 4-91
Diet.
  *Basic food elements, 4-51-61
  *Carbohydrates, 4-76-78
  *Regulation of, 5-267-75
  *Vitamins, 5-38-49
  Adaptation of animals and plants to, *with illus.,* 3-235-38
  Allergies controlled by food substitutes, 4-264
  Deficiencies due to excessive alcohol consumption, 4-411
  Evolution of human diet, 1-66
  Germ-free animals, 7-155
  Health affected by, 10-77
  Meat important in, 5-163, 172
  Older persons, 8-81-82
  Rickets due to faulty diet, 3-84
  Sick persons', *with illus.,* 10-64-66
  Teeth health influenced by, 5-134
  Tubercular patients, 9-183
  Zoo animals, 10-159-60, *illus.,* 158
Diethyl ether, anesthetic. 7-273
Differential calculus, branch of mathematics. *with diagrams,* 4-436-39
  Newton invented, 1-20-21
Differential gears, for automobiles. 2-141-42, *illus.,* 140, 141
Differential psychology. 9-320
Differential thermometers, Beckman. 3-411
Differential white-cell count, blood count. 3-329
Differentiation, cell. Plants, 3-50
Difflugia, genus of one-celled animals. 2-64-65, *illus.,* 63
Diffraction, optical phenomenon. 7-282, *with illus.,* 250, *illus.,* 284
  Crystal diffraction, 7-144-45
  Phonograph record showing, *illus.,* 7-284c
Diffraction grating.
  Explanation of, 7-144
  Incandescent light broken up by, *illus.,* 7-284a
Diffraction-grating spectroscopes. 7-279, 282, *illus.,* 284
Diffractometers, X-ray. *illus.,* 7-358

Diffusion. *with illus.,* 5-373-74
Cells use process for exchange of materials,
2-6, 7, 11, 13
Exchange of materials in capillary network, 3-385;
illus., 4-202
Gas exchange in lungs by, 4-206, *illus.,* 202
Sound, 5-128
Digester gas. By-product of sewage treatment,
5-332-33
Digesters, vessels in which wood chips are cooked.
with illus., 4-366-67
Digestion. *4-321-35
Bacteria that play part in, 3-69-70
Carbohydrates, 4-52
Colloid phenomena in, 5-301
Development in human baby, 8-95
Development of digestive system in unborn human
young, 8-27
Fats, 4-53
Liver involved in, 5-15
Nineteenth-century developments in study of,
7-372-73
Plants' digestion, 3-46-47
Products of digestion, 2-10-11
Proteins, 4-54
Seeds may resist, 5-5
See also **Digestive systems**
Digestive systems.
Birds, 5-420, *illus.,* 421
Coelenterates, *with illus.,* 2-148
Cud-chewing mammals, *with illus.,* 7-10
Echinoderms, 2-152
Insects, 2-405
Lobsters, *illus.,* 2-239
Man, *diagram,* 1-146, *illus.,* 148d
Oysters, *illus.,* 2-197
Sponges, 2-146
See also **Digestion**
Digital computers. *9-143-52
Automation, used in, *illus.,* 10-234b
Space and missile flights guided by, 8-128, 130
Digitalis.
Heart failure, use in, 3-390
Introduced into medical practice, 3-380
Digits, numerical figures.
Mathematical recreations involving, 4-443-45
Dihedral angles, in solid geometry. *with illus.,* 3-
440-41
Dihydrotachysterol, compound related to vitamin D and
used to treat tetany. 5-18
Dik-diks, antelopes. 8-387
Dikes, geologic formations. 3-420, *illus.,* 420-21
Dimensional analysis, in mathematics. 1-78
Dimensions (sizes), galactic. 8-51
Dimethyl butadiene.
Synthetic rubber made from, 6-358
Dimetrodon. See **Sail-fin reptiles**
Dimorphism, difference of form, color, or structure
between members of same species.
Butterflies and moths, 3-197, *illus.,* 199
Screech owls, 6-165
Dingoes, wild dogs. 8-138-40, *illus.,* 132
Dinichthys, primitive fish. 1-389
Dinnerware. Modern design, example of, *illus.,* 10-119
Dinoflagellates, protozoans. 2-61, *illus.,* 60
Dinosaurs. 1-392-93, 394, *illus.,* 391, 392, 395; *illus.,*
6-373
Extinction of, 3-181-82
Suspension of backbone, *illus.,* 1-286
Dinotherium, genus of extinct elephants. 7-408

Diodes, electron tubes. *with illus.,* 6-295-98, 301-03
Audion tube, development of, 8-85-87
Diogenes of Apollonia, Greek philosopher. Blood
circulation, 1-365
Dione, satellite of Saturn. 5-113
Diophantus, Greek mathematician. 1-360; 2-68
Diorites, igneous rocks. 2-83; 3-423; 9-308
Dioscorides, Pedanius, Greek physician.
Drugs and botany, authority on, 1-366
Dip of the compass. *with diagram,* 7-168-69
Experiment showing, *with illus.,* 8-144
Dip tubes. *with illus.,* 8-115
Diphosphopyridin nucleotide, organic compound in
luciferin. 2-188-89
Diphtheria. Antibodies and immunization against,
7-350
Bacteria that cause, *illus.,* 3-71
Diplodocus, herbivorous dinosaur. 1-393, *illus.,* 391
Dipole antennas. *with illus.,* 3-90
Diprotodon, genus of extinct marsupials. 7-421
Diptera, order of insects. *3-283-92
General description of order, 2-414
Direct current. Electrical, *with illus.,* 6-129-30
Electronics, 6-298, 301, 303
Direct dyes. 8-186
Directional gyro, airplane compass. 6-193
Directional sound.
Perception of by vertebrate ear, 4-380
Directions in space.
Parity law of physics and, *with illus.,* 7-108
Wind directions, measuring and recording, 1-249,
illus., 248, 250
Dirigibles, controlled balloons. *with illus.,* 6-178-81
World War I, 9-214
Disaccharides, sugar compounds. 4-51-52, 78, 79
Cells contain, 2-5
Disasters. Earthquakes, *with illus.,* 9-110-11, *illus.,* 117
Disc method, of testing antibiotics. *illus.,* 10-130d
Discharge lamps. 4-239-40
Discoverer XIII, artificial satellite launched by United
States. 10-47
Discoverer XIV, artificial satellite launched by United
States. *with illus.,* 10-47
Disease transmission. Viruses, 3-456-57
Diseases.
*Allergies, 4-257-64
*Body defenses, 7-346-53
*Cancer, 8-265-72
*Mosquito as vector of malaria and yellow fever,
10-30-39
*Pasteur's contributions to bacteriology, 9-71-80
*Progress in medicine, 10-127-34
*Tuberculosis, 9-175-84
*Viruses, 3-451-58
*Vitamin-deficiency diseases, 5-39-49
Bacteria that cause diseases, 3-66-67
Black Death, or plague, in the Middle Ages,
2-312-13
Blood diseases, *with illus.,* 3-330-32
Bone diseases and injuries, 3-73-76, 79, 83-84
Bursitis, 3-211
Circulatory-system disorders, *with diagrams,* 3-390-92
Contrast between those that attack youth and age,
8-79, 82
Deafness, 5-125
Diagnosis of
Electroencephalograph and electrocardiograph
used in, *with illus.,* 2-426-28
X rays used in treatment and, *with illus.,* 7-149-50
Digestive tract disorders, *with illus.,* 4-332-35
Fish in aquariums, diseases of, 8-116

Diseases (continued)
Fungi that cause, 3-27, 32
Glands and, 5-8-9, 12-13, 17-18, 19
Hair and scalp disorders and baldness, with illus., 2-180
Inheritable diseases, 8-342, 344
Insects responsible for, 2-410, 411, 413
Molecular basis of, 9-386
Muscles, disorders and injuries of, 3-212-13
Nervous system, diseases of, 6-329-30
Nineteenth-century developments in control of, with illus., 7-374-89
Parasitic-worm infestations, 2-154-59
Preventive medicine, development of, with illus., 4-400-03
Public-health movement, with illus., 9-36-42
"Quacks" who treat for cancer, 8-272
Race, relation to, 8-220
Scurvy, prevented by dietary use of lime juice, 3-380
Silkworm diseases, 5-173, 175, 178
Tooth diseases and disorders, 5-130-33, illus., 135, 137
Trichinosis, 5-336
Wastes may cause, 5-328, 336
Weeds, role in spreading of disease, 7-111-12
White blood cells defend against, 3-328-29
Zoo animals, diseases of, 10-157-58
See also **Colds; Drugs; Flies; Immunity to disease; Malaria; Medicine; Mosquitoes; Plant diseases; Tuberculosis;** etc.
Diseases of plants. See **Plant diseases**
Disk flowers. with illus., 4-124
Dislocations of bones. First aid for, 10-11-12
Dislocations of earth's crust. *Earthquakes, 9-105-19
Dispersal of seeds and fruits. *5-1-7
Displacement. Floating bodies, 2-32-33
Displacement law, Wien's, of radiant energy distribution. 7-201
Dissecting instruments. illus., 2-376
Dissonance, of musical tones. 5-213
Distance. Force and work, relation to, with illus., 1-82-83, 84
Distances, galactic. 8-50-51
Distant Early Warning (DEW) line. 9-390
Distillation. 1-168
Petroleum industry uses, 4-143, 147
Water desalted by, 2-284
Zinc refining, with diagram, 1-380
Distilled water.
Construction of distilling apparatus for home laboratory, with illus., 4-225-26
Experiments with, with illus., 8-5-6
Distilling devices. Water, with illus., 8-5
Zinc refined in, with diagram, 1-380
Distributary channels, in deltas. 8-17
Distribution.
Natural gas, with illus., 5-105-06
Petroleum products, 4-152
Water supply, with illus., 2-284-86, illus., 282-83
Distribution (electricity) systems. 9-236-38, illus., 238-39
Distributive law of multiplication. 2-69-70
Disturbances, periods of geologic change. 1-385
See also **Mountain making**
Diurnal motion. Sun's, diagram, 1-263
Diurnal tides. 6-204-05
Divers, Cartesian. with illus., 1-281; with illus., 7-221-22
Diversion dams. 8-307
Divides, watersheds. 6-412; 8-18
Dividing, breadmaking operation. with diagram, 9-297

Dividing, method of plant propagation. 9-7
Diving. Compressed air used in diving operations, 9-68
Ocean depths explored by divers, 6-73, illus., 76
Scuba diving, with illus., 6-26a-d
Diving beetles. with illus., 3-338
Diving bells. 9-68
Diving masks. with illus., 6-26b
Diving suits. 9-68
Divining rods, devices that are supposed to point to underground water. 8-331
Division, arithmetical operation. 1-158
Dix, Dorothea Lynde, American reformer. 9-103
DNA. See **Deoxyribonucleic acid**
Doctor blades, in printing presses. 1-213
Doctors. See **Diseases; Drugs; Medicine**
Dodders, plants. 8-366
Degenerate forms, 6-284
Dodoes. 6-304
Doebereiner, Johann Wolfgang, German chemist. 5-83
Dog family. *8-132-41
Dog fleas. illus., 8-367
Dogfish. 4-290
Spined dogfish, illus., 4-291
Dogs.
Breeds developed by artificial selection, 6-275-76, 279, illus., 269
Classification of, 1-289, 291
Domestication of, with illus., 10-240-43
Evolution of, 1-396
Intelligence, illus., 2-26
Parasitic-worm infestations, 2-155, 159
Pavlov's work with, with illus., 9-51-52
"Silent" dog whistles, 8-104
Skeleton compared with that of man, illus., 1-57
Skull compared with man's, illus., 3-78
Sweating and cooling of, 2-177
Teeth of, illus., 1-59
Transportation, use in, 1-99-100, illus., 101
See also **Dog family**
Dogwood trees. 5-150, illus., 151
Bark, illus., 5-140
Doisy, Edward A., American biochemist. Vitamin K₂ isolated by, 5-48
Doldrums, equatorial wind belt. 1-244; 2-93, diagram, 92
Doll, R., English physician. Lung cancer, investigation of, 5-349-50
Dollond, John, English optician. 7-158
Dolphins. with illus., 7-189, illus., 185
Domagk, Gerhard, German chemist. 9-33
Discovery of prontosil, 10-127
Dome cars, of railroad trains. with illus., 1-188
Domes, of astronomical observatories. 8-56
Domes, geological. See **Anticlines; Folds; Salt domes**
Domestic animals.
Virus diseases of, 3-452, illus., 454
Domestication of animals. *7-327-33; *10-239-50
Elephants, 7-410-11, illus., 411, 413
Dominance, phenomenon of inheritance. 8-340-44, diagram, 341
Dominance, social force displayed by animals.
Birds, 5-425
Mammals, 7-11-12
Primates, 9-261-62
Dominican (religious) order. Medieval universities influenced by, 2-304-05
Dominion Astrophysical Observatory, Canada. 8-64; 9-156
Donati's comet. 5-398, illus., 393; 6-393, illus., 392

Donkeys. Domestication of, **10**-250
Transportation, use in, **1**-102, *illus.,* 103
Donn, William, American geologist. **5**-193
Donora, Pennsylvania. Smog damage (1948), *with illus.,* **3**-353
Donors, blood givers. **3**-332-33
Dope. See **Drugs; Narcotics**
Doppler, Christian Johann, Austrian physicist. **6**-391
Doppler effect.
Aircraft sounds exhibit, *with diagram,* **10**-229
Heavenly bodies, relation to motion of, **6**-391; **8**-52, 54
Rotational speed of sun measured by, **3**-107-08
Sound, **5**-127, *diagram,* 126
Experiments with, *with illus.,* **5**-229, *illus.,* 227
Space vehicles and missiles guided by radar Doppler effect, **8**-131
Dormant animals. See **Estivation; Hibernation**
Dormant buds **4**-67
Dormant period, of plants. **2**-418; **5**-63
Dormice, rodents. **8**-164
Dorsal fins, of fishes. *with illus.,* **4**-96
Dorset, Marion, American scientist. **9**-290
Dosing, medicinal. Nursing procedure in, *with illus.,* **10**-63-64
Double bedrooms, Pullman sleeping cars. **1**-187
Double stars. Solar system, as origin of, **1**-29-30
Dough, bread. **9**-294-95, *with diagrams,* 297-98, *diagrams,* 296
"Doughnuts," vacuum chambers of betatrons. **9**-247
Douglas, Sholto, English agricultural expert. **8**-36
Douglas Aircraft Company. **7**-74
Douglas DC-8, United States jet liner. **9**-219
Douglas fir trees. **5**-142, *illus.,* 143
Conservation of, *illus.,* **6**-9
Douglass, Andrew Ellicott, American astronomer. **9**-29
Annual rings of trees, investigations of, **3**-107
Doves. *with illus.,* **6**-304-05
Dow process, for magnesium production. **3**-172
Downcutting, stream erosion. **8**-17
Downdrafts, air currents. **1**-242
Downy mildews. **3**-25-26
Downy woodpeckers. **6**-211
Dowsers. See **Water Witches**
Draco (Dragon), constellation. **1**-330
Drag, resistance of air to flying object. **6**-186-87; **10**-230-31, 232
Dragonflies. *illus.,* **1**-296; **2**-408
Fossil dragonflies, *illus.,* **6**-372
Metamorphosis of, *illus.,* **2**-408-09
See also **Odonata**
"Dragon's blood," powder used in making photoengraved plates. **1**-205-06
Drainage.
Coal mines, draining water from, **1**-414
Crops require adequate drainage, **8**-198
Soil drainage, **2**-20, 23; *with illus.,* **5**-26-28
Drainage basins, areas drained by rivers. **8**-12
Drake, Edwin L., American oilman (1819–80). Petroleum industry in the United States begun by, *with illus.,* **4**-141
Drake, Sir Francis, English navigator. **2**-366
Tobacco brought to England by, **5**-343
Drakensberg, mountain range of southern Africa. **10**-26
Draper, John, scientist and author. **6**-386
Dravidian local race. **8**-218
Draw works, block-and-tackle drums. *diagram,* **4**-144
Drawbaugh, Daniel, American inventor. **5**-243
Drawing.
Glass products shaped by, **3**-311, *illus.,* 314a, 314b-c
Steel products shaped by, **1**-349, *illus.,* 351

Drawing rooms, Pullman sleeping cars. **1**-187
Drawings, topologic. *with diagrams,* **4**-451
Drawsheets, bed. Sickbed, **10**-59, 60, *illus.,* 59
Dreams. **6**-145
Drebbel, Cornelius van, Dutch physician. Submarine, first practical, **5**-31
Dredges.
Gold-extracting operations, **4**-248
Dredging. Reservoirs, **2**-273
Dresden porcelain. *illus.,* **7**-399
Dressing, ore. *with diagrams,* **1**-371-76
Dressings. First aid, **10**-15
Dreyer, John L. E., Danish-Irish astronomer. Nebulae and star clusters catalogued by, **8**-49
Dreyfus, Henry, American designer. **10**-119, 120
Dried manures, soil fertilizers. **2**-165
Driers, in papermaking. *with illus.,* **4**-372, *illus.,* 374b-c
Driffield, V. C. D., English photographer. **9**-403-04
Drift bottles. Oceanic circulation determined by, **6**-230
Drift mines, for coal. *with illus.,* **1**-410
Drift nets. Pelagic fishing, use of nets, **4**-311
Drifter drills, tunneling tools. *illus.,* **2**-44
Drill mud, lubricant in well drilling. **2**-274; **4**-145, *diagram,* 144; **5**-100
Drill pipe, piping used in well drilling. **4**-145, *diagram,* 144; **5**-100
Drilling.
Exploration (scientific) in Pacific atolls, **6**-77
Natural-gas wells, **5**-98, 100-01
Oil wells, *with diagrams,* **4**-144-46
Pneumatic tools, used in, **9**-66, *illus.,* 65
Wells for water supply, **2**-273, *with illus.,* 274; *illus.,* **8**-330
Drilling, tooling operation. **10**-109, *illus.,* 111
Drilling log, record of well drilling. **5**-100
Drillmasters, combination air compressors and drills. *illus.,* **9**-65
Drills, Old World monkeys. **9**-258
Drills, tools. **10**-109, *illus.,* 111
Drifter tools used in tunneling, *illus.,* **2**-44
Pneumatic drills, *illus.,* **8**-42; **9**-66
Drills, dental. **5**-137
Drinker-Collins Respirators. *with illus.,* **4**-205-06
Drinking. See **Water**
Dripstone, calcium carbonate formation, in caves. *with illus.,* **5**-55
Driven wells. **2**-274
Driver (army) ants. **3**-364-65
Dromedaries, camels. *with illus.,* **7**-329-31
Drone honeybees. **3**-368, 370, *illus.,* 372
Drongo cuckoos. **6**-306
Drongo shrikes. **6**-306
Drossing kettle, for refining lead. **1**-379
Drowned river valleys. *with illus.,* **8**-358
Drowsiness, preparatory stage of sleep. **6**-143
Drug addiction. Definition of, **4**-409
See also **Drugs; Narcotics**
Drugs.
*Antibiotics, **10**-130a-d
*Narcotics, **5**-400-07
*Penicillin and streptomycin, **7**-52-54
*Tranquilizers, **5**-377-79
Alcoholic beverages as habit-forming drugs, **4**-409-11
Allergic reactions to, **4**-260
Allergies controlled by, **4**-264
Aralen preparation, *illus.,* **8**-183
Cancer treatment with, **8**-270
Dosing procedure, *with illus.,* **10**-63-64
Effects of, studied with radioisotopes, **10**-100
Hashish, **4**-180-81
Pain-killing drugs, dangers of, **7**-347

Drugs (continued)
Quinine a "specific," 10-37
Sleep, relation to, 6-150
Synthesis of, 8-187-88
Synthetic-drug industry, beginnings of, 5-80
Tuberculosis treated with, 9-183, illus., 184
Twentieth-century developments in use of, with illus., 9-32-35
See also **Antibiotics; Laughing gas;** etc.
Drugstore beetles, 3-344
Drum driers, devices for dehydrating food. 4-166
Drumlins, glacial deposits. 9-173, illus., 171
Islands formed by, 8-356, illus., 357
Drummond, Captain Thomas, British inventor.
Limelight, invention of, 4-235-36
Drums. Sound production in, 5-218
Drums, in automobile brake assembly. with illus., 2-143-44
Drupes, fleshy fruits. with illus., 4-129-30
Dry assays, analyses of precious-metal ores. 1-376
Dry cells, for generating electric current. with illus., 5-94-95; with illus., 6-127-28; 9-228
Experiments with, with illus., 6-288-94; with illus., 8-144-49
Dry fruits. with illus., 4-130-31
Dry ice. Crystalline structure, 5-337-38
Experiments with, with illus., 7-130-32
Refrigeration, use of dry ice in, 4-160
Sublimation of, 1-171; 3-418
Dry (hot) manures, soil fertilizers. 2-165
Dry measures. United States, table, 10-295
Dry-plate process. In photography, 9-403
Dry seasons.
Animals affected by, 5-412-13
Dry wines. 4-168
Drying, method of food preservation. with illus., 4-165
Drying, of ores. 1-376
Drying, of sludge. 5-333
Dubois, Eugene, Dutch anatomist and paleontologist.
9-22-23
Dubois, Raphael, French physiologist.
Bioluminescence, researches in, 2-188
Du Bois-Reymond, Emil, German physiologist.
Experiments with animal electricity, 2-421
Dubos, René-Jules. Work with tyrothricin, 9-34
Du Bridge, Lee A., American physicist. 9-289
Duck-billed platypuses. See **Platypuses**
Duck hawks. 6-159
Ducks. 6-400-03
Mallard, illus., 5-414
Raising of, 7-23
Ring-necked ducks, illus., 5-418e
Duckweeds, aquatic plants. 6-223
Duct, common bile. illus., 1-148d
Duct, pancreatic. illus., 1-148d
Duct glands, glands with ducts. 5-8-9, 10-15
Ductility. 5-376
Ductless glands. 5-15-19, illus., 16-17, 19
See also **Endocrine glands**
Ductus epididymis, tube leading from testis. 8-21, illus., 20
Du Fay, Charles, French scientist. Work on electricity, 4-359
Dugongs, aquatic mammals. 7-181-83, illus., 16
Adaptations for feeding, 7-9
Dugouts, primitive boats. Origin of, 4-106
Duikers (duikerboks), antelopes. 8-386, illus., 381
Dujardin, Félix, French zoologist. 7-159
Dulosis, slavery among ants. 3-365
Dumas, Jean-Baptiste-André, French chemist. 7-378, 380

Dumps. See **Open-dump method**
Dunant, Jean-Henri, Swiss philanthropist. 7-389
Dunes. 7-319-24, illus., 318, 322-24
Dung beetles. 3-345
Dunlap Observatory. See **David Dunlap Observatory**
Dunraven, fourth Earl of. Description of Yellowstone geysers, 8-289-90
Duodecimal system, of calculation. 1-156
Duodenal ulcers. 4-335, illus., 334
Duodenum, part of small intestine. illus., 1-148d; 4-327, illus., 322, 334
Duplation, form of multiplication. 1-157-58
Duplication. *Microfilming, 10-68-74
*Printing and engraving, 1-196-214
Duplicators. Design improved by Raymond Loewy, 10-120
Dura mater, one of the meningeal membranes. with illus., 6-327-28
Duralumin, alloy. 3-172
Duration, of sounds. 5-213
Durez phenolic resin, plastic. illus., 8-227
Duryea, Charles E., American automobile manufacturer. 2-130; 6-380-81
Duryea, J. Frank, American automobile manufacturer. 2-130
Dust. *7-137-42
Allergic reactions to, 4-260
Atmospheric and meteoritic, 1-232, 236, 238
Clouds formed about, 2-213, 216
Coal-mine explosions due to, 1-413; 8-273
Explosions due to, 2-229
Sunsets affected by volcanic dust, 7-342
Volcanic, 8-302
Wind distribution of, 7-319, 324-26, illus., 325
Dust Bowl. Formation of, 7-138
Dust-cloud hypothesis, of origin of solar system. 1-30; 9-225
Dust storms. 7-324-25
Dutch elm disease. Chemical treatment of, 10-153
Dutch metal, alloy of copper and zinc. 3-36
Dutton, Clarence Edward, American geologist. 7-32
Dwarfism, condition caused by underactivity of the pituitary gland. 5-17
Dwarfs. General Tom Thumb, illus., 8-94
Dye-transfer color photographs. 9-413
Dyes.
Dyeing leather, used in, 7-234
Roots that yield dyes, 4-75
Silk dyeing, 5-182, 184
Synthetic dyes, development of, 5-80-81; 8-183-84, 186-87
Dynamic geometry. 3-440
Dynamic loud-speakers, in radio. with illus., 3-96-97
Dynamics. See **Force; Motion**
Dynamite. illus., 8-284
Earthquakes induced by explosions in prospecting, 5-99, illus., 100; with diagrams, 7-357-58, illus., 354
Invention and development, with illus., 5-81-82; 8-182-83, 276
Marble quarried by, 2-87
Uses of, 8-287
Dynamos. See **Electric generators**
Dynel fibers. illus., 2-233
Dynes, units of force. 10-295
Barometric scales based on, 1-249
Dyrenforth, Robert G., American army officer.
Rain-making experiments of, 2-216
Dysentery. See **Amebic dysentery; Bacillary dysentery**
Dysprosium (Dy), chemical element. Atomic number, 66; atomic weight, 162.50. Rare-earth metal of the yttrium

Dysprosium (continued)
group. Discovered in 1886 by Lecoq de Boisbaudran.
Name derived from Greek *dysprositos:* "hard to get at."
Not yet isolated in free state, it is usually found in
minerals contained in granite or pegmatite veins.

E

E layer, ionized atmospheric region. 1-240, *diagram,*
239
Eads, James Buchanan. Born in Indiana, 1820; died in
the Bahamas, 1887. His family moved to St. Louis when
he was a child. During the Civil War he constructed
ironclads and gunboats for the Federal Government. He
built a bridge across the Mississippi at St. Louis, a feat
considered impossible at that time. He also invented a
system of jetties to control the channel at the mouth of
the Mississippi.
Eagle rays. 4-295
Eagles. 6-157, *illus.,* 156, 157
  Bald eagle in flight, *illus.,* 5-418
Eames, Charles, American designer. 10-121
Ear defenders, to ward off noise. 5-128
Ear trumpets, for deafness. *with illus.,* 5-125
Eardrum, tympanum of ear. *illus.,* 5-123; *with illus.,*
7-298, 299
Earphones. Prospecting, use of in, *with illus.,* 7-360
Ears.
  *Human ears, 7-298-301
  *Vertebrate ears, development of, 4-379-85
    Amphibians, *with illus.,* 1-282
    Balancing function in fish, *with illus.,* 1-281
    Care of, *with illus.,* 10-80
    Development in unborn human young, 8-30
    Embryonic development in humans, *with illus.,* 4-385
    Mechanism of, *with illus.,* 1-282
    Middle ear, evolution of, 7-2
    Sound waves affect, 5-114-15, 118-19, 122-23, 125-26,
      128, *illus.,* 114-15, 119, 123, 125
    Wax glands of, 5-11
  See also **Hearing**
Earth. *4-42-50
  *Atmosphere, 1-230-40
  *Caves, 5-50-60
  *Climates of past, 3-177-85
  *Clouds, 2-212-22
  *Dust, 7-137-42
  *Earthquakes, 9-105-19
  *Geysers, 8-288-92
  *Glaciers and icebergs, 9-162-74
  *Ground water, 8-321-32
  *Icebergs, 9-333-39
  *Interior, 4-169-76
  *International Geophysical Year, 5-186-95
  *Introduction to study of earth, 1-27-36
  *Islands, formation of, 4-133-39
  *Jet streams, 2-358-60
  *Lakes, 7-55-66
  *Lightning, 1-398-404
  *Meteorites and meteors, 6-87-98
  *Mineral deposits, 4-140-52; 5-248-56; 7-354-61
  *Mountain-building forces, 10-213-23
  *Mountains, 10-18-29
  *Oceanography, 6-26a-36
    *Bed of the sea, 6-69-77
    *Currents, 6-229-38
    *Tides, 6-201-08
    *Waves, 6-361-68
  *Precipitation, 2-346-57
  *Rivers, 6-409-18
  *Rocks, formation of, 3-419-26

Earth (continued)
  *Shoreline changes, 8-348-59
  *Soil, 2-15-25, 203-11; 5-25-30; 6-136-42
  *Soil fertility, 2-163-72
  *Time scale of earth's history, 6-369-74
  *Volcanoes, 7-334-45; 8-293-304
  *Water, erosive action of, 8-9-18
  *Winds, 2-89-98
    *Erosive agents, 7-318-26
  Age of, 4-46-47
  Aphelion of, 3-185
  Axis, inclination of, 3-182-83, 185
  Coal, formation and occurrence of, *with illus.,*
    1-405-08
  Composition of interior, 4-174-76
  Crust of
    Chemical elements, 1-80
    Density, variations in, 2-318-19, 320
    Equilibrium in, theory of, 7-32
  Data, 10-298
  Density of, 4-44
  Density of and internal pressure of, 4-173-74
  Deserts, *with illus.,* 6-113-18
  Elasticity and rigidity of, 4-174
  Expanding earth, theories of, 5-189-90
  Gravitational force exerted by. See **Gravity**
  Heat, sun as source of internal, 3-407
  Magnetic field of, 4-44, 176; *with diagrams,* 7-166-72
  Magnetic field's influence on cosmic rays, *with dia-
    gram,* 8-394-95
  Mantle, core and crust of, 4-171, 173, *illus.,* 170, 172
  Mass of, *with illus.,* 4-43-44
  Moon's movement around, *with illus.,* 2-316
  Movements of, *with diagrams,* 4-47-50
  Orbit of, 3-185, *illus.,* 99
  Origin and structure, theories of, *with illus.,* 1-27-30;
    with illus., 4-392-98
  Parts of, *with illus.,* 4-45-46
  Population, distribution of, 3-230-34, *map,* 230-31
  Rotation influences air circulation, 2-91
  Rotation influences ocean circulation, 5-191
  Shadows of, 3-132
  Shape of, *with illus.,* 4-42-43; 5-187-88
  Sunspot activity affects earth, 3-106-07
  Temperature, internal, 4-174
  See also **Astronomy; Geology; Geophysics; Paleon-
    tology; Physiography; Prehistoric times; Pros-
    pecting; Solar system; Universe**
Earth currents, electrical. See **Telluric currents**
Earth-fill dams. 2-272-73; 8-311-12, *illus.,* 310, 316c
  History of, 8-308
Earth satellites. See **Satellites, artificial**
"Earth watch," by artificial satellites. 10-52-53, *illus.,*
51
Earthenware. 7-396
Earthquakes. *9-105-19
  Artificial earthquakes used in prospecting, 4-145,
    diagram, 143; 5-99, *illus.,* 100; *with illus.,* 7-
    357-58
  Dams affected by, 8-317
  Earth's interior studied by means of earthquake
    waves, 4-170-71, 173, *illus.,* 170
  Lakes formed by, 7-55
  Ocean waves caused by, 6-368
  Submarine, 6-74
  Zones of, in Antarctica, 5-191
Earthshine, lunar phenomenon. 4-278
Earthworms. 2-159-61, *illus.,* 153, 159
  Fertilizers benefit, 2-170
  Gland cell of, *illus.,* 2-12d
  Movement of, *with diagram,* 1-279-80

Earthworms (continued)
  Respiration of, 4-200, illus., 201
  Soil development aided by, 2-204
Earwax. 5-11
Earwigs, insects. illus., 1-296; illus., 2-405; with illus., 3-151-52
East Greenland Current, oceanic current. 6-238, map, 232-33
East Pacific Rise, submarine ridge. 6-74-75
Eastern chipping sparrows. Migrations of, 5-418e
Eastern Hemisphere (Old World). Populations, development and size of, 3-226-28, 231-32
Eastman, George, American inventor and industrialist. 6-382
  Development of photography, 9-403
Ebbinghaus, Hermann, German psychologist. 9-56
  Study of forgetting process, 9-316
Ebers Papyrus. 1-128
Eberth, Karl Joseph, German anatomist and bacteriologist. 7-382
Eberthella typhi, bacterium causing typhoid fever. illus., 3-64
Eccentricity, of ellipses and orbits. 8-126-27
  Jupiter, 5-24
Eccles, W. H., American physicist.
  Electronic "trigger circuit" suggested by, 9-144
Echinoderms. 2-151-52, illus., 150-51
  Classification of, 1-293-94
  Fossil representatives, 1-388
  Larvae of, 4-3, illus., 2
  See also **Sea stars**
Echiuroidea, phylum of worms. 1-295
Echo satellites, communication satellites launched by the United States. 9-380; 10-47
Echo sounding. 6-69-70, 74, diagram, 70; 9-221-22
Echoes. 5-120-21, 128, illus., 121
  High-frequency sound produces, with illus., 8-105-06, 108-09
  Seismic echoes in prospecting, 4-145, diagram, 143
Eckert, J. P., American engineer. 9-145
Eclipses. *3-130-37
  Antiquity, eclipses in, 1-129-30
  Light velocity determined from eclipses of Jupiter's satellites, 5-21
  Prominences and Baily's beads discovered during, with illus., 6-393
  Solar, with illus., 6-393
  Solar and lunar eclipses, how to observe, with illus., 6-82-83
  Superstitions, ancient, 1-24, 26, illus., 23
  See also **Astronomy; Earth; Sun; Universe**
Eclipsing binaries, double stars. 7-229
  Algol, in Perseus, 1-334
Eclipsing variables, stars. 7-45-46
Ecliptic system, in astronomy. 1-260, 261, 263
  Signs of the zodiac, 10-298
Ecole des Ponts et Chausées (School for Bridge and Highway Construction). 2-333
Ecology, science dealing with relations between organisms and environment.
  *Adaptations, 3-235-44
  *Plants, 6-218-28
  *American forests, 5-257-62
  *Animal migrations, 9-415-32
  *Communities, plant and animal, 10-181-90
  *Habitats, 10-135-42
  *Human populations, 3-225-34
  *Parasites, 8-360-68
  *Seasonal changes and life, 5-408-13
  *Seed and fruit dispersal, 5-1-7
  *Soil organisms, 2-203-11

Economics.
  *Design of products, 10-117-26
  *Population problems, 3-225-34
  Automation, effects of, 10-237-38
  Industrial Revolution, effects on society, 4-35, 41
  Older population, effects on, 8-79-80
  Zoo management, economics of, 10-156-57
  See also **Industry**
Ecosystems, communities in which plants, animals and environment are linked together. 10-183-86, illus., 184-85
Ectoderm, layer of cells in early development of embryo. 8-23, illus., 24
Ectoparasites, true parasites living outside of host. with illus., 8-366-68
Eczema, rash caused by allergy. 4-257
Eddington, Sir Arthur Stanley, English astronomer (1882–1944). He was astronomy professor at Cambridge and director of its observatory. Eddington demonstrated that the sun is gaseous and that a star gives off light through subatomic energy. He investigated stellar motion and evolution, was a leading advocate of the relativity theory and published important works on the nature and laws of the universe.
Eddy currents, electrical. Currents induced in conducting material by a varying magnetic field. They are sometimes known as Foucault currents. See also 5-210
Edentata, order of mammals. with illus., 7-14
Edge-tone instruments. Sound production in, with illus., 5-217
Edible mushrooms. with illus., 3-30-31
Edison, Thomas Alva, American inventor. with illus., 5-244-47
  Electric lighting, contributions to, with illus., 4-235
  Phonograph, invention of, with illus., 7-363-66
  Radio emanations from sun studied by, 9-207
Edison effect. 9-286
Edison storage batteries. 5-96
Edmonton-Great Lakes pipeline. 4-147
Education.
  Behaviorist psychology applied to, 9-52
  Career in science, education needed, 10-194-95
  Industrial design, training in, 10-126
  Public-health movements, education in, 9-41
  Typing courses in schools, development of, with illus., 1-268-69
  See also **Binet, Alfred; Brain**
Educational psychology. 9-320
  Intelligence testing, development of, 9-54-56
Eductors, components of air-lift pumps. 2-275
Edwin Smith Surgical Papyrus. 1-127-28
Eels, fishes.
  Electric, 2-428
  Land travelers, 4-99
  Migrations, 3-243-44; 9-427
  Swimming movements of, 4-98
Efferent (motor) nerves and fibers.
  Definition and functions of, 6-318, illus., 322
Efficiency.
  Design of products, factor in, 10-120
  Noises affect, 8-43
Effinger, Cecil, American musicologist.
  Music typewriter developed by, with illus., 1-275
Effort.
  Force applied to lever, with illus., 1-283; 3-57, 58, illus., 56-58; with illus., 7-215
  Relation of, to work, 3-56-57
Efts, immature forms of newts. with illus., 5-161
Egg cells, female sex cells.
  Heredity, role in, 8-334-37
  Human, illus., 1-43

Egg-eating snakes. 5-360-61
Egg sacs.
  Spiders, 2-262, illus., 258, 260, 267
Egg teeth, lizards. 5-205
Eggs.
  Birds
    Cuckoos, 6-306, 308
    Hawks, illus., 6-158
    Hens, illus., 1-43
    Kinglets, 6-44
    Nuthatches, 6-42
    Robins, 6-38
    Vireos, 6-64
    Woodpeckers, 6-210
  Cooking with high-frequency sound, illus., 8-107
  Fossil dinosaur eggs, 1-385
  Frogs, with illus., 5-158-59
  Human egg cell, illus., 1-43
  Insects, 2-406
    Ants, illus., 3-360
    Flies, 3-283, illus., 285-86, 288
    Mantes, illus., 8-68
    Moth and butterflies, illus., 2-408; 3-195, illus., 194, 197, 202
    Orthopterous insects, 3-139, 142, illus., 138, 142
    Silkworms, with illus., 5-174, 175-76
    Social insects, 3-357, 358, 362, illus., 360, 365
    True bugs, 3-255
  Protection of, with illus., 3-241-43
  Raw-egg diet, dangers of, 5-43-44
  Reptiles, 5-381-82
  Salamanders, with illus., 5-160
  Snakes, 5-355, illus., 354
  Spiders, 2-262
  Toads', illus., 3-226
Egypt, Ancient.
  Algebra, contributions to, 2-68
  Animal skins, preparation of, in Egypt, 7-231, illus., 232
  Archaeological materials dating from, 10-96-97, illus., 92
  Architecture of, 3-114
  Breadmaking in, 9-294
  Buttons of, 7-209
  Calendar of, 10-171-72
  Engineering in, 1-216
  Illumination in, 4-232
  Irrigation in, with illus., 8-192
  Mathematics, contributions to, 3-427-28
  Number system of, 1-150, 152, illus., 151
  Pottery of Twelfth Dynasty, illus., 7-398
  Science in, with illus., 1-124-28
  Sea voyages of Egyptians, 6-27
  Ships and boats of, 4-106
  Stone buildings, with illus., 7-116
  Water supply in, 2-271
  Writing developed by ancient Egyptians, 1-111, 113, illus., 116-17
Egypt, Modern. Irrigation, with illus., 8-200
Egyptian lotuses. illus., 5-65
Egyptian mongooses. See Ichneumons
Ehrlich, Paul, German bacteriologist. with illus., 9-32-33
Eider ducks. 6-403
Eiffel Tower, Paris. 3-115; illus., 7-123
Eijkman, Christiaan, Dutch hygienist. 8-404
  Vitamin study pioneered by, 5-39
Einstein, Albert, German-born American physicist.
    with illus., 9-279-82, 284
  *Relativity theory, 4-210-20
  Law of gravitation, modification of, 3-164
  Mass-energy equation, 1-84-85, 329-30

Einstein, Albert (continued)
  Quotation from, 10-202
  Tests of his theory, 3-136-37
Einstein equation. 1-84-85; 4-217; 9-329-30
Einsteinium (Es), chemical element. Atomic number, 99; atomic weight, 254(?). Radioactive actinide metal with chemical properties similar to those of the rare earth holmium. First discovered in dust and debris from the 1952 H-bomb explosion at Eniwetok. Subsequently made by a group led by Ghiorso at the University of California through bombardment, in a cyclotron, of uranium-238 with nitrogen-14 at 100,000,000 electron volts. Also produced in a reactor by successive irradiations of plutonium.
Einthoven, Willem, Dutch physiologist. 2-421
Ekman current meter. 6-229-30
Elands, antelopes. 8-379, illus., 380
Elasticity. 5-375
  Boyle's experiments, 3-271
  Earth's elasticity and earthquakes, 4-174; 7-357-58
  Sound, speed of, and elasticity of medium, 5-119
  See also Solids; Vibration; Waves
Elbows. Action of, with illus., 1-283
  Muscles acting on, with illus., 3-208-09
Elder trees. 5-150
El Dorado, mythical kingdom of New World. 4-244
Electric-arc process, for fixing nitrogen. 3-127
Electric charges. Experiments showing effects of, with illus., 6-286-88
Electric current.
  Animal light stimulated by, 2-187
  Atmosphere, currents in upper part of, 1-240
  Experiments with, with illus., 6-288-94
  Oscillations in, and radio waves, 3-86
  Prospecting with, with diagram, 7-359-61
  See also Current electricity; Electricity
Electric distributing stations. 9-236-37, illus., 238
Electric drive. Ships, 4-114, 115
Electric eels, fishes. 2-428; with illus., 4-103
Electric eye. See Photoelectric cells
Electric furnaces. Process of steelmaking, 1-340, with illus., 346-47, diagram, 348c
Electric generating stations. 9-234-35, illus., 236
Electric generators. illus., 5-308; with illus., 9-228-36
  Direct current, with illus., 6-129-30
  Electrolysis brought about by, 5-89
  Nineteenth century, development of, with illus., 5-236, 247
  Radioisotope-fueled thermoelectric generators, with illus., 6-172-75
  Rotor assembly of, illus., 5-309
  Stator assembly of, illus., 5-309
  Steam turbine-generator unit, illus., 5-310-11
Electric heating units. Home laboratory, with illus., 4-223
Electric light bugs. 3-263
Electric lighting. with illus., 4-234-35, 237-41
  *Electroluminescence, 9-344-47
  Nineteenth century, development of, 5-246-47, illus., 244
  See also Illumination; Lamps
Electric locomotives. See Locomotives, electric
Electric motors. with illus., 6-131
  Airplanes, use in, 6-192
  Forerunner of, 5-236
  Homemade, with illus., 8-147-49
  Shaft power by means of, 9-239-40
  Ships, 4-114, 115
Electric oscillators. with illus., 6-299-300
  Development of, 6-244
Electric portable typewriters. with illus., 1-273

Electric power. See Power
Electric rays, fishes. 3-237-38
Electric resonators. Detecting electromagnetic radiations, 6-245, illus., 244
Electric shock. Prevention of in home, 7-196-97
Electric signal system. Invention of, for railroads, 6-379-80
Electric telegraphs. Invention and development of, in nineteenth century, with illus., 5-238-41, 244
Electric transformers. See Transformers, electric
Electric typewriters. with illus., 1-273
Electric well logging, electrical measurements in wells. 7-361
Electrical appliances. Safety measures with, 7-191-92, 196-97
Electrical circuits.
  *Printed circuits, 6-49-51
  Electric generating and distributing stations, circuits in, 9-234-38, illus., 236, 238-39
  Homemade circuits, with illus., 6-288-94
  Prospecting with, with diagram, 7-359-61
  UNIVAC computers, 9-149
  See also Electricity; Electronics
Electrical conduction. See Conductors, electrical
Electrical energy. 1-83
  *Generation, transmission and distribution of, 9-226-40
  Conversions of, to other forms of energy, 9-226-27
  Light energy transformed into, with illus., 7-103-06
  Transformations of, 6-247, illus., 248-49
Electrical engineering. 1-219, 223-24
Electrical hygrometers, humidity gauges. 1-251
Electrical impulses. Living organisms have, 2-421-28
  Prospecting with electrical pulses, 7-361
Electrical industry. Transportation in nineteenth century, 6-380
Electrical phenomena. Atmospheric, 1-238, 240, illus., 236
Electrical potential. 9-227
  Prospecting with, with diagram, 7-359-61
Electrical precipitators, for smoke. with diagram, 5-304
  See also Electrostatic precipitators
Electrical systems, automobile. with illus., 2-137-38
Electrical terms. Faraday introduced, 5-236
Electrical winds, in upper atmosphere. 1-240
Electricity. *6-119-35
  *Bioelectricity, 2-421-28
  *Electrochemistry, 5-87-96
  *Electroluminescence, 9-344-47
  *Electronics, 6-295-303
  *Experiments with, 6-286-94
  *Generation, transmission, distribution, 9-226-40
  *Lightning, 1-398-404
  *Piezoelectricity, 2-293-94
  *Printed circuits, 6-49-51
  *Radioisotope-fueled thermoelectric generators, 6-172-75
  *Telegraph and telephone, 2-377-95
  Abrasives, use in manufacture of, 1-88
  Absolute zero, electrical phenomena at temperatures near, 5-209-10
  Airplanes, use in, 6-191-92
  Atmospheric phenomena, 1-238, 240, illus., 236
  Atom, charges within, 9-125
  Atom, electrical forces in, 1-310, 311
  Charged particles affected by electric field, 9-241, 345
  Coal burned to generate electricity, 1-416-17
  Colloidal suspensions, electrical forces in, 5-300-01
  Electrolysis of water by homemade apparatus, with illus., 4-348-49
  Fishes, electrical discharges of, 3-237-38; 4-103, 293

Electricity (continued)
  Frictional-electricity machine, invention of, 3-18
  History
    Sixteenth-century study, 2-371
    1765–1815, research, with illus., 4-358-63
    Nineteenth century, with illus., 5-231-47
  Illumination, with illus., 4-234-35, 237-41
  Light and magnetism, relation to, 6-239, 242-45
  Metals recovered by electrolysis, 1-380, with diagram, 378, 381
  Molecular forces due in part to electrical attraction, 1-166
  Nuclear reactors generate electricity indirectly, 9-358, illus., 357
  Photography, electrical devices in, 9-408-09, 410-11, 412, illus., 409
  Piezoelectric effect, 8-107
  Precautions to be taken in using, 7-191-92, 196-97
  Prospecting with, with diagram, 7-359-61
  Recording method, electrical, 7-368
  Ships powered by, 4-114, 115
  Solutions, testing conductivity of, with illus., 4-345
  Steam turbine-electric generator unit, 5-310-11
  Sun, generation of electricity due to heat of, 3-407-08
  Weather and rain, atmospheric electricity in, 1-245
  X rays, production of, 7-143-46, 148
  Xerographic printing, 1-214
  See also Electric lighting; Electrolysis; Electromagnetic radiation; Electromagnetism; Electronics; Electrons; Electroplating; Henry, Joseph; Maxwell, James Clerk; Photoelectric cells; Radio
Electro shock, treatment for mental illness. 9-203
Electrocardiographs, devices for recording electric impulses accompanying beat of heart. 2-428, illus., 426
Electrochemical analysis. 5-91
Electrochemistry, study of electricity in chemistry. *5-87-96
  Metals recovered by electrolysis, 1-380, with diagram, 378, 381
  Ore bodies generating electrochemical currents, 7-359-60
  See also Electrolysis; Electroplating; Electrotypes
Electrodes. 5-89
  Electric steelmaking furnaces, function in, 1-346
  Faraday introduced name, 5-236
  Prospecting with, with diagram, 7-360-61
Electrodialysis, electrical filtering of solutions through membranes. Water desalted by, 2-284
Electroencephalograph, for recording brain waves. with illus., 2-427-28
Electrojet, atmospheric electric current. 1-240
Electroluminescence. *9-344-47
Electrolysis, chemical decomposition by action of electric current. with illus., 5-89-94
  Discovery of, 4-363
  Faraday's researches, 5-236
  Hair removed by, 10-84
  Metals recovered by, 1-380, with diagram, 378, 381
  Printing plates made by, 1-207, diagram, 208
  Water, decomposition into oxygen and hydrogen, with illus., 4-348-50
  Water desalted by a form of, 2-284
Electrolytes, substances whose aqueous solutions conduct electricity. 2-423; with diagram, 4-298; 5-89
  Faraday introduced name, 5-236
  Voltaic cells, use of electrolytes in, with illus., 5-94-96
Electrolytic tank. See Tank, electrolytic
"Electrolytic-zinc process." 1-380

Electromagnetic radiation. *7-199-207
Atomic particles involved in, 1-314
Light as form of, 7-278
See also Electromagnetic waves; Radio telescopes
Electromagnetic spectrum. 6-245
*Electromagnetic radiation, 7-199-207
Discovery and formulation of, 6-245
X rays in, 7-145
Electromagnetic theory of light. Faraday foreshadowed, 5-236
Electromagnetic waves.
*Electromagnetic radiation, 7-199-207
*Optics, 7-249-62
Nineteenth-century study, with illus., 6-239-47
See also Color; Electronics; Radiation; Radio; Radio astronomy; Television
Electromagnetism.
*Experiments with, 8-144-50
Electromagnetic separation of uranium isotopes, 9-134
Generators, use in, 6-129-30, illus., 128, 129
Nineteenth-century development and application, with illus., 5-231-47; with illus., 6-239-47
Ore separation, use in, 1-374-75
Prospecting with electromagnetic methods, 7-361
See also Electricity; Electromagnetic waves
Electromagnets. 6-130; 7-166, illus., 162
Homemade working models, with illus., 8-144-49
Invention and development of, with illus., 5-232-47
Ore separation, use in, 1-374-75
Superconductive alloys used for, 5-210
Electrometallurgy. 9-240
Electromotive force. See Voltage
Electromyographs. Dentistry, use in, 5-137
Electron microscopes. with illus., 9-94; illus., 10-169
Development of, 9-289
Micrograph taken with electron microscope, illus., 10-169
Virus crystals photographed with, illus., 5-342
Virus study, use in, 3-455-56, 457, illus., 451
Electron synchrotrons, atom smashers. 9-248-49
Electron tubes. *6-295-303
*Audion, development of, 8-84-89
Bioelectricity, studied with, 2-422
Development of, 8-409; 9-287-89
Radio detectors, 3-96
Television, use in, with illus., 5-280-86
Transistors compared with, with illus., 10-104
See also Diodes; Gas-filled tubes; Triodes; Vacuum tubes; etc.
Electron volts, units of energy. 8-397
Electronic computers. *9-143-52; illus., 6-298a, 298b-c
Automation, use in, 10-236-37, illus., 234b
Electric typewriters used with, with illus., 1-276
Printed circuits used in, 6-50-51
Radiation thickness gauges used with, 9-45
Telegraphic systems used with, 2-383-84
Electronic hearing aids. 5-125
Electronic music synthesizer. with illus., 5-220
Electronic musical instruments. 5-220, illus., 219-20
Electronic oscillators. with illus., 3-86-88; 6-297, 299-300, illus., 299
Electronics. *6-295-303
*Applications, practical, 10-168-70
*Audion, development of, 8-84-89
*Facsimile transmission, 7-390-92
*Noise meters, 8-38-46
*Piezoelectricity and electrostriction, 2-293-94
*Printed circuits, 6-49-51
*Radar, 9-387-90
*Radiation thickness gauges, 9-43-46

Electronics (continued)
*Radio, 3-85-98
*Solar battery, 7-103-06
*Television, 5-276-88
*Transistors, 10-102-04
Cathode-ray oscillograph, illus., 10-201
Coal industry uses, 1-416, illus., 409
Development of, with illus., 9-285-89
Electricity, electronics as application of, 9-240
Inventions using, illus., 10-168-70
Mass spectrometer, illus., 10-200-01
Photography, electronic flashes for, 9-411, illus., 412
Recording, 7-368
Space vehicles and missiles guided by electronic devices, 8-128-31
See also Electron microscopes; Electronic computers
Electrons. 6-286
*Solar battery, role of electrons in, 7-103-06
Accelerated by linear accelerators, 9-247
Arrangement of, with illus., 3-246-47
Atmospheric, 1-238, 245
Atomic particles, 1-310, diagrams, 311-13, with table, 314; 9-123, 125, 128
Cosmic-ray showers, 8-396, 397
Discovery of, 8-403-04, 416; 9-285
Electric charge of, 6-120-21
Electricity as flow of electrons, with illus., 9-227-28
Electromagnetic theory of matter and radiation, part in, 7-205, 249, 250, 252
Electronics, electrons basis of, with illus., 9-285-89
Geiger-Mueller counters, behavior of electrons in, 9-342
Ionization involves, with illus., 5-88-89
Magnetism, theoretical role in, 7-172
Oxidation and, 3-317
Parity law of physics violated by, 7-110
Phosphors, excitation of, for light production, 9-344
Radiation thickness gauges use beams of electrons, with illus., 9-43
Radio waves result from movement of, 3-86
Television transmission, electrons basis of, 5-279-84
Transistors, flow of electrons in, 10-103-04
X rays produced by high-speed electrons, 7-144-46 148
See also Beta particles; Electron tubes; Electronics
Electroosmosis. 5-301
Electrophoresis. Technique used to separate mixtures into their components. It is based on the fact that the components carry electric charges of varying amounts; therefore they will move at different rates in a salt solution through which a current is passed. In paper electrophoresis the mixture to be separated is poured on a strip of paper after the paper has been moistened by the salt solution. Each end of the strip is put into a container filled with the solution. An electrode is submerged in each container; direct current is passed through the solution. The different components migrate at different rates according to their electric charges. After they have been separated they are identified by various means.
Electroplating. 5-91-92, illus., 90; 9-240
Demonstration of, with illus., 7-134
Printing plates made by, 1-207, diagram, 208
Electropositiveness. 3-33, 165
Electroscopes.
Electrical charge identified by, with illus., 6-121-22
Experiments with homemade electroscopes, 6-287, illus., 286
Electrostatic attraction.
Atoms, with diagram, 2-422
Ore separation, use in, 1-375

Electrostatic generators (Van de Graaff accelerators), atom smashers. *diagram,* 1-309; 8-419-20, *illus.,* 418; 9-131, 330, *with illus.,* 242-44, *illus.,* 129, 241; 10-200
Preservation of food by, *illus.,* 4-168
Electrostatic precipitators, smoke-control devices, *with illus.,* 3-355
See also **Electrical precipitators**
Electrostatic separation, in ore dressing. 1-375
Electrostriction. *2-293-94
Minerals identified by, 5-256
Electrotypes, in printing. 1-207, *diagram,* 208
Electrotypesetters, coded type-casting machines. 1-202
Electrovalence. *with illus.,* 3-247-50
Electrum, alloy of silver and gold. 3-34
Elements. Four elements of antiquity, 1-137, *with illus.,* 132
Elements, chemical. 1-79-81
*Atomic structure, 1-307-14
*Carbon, synthetic diamonds made from, 4-273-76
*Metals, survey of, 3-33-42, 165-76
*Nitrogen, fixation of, 3-126-29
*Nonmetallic elements, 3-317-24
*Periodic table of elements, 4-304-10
Boyle's introduction of modern concepts, 3-270
Classification of, in nineteenth century, *with illus.,* 5-83-86
Lavoisier's classification, 4-357
Comets, found in, 5-392-93
Discoveries in nineteenth century, 5-76-77, 85-86
Disintegration of, 8-416
List of, 10-293
Mendeleev's predictions of, 5-85
Meteors and meteorites, found in, 6-92-93
Minerals as, 5-248
Native elements, examples of, 9-306
Oxygen as an active element, 8-273
Plants, elements required by, 2-23-24; 8-34-35
Plants' absorption and use of soil nutrients, 3-44-45
Plastics, elements in, *with diagram,* 8-222
Protoplasm, elements in, 2-3-6
Sea, kinds and amounts found in, *with chart,* 6-30-32
Soil fertility, factors in, 2-163, 164
Stellar bodies, discovery and identification of elements in, 6-390-91
Sun, elements found in, 3-108-09
Transmutation of, *with illus.,* 8-410-20; *with illus.,* 9-328-32
See also **Chemistry** and names of individual elements
Elements, periodic law of. *4-304-10
Elephant beetles. 3-346
Elephant fish. 4-295
Elephant seals. *illus.,* 7-91
Elephant shrews. 7-102, *illus.,* 13, 100
Elephantiasis. 2-158
Elephants. *with illus.,* 7-409-13, *illus.,* 12, 16
Adaptation to climate, 3-179
African elephant, 3-frontispiece
Domestication of, 7-328
Intelligence, *illus.,* 2-29
Transportation, use in, *with illus.,* 1-100-01
Trunk of, 7-409-10
Elevated storage tanks, for water-supply systems. *with illus.,* 2-285-86
Elevators. Mines, 1-410
Elevators, movable parts of airplane tails. 6-188
Elf owls. 6-165
Elfin sharks. 4-290
Elimination of body wastes. 10-83
Elizabeth River Tunnel, Norfolk, Va. Section of unfinished tunnel, *illus.,* 2-51

Elks, wapiti. *illus.,* 8-238
Migration of, 9-422
Ellesmere Island. Source of ice islands, 9-338, *map,* 336-37
Ellipses, plane curves. *with illus.,* 3-438-39
Analytic geometry, equations in, 4-427-28, *diagram,* 429
Cometary orbits depicted as, 5-394-95, *illus.,* 396
Earth's revolution around sun is elliptical, 4-48-49, *diagram,* 46
Heavenly bodies that move in ellipses, 1-20
Space-flight orbits are elliptical, 8-126-28, 131, *diagrams,* 126, 131
Elliptical-equator theory. 5-188
Elliptical galaxies. 8-50, *diagram,* 48; 9-363
Elliptical orbits. Meteorites, *with diagram,* 6-98
Ellis Island, New York City, former immigration center. *illus.,* 3-233
Elm trees. *with illus.,* 5-145
Bark, *illus.,* 5-140
Fruits, *illus.,* 5-3, 141
Leaves, *illus.,* 5-140
Seeds, *illus.,* 5-63
El Nath, star in Taurus. 1-336
Elodea, aquatic plant. *illus.,* 8-114
El Salvador, republic of Central America.
Cuscatlán Bridge, *illus.,* 3-302
Izalco, volcano, *illus.,* 8-300a
Elsasser, Walter, German-born American physicist.
Earth's magnetic field, possible explanations of, 4-176
Elton, Lake. Russia, 7-64
Elytra, modified beetle wings. *illus.,* 2-405; 3-335, *illus.,* 336
Embankments, railway. 1-192
Embioptera, order of insects. 2-413
Emboli, abnormal particles in blood stream. 3-332, *illus.,* 331
Embolism. See **Emboli**
Embryo sacs, cells within ovules. *with illus.,* 4-125
Embryology.
Aristotle's work, 1-138
Cell theory, revolutionized, *with illus.,* 7-161
Human embryo, development of, *with illus.,* 8-19-33
Embryonic shield, early structure in product of conception. *with illus.,* 8-23
Embryos, miniature plants arising from seeds. 2-415, 417, 418-19, 420, *illus.,* 416
Embryos, undeveloped forms of immature organisms.
Gill pouches in, *illus.,* 1-58
Human, *with illus.,* 8-25
Plants, 4-131; 5-62
Virus cultures, chicken embryos for, 3-457-58
See also **Embryology**
Emerald hummingbirds. *illus.,* 6-213
Emerging coasts. 8-354-55
Emission of electrons. *with illus.,* 6-295-97, 300-02
See also **Photoelectric emission**
Emission theory of light. See **Corpuscular theory of light**
Emotions.
Baby, human, development in, 8-97-98
Colors produce, 7-290
Digestive tract affected by emotional disturbances, 4-332
James-Lange theory of, 9-50
Psychology of, 9-318
Psychopathic personalities, 9-199-200
Empedocles, Greek philosopher. *with illus.,* 1-132
Four body humors, theory of, 1-365
Light, comment on velocity of, 5-21

Empedocles (continued)
Matter, explanation of, 1-307
Empire State Building, New York City. **3-114**
Struck by lightning, illus., 6-126
Studies of lightning striking building, with illus., 1-401-02
Television antenna, illus., 5-283
Transmitting tower atop, 3-86
Empire State Express, steam locomotive. **6-379**
Empirical formulas. 3-246
Employment. Older persons, 8-83
Typewriter provides, 1-269
Empty (null) sets, in mathematics. with diagram, 4-442
Emulsification. High-frequency sound, 8-109, illus., 110
Emulsions.
Colloidal, 5-296-97, 300
Photographic, 9-403, 404, 408, 413, 414, illus., 400a-b
Enamel, tooth tissue. 5-129, 131, illus., 134-35
Enamels. Cans coated with, 4-155
Enceladus, satellite of Saturn. 5-113
Encephalitis, lethargic, sleeping sickness. 6-151, 330
Encke, Johann, German astronomer. Saturn's rings described by, 5-110
Encke's comet. 5-396
Endives. Air pollution detected by, illus., 3-352
Endocrine glands. illus., 1-148g; 5-8, 15-19, illus., 16-17, 19
Luminous secretions in animals, 2-186
Endocrine system. See **Endocrine glands**
Endoderm, layer of cells in early development of embryo. with illus., 8-23, 24
Endodermis, layer of plant cells. with illus., 4-64
Endolymph, liquid of inner ear. 7-299
Endoparasites, true parasites living within host. 8-364-66, illus., 363
Endoplasmic reticulum, internal membranes of cells. 2-6-9, illus., 12b-c
Endosperm, seed food tissue. 2-415, 417, 418-19, 420, illus., 416; 4-131; with illus., 5-62
Energy.
*Atom smashers, 9-241-49
*Atomic energy, 9-120-42
*Bodily energy, **10-85-91**
*Cosmic rays, 8-393-99
*Electricity, 6-119-35; 9-226-40, 344-47
*Electrochemistry, 5-87-96
*Electromagnetic radiation, 7-199-207
*Explosives, 8-273-87
*Geiger-Mueller counters, 9-340-43
*Heat, 3-407-18; 4-9-16
*Heat engines, 4-80-92
*Irrigation, 8-191-201
*Light, experiments with, 8-117-24
*Liquids and gases, forces in, 2-30-42
*Magnetism, 7-162-72
*Matter and energy, 1-79-86
*Noise meters, 8-38-46
*Optics, 7-249-62
*Radioisotope-fueled thermoelectric generators, 6-172-75
*Solar battery, 7-103-06
*Sounds, musical, 5 211-20
*Turbines, 5-305-12
*Ultrasonics, 8-103-10
Atomic Age, dawn of, with illus., 9-328-32
Conservation of (historical background), 6-247-54
Conversion of, illus., 3-408-09; with illus., 9-226-34

Energy (continued)
High-frequency sound, 8-108
Kinetic, in turbines, 5-307
Mass, relation to, 9-131
Muscle contraction, required for, 3-205-07
Plant processes, sources and uses of energy in, 3-43-45, 47-48, 50
Potential, in turbines, 5-307
Solar, with illus., 3-109-12; 9-139-40, 224
Sound waves, 5-118-19, 122, illus., 118
Thermodynamics, rise of science of, 6-253-54
Ultrasonic, illus., 1-89
See also **Atoms; Calories; Chemistry; Electricity; Heat; Kinetic theory; Light; Motion; Parity law; Power; Sound; X rays**
Energy cycles. 6-247, illus., 248-49
Engineering. 1-215-29
*Aeronautics, 6-176-200
*Automation, 10-235-38
*Automobiles, 2-129-45
*Bridges, 2-332-45
*Electricity, generation, transmission, distribution of, 9-226-40
*Guidance of missiles and space vehicles, 8-125-31
*Heat engines, 4-80-92
*Hydrofoils, 4-5-8
*Irrigation, 8-191-201
*Road making, 3-293-306
*Science and industrial progress, 1-87-97
*Ships, 4-106-18
*Space travel, 10-40-54
*Steam engines, 5-305-12
*Tunnels, 2-43-57
*Waste disposal, 5-326-36
*Water supply, 2-270-86
Acoustical, 5-128, illus., 127
Calculus used in, with diagram, 4-435
Development in ancient Rome, 1-363, illus., 364
Petroleum engineering, with d.agrams and illus., 4-144-52
See also **Bridges; Building; Canals; Chemistry; Electricity; Electronics; Engines; Roads; Tunnels; and names of industries**
Engineers' Council for Professional Development. 1-215, 229
Engines.
*Heat engines, 4-80-92
*Turbines, steam, 5-305-12
Atomic-submarine engine, used in, illus., 4-342d
Automobile, automatic production of, with illus., 10-237-38
Digester gas as fuel for, 5-332
Internal-combustion engines, development of, 6-254, illus., 252-53
Reciprocating, compared with turbine, 5-311
Ships powered by various, with illus., 4-109-18
See also **Automobiles; Diesel engines; Gasoline engines; Inventions; Jet propulsion; Locomotives; Rockets; Steam engines; Turbines**
England.
Archaeological materials dating from, **10-97,** illus., 92
Calendar reform, 10-176
Coal, medieval use of, 1-408-09
Evolutionary controversy in, 8-261-62
Industrial Revolution, birth of, with illus., 4-36-41
Irrigation in, 8-193
Library materials microfilmed, 10-73-74
Manchester Ship Canal, 4-186
Roads of, with illus., 3-298-99
Salisbury Cathedral choir, illus., 7-117

England *(continued)*
   Scientific contributions
      1600–1765, *with illus.,* **3**-266-67, 270-71, 273,
         275-82
      1765–1815, *with illus.,* **4**-353-55, 359, 361, 363
   Semaphore system, **2**-378
   Transportation on land, early, **1**-103, *with illus.,* 104-
      05
   World exploration, contributions to, **2**-365-66; *with*
      illus., **7**-31-34
   See also **Great Britain; London**
English Channel. Airplane crossing, first, **6**-183; **9**-
   216-17
English language. Characteristics and development,
   1-116-17
English lime trees. **5**-146
English sparrows. City-dwelling birds, **10**-256
Engraving.
   *Printing and engraving, **1**-196-214
   Halftone engraving process, invention of, **6**-381
Eniwetok Atoll, in the Marshall Islands. Drilling ex-
   ploration in, **6**-77
Enlarging, photographic. **9**-406, 410, *diagram,* 411
Enrichment, of food.
   Bread, **9**-299
   Malnutrition combatted by, *with illus.,* **4**-61
Entamoeba, genus of one-celled animals. **2**-64, *illus.,*
   62
Entamoeba histolytica, species of ameba. Amebic
   dysentery, **4**-333-34, *illus.,* 333
Enterogastrone, hormone functioning in digestion.
   4-326
Enterprise, nuclear-powered aircraft carrier of United
   States Navy. **4**-118, *with illus.,* 114a
Entomology, science that treats of insects. *****2**-402-14
   *Ants, bees and wasps, **3**-357-72
   *Ants, keeping colony of, **3**-393-96
   *Beetles, **3**-335-48
   *Butterflies and moths, **3**-193-202d
   *Flies and mosquitoes, **3**-283-92
   *Grasshoppers and kin, **3**-138-52
   *Insect collecting, **3**-153-56
   *Mosquito as transmitter of disease, **10**-30-39
   *Plant pests, **9**-185-95
   *True bugs, **3**-252-64
   Beginnings of, **3**-274
   Disease germs, insects as transmitters and carriers
      of, **7**-382-83
   See also **Insects; Parasites**
Entoprocta, phylum of mosslike animals. **1**-293
Environment.
   *Adaptations, **3**-235-44
      *Plant, **6**-219-28
   *Communities, plant and animal, **10**-181-90
   *Seasonal changes and life, **5**-408-13
   Allergy and, **4**-262
   Animal migration, influence on, **9**-416, 418
   Caves as dwelling places for plants and animals,
      with illus., **5**-58-60
   Effects of, *illus.,* **8**-347
   Evolution influenced by, *with illus.,* **6**-276-77
   Factors of, affecting mammals, *with illus.,* **7**-6-11
   Factors of, affecting plants, *with illus.,* **6**-218-28
   Fruits and seed in relation to, **5**-6-7
   Heredity and, **8**-334, 346-47
   Human growth, role in, **8**-92-93
   Plant growth and response, influence on, *with illus.,*
      3-50-54
   Plants adapted to various environments, **1**-49
   Populations and, **3**-225-28

Enzymes, organic substances speeding up chemical re-
   actions.
   Aging process, enzymes may affect, **8**-81
   Breadmaking fermentation due to, *with diagrams,*
      9-296-97
   Digestive and respiratory enzymes of plants, **3**-46-48
   Digestive enzymes of humans, **4**-321, 325, 328
   Fungi, enzyme activities of, **3**-23
   Nucleic acids synthesized by aid of, **9**-386
   Plant and animal cells, found in, **2**-3, 6
   Sugar fermentation, **8**-184
   Synthesis, catalytic role in, **8**-190
"Eoanthropus." Discovered by Dawson, **9**-23
Eocene epoch, time in earth's history. **6**-374
Eohippus, ancestor of horse. *with illus.,* **1**-396, *with*
   illus., **6**-281
Eolian soils, wind-deposited soils. **6**-142
Eosinophils, white blood cells. **3**-328, *illus.,* 329
   See also **White blood cells**
Eötvös torsion balance. *with illus.,* **7**-359-60
Ephemerida, order of insects. **2**-413
Ephemeris, table showing assigned places of celestial
   body for regular intervals.
   Comets, **5**-396
Epicenters. Of earthquakes, **9**-107, 114, *diagram,* 114
Epicotyls, seed parts. *with illus.,* **4**-131; **5**-62, 66, *illus.,*
   62, 67
Epicureans, Greek philosophers. **1**-138
Epicurus, Greek philosopher. Philosophy of, as ex-
   pounded by Lucretius, **1**-361
Epicycles, theory of, in astronomy. **3**-162
Epidemics. Study of, **2**-367-68
   See also **Infectious diseases; Malaria; Mosquitoes;**
      Rats; Smallpox; Ticks
Epidemiology. Theobald Smith's contributions to,
   7-384
Epidermis, outer layer of skin. **2**-173, 179, 181,
   illus., 174
Epidermis, surface layer of plants. *illus.,* **3**-42b; **4**-63,
   68, 72, 73, *illus.,* 64, 69, 73
Epidinium, genus of protozoans. **2**-66, *illus.,* 65
Epiglottis. Function in swallowing food, *with diagram,*
   4-323
Epilepsy, mental disorder. **9**-201
   Sleep, not similar to, **6**-150
Epileptic convulsions.
   Alcoholics may suffer from, **4**-412
   First aid for, *with illus.,* **10**-14-15
Epinephrine. See **Adrenaline**
Epiphyses, centers of bone formation. **8**-96
Epiphytes. **6**-222
Epithelium, lining tissue. **1**-144-45, 147
Epochs, lesser geologic-time units. **6**-370
   See also **Eras; Periods**
Epoxy resins, plastics. **8**-227
Epsilon Lyrae, double star in Lyra. **1**-333
Epsom salts. **3**-172, 425
Epsomite. Cave deposits of, **5**-56
Equal-arm balances.
   How to make, *with illus.,* **7**-216
Equal sets, in mathematics. **4**-442
Equal triangles. *with illus.,* **3**-433
Equations, algebraic. **2**-72-73
   Einstein's equation, **1**-84-85
Equations, chemical. **2**-225-27, 229, 230, 231, *dia-*
   gram, 225-27
Equator, celestial. See **Celestial equator**
Equator, terrestrial.
   Air masses warmed at, *with diagrams,* **1**-242-44; **2**-
      89-90, *diagram,* 91

Equator, terrestrial (continued)
Atmospheric phenomena over equatorial regions, 1-238
Elliptical rather than circular, 5-188, 189

Equator system. Determining star positions by, with diagram, 6-80-81

Equatorial Countercurrent, oceanic current. 6-238, map, 232-33

Equatorial mounts, for telescopes. with diagram, 9-373

Equatorial orbits, parallel to earth's equator. with diagram, 8-127

Equatorial system, in astronomy. with illus., 1-259-60

Equilibrium, state of balance.
Cerebellum controls, 6-326
Chemical reactions, reversible, 2-229-30, 231, diagram, 230-31
Gravitational, 2-322, illus., 321
Melting points represent, 1-171
See also **Balance**

Equinoxes. 1-260, 263
See also **Astronomy; Seasons**

Equipotentials, lines of equal electrical potentials.
Prospecting, detection in, with diagram, 7-360

Equisetum, genus of horsetails. 3-192, illus., 191

Equivalent population. Sanitary engineer's measure of wastes, 5-329

Equivalent sets, in mathematics. 4-442

Eras, largest geologic-time units. 6-370
See also **Epochs; Periods**

Eraser. Rubber first used as, 6-351

Erasistratus of Chios, Greek physician and anatomist.
Anatomical dissection, work in, 1-366

Erasmus, Desiderius, Dutch scholar. 2-364

Eratosthenes, Greek geographer and librarian. 1-358, illus., 259
Suggested route to India, 2-364

Erbium (Er), chemical element. Atomic number, 68; atomic weight, 167.26; specific gravity, 4.77(?). Rare-earth metal. Discovered in 1843 by Mosander; name derived from Swedish town of Ytterby. Occurs in minerals normally found in granite or in pegmatite veins. Best obtained by crystallization of the bromates, or by boiling the nitrate solution with sodium nitrate.

Erbium oxide. Lighting experiments with, 4-236

Ergs, units of work or energy. 10-295

Ericsson, John, Swedish-American engineer (1803–89). 6-378
Screw propeller perfected by, 4-111

Eridanus, constellation. 1-337

Erie Canal. Difficulties in building of, 4-190

Ermine fur, winter coat of weasel. 7-238; 8-174

Eros, asteroid. 4-421-22
Space flight to, 10-54

Erosion.
*Water as erosive agent, 8-9-18
*Winds as erosive agents, 7-318-26
Effects of, illus., 5-29; illus., 6-11
Glacial erosion and deposits, with illus., 9-168-72, diagram, 164-65
Ground water, erosive action of, 8-328
Measures to combat, 6-5-6
Mountains, effects on, 10-214, with illus., 220-23
Rain-caused, 2-351, illus., 351, 352
Rocks affected by, 3-419
Soil formation and transportation, factor in, 2-16, 21
See also **Soil**

Erosion base, of streams. 8-14

Erosion remnants, landscape features. illus., 8-10, 11, 15

Erosion terraces, of streams. 8-18

Eryngo. Flowers and leaves of, illus., 7-79

Erythrocytes. See **Red blood cells**

Erythroxylon coca, plant yielding cocaine. 5-401, illus., 400

Escape velocity, for space rockets. 10-43-44

Escapement wheels. Typewriters, 1-269-70

Escherichia coli, bacterium found in human digestive tract. 3-69-70
Bacteriophage effect on, 2-457
Nucleic acid synthesized by aid of, 9-386
Water contamination, indicator of, 2-276

Eskers, glacial deposits, 9-173, illus., 171, 172

Eskimos.
Food chain involving, 10-187
Skins and furs, processing and trading, illus., 7-230
Transportation methods on land, 1-100, illus., 101
Walruses valuable to, 7-91

Esophagus. illus., 1-148d-e; 4-323, illus., 322

Esparto grass. Paper made from, 4-370

Esperanto, artificial language. 1-120

Espionage, spying activities. Microfilming in, with illus., 10-74

Essential amino acids. See **Amino acids**

Essential oils. Gymnosperms yield, 3-400

Esters, derivatives of organic acids. 7-273

Estivation. 5-412-13, illus., 411
Amphibians, 5-162

Eta-Aquarids, meteor shower. table, 6-97

Etchants. Chemicals for etching, 1-205

Etching. Glass etched with hydrofluoric acid, with illus., 3-320-21
Meteorites, test for, 6-92-93, illus., 93
Photoengraving, etching process in, with diagram, 1-205-06
Printing, etching in, 1-211, 212

"Eternal fires," burning oil seeps. 4-140

Ethane, a methane hydrocarbon. with diagram, 7-268
Ethyl alcohol produced from, 7-272
Production from ethylene, 7-270

Ether.
Anesthetic, developments in use of, with illus., 7-375-77
Evaporation of, 1-167

Ether Day. 7-375-76

Ether theory. 4-210-12
Nineteenth-century contribution to, 6-241, 243, 246-47

Ethers, alcohol derivatives. 7-273

Ethiopian highlands. 10-24, 26

Ethyl acetate. 7-273

Ethyl alcohol. 7-272
*Beverages containing, 4-405-14
Rocket fuel, used as, 10-45
See also **Alcohol**

Ethyl bromide. 7-271

Ethyl chloride. 7-271
See also **Chlorine.**

Ethylene. Structural formula, 7-270

Ethylene glycol. Molecular structure, 7-272

Eucalyptus trees. Koalas feed on leaves of, 7-6

Euclid, Greek geometer. 1-355-56; with illus., 3-429

Euclid's postulate. 4-439, diagram, 438

Eudorina, genus of one-celled animals. 2-62, illus., 61

Euergetes I. See **Ptolemy III**

Eugenics.
Galton's contributions to, 8-264
Undesirable genes, problem of eliminating, 8-344
See also **Evolution; Heredity; Natural selection**

Euglena, genus of fresh-water plantlike flagellates. 1-42, illus., 41, 300; 2-62; 3-215

Euglenophyta, phylum of algae. 1-300; 3-215

Euhominids, true men. 1-397

Europa, satellite II of Jupiter. 5-24

Europe.

Breadmaking in medieval Western Europe, 9-294-95

Mountain systems of, 10-21

Petroleum production and reserves, 4-150

Plains and plateaus, 6-109-12

Rainfall statistics, 2-347

Rivers of, 10-27

Silk industry, 5-173, 176

Transportation on land, primitive and early, 1-98, with illus., 102, 103-05, illus., 99-100

See also England; France; etc.

European cuckoos. 6-306

European earwigs. 3-152, illus., 151

European geographical race. with illus., 8-215-16

European horse chestnut trees. 5-147

European linden trees. 5-146

European mantids. 3-150-51

European pine squirrels. 8-162

European salamanders. illus., 5-152

Europium (Eu), chemical element. Atomic number, 63; atomic weight, 151. 96; melting point, about 1,150° C. Rare-earth metal. Discovered in 1896 by Demarcay; name derived from continent of Europe. Rare; best obtained from a crude mixture of samarium and gadolinium oxides derived from monazite. No practical uses at present.

Eurypterids, extinct scorpionlike arthropods. with illus., 1-388; with illus., 6-371

Eustachian tube, of ear. with illus., 4-380; 7-299, illus., 298

Birds', reptiles' and frogs'. illus., 4-381

Eutectic ice. 4-160

Evans, Oliver, American inventor. 2-130

Conveyer belt, eighteenth century, described by, 6-168

Evanston, city in Illinois.

Test of fluoridation at, 5-133

Evaporation. with illus., 3-417-18

Mineral deposits formed by, 3-178; 5-251

Molecular behavior in, with illus., 1-163, with diagram, 167

Perspiration regulates bodily temperature through evaporation, 5-10

Reservoirs, problem in, 2-273

Salt extraction, 5-98, 315

Soil water, diagram, 2-25

Water desalted by, 2-284

Evaporation, vacuum. 3-418

Evaporites, sedimentary rocks. 3-425

Even parity. See Parity law

Evening star.

Mercury as, 4-25

Venus as, 4-28

Everest, Sir George, British military engineer. 7-32

Everest, Mount, highest mountain in world. 10-22, 222

Ascent of, 4-209, illus., 208

Everglades kites. 6-161

Evergreen magnolia trees. 5-148

Evergreens, plants. 6-57

Seed dispersal in, 5-1, illus., 3

See also **Fir trees; Pine trees; Spruce trees;** etc.

Evolution. *6-269-85

*Coelacanths, 4-196-99

*Time scale of evolutionary history, 6-369-74

Animals

Amphibians, 5-153-54

Antelopes, 8-377

Birds, 5-415-16, illus., 417

Carnivores, 7-307

Evolution (continued)

Cats, 8-202

Cetaceans, 7-181

Coelenterates, 2-151

Darwin's finches, with illus., 6-282

Deer family, 8-235

Dog family, 8-133

Elephants, 7-408-09

Horses, with diagram, 6-281

Insectivores, 7-95-96

Irish elks, 6-282

Mammals, with illus., 7-1-6

Marsupials, 7-420-22

Millipedes, with illus., 6-278

Primates, 9-251

Man, 1-65-66

Reptiles, 5-381-82; 6-282-83

Rodents, 8-161

Seals and walruses, 7-85

Sharks and rays, 4-286-87

Snakes, 5-351

Sponges, 2-148

Turtles, 5-388

Weasel family, 8-171

Bioluminescence, 2-190

Cataclysmic evolution, 9-291

Climate changes affect, 3-178

Count de Buffon as forerunner of theory, 3-378

Ear, bony structure of, with illus., 4-382-85

Heart of chordates, with illus., 1-277-79

Heredity and environment, 8-334, 346-47

History of theory, with illus., 8-256-60

Lamarck's theory of, with illus., 4-389-90

Plants

Angiosperms, 3-404

Fungi, 3-24

Gymnosperms, 3-401

Monocotyledons, 3-404

Seed plants, 3-401, 404

Theory of, as aid in studying man, with illus., 9-21-24

See also **Animals; Biology; Fossils; Geology; Heredity; Java Man; Natural selection; Paleontology**

Evolution, arithmetical operation. 1-158

Evolution of stars. 7-45

See also **Stellar evolution**

Ewes. illus., 10-246

Ewing, Maurice, American geologist. 5-190, 193

Ewing-Donn ice-ages theory. 5-193-94

Ewing theory of earth expansion. 5-190

Examinations, health. 10-75

Excavating, for roads. illus., 3-298b

Exchange. See Trade

Exchanges, telephone. with illus., 2-388-91

Excitants, drugs. 5-401-03, illus., 400

Excitation. Phosphors, 9-344-45

Excretion. illus., 1-148e

Elimination of wastes by cells, 2-13

Glandular secretion and excretion of wastes, 5-11-15

Kidneys, 5-11-13, diagram, 12

Sweat glands, 2-176-77, illus., 174, 177

Excretory system. See Excretion

Exercise. *10-85-91

Muscular exercise, biology and mechanics of, 3-205-09, 210-13

See also **Fatigue; Muscles**

Exhaltation, of air. 4-205-06, illus., 204

Exhaust manifolds, of automobile engines. with illus., 2-135

Exhibitions.

Scientific, 8-69-70, 72-74

Exhibitions (continued)
Zoo animals, with illus., 10-160-62, illus., 154
Exoskeletons. Insects, 2-402
Expanding universe. 8-54; 9-225
Expansion, due to heat. with illus., 3-414-16
Atmospheric expansion and movements, with diagrams, 1-242-44
Convection currents caused by, with illus., 4-12-14
Experiments with, with illus., 4-22-24
Expansion steam engines. See **Compound (expansion) steam engines**
Expansion tanks. with illus., 2-249; 4-13, diagram, 12
Experimental method. Psychology, applied to problems of, 9-312
Experimentation.
*Industry and scientific research, 1-87-97
Académie des Sciences and, 3-268
Aerodynamic ground tests on model aircraft and missiles, with diagrams, 10-233-34
Bacon, Sir Francis: ideas on experimentation, 2-307-08
Bacon, Roger: ideas on experimentation, 2-307-08
Descartes, René: ideas on experimentation, 3-8-9
Goals of, 1-123
Nineteenth-century ideas on, 5-73
Royal Society and, 3-265-67
Scientific experiments by youngsters in competitions, 8-70-72, 74-77, illus., 75, 76
Experiments. Definition of, 1-141
See also **Projects and experiments**
"Exploding" fruits. Adaptations for seed dispersal, 5-2, illus., 6
Exploding stars, novae. 6-267-68
Explorations.
Atmosphere, 1-235-36
Bathyscaphes exploring ocean bottoms, with illus., 6-74a-d
History
Early sea voyages, with illus., 6-27-28
Fifteenth and sixteenth centuries, with illus., 2-364-67
Seventeenth and eighteenth centuries, with illus., 3-373
Nineteenth century, with illus., 7-27-34
Twentieth century, with illus., 9-220-25
Explorer I, artificial satellite launched by United States. 9-380; 10-46
Explorer II, stratosphere balloon. 1-235
Explorer XII, artificial satellite launched by United States.
Magnetosphere discovered through observation of, 5-195
Solar cells used in, 7-106
Explosion craters. Meteorites may produce, 6-91, 92, diagram and illus., 90, 91
Explosion process, for preparing wood chips for paper-making. 4-369
Explosions. 8-274
Coal-mine explosions, 1-413
Earthquakes induced by explosions in prospecting, 4-145, diagram, 143; 5-99, illus., 100; with diagram, 7-357-58
Experiments and tricks with, with diagrams, 7-177-78
Man-made explosives, 8-273, illus., 277
Prevention of, in home, 7-190-94
Explosive warmings, stratospheric phenomena. 1-238
Explosives. *8-273-87
Coal mining, explosives in, 1-412
Dam construction, explosives used for, 8-309
Dynamite, invention of, with illus., 5-81-82
Methane mixed with oxygen, 7-267
Military, 9-211-12

Explosives (continued)
Nitrogen compounds, 3-317-18
See also **Blasting; Haber process; Maxim, Sir Hiram; Maxim, Hudson; Nobel, Alfred Bernhard**
Exponents. 2-73-74
Exports. See **Trade**
Exposure meters, light. with illus., 9-409
Exposures, photographic. 9-398-403, 405, 407, 409-11
Express trains. with illus., 1-186-89
Expression, facial. Muscles of, 3-210
Extended forecasts. 1-254
Extensometers, instruments registering gradual earth movements. 5-187
Extensor digitorum longus, lower-leg muscle. illus., 3-213
External-combustion engines. Distinguished from internal-combustion engines, 4-86
See also **Steam engines; Turbines**
External respiration. See **Surface (external) breathing**
Extragalactic nebulae, island universes outside the Milky Way. *8-47-54
Extrasensory perception (ESP).
Study of, 9-57
Testing for, illus., 9-321
Extratropical cyclones. 2-97, diagram, 98
Extreme-Mongoloid local race. 8-219
Extrusion molding. Plastics, with diagram, 8-231, illus., 220b
Extrusion process. Manufacture of seamless steel tubing. 1-351
Extrusive masses, geologic formations. 3-420, 422
Eye color. Inheritance of, 8-342
Eye sockets, of skull. with illus., 3-78
Eye teeth. See **Canine teeth**
Eyeglasses, lenses used to correct defects of vision. 7-296
Earliest use of, 9-82
Eyelids. Muscles of, 3-209-10
Eyes.
Action of, 9-84, 86
Animals
Birds, 5-422-23
Crustaceans, 2-237
Insects, 2-403, illus., 403, 404; 3-253; 7-262
Man, with illus., 7-291-97
Pearly nautiluses, 7-262
Spiders, 2-259, illus., 261
Development in unborn human young, 8-30
Foreign bodies in eyes, first aid for, 10-15
Image-forming devices, 7-251, 262
Injuries to eyes, first aid for, 10-15
Movements of, during sleep, 6-146
Ophthalmoscope, invention of, 6-253
Protection of, 10-78-80
See also **Color blindness; Vision**
"Eyes" of potatoes, seeds. 2-420
Eyesight. See **Color blindness; Eyes**

F

F₁ layer, ionized atmospheric region. 1-240, diagram, 239
F₂ layer, ionized atmospheric region. 1-240, diagram, 239
F-86. See **Sabre jets**
f number, of lenses and mirrors.
Lenses of cameras, 9-406-07
Mirrors of reflecting telescopes, 9-366
F. N. R. S. III, bathyscaphe of French Navy. with illus., 6-74b-c
Fabre, Jean-Henri, French naturalist. 8-255

Fabricators, manufacturers. Plastics products, **8-233**
Fabricius, David, German theologian and astronomer.
  Discovery of variable star, Mira, **7-48**
Fabricius, Hieronymus, Italian physician. **2-376**
Fabrics.
  Bacteria that decompose, **3-67**
  Pineapple leaves used for, **4-182**
  Printing of, *illus.*, **1-92c**
  Research on cotton, *illus.*, **1-92**
  See also **Cotton; Linen; Silk; Wool**
Fabrics, synthetic. *with illus.*, **8-189**
Face.
  Bones of, **3-78**, 79, *illus.*, 77
  Muscles of, **3-209-10**
Face angles, in solid geometry. *with illus.*, **3-441**
Facial nerves. *illus.*, **1-148h**; **6-328**
Facsimile transmission. *****7-390-92**
  DeskFax, *illus.*, **2-382**
Factor analysis, statistical method.
  Application to problems of psychology, **9-313**
Factor P, human blood factor. **3-334**
Factor S, human blood factor. **3-334**
Factories.
  Automatic, **10-237-38**
  Windows in early factories, **8-390**
  See also **Industry; Machines**
Factory system. Establishment of, **4-35-41**
Faculae, markings on sun. **3-100**, 106
Fading, in radio. **3-93**
Fahrenheit, Gabriel Daniel, German physicist. **3-19**,
  410
Fahrenheit scale. *with diagram*, **1-164**; *with illus.*, **3-**
  410-11
  Compared with centigrade and Réaumur scales,
    illus., **3-411**; **10-297**
  Introduction of, **3-19**
Fainting. First aid for, **10-14**
Fairchild XC-120, "flying boxcar." *illus.*, **6-197**
Fairs. See **Exhibitions**
Fairy terns. **6-396**
Falanoucs, civets. **8-247**
Falconry. **6-159**
  Middle Ages, **2-310**, *illus.*, 308
Falcons. *with illus.*, **6-159**
Falkland Current, oceanic current. **6-237**, map, 232-33
Fall, chain, combination of pulleys. **7-217**
Fall, free. Rates of falling, *with diagram*, **4-437-38**
Fall season.
  *****Autumn as storage season for plants, **6-52-59**
Fallen arches, in feet. **3-83-84**
Fallopian tubes, tubes leading from ovaries to uterus.
  with illus., **8-20**, 21, 23
Fallopius, Gabriel, Italian physician. **2-376**
Fallout. See **Radioactive fallout**
Fallow deer. **8-239**, *illlus.*, 242
Falls. See **Water power**
Falls (accidents). Prevention of, in home, **7-194-95**
False buckwheat. Fruit of, *illus.*, **5-3**
False coral snakes. **5-358**
"False Cross," group of stars in constellation Vela. **1-337**
False ribs. **3-77**, *illus.*, 74
False teeth. See **Artificial teeth**
Falsework, scaffolding. **2-343**, 344
Families, groups in classification of living things. **1-289**
  Mammals, **7-12**
Fan kelps. *illus.*, **3-220**
Fangs.
  Snakes, *with illus.*, **1-285**; **3-237**; **5-360-61**, 364
  Spiders, *with illus.*, **2-261**
Fans, cooling.
  Automobile cooling system, **2-136**

Fans, cooling *(continued)*
  Ventilation, fans for, **2-255**
Fantails, pigeons. **6-306**
Fantus, Bernard, American physician.
  Blood storage, research in, **9-35**
Fanworts, aquatic plants. *illus.*, **8-114**
Faraday, Michael, English physicist and chemist. *with*
    illus., **5-231**, 233-37
  Benzene first obtained by, **7-274**
  Electricity, experiments in, **6-124**, 129
  Electrolysis, laws of, **5-91**
  Electromagnetic theory of light, contributions to,
    6-242
  Rubber molecule's formula discovered by, **6-357**
Faraday's laws of electrolysis. **5-91**
Farm machinery. *illus.*, **2-164**, 168, 169
Farm (animal) manures. **2-163**, *with diagram*, 165-67
Farming.
  *****Atomic farming, **10-251-53**
  *****Chemurgy, **7-35-44**
  *****Soil fertility, **2-163-72**
  *****Soilless agriculture, **8-34-37**
  *****Vegetable fibers, **4-177-82**
  *****Water of soil, **5-25-30**
  *****Weeds, **7-111-14**
  Gas, farm uses of, **5-106**
  Nineteenth-century inventions in farm machinery, **6-383**
  See also **Agriculture; Fertilizers; Grain; Irrigation;**
    Pests; Plowing; Soil
Farnsworth, Philo T., American inventor.
  Television system of, **5-279-80**
Farrell, Thomas F., American general.
  Quotation from, **9-329**
Farsightedness (hyperopia). **7-296**, *illus.*, 297
Farsinaj, Turkey. Earthquake at, **9-119**
Fast breeders, nuclear reactors. **9-138**
Fasting. Reducing quickly by fasting, **5-270**
Fat droplets, in cells. **2-5**, *illus.*, 4
Fat tissue.
  Dietary control of fatness, *with tables*, **5-268-71**, 273,
    diagrams, 267, 269
Fathometers, sonic depth finders. **5-120**; *illus.*, **6-70**
Fatigue.
  Muscular fatigue, causes of, **3-206-07**, 213
  Results of, **10-91**
  Retina, fatigue of, *illus.*, **7-284d**
Fatigue-toxin theory of sleep. **6-148**
Fats, food elements.
  Balanced diets, content in, **5-269**, 271
  Breadmaking utilizes fats and oils, **9-295**
  Components of, **7-275**
  Digestion and assimilation of, **2-10-11**
  Endocrine control of fat metabolism, **5-19**
  Essential food elements, *with illus.*, **4-52-53**, *table*,
    55-57
  Insect diet includes, **3-358**
  Meat as important source of, **5-163**
  Muscular energy furnished by, **3-205**
  Older person's diet, **8-82**
  Plants, found in, **2-417**
  Protoplasm, fat content found in, **1-43**; **2-3**, 5
  Test for, **7-136**
Fatty acids, components of fats. **4-52-53**
  Saturated and unsaturated components of, **7-275**
Faults, geological. *with illus.*, **10-215**, *illus.*, 221
  Coasts affected by, *with illus.*, **8-357**
  Petroleum trapped by, **4-143**, *diagram*, 142
  See also **Geology; Physiography**
Fear. Dark as cause of, **4-232-33**
Feather-compound leaves. *with illus.*, **5-139-40**
Feather stars. **2-152**

Feathering, term used in aeronautics. **6-188**
Featherlike muscles. *with diagram,* 3-210
Feathers.
Bluebirds, **6-38**
Secondaries, definition, **6-210**
Structure and function of, **5-416-17, 419**
Thrushes, **6-38-39**
February. Book of Hours, depicted in, *illus.,* **10-177**
Feces, digestive wastes.
Fertilizer, human wastes used as, **5-327,** *illus.,* 328
Production and elimination of, **4-330-31**
Seeds dispersed with, **5-5**
Federal Communications Commission (FCC), United States. **3-91**
Federal Government. See **United States**
Federal Telecommunication Laboratories. *illus.,* **4-342b**
Feeble-mindedness. 9-199
Feedback, principle of automatic control. **10-235-36, 238,** *with illus.,* **234c**
Feeding, tree. **10-151**
Feeding devices.
Birds attracted by, **6-341, 343-44,** *illus.,* 342; *with illus.,* **10-255**
Feeding habits, animal. *with illus.,* **3-235-38**
Amphibians, **5-161-62**
Bears, **7-308, 310, 311, 313**
Beetles, **3-336,** *illus.,* 338
Birds
Birds of prey, **6-153**
See also articles on birds
Cats, **8-204-06, 208, 210, 212**
Fishes, *with illus.,* **4-103**
Fruits and seeds dispersed by being eaten, **5-5-6,** *illus.,* 7
Insects, **2-403, 405-07, 410-14; 3-358, 366-67, 368, 370,** *with illus.,* **360-65, 371-72**
Jackals, **8-138**
Koalas, **7-426**
Lizards, **5-204**
Snakes, **5-353,** *illus.,* 355
Turtles, **5-386**
Feeding of ill persons. *with illus.,* **10-64-66**
Feeding of pets.
Fish, **8-115**
Wild animal pets, **7-20**
Feelers. See **Antennae; Palpi**
Feeling. Psychology of, **9-318**
Feet.
Birds', **5-419-20**
Bones of, *with illus.,* **3-83-84,** *illus.,* **74-75, 82**
Care of, **10-81-82**
Levers, human feet as, *with illus.,* **1-283**
Tendons, ligaments and bones of, *illus.,* **3-212, 213**
Toenails, **2-180-81**
Feldspars, minerals. **3-422**
Climatic types indicated by condition of, *with illus.,* **3-179**
Felines. See **Cats**
Felix atrox, extinct lion. **1-397**
Fels Planetarium, Philadelphia. **2-398**
Felsite, igneous rock. **3-423**
Felt. Shelter, material for, **7-115-16**
Female sex cells. See **Egg cells; Ova**
Femoral nerve. *illus.,* **1-148h**
Femur, thighbone. *illus.,* **1-148b;** *with illus.,* **3-82,** *illus.,* 74-75
Fennecs, African foxes. **8-141**
Fenton, Roger, English photographer. **9-403**
Fer-de-lances, snakes. **5-364**
Ferdinand II, Grand Duke of Tuscany. **3-18, 265**

Fergusson rain gauges. See **Weighing rain gauges**
Fermat, Pierre, French mathematician. **3-21, 277**
Fermentation. *with illus.,* **7-135**
Acetone produced by bacteria from starches, **9-212**
Alcoholic beverages, **4-405-06**
Bacterial, **3-66**
Breadmaking utilizes, **9-293, 294,** *with diagrams,* 296-97
Food preservation by, **4-167-68**
Pasteur's work on, **7-378, 380; 9-71-76**
Sugars, **4-79; 8-183**
Yeast, **3-27**
See also **Anaerobic respiration**
Fermentation rooms. Breadmaking, *with diagrams,* 9-296
Fermi, Enrico, Italian physicist. **9-330;** *illus.,* **10-303**
Cosmic rays, theory accounting for energies of, **8-399**
Uranium bombardment proposed by, **9-132**
Fermium (Fm), chemical element. Atomic number, 100; atomic weight, 253(?). Radioactive actinide metal, chemically analogous to erbium. Originally found in dust and debris from the 1952 H-bomb explosion at Eniwetok; subsequently made in a cyclotron by Seaborg, Harvey, Thompson, Ghiorso and Choppin by bombardment with nitrogen-14, and in a reactor by successive neutron irradiations of plutonium. Formed by converting plutonium-239 into californium, then adding neutrons. Half-life period of about sixteen hours, decaying by shooting off alpha particles.
Fern mosses. 3-188
Ferns. *illus.,* **1-302; 3-190-92,** *illus.,* **186, 188-89**
Ferrets. 8-175
Ferric acid. Etching in printing, **1-212**
Ferric (iron) chloride. Experiments and tricks with, **7-179,** *with diagram,* 177
Ferrosilicon, deoxidizing alloy. **3-322**
Ferrous alloys. Nonferrous alloys, distinguished from, **1-382**
Ferrous metallurgy.
Nonferrous metallurgy, distinguished from, **1-376**
See also **Iron; Steel**
Fertility of soil. See **Soil**
Fertilization, reproductive process.
Chromosome arrangement in human, **8-91**
Flowering plants, **3-406**
Sex-cell nuclei, fusion of, **8-334**
Fertilizers.
*Soil fertility, **2-163-72**
'Ammonium-sulfate fertilizer derived from coal, *with illus.,* **1-419**
Wastes used as, **5-327, 333, 336,** *illus.,* **328, 333; 8-36**
See also **Nitrates**
Fertilizing the sea.
Growth of fish increased by, **4-312**
Fetches, areas where ocean waves are generated. **6-364-65**
Fetus, later stage of unborn young. *with illus.,* **8-25-31**
Food demands of, on mother, **5-272-73**
Fever ticks. 8-368
Fiber board. Sugar-cane fibers for, **7-39**
Fiber glass. 3-315-16
Building construction, use in, *illus.,* **7-126**
Fibers.
*Vegetable fibers, **4-177-82**
Cotton, research in, *illus.,* **1-92**
Dynel, *illus.,* **2-233**
Synthetic, *with illus.,* **8-189**
See also **Cotton; Paper; Silk; Wood**
Fibers, muscle. 3-208, 210, 212, *with illus.,* **204-05**

Fibers, nerve. Muscular activity, role in, **3**-208, *illus.*, 206

Fibers, skin. **2**-174-75

Fibonacci, Leonardo, Italian mathematician. **2**-310

Fibrin, material of blood clots. *with illus.,* **3**-329-30

Fibrinogen, blood-clotting protein. **3**-330, 331

Fibrous systems, of roots. **4**-64, *illus.,* 65

Fibula, bone in lower leg. *illus.,* **1**-148b; **3**-83, *illus.,* 74-75, 82
  Fracture, healing of, *illus.,* **7**-352

Fiddler crabs. **2**-241, *illus.,* 240

Field, Cyrus West, American financier. **5**-241
  Transatlantic cable, **2**-384

Field glasses.
  Nature study, use in, **10**-258, 259-60

Field sparrows. **6**-108

Field study.
  *Exploring animal world, **10**-254-64
  *Exploring plant world, **10**-203-12
  Earthquakes, **9**-111-12

Fields, magnetic. *with illus.,* **7**-164-68

Fifth wheel, of wagon. **1**-103

Figs. Pollination in, *illus.,* **3**-405

Figure-of-eight turns, in bandaging, **10**-16, *illus.,* 17

Figures, topologic. *with diagrams,* **4**-451

Filaments.
  Electric lighting, **4**-235; **5**-246
  Electron tubes, *with illus.,* **6**-296
  See also **Cathodes; Fibers**

Filarial worms. **2**-158

Filariasis, filarial-worm infestation. **2**-158

Filatures, silk-spinning factories. **5**-179-80, *illus., 183*

Filing, of records. Microfilming helps, **10**-69-73, *illus.,* 72-73

Fillers. Plastics, used in manufacture of, **8**-225

Fillings, teeth. Materials used for, **5**-136-37

Film.
  Color film principles, *illus.,* **9**-400a-b
  Flexible film, invention of, **6**-382
  Photographic, **9**-403, 405, 408-10, 414

Film, photographic. *Microfilm, **10**-68-74

Film water, water held by soil. **5**-25-26, 27

Films, chemical. Water evaporation reduced by, **2**-273

Filterable viruses. See **Viruses**

Filtering, in ore dressing. *with diagram,* **1**-374

Filters.
  Air conditioning, filters for, **2**-257
  Aquarium, filtering installation for, *illus.,* **8**-113
  Blood filtered by various organs, **5**-8-9, 11-12, 15
  Sand filters for water, **2**-277, 279-80, *illus.,* 279, 283
  Sewage, purification of, *with illus.,* **5**-331
  Viruses pass through most laboratory filters, **1**-39; **3**-451, 452, 456

Filters, light.
  Astronomy, colored glass filters used in, **8**-60
  Color photography, *diagram,* **9**-400b
  Color-printing plates prepared with, **1**-213-14
  Nature photography, use in, **6**-314-16
  Photography, use in, **9**-408, 412-14
  Vision experiments with colored filters, **8**-180, *diagram,* 179

Filtration, water. **2**-277, 279-80, *illus.,* 279, 282, 283

Fin rot, fish disease. **8**-116

Finance. See **Economics**

Finback whales. *illus.,* **7**-184

Finches. **6**-108

Fingal's Cave, sea cave on island of Staffa. *with illus.,* **5**-57

Finger Lakes, New York. **7**-57

Fingernails. See **Nails,** of man

Fingerprints. **2**-175, *illus.,* 174-75

Fingers.
  Bones (phalanges) of, *illus.,* **1**-148b; *with illus.,* **3**-81, *illus.,* 74, 80
  Muscles of, **3**-210-11, *illus.,* 208
  Nails of, **2**-180-81, *illus.,* 181

Fingertips. *illus.,* **2**-181

Fining, glassmaking process. **3**-309

Finishers, in photoengraving. **1**-206

Finishes.
  Leather, finishing of, **7**-234-35

Finishing mills.
  Plastics products, finishing of, **8**-233
  Steel products, shaping of, **1**-349, *diagram,* 348d

Finlay, Carlos Juan, Cuban physician and biologist. **7**-384; **10**-38

Finley, James, American bridgebuilder. **2**-338

Fins, of fishes. *with illus.,* **4**-96

Fins, used in free diving. *with illus.,* **6**-26b

Fiords. Glacial erosion creates, **6**-71; **9**-170

Fir trees.
  Douglas fir, **5**-260
  How to recognize, *with illus.,* **5**-142
  White fir, **5**-260

Fire.
  Coal-mine fires, **1**-413-14
  Combustion, requirements for, **4**-351
  Experiments and tricks with, *with diagrams,* **7**-174-75, 177-80
  High-frequency sound can cause, **8**-108, *illus.,* 105
  Nuclear-bomb explosion may be followed by, **9**-393
  Photography of, **6**-315, *illus.,* 314
  Prehistoric discovery of, *with illus.,* **1**-123-24
  Prevention in home, **7**-190-94
  Starting of, by friction on wood, *with illus.,* **4**-18
  See also **Combustion; Oxidation**

Fire assays. See **Dry assays**

Fire beetles. **3**-341-42

Fire bosses, safety supervisors in coal mines. **1**-414

Fire extinguishers.
  Fire-fighting principles, *with illus.,* **4**-351-52
  Home use of, **7**-194
  Soda-acid fire extinguisher, homemade, *with illus.,* **4**-352

Fire fighting.
  Forest fires, *illus.,* **5**-265
  Principles of, **4**-351-52
  Water made available for, **2**-286

Fire-resistant materials. Home use of, **7**-193

Fire storm. Atom-bomb explosion as cause of, **9**-351

Fire-tube boilers. *with illus.,* **4**-83
  Ships, used in, **4**-111, 114

Fireballs, ultrabrilliant meteors. *with illus.,* **6**-89
  Atom-bomb explosion produces, *with illus.,* **9**-391

Firedamp, methane gas in coal mines. **1**-413

Fireflies, beetles. *illus.,* **2**-189; **3**-342, *illus.,* 340
  "Cold" light produced by, **2**-189; **8**-118
  Luminous ingredients of, *illus.,* **2**-188

Fireplaces.
  Convection currents through, *with illus.,* **4**-13-14
  Dangerous in thunderstorm, **1**-404
  Precautions in using, **7**-192-93

"Fireproofing" paper trick. *with diagram,* **7**-177

Fireworks. Rockets, **10**-1

Firn, compacted snow and ice.
  Glacier formation, role in, **9**-164-65

First aid. ***10**-5-17

First-class levers. *with illus.,* **1**-283; **3**-57-58, *illus.,* 56; *with illus.,* **7**-215

First quarter, lunar phase. **4**-278

Firth of Forth Bridge, Scotland. **2**-336

Fischer, Emil, German chemist (1852–1919). He taught chemistry at the universities of Erlangen, Würzburg and Berlin. His analysis of organic compounds, particularly proteins, and his researches on the structure and synthesis of sugars won him the 1902 Nobel Prize in chemistry. Fischer was one of the founders of enzyme chemistry. See also **8-184**
  Veronal developed by, **8-408**
Fischer-Tropsch water-gas process. *with illus.,* **1-418**
Fish, Marie P., American biologist. **8-41**
Fish. **4-93-105*
  *Aquariums, fish as pets in, **8-112-16**
  *Coelacanths, **4-196-99**
  *Fisheries, **6-15-26**
  *Salt-water fish, **4-311-20**
  *Sharks, rays and kin, **4-285-95**
  Adaptations for survival, **3-237-38, 241,** *with illus.,* **242-44;** *with illus.,* **10-141-42**
  Amphibians compared to, **5-153**
  Brain compared to those of other vertebrates, *illus.,* **1-63**
  Breathing mechanism, *with illus.,* **1-279**
  Classification of, **1-297-98**
  Cross section of fish's body, *illus.,* **4-382**
  Deep-sea fish, *illus.,* **7-33**
  Ears used as balancing organs, *with illus.,* **1-281**
  Fossil fish, *illus.,* **6-371, 372**
  Heart of, **1-277,** *illus.,* **278**
  Luminescence displays of, **2-183, 185, 190,** *illus.,* **186, 190-91**
  Lungfish, estivation of, **5-412-13,** *illus.,* **411**
  Migrations of, **9-415-16, 418, 424-25, 427,** *illus.,* **426, 428**
  Oceanic banks abound in, **6-71**
  Pollution may destroy, **5-328**
  Sense organs of, *with illus.,* **4-381-82**
  Sounds made by, **8-43**
  Swimming and floating mechanism, air bladder used as, *with illus.* and *diagram,* **1-280-81**
  See also **Sharks.**
Fish and Wildlife Service, United States. **9-277-78**
Fish hawks. 6-160
Fish killers, true bugs. **3-263**
Fish ladders, accessory structures of dams. **8-316**
Fish tapeworms. 8-361
Fishbein, Morris, American physician and editor.
  Medical drugs listed by, **9-36**
Fisher spiders. 2-266
Fisheries. **6-15-26*
  International agencies devoted to conservation of, **6-36**
  See also **Fish**
Fishers, carnivorous mammals. **8-171**
  Fur, **7-238**
"Fishtail burners." See **"Batswing burners"**
Fission, reproductive process. **2-287-92,* **13-14,** *illus.,* **13**
  Bacteria, **3-64**
Fission, atomic. 9-133, 135, 136-37
Fission-fusion-fission bombs. 9-141, 354
Fissure eruptions. 8-304
Fissures of cerebrum. 6-324
Fissures of spinal cord. 6-327
Fitch, John, American inventor.
  Steamboats of, *with illus.,* **4-109; 6-377,** *illus.,* **378**
Fitches, animals. Fur, **7-238**
Fitzgerald, G. F., Irish physicist.
  Fitzgerald-Lorentz contraction, **4-214**
Fitzgerald-Lorentz contraction. 4-214
Fixed bridges. *with illus.,* **2-334-40**
Fixed stars. 1-264; 7-223
Fixing, photographic. 9-410

Fizeau, Armand-Hippolyte-Louis, French physicist.
  6-241-42, 386-87, 391
Flacherie, silkworm disease. **9-77**
Flagella, threadlike processes of cells.
  Algae, **3-215**
  Bacteria, **3-64**
  Movements of, *illus.,* **2-11**
  Protozoans, **2-60, 61, 62**
  Slime molds, *with illus.,* **3-24**
Flagellates. See **Mastigophora**
Flame retardants, fireproofing compounds.   **Plastics,** used in manufacture of, **8-225**
Flame throwers.
  World War I, **9-213**
  World War II, **9-326**
Flamingos, birds.
  Nesting activities of, *with illus.,* **5-418f**
Flammarion, Camille, French astronomer and author (1842–1925). Serving for a time at the Paris observatory he later established a private observatory at Juvisy. He investigated double stars, the color of stars and the topography and physical constitution of Mars and the moon. He wrote several popular handbooks on the subject of astronomy. In 1887 he founded the French Astronomical Society.
Flamsteed, John, English astronomer. **3-281-82**
  Star designation, contributions to, **6-260**
Flank bone. See **Innominate bone**
Flares, solar. See **Solar flares**
Flash bulbs, camera. 9-411
Flash-camera traps. Wildlife photographed by, *with illus.,* **6-313**
Flash pasteurization. 4-157
Flash powder, photographic. Magnesium in, **9-411**
Flashlights. *with illus.,* **6-127-28**
  Homemade flashlights, *with illus.,* **6-288-89**
  Nature study, use in, **10-260**
Flashlights, camera. 9-411-12
Flasks.
  Home laboratory use, *with illus.,* **4-224**
Flat bugs. 3-260-61
Flat color printing. See **Color printing**
Flat feet. See **Fallen arches**
Flat sours, certain types of spoiled canned foods.   **4-158**
Flatcars, freight cars. *with illus.,* **1-190**
Flatfish. *with illus.,* **4-315-17**
  Young flatfish, *illus.,* **6-34**
Flats, in photoengraving. **1-204-05**
Flatworms. *with illus.,* **2-153-54**
Flavin mononucleotide, organic compound in luciferin. **2-188**
Flax.
  Fiber from straw, **7-39,** *illus.,* **38**
  Paper made from, **4-370; 7-39**
  Plant and fiber, *with illus.,* **4-179-80**
Flea hoppers, insect. *illus.,* **2-407**
Fleas.
  Carriers and transmitters of disease, **7-383-84**
  Common dog flea, *illus.,* **7-204**
  Dog fleas, *illus.,* **8-367**
Fleeces. See **Wool**
Fleming, Sir Alexander, Scottish physician and bacteriologist. **9-33**
  Penicillin, discovery of, **10-128**
Fleming, Sir John A., English electrical engineer.   **9-286**
  Electron tube of, **8-409**
Flemming, Arthur S., American administrator. **8-268-69**
Flesh eaters. See **Carnivores**
Fleshy fruits. *with illus.,* **4-129-30**
Fletcher, John, Elizabethan dramatist.
  Glowworms described by. **2-187**

Flexner, Abraham, American educator. **9-31**
Flexner, Simon, American pathologist (1863-1964). Before becoming director of the Rockefeller Institute for Medical Research in 1920, he was professor of pathology at Johns Hopkins University and the University of Pennsylvania. He prepared a serum to combat cerebrospinal meningitis and isolated the infantile paralysis virus.
Flexographic printing. **1-214**
Flexure lines. Palms of hands, lines in, **2-175,** *illus.,* 176
Flickers, birds. **6-210-11,** *illus.,* 210, 347
    Nesting boxes (artificial) used by, **6-210**
Flies, insects. *3-283-92
    Bee flies, **3-240**
    Bolitophila luminosa, a cave dweller, **5-60**
    Transmitters and carriers of disease germs, **7-382-84**
Flight. Birds, with *illus.,* **5-416-19; 10-138**
    See also **Aeronautics; Supersonics**
Flight controls. Space-flight guidance effected by, **8-128-31,** *diagrams,* 129, 130
Flippers, animal limbs adapted for swimming.
    Whales', **7-183**
Flippers, distorted cans. **4-158**
Floating bodies. Explanation of, **2-32-33**
Floating bridges (pontoon bridges). *with illus.,* **2-341-42**
Floating ribs. **3-77,** *illus.,* 74
Floats, air or gas containers for buoyancy.
    Living, *with illus.* and *diagram,* **1-280-81**
Floc, light, loose mass formed by coagulant. **2-278-79,** *illus.,* 278
Flood control. **6-417**
    Dams that help bring about, **8-307**
Flood irrigation. **8-196**
Flood plains, areas covered by stream sediment. **8-16,** 17, 18
Flooding, means of distributing irrigation water. **5-30**
Floodlights, photographic. **9-410-11**
Floods. *with illus.,* **6-416-17**
    Mud flows, **2-351-52**
    Sheet floods, **8-10-11,** 12, 13, 16, 17
    Storm winds cause, **8-350**
Floor plans. Small house, **4-266,** 267, 269, *illus.,* facing 266
Flora. See **Flowers; Plants**
Floral arrangements.
    Wild plants, use in, **10-212**
Florentine thermometer. **3-18**
Florey, Howard Walter, British pathologist. **9-34**
Floriculture. See **Horticulture**
Florida Current, oceanic current. **6-237,** *map,* 232-33
Florida gallinules, birds. *with illus.,* **6-403-04**
Florida Keys. Formation of, **4-137**
Florigens, hormones. **4-120**
Flotation process, in ore dressing. *with diagram,* **1-374; 5-303**
    Gold obtained by, **4-248**
    Molybdenum obtained by, *illus.,* **3-38-39**
Flounders. *with illus.,* **4-317**
Flour, baking. *with diagrams,* **9-295-97**
    Experiments and tricks with, *with diagrams,* **7-177-78**
    See also **Grain**
Flower flies. **3-290**
Flowering plants. **3-399-400,** 403-06, *illus.,* 398, 402-05
    *Germination, **5-61-67**
    *Seed and fruit dispersal, **5-1-7**
    Flowers, formation of, **3-54-55**
    See also **Angiosperms**
Flowers. *4-119-28
    Collecting and preserving, *with illus.,* **10-206-12**
    Formation of, **3-54-55**
    Hummingbirds feed on, **6-212**

Flowers *(continued)*
    Photography of, *with illus.,* **6-313-14**
    Structure of, **3-404-05,** *illus.,* 398
    Trees can be recognized by, **5-140**
    Uses of, **4-132**
    See also **Horticulture**
Flowstone, calcium carbonate formation in caves. *with illus.,* **5-55**
Flue pipes, of organs.
    Sound production in, *with illus.,* **5-217**
Fluid drive, for automobiles. *with illus.,* **2-138**
Fluids. See **Gases; Liquids**
Flukes, flatworms. **2-155-56,** *illus.,* 154
    Fish in aquariums menaced by, **8-116**
Flukes, lobes of whale's tail. **7-183**
Flumes. Water conveyed in, **2-276,** *illus.,* 277
Fluorescence. **7-280-81**
    Minerals identified by, **5-256**
    Ultraviolet rays, produced by, **7-200, 206**
    X rays, produced by, **7-146,** 148
    See also **Luminescence; X rays**
Fluorescent lamps. **4-240-41; 9-344,** *illus.,* 237
    "Cold" light produced by, **8-118**
    Ultraviolet rays used in, **7-206,** *illus.,* 201-02
Fluoridation, treatment of water supply with fluorides. **5-133**
Fluorine (F), chemical element. Atomic number, 9; atomic weight, 18.9984; melting point, $-223°$ C.; boiling point, $-188°$ C.; specific gravity (air $=$ 1), 1.312. Halogen; pale yellow gas, decomposing almost all compounds to form fluorides. Discovered by Scheele in 1771; isolated in 1886. Name derived from Latin *fluere:* "to flow." Widely distributed; found chiefly in fluorspar and cryolite. Compounds useful in etching glass and in air conditioning; also added to water to combat dental decay.
    Dental caries prevented by use of, **5-133; 10-78**
    Diet place in, **4-60**
    Electron arrangement of, *illus.,* **3-247**
    Freon refrigerating fluids, use in, **4-310**
    High-energy fuels, use in, **10-4**
    Hydrogen fluoride as air pollutant, **3-352,** 353
    Nonmetal, most active, **3-320**
    Plastics often contain, **8-222**
    Refrigerants, fluorine as component of, **4-310**
Fluorite, mineral. **5-256,** *with illus.,* 255, *illus.,* 254
Fluorocarbons, plastics. **8-227**
Fluoroscopes. **7-148,** *illus.,* 149
    Food containers inspected with, *illus.,* **7-204**
    Tuberculosis detected with, **9-180,** *illus.,* 181
Fluoroscopy. See **X rays**
Flutes. Sound production in, **5-217**
Fluxes, in smelting. **1-371,** 375
Fly amanita, poisonous mushroom. *with illus.,* **3-31**
Flycatchers, birds. **6-99**
Flying. See **Aeronautics**
Flying, of animals. Bird flight, mechanism of, *with illus.,* **1-284-85**
"Flying boxcar." *illus.,* **6-197**
Flying dragons. See **Flying lizards**
Flying fishes. *with illus.,* **4-97**
Flying lemurs. **7-9,** *illus.,* 13
Flying lizards (flying dragons). *with illus.,* **5-202,** 203
Flying phalangers, gliding marsupials. **7-9**
Flying reptiles. See **Pterodactyls**
Flying saucers. *9-16-20
Flying shuttles. Invention of, **4-36**
Flying snakes. **5-361,** *with illus.,* 354c
Flying squids. **2-194**
Flying squirrels. **7-9; 8-163,** *illus.,* 166
"Flying stovepipe," a ramjet. **6-195**

Flying Wing, airplane. **6**-193, *illus.,* 192
Flyoff, phase of atmospheric precipitation. **8**-9
Flyways, bird migration routes. **5**-423
Flywheels, of engines.
   Gasoline engines, **4**-88
   Steam engines, *with illus.,* **4**-84
Foam glass. Manufacture, **3**-316
Foam rubber. Processing method, **6**-356
Foaming, industrial. Plastics, **8**-229, 233
Focal lengths. **7**-259, 262
   Camera lenses, **9**-406-07
   Telescopes, **9**-366, 370, *diagrams,* 366, 367
Focal planes. Photography, **9**-407
Foci. Earthquakes, **9**-107
   Light rays, *with illus.,* **7**-256-57, 258, 259, 261, 262
Focke, Heinrich, German aeronautical engineer. **9**-220
Focuses (foci), fixed points in geometry. *with illus.,* **3**-438-39
   Ellipses, **8**-126-27, *diagrams,* 126
Focusing.
   Microscopy, **9**-86, *illus.,* 87
   Photography, **9**-405, 406-07, *diagram,* 407
Foehn, a warm dry wind. **2**-94; **10**-28
Fog. **2**-213
   Plane landings in, **6**-198, 200
   Smog formation, contribution to, *with illus.,* **3**-349-50
Folds, bends produced in rock. **10**-215
   See also **Anticlines; Domes; Synclines**
Folic acid, B vitamin. **5**-44
Folkways. Concept in study of society, **9**-26
Follicles, dry fruits. **4**-130, *illus.,* 131
Follicles, of hair. **2**-179, 180, *illus.,* 179
Fomalhaut, star in Piscis Austrinus. **1**-335
Font-de-Gaume, France.
   Prehistoric cave paintings at, **9**-29-30
Fontanelles, areas of skull covered only by membrane in newborn babies. **3**-78; **8**-29
Fonts, assortments of printing type. **1**-199
Food.
   *Basic food elements, **4**-51-61
   *Bread, **9**-293-99
   *Carbohydrates, **4**-76-79
   *Diet, regulation of, **5**-267-75
   *Meat packing, **5**-163-72
   *Plant nourishment in soil, **2**-163-72
   *Preservation of, **4**-153-68
   *Preservation of, by atomic radiation, **10**-114-16
   *Vitamins, **5**-38-49
   Adaptations of animals and plants for obtaining food, **1**-52-53; *with illus.,* **3**-235-38
   Algae as source of, **3**-220, 224
   Allergic reaction to, **4**-260, 264
   Animals attracted by means of, *with illus.,* **10**-254-55
   Babies', **8**-95
   Bacteria that help produce food, **3**-67
   Bacteria that spoil food, **3**-67
   Cellular absorption and use of, **2**-8-12
   Chemical additives to food may cause cancer, **8**-268-69
   Colloidal phenomena in, **5**-302
   Energy, transformation into, **10**-85-86
   Fish pets, food for, **8**-115
   Fishes as, **4**-105
   Food chains among plants and animals, *with illus.,* **10**-186-87
   Food tests made at home, *with illus.,* **7**-135-36
   Health, effect on, **10**-77
   Ill persons, food for, *with illus.,* **10**-64-66
   Industries, *illus.,* **1**-92c
   Insect feeding, **2**-403, 405-07, 410-14; **3**-358, *with illus.,* 360-68, 370-72; *with illus.,* **5**-174-79

Food *(continued)*
   Insects used as human food, **3**-256, 264
   Leaves that supply food, **4**-75
   Lizards as, **5**-206
   Muscular energy, food for, **3**-205-06
   Nuclear blasts may cause contamination of, **9**-396
   Nutritional values of, *table,* **4**-55-57
   Older persons, food for, **8**-81-82
   Plants: seed digestion and storage, **5**-62, 64
   Populations and, **3**-225, 227-30
   Preventing food particles from entering trachea, **4**-203
   Quick-freezing of, *illus.,* **4**-318-19
   Radiation contamination, **9**-396
   Salivary reflex to, **6**-323
   Soil water a food solution for plants, **5**-25, 26
   Tubercular patients, food for, **9**-183
   Water content of, testing for, *with illus.,* **4**-344
   Wild animal pets, food for, **7**-20-26
   Zoo animals, food of, **10**-159-60, *illus.,* 158
   See also **Calories; Carbohydrates; Digestion; Fats; Proteins; Nutrition; Vitamins**
Food and Agriculture Organization (FAO), United Nations agency. **6**-14
Food and Drug Administration. See **United States Food and Drug Administration**
Food and Nutrition Board of National Research Council, United States. Bakery-product enrichment standards recommended by, **9**-299
Food chains. **4**-285; *with illus.,* **10**-186-87
Food dances, of honeybee. **3**-370
Food storage.
   *Plants, **2**-415-20
   Roots, **4**-65
   Starch storage in organisms, **4**-76, 77
   Time limits for different foods, *table,* **4**-161
   Wheat stored in grain elevators, **9**-295, *diagram,* 294
Food supply. Animal migrations influenced by, **9**-418
   Ants that consume human food, **3**-361-62
   Estivation of animals and, **5**-412-13
   Hibernation of animals and, **5**-410-12
Fool hens. **6**-344, 355
Fool quail. **6**-334
"Fool's gold." See **Iron pyrites**
Foot. See **Feet**
Foot-pounds, units of work. **10**-295
Football. **10**-90
Forage crops. Weed damage, **7**-111
Foramen magnum, bottom opening of skull. **3**-78, *illus.,* 77
Foramina, openings in body parts. Spinal column, **3**-75
Foraminifera (foraminifers), marine protozoans. **1**-384, 390; **2**-65, 288-89
Foraminifers. See **Foraminifera**
Forbes, Edward, British biologist.
   Marine biology, contributions to, **6**-29
Forbidden lines, lines seen in nebular spectrum. **9**-362
Force.
   *Atomic energy, **9**-120-42
   *Electricity, **6**-119-35
   *Forces in liquids and gases, **2**-30-42
   *Gravitation, **2**-315-22
   *Magnetism, **7**-162-72
   *Magnetism, experiments with, **8**-142-50
   *Matter and energy, **1**-79-86
   *Motion, **2**-118-28
   *Properties of matter, **5**-369-76
   *Ultrasonics, **8**-103-10
   Centrifugal, **4**-219
   Dams, forces that affect, *with illus.,* **8**-316-17

Force (continued)
    Electrical forces within the atom, 1-310, 311
    Molecules, forces among, *with diagram*, 1-166-68
    Muscular force, 3-205, 208-10
    Space flight, forces and motions in, 8-126-31
    Trigger force producing earthquakes, 9-107
    Work, relation to, 3-56-57
    See also **Engines; Energy; Heat; Lines of force**
Force, lines of. See **Lines of force**
Force cups, plumber's suction devices. *with illus.*, 7-220
Forced-circulation hot-air heating systems. 2-247
Forced vibrations, of sound waves. 5-117-18
Ford, Henry, American automobile manufacturer. 2-130-31
Ford Motor Co.
    Automation in Cleveland plant, 10-237
Fore-and-aft sails. 4-107-08
Forebrain. 6-323
    See also **Brain; Cerebrum**
Forecasting. *Weather, 1-241-54
    Waves, ocean, forecasting of, *with illus.*, 6-366-67
    See also **Barometers; Weather**
Foregut, pouch formed in early stage of digestive-system development, 8-27
Foreign bodies, in various body structures.
    First aid for, 10-15
Forel, Auguste-Henri, Swiss psychiatrist and entomologist. 8-254
Forel, François-Alphonse, Swiss naturalist. 8-254
Forel arena, device for preventing escape of ants. 3-395-96
Foreshocks, preliminary earthquake tremors. 9-108
Foreshores, of beaches. *with diagram*, 8-352
Forest, Fernand, French inventor. 6-380
Forest fires. 2-350
    Dust derived from, 7-141
Forest Negro local race. 8-218
Forest terrariums. 5-366
Forestry.
    *American forests, 5-257-66
    See also **Forests; Timber; Trees; Wood**
Forests. *5-257-66
    *Lumbering, 2-105-17
    Conservation of, 6-8, *illus.*, 3, 9
    Rain attracted by, 2-350
    Virgin forest, 5-260
Forging, tooling operation. 10-108
    Aluminum forgings, *illus.*, 1-92b
    Steel products shaped by, 1-351
Forked sticks. Prospecting, former use in, 7-355
Forlanini, Enrico, Italian inventor.
    Hydrofoil boat built by, 4-6
Formaldehyde. 7-273
    Plastics produced with, 8-223-24, 225, 227
Formations, rock deposits. See **Sedimentary rocks**
Formed elements. See **Blood cells**
Formic acid. 7-273
Formosa. Camphor trees of, 8-184
Forms, in printing. *with illus.*, 1-206-07, *diagram*, 209
Formulas.
    Algebraic, 2-69-70, 72
    Chemical, 2-224, 225-26, 227, 229, 230, 231, *diagrams*, 224, 225-26
    Graphic formulas of organic compounds, 5-78-80
    See also **Structural formulas**
Fort Peck Dam, Montana. 8-312
Fort Rock Cave, Oregon.
    Dating of sandals found in, 10-97
Fortified wines. 4-168
Fossas, largest carnivores of Madagascar. 8-247-48

Fossilization. Replacement as form of, 8-328
Fossils. *1-383-97
    *Time scale of evolutionary history, 6-369-74
    Climates of past revealed by, 3-177-81, *illus.*, 178
    Hemipterous, 3-254-55
    Human populations, evidence of prehistoric, 3-226-27
    Man, fossil remains of, *with illus.*, 9-21-25
    Marine diatoms, *illus.*, 6-33
    Microscopic study of ancient plants and animals, 5-100, *illus.*, 101
    Mountain origins revealed by, 10-214
    Natural gas derived from remains of ancient plants and animals, 5-97, 100
    Sedimentary formations often contain, 9-308-09
    Study of fossils, 4-386-94, 397
    See also **Evolution; Diatoms; Geology; Paleontology**
Foster, George.
    Co-inventor of radiation thickness gauges, 9-46
Fotosetter machines, for typesetting. 1-203, *illus.*, 202
Foucault, Jean Bernard Léon, French physicist. 6-386-87, *with illus.*, 241-42
    Earth's rotation demonstrated by, 4-47-48
Foucault pendulums. See **Pendulum**
Foucault test, for optical mirrors. 9-369-70
Fountains.
    Granite fountain in Washington, D.C., *illus.*, 2-83
    Trick fountain, *with diagrams*, 7-173-74
    Water fountain caused by compressed air, *with illus.*, 7-220-21
Fountains, reservoirs for ink in printing presses. 1-209
Four-dimensional continuum, important concept in relativity theory. 4-214
Four-dimensional geometry. 4-431
4-H Clubs, agricultural organizations. Competitions for young scientists sponsored by, 8-73
Four-horned antelopes. 8-383
Four-stroke cycle, of automobile engines. *with illus.*, 2-133-34
Fourdrinier papermaking machines. 4-371-73, *illus.*, 370-71, 372-73, 374a, 374b
    Development of, 4-365
Fovea centralis, of eye. 7-293, *illus.*, 294
Fowl pox, virus disease. *illus.*, 3-454
Fowler's toads. *illus.*, 5-158
Fowls. See **Chickens; Ducks; Geese**
Fox fire. 2-182
Fox snakes. Pets, 7-25
Fox sparrows. 6-108
Foxes. *with illus.*, 8-140-41
    Color changes with seasons, 5-413
    Fur, 7-238
    Pets, foxes as, 7-21
Fracastoro, Girolamo, Italian physician. 2-367-68
Fractionating, of fluids. Petroleum refining uses, 4-148, *illus.*, 149
Fractionation of blood plasma. 3-326
Fractions, in arithmetic. 1-158-59
    Exponents in form of, 2-74
Fracture, identifying characteristic of minerals. 5-255
Fractures. 3-84; *illus.*, 7-352
    First aid for, *with illus.*, 10-11
Fractures, geological. See **Faults, geological**
Fraenkel, Karl, German bacteriologist. 7-382
Fragilitas ossium, bone brittleness. 3-84
Fragmental rocks, sedimentary rocks. 3-424
Frame houses. *with illus.*, 7-120
Frames, automobile. 2-142, *illus.*, 141
Framework. Building construction, *illus.*, 3-120, 121
France.
    Calendar reform, 10-176, 178
    Contributions to science

France (continued)
   Early exploration in North America, 2-366
   1600–1765, 3-267-69, 277-78
   1765–1815, with illus., 4-356-57, 359, 361-62
   Nineteenth and twentieth century naturalists,
      8-254-55
   Darwinism in, 8-262
   Dating archaeological material from, 10-97
   Engineering developments in, 1-218
   Fisheries, 6-20
   Industrial research, 1-95-96
   Pottery-making, illus., 7-400
   Puy-de-Dôme, extinct volcano, illus., 4-394
   Saltern, illus., 5-315
   Silk industry, 5-173
   Wine industry threatened by mildew of grapes,
      3-25-26
Francis, Thomas, Jr., American physician.
   Salk vaccine report of, 10-131, 133
Francis reaction turbines, 9-234, illus., 232
Franciscan order.
   Medieval universities influenced by, 2-304
Francium (Fr), chemical element.   Atomic number, 87;
atomic weight, 223(?).   Alkali metal; a natural isotope
in the actinium series.   Discovered in 1939 by Mlle.
Marguerite Perey of the Curie Institute in Paris; named
after France.   Occurs as a result of alpha disintegra-
tion of actinium.   See also 3-169-70
Franco-Prussian War.   Balloons used in, 6-177-78
Frank, Canada.   Catastrophic landslide, 2-353
Frankland, Sir Edward, English chemist.   5-78, 86
   Helium discovered by, 1-20; 6-391
Franklin, Benjamin, American statesman, scientist and
   essayist.
   Electricity, research in, 4-359-61, illus., 358
   Lightning, experiment with, 1-400-01; with illus.,
      6-124-25
   Magic squares prepared by, with diagram, 4-450
   Overpopulation, statement on, 4-403
   Sea light, experiments with, 2-183
Franklin, Sir John, English arctic explorer.   7-34
Franklyn's grouse.   6-335
Frasch process, for sulfur extraction.   3-321, illus.,
   318
Fraternal twins.   8-336, illus., 337
Fraunhofer, Joseph von, Bavarian physicist and optician.
   5-85; 6-387, 390
Fraunhofer lines.   3-108; 5-85-86
Frazer, Sir James George, Scottish anthropologist.
   9-25-26
Freccia del Garda ("Arrow of Garda").   Italian hydro-
   foil boat, with illus., 4-7
Freccia del Sole ("Arrow of the Sun").   Italian hydro-
   foil boat, 4-7
Frederick II, King of Sicily and Holy Roman Emperor.
   2-310
Fredonia, New York.   Natural-gas industry, early,
   5-98
Free balloons.   6-177-79, 181
Free fall.   Rates of falling, with diagram, 4-437-38
"Free fixers," nitrogen-fixing bacteria living freely in
   soil.   2-209
Free flight.   Space vehicles and missiles, 8-126
Free-trial selling method.   1-268
Free vibration, of sound waves.   5-117
Free water, surplus water in soil.   with illus., 5-26-28
Freedom VII, American manned space vehicle.   9-382,
   with illus., 381
Freeze-drying (lyophilization), method of preserving
   food.   4-166-67

Freezing.
   Ice, physical properties of, with illus., 8-1-2
   Meats processed by, 5-168
   Molecular behavior in, 1-162-63
   Quick-freezing of foods, with illus., 4-160-63
   Soil formation, factor in, 2-15
   Water desalted by, 2-284
   See also **Refrigeration**
"Freezing liquid" trick.   with diagram, 7-175-76
Freezing points.   3-416
   Solutions, 4-301
Freight cars.   with illus., 1-190
Freighters.   illus., 4-187-89; illus., 7-61
Freighting, transport of goods.   Early, with illus., 1-
   105-06
French Equatorial Africa.
   Forest acreage of, diagram, 2-113
French horns.   Sound production in, 5-219
French Revolution.   with illus., 4-33-34
Freons, refrigerants.   4-160, 310
Frequencies, of sound waves.   5-117-18, 120, 123-24,
      125, 127, illus., 126; 8-103-04
   Musical sounds, with illus., and tables, 5-211-14
   Regulated in radio transmitters and clocks by elec-
      trostriction crystals, 2-294
   Tones produced by musical instruments, with illus.,
      5-215-20
Frequency allocations.   United States, with table, 3-91
Frequency (sound) analyzers.   8-46
Frequency-division multiplex.   2-383
Frequency modulation (FM).   with illus., 3-89
   Wave lengths used for, diagram, 7-200
Frères Pontifes, bridge-building monks.   3-298
Fresh water.   Sea water, derivation from, 2-283-84
Fresnel, Augustin-Jean, French physicist.   6-240-41
Freud, Sigmund, Austrian psychoanalyst.   with illus.,
      9-96-102
   Case-study methods of, 9-314
   Subconscious mind revealed by, 8-403
Friction.
   Heat, mechanical energy changed through friction
      into, with illus., 7-219
   Hydrofoil hulls escape surface friction, 4-6
   Motion and heat related to, 4-17-18
Frilled lizards.   5-202
Frilled sharks.   4-287, illus., 291
Fringing reefs.   4-135; 6-72, 75, illus., 77
Frisch, Karl von, German zoologist.
   Honeybees, researches on, 3-370
Frisch, Otto Robert, Danish physicist.   9-330
Frogs.   5-154-56, 157-60, 161, 162, illus., 155, 158-59,
      162
   Ear and jaw structure.   with illus., 4-381
   Electricity, frogs used in early experiments on, 4-362,
      illus., 360-61
   Field study of, 10-261-62
   Inactivity in cold season, 5-411
   Migration of, 9-428
   Pets, with illus., 7-26
   Terrarium animals, 5-366-67
Fronds, fern leaves.   3-191, illus., 186, 188-89
Front-wheel assembly, automobile.   with illus., 2-142-43
Frontal bone, in skull.   illus., 3-74, 75, 77
Frontal lobes, of cerebrum.   with illus., 6-324-25
Frontal sinus, in skull.   illus., 3-77
Frontalis, forehead muscle.   illus., 3-204
Fronts, boundaries between air masses.   with diagram,
      1-244, 254, illus., 250; 2-95, 359-60
   Weather-map symbols for, diagrams, 2-94-95
Frosch, Paul, German bacteriologist.   3-452
   Viruses discovered by, 8-405

Frost. 2-220
See also **Ice**
Frostbite. First aid for, 10-13-14
Frozen dinners. 5-168
Frozen-section technique. 8-270
Fructose, fruit sugar. 4-79
Fruit cacti. *illus.,* 3-49
Fruit flies. 3-290; 10-254-55
Cherry fruit flies, 9-194
Fish in aquariums, fruit flies as food for, 8-115
Genetic research based on, 9-356, *with diagram,* 384-85
Maggots, *illus.,* 9-195
Fruit sugar. See **Fructose**
Fruit trees. *with illus.,* 5-148-49
Fruiting bodies, reproductive parts of fungi. *with illus.,* 3-23, 29-30
Fruits. *4-128-31
*Dispersal, 5-1-7
*Insect enemies of fruit crops, 9-185-96
Diseases of, 8-375, *illus.,* 374-75
Dispersal in nature, *with illus.,* 3-240-41
Formation of, 3-55
Preservation of, 10-211
Soilless-agriculture methods applied to, 8-35-36
Sugars, fruit, 4-79
Trees can be recognized by, *with illus.,* 5-140-41
Uses of, 4-132
See also under names of fruits
Frustration. Psychology of, 9-319
Frustums of cones. *with illus.,* 3-443
Frustums of pyramids. *with illus.,* 3-443
Fucino, Lake, Italy. Draining of, 8-310
Fucus, genus of brown algae. 3-220-21
Fuel oils. 4-148, 149
Steamships, 4-114
Fuel pumps. Automobiles, 2-135
Fuel systems, of engines.
Automobiles, 2-135, *illus.,* 134
Diesel, *with illus.,* 4-90-92
Gasoline, *with illus.,* 4-88-89
Jets, 4-92
Fuels.
*Coal, 1-405-20
*Natural gas, 5-97-106
*Petroleum, 4-140-52
Carbohydrates as body fuels, 4-76, 77, 79
Carbon-dioxide content of atmosphere increased because of use of, 5-193
Carbon dioxide given off by burning fuel, test for, *with illus.,* 7-130
Corncobs as, 7-36
Digester gas, 5-332-33
Dust derived from burning of, 7-141-42
Electricity generated by use of, *with illus.,* 9-229-33
Hazards in homes, 7-190-91, 192-93, 197
Heat of combustion, determination of, *with illus.,* 3-414
Human body's consumption of, 3-205-06
Manufactured gas, 5-106
Plants use stored food as, 2-417, 418, 419-20
Refuse used as, 5-335
Rocket propulsion, 10-4, 41-44, 45, *illus.,* 43
Scientific industrial research in, 1-88, 89, *diagram,* 90, *illus.,* 92b
Space-rocket propulsion, 10-53-54
Steamship, 4-111, 114
See also **Coal; Coke; Electricity; Gasoline; Petroleum**
Fujiyama. *illus.,* 8-296

Fulcrum, pivot of a lever. 3-57, 58, *illus., 56-58;* *with illus.,* 7-214, 215-16
Human body, examples in, *with illus.,* 1-283
Fulgurites, formations caused by lightning. 1-403, *illus.,* 402
Full moon, lunar phase. 4-278
Fulton, Robert, American engineer and inventor. 6-378, *illus.,* 379
Steamboat of, *with illus.,* 4-109-10; 6-378, *illus.,* 379
Submarine *(Nautilus)* of, 5-31-32, *illus.,* 33
Functionalism, psychological theory. 9-50-51
Fundamental astronomy. 8-62
Fundus, part of stomach. 4-324, 325
Fundy, Bay of. Tides at, 6-203-04
Funerary ship. Determining date of, 10-96-97, *illus.,* 92
Fungi. *3-22-32
Algae, partnership with, 10-187, *illus.,* 188
Ants cultivate, *with illus.,* 2-412b; 3-362, 364
Bacteria, similarities with, 3-63
Bread mold, *illus.,* 1-37
Cave-dwelling species, 5-59
Chemicals used against, 10-151
Classification of, 1-301
Fish diseases caused by, 8-116
Lichens formed by combination of algae and, *with illus.,* 3-32
Luminous, *with illus.,* 2-182-83
Plant diseases caused by, *with illus.,* 8-370-73
Seeds attacked by, 5-67
Yeasts, anaerobic respiration of, 3-48
Fungicides. 8-370
Funiculi, columns of spinal cord. 6-327
Funk, Casimir, Polish chemist.
Vitamin study pioneered by, 5-39
Funny bone. 3-80
Fur, animal hair.
Seeds and fruits carried in, 5-5
Fur-bearing animals. 7-236-38
Fur farming. 7-236-37, *illus.,* 235
Fur seals. 7-86, 88, 89-90, *illus.,* 87, 89
Laws governing killing of, 7-89
Migration of, 9-423
Refuge in Pribilof Islands, *illus.,* 6-14
Furfural, chemical compound. 7-35-36, *diagram,* 36-37
Furnaces.
Glassmaking, used in, 3-309-10
Heating by hot air, 4-14
Safety precautions for home furnaces, 7-190-91
Smelting, *with diagrams,* 1-377, 379, 380
See also **Blast furnaces**
Furnaces, electric.
Steelmaking, used in, *with illus.,* 1-346-47
Furnas County meteorite, from Nebraska. 6-90
Furniture.
Designs related to architecture, 10-118
Homes, used in, 4-272, *illus.,* 271
Modern design, example of, *illus.,* 10-118, 120
Furniture, blocks for holding printing material. 1-207, *illus.,* 206
Furrow irrigation. 8-196
Furrows.
Irrigation water distributed by, 5-30
Furs. *with illus.,* 7-235-38
Fusarium wilt, plant disease. 8-372
Fuse boxes. 9-238, *illus.,* 239
Fuselages, bodies of airplanes. 6-189, 191
Fuses, devices used in electric circuits. 6-134; 7-191-92
Principles of, and experiments with, *with illus.,* 6-291-92
Fusion. See **Melting points**

Fusion, atomic. 9-139-41, 142
  Plasmas and, *with illus.,* 1-173-78
  Power to be produced by?, 9-332
Fusion, heat of. 3-416-17
Future Scientists of America, Washington, D. C. Competitions for young scientists sponsored by, 8-72

G

G, rate of acceleration due to gravity. *with table,* 2-318; 10-48-50
Gabbro, igneous rock. 3-423; 9-308
Gaddum, J. H., American scientist. Quotations from, 5-346
Gadolinium (Gd), chemical element. Atomic number, 64; atomic weight, 157.25. Rare earth. Separated in 1880 by Marignac; name derived from gadolinite, a vitreous silicate and source of rare earths, named after Gadolin, a Finnish chemist. Free element not yet isolated.
Gagarin, Yuri A., Russian Air Force officer. Space flight by, *with illus.,* 9-380-81
Gagnan, E. Aqualung developed by, 6-26a
Gaillard Cut, Panama Canal. 4-194, *illus.,* 193
Gain. Amplification of input in electron tubes, 6-299
Galactic clusters. 6-267; 8-155
Galactic rotation. 7-229
Galactic system, in astronomy. 1-261
Galactose, a simple sugar. 4-79
Galagos, lemurlike primates. 9-265
Galalith, plastic. 8-223
  Buttons made from, 7-210, 212
Galápagos Islands. *with map,* 10-183
  Darwin's finches, evolution of, *with illus.,* 6-282
  Darwin's visit to, 8-257
  Turtles of, 5-389
Galápagos tortoises. *illus.,* 5-387
  Migration of, *with illus.,* 9-425
Galápagos turtles. 5-389
Galaxies, island universes. 6-259, *illus.,* 258-59; *8-47-54
  *Interstellar materials, 9-359-64
  *Milky Way, 8-151-59
  Andromeda, Great Galaxy in, *illus.,* 8-156c
  Milky Way, size of, 8-158
Gale, Leonard Dunnell, American chemist. 5-239-40
Galen, Greek physician. *with illus.,* 1-366-67
  Blood circulation, doctrine of, 3-10
Galena, ore of lead.
  Crystals used as radio detectors, 3-95-96
  Semiconducting crystals, 6-303
Galidines (Malagasy mongooses). 8-247
Galileo (Galileo Galilei), Italian astronomer and physicist. *with illus.,* 3-1-5, 14-15, 18
  Air has weight: demonstration, 9-59
  Gravity, experiments with, 2-120
  Jupiter's satellites (first four), discovery of, *illus.,* 3-163; 5-24
  Lunar craters observed by, 4-279
  Pendulum principle, experiment with, 2-121
  Pressure of water and atmosphere, observations on, 1-233
  Refracting telescope of, 7-262
  Saturn's rings observed by, 5-109
  Sunspots discovered by, 3-100
  Thermoscope, invention of, *with illus.,* 3-410
Gall bladder. *illus.,* 1-148d; 4-328, *illus.,* 322; 5-13, 15
Gall wasps (gallflies). 3-367
Galle, Johann Gottfried, German astronomer. 6-392
  Neptune discovered by, 2-317; 5-291
  Saturn's third ring, discovery of, 5-110
Galleys, ancient ships. 4-107

Galleys, long trays of printing type. 1-199
Gallflies (gall wasps). 3-367
Gallinaceous birds. *6-331-40
Gallinules. 6-403-04
Gallium (Ga), chemical element. Atomic number, 31; atomic weight, 69.72; melting point, 29.78° C.; boiling point, 1,983° C.; specific gravity, 5.91. A hard, steel-gray metal; very rare. Discovered in 1875 by Lecoq de Boisbaudran through use of the spectroscope and by electrolysis; name derived from Latin *Gallia:* "France." Widely distributed in minute quantities; found especially in many zinc blendes and bauxites. One of four metals that can liquefy at or near room temperatures (others, mercury, cesium and rubidium); is therefore useful in high-temperature thermometers. Discovery of, 5-85
Gallstones. *with illus.,* 4-335
  Removal by means of high frequency sound, 8-110
Galton, Sir Francis, English scientist. 8-264, *illus.,* 263
  Introspective method to determine mental images, 9-312
  See also **Evolution; Heredity**
Galvani, Luigi, Italian physicist.
  Animal electricity, experiments with, 2-421
  Electricity, experiments with, 4-362, *illus.,* 360-61; 6-125
Galvanized steel. Manufacture and uses of, 1-350
Galvanometers. *with illus.,* 6-131-32
  Faraday's use of, 5-236
  Homemade, *with illus.,* 8-147
  Mirror galvanometer, 5-241-42
  String galvanometer, 2-421
Galvanometric system of magnification. Seismometers, use in, 9-113
Galveston, Texas. "Storm tide" damage to, 8-350
Gama, Vasco da, Portuguese navigator. 2-364
Gambel's quail. 6-334
Game birds. See names of birds.
Game protection. *9-266-78
Games. See **Exercise**
Gametes.
  Heredity, role in, *with illus.,* 8-334-37
  See also **Reproduction; Sex cells**
Gametophytes, sex-cell-producing generations of plants. Mosses, 3-187
  See also **Alternation of generations; Reproduction**
Gamma globulins, blood-plasma fractions. 3-326
  Measles immunization with, 7-350
  Poliomyelitis, prevention of, 10-130-31
Gamma rays. 7-205-06, *diagram,* 201
  Atomic farming, uses, 10-251-52
  Cosmic-ray showers, 8-396, 397
  Detection by Geiger-Mueller counter, *with illus.,* 9-343
  Emitted by certain radioactive elements, 8-416
  Food preserved by, 4-168; *with illus.,* 10-114-16
  Medical uses of, 10-98, 99
  Nuclear explosions release, 9-391, 394
  Radiation thickness gauges use gamma rays, 9-45
  Radioactive elements emit, 9-349
Gamow, George, American scientist. Explanation of beta particles, 9-128
Ganges River, India. Sediment carried by, 10-214
Ganglia.
  Insect nerve centers, *with illus.,* 2-406
  Nature and functions of, 6-329
Ganglion cells, of eye. 7-293, *illus.,* 292
Gangue, mineral waste. 1-371
Ganswindt, Hermann, German inventor. Space travel proposed in 1890 by, 10-42
Ganymede, satellite III of Jupiter. 5-24

Garbage disposal. 5-334-36, *illus.*, 334, 335
Garda, Lake, Italy. *illus.*, 7-58
Garden flea hoppers, true bugs. 3-261
Garden spiders. With egg sac, *illus.*, 2-260
Gardening. See **Horticulture**
Gardening ants. 3-362, 364
Gardens, miniature. See **Terrariums**
Garett, G. W., English cleryman and inventor.
   Steam-powered submarine, 5-32
Garnet, mineral. *illus.*, 9-304
Garofalo, whirlpool. 6-207
Garter snakes. 5-359, *illus.*, 354
   Pets, 7-25
Garwin, K., American atomic scientist. 7-110
Gas. See **Gases**
Gas appliances. 5-106
   Safety precautions, 7-190, 191, 197
Gas engines. See **Internal-combustion engines**
Gas-filled tubes (electronic). 6-298, *with illus.*, 300-02
Gas illumination. 4-233-37
Gas lighting. See **Gas illumination**
Gas ranges, stoves. 5-106
Gas-sensitive plants. Air pollution detected by,
   3-351-52, 354, *illus.*, 352
Gas shells. World War I, use in, 9-213
Gas turbines. See **Turbines**
Gas wells. See **Wells, natural-gas**
Gascony. Landes of, *with illus.*, 6-111
Gaseous diffusion. Uranium isotopes, 9-134-35
Gases.
   *Atmosphere, 1-230-40
   *Compressed air, 9-58-70
   *Forces within gases, 2-36-42
   *Natural gas, 5-97-106
   *Nitrogen, fixation of, 3-126-29
   Adhesive forces, 5-374
   Air pressure, experiments with, *with illus.*, 7-220-22
   Ammonia synthesis, *with diagram*, 2-230-31
   Boyle's law, 3-416
   Carbon dioxide, experiments with, *with illus.*,
     7-129-32
   Charles' law, 3-416
   Coal, manufacture of fuel gases from, *with illus.*,
     1-418
   Coal mines, gases a hazard in, 1-413-14
   Colloidal particles, 5-296
   Combustion, heat of, *with illus.*, 3-414
   Comets contain, 5-392
   Diffusion of, 4-206-07, *illus.*, 202; 5-373, 374
   Digester gas, 5-332-33
   Discharge lamps, use in, 4-239-40
   Expansion due to rise in temperature, 3-415-16
   Gay-Lussac's law, 3-416
   Heat transfer and insulation by air, 4-10-14, 16, *illus.*,
     11, 15
   Hydrocarbons, 7-267
   Ideal gases, laws of, *with diagram*, 1-165-66; 3-416
   Incandescent, of bright nebulae, 9-361
   Incandescent-lamp bulbs filled with, 4-239
   Inert (noble) gases, *with diagram*, 3-247
   Lighting, use of gases for, 4-233-37
   Lungs, exchange of gases in, 4-206, *illus.*, 202
   Manufactured gas and natural gas, 5-106
   Molecules, behavior of, 1-162, 164, 171, 172, *with*
     illus., 163, *with diagrams*, 165-66, 167-69; 3-416
   Nebulae composed of, 8-47, 49
   Petroleum-refinery gases, 4-148, 151
   Plants affected by, 3-51
   Plasmas derived from, *with illus.*, 1-173-78
   Poisoning in home, prevention of, 7-197
   Pollution of air by, 3-351-56

Gases *(continued)*
   Research on, between 1765–1815, *with illus.*,
     4-353-57
   Rocket and jet propulsion uses, 10-41, 54, *illus.*, 43
   Schlieren photographs of, *illus.*, 10-165
   Sea, occurrence of gases in, 6-32
   Solubility of, in water, *with diagram*, 4-300
   Temperature changes affect, 3-415-16
   Uses of gas in communities and industries, 5-106
   Viscosity of, *with illus.*, 5-370-71
   Warfare, see **Poison gases**
   See also **Air; Evaporation; Matter; Molecules; Super-**
     sonics; Water vapor
Gasification, of coal. 1-418
Gasoline. 4-148
   Bathyscaphe rendered buoyant by, *with illus.*, 6-74a,
     74b, 74c
   Combustion products as air pollutants, 3-353, 354,
     356
   Hydrocarbons in, 7-269
Gasoline engines, *with illus.*, 4-86-89
   Aircraft, 6-178, 182, 187
   Automobiles, *with illus.*, 2-131-38
   Diesels compared with, 4-91
   World War I, 9-213-14
Gasoline vehicles. World War I, *with illus.*, 9-213-14
   See also **Automobiles**
Gastric juice. 4-325-26
Gastric ulcers. 4-335
Gastrocnemius, lower-leg muscle. *illus.*, 1-148c; *illus.*,
   3-205, 213
Gastrointestinal tract. See **Digestion**
Gastroliths. Fossil remains?, 1-385
Gastropods. 2-200-01, *illus.*, 193, 198
   Shell collecting, 2-99, 101-04, *illus.*, 100
Gathering, of glass. 3-310, *illus.*, 314a
Gatun Locks, Panama Canal. *with illus.*, 4-193
Gauges.
   *Radiation thickness gauges, 9-43-46
   Automobiles, 2-144-45
   Machined work tested by, 10-112
   Piezoelectric crystals used in pressure gauges, 2-294
   Railroad, 1-182-83
   Standard railroad, 1-183
Gaurs, wild oxen of India. 10-248
Gauss, Karl Friedrich, German mathematician. 9-282
   Ceres' orbit calculated by, 4-420-21
Gautier, Hubert, French architect. 2-333
Gavials. *illus.*, 5-384
Gay-Lussac, Joseph-Louis, French chemist and physicist
   (1778–1850). He taught at the Polytechnic School,
   the Sorbonne and the Botanical Gardens (all in Paris)
   and was consultant to the French chemical industry. He
   isolated boron from boric acid, prepared potassium
   from fused potash and discovered new methods of analyzing organic compounds. He discovered that all
   gases have almost the same expansion coefficient; he
   formulated the law of combining volumes (Gay-Lussac's
   law). In the course of balloon ascents he investigated
   the effects of terrestrial magnetism and the composition
   of air at high elevations.
Gay-Lussac's law, of gases. 1-165-66; 3-416
Gayals, partly domesticated oxen. 10-248
Gazelles. 8-387
Geanticlines, uparchings of earth's crust. 10-215
Gears.
   Homemade versions of, *with illus.*, 7-217-18
   Rear- axle gears, used for automobiles, 2-141, *illus.*,
     140
   Tooling of, by hobbing machine, *illus.*, 10-108
   Transmission gears for automobiles, *with illus.*, 2-139

Gears *(continued)*
Wheel and axle gears as variation of, **3**-61
See also **Linkages**
Geber, Arab physician and alchemist. **2**-299-300
Geckos, lizards. *with illus.,* **5**-198, 205, 206
Geddes, Norman Bel, American designer. **10**-119, 120
Geese. *with illus.,* **6**-399-400
Canadian geese, *illus.,* **5**-418e; *illus.,* **9**-268-69; **10**-257
Migration of, **9**-420, *illus.,* 416-17
Raising of, **7**-23
Snow geese, *illus.,* **5**-418e
Gegenschein, atmospheric glow. **1**-240
Geiger, Hans, German physicist.
Radiation detectors, development of, *with illus.,* **9**-340-43.
Geiger counters and Geiger-Mueller counters.
****9**-340-43
Medical use of, **10**-99, *illus.,* 100
Prospecting with, **7**-361
Radiocarbon dating, used for, *with illus.,* **10**-95-96
Uranium ore, used for detecting, *illus.,* **9**-140
Geikie, Sir Archibald, Scottish geologist (1835–1924). He taught geology at the University of Edinburgh and directed the geological survey of Scotland and, later, of the United Kingdom. His *Scenery of Scotland* was one of the first works to describe in detail the topographical history of a country. Geikie studied the effects of glacial action in Scotland and determined the history of volcanic action in the British Isles.
Geissler, Heinrich, German glass blower. **8**-411
Gekkonids (Gekkonidae), family of lizards. **5**-198
Gelatin.
Bacteria cultivated in, *with illus.,* **3**-72
Photographic use of, **1**-212; **9**-403, 408, 413
Gels, forms of colloidal suspension. *with illus.,* **5**-297
Living matter, found in, **2**-6, 8, *illus.,* **10**; **5**-301
Gemini (Twins), constellation. **1**-337
Geminids, meteor shower. *table,* **6**-97
Gemmae, vegetative outgrowths capable of producing new plants.
Liverworts, **3**-189-90
Gemmae cups. Liverworts, **3**-189, *illus.,* 186
Gems. **9**-307
See also **Diamonds.**
Gemsboks, antelopes. **8**-383
Genera, groups in classification of living things. **1**-289
General Catalogue, classification of nebulae and star clusters. **8**-49
General Electric Company. **4**-275
High voltage and artificial lightning, experiments in, *illus.,* **1**-400-01
Laboratory for fundamental research, **8**-407-08
Synthetic diamonds produced by, **4**-253
Natural lighting, studies of, *with illus.,* **1**-401-02
General Electric Research Laboratory. **4**-275
General Motors Corporation.
Metallurgy, research in, *illus.,* **4**-342a
Technical research center, *illus.,* **4**-342b
General theory of relativity. *with illus.,* **4**-218-20
Generators.
Electrostatic generators (Van de Graaff accelerators), *diagram,* **1**-309; **9**-131, *illus.,* 129; *illus.,* **10**-200
Steam turbine, *illus.,* **9**-234a
See also **Electric generators; Electricity; Steam; Turbines**
Genes, carriers of hereditary traits. *with illus.,* **6**-271, 272; *with illus.,* **8**-91-93
Heredity, role in, **8**-339-44
Human differences due to recombinations of, **8**-213-14

Genes *(continued)*
Molecular nature of, **9**-385-86
Mutations due to radiation, **9**-356
Radiation effects on, **9**-358
Genetics.
Heredity in man, **8-333-47
Agriculture, genetics as factor in, **9**-291
Human heredity, basis of, *with illus.,* **8**-91-92
Mathematics and, **1**-78
Molecular basis of heredity, *with diagrams,* **9**-383-86
Mutations caused by gamma radiations, **10**-252
See also **Evolution; Heredity; Life; Mendel, Gregor Johann**
Genets. *with illus.,* **8**-245-46
Geneva, Lake. Regulating action of, **7**-61
Geneva Convention (1864). **7**-389
Genotypes, gene patterns. *with illus.,* **6**-271-73; **8**-340
Genus. See **Genera**
Geochronology, scientific dating of geologic events.
Time scale of earth's history, **6-369-74
Geodes, crystal formations. **8**-328
Geodesics, shortest distances between points. **4**-440-41, *diagrams,* 438-39
Geoffroy Saint-Hilaire, Etienne, French naturalist. **4**-390
Geographical races, of mankind. *with illus.,* **8**-215-17
Geography.
Caves, **5-50-60
Deserts, **6-113-18
Earthquakes, **9-105-19
Flattened areas of earth, **6-109-18
Geysers, **8-288-92
Glaciers and icebergs, **9-162-74
Ground water, **8-321-32
Islands, **4-133-39
Lakes, **7-55-66
Mineral deposits in rocks, **5-248-56; **7**-354-61
Mountains, **10-18-29, 213-23
Ocean depths, **6-69-77
Oceanic currents, **6-229-38
Oceanic tides, **6-201-08
Oceans, **6-26a-36
Plateaus, **6-109-13
Precipitation, **2-346-57
Rivers, **6-409-18
Shoreline changes, **8-348-59
Soil, **2-15-25
Volcanoes, **8-293-304
Water, erosive action of, **8-9-18
Barriers limit plant and animal communities, **10**-182
History
Antiquity, *with illus.,* **1**-130-31; 358-59
Fifteenth and sixteenth centuries, *with illus.,* **2**-364-67
Nineteenth century voyages of discovery, *with illus.,* **7**-27-34
See also **Africa; Asia; Australia; Europe; Explorations; Geology; Geysers; North America; Physiography; South America; United States**
Geologic column. See **Stratigraphic column**
Geologic thermometer. **3**-181-82
Geological time. ****6**-369-74
Geologists. See **Geology;** also names of geologists
Geology.
Caves, **5-50-60
Climates of past, **3-177-85
Dust, **7-137-42
Earthquakes, **9-105-19
Flattened areas of earth, **6-109-18
Geysers, **8-288-92

Geology *(continued)*
*Glaciers, and icebergs, 9-162-74
*Ground water, 8-321-32
*Iceberg formation, 9-333-39
*Interior of earth, 4-169-76
*Introduction to study of geology, 1-27-36
*Islands, formation of, 4-133-39
*Lakes, 7-55-66
*Meteorites, 6-87-98
*Mineral and rock collecting, 9-300-09
*Mineral deposits in rocks, 4-140-52; 5-248-56; 7-354-61
*Mountain-building forces, 10-213-23
*Mountains, 10-18-29
*Oceanography, depths of sea, 6-69-77
*Prospecting, 7-355-61
*Rivers, 6-409-18
*Rocks, formation of, 3-419-26
*Shoreline changes, 8-348-59
*Soil, 2-15-25
*Time scale of earth's history, 6-369-74
*Volcanoes, 7-334-45; 8-293-304
*Water, erosive action of, 8-9-18
*Winds, erosive action of, 7-318-26
Astronomy, relation to, 1-21-22
Carboniferous period, 1-410
Coal, formation and occurrence of, *with illus.*, 1-405-08
Development in eighteenth and nineteenth centuries, *with illus.*, 4-392-98
Formation of earth, theories concerning, *with illus.*, 1-27-30
Fossils in relation to, *with illus.*, 4-386-94, 397
Isostasy, 7-32
Job opportunities in field of, *illus.*, 10-202
Salt beds deposited, 5-318
Subdivisions of, 1-36
Submarine geology, 9-221-22
See also **Climate; Earth; Fossils; Geophysics; Ocean; Paleontology; Weather**
Geomagnetic electrokinetographs, oceanic current speed and direction recorders. *illus.*, 6-232
Geomagnetism, magnetism of earth. *with diagrams*, 7-168-71, 356-57
Geometer moths. 3-202
Geometric progressions. Malthusian theory, 3-229
Geometric sequences. 2-77-79
Geometric spiders. 2-266
Geometry. *3-427-46
*Analytic geometry, *with diagrams*, 4-423-31
Invention of, 3-20-21
*Plane geometry, 3-429-40
*Solid geometry, 3-440-46
Antiquity, development in, 1-127, 130, 133-34
Euclid, 1-355-56
Non-Euclidean, *with diagrams*, 4-438-41; 9-282
Recreations, geometrical, 4-445-46, *with diagrams*, 451-53, *diagrams*, 446-47
Geomorphology, scientific study of landscape features.
*Glaciers as factor in land erosion, 9-162-74
*Mountain-building, 10-213-23
*Ocean waves as factor in land erosion, 8-348-59
*Water erosion of land, 8-9-18
*Wind as factor in land erosion, 7-318-26
Geophones, ground-vibration detectors. *diagram*, 4-143; 7-358
Geophysics, application of physics to study of the earth.
*Earth, 4-42-50
*Earth's interior, 4-169-76
*International Geophysical Year, 5-186-95

Geophysics *(continued)*
*Prospecting by geophysical methods, 7-354-61
Natural-gas prospecting by geophysical methods, *with illus.*, 5-99-100
Petroleum prospecting by geophysical methods, 4-144-45, *diagram*, 143
Twentieth century, 9-220-23
See also **Earth**
George Washington Bridge, New York City. 2-339, *illus.*, 332
Geosynclines, deep troughs in earth's crust. 10-213-14, 215, 218, 220
Geotropism, organic movement in reaction to gravity.
Beans, *illus.*, 1-47; *illus.*, 6-218c
Plants, 3-53, *illus.*, 51
Geraniums. *illus.*, 4-123
Flower parts of, 4-120-21
Gerard de Geer Glacier, West Spitsbergen. *illus.*, 9-334
Gerard of Cremona, Italian translator. 2-303
Gerbils, rodents. 8-164
Gerenuks, antelopes. 8-387
Gerhardt, Charles-Frédéric, French chemist. 5-78
Geriatrics, science treating of old age and its diseases. *8-78-83
Gericke, W. F., American botanist.
Soilless agriculture experiments, 8-35
Germ cells.
Heredity, role in, *with illus.*, 8-334-37
See also **Cells; Chromosomes; Evolution; Sex cells**
Germ-free animals. *7-151-55
Germ plasm.
See **Cells; Chromosomes; Evolution; Gametes; Genetics; Germ cells; Heredity**
Germ theory of disease. Development of, *with illus.*, 7-378-85
Pasteur's contributions to, 9-77-78
See also **Germs**
German cockroaches (croton bugs). 3-148
German silver. 1-382
German Society for Space Travel. 9-377
German tribes. Overthrow of Western Roman Empire, 1-368
Germanic (language) stock. 1-118
Germanium (Ge), chemical element. Atomic number, 32; atomic weight, 72.59; melting point, 958.5° C.; boiling point, volatilizes at 2,700° C.; specific gravity, 5.36. Metal; gray-white, brittle, crystalline, lustrous at room temperatures. Discovered by Winkler in 1886; name derived from Latin *Germania*: "Germany." Two main ores are germanite and argyrodite; also found in small amounts in many other ores. Prepared by reducing the oxide with carbon or hydrogen; by-product of smelting zinc and cadmium. Used on wide scale for transistors; see **Transistors.** See also 3-42
Discovery of, 5-85
Transistors, made of, 6-303; 10-103-04
Germany.
Digester gas for fuel, 5-332-33
Evolutionary controversy in, 8-262
History of science in
1600–1765, 3-268-70, 275
1765–1815, 4-355-56
Hydrofoil development in, 4-6-7
Industrial research, 1-95
Jet aviation, contributions to, 7-68-69; 9-218
Kiel Canal, *with illus.*, 4-186
Military science and technology, *with illus.*, 9-211-15
Printing developed in, 1-197
Rocketry, contributions to, 9-218
Salt mine as art storehouse, *illus.*, 5-319

Germany (continued)
Space and rocket research in, 9-218, with *illus.,* 377-79; **10-42, 44-46,** *illus.,* **47**
Synthetic chemistry in, 8-187
Synthetic rubber first produced by, 6-57-58
See also **World War I; World War II**
Germination. *5-61-67
Environmental factors affecting fruits and seeds, 5-6-7
Germs.
*Germ-free animals, 7-151-55
*Parasitic microorganisms, 8-360-68
*Pasteur's contributions to bacteriology, 9-71-80
*Protozoans, 2-58-66
*Viruses, 3-451-58
Body's defenses against, 7-347-51, *diagrams,* 348, 349
Coliform bacterium as indicator of water purity, 2-276
Development of germ theory of disease, with *illus.,* 7-378-85
Killed by ultrasonic waves, *illus.,* 8-103
Nursing precautions against, 10-55-57, 65-66
Tuberculosis, with *illus.,* 9-175-78
White blood cells defend against, 3-328
See also **Bacteria; Diseases; Medicine; Microbes; Parasites; Tuberculosis; Viruses**
Gerontology, science dealing with aging. 8-79
Possibilities in science of, 10-225
See also **Geriatrics**
Gerrids, family of true bugs. with *illus.,* 3-262
Gesell, Arnold, American psychologist and pediatrician. with *illus.,* 9-56-57
Gesner, Abraham, Canadian physician and geologist (1797–1864). Kerosene discovered by, 4-141
Gesner, Konrad von, German-Swiss editor. with *illus.,* 2-370
Gestalt psychology. 9-315
Theory of, 9-54
Gestation period.
Camels, 7-329
Cats, 8-204, 206, 208, 210, 212
Elephants, 7-328
Hyenas, spotted, 8-250
Hyenas, striped, 8-250
Insectivores, 7-98-99
Jackals, 8-138
Marsupials, 7-419
Primates, 9-260
Snakes, 5-355
Sperm whales, 7-188
Gestetner, Sigmund, British manufacturer. Duplicating machine of, 10-120
Getters, substances used to remove traces of free gas. Barium used as, 3-174
Geysers. *8-288-92
Formation of, 8-325-26, *illus.,* 327
Ghee, semifluid buffalo butter. 7-329
Ghiraldi, Luigi Lilio, Italian astronomer and physician. Calendar reform, 10-176
Giacobini-Zinner comet. 6-96, 97
Giacobinids, meteor shower. 6-96, 97, *illus.,* 96, *table,* 97
Giant anteaters. *illus.,* 7-14
Giant armadillos. *illus.,* 7-11
Giant clams. 2-199
Giant elands, antelopes. *illus.,* 8-380
Giant hummingbirds. 6-212
Giant kelps. 3-220
Giant marine toads. 5-162
Giant pandas. 7-6, 315, *illus.,* 313
Giant salamanders. with *illus.,* 5-157
Migration of, 9-428-29

Giant sequoia trees. with *illus.,* 5-142-43
Giant squids. 2-194
Giant water bugs. with *illus.,* 3-263-64, *illus.,* 254
Giantism. Pituitary gland may cause, 5-17
Giant's Causeway. Basalt formation in Northern Ireland, 4-395, *illus.,* 394
Giants, stars. 6-264, 265, 266, *table,* 264
Gibbons. 9-252, 254, 260-62, *illus.,* 253; 10-136
Adapted for swinging through trees, 7-9
Gibbs, Erna, American psychiatrist. 9-104
Gibbs, Frederick, American psychiatrist. 9-104
Gibbs, Josiah Willard, American physicist (1839–1903). He was professor of mathematical physics at Yale. His greatest work was in thermodynamics; among other contributions, he formulated a law (Phase Rule) expressing the conditions of equilibrium in a heterogeneous system. He developed vector analysis, applying the method to problems of crystal structure and to the calculation of the orbits of planets and comets. See also 5-83
Gieber, A., German biologist. Virus experiments of, 9-385
Giffard, Henri, French pioneer in aeronautics. 6-178
Gila monsters, lizards. with *illus.,* 5-200, 206
Gila woodpeckers. 6-212
Gilbert, Sir William, English physician and physicist. 2-370-71
Electricity, experiments with, 6-124
Magnetic field of the earth proposed by, 4-44
Magnetism, work on, 7-167-68
Theory of earth's magnetic field set forth, 4-176
Gill arches. Fishes' inner ear evolved from, 4-382
Vertebrate embryos have, 4-385
Gill chamber, of fishes. with *illus.,* 4-100
Gill covers (opercles), of fishes. with *illus.,* 1-279; with *illus.,* 4-96
Gill filaments, of fishes. 4-100
Gill fungi, mushrooms. with *illus.,* 3-29-30
Gill pouches, in vertebrates. with *illus.,* 1-58
Gill slits. Acorn worm's, with *illus.,* 4-2
Chordates all possess gill slits at some time, 4-1
Gills, organs for respiration.
Fish, 1-277, with *illus.,* 279; with *illus.,* 4-100; 10-141
Gills, platelike spore-producing organs of mushrooms. with *illus.,* 3-29-30
Gingivitis, inflammation of the gums, 5-131-32
Ginkgo trees. 3-402, *illus.,* 401; with *illus.,* 5-144
Unchanged for millions of years, 6-283
Ginkgoales, order of gymnosperms. 3-402, *illus.,* 401
Giraffes. with *illus.,* 7-414, 416-17
Girder bridges. with *illus.,* 2-334-35
Girders, construction elements. with *illus.,* 2-334-35
Girdling roots, tree deformity. 10-150
Girls. Puberty in, 8-99
Gisborne, Frederick N., Canadian inventor. 2-384
Glacial climates. Causes of, 9-174
Glacial deposits. 3-179-80
Glacier National Park, United States. *illus.,* 7-57; 9-276
Avalanche Lake, *illus.,* 6-415
Game and bird preserve, 9-276
Glaciers. *9-162-74
*Iceberg production, 9-333-39
Atolls and barrier reefs due to ?, 6-75, 77
Coasts shaped by, with *illus.,* 8-356
Continental shelves, action on, 6-71
Debris of, 9-173-74, *illus.,* 166-67, 171, 172
Dust storms arise in vicinity of, 7-325
Earth formation, glacier action in, 4-396
Great Illecillewaet, Canada, *illus.,* 6-413
Greenland, *illus.,* 3-184
IGY investigations of, 5-190

Glaciers (continued)
  Lakes formed by, 7-55, 57, illus., 56
  Soil formation partially due to, 2-16
  Streams and valleys, effects on, 8-15
  Till, 9-173, illus., 171
  Weathering effects of, with illus., 6-137-38
  See also **Ice; Ice ages; Pleistocene epoch**
Gladioli. illus., 6-59
  Bulb and bulblets of, illus., 9-15
Gladstone, William, British statesman. 5-231
Glands. illus., 1-148g; *5-8-19
  Body's defenses, role in, 7-347-48, 352-53
  Cell in earthworm gland, illus., 2-12d
  Growth and aging, action on during, 8-94-95, 101
  Insects', 2-405-06, 409
  Lachrymal, 7-293
  Luminous secretions in animals, 2-186
  Scent glands as defense, with illus., 3-238-39
  Skin glands, 2-176-77, 180, illus., 174, 177
  See also **Endocrine glands; Goiter**
Glands of internal secretion. See **Endocrine glands**
Glass. *3-307-16
  *Construction material, glass used as, 8-388-92
  Aquariums, glass covers for, 8-112
  Building material, 7-122, illus., 124, 127
  Crown glass, 9-91
  Etching with hydrofluoric acid, with illus., 3-320-21
  Expansion due to rise in temperature, 3-415
  Flint glass, 9-91
  Food containers, made of, 4-156
  Heat conductivity of, 4-10-12, 16, illus., 15
  Index of refraction of common glass, 7-254
  Lever House (New York City), a building of glass, 3-117
  Molecular structure and behavior of, 1-170-71
Glass blocks. *8-388-92
Glass blowing. with illus., 3-310; illus., 314a-c
Glass ceramic. 3-315
Glass prisms. See **Prisms**
"Glass sand," used in glassmaking. 3-308
Glass snakes. with illus., 5-200, 206
Glass tubing. Preparation of, for home laboratory, with illus., 4-224-25
Glassine, semitransparent paper. 4-378
Glassware.
  Home chemical laboratory, with illus., 4-224-27
Glauber, Johann Rudolf, German scientist. 3-270
Glauber salts. 3-425
  Solar heating, use in, 2-252
Glaze, icy deposit resulting from freezing rain, 2-355
Glazes of pottery. 7-396, 406, illus., 405
Glidden, Carlos, American inventor. 1-266-67; 6-381
Gliders. Development of, 6-181-82, 195-96, illus., 183
  Jet streams studied by use of, illus., 2-358
Gliding phalangers. See **Flying phalangers**
Gliocladium roseum, mold. illus., 10-130b-c
Gliomas, cancers in supporting connective tissue in brain and central nervous system. 8-266-67
Globigerina, genus of protozoa. with illus., 6-33
Globigerina ooze, marine deposit. 6-33
Globin, protein in hemoglobin. 3-326
Globular clusters. with illus., 6-267; 8-155-56; illus., 9-161
  Orbital motion of, 7-229
Globulins, blood proteins. 3-326
  Red blood cells contain globulin, 5-13, 14
  See also **Gamma globulins**
Gloeocapsa, blue-green algae. with illus., 3-214-15
Gloger's rule, concerning skin pigmentation. 8-219
Glomeruli, tufts of capillaries in kidney. diagram, 5-12

Glossopharyngeal nerves. 6-328
Glossopteris, genus of extinct fernlike plants, 3-180
Gloucester, Massachusetts. Fishing industry, 6-23, illus., 22-23
Glow, thermoluminescent. 6-375, 376
Glowworms, beetles. 2-183, 185; 3-342
Glowworms, larval flies. 5-60
Glucinum. See **Beryllium**
Glucose, a simple sugar. 4-79
  Body's use of, 4-52
  Cells, important carbohydrate in, 2-5, 11
  Laboratory production of, 8-190
  Molecular structure, 7-276
  Plants' manufacture and use of, 3-45-48
  Regulation in blood, 5-15, 19
Gluteus maximus, buttocks muscle. illus., 3-205
Gluttons (wolverines). with illus., 8-172
Glycerol. 7-272
  Component of fat, 4-52-53; 7-275
  Molecular structure, 7-272
Glycine, amino acid. 7-275
Glycogen, animal starch. 4-77; 7-276
  Animal cells, 2-5
  Body's use of, 4-52
  Muscular energy furnished by, 3-205, 206
  Regulation in body, 5-15, 19
Gnatcatchers. 6-44
Gnats. See **Buffalo gnats; Diptera**
Gnawing animals. See **Rodents**
Gneiss, metamorphic rock. 3-426; 9-308
Gnetales, order of gymnosperms. 3-401
Gnus, antelopes. 8-386, illus., 387
Goat antelopes. 8-377-79
Goats.
  Domestication of, 10-245
  Glacier National Park, 9-276
  Sheep distinguished from, 10-245, 248
Goatsuckers, birds. with illus., 6-216-18
Gobi Desert, Asia. 6-118
Goddard, Henry Herbert, American psychologist. 9-56
Goddard, Robert H., American rocket experimenter. 9-377; illus., 376; 10-42, 44
Goethals, G. W., American engineer. 4-192
Goiter, enlargement of thyroid gland. 5-18
  Radioiodine used to treat, illus., 10-100
Gold (Au), chemical element. Atomic number, 79; atomic weight, 196.967; melting point, 1,063° C.; boiling point, 2,600° C.; specific gravity, 19.32. Most ductile and malleable of the metals and one of the softest. A good conductor of heat and electricity. Known from earliest recorded times. Name derived from Sanskrit Jval, by way of Anglo-Saxon; chemical symbol (Au) derived from Latin aurum: "gold." Found in free form and in telluride ores; often associated with silver, copper and other metals. Obtained from its ores by cyanidation, amalgamation and smelting. Often refined by electrolysis. Used in alloys for ornaments and coins; in its pure form as a standard of value for money. Some compounds are useful in photography, gold paints and medicine. See also *4-242-50
  Crystalline structure, 5-340, diagram, 339
  Radiogold, medical uses of, 10-100
  Mercury, gold produced from, 8-420
  Ore, treatment of, 1-375; 4-248, 250
  Properties and uses, 3-34
  Teeth fillings made of, 5-136-37
  White gold, 1-382
Gold leaf. 3-34
Gold mining. *4-242-50
  Scuba divers employed in, illus., 6-26d
Golden cats. 8-211

Golden-crowned kinglets. 6-42

Golden eagles. 6-156, *with illus.*, 157

Golden-fronted woodpeckers. 6-212

Golden Gate Bridge, San Francisco. 2-340

Golden moles. 7-102

Golden pheasants. *illus.*, 6-340

Golden plovers. 6-407-08

    Migration of, 9-420

Goldenrod. 10-205

Goldfinches. 6-108

Goldfish. 8-113, 115

Goldschmidt process. Iron, melting of, 3-317

Golgi, Camillo, Italian physician.

    Malarial parasites, work on, 10-32

Golgi substance, or Golgi apparatus, cell structures.
    1-143; 2-8-9, illus., 4, 8

Goliath beetles. 3-346

Gomphotherium, genus of extinct elephants. 7-408

Gonads, sex glands. *illus.*, 1-148g; *with illus.*, 8-19-21

Gondolas, freight cars. *with illus.*, 1-190

Gonyaulax, genus of protozoans. *illus.*, 2-60

"Good-luck spots," in fingernails. 2-181

Goodricke, John, English astronomer. 7-46

Goodyear, Charles, American inventor.

    Vulcanization discovered by, 6-351-52

Googolplexes, numerical units invented by Edward Kas-
    ner. 2-74

Googols, numerical units invented by Edward Kasner.
    2-74

Goose barnacles. 2-242

"Goose pimples." 2-180

Goose plants. *illus.*, 7-83

Gopher snakes. Pets, 7-25

Gophers. *illus.*, 2-203

    Pocket gophers, 10-137, illus., 140

Gorals, goat antelopes. 8-377

Gorgas, William C., American army surgeon. 4-192;
    7-385

Gorges. Cut by young streams, 8-17, illus., 18

Gorillas. *illus.*, 7-14, 9-252-53, 260-62, illus., 250

    Hand of, 2-176

    Skeleton compared with those of other vertebrates,
      illus., 1-57

    Teeth of, illus., 1-59

    Zoo, illus., 10-159, 160

Goshawks. 6-157

Gothic architecture. *with illus.*, 7-117

    Stained-glass windows, *with illus.*, 8-389

Government.

    Industrial research conducted by governments, *with
      illus.*, 1-90-97

Government service. Scientific positions in,
    10-198-99, illus., 197

Governors, automatic controlling devices.

    Watt's centrifugal governor, 10-235

Graafian follicles, sacs in which eggs are enclosed in
    the ovary. 8-20, illus., 21

Gracilis, thigh muscle. *illus.*, 1-148c

Grackles. 6-104

Gradient, stream. 8-12, 13

Grading.

    Coal, 1-416

    Roads, illus., 3-298b

Graebe, Karl, German chemist. 5-80

    Alizarin synthesized by, 8-183

Graf Zeppelin. Dirigible, *with illus.*, 6-180

Grafting, method of plant propagation. 9-8, 10-12, 14,
    illus., 13

    Hybrid allegedly produced by, 9-10-12

Graham, E. A., American surgeon. Cancer, investiga-
    tion of, 5-348, 350

Graham, Thomas, Scottish chemist. 5-83

    Colloids, investigation of, *with diagram*, 5-295

Graham Island, islet produced by volcanic action.
    8-303

Grain.

    Conveyor belts carry, 6-168

    Damage to, from weeds, 7-111

    Insects, determining presence of, in grain, 8-44-45

    See also **Corn; Flour; Seeds; Wheat**

Grain, dry fruits. *with illus.*, 4-131

Grainer pans. Salt extraction by use of, *with illus.*,
    5-321-22

Gram-calories. See **Calories**

Grammar. 1-110, 116

Gramme, Zénobe-Théophile, Belgian electrician.
    5-247

Gramophones. See **Phonographs**

Grampuses. *illus.*, 7-185

Grand Bank, off Newfoundland. *illus.*, 6-71

Grand Canyon, gorge formed by Colorado River.
    with illus., 8-11; 10-213

Grand Coulee Dam, Washington. 8-309-10

Grand Ferghana Canal, Russian irrigation project.
    8-201

Grand Saline, Texas. Salt mine, illus., 5-317

Granite, igneous rock. *illus.*, 1-31; *with illus.*, 3-423;
    9-308

    Blasting needed to detach, 2-84

    Decomposition by water, 2-351

    Origin, distribution and uses of, *with illus.*, 2-83-85

    Sawing by steel bar, 2-84

Granular (crumblike) soils. *with illus.*, 2-19

Granulations, markings on sun. 3-100

Granules, grainlike particles. Starch granules, 4-76-77,
    78

Grape ferns. *illus.*, 3-189

Grape leafhoppers. 9-195, illus., 196

Grapefruit. Seedlings as terrarium plants, 5-367

Grapes. *illus.*, 1-304

    Mildew of, 3-25-26

    Vines, illus., 3-44; 10-140

Grapevines. Grape leafhoppers attack, 9-195

Graphic arts. *Printing and engraving, 1-196-214

Graphic formulas. Organic compounds, 5-78-80

Graphite, form of carbon. 3-324; 4-273, 274, 276

    Crystal structure of, 5-374, with diagram, 338, illus.,
      375

    Formation of, 5-248

    Rings of, in turbines, 5-310

    Specific gravity of, 5-254

Graphs. *with illus.*, 2-70-72

    Analytic geometry, use of graphs in, *with diagrams*,
      4-425-31

Graptolites, extinct floating animals. 1-387-88; *illus.*,
    6-371

Grass bugs. 3-258

Grasses. *illus.*, 1-303

    Grasslands of the world, 6-112-15

    Leaves of, illus., 4-72

    Seeds, illus., 5-63

Grasshopper robot weather stations. illus., 1-252

Grasshoppers. *illus.*, 1-296

    Anatomy of, external, illus., 2-403

    Cell of, illus., 2-9

    Field study of, 10-262

    Migration of migratory locusts, 9-432, illus., 431

    See also **Long-horned grasshoppers; Short-horned
      grasshoppers**

Grassi, Giovanni Battista, Italian physician and zoolo-
    gist, 7-384; 8-405; 10-33

Graunt, John, English statistician. 3-21

Grave mounds, China.
Irrigation projects hampered by, **8**-201
Gravel. Size of particles of, **3**-424
Soil texture, *with illus.,* **2**-18
Streams carry and deposit, **8**-13
Water filtered through, **2**-280, *illus.,* 279
See also **Rocks; Soil**
Gravel-packed (gravel-wall) wells. **2**-274, *illus.,* 275
Gravel-wall wells. See **Gravel-packed wells.**
Gravimeters. See **Gravity meters**
Gravitation. *2-315-22
Acceleration as, **2**-318
Earth's air circulation affected by, **2**-89
Effect of, as force, *with illus.,* **1**-83, 84
Einstein's theory of, *with illus.,* **9**-282
Gravity distinguished from, **2**-318
Heavenly bodies subject to laws of, **3**-163-64
Jupiter's gravitational pull on asteroids and comets, **5**-24
Light rays effect on, **3**-137
Molecular attraction due in part to, **1**-166
Newton's pioneer work, **3**-278-81
Space flight, gravitation as factor in, **8**-126, 127, *diagram,* 126
Tides caused by moon's and sun's gravitational pull, *with diagrams,* **6**-201-04, 205
Gravitons, gravitational units. *table,* **1**-314
Gravity. *2-315-22
Acceleration as, *with table,* **2**-318
Center of, **2**-322, *illus.,* 320, 321
Earthquakes, relation to, **9**-105-06
Falling bodies affected by, **2**-119-20, *illus.,* 120, 121
Force in colloidal suspension, **5**-300
Geotropism as manifestation of, **3**-53, *illus.,* 51; *illus.,* **6**-218c
Gravitation distinguished from, **2**-318
Measurement of, **2**-319-20, *with table,* 318
Muscular action affected by, **3**-209
Natural-gas deposits located by gravity methods, **5**-99-100
Ore and petroleum deposits located by gravity methods, *with diagrams,* **1**-373; **2**-320
Prospecting by measuring variations in, **5**-99-100; *with illus.,* **7**-358-60
Soil water affected by, **5**-26
Space travel, problems of gravity in, **10**-43-44, 48-50, 52, 53
Specific gravity, explanation of, **2**-31-33
Terrestrial gravity, **4**-44
Gravity-arch dams. **8**-315, *illus.,* 310
Gravity-circulation hot-air heating systems. *with illus.,* **2**-246
Gravity concentration, in ore dressing. *with diagrams,* **1**-373
Gravity dams. **8**-312-14, *illus.,* 310
History of, **8**-308
Gravity meters, instruments measuring the earth's gravity. **5**-99-100
Prospecting with, *with diagram,* **7**-359
Gravity-type dams. *illus.,* **8**-316a
Gravure, printing process. **1**-212-13, *diagram,* 211
Gray, Asa, American botanist (1810–1888). Author of the *Manual of Botany,* first written in 1848 and still highly regarded today. With John Torrey, he wrote a *Flora of North America.* He was curator of the New York Lyceum of Natural History and professor of natural history at the University of Michigan and at Harvard, where he developed the famous Botanical Garden.
Gray, Elisha, American inventor. **5**-243
Telephone invention claimed by, **2**-388

Gray, Stephen, English scientist. Electricity, work on, **2**-378; **4**-359
Gray birch trees. **5**-145
Gray-brown podsolic soils, soil type. **2**-22
Gray-cheeked thrushes. **6**-39
Gray foxes. *with illus.,* **8**-141
Gray matter, of nervous system. Nature and locations of, **6**-324, 326-27
Gray squirrels. **8**-162
Gray wolves. **8**-136-37, *illus.,* 134
Gray wooded soil, soil type. **2**-22
Graying of hair. **2**-179
Graylag geese. **6**-400
Grease. Lubricating greases, **4**-149
Greasewood. Underground water indicated by presence of, **8**-331
Great Barrier Reef, Australia. **4**-135; **6**-72; **8**-359
Coral formations, *illus.,* **4**-137
Great birds of paradise.
Courtship behavior of, *with illus.,* **5**-418c
Great Britain.
Atomic bombs, **9**-354
Digester gas in bombs, use of, **5**-333
Fish industry, **6**-15, 16, 18
Industrial research in, **1**-93-95
Jet aviation, contributions to, **7**-67-69, 72-73, *illus.,* 73; **9**-218
Library materials microfilmed, **10**-73-74
Military science and technology, *with illus.,* **9**-212-15
Transportation on land, early, **1**-103, *with illus.,* 104-05
Great Britain, steamship. **4**-110, 111
Great circles. **3**-444, *illus.,* 445
Glassy meteorites (tektites) distributed along, **6**-94
Great Danes, dogs. **10**-243
Great Eastern, steamship. **4**-110-11
Great Falls of the Yellowstone, Wyoming. **8**-15
Great Geyser, Iceland. *with illus.,* **8**-290-91
Great gray owls. **6**-164
Great horned owls. **6**-163, *with illus.,* 164
Nesting activities of, *with illus.,* **5**-418g
Great Illecillewaet Glacier, Canada. *illus.,* **6**-413
Great Lakes. **7**-61-62
Great manta rays, fish. **4**-295
Great Nebula, galaxy in Andromeda. **1**-334; **9**-363
Great Nebula, nebula in Orion. *illus.,* **9**-359, 360
Orion, **9**-360-61
Great Plains, United States. Dust storms, **7**-324-25
Great Pyramid, Egypt. **8**-309
Great Red Spot, marking on Jupiter. *with illus.,* **5**-23-24
Great Rift Valley, Africa. **7**-56; **10**-24, 26
Great Salt Lake, Utah. **7**-64
Salt-making operations, **5**-316
Great Salt Lake Desert, Utah. **6**-118
Great Sandy Desert, Australia. **6**-118
Great Western, steamship. **4**-110
Greater occipital nerve. *illus.,* **1**-148h
Grebes, birds. **6**-395, *illus.,* 396
Greece, Ancient.
Algebra, contributions to, **2**-68
Alphabet of early Greeks, **1**-115
Architecture of ancient, **3**-114
Breadmaking in, **9**-294
Engineering in, **1**-216
Illumination in, **4**-232
Malaria-carrying mosquitoes, war on, *illus.,* **10**-36
Marble buildings, **7**-116
Mathematics, contributions to, *with illus.,* **3**-428-29
Matter, ancient Greek concepts of, **1**-307
Number system of, *with illus.,* **1**-152
Pottery of ancient, **7**-396, 398

Greece, Ancient (continued)
  Science, contributions to
    Early Greek scientists, with illus., 1-129-38
    Alexandrian school, with illus., 1-354-60
  Ships and boats of ancient Greece, 4-107
  Signal system, in antiquity, 2-377
  Steam engine experiments in, 5-305
Greece, Modern. Hydrofoil boats in, 4-7
Greek alphabet. table, 1-325
  Letters used to designate stars, 1-323
Greek language.
  Living things named in Latinized Greek, 1-291
Greek learning and arts. Rebirth of, in the Italian Renaissance, 2-362
Green algae. with illus., 3-216-19
  Lichens formed by combination of fungi and, with illus., 3-32
  Spirogyra, illus., 1-45
Green crops. See **Green manures**
Green filters, for light.
  Vision experiments with, 8-180, diagram, 179
Green manures. 2-163-65
Green molds. with illus., 3-27
Green Mountains (Vermont) Disturbance, time of mountain making, 6-371
Green snakes. Pets, 7-25
Green turtles. 5-388
  Migration of, 9-429
Greenhouse effect, atmospheric. 1-232
Greenhouses. Heated by radiant heat, 4-16
Greenland.
  Icebergs produced from Greenland glaciers, with illus., 9-334, 335, map, 336-37
  Icecap, 9-166
  IGY investigations of, 5-190
Greenland sharks. 4-290
Greenstein, Jesse L., American astronomer. 9-209
Greenstick fractures, of bones. 3-84
Greenwich Observatory. See **Royal Greenwich Observatory**
Gregorian calendar. 10-176, 178, illus., 175
Gregory XIII, Pope. Calendar reform, 10-176, 178, illus., 175
Gregory, James, Scottish telescope designer. 9-153
Gresham College, London. illus., 3-267
Grew, Nehemiah, English scientist. 3-275
  Cell structure, investigations of, 7-157
Greyhounds. 10-240, illus., 241
Gribbles, crustaceans. 2-242
Grids, electrodes in electron tubes. 6-298-301
  *Audion (grid tube), invention of, 8-84-89
Griffin, legendary creature. illus., 1-363
Griffith, A. A., English scientist. Jet aviation pioneer, 7-67-68
Griffith Planetarium, Los Angeles. 2-398, illus., 396
Griffon vultures. illus., 6-155
Grilles, heating. See **Registers, heating**
Grimaldi, Francesco Maria, Italian mathematician. 3-275
Grinding, in ore dressing. with diagrams, 1-372
Grinding, of waste materials. 5-330, 335-36
Grinding, tooling operation. 10-111-12, illus., 109
Grinding, grain. See **Milling, grain**
Grisons, animals. with illus., 8-172
Grit chamber. Sewage purifying, with illus., 5-330
Grizzlies, in ore dressing. with diagram, 1-372
Grizzly bears. 7-308, 311, 312, illus., 314
Grooming. Primates, 9-262
Gropius, Walter, German architect. 8-390; 10-119
Gros Ventre Valley, Wyoming. Landslide in, 2-353
Grosbeaks. 6-108

Gross, Herbert, American astronomer. 9-150
Grosseteste, Robert, English theologian and scholar. 2-306
Ground. Atmospheric heat balance affected by, 1-241-42
Ground, in radio. 3-93
Ground beetles. 3-337-38, illus., 336-37
Ground Control Approach. 6-200
  Radar-operated system, illus., 9-387
Ground currents, electrical. Prospecting with, with diagram, 7-359-61
Ground doves. 6-305
Ground pines, club mosses. 3-192, illus., 190
Ground squirrels. illus., 8-160
  Hibernation, 5-410
  Home building, 9-6
  Pets, 7-21
Ground water. *8-321-32
  Limestone caves, water as an erosive agent in formation of, with illus., 5-51-54
  Water supply, source of, 2-273-75, 280-82
Ground waves, in radio. 3-92
Groundwood, wood pulp prepared by grinding process. 4-369-70
Group A, human blood group. with table, 3-333
Group AB, human blood group. with table, 3-333-34
Group B, human blood group. with table, 3-333
Group dynamics. Study of, 9-322
Group M, human blood group. 3-334
Group MN, human blood group. 3-334
Group MS, human blood group. 3-334
Group N, human blood group. 3-334
Group O, human blood group. 3-334, with table, 333
Groups of galaxies. 8-53-54, diagram, 52
Grouse. 6-334-35, 337, illus., 332
  Courtship display of sage grouse, illus., 5-422
Grouting, process used in construction with cement. 8-313
Groves, Leslie R., American army officer. 9-330-31
Growdon, James. Rock-fill construction of dams, contribution to, 8-312
Growth.
  *Human growth and development, 8-19-33, 90-100
  *Plant growth and soil fertility, 2-163-72
  Bone growth, 3-73
  Coral reefs, 6-72, 75, 77
  Difference in, between living and nonliving things, 1-38
  Dimensional analysis used to measure, 1-78
  Fishes, 4-96
  Index of health in children, 10-76-77
  Insect growth and development, 2-406-09, illus., 408-09
  Pituitary gland controls, 5-15, 17
  Plant movement caused by growth reactions, 3-52-54, illus., 51, 55
  Plants, growth of, 3-49-52, 399, illus., 46, 50; 5-66-67
  Sign of a young organism, 8-80
  Skin, hair and nails, 2-173, 174, 179-81
Growth hormones. Plants, 3-50, 53
Growth plates, in bones. 3-73
Grubb, Thomas. Irish optician. 9-156
Grubs. See **Larvae**
Grumman Aircraft Engineering Corporation. 4-8, illus., 5
Grunions, fish. Migration of, 9-427
Grylloblattodea, order of insects. 2-412; 3-417
Grysboks, antelopes. 8-387
Guacharos, birds. 5-59
Guanacos. 7-331-32, illus., 329

Guano, animal excrement.
  Bat excrement a source of nitrate, 5-59
  Fertilizer, used as, 2-171
Guar plants. 7-44, illus., 43
Guard cells, of leaves. with illus., 4-73
Guayule plants. 7-44, illus., 43
  Rubber produced from, 6-353
Guenons, Old World monkeys. 9-258, 260
Guerezas, South American monkeys. 7-9; 9-257
Guericke, Otto von, German physicist. with illus.,
    3-17-18
  Electric lighting, experiment, 4-234
  Electricity, experiments with, 6-124, illus., 123
  Magdeburg hemispheres, experiments, 1-233-34, illus.,
    234-35; with illus., 2-325-26
Guernsey, English Channel island. Sea water converted
    into fresh water in, 2-283
Guest animals, of social insects. 3-361
Guettard, Jean-Etienne, French physician and geologist.
    4-394-95
Guhr dynamite. 8-276
Guidance of missiles and space vehicles. *8-125-31
Guilds, bakers'. Medieval, 9-294-95
"Guillotines." See Paper trimmers
Guinea hens. 6-337
Guinea pigs. 8-168
  Experiments, use in, illus., 8-169
  Pancreas cell, illus., 2-8
Guinea worms. 2-158-59
Guitarfish. 4-292
Gulf Intracoastal Waterway. illus., 4-188
Gulf of St. Lawrence. See St. Lawrence, Gulf of
Gulf Stream system, oceanic current. 6-236, 237-38,
    diagram, 235, map, 232-33
  Current flow in, 5-192
  Icebergs in, 9-336, map, 336-37
  Seeds and fruits dispersed by, 5-4-5, 7
Gulfweeds, brown algae. 3-221
Gullet, food pipe. Windpipe, relation to, with illus.,
    4-203
  See also Esophagus
Gullies, gorges excavated by rain water. 8-10-11,
    illus., 10
Gulls. with illus., 6-395-96
Gum arabic. Tungsten filaments, use of gum arabic in
    production of, 4-238
Gummed paper. 4-375
Gums. Diseases of, 5-131-32
  Newborn baby, illus., 10-164
Guncotton. 8-276, 278
  Discovery and use of, in dynamite, 5-81-82
  Manufacture of, 8-282-84
Gunpowder.
  Formula of, developed by Roger Bacon, 2-307
  Invention and early use, 8-275, 276
Guntersville, Lake, Alabama. illus., 6-11, 13
Guppies, tropical fish, 8-115, illus., 116
  Reproduction, 4-104
Guppy, H. B. Theory of coral-reef formation, 4-138
Gutenberg, Beno, geophysicist. Calculation of thick-
    ness of earth's mantle, 4-171
Gutenberg, Johann, German inventor of printing from
    movable type, 1-197; with illus., 2-313-14
Gutenberg Bible, first book printed from movable type.
    1-197
Guyots, oceanic peaks. with diagram, 6-75
Gymnastics. See Exercise
Gymnosperms, seed plants. with illus., 3-399-403
  *Germination, 5-61-67
  Classification of, 1-302

Gymnosperms (continued)
  Seeds and seed dispersal, 5-1, illus., 3
  See also Seed plants
Gymnuras, animals. 7-99-100
Gypsum, mineral. 5-250, illus., 249; illus., 9-304
  Cave deposits of, 5-56, illus., 58c
  Deposits laid down in arid climate, 3-178
  Plaster contains, 7-121
  Soil fertilizer, used as, 2-169
Gypsy moths. Larvae, 3-197
Gyratory crushers, in ore dressing. with diagram, 1-372
Gyrfalcons. with illus., 6-159
Gyri, of cerebral cortex. 6-324
Gyro-artificial horizon. 6-193
Gyropilots, course setters. Ships, 4-117
Gyroscopes. Airplanes, 6-193
  Invention of, 6-242
  Perfect (theoretically), at low temperatures, 5-210
  Space vehicles and missiles guided by, 8-129-30,
    diagram, 130

H

Haagen-Smit, A. J., Dutch-American biologist.
  Artificial production of typical smog, 3-356
Haber, Fritz, German chemist. 9-211-12
  See also Haber process
Haber process, for ammonia production. 3-127, illus.,
    128-29; with diagram, 2-230-31; 9-211-12
Habit-forming drugs. *Narcotics, 5-400-07
Habitats. 10-135-42
Habits.
  Sleep considered a habit, 6-149
  Smoking as habit, 5-346
Hackberry trees. with illus., 5-145
Haddock. 4-320
Hadley, John, English mathematician. Reflecting tele-
    scope made by, illus., 9-153
Haeckel, Ernst Heinrich, German biologist. 8-262,
    illus., 260
Hafnium (Hf), chemical element. Atomic number, 72;
  atomic weight, 178.49; melting point, 1,700° C.; boiling
  point, above 3,200° C.; specific gravity, 13.3. Metal;
  resembles zirconium in chemical properties and com-
  pounds. Discovered by Coster and von Hevesey in
  1923; name derived from Hafnia, the neo-Latin name
  for Copenhagen. Found in all zirconium minerals; separated by repeated recrystallization of the double ammonium or potassium fluorides, or prepared by passing
  tetraiodide vapor over a heated tungsten filament.
Hagfishes, fishes. 4-94; 8-364
Hahn, Otto, German physical chemist. 9-330
Hailstones. with illus., 2-356-57
Hailstorms. 2-357
Hair.
  Heat, insulating properties of hair and fur, 4-11
  Man, *2-178-80
    Care of, with illus., 10-82-83
    Removal of unwanted, 10-84
    Respiration, function of hair and cilia in, 4-201,
      203, 204
    Sebaceous glands of, 5-11
  Seed and fruit tufts, 5-4, illus., 2-3
Hair hygrometers, humidity gauges. 1-250-51, illus.,
    248
Hair seals. 7-86
Hairy woodpeckers. 6-211
Hale, George Ellery, American astronomer (1868–1938).
  He organized and directed the Yerkes and Mount Wil-
  son observatories and was professor of astrophysics at
  Chicago University. With his invention, the spectro-

Hale, George Ellery (continued)
heliograph, he analyzed the sun's atmosphere by photographing its layers. He made lasting contributions to solar and stellar spectroscopy and discovered the magnetic fields in sunspots.
>Mount Wilson 100-inch reflecting telescope erected by, 8-64
>Tower telescope, development of, 3-103

Hale, William J., American chemist. 9-292
Halemaumau, fire pit of the volcano Kilauea. 7-345, illus., 344; illus., 8-300c
Hales, Stephen, English clergyman and physiologist.
>Plant physiology, with illus., 3-379
>Pneumatic trough, with illus., 4-353

Half life, of radioactive isotopes.
>Definition, 4-215; 9-43, 352
>Fluorine 17, 9-352
>Idea introduced by Rutherford, 8-416
>Radioactive carbon, 10-94
>Radioactive thallium-204, 9-43
>Radioactivity, definition, 9-127
>Radioisotopes used in medicine, 10-98
>Strontium 90, 9-43, 352

"Half-moons" (lunulae) of fingernails. with illus., 2-181
Halftone screens, in printing. with illus., 1-204
Halftones, photoengraved pictures in printing. with illus., 1-204-06
Halibuts. 4-292
Halides.
>Minerals in the form of, with illus., 5-250; 9-306

Hall, Asaph, American astronomer.
>Satellites of Mars, discovery of, 4-417
>Saturn, observation of rotation period of, 5-108

Hall, Charles Martin, American chemist and manufacturer. 6-385
Hall, G. Stanley, American psychologist. 9-49
Hall, H. T., American physical chemist. 4-275, 276
Hall, Sir James, Scottish geologist and chemist. 4-397
Hall, Thomas S., American inventor. 6-379-80
Hall-Héroult process, for extracting aluminum. 3-40; 6-385
Haller, Albrecht von, Swiss physician. Work in physiology, 3-379-80
Halley, Edmund, English astronomer.
>Cometary motion studied by, 5-394
>Newton and, 3-279
>Scientific contributions, 3-282
>Star motions, studies of, 7-223
>See also **Halley's comet**

Halley's comet. 5-392-94, 397-98, illus., 390, 394, 399
Hallucinations. 6-145
Hallucinosis, acute alcoholic, condition resulting from withdrawal of alcohol. 4-412
Halobates, genus of true bugs. 3-262
Halogens. Name applied to five nonmetallic elements—fluorine, chlorine, bromine, iodine and astatine—making up Group VII-VIIb of the periodic table. The halogens are the most active nonmetals. They react readily with metals to form salts; that accounts for the name "halogens," from two Greek words meaning "salt-producers." See also 3-320; also **Astatine; Bromine; Chlorine; Fluorine; Iodine.**
Halos, atmospheric phenomena. 7-279
Halteres, reduced hind wings of flies. 2-404; 3-283
Hamitic local race. 8-218
Hammer (malleus), bone of ear. with illus., 4-380; 7-299, illus., 298
Hammerhead sharks. 4-290, illus., 289
Hammering, tooling operation. with illus., 10-107-08

Hammers.
>Claw hammer as example of lever, with illus., 7-215-16
>Pneumatic hammers, 9-66
>Sledge hammer used in collecting minerals, with illus., 9-302

Hammers, drop, machine tools. with illus., 10-107-08
Hammon, William McD., American medical researcher. Poliomyelitis, work with, 10-130-31
Hammond, E. Cuyler, American statistician. Lung cancer, investigation of, 5-348-49
Hammond organs. 5-220, illus., 219
Hammurabi, Code of. with illus., 1-128
Hampshire, breed of sheep. illus., 10-247
Hampton, Virginia. Unloading oysters at, illus., 6-17
Hams. Preparation of, 5-167
Hamsters. 8-164
Hanaman, Franz. Tungsten electric-light filament, 4-238
Hand cameras. 9-403, 405-06, illus., 404-05, 406
Hand lenses. Nature study, use in, 10-263
Hand-setting, of printing type. with illus., 1-199-200
Handmade products. Design of, 10-118
Hands.
>Bones of, illus., 1-148b; with illus., 81, illus., 74, 80
>Care of, with illus., 10-81
>Muscles and tendons of, 3-210-11, illus., 208
>Skin and nails of, 2-175, 180-81, illus., 176, 181
>X-ray photograph, illus., 7-144

Hanford, Washington. Nuclear-energy production center, with illus., 9-137-39
Hanging valleys, land forms due to glacial erosion. 9-170, diagram, 164-65
Hankel, Wilhelm Gottlieb, German physicist. Piezo-electricity named by, 2-293
Hannay, J. B., Scottish researcher. 4-274
Hansen, Armauer Gerhard Henrik, Norwegian physician. 7-382
"Happy pills," mild tranquilizers. 5-379
Harbor seals. illus., 7-93
Harbors. *Buoys, 5-68-71
Hard coal, anthracite. 1-408
Hard palate, in skull. 3-79
Hard rubber. Uses of, 6-356
Hard-shelled clams. 2-198-99
Hard-shelled crabs. 2-240
Hard water.
>Experiments with, with illus., 8-5-6
>Treatment of, 2-280-82

Hard X rays. 7-145
Hardboards. 7-125
Hardening of the arteries. 5-14
>Brain, 9-201

Hardening processes.
>Plastics, with diagram, 8-223
>Steel, 1-353

Hardie Sprayers. illus., 9-186
Hardness. 5-376
>Minerals identified by, with illus., 5-253-54
>Plastics, heat affects hardness of, with diagram, 8-222-23

Hardness test. Minerals, 9-303, 305
Hardwoods.
>*United States, 5-257-66
>See also **Forests; Timber; Wood**

Harelip, abnormal condition of upper lip. 8-29
Hares. 8-170
>Fur, 7-238
>Varieties of, with illus., 5-263
>Varying hares (snowshoe rabbits), 5-413, illus., 412

Hargreaves, James, English inventor. with illus., 4-36-37

Harlequin bugs (calico bugs). *with illus.,* **3-257**
Harmattan, a dust-laden wind. **2-94**
Harmonic telegraph. Alexander Graham Bell, **2-386-87**
Harmony. Elements of, *with table,* **5-213-15**
    Interior decoration uses, *with illus.,* **4-271-72**
Harnessed antelopes. 8-382-83
Harp seals. 7-91
    Migration of, **9-423**
Harris hawks. 6-156
Harrows, farm machines. *illus.,* **2-168**
Hartebeests, antelopes. **8-386**
Harvard Geological Laboratory. 4-275
Harvard Observatory. 5-395-96
Harvestmen (daddy longlegs). **2-268,** *illus.,* **258**
Harvey, William, English physician. *with illus.,* **3-10-13**
Hashish, stimulant narcotic. **4-180-81; 5-402**
Hastelloy-C, alloy. Radioisotope-fueled thermoelectric generators, use in, **6-174**
Hatchet fish, luminous fish. *illus.,* **2-190**
Haustoria, adventitious roots. **8-366, 368**
Hawaiian Islands.
    Lava cave at Hawaii, *illus.,* **5-57**
    Submarine ridges form, **6-74**
    Volcanic islands, *with illus.,* **4-134**
    Volcanoes of, *with illus.,* **7-344-45**
Hawk cuckoos. 6-306
Hawk moths. 3-200
Hawk owls. 6-165
Hawks. *with illus.,* **6-156-61**
    Adaptations for obtaining food, **3-237,** *illus.,* **239**
    Cooper's hawk trained for hunting, *illus.,* **6-343**
    Courtship behavior of, *with illus.,* **5-418a**
    Marsh hawks, *with illus.,* **5-418b**
    Pets, **7-23**
    Swainson's hawk on nest, *illus.,* **10-258**
Haws. See **Hawthorns.**
Hawthorn trees. 5-149, *illus.,* **148**
Hawthorns (haws). Fruits, *illus.,* **5-7, 141**
Hay. Weed damage, **7-111**
Hay fever. Allergy as cause of, **4-257**
    Hyposensitization as weapon against, **4-264**
    Symptoms of, **4-261**
Hayden Planetarium, New York. **2-398,** *illus.,* **399-400**
Hazes. See **Smoke**
Head.
    Blood vessels of, *illus.,* **1-148f**
    Development in unborn human young, **8-29-30**
    Human skull, *illus.,* **1-148b;** *illus.,* **3-74-75, 77**
    Insect heads, **2-402-03, 406,** *illus.,* **403, 404**
    Muscles of, *illus.,* **1-148c;** *with illus.,* **3-209-10,** *illus.,* **204**
    See also **Ears; Eyes; Mouth; Nose;** etc.
Head boxes in Fourdrinier paper machines. *illus.,* **4-374b**
Heads, flower clusters. *with illus.,* **4-123-24**
Heads, pressure. **2-285**
Healing. Natural, **7-351-53**
Health.
    *Accident prevention at home, **7-190-98**
    *Aging problems, **8-78-83**
    *Air pollution, **3-349-56**
    *Allergies, **4-257-64**
    *Atomic medicines, **10-98-101**
    *Body defenses, **7-346-53**
    *Diet, regulation of, **5-267-75**
    *Exercise, **10-85-91**
    *First aid, **10-5-17**
    *Food elements, **4-51-61**
    *Food preservation, **4-153-68; 10-114-16**
    *Heating and ventilation, **2-244-57**
    *Introduction, **1-67-72**

Health *(continued)*
    *Keeping fit, **10-75-84**
    *Medicine, progress in, **10-127-34**
    *Microorganisms, dangerous, **8-360-68**
    *Mosquito as vector of malaria and yellow fever, **10-30-39**
    *Narcotics, **5-400-07**
    *Nursing patients at home, **10-55-67**
    *Parasites, **8-360-68**
    *Pasteur's contribution to bacteriology, **9-71-80**
    *Penicillin and streptomycin, **7-52-54**
    *Psychiatry, **9-197-205**
    *Smoking, effects of, **5-343-50**
    *Sleep, **6-143-51**
    *Teeth, **5-129-37**
    *Tobacco problem, **5-343-50**
    *Tranquilizers. **5-377-79**
    *Tuberculosis. **9-175-84**
    *Viruses, **3-451-58**
    *Vitamins, **5-38-49**
    *Waste disposal, **5-326-36**
    *Water supply, **2-270-86**
    Electroencephalograph and electrocardiograph to diagnose diseases, *with illus.,* **2-426-28**
    Laboratory animals, use of, *illus.,* **8-169**
    Noise, effects on health, **8-43**
    Parasitic-worm infestations, **2-154-59**
    Sounds affect, **8-43**
    Twentieth-century developments in public-health movement, *with illus.,* **9-36-42**
    Zoo animals, care of, **10-157-58**
    See also **Air; Body; Breathing; Digestion; Diseases; Food; Medicine**
Health, public. See **Public health**
"Healthy carriers." 9-40
"Heard sound." 5-115
Hearing. *7-298-301**
    *Sound waves and sound, **5-114-28**
    *Vertebrates' hearing, **4-379-85**
    Amphibians, *with illus.,* **1-282**
    Ants may possess sense of, **3-360**
    Bats', **10-140**
    Fishes, **4-102**
    Insects, **2-402, 406**
    Mechanism of, *with illus.,* **1-282**
    Musical sounds, **5-211-20**
    Sense of, in birds, **5-422**
    Sound waves, audible, **8-104-05**
    Sounds of different pitches and intensities, response to, *chart,* **8-40**
    Tests for, *with illus.,* **10-80**
    See also **Deafness; Ears**
Hearing aids. *with illus.,* **5-125**
Heart. *illus.,* **1-148f; 3-381, 382-83, 386, 387,** *diagrams,* **381-84, 386**
    Action of, discovery of, *with illus.,* **3-10-12**
    Aging, effects on, **8-80-81**
    Baby, human, development in, **8-95-96**
    Development in unborn human young, **8-26**
    Disorders of, *with diagram,* **3-390-91**
    Electrical impulses accompanying heart beat, **2-428,** *illus.,* **426**
    Evolution in chordates, *with illus.,* **1-277-79**
    Evolution of, *with illus.,* **7-3**
    Muscle of, **3-204;** *illus.,* **9-93**
    Muscle structure, *with illus.,* **1-145**
Heart attack. First aid for, **10-14**
Heart disease. 3-390-91
    Race, relation to, **8-220**
    Smoking may contribute to, **5-345**
    See also **Heart attack**

Heart failure. 3-390

Heart worms. 2-159

Heartbeat. *with diagram,* 3-386-87
  Pulse reading, *with illus.,* 10-58

Heartwood, inner wood of trees. *with illus.,* 4-70

Heat. *3-407-18
  *Engines, heat, 4-80-92
  *Experiments with, 4-17-24
  *Heating and ventilation, 2-244-57
  *Thermoluminescence, dating by, 6-375-76
  *Transmission of heat, 4-9-16
  Air circulation affected by land and sea temperatures, *with diagrams,* 1-241-44; 2-90-91
  Atom-bomb flash, 9-351
  Balloons inflated by heated air, 6-177, *illus.,* 176
  Birds, regulation of body temperature, 5-419, 421
  Chemical reactions influenced by, 2-227, 228, 229, 230, 231, *diagram,* 226; 7-264
  Clouds conserve, in atmosphere, 2-218
  Earth's heat moderated by atmosphere, 1-232, 237, 238
  Food preservation by, 4-154-58
  Friction changes mechanical energy into heat, *with illus.,* 7-219
  Glass that helps keep out solar heat, 8-392
  High-frequency sound gives rise to, 8-108, *illus.,* 105, 107
  Infrared rays, 7-200-01, 205-06, *diagram,* 200
  Light developed from, 2-187
  Light given off by hot substances, 8-117
  Light transformed into, 7-250
  Molecular motion and, 1-163-66, 170-72, *with diagrams,* 167-69
  Mountain building, earth's internal heat in, 10-216, 218-20, 223
  Muscular energy and body heat, 3-207-08
  Nineteenth-century developments in theory of, 6-248-54
  Oxidation process, emits, 8-273
  Plastics, effect of heat on, *with diagrams,* 8-222-23, 230-33
  Radiant energy, heat as form of, *with illus.,* 1-83; 7-250
  Radiation caused by nuclear blast, 9-393
  Radio waves compared to heat rays, 3-85
  Regulation in body during muscular exercise, 10-87-88, 90
  Sound energy transformed into, 5-122
  Space travel and, 10-52
  Sun's heat, 3-107
  Treatments using, *with illus.,* 10-66-67
  See also **Boilers; Energy; Engines; Oil; Steam; Temperature**

Heat, sense of. *with illus.,* 7-304-05

Heat absorption. *with illus.,* 3-413-14

Heat energy.
  Bacterial respiration releases, 3-66
  Conversion to electrical energy, *with illus.,* 9-229-33
  Transformations of, 6-247, *illus.,* 248-49

Heat engines. *4-80-92

Heat equator. 6-34

Heat exchangers.
  Atomic-powered submarines, 5-36
  Hot-water heating systems 2-249

Heat exhaustion. First aid for, 10-13

Heat hazes. See **Blue heat hazes**

Heat lamps. Infrared rays used in, 7-206

Heat lightning. Explanation of, 1-399-400

Heat of combustion. *with illus.,* 3-414

Heat of fusion. 3-416-17

Heat of vaporization. 3-418

Heat pumps. *with illus.,* 2-251

Heat-resistant glasses. 3-315

Heat, specific, heat unit. 3-413-14

Heat treatment. Steel, 1-352-53

Heath hens. 6-337, *illus.,* 335

Heating. *2-244-53
  *Transmission of heat, 4-9-16
  Coal heating, 1-416
  Electric heating, 9-239
  Gas-heating systems, automatic, 5-106
  Mechanical engineering and, 1-224
  Oil for heating, distribution of, 4-152
  Precautions, 7-190-91, 192-93, 197
  See also **Boiling points; Distillation; Energy; Fuels; Temperature; Thermometers**

Heating equipment. Home laboratory, *with illus.,* 4-223-24

Heatstroke. First aid for, 10-13

Heavens. See **Astronomy; Aurora borealis; Comets; Mars; Milky Way; Neptune; Sky; Solar system; Stars; Sun; Universe; Venus; etc.**

Heavier-than-air-flight. *with illus.,* 6-181-200

Heavy hydrogen. See **Deuterium; Tritium**

Heavy water. Water consisting of molecules in which an atom of oxygen is combined with two atoms of heavy hydrogen. The ordinary water molecule contains one atom of oxygen associated with two atoms of hydrogen of normal weight. Heavy hydrogen, or deuterium, has two times the atomic weight of common hydrogen. This is because it carries a neutron, or neutral particle, in its atomic nucleus, in addition to the proton, or positive unit of electrical charge, which is found in the nucleus of ordinary hydrogen. Although the chemical properties of normal and heavy water are generally alike, their physical characteristics differ appreciably. Among other things, heavy water is denser and freezes and boils at higher temperatures. It is used as a moderator in atomic reactors. See also **Deuterium; Hydrogen; Nuclear reactors; Water**
  Heavy-water reactor, *illus.,* 1-94

Hebrews.
  Number system of, *with illus.,* 1-152
  Science in Biblical times, 1-128

Hecataeus of Miletus, Greek explorer. 1-131, *illus.,* 130

Hedgehogs. *with illus.,* 7-99-100

Heel bones. *with illus.,* 3-83, *illus.,* 75, 212, 213

Heezen, Bruce C., American geologist. 5-189

Heezen theory of earth expansion. 5-189

Hefner, Lake, in Oklahoma. Evaporation in, 2-273

Height. Index of health in children, 10-76-77

Height-weight tables. 10-76-77

Heinkel 178, German jet plane. Jet-powered flight, first successful one made by, 7-68

Heisenberg, Werner, German physicist. *with illus.,* 9-284

Heliacal rising, in astronomy. 1-126

Helicopters. 6-193-94, *illus.,* 182, 193
  Development of, *with illus.,* 9-919-20
  Uses of, *illus.,* 6-19; 10-163
    Fishermen, *illus.,* 6-19
    News photographers, *illus.,* 10-63

Helictites, calcium-carbonate deposits in caves. *with illus.,* 5-55, *illus.,* 58c

Heliocentric theory, of Copernicus. *with illus.,* 2-372-73

Heliocentric velocity, orbital speed around sun. Meteorites, 6-97-98

Heliographic technique. Early photography, 9-399

Heliozoans, fresh-water protozoans. 2-65, *illus.,* 63

Helium (He), chemical element. Atomic number, 2; atomic weight, 4.0026; melting point, below —272.2° C.; boiling point, —268.9° C.; specific gravity (air = 1), 0.13804. Inert gas; second lightest gas. Existence first shown during eclipse of 1868 with detection of new line on solar spectrum; first isolated in 1895. Name derived from Greek *helios*: "the sun." Widely distributed in nature, though usually in very small amounts; obtained commercially by compression and fractionation of the gas from natural gas wells and from many radioactive minerals. Used for inflating balloons, because it will not burn. A mixture of helium and oxygen serves as an artificial atmosphere for divers and others because it will not cause caisson disease. Helium is also used in treating certain respiratory diseases.
  Atomic structure, 1-311, *diagram*, 312
  Balloons filled with, 3-319
  Discovery of, 1-20; 5-86, 207; 6-391
  Electron arrangement, *illus.*, 3-247
  Fusion of hydrogen, formed by, 3-318
  Interstellar space contains, 9-362
  Lighter-than-air craft inflated with, 6-180-81
  Liquefaction of, *with illus.*, 5-207, 208-09
  Nucleus of, as a primary cosmic-ray particle, 8-397
  Sources of, 5-207-08
  Sun, helium found in, 3-109; 9-140
  Superfluid, *with illus.*, 5-208-09, *illus.*, 207
Hell Gate Bridge, New York City. 2-337
Hellbenders, salamanders. 5-156, 161
  Pets, 7-26
Hellebores. Flowers and leaves of, *illus.*, 7-77
Helmet quail, birds. 6-333-34
Helmholtz, Hermann von, German physicist, anatomist and physiologist. 6-252-53, *illus.*, 251
  Color-vision theory, *with diagram*, 7-288-89, *illus.*, 287; 8-179
  Psychology, development of, 9-48
  Solar energy, theory of source of, 3-109; 9-140
Helmont, Jan Baptista van, Belgian scientist. 3-270
Helodermatids (Helodermatidae), beaded lizards. 5-200
Helsingfors 956, star. Radial velocity of, 7-226
Hematin, dye that gives red blood cells their color. 5-13-14
Hematite, iron-ore mineral. 1-340; 5-254
Hematocrits, tubes for measuring red-cell content of blood. 3-327-28
Hematology, scientific study of blood. *3-325-34, 381-92
Heme, pigment in hemoglobin. 3-326
Hemelytra, forewings of true bugs. 3-253
Hemichordates, class of chordates. *with illus.*, 4-2-3
Hemigales. 8-246-47
Hemipseudospheres. Distances on, 4-440-41, *diagram*, 439
Hemiptera, insects. *3-252-64; 2-413
Hemispheres. Distances on, 4-440-41, *diagram*, 439
Hemlock trees. *with illus.*, 5-142
Hemocyanin, respiratory pigment. 3-37
Hemoglobin, respiratory pigment. 3-40, 326-28, 330-31; 4-206
  See also **Blood**
Hemolytic anemias, anemias due to red-blood-cell destruction. 3-330
Hemophilia, disease due to failure of blood to clot. 3-332; 5-14
  Inheritance of, 8-342
Hemorrhage. See **Bleeding**
Hemp.
  Marijuana obtained from, 5-402, *illus.*, 400

Hemp *(continued)*
  Naturalization of, 5-6
  Plant and fiber, 4-180-81, *illus.*, 177, 181
Henderson, Thomas, Scottish astronomer. 6-390
Henequen. Plant and fiber, 4-182
Henry, Joseph, American physicist. *with illus.*, 5-237, 240
  Electromagnetism, contributions to, 2-379
Henry the Navigator, Prince, Portuguese explorer. 2-364
Henson, William S. Steam-powered monoplane, *with illus.*, 6-182
Heparin, blood anticoagulant. 3-328
Hepatic tanagers, birds. 6-108
Heptane. 7-269
Heraclitus of Ephesus, Greek philosopher. 1-131
Herbaceous stems. 4-66, 70-71, *illus.*, 70
Herbals, medieval books on plants. 2-309
Herbivores, plant-eating animals. 10-184
  Fruits and seeds scattered by, 5-5-6, *illus.*, 7
Herculaneum. Destruction by eruption of Vesuvius, 7-335-37; 8-303
Hercules, constellation. 1-333
  Globular cluster, *illus.*, 9-161
  Solar system moving toward, 7-227-28
Hercules beetles. 3-346, *illus.*, 345
Heredity.
  *Human heredity, 8-333-47
  Allergy, role in, 4-258
  Hemophilia, factor in, 3-332
  Human heredity, basis of, *with illus.*, 8-91-92
  Molecular basis of, *with diagrams*, 9-383-86
  Neurospora, bread mold, used in study of, 3-28
  Rediscovery of "lost" paper of Mendel, 8-405-06
  Role of cancer in, 8-269
  See also **Evolution; Genes; Hybrids; Races; Society; Weismann, August**
Herget, Paul, American astronomer. 9-150
Hermaphrodites, individuals in whom male and female characteristics are blended. 8-28-29
Hermes, asteroid. 4-422; 6-92
Hermes Trismegistus, supposed father of alchemy. 2-311
Hermit crabs. *with illus.*, 2-241
Hermit thrushes. 6-30
Hero of Alexandria, Greek mathematician, physicist and inventor. *with illus.*, 1-359-60
  Aeolipile of, 1-359; *with illus.*, 4-80
  Steam turbine, early experiments with, *with illus.*, 5-305
Herodotus, Greek historian.
  Breadmaking in Egypt described by, 9-294
  Eclipse of 585 B.C., predicted by, 3-134
  Petroleum described by, 4-140
Heroin. 5-404-05, *illus.*, 400, 406
Herons. 6-397, *illus.*, 398
  Adaptation for obtaining food, 3-236, *illus.*, 237
Héroult, Paul-Louis-Toussaint, French metallurgist. 6-385
Herrings. 4-313
  Catches of, 6-22
  Migration of, 9-427
Herschel, Caroline, English astronomer. 4-399; 9-154
Herschel, Sir John F. W., English astronomer (1792—1871). Sir John re-examined the double stars that his father, Sir William Herschel, discovered and added many more to this list. Leading a private expedition to the Cape of Good Hope, he made the first exhaustive survey of the southern sky. He carried on researches of the Milky Way, stellar color and brightness, variable stars, nebulae and Magellanic Clouds. Among

Herschel, Sir John F. W. (continued)
his contributions to photography was the discovery of
the solvent action of sodium hyposulfite on silver salts.
  Nebulae and star clusters catalogued by, 8-49
  Photographs of stars, 1-24
  Photography terms coined by, 9-401
  Solar system, quotation concerning scale of, 5-20
Herschel, Sir William, English astronomer. with illus.,
    4-398-99; 9-154, 159-60
  Classification of stars in order of brightness, 6-389
  Heat (infrared) rays, discovery of, 7-200
  Nebulae and star clusters classified by, 8-49
  Saturn, discovery of rotation period of, 5-108
  "Star gauging," devised by, 8-154
  Sun's course in heavens studied by, 7-227
  Uranus, discovery of, 5-289, illus., 290-91
Hertz, Heinrich Rudolph, German physicist. with
    illus., 6-243-45
  Electromagnetic waves, work with, 7-202
Hertzian waves. 6-245; 7-202, diagram, 200
  See also **Marconi, Guglielmo; Radio waves**
Hesperornis, extinct bird. 1-394; 5-416
Hess, Victor F., Austrian physicist. Cosmic-ray investi-
    gations, 8-393
Hessian flies. with illus., 3-289
Heterogeneous mixtures. 1-82
Heteroptera, suborder of insects. 3-252
Heteroteuthis, squid genus. 2-191
Heterotrophic organisms, obtaining nourishment from
    organic matter.
  Bacteria that are heterotrophic, 3-65
Hevea brasiliensis, rubber tree. with illus., 6-352
Hevelius, Johann, German astronomer. 3-15
Hewitt, Abram Stevens, American industrialist and
    political leader. 6-384
Hexagonal system. External crystal structure, 5-342,
    diagram, 341
Hexane. 7-269
Hey, J. S., British physicist. 9-208, 209
Hibernation. 5-410-12; 6-149-50
  Amphibians, 5-162
  Insects, 3-358, 365
  Poorwills, 6-216; 8-385
  True bugs, 3-254
Hibiscuses. Pollination by bumblebee, 8-frontispiece
Hickory trees. 5-146, illus., 147
  Nuts, illus., 5-141
Hidalgo, asteroid. 4-422
Hides.
  Building material, use as, 7-115
  Leather manufacture, used in, with illus., 7-231-35
  Leatherbacked turtles', 5-388
Hieratic number system, of ancient Egypt. 1-152
Hieroglyphics, ancient Egyptian writing system. illus.,
    1-116
  Development in ancient Egypt, 1-125, illus., 127
  Numbers expressed in, 1-150, 152, illus., 151
Hierophilus of Chalcedon, Greek physician and anat-
    omist.
  Anatomical dissection, work in, 1-366
High-analysis fertilizers. 2-171
High-fidelity phonographs. 7-369
High-pressure chambers. Shock-tube chambers, with
    diagram, 10-234
High-Speed-Fax, facsimile machine. 7-392
High-speed photography. illus., 9-397, 412
Higher geometry. 4-431-32
Higher mathematics. *4-423-42
Higher physics. Twentieth-century developments in,
    with illus., 9-279-85

Highs, atmospheric high-pressure areas. with diagrams,
    1-242-44, illus., 250
Highways. See Roads
Hill, A. B., English physician. Lung cancer, investiga-
    tion of, 5-349-50
Hill, Archibald V., English physiologist. Measurements
    of breathing and recovery time in athletes,
    10-88, 91
Hillary, Sir Edmund, English explorer. 9-221
  Everest scaled by, 4-209, illus., 208
Hilo, Hawaii. Bridge, illus., 9-109
Himalayan black bears. 7-315
Himalayas. 10-22-23
  Gravitational attraction of, 7-32
  History of, 10-222
  Pamir plateau, illus., 6-115
  Plateaus of, 6-109
  Rainfall of, 2-347
Hindbrain. 6-323-24
  Nicotine's effects on, 5-345
  See also **Brain; Cerebellum; Medulla oblongata**
Hindenburg, dirigible. 6-180
Hindgut, pouch formed in early stage of digestive-
    system development. 8-27
Hindu-Arabic numerals. See Arabic numerals
Hindu Kush Mountains, Central Asia. 10-222
Hindu local race. 8-218
Hindus.
  Mathematics, contributions to, 2-298
Hip. Bones of, illus., 1-148b; 3-81-82, illus., 74-75
Hipparchus of Nicaea, Greek astronomer and mathe-
    matician. 1-358
  Stars, arrangement of, according to brightness,
    6-389
  Trigonometry developed by, 3-449
Hippocrates, Greek physician. 1-363-65
  Epilepsy, nature of, 9-102
  Quotation from, concerning obesity, 5-268
Hippocratic oath. 1-363
Hippopotamuses. 7-412, 414, illus., 415, 416
Hiroshima, Japan.
  Blasted by atomic bomb, 9-351-52, illus., 328
Hirudin, blood anticoagulant. 2-162
Histology, study of body tissues.
  *Bones, 3-73-84
  *Skin, hair and nails, 2-173-81
  Human body, tissues of, with illus., 1-144-45, 147
  Muscles, with illus., 3-203-05
  See also **Blood; Brain; Cells; Heart; Skin; Tissues;**
    etc.
Historical geology, science dealing with earth's past
    and with prehistoric life.
  *Time scale of earth's history, 6-369-74
  See also **Earth; Evolution; Fossils; Geology; Paleon-
    tology; Stratigraphy**
History of science.
  *Antiquity (to 450) I, with illus., 1-122-38
  *Antiquity (to 450) II, with illus., 1-354-68
  *Middle Ages (450–1450), with illus., 2-295-314
  *Renaissance (1450–1600), with illus., 2-361-76
  *Science grows up (1600–1765) I, with illus., 3-1-21
  *Science grows up (1600–1765) II, with illus., 3-265-82
  *Science grows up (1600–1765) III, with illus.,
    3-373-80
  *Science in revolution (1765–1815) I, with illus.,
    4-32-41
  *Science in revolution (1765–1815) II, 4-353-63
  *Science in revolution (1765–1815) III, with illus.,
    4-386-404
  *Science and progress (1815–95) I, 5-72-86
  *Science and progress (1815–95) II, 5-231-47

History of science (continued)
*Science and progress (1815–95) III, 6-239-54
*Science and progress (1815–95) IV, 6-377-93
*Science and progress (1815–95) V, 7-27-34
*Science and progress (1815–95) VI, 7-156-61
*Science and progress (1815–95) VII, 7-370-89
*Science and progress (1815–95) VIII, 8-251-64
*Twentieth century (1895–   ) I, 8-400-20
*Twentieth century (1895–   ) II, 9-21-42
*Twentieth century (1895–   ) III, 9-47-57
*Twentieth century (1895–   ) IV, 9-96-104
*Twentieth century (1895–   ) V, 9-211-25
*Twentieth century (1895–   ) VI, 9-279-92
*Twentieth century (1895–   ) VII, 9-323-32
*Twentieth century (1895–   ) VIII, 9-375-86
*Twentieth century (1895–   ) IX, 10-191-202
*Twentieth century (1895–   ) X, 10-224-27
*Audion, development of, 8-84-89
*Medicine, progress in, 10-127-34
*Pasteur's contributions to bacteriology, 9-71-80
  Engineering, history of, with illus., 1-216-19
  Weather study and forecasting, 1-245-46
Hives, of bees. See Beehives
Hoactzins, South American birds. 10-136
Hoary bats. Migration of, 9-422
Hoba, South-West Africa.
  Meteorite found near, 6-90
Hobbs, tools. 10-110, illus., 108
Hodgkin's disease. 8-267
  Alcoholic beverages used in diagnosis of, 4-408
Hoe, Richard, American inventor and industrialist.
  with illus., 6-381
Hoff, Jacobus Hendricus van't, Dutch chemist (1852–
1911). One of the founders of physical chemistry, he
was a professor at the University of Amsterdam and
at the Prussian Academy of Science. He founded the
science of stereochemistry, dealing with the arrangement of atoms and molecules in space. He applied
thermodynamic principles to chemical reactions and
showed that gases and substances in dilute solutions
obey the same laws; for this work he won the first
Nobel award in chemistry (1901). See also 5-83.
Hofmann, August Wilhelm von, German chemist (1818–
92). Founder of the German Chemical Society, first
director of London's Royal College of Chemistry and
chemistry professor at Berlin University, he was noted
for his researches in organic chemistry. He discovered
aniline and he prepared various dyes from this chemi-
cal. He also introduced a method for finding molecular
weights of liquids by means of their vapor densities.
Hofmann, Klaus, American biochemist. 10-134
Hog-nosed snakes. 10-261
  Death feigned by, 3-240
  Pets, 7-25
Hogarth, William, English artist. Etchings showing
  conditions of insane, 9-102
Hogbacks, rock features. illus., 10-223
Hogs. See Pigs
Hohmann, Walter, German rocket expert. 10-42
Holland, Clifford M., engineer. 2-54
Holland, John P., American inventor.
  Submarine perfected by, 5-32; 9-214
Holland.
  Peat pits, illus., 6-112
  Scientific contributions
    1600–1765, 3-372-74, 276-77
    1765–1815, 4-359
    World exploration, 2-366
Holland No. 9, early submarine. 9-214
Holland Tunnel. with illus., 2-54-56

Hollanders, devices for preparing wood fibers for
  papermaking. with illus., 4-368-69
  Development of, 4-365
Hollerith, Herman, United States Census Bureau official.
  Punched-card tabulating system developed by, 9-144
Hollow-toothed deer, large subfamily of deer. 8-241
Holly trees. with illus., 5-149
Holmes, Oliver Wendell, American physician and
  writer. with illus., 7-374-75
Holmium (Ho), chemical element. Atomic number, 67;
atomic weight, 164.930. Rare-earth metal. The oxide
dissolves in certain acids to produce yellow or orange
salts. Discovered by Cleve in 1879; pure holmia earth,
containing holmium, isolated by Homberg in 1911.
Named after Holmia, the Latin name for Stockholm.
Found in gadolinite and similar metals. The element
has not yet been isolated.
Home. See Accident prevention; Housebuilding;
  Interior decoration
Home bakeries. 9-294, 295
Home economics. See Housebuilding; Interior decora-
  tion
Home gardens. See Terrariums
Home nursing. *10-55-67
Home projects and experiments. See Projects and
  experiments
Homing pigeons. 6-306
Homogeneous mixtures. 1-81
Homogeneous photographic surveys, of nebulae and
  star clusters. 8-49
Homogenized milk. 5-302
Homologies, similarities of structure due to descent
  from common ancestral form.
  Vertebrates, 4-385
Homologous series. Introduction of, into organic
  chemistry, 6-78
Homoptera, order or suborder of insects. 2-413; 3-252
Honey. 3-367, 370, 372
  Sugar, 4-79
Honey ants. 3-364
Honey extractors. 3-372, illus., 371
Honeybees. illus., 2-404, 405; illus., 3-366
Honeycombs, of honeybees. 3-368, with illus., 370-72
Honeydew, aphid secretion. Ants obtain, 3-361
Honors Certificates, awards to young scientists. 8-74
Hooded mergansers, birds. illus., 6-400
Hooded seals. 7-91
Hoods, for ventilation. 2-255
Hoofs. Buttons made from, 7-210, 213
Hook-and-swivel assemblies. Well drilling, use in, dia-
  gram, 4-144
Hooke, Robert, English scientist. 3-267, 271, 273,
  illus., 272
  Cell's structure first made out by, 2-1-2, illus., 2; 7-
    157
  Compound microscope of, 3-16
Hooker, Joseph Dalton, English botanist and physician.
  8-252
Hooker telescope, 100-inch reflector at Mount Wilson
  Observatory. illus., 8-65; 9-156, illus., 155
Hooke's law. 5-375
Hookworms. illus., 1-293; 2-157-58
Hoosac Tunnel, Massachusetts. 2-45-46
Hoover (Boulder) Dam, Arizona-Nevada. 8-307,
  illus., 316b
Hop hornbeam trees. with illus., 5-145
Hopkins, Sir Frederick Gowland, British nutritionist.
  Vitamin study pioneered by, 5-39
Hopper cars, freight cars. with illus., 1-190
Horizon.
  Astronomical horizon, with diagrams, 1-260-61

Horizon system, in astronomy. *with diagrams,* 1-260-61

Horizons, soil. 2-17-18, 19, 22, *illus.,* 17, 25

Horizontal undulatory movement, of snakes. *with illus.,* 5-354a

Horizontally opposed airplane engines. 6-187

Hormones.
　Cancer and, 8-268
　Cortisone and ACTH, 10-133-34, *illus.,* 132
　Ductless glands, secretions of, 5-8, 15-19
　Functions of, 5-14
　Insects controlled by means of, 9-189, 191, *illus.,* 190-91
　Psychological states, relationship to, 9-52
　Sex hormones during growth and aging, 8-98-99, 101
　See also **Auxins; Plant hormones**

Horn, Daniel, American statistician. Lung cancer, investigation of, 5-348-49

Hornaday, William T., American zoologist. Description of the bison's range, 9-268

Hornbeam trees. *with illus.,* 5-145

Hornbills. Adaptation for survival, 3-242, *illus.,* 242-43

Hornblende, mineral. 3-422

Horned larks. *with illus.,* 6-100-01, *illus.,* 106; 9-421

Horned lizards (horned toads). *with illus.,* 5-201
　Inactivity in dry season, 5-412

Horned rattlesnakes. See **Sidewinders**

Horned toads. See **Horned lizards**

Hornets. 3-366
　Bald-faced hornet and nest, *illus.,* 3-361

Horney, Karen, American psychoanalyst. 9-102

Horns. Buttons made from, 7-210

Horns, land forms due to glacial erosion. 9-169, *diagram,* 164-65

Hornworts, aquatic plants. 6-223

Horse ants. 3-365

Horse chestnut trees. *with illus.,* 5-147
　Buds, *illus.,* 5-140; 6-55
　Leaves of, *illus.,* 4-72
　Seeds, *illus.,* 5-62

Horse latitudes, wind belts. 1-244; 2-93, *diagram,* 92

Horse manure, as soil fertilizer. 2-165

Horseflies. 3-286, 287, 290

Horsepower.
　Ship horsepower, calculation of, 4-117-18
　Watt's definition of, 4-40

Horses.
　Domestication of, 10-249-50
　Evolution of, 1-396; *with diagrams,* 6-281
　Feeding, method of, 7-9
　Intelligence, *illus.,* 2-27
　Transportation, use in, 1-98, 102-03, *with illus.,* 99-100, 104-06

Horseshoe crabs. *illus.,* 1-295; 2-242
　Unchanged for millions of years, *with illus.,* 6-283

Horseshoe magnets. 7-165

Horsetails. 3-192, *illus.,* 191
　Unchanged for millions of years, *with illus.,* 6-283

Horticulture.
　*Artificial propagation of plants, 9-7-15
　*Diseases of plants, 8-369-75
　Wild flowers and plants for garden use, 10-212
　See also **Flowers; Plants; Vegetables**

Horus, Temple of. *illus.,* 1-117

Hospitals. Organization of, in the Middle Ages, *with illus.,* 2-312

Hot-air heating systems. *with illus.,* 2-246-47; 4-14

Hot (dry) manures, soil fertilizers. 2-165

Hot-metal machines, for type casting.
　Cold-type typesetters distinguished from, 1-203
　See also **Intertype machines; Linotype machines; Monotype machines**

Hot springs. 8-325-26, *illus.,* 327

Hot-water bags. Nursing use of, 10-66-67

Hot-water heating systems. *with illus.,* 2-248-49; 4-13, *illus.,* 12

Hôtel Dieu, hospital in Paris. *with illus.,* 2-312

Hothouses. Ancient, 8-388

Hottentot local race. 8-218

Hounds. 10-242

Hound's-tongues. Fruit of, *illus.,* 5-5

Hour-circles. 1-260, *diagram,* 259

Housatonic, Federal ship. Sinking by early submarine, 5-32

House cleaning.
　Vacuum cleaner, *with illus.,* 9-70

House decoration. *with illus.,* 4-269-72
　Color and color values. 4-269-71
　See also **Furniture**

House sparrows. 6-108

House wasps. Comb, *illus.,* 3-365

House wrens. 6-45, *illus.,* 44

Housebuilding.
　*Concrete construction, 3-113-25
　*Glass as construction material, 8-388-92
　*Materials, 7-115-28
　*Modern homes, 4-265-72
　*Wood substitutes, 2-105
　Insulation and heating of, 4-11-14, 16, *illus.,* 11-15

Houseflies. 3-285, 287, 292, *illus.,* 285

Household chemicals. List of, 4-228

Houtermans, F. G. Theory of stellar energy, 9-224

Howard, Luke, English scientist. Cloud classification of, 2-220

Howdahs, elephant seats. *with illus.,* 1-101

Howe, Elias, American inventor (1819–67). His work in a machine shop gave him the knowledge of machinery necessary for the invention of the sewing machine. The patent on his first model was issued in 1846. See also 6-383

Howling monkeys. *illus.,* 7-9; *with illus.,* 9-259-63
　Family groups, 7-12

Hrdlicka, Ales, American anthropologist. 9-24-25

HTST process. See **Martin aseptic canning process**

Hubble, Edwin P., American astronomer.
　Galaxies studied and classified by, 8-49, 50, 54, *diagram,* 48

Huber, François, Swiss naturalist. 8-254

Hudson, Henry, English navigator. *with illus.,* 2-366

Hudson, William Henry, English naturalist. 8-252

Hudson and Manhattan Railroad tunnel. 2-53-54

Hudson River. First tunnel under, 2-53-54

Hudson seals. Fur, 7-238

Hudson's Bay Company. 7-236

Hue, characteristic of color. 7-286

Huggins, Sir William, English astronomer (1824–1910). In his observatory in London, Sir William pioneered in spectroscopy and photography. He invented (with W. A. Miller) the stellar spectroscope; with it he showed that stellar structure was similar to that of the sun and that certain nebulae were gaseous. Sir William adapted the gelatin dry-plate negative for astronomical photographs. He determined the motion of stars by the shift of their spectral lines. See also 6-391; 8-47, 49

Huguenots, French Protestants. Silk industry and, 5-173

Hulett electric unloader. Iron-ore crane, 1-341

Hull-Rust-Mahoning iron-ore mine, Minnesota. *illus.,* 1-340-41

Hulls, ships'. 4-107, 108

Human beings. See **Man**

Human nature. *Psychology, 9-310-22

Human relations. Study of, 9-322

Human resources. Conservation of, 6-10, 12
Human skeleton. *3-73-84
Human wastes. Fertilizer, use as, 5-327, *illus.*, 328
Humanism. Origin of, in Renaissance Italy, 2-362
Humanity. See **Civilization; Man; Society**
Humason, Milton L., American astronomer.
    Galactic velocities measured by, 8-54
Humboldt, Alexander von, German naturalist, traveler
    and statesman. *with illus.*, 7-29-31
    Nebulae called island universes by, 8-47
Humboldt Current. See **Peru Current**
Humerus, bone of upper arm. *illus.*, 1-148b; 3-80, *illus.*,
    74-75, 81
Humid (wet) regions. Soils of, 2-19, 21
Humidification. 2-256
    Breadmaking proofing operations, *with diagram*, 9-
    297-98
Humidity, relative
    Control of, *with illus.*, 2-255-57
    Mammals affected by, 7-7
    Measuring and recording, 1-249-51, *with diagram*,
      320-21, *illus.*, 248, *diagram*, 316
    Nature of, 2-255
    Plant communities affected by, 10-182
    Seed dispersal affected by atmospheric moisture, 5-2
    See also **Water; Water vapor**
Hummingbird moths. 3-200, *illus.*, 201
Hummingbirds. 6-212, 214, *illus.*, 213
    Flight of, *illus.*, 5-418
    Migration of, 9-420
    Pollen carriers, *with illus.*, 7-248
    Pollination brought about by, 4-126, *illus.*, 127
Humors, body. Theory of, 1-365
Humpback whales. *illus.*, 7-185
    Migration of, 9-423-24
Humus. 2-16-17, 22, 24
    Soil effects of, *illus.*, 2-167
Hundley, Confederate submarine. 5-32
Hunger.
    Basic drive, 4-331-32
    Sensation of, 9-314
Hunsaker, Jerome C. NACA chairman, 9-219
Hunter, John, English physiologist and surgeon (1728–
93). Through his efforts surgery became a science; it
owes much to his contributions. Described as the bold-
est and best operator of his time, an anatomist of mar-
velous knowledge and one of the fathers of zoological
science, he founded London's great Hunterian Museum,
which at his death comprised nearly 14,000 specimens.
Hunting, oscillation of feedback system. 10-236
Hunting dogs, wild. 8-140, *illus.*, 139
Hurdles, primitive hauling devices. *with illus.*, 1-98
Huron, Lake. *illus.*, 7-62
Hurricanes. 2-96
    Erosive agents. unimportant as, 7-319
    Ocean waves produced by, 8-350
    Radar used to spot hurricanes, 9-390
    Storm warnings, loss of life reduced by, 1-254
Hurter, F., English photographer. 9-403-04
Hussey, Obed, American inventor. 6-383
Hutton, James, Scottish geologist. *with illus.*, 4-395-97
Huxley, Julian, English biologist and author (born 1887).
He was professor of zoology at London's King's College
and professor of physiology at the Royal Institution.
Writing on biological and cultural subjects, he popular-
ized science and showed its vast influence. In 1946 he
was elected director-general of the United Nations Edu-
cational, Scientific and Cultural Organization (UNESCO).
Huxley, Thomas Henry, English biologist (1825–95); a
famous exponent of Darwin's doctrine of evolution. One
of the outstanding scientists of the 19th century, he laid

Huxley, Thomas Henry *(continued)*
down many of the foundations of political, social and
moral reform. In 1845 he entered the medical service
of the British Navy, from which he retired in 1853. Later
he was lecturer on natural history at the Royal School
of Mines. He was elected president of the Royal Society in 1883. See also 8-252
Huygens, Christian, Dutch scientist. 3-276
    Clocks, work with, 3-19
    Ether, concept of, 6-241
    Internal-combustion engine, ideas of, 2-130; 4-86
    Saturn's rings described by, 5-110
    Temperature scales, work with, 3-18
    Wave theory of light, 6-239; 7-199
Hyacinths, flowering plants. Bulbs of, *illus.*, 4-68
Hyades, group of stars in Taurus. 1-335
Hyatt, John Wesley, American inventor. 8-223; 9-292
Hybrid corn, 9-291
Hybrid guidance systems, for space vehicles. 8-131
Hybrid onions. 9-291
Hybrids.
    Crossing, results of, 8-340-44, *diagram*, 341
    "Graft-hybrids," 9-10-12
    Polyploidy as factor in development of, 6-280
    "Purebred" individuals really hybrids, 6-273
Hydra, constellation. 1-332
Hydrants, fire. 2-286
Hydras. *illus.*, 1-292; 2-150
Hydration.
    Rocks, 2-351
    Soil formation, 2-16
Hydraulic action. Streams wear away rocks by, 8-13-14
Hydraulic brakes, for automobiles. *with illus.*, 2-143-44
Hydraulic engineering, management of water and other
    liquids in motion.
  *Canals, 4-183-95
  *Dams, 8-305-20
  *Irrigation, 8-191-201
  *Sewage disposal, 5-326-36
  *Water supply, 2-270-86
Hydraulic-fill method, for constructing earth-fill dams.
    8-312
Hydraulic giants, gold-extracting devices. 4-248
Hydraulic gradient. 2-275-76
Hydraulic lifts. *with illus.*, 2-34
    Homemade version of, *with illus.*, 7-222
Hydraulic presses. *with illus.*, 2-34-35
    Diamond synthesis requires powerful, 4-275
Hydraulic pressure.
    Airplanes, used in, 6-191
    Automobiles, used in, *with illus.*, 2-143-44
    See also **Water pressure**
Hydraulics, science dealing with water or other liquid.
    in motion. See **Liquids; Water**
Hydrocarbons.
    Air pollutants. 3-353, 354
    Aromatic, 7-274-75
    Carbohydrates distinguished from, 2-5
    "Cracking," explanation of, 7-269
    Methane series, 7-267-69
    Natural gas contains, 5-100-01
    Paraffin series, 7-267-69
    Petroleum composed of, 7-267
    Saturated, 7-267-69
    Unsaturated, 7-270
    See also specific compounds
Hydrochloric acid.
    Behavior as typical acid, 4-338-39
    Experiments and tricks with, *with diagram*, 7-176-77
    Minerals tested with, 9-305
    Preparation of, 5-325

Hydrocortisone. Allergies controlled by, 4-264
Hydroelectric power.
Dams used to generate, *illus.,* 8-316, 316d
Electricity, generation of, 9-233-34, *illus.,* 232-33
See also **Dams**
Hydrofluoric acid. Etching glass, used in, *with illus.,* 3-320-21
Hydrofoils. *4-5-8
Hydrogen (H), chemical element. Atomic number, 1; atomic weight, 1.00797; melting point, —259.14° C.; boiling point, —252.8° C.; specific gravity (air = 1), 0.06952. Lightest gas, insoluble in water, forming many compounds. First recognized as distinct substance in 1766 by Cavendish; name derived by Lavoisier from Greek *hydor:* "water," and *genes:* "forming." Combines with oxygen to form water; found in acids, bases, alcohols, petroleum and other hydrocarbons and food. Prepared by action of steam on heated carbon, by decomposition of certain hydrocarbons with heat, by electrolysis of water or by displacement from acids by certain metals. Used as reducing agent; serves in welding, hydrogenation of oils and formation of ammonia in the Haber process. (See **Haber process.**) Hydrogen bomb is based on fusion of hydrogen atoms. Two isotopes of hydrogen — deuterium, with atomic weight 2, and tritium, with atomic weight 3 — are used extensively in modern nuclear physics. See also 3-318-19
Acids contain atoms of, 4-338, 340
Ammonia synthesis, 3-127, *illus.,* 128-29
Atomic energy from, 9-133-34, 136
Balloons inflated with, 6-177, 180
Bomb, 9-141
Cellular respiration involves, 2-11-12
Discovery of, 4-354
Electrolytic preparation of, 5-92
Electron arrangement, *illus.,* 3-247
Function of, in stellar radiation, 7-51
Hydrogen gas, home preparation of, 4-348-50, *illus.,* 349, 351
Interstellar clouds of, 7-207; 9-361, 363
Isotopes, 1-312, *diagram,* 313
Jupiter's atmosphere contains, 5-21-22
Liquid hydrogen in atomic engines, 9-381-82; 10-4
Nucleus of, as a primary cosmic-ray particle, 8-397
Oxidation of, 3-317, 319
Plastics containing, *with diagram,* 8-222
Prout's theory of hydrogen atoms as building blocks of matter, 5-75
Radio waves emitted by hydrogen atoms in space, 9-210
Stellar energy based on reactions of, 6-265-66
Structure of atom, 1-311, *with diagrams,* 312, *diagram,* 313
Sun, hydrogen found in, 3-109; 9-140
Water molecules contain, 2-223-24, 225, *diagram,* 223-24
Weight as standard for other atoms, 1-308, 310
Hydrogen acceptors, metabolic agents. 2-12
Hydrogen bombs. 9-352
Fusion of atomic nuclei, basis of, 9-141, 331
Tritium obtained from lithium isotope, 3-166
See also **Nuclear bombs**
Hydrogen donors, metabolic agents. 2-12
Hydrogen fluoride. Air pollutant, 3-352-53
Hydrogen ions (protons), nuclei of hydrogen atoms.
Acids contain, 3-319; 4-338-41
Formation and effects of, 2-423-24
Soil, ion exchanges in, 2-24, 169
Hydrogenation.
Coal hydrogenated into liquid fuels and chemicals, *with illus.,* 1-418

Hydrogenation *(continued)*
Oils and petroleum, 3-319; 4-148
Hydrographic Office. See **United States Hydrographic Office**
Hydroids, coelenterates. *with illus.,* 2-149-50
Luminous, *illus.,* 2-184
Hydrologic cycle. See **Water cycle**
Hydrology. *Water supply, 2-270-86
Hydrolysis. Soil formation, 2-16
Carbohydrates, 4-78-79
Hydrometers. Accademia del Cimento, use by, *illus.,* 3-266
Hydrometrids, family of true bugs. *with illus.,* 3-262
Hydronium ions.
Acid-base reactions, 4-338-40
Acids contain, 3-319; 4-338-41
Hydrophobia.
Pasteur's work on, 7-381
See also **Rabies**
Hydrophones, devices for detection of sound transmitted through water. 5-191, *illus.,* 193
Oceanic research uses, 6-70
Hydrophytes, water plants. Adaptations of, *with illus.,* 6-223, 226
Hydroplanes. Submarine diving planes, 5-35
Hydroponics, soilless agriculture. *8-34-37
Substitute for conservation of soil?, 6-14
Hydroponicums, soilless farms. 8-35-36
Hydrosphere. 1-33; *with illus.,* 4-45-46
Hydrostatic organ. Fishes, 4-196
Hydrotropism, organic movement in response to water.
Beans, *illus.,* 1-47; *illus.,* 6-218c
Hydroxyl ions.
Definition and properties of bases, 4-338-41
Formation and effects of, 2-423-24
Hyenas. *with illus.,* 8-249-50
Hygiene.
*Exercise, 10-85-91
*Keeping fit, 10-75-84
Development in antiquity, 1-128
Sickroom, 10-56-57, 61-63, 65-66, *illus.,* 56-57, 62-63
See also **Health; Public health**
Hygrographs, humidity recorders. 1-251
Hygrometers, humidity gauges. 1-250-51, *illus.,* 248
Hygroscopes, humidity gauges. 1-250-51, *illus.,* 248
Hygroscopic mechanisms. Seed dispersal by means of, 5-2
Hygroscopic moisture, water locked in soil. 5-26
Hyla, genus of tree frogs. 5-155-56
Hymenoptera, order of insects. 2-414
*Ants, bees and wasps, 3-357-72
Hyoid, bone in mouth and neck. 3-79
Jaw support of fishes evolved from, 4-382
Hyomandibular, bone. Evolution in fish, 4-382-83
Hyperbolas, plane curves. *with illus.,* 3-439-40
Analytic geometry, equations in, 4-428, *diagram,* 429
Cometary orbits depicted as, 5-395, *illus.,* 396
Hyperbolic orbits. Meteorites, *with diagram,* 6-98
Hyperion, satellite of Saturn. 5-113
Hyperons, atomic particles. *with table,* 1-314
Hyperopia. See **Farsightedness**
Hyperplane, in four-dimensional space. 4-431
Hypersphere, sphere with more than three dimensions. 4-432
Hypersonic velocities, far exceeding the velocity of sound in air. 10-232-33, 234
Hypertension, high blood pressure. 3-392
Hyperthyroidism, thyroid-gland condition. 5-17-18
Hyphae, branching filaments of fungi. 3-22, *illus.,* 26
Hypnagogic stage of sleep. 6-144-45
Hypnosis. Sleep differs from, 6-150

Hypnotism.
Nineteenth-century development in, *with illus.,* 9-99-101
Hypnotoxin theory of sleep. 6-148
Hypo (sodium thiosulfate).
Photography, use in, 9-410
Supersaturated solution of, 4-303; *with diagram,* 7-176
Hypocotyls, seed parts. *with illus.,* 4-131; *with illus.,* 5-62, 66, *illus.,* 67
Hypoglossal nerves. 6-328
Hypoid gears, for automobiles. 2-141
Hypophysis (pituitary gland). 5-15, 17, *illus.,* 16-17
Hyposensitization, used against allergy. 4-264
Hypotension, low blood pressure. 3-392
Hypothalamus, part of forebrain. 5-377
Sleep, relation to, 6-148, 150
Hypotheses, scientific. Experiments and observations testing, 8-71-72
Hypothyroidism, thyroid-gland condition. 5-23
Hyracoidea, order of mammals. 7-16
Hyraxes, mammals. 7-16
Hysteria, mental illness. 9-202
Nineteenth-century studies in, *with illus.,* 9-100-01

I

I.Q. (Intelligence Quotient). 9-198
Iapetus, satellite of Saturn. 5-113
Iatrochemistry. 3-269-70
Icarus, asteroid. 4-422
ICBM (Intercontinental Ballistics Missile). 10-3, *with diagram,* 232-33
Ice.
*Glaciers, 9-162-74
*Icebergs, 9-333-39
Crystalline structure, 5-337
Dams affected by, 8-316
Dated by thermoluminescence, 5-191
Jupiter contains, 5-22
Molecular behavior of, 1-171, *with illus.,* 162-63
Physical properties of, and experiments with, *with illus.,* 8-1-2
Soils formed by, 2-16; 6-142
Water, relation to, 3-417
Water-supply problem, 2-270
Weathering effects of, *with illus.,* 6-137-38
See also **Dry ice; Eutectic ice; Glaciers; Icebergs; Reusable ice**
Ice ages. 1-396
Causes of, 3-183-85; 9-174
IGY program for study of, 5-193-94
See also **Pleistocene epoch**
Ice bags. Nursing use of, 10-67
Ice forecasting service. By U.S. Hydrographic Office, 9-336-37, 338
Ice islands. 9-338-39, *map,* 336-37
Ice peaks, in glaciers, 9-169, *illus.,* 163
Ice sheets (icecaps), continental glaciers. 5-190, 193-94; 9-163, 165-66, 170-73
See also **Continental glaciers**
Ice storms. 2-356
Effects of, *illus.,* 2-355
Icebergs. *9-333-39
Antarctic origin of, 5-190
Icebreakers.
Lenin, Russian nuclear-powered icebreaker, 4-118, *with illus.,* 114a
Icecaps. See **Ice sheets**
Iceland.
Fissure eruptions in, 8-304
Geysers of, *with illus.,* 8-290-91

Ich, fish disease. 8-116
Ichneumon flies. See **Ichneumon wasps**
Ichneumon wasps. 3-367, *illus.,* 362; 8-362
Ichneumons (Egyptian mongooses). 8-247
Ichthyology, science treating of fishes. See **Fish; Fisheries**
Ichthyornis, extinct bird. 1-394; 5-416
Ichthyosaurs, primitive marine reptiles. *with illus.,* 1-391
See also **Ichthyosaurus**
Ichthyosaurus, genus of prehistoric reptiles. *illus.,* 4-386
Ichthyostega, genus of early amphibians. 5-153; *illus.,* 6-372
Iconoscopes, television tubes. *with illus.,* 5-280-82
Icy conglomerate theory of comets. 5-393
Ideal-gas laws. *with diagram,* 1-165-66
Identical twins. *with illus.,* 8-336-37
Identities, algebraic. 2-73
Identra. See **Automatic train identification**
Ides. Roman dates, 10-173
Idlewild Airport, New York. *illus.,* 6-199
"Idols." Prejudices analyzed by Sir Francis Bacon, 3-8
Ifkakhs, desert lizards. *illus.,* 5-196
Igneous rocks. *with illus.,* 3-419-24; 9-307-08
Formation, properties and uses of, *with illus.,* 2-82-85
Mountain formation, 10-223, *illus.,* 222
Ignition systems, of engines.
Automobiles, *with illus.,* 2-137-38
Diesel, *with illus.,* 4-90-91
Gasoline, 4-89
Jets, 4-92; 10-41, *illus.,* 43
Rockets, 10-41, 45, *illus.,* 43
Ignitrons. Mercury-filled electron tubes, *with illus.,* 6-301-02
Iguanas, lizards. *with illus.,* 5-201, 203, 204, 206; *illus.,* 8-256
See also **Lizards**
Iguanids (Iguanidae), family of lizards. *with illus.,* 5-201, 203, 204, 206
IGY. See **International Geophysical Year**
Ileocaecal valve. *with illus.,* 4-329
Ileum, part of small intestine. 4-327, *illus.,* 322, 329
Iliac artery and vein, in abdomen. *illus.,* 1-148f
Iliohypogastric nerve. *illus.,* 1-148h
Ilioinguinal nerve. *illus.,* 1-148h
Ilium, bone of hip. 3-81-82, *illus.,* 74-75
Illness. See **Sickness**
Illumination. *4-232-41
*Electroluminescence, 9-344-47
Electrical engineering and, 1-223
Photography, artificial lighting in, 9-408-09, 410-11
See also **Electricity; Lamps; Lighting; Lighthouses**
Illusions, false sensory impressions. 9-315
Illustrations.
Reproduction for printing purposes, *with diagrams,* 1-204-06
Images, visual. *with illus.,* 7-295, 296
Colored images, perception of, *with diagram,* 7-288-90, *illus.,* 287
Formation of optical images, *with illus.,* 7-255-56, 257, 258, 259, 260, 261, 262
Interpretation of, in brain, 6-317
Land theory of, *with illus.,* 8-178-80
See also **Parity law**
Images, camera and film. 9-397-402, 404, 405, 406-07
Imaginary numbers (complex numbers). *with illus.,* 1-161
Imagos, adult insects. 2-407, 408, *illus.,* 409
Imhoff tanks. Sewage disposal, used for, 5-333
Imhotep, Egyptian architect-physician. *with illus.,* 1-127
Imitation. Ants learn by, 3-359

Immature (young) forms, of animals. Praying mantes, *illus.,* 8-68

Immature soils. 2-23

Immigration.
Overpopulation problem solved by, 3-233-34
Immigration to planets?, 6-12

Immiscible liquids. 4-301

Immunity. Insects acquire immunity to insecticides, 9-189

Immunity to diseases. 7-350-51
Cancer research to develop, 8-272
Gamma globulins produce, 3-326
Nineteenth-century developments in study of, 7-380-81
Vaccines and serums used to bring about immunity, 3-70

Immunization. 7-350-51
Pasteur's work in, 9-78-80

Immunology. See **Immunity to diseases; Immunization**

Impactites. 6-94
See also **Silica glasses**

Impalas, antelopes. 8-387

Impellers. Vertical turbine pumps, components of, 2-274-75

Imperfect flowers. 4-122

Imperfect fungi. 3-32

Imperial swallowtail butterflies. *illus.,* 3-202c

Imperial Valley, California. Irrigation in, *illus.,* 10-28

Implantation, implanting of product of conception in lining of uterus. 8-23

Implements. See **Tools**

Imposition, of printing material. 1-206-07

Impression cylinders, in printing presses. *with diagram,* 1-208-09

Impulse turbines. 9-234, *illus.,* 233

Impurities, metallurgical.
Removal of, *with diagrams,* 1-371-82

In-line airplane engines. 6-187

Inbreeding. 10-240

Inca doves. 6-305

Inca Lake, Chile. *illus.,* 10-27

Incandescence. Color changes of incandescent bodies at different temperatures, 8-117

Incandescent electric lamps. 4-234-35; 9-344
Homemade model of, *with illus.,* 6-291
Invention and development of, 5-246-47

Incas, South American Indians.
Irrigation systems of, 8-192

Incidence, angle of. *with illus.,* 7-251, 254, 255

Incident rays. 7-251, 253, 255, *illus.,* 254, 255

Incinerators. Waste disposal, 5-333, 335

Incisors, teeth. 5-129-30, *table,* 130, *illus.,* 132
Development of, in man. 8-95
Rodents, 3-236; 8-162

Inclination of the compass. *with diagram,* 7-168-69

Inclined orbits, inclined to earth's equator. *with diagrams,* 8-127

Inclined planes, simple machines. *with illus.,* 3-59-60

Inclinometers. Ocean-bottom analysis, by means of, *illus.,* 6-26d

Incomplete fertilizers. 2-171

Incomplete metamorphosis, of insects. 2-407-08, 412-13

Incontinence, lack of kidney or bowel control. **Nursing,** 10-63

Incubation. Silkworm eggs, 5-176

Incus. See **Anvil**

Indehiscent fruits. *with illus.,* 4-130-31

Independence, ocean liner. *illus.,* 4-116

Independent assortment, law of heredity. 8-340-41

India.
Elephants used as beasts of burden in, *illus.,* 7-413

India *(continued)*
Exploration of, in nineteenth century, 7-31-32
Fissure eruptions in, 8-304
Hydroponic-farming experiments in, 8-36
Industrial research, 1-96-97
Irrigation in ancient, 8-192
Irrigation in modern, 8-200, *illus.,* 201
Road construction in, *illus.,* 3-303
Steel, ancient Indian, 1-339

India rubber. See **Rubber**

Indian geographical race. *with illus.,* 8-216-17

Indian hemp. 4-180-81

Indian Ocean. Bottom features of, 6-74, 75

Indian rhinoceroses. 7-414, *illus.,* 415

Indian snakeroots, plants.
Reserpine, tranquilizer, derived from, 9-104

Indians, American.
Petroleum used by, 4-141
Picture writing of, *with illus.,* 1-112
Preserved food by drying, 4-165
Shelters made of hides, 7-115
Signal system, 2-377
Transportation methods on land, 1-102, *with illus.,* 99-100, *illus.,* 103
Zuñi pottery-making, *illus.,* 7-400

Indicators, acid-base (pH). 4-341-42, *table,* 339
Examples of, 4-231

Indigo. Synthesis of, 8-183-84, 186
See also **Dyes**

Indigo snakes. Pets, 7-25

Indium (In), chemical element. Atomic number, 49; atomic weight, 114.82; melting point, 156.4° C.; boiling point, about 2,000° C.; specific gravity, 7.28. Soft, silvery, malleable metal, not affected by air or water. Discovered in 1863 by Reich and Richter with aid of spectroscope; later isolated by this team. Named for its indigo blue spectrum. Found chiefly in zinc blendes, sometimes with pyrites and siderite. Obtained by electrolysis from baths of complex cyanide, chloride and sulfate. Used in electroplating to increase resistance to organic acid corrosion. Indium alloys are used for jewelry and in dentistry.

Indo-European language stock. 1-119

Indole-3-acetic acid, plant growth hormone. 3-50, 53; 5-66

Indris, lemurs. 9-265

Induced radioactivity. 9-394

Inductance coils. *with illus.,* 6-299-300

Induction. Electrical charge, 6-122-23
Electrical current, 5-236-37
Prospecting by applied electric potential, *with diagram,* 7-360-61

Induction coils. Homemade, *with illus.,* 8-149-50

Induction heating. 9-239

Inductor-couplers. 3-94

Inductors (organizers), cells or tissues that affect neighboring cells. 2-289

Indus River, India. 10-222

Industrial chemistry. See **Chemistry**

Industrial design. *10-117-26

Industrial Designers' Institute. 10-126

Industrial diamonds. 4-256

Industrial management. 1-225

Industrial psychology. 9-321

Industrial research laboratories. Types of, 10-199

Industrial Revolution. *with illus.,* 4-33, 35-41
*Design of products, 10-117-26
Automation, 10-235-38
Machine tools developed during, 10-105-06
Rubber industry stimulated by, 6-352

Industry.
  *Automation, 10-235-38
  *Breadmaking, 9-293-99
  *Buttons, 7-208-13
  *Ceramics, 7-393-407
  *Chemical industries, 7-35-44; 8-181-90, 221-33, 273-87
  *Chemurgy, 7-35-44
  *Coal industry, 1-405-20
  *Compressed air, 9-58-70
  *Construction industry, 2-43-57; 3-113-25; 4-265-72; 7-115-28; 8-305-20, 388-92
  *Conveyer belts, 6-168-71
  *Design of products, 10-117-26
  *Diamond industry, 4-251-56
  *Diamond synthesis, 4-273-76
  *Electrical industries, 4-232-41; 9-226-40
  *Electronic computers. 9-143-52
  *Electronics industries, 3-85-98; 5-276-88; 7-390-92; 9-387-90; 10-102-04, 168-70
  *Engineering, 1-215-29
  *Fisheries, 6-15-26
  *Glass, 3-307-16; 8-388-92
  *Gold mining, 4-242-50
  *Illumination, 4-232-41
  *Irrigation, 8-191-201
  *Leather and furs, 7-230-38
  *Lumbering, 2-105-17
  *Machine tools, 10-105-13
  *Meat packing, 5-163-72
  *Metallurgy, 1-369-82
  *Natural gas, 5-97-106
  *Papermaking, 4-364-78
  *Petroleum industry, 4-140-52
  *Phonographs, 7-362-69
  *Plastics, 8-221-33
  *Printing and engraving, 1-196-214
  *Prospecting for minerals, 7-354-61
  *Quarrying, 2-81-88
  *Radiation thickness gauges, 9-43-46
  *Rubber, 6-350-60
  *Salt industry, 5-313-25
  *Science and industrial progress, 1-87-97
  *Silk industry, 5-173-85
  *Steel industry, 1-338-53
  *Streamlining in, with illus., 3-407-18
  *Typewriters, 1-265-76
  *Vegetable fibers, 4-177-82
  Air pollution caused by, with illus., 3-349-56
  Airplane manufacture, 6-184-85, illus., 188
  Colloidal phenomena in, with illus., 5-302-04
  Diamonds used in, 4-256
  Disposal of wastes, 5-329
  Electronic data-processing systems, 9-152
  Employment of older persons, 8-83
  Gold used in, 4-250
  High-frequency sound used by, 8-108-09, illus., 108-10
  History
      Middle Ages, 2-313
      Industrial revolution, with illus., 4-35-41
      Nineteenth century, with illus., 5-238; 6-377-85
      World War II, with illus., 9-323-27
  Mathematics used in, 1-76
  Microfilming in, with illus., 10-71-72
  Nuclear reactors used as power sources, 9-358
  Science in industry, illus., 2-232-35
  Scientific positions in industrial research, with illus., 10-199-202
  X rays use in, with illus., 7-150
  See also **Agriculture; Communications; Construction; Economics; Labor; Mining; Natural resources; Steel; Transportation; Wastes**

Inebriation. Alcoholic beverages bring about, 4-409
Inert gases. Name applied to six elements—helium, neon, argon, krypton, xenon and radon—making up Group 0 of the periodic table. They are all gases at ordinary temperatures and are chemically inert; that is, they do not form stable compounds. They are known also as noble gases and rare gases; all are present in the atmosphere. See also 1-80; 3-247
  See also **Argon; Helium; Krypton; Neon; Radon; Xenon**
Inertia. with illus., 2-124-26
  Space flight, factor in, 8-126, 129-31
Inertial guidance, of space vehicles and missiles. 8-130, diagram, 131
Infantile paralysis. See **Poliomyelitis**
Infectious diseases.
  *Tuberculosis, 9-175-84
  Body's defenses against, 7-348-51, illus., 348, 349
  Bone, 3-84
  Luminous bacteria as cause, 2-186
  Nervous system, 6-330
  Nineteenth-century developments in control of, with illus., 7-374-89
  Nursing of patients with, 10-55-57
  White blood cells defend against, 3-328-29
  See also **Bacteria; Diseases; Fungi; Germs; Health; Malaria; Microbes; Parasites; Protozoa; Public health; Tuberculosis; Viruses; Yellow fever**
Infectious mononucleosis, disease. 3-331
Inferior ovaries, of flowers. 4-123
Inferior vena cava, great vein in abdomen. illus., 1-148f
Infiltration galleries, in wells. 2-274
Infinite series and sequences, in numbers. 4-433-34, 436-37
Inflammable liquids. Fire hazard, 7-190-91, 192, 193
Inflammation. Bodily reaction to injuries and infections, 7-348
Inflorescences, flower clusters. with illus., 4-123-24
Influenza. Virus of, 3-455, 457-58, illus., 454
Infrared rays. 7-200-01, 205-06, diagram, 200
  Atmospheric effect on, 1-237
  Atomic-bomb explosion produces, 9-351
  Paintings analyzed by use of, illus., 7-203
Ingot strippers. 1-347, illus., 348, 348b
Ingots. Steel, pouring and processing of, 1-347-48, illus., 348, 348b-c
Ingrain dyes. 8-186
Inguinal nodes, lymphatics in groin. illus., 1-148g
Inhalants, substances that cause allergic attacks when inhaled. 4-259-60
Inhalation, of air in breathing. 4-205-06, illus., 204-05
Inhalation, steam or vapor. 10-66, illus., 67
  Allergenic substances in inhalants, 4-259-60
Inheritance. See **Evolution; Genetics; Germ cells; Heredity; Natural selection; Races; Society**
Inhibition theory of sleep. 6-149
Inhibitors, chemical. Germination, role in, 5-64
Injection, in creating ultrahot plasmas. 1-177-78
Injection molding.
  Plastics, 7-210, illus., 211; with diagram, 8-230-31, illus., 220b
Injectors, fuel, of diesel engines. with illus., 4-90-91
Injuries.
  *Accident prevention at home, 7-190-98
  *First aid, 10-5-17
  Bodily reactions to, 7-348, 351-53
  Bone injuries and diseases, 3-73-76, 79, 83-84
  Muscular injuries, strains and bruises, 3-212-13
Ink-blot tests. with illus., 9-57
Ink sacs, in mollusks. 3-239-40

Inking rollers, in printing presses. 1-208, with diagrams, 209, 211-12

Inks.
Printing inks, 1-209, 211, 213-14

Inner ear. 4-382, 383, 385, with illus., 380

Innominate bone. See Hip

Inoculation.
Antipolio, illus., 7-350
Smallpox preventive, with illus., 4-401-02

Inorganic chemistry. Definition, 7-263
See also Chemistry

Inorganic insecticides. 9-187

Inorganic substances. Bacterial action makes them available to living things, 3-68
Protoplasm contains, 2-5-6, 10, 11

Inquilines, parasitic insects. 3-368

Inquisition. Banning of Copernican system, 3-3-4

Insanity. See Mental Illness

Inscribed angles. with illus., 3-436-37

Insect collecting. *3-153-56

Insecticides. with illus., 9-185-91
Mosquito pests, use against, illus., 10-36, 37

Insectivora, order of mammals. with illus., 7-13
See also Insectivores

Insectivores. *7-94-102

Insects. *2-402-14
*Ants, bees and wasps, 3-357-72
*Ants, keeping colony of, 3-393-96
*Beetles, 3-335-48
*Butterflies and moths, 3-193-202d
*Flies and mosquitoes, 3-283-92
*Fruit crop pests, 9-185-96
*Grasshoppers and kin, 3-138-52
*Insect collecting, 3-153-56
*Mosquito as transmitter of disease, 10-30-39
*Parasites, 8-360-68
*Plant pests, 9-185-95
*Pollination of plants by, 7-239-48
*Silkworms and silk, 5-173-85
*True bugs, 3-252-64
Adaptations for survival, 3-238, 239, with illus., 240
Allergic reactions to, 4-260
Birds that devour, 6-341
Chemicals used against, 10-151
Classification of, 1-295-97
Compound eyes of, 7-262
Defense methods against, survey of, with illus., 9-185-91
Disease germs transmitted by, 7-382-83
Environment adaptation to, 10-138
Field study of, with illus., 10-262-63
Flowers attract, 10-255
Fossil insects, illus., 6-372
Legs of, with illus., 1-283-84
Long-horned wood borer, illus., 9-95
Luminous, 2-183, 185
Mantes, experimental study of, 8-67-69
Migrations of, with illus., 9-430-32
Muscles of, with illus., 1-283-84
Plants that protect themselves from, 7-82
Pollination of plants by, illus., 3-405; with illus., 4-126-27
Prehistoric forms, 1-390
Presence of, determined by "sound microscopes," 8-44-45
Respiration of, 4-200, illus., 201
Seeds attacked by, 5-67
Terrarium animals, insects as, 5-366
Weed-killers, 7-114
See also Ants; Bees; Flies; Mosquitoes; Wasps; etc.

Insomnia. 6-150-51

Inspection, United States government.
Meats, 5-166, 167

Inspection galleries, in dams. 8-313, illus., 312

Installation, as function of engineers. 1-227, illus., 229

Instars, stages between moltings in insects. 3-139

Instincts.
Ants, automatic behavior of?, 3-359-60
Sleep considered an instinct, 6-149
See also Fear; Habits; Mind; Pyschology

Institute of Microbiology, Rutgers University. illus., 10-130c

Institution of Civil Engineers. 1-218

Institution of Mechanical Engineers. 1-219

Institutions of society.
Theory of origin of, 9-26

Instrument landing system, for airplanes. 6-200

Instrument panels.
Air liner, 6-192-93, illus., 190
Automobile, 2-144-45

Instruments, scientific.
Exhibiting, 8-70
Seventeenth and eighteenth centuries, developments, with illus., 3-14-19
See also Microscopes; Prospecting; Seismographs; Spectroscopes; Telescopes; etc.

Insulation. Buildings, with illus., 7-124-25
Glass construction, insulating properties of, 8-388, 391-92

Insulators, electrical nonconductors. 6-302; 9-234-35

Insulators, heat. with illus., 4-10-12
Fiber glass, 3-315-16

Insulin, a hormone. 5-13, 15, 19
Discovery of, with illus., 9-34-35
Schizophrenia, used in, 9-203

Insurance. Probabilities, calculations of, 2-80

Intaglio printing. 1-212-13, 266, with illus., 270, with diagrams, 198-99, diagrams, 211

Intake manifolds, of automobile engines. 2-135

Intake works, in dams. 2-273

Integers, in arithmetic. 1-158-60

Integral calculus, branch of mathematics. with diagrams, 4-433-35

Integration, in automation, with illus., 10-234a

Intelligence.
*Animal intelligence, 2-26-29
Aging affects, 8-82-83
Ants—do they possess intelligence? 3-359-60
Human growth and aging, role of intelligence in, 8-97-98, 100-02
Measurement of, with illus., 9-54-56
Primates, 9-263-64
Race, relation to, 8-220
See also Brain; Intellect; Mind; Psychology

"Intelligence Quotient" (I.Q.). 9-198
Developments in measurement of, with illus., 9-55

Intelligence tests. illus., 9-198, 310, 320
Development of, 9-54-56

Intensity.
Color, illus., 7-284b
Sound, 5-119, 124, 212, illus., 214

Interaction, galactic. 8-54, diagram, 53

Inter-American Highway. 3-303

Intercellular bridges. 2-174

Interchangeable type, for typewriters. 1-274

Intercontinental Ballistic Missiles. See ICBM

Intercostal nerves, nerve group. illus., 1-148h

Interference, optical phenomenon. with illus., 7-281-82

Interference of light. illus., 7-284c
Wave theory of light, demonstration of, with illus., 6-239-40

Interference of sound. 5-125-26
    Experiments with, *with illus.*, 5-228-29
Interior decoration. *with illus.*, 4-269-72
Interjectional theory. Origin of language explained
    by, 1-107
Interlingua, artificial (auxiliary) language. 1-120-21
Interlocking signal systems, for railroads. 1-192-93
Intermittent sand filters. Sewage purification, 5-331
Internal-combustion engines. *with illus.*, 4-86-92
    Digester gas as fuel for, 5-332
    Electricity generated by use of, 9-231, 233, *illus.*, 230,
        232
    Nineteenth-century development, 6-254, *illus.*, 252-53
    See also Jet propulsion; Rockets
Internal jugular vein, in neck. *illus.*, 1-148f
Internal respiration, breathing in cells. 4-200, 206,
    illus., 202
Internal secretions. 5-15-19
    See also Hormones
International Astronomical Union. Sky map, 8-62-63
International Auxiliary Language Association (IALA).
    Interlingua developed by, 1-121
International Business Machines Corporation.
    Electronic computers developed by, 9-145
International Commission on Radiological Protection.
    9-350
International Commission on Zoological Nomenclature.
    1-288
International Council of Scientific Unions. 5-186
International Geophysical Year (IGY). *5-186-95; 9-
    221
    Air currents investigated during, 1-237
International Meteorological Committee.
    Cloud classification of, 2-220
International Office of Public Hygiene. 9-42
International Phonetic Association. Phonetic alphabet,
    1-110
International Polar Years. 5-186
International relations.
    Automation, effect of, 10-238
International Rules of Botanical Nomenclature.
    1-288-89
International Union for the Conservation of Nature
    and Natural Resources. 9-278
Interphase, resting stage of cells. 2-14, *illus.*, 13
Interrupted ferns. 3-192
Intersection, in mathematical sets. *with diagram*, 4-442
Interstellar materials. *9-359-64
Interstream profiles, in geography. 8-18
Intertype machines, for typesetting. *with illus.*, 1-200-
    01
Intervals, musical. *with table*, 5-214-15
Intervertebral discs. 3-75, 76
Intestinal juice. 4-327, 329
Intestine, large. *illus.*, 1-148d; 4-329-31, *illus.*, 322,
    329-30, 331
Intestine, small. *illus.*, 1-148d; 4-327-29, *illus.*, 322,
    327, 329, 334
Intestines.
    By-products from intestines of meat animals, 5-169
    Development in human body, 8-95
    Peristalsis in, *with illus.*, 1-179-80
Intoxication. See Alcohol
Intradermal tests, in allergy detection. 4-263
Introspection. Psychological method of, 9-312
Intrusions, masses of molten rock penetrating into or
    between other rock formations. *with illus.*, 3-420-22
Invariants, properties of geometric figures. *with illus.*,
    3-435
Invasions. Overpopulation relieved by, 3-233

Inventions. See History of science; also names of in-
    ventions and inventors
Inventors. See Inventions; also names of inventors
Inverse proportion. 2-315
Invert sugar, honey sugar. 4-79
Invertase, digestive enzyme. 3-47
Invertebrates.
    Cave-dwelling species, 5-59, 60
    Cold weather, effect on, 5-409
    Fossil invertebrate animals, *with illus.*, 6-370-72
    Migration of, 9-415-16, 430-32, *illus.*, 428, 431
    Skeletal remains of, form chalk and limestone deposits,
        4-134
    Vertebrates distinguished from, 3-74-75
    See also Crustaceans; Insects; Mollusks; Spiders;
        Worms; etc.
Invisible colleges. *with illus.*, 3-265-69
Involuntary muscles. See Smooth muscles
Involution, arithmetical operation. 1-158
Io, satellite I of Jupiter. 5-24
Iodine (I), chemical element. Atomic number, 53; atomic
    weight, 126.9044; melting point, 113.5° C.; boiling point,
    184.35° C.; specific gravity, solid: 4.93. Member of the
    halogen group. Shiny, grayish black solid; at ordinary
    temperatures vaporizes as violet gas, giving off irritating
    odor. Discovered by Courtois in 1811; name derived
    from Greek *iodes*: "violet." Widely distributed in both
    organic and inorganic matter, in sea water and in the
    thyroid gland of vertebrates. Obtained from brines in
    salt wells and old sea deposits, from its iodides by treat-
    ment with sulfuric acid and an oxidizing agent and from
    iodates by heating with sodium bisulfate. Used to pre-
    vent goiters, on external wounds and sometimes in pho-
    tography. Compounds of iodine are important in the
    chemical industry.
    Diet, essential to, 4-59-60
    Goiter, treatment of, 5-18
    Radioactive isotopes, 9-132
    Radioiodine, 9-132
        Medical uses of, 10-98, 99, *illus.*, 100
    Starch, test for, 4-77; *with illus.*, 7-135-36
    Sublimation of iodine crystals, 3-418
    Vitamin C, test for, 7-136
Ion exchanges. Soil, exchanges in, 2-24
Ionia, district of ancient Greece. Center of learning,
    1-129
Ionic jets, atomic engines. 9-382; 10-4
Ionization. *with diagram*, 2-422-24; *with illus.*, 5-87-93,
    95-96
    Acids, bases and salts, 4-338-40
    Atmospheric, 1-238, *diagram*, 239
    Gas-filled electron tubes, 6-301-02
    Ionospheric, 5-194-95
    X rays, produced by, 7-146
    Soil solution, ionization in, 2-16, 23
    Thermal, 1-174
Ionization chambers. 8-393; *illus.*, 9-43
    Radiation thickness gauges use ionization chambers,
        9-45
Ionosphere, layer of atmosphere. 1-22, *with diagram*,
    238-40; 4-45
    IGY studies of, 5-194-95
    Radio reception affected by, *with illus.*, 3-92-93
Ions, charged atomic particles. *with diagrams*, 2-422-
    26; *with illus.*, 5-87-91
    Acids, bases and salts, 4-338-41
    Atmospheric charged atoms, 1-240
    Crystals made up of, *with diagrams*, 5-338-40
    Electron tubes, gas ions in, 6-301-02
    Name introduced by Faraday, 5-236
    Nerve-impulse conduction, role of ions in, 6-321

Ions (continued)
  Plants' absorption and use of nutrient ions, **3-44-45**
  Protoplasm, salt ions of, **2-3, 6, 7, 10, 11**
  Solutions, ions in, *with diagram,* **4-297-98**
  Water-condensation centers in atmosphere, **2-218**
  See also **Ionization**
I. Q. See **"Intelligence Quotient"**
Iranian Plateau, 6-109
Iraq. Petroleum pipelines, **4-147**
IRBM (Intermediate Range Ballistics Missile). 10-3
Ireland.
  Famine of 1845, **3-25**
  Giant's Causeway, **4-395,** *illus.,* **394**
Iridium (Ir), chemical element. Atomic number, 77;
atomic weight, 192.2; melting point, 2,454° C.; boiling
point, above 4,800° C.; specific gravity, 22.42. Metal
(platinum family); white, very hard, brittle. Discovered
in 1803 by Tennant; name derived from Latin *iris:*
"rainbow," so called because of the green, red and
violet color of its salts. Found uncombined, together
with various members of platinum family, in alluvial
deposits; usually separated as ammonium iridium chloride, which is then ignited to give a pure, spongy
iridium. Useful in apparatus for high temperatures,
alloyed with platinum for standard weights and measures, with osmium in tipping pens and compass bearings and as a catalytic agent. See also **3-42**
Iris diaphragms, of cameras. **7-261; 9-406-07**
Iris of the eye. 7-262, 293, 294, *Illus.,* **292**
Irises, plants. *with illus.,* **7-242-43**
Irish elks.
  Evolution of, **6-282**
Irish moss, red algae. **3-224**
Irminger Current, oceanic current. **6-238,** *map,* **232-33**
Iron (Fe), chemical element. Atomic number, 26;
atomic weight, 55.847; melting point, 1,535° C.; boiling
point, about 3,000° C.; specific gravity, 7.85-7.88.
Pure metal, which is silver-white, ductile and magnetic,
is found in limited quantities in basalts and meteorites.
Combined with oxygen and other elements, iron is
widely distributed. Known and used long before recorded history. Name is derived from Anglo-Saxon
iron; chemical symbol (Fe), from Latin *ferrum:* "iron."
Pure metal is prepared by electrolytic deposition from
ferrous sulfate or by reduction of the pure oxide. Iron
is used as alloy in a great variety of industries, espe-
cially in the making of steel; ferrous metals are found
in tools, weapons of war and so forth. See also **3-37, 40**
  *Steel, alloy of iron, **1-338-53**
  Anemia due to iron deficiency, **3-330**
  Bacteria that act upon certain compounds of, **3-65**
  Blood, role in, **3-326-27, 331**
  Bread enriched with, **9-299**
  Bridges made of, **2-333**
  Building material, **7-122,** *illus.,* **123**
  Cells, iron in, **2-6**
  Combustion of, **4-352**
  Crystalline structure, **5-340,** *diagram,* **339**
  Diet, essential to, **4-59**
  Goldschmidt process, iron in, **3-317**
  Interstellar space contains, **9-363**
  Magnetite, **7-356,** *with illus.,* **163-64**
  Meteorites, alloy with nickel found in, **6-92-93, 98**
  Nickel-iron alloy in earth's core, **4-175**
  Nineteenth-century developments in steelmaking,
    with illus., **6-383-85**
  Nutritional requirement and food sources of, *table,*
    4-55-57
  Plant's use of, **3-44-45**
  Pregnancy, mothers need iron during, **5-272**
  Prospecting for iron ores, **7-356,** *diagram,* **357**

Iron (continued)
  Sewer pipes made of, **5-328**
  Ship hulls made of, **4-110-11**
  Sulfur, reaction with **4-230**
  Water supply, impurity in, **2-282**
  Wood, greatest competitor of, **5-266**
  See also **Pig iron; Steel**
Iron chloride (ferric or ferrous chloride).
  Experiments and tricks with, **7-179,** *with diagrams,*
    177
Iron deposits. Discoveries of, in nineteenth century,
  6-383-84
"Iron chinks," devices used for cutting off heads and
  tails of salmon. *illus.,* **6-24**
Iron lungs. *with illus.,* **4-205-06**
Iron meteorites. See **Siderites**
Iron ore, raw material in iron- and steelmaking.
  1-340-41, 343, 345-46, *illus.,* **340**
Iron ore mining. *with illus.,* **1-340-41**
Iron pyrites ("fool's gold"), mineral. *with illus.,* **5-249**
  Semiconducting crystals, **6-303**
Iron sulfide. Formation of, **4-230**
Irrational numbers. 1-160-61
Irregular galaxies. 8-50, *diagram,* **48; 9-363**
Irrigation. *8-191-201**
  Dams store water for, **8-306**
  Imperial Valley, California, *illus.,* **10-28**
  Modern systems, **5-29-30**
  Salt water as source of fresh water for, **2-283-84**
  Well water used in, *with illus.,* **8-330**
Irritability, responses of organisms to stimuli. **1-37-38**
  Plants, **3-52**
Irritation, chemical. Cancer may be caused by, **8-268**
Irritation, chronic. Cancer may be caused by, **8-267**
Irruptive movements, one-way movements of animal
  groups. **9-415**
  Lemmings, mass movements of, **9-422-23**
Irvin Cobb Bridge, Kentucky-Illinois. *illus.,* **2-335**
Isaiah, Book of. Manuscript dated by radiocarbon
  method, **10-97**
Isaria, mold. *illus.,* **10-130b-c**
Ischium, bone in hip. **3-81, 82,** *illus.,* **74**
Isidore of Seville, Bishop and Spanish scholar. **2-295,**
  297
Islam. See **Mohammedanism**
Island superstructures, of aircraft carriers. *with illus.,*
  4-114d
Island universes. *8-47-54, 158**
  Sir William Herschel's contributions to theory of,
    4-399
  See also **Galaxies**
Islands. *4-133-39**
  Appearing and disappearing with eruption of vol-
    canoes, **8-303**
  Coral-reef formation, theories of, **6-75, 77,** *illus.,* **77**
  Ice islands, **9-338-39,** *map,* **336-37**
Islands of Langerhans, in pancreas. See **Langerhans,
  islands of**
Ismailia, Egypt. Malaria conquered in, **10-34-35**
Isobaric lines. 9-223
Isobars, lines of equal air pressures. **1-249, 254,** *illus.,*
  250; 9-223
Isobutane. 7-269
Isoclinic charts of magnetic inclination. 7-169, *illus.,*
  169, 170-71
Isolation.
  Factor in development of new species, *with illus.,*
    6-279-80
Isomagnetic charts. 7-169, *illus.,* **170-71**
Isomerization, molecular rearrangement. Petroleum re-
  fining uses, **4-148**

Isomers. Definition, 7-269
  Stereoisomers, 9-72
Isometric system, of external crystal structure. 5-342,
  diagram, 340
Isopentane. Structural formula, 7-269
Isopods, crustaceans. 2-242
Isoprene, main component of natural rubber. *with
  diagram,* 6-357
  Molecular structure, 7-270
  Synthetic rubbers and, 8-185
Isoptera, order of insects. 2-413
  Termites, 3-362
Isostasy, geological term. 9-105-06; 10-220, 223
  Theory of, 7-32
Isothermal region of atmosphere. See **Stratosphere**
Isotopes, different forms of one element. 1-312, *with
  diagram,* 313; 9-43
  Artificial, 8-420
  Atomic energy, production of, 9-125-26, 131-34,
    137-38, 331-32
  Climates of past indicated by analysis of oxygen
    isotopes, 3-181-82
  Discovered by Soddy, 8-416
  Hydrogen, isotopes of, 3-319
  Radiation thickness gauges use isotopes, 9-43
  Radioisotope-fueled thermoelectric generators, *with
    illus.,* 6-172-75
  Separation methods, 8-418
  See also **Radioactive isotopes**
Israel. Irrigation in, 8-200, *illus.,* 201
Italia, airship. 6-180
Italy.
  Bridges, medieval, 2-333
  Catastrophic mud flood and landslide, 2-351-52
  Contributions to science
    1600–1765, *with illus.,* 3-265-66, 273-75
    1765–1815, 4-362-63, *illus.,* 360-61
  Hydrofoil boats in, 4-7
  Jet aviation, contributions to, 7-68
  Messina-Reggio earthquake, 9-110
Ives, Frederick Eugene, American inventor. 6-381
Ives, N. E., American physicist. 4-216
Ivory, vegetable. Buttons made from, 7-210, 212,
  illus., 213
Ivory-billed woodpeckers. 6-211
Iwanowski, Dimitri, Russian scientist. Work on tobacco
  mosaic disease, 1-39; 3-451
Izalco, volcano in El Salvador. 8-298, *illus.,* 300a
Izsak, Imre G., American astrophysicist. 5-188

J

J.N.D's. See **Just-noticeable-differences**
Jabir. See **Geber**
Jack-in-the-pulpits, woodland herbs. *with illus.,* 7-244
Jack rabbits. *illus.,* 7-15; 8-170
Jackals. 8-138, *illus.,* 135
Jackhammers, pneumatic hammers. 9-66
Jackscrews, simple machines. *with illus.,* 3-60
Jackson, Charles Thomas, American scientist. 5-239;
  7-376-77
  Telegraph patent to Morse contested by, 2-379
Jacob's Creek, Pennsylvania. Bridge over, 2-338
Jacquard, Joseph Marie, French inventor (1752–1834).
The son of silk weavers, he invented a loom that could
weave complicated patterns in silk and other fabrics.
Jaguars. 8-210, *illus.,* 207
Jaguarundis, cats. 8-211
Jakobshavn Glacier, Greenland. *illus.,* 9-335
James, Henry, American novelist. 9-50

James, William, American psychologist and philosopher.
  with illus., 9-49-51
James-Lange theory of emotions. 9-50
Jansky Karl G., American radio engineer. 9-207, 224
Janssen, Pierre-Jules-César, French astronomer. 5-86
  Helium, discovery of, 1-19-20; 6-391
  Solar observations, 3-105
Janssen, Zacharias, Dutch spectacle-maker. 3-14, 16
Japan.
  Earthquakes, 9-111, *illlus.,* 118
  Human wastes used as fertilizer, 5-327, *illus.,* 328
  Hydroponic farming in Japan by United States Army,
    8-36
  Industrial development of, 1-97
  Jet stream over, 2-359
  Saltern, *illus.,* 5-314
  Silk industry, 5-184, *illus.,* 176, 181, 185
Japanese.
  Blood groups, *with table,* 3-333
  Skin and hair of, *illus.,* 2-173, 178
Japanese beetles. 3-345; 9-196
Jato units, rocket engines. 7-70
Jaundice. 4-335
Java. Volcanoes, *illus.,* 8-297
Java man. *illus.,* 3-227
  Discovery by Dubois, 9-23, *illus.,* 22
Javelle water, bleaching agent. 3-319
Jaw crushers, in ore dressing. *with diagram,* 1-371-72
Jawbones.
  Human, *with illus.,* 3-78-79, *illus.,* 74, 75, 77
  Muscle operating lower jaw, *illus.,* 3-209
Jaws.
  Birds, *with illus.,* 1-285
  Insects, 2-403, *illus.,* 404
  Man, 8-29
  Muscle operating lower jaw, *illus.,* 3-209
  Rattlesnake, 3-237
  Snakes, *with illus.,* 1-285
  Spiders, *with illus.,* 2-261
  See also **Beaks; Mandibles**
Jays. *with illus.,* 6-101-02
  Pets, 7-23
Jeanneret, Charles-Edouard. See **Le Corbusier.**
Jeans, Sir James H., English mathematician (1877–
1946). He taught applied mathematics at Princeton
and Cambridge and was astronomy professor at the
Royal Institution. Jeans advanced a famous theory of
the creation of the universe. He worked on radiations,
the kinetic theory of gases, the quantum theory and
stellar formation; he also studied the effects of gravita-
tional attraction on the motion of stars.
  Tidal theory, 1-29, *illus.,* 28; 9-225
Jefferson, Thomas, American political leader, states-
man and scientist. 4-33-34
  Louisiana Purchase, 7-27
  Memorial, Washington, D.C., *illus.,* 7-118
Jeffreys, H., English scientist.
  Tidal theory, 1-29, *illus.,* 28; 9-225
Jejunum, part of small intestine. 4-327, *illus.,* 322
Jellyfish. 2-150
  Fossil jellyfish, *illus.,* 6-370
  Luminous, *illus.,* 2-184
Jelutongs, Malayan trees. 6-353
Jenner, Edward, English physician. *with illus.,*
  4-401-03; 7-350
Jerboas, rodents. 8-164
Jerusalem crickets. *with illus.,* 3-145-46
Jespersen, Otto, Danish linguist. 1-117
Jet condensers, in ships' steam engines. 4-111
Jet fuels. 4-148
Jet planes. *7-67-74

Jet planes (continued)
Development of, with illus., 6-185, 194-95; with illus., 9-218-19, illus., 217
Link jet trainer, illus., 2-235
Take-off, 6-frontispiece
See also **Supersonics**
Jet propulsion. 2-329; 7-67; illus., 10-43
Jet engines, illus., 1-92b
Rockets, 10-41-42
See also **Jet planes**
Jet streams. 1-237-38; *2-358-60
Jet water pumps. with illus., 2-35-36
Jetlike air streams. 1-242
Jetties. Beach changes due to, 8-351
Jews.
Calendar, 10-178
Science in Biblical times, 1-128
Jig washing, of coal. 1-415
Jiggers, machines used in making pottery. 7-401, illus., 403
Jigs, in ore dressing. with diagram, 1-373
Jobs.
Available in scientific fields, with illus., 10-197-202
Psychology, 9-322
Job's Coffin, name given to constellation Delphinus. 1-334
Jodrell Bank Radio-Astronomical Observatory, England. with illus., 9-208
Jodrell Bank radio telescope, Manchester, England. 9-225
Johannesburg, South Africa. illus., 6-114-15
John Dory, fish. 4-314-15
Johnson, Douglas W., American geologist.
Coastline classification proposed by, 8-354-55
Johnson grass. 7-113
Joints.
Action of, with illus., 1-283-84
Muscle and joint disorders, 3-211, 213
Sprains, first aid for, 10-12
See also **Bones; Muscles**
Joliot-Curie, Frédéric, French physicist. 8-420
Discovery of artificial radioactivity, 9-132
Joliot-Curie, Irène, French physicist. 8-420
Discovery of artificial radioactivity, 9-132
Jolliffe, Norman, American nutritionist. Biotin-deficiency case described by, 5-44
Joly, John, Irish physicist and geologist. Mountain-building forces, theory of, 10-219-20
Jordan, F. W., American physicist.
Electronic "trigger circuit" suggested by, 9-144
Jordans, devices for processing wood fibers used for papermaking. with illus., 4-369
Jorgensen, Lars, American engineer. 8-308
Jouffroy d'Abbans, Marquis Claude de, French inventor (1751–1832). Steamboat of, 4-109
Joule, James Prescott, English physicist. with illus., 6-247, 250-52, 254
Electricity, work in, 5-238
Heat, experiments on, 3-408
Joule's law. 5-238
Joysticks. Airplanes controlled by, 6-188
Jugular vein, in neck. illus., 1-148f
Julian, Percy L., American Negro chemist (born 1899). He taught at Howard and Depauw universities; later he worked as an industrial research chemist. He was the first to synthesize physostigmine, a drug used in the treatment of the eye disease called glaucoma. His research on the uses of soybean protein led to his invention of an important paper coating and a liquid for extinguishing gasoline and oil fires. He also made a study of hormones for medical research.

Julian calendar. 10-173-76, illus., 172
Julien-Dubuque Bridge, Iowa. 2-336
July. Origin of name, 10-175
Jumping shrews. 7-102, illus., 100
Jumping spiders. 2-266-67, illus., 258-262
June bugs, beetles. 3-345
Jung, Carl Gustav, Swiss psychiatrist. 9-102
Junior Engineering Technical Society (JETS), East Lansing, Michigan. National Project Exposition for young scientists sponsored by, 8-73
Junipers, trees. illus., 6-140
Juno, asteroid. 4-421
Jupiter, planet. *5-20-24; illus., 9-150
Asteroids, influence on, 4-422
Comet family of, 5-396-97
Data, 10-298
Observing, means of, 6-84
Satellites of, 3-158-59, illus., 162
Discovered by Galileo, 3-2
Jupiter VIII, satellite of Jupiter.
Rediscovered with electronic computer, 9-150-51
Jurassic period, time in earth's history. 1-392-93; 6-373
Just, Alexander, Austrian inventor.
Tungsten electric-light filament, experiments with, 4-238
Just-noticeable-differences (J.N.D's.), of sensation. 7-291
Justification, of printing type. 1-199, 200
Jute. Plant and fiber, 4-181, illus., 180
Juvenal, ancient Roman satirist.
"Bread and circuses" quotation, 9-294
Juvenile hormones.
Insects controlled by means of, 9-189, 191, illus., 190-91

K

K3, U.S. Navy submarine. illus., 5-34
K mesons, atomic particles. table, 1-314
Kadiak (Kodiak) bears. 7-312
Kala azar, disease. Triatoma transmits, 3-260
Kamchatka bears. 7-312
Kames, glacial outwash deposits. 9-173-74
Kamishiiba Dam. illus., 8-316b
Kangaroo rats, rodents. 8-163
Kangaroos. illus., 1-299; 7-422, 424-25, illus., 418, 420-21
Adaptation for feeding, 7-9
Adaptation for preservation of offspring, 3-242, illus., 243
Kant, Immanuel, German philosopher.
Nebular theory of, 8-47
Solar system, theory about, 1-27
Kaolin.
Processing of, illus., 7-395, 397
Kaons. See **K mesons**
Kaplan reaction turbines. 9-234
Kapteyn, J. C., Dutch astronomer. 8-154
Kara-Baghas, inlet of Caspian Sea. 7-63
Karakoram, mountains in Kashmir and Tibet. 10-22
Karakul, fur. 7-238
Karroo, South African plateau. 2-216
Karst region, Yugoslavia. Limestone caves in, 5-53
Kashmir.
Liddar Valley, illus., 10-26
Kasner, Edward, American mathematician. 2-74
Katiusha, Russian rocket-firing gun. 9-327
Katmai Volcano, Alaska. Volcanic ash from, 7-326
Katydids. with illus., 3-144-45
Kay, John, English inventor. 4-36

Keds, flies. 3-292, *illus.,* 291

Keeler, J. E., American astronomer.
Saturn's rings, observations of, 5-110-11

Keels, boat and ship. Origin of, 4-106, 107

Keith, Sir Arthur, British anthropologist. 9-24-25

Kekule, Friedrich August, German chemist. *with illus.,* 5-79-80

Keller, Albert G., American sociologist. 9-26

Kellies, well-drilling pipes. *diagram,* 4-144

Kelly, William, American inventor. 6-384

Keloids, scar tissues. 7-353

Kelps, brown algae. *with illus.,* 3-220

Kelvin, Baron (William Thomson), British mathematician and physicist. 5-241-42
Earth's rigidity calculated by, 4-174
Thermodynamics, work in, 6-254

Kelvin scale. See **Absolute scale**

Kenaf, fiber. Retting of, *illus.,* 3-69

Kenny, Elizabeth, Australian nurse. Poliomyelitis treatment, 10-129-30

Kentucky coffee trees. *with illus.,* 5-148
Leaves, *illus.,* 5-139

Kenya, Mount, Africa. 10-26, *illus.,* 23

Kepler, Johannes, German astronomer. 3-5-6, 15
Galileo's letter to, 3-2
Vision, explanation of, 3-276
See also **Kepler's laws of planetary motion**

Kepler's laws of planetary motion. 3-5-6

Kerosene. 4-141, 148
Safety measures with, 7-192
Woolly aphids controlled by, 9-193

Kerst, Donald W., American physicist. Betatron, development of, 9-247

Kestrels, falcons. 6-159

Ketones. 7-273

Kettle, drossing. See **Drossing kettle**

Kettledrums. Sound production in, 5-218

Kettles, chemical vessels. Plastics manufacture uses, 8-225

Key West. Origin of, 4-137

Keyboards, typewriter. *with illus.,* 1-272-73

Keyhoe, Donald E., American author. Flying saucers, account of, 9-19

Keys, Florida. Formation, 4-137

Keys, typewriter. 1-270, 272, *illus.,* 270, 271

Khartoum, Sudan. Solar eclipse observations near, *illus.,* 3-136

Khayyam. See **Omar Khayyam**

Khimki, Russia, rocket-research center. 9-379

Kidder, W. P., American manufacturer.
Noiseless typewriter developed by, 1-273

Kidneys. 5-11-13, *diagram,* 12
Development in
Human baby, 8-96
Unborn human young, 8-28
Mammalian kidney, 7-4
Scarlet fever may damage, 7-352
Stones of, 5-18

Kiel Canal, Germany. *with illus.,* 4-186

Kilauea, Hawaiian volcano. 7-345, *illus.,* 344; *illus.,* 8-300c
Caldera of, 8-298

Kilimanjaro, Mount, highest peak of Africa. 10-26, 213

Killarney Revolution, time of mountain making. 6-370

"Killed" vaccines. Virus, 3-458

Killer whales. 7-189, *illus.,* 185

Killing bottles. Insect collecting, use in, *with illus.,* 3-153-54

Kilns.
Dehydrating foods, used in, 4-166
Firing pottery, used in, 7-402, *illus.,* 404

Kilocycles. 3-91

Kilogram-calories. See **Calories**

Kimberlite, diamond-bearing soil. 4-253, *illus.,* 252

Kindling temperature, temperature at which combustion takes place. 4-19, 351

Kinescopes, television tubes. 5-283-84

Kinesthesia (muscle sense). 7-306

Kinesthetic sensations. 9-314

Kinetic energy. *with illus.,* 1-82, 83
Conversion to electrical energy, 9-229
Distinguished from potential energy, 6-247
Heat as energy of motion, 7-250

Kinetic (kinetic-molecular) theory. 1-163-64, 170, 172, *with diagrams,* 167-68
Chemical reactions and, 2-228
Demonstration of, 6-254

King birds. 6-99

King crabs. 2-242

King snakes. *illus.,* 5-355
Pets, 7-25

King termites. 3-362

Kingdoms, groups in classification of living things. 1-291

Kingfishers. *with illus.,* 6-309-10

Kinglets. 6-42, 44, *illus.,* 43

Kingsley Dam, Nebraska. 8-312

Kinkajous, carnivorous mammals. 7-317

Kircher, Athanasius, German scientist. 3-275
Camera obscura of, *illus.,* 9-398

Kirchhoff, Gustav, German physicist. 5-86
Cesium and rubidium, discovery of, 3-169
Science of astrophysics, founding of, 6-390-91

"Kissing bugs." 3-260

"Kissing disease," infectious mononucleosis. 3-331

Kissing gouramis, tropical fish. *illus.,* 8-116

Kitazato, Shibasaburo, Japanese bacteriologist. 7-383

Kitchens.
Garbage grinders, 5-336
Gas appliances, 5-106
Housebuilding plans, 4-267, 269
Modern design, example of, *illus.,* 10-122

Kites, birds. *with illus.,* 6-160

Kitt Peak National Observatory, Arizona. 8-64
Mirror for 84-inch telescope, construction of, *illus.,* 3-314

Kitty Hawk, North Carolina. Wright brothers at, 6-182-83; 9-216
Wright brothers, *illus.,* 9-217

Klebs, Edwin, German pathologist. 7-382

Kleist, Ewald Georg von, German scientist. Invention of Leyden jar, 4-359

Kline, Nathan S., American psychiatrist. 9-104

Klingenstierna, Samuel, Swedish physicist. 7-158

Klipspringers, antelopes. 8-387

Klystrons, high-frequency electron tubes. 6-302, *illus.,* 298d

Kneading, of dough. Rome, Ancient, 9-294

Knee jerk, a reflex movement. 6-323

Kneecap. See **Patella**

Knees, exposed roots of bald cypress trees. 4-65

Knees, leg joints. 3-82, 83

Knot, marine measure. See **Nautical measures**

Knowledge.
Aristotle's theory of, 9-47
See also **Intelligence; Mind; Senses**

Knuckles, of hands. 3-81

Koalas, mammals. 7-6, *with illus.,* 425-26

Kobs, antelopes. 8-386

Koch, Robert, German physician. *with illus.,* 7-382
Tuberculosis, work on, 9-175, 180, *illus.,* 177

Kodachrome film. 9-414

Kodacolor film. 9-414

Kodak cameras. 9-403, *illus.,* 404

Kodiak bears. See **Kadiak bears.**

Koebele, Albert, American entomologist. 9-290

Koehler, Wolfgang, German psychologist. *with illus.,* 9-52-54

Koelliker, Albert von, anatomist and zoologist. 7-161

Kok-sagyz plants. *illus.,* 7-43
  Rubber from, 7-44

Kolbe wheels, mine-excavating machines. 1-409

Kolhörster, Werner, German physicist. Cosmic-ray investigations, 8-393, 394

Kolinsky, fur. 7-238

Komodo dragons, largest lizards. *with illus.,* 5-200, 204

Kookaburras, kingfishers. 6-310

Koosah Falls, Oregon. *illus.,* 8-15

Korea.
  Printing in, 1-197

Kornberg, Arthur, American biologist. Nucleic acid synthesized by, 9-386

Koroseal. Conveyer belts made of, 6-170

Korsakoff's psychosis, mental disturbance. 4-412

Kozyrev, N. A., Russian astronomer. 4-284

Kraepelin, Emil, German psychiatrist. 9-49

Kraits, snakes. 5-362

Krakatoa, Indonesian volcano. 8-298
  Eruption of, *with illus.,* 7-340-42
    Sound intensity of, 8-40
  Succession, example of, 10-189-90
  Volcanic ash from, 7-326
  Waves produced by eruptions of 1883, 8-350

Krebs, A. C., French pioneer in aeronautics. 6-178

Krimmer, fur. 7-238

Krische, Wilhelm, German chemist. 8-223

Kroeber, A. L., American archaeologist. 9-30

Krueger 60, star.
  Orbital motion of, *illus.,* 7-226-27

Krypton (Kr), chemical element. Atomic number, 36; atomic weight, 83.80; melting point, —156.6° C.; boiling point, —152.9° C.; specific gravity (air = 1), 2.868. Rare, inert gas, characterized by brilliant green and yellow lines in spectrum. Discovered in 1898 by Ramsay and Travers; name derived from Greek *kryptos:* "hidden." One part krypton to every million parts of air. Found, with xenon, in certain mineral springs, but obtained from the atmosphere. Condenses as liquid or solid if slow stream of dry air is passed through a tube cooled by liquid air. Used chiefly for lighting devices.
  Fission of uranium, 9-133, 330

Kublai Khan, Chinese emperor. Oil fields of, 4-140

Kudus, antelopes. 8-379-80, *illus.,* 376

Kuiper, Gerard P., Dutch-born astronomer.
  Jupiter's satellites I-IV, observations of, 5-24
  Miranda and Nereid discovered by, 5-289-90, 292
  Nebular hypothesis of, 1-30
  Saturn's rings, observations of, 5-112

Kunlun Shan, mountains in China. 10-22

Kuroshio, oceanic current. 6-238, *map,* 232-33

Kuwait, sheikhdom in Arabia. Sea water converted into fresh water in, 2-283

Kwakiutl Indians. Cultural studies of, *with illus.,* 9-26-27

Kwashiorkor, protein-deficiency disease. 4-54

KWIC ("key word in context") **system.** 10-226

L

L-head engines, for automobiles. *with illus.,* 2-133

Labella, liplike processes. Insects, *illus.,* 2-404

Labium, liplike structure. Insects, *illus.,* 2-404

Labor.
  Automation, effects of, 10-238
  See also **Industry**

Labor pains. 8-32

Laboratories.
  *Amateur chemistry at home, 4-221-31, 343-52; 7-129-36
  Bathyscaphes as marine laboratories, *with illus.,* 6-74d

Laborit, Henri, French psychiatrist. 9-104

Labrador Current, oceanic current. 6-238, *map,* 232-33
  Iceberg movements in, 9-336, *map,* 336-37

Labyrinth, of ear. 4-380

Labyrinthodonts, primitive group of amphibians. 5-154

Laccoliths, geologic formations. 3-421, *illus.,* 420

Lace bugs. 3-259

Lacertids (**Lacertidae**), family of lizards. 5-199

Lacewings, insects. See **Neuroptera**

Lacey Act, conservation measure. 9-273

Lachrymal glands. 7-293

La Condamine, Charles de, French mathematical geographer. 6-351

Lacquers. Cans, used in, 4-155

Lactic acid.
  Food preservative, 4-164-67
  Muscular activity, role in, 2-12; 3-206, 207

Lactose, milk sugar. 4-79

Ladders. Use of, 7-194-95, *illus.,* 195

Ladino local race. 8-219

Ladles. Containers for molten metal, 1-343, 346, *illus.,* 342, 345
  Teeming steel from, 1-347, *illus.,* 348b

Ladoga, Lake, U.S.S.R. 7-56

Lady-slipper orchids, flowering plants.
  Pollination of, *illus.,* 4-127

Ladybirds, beetles. *illus.,* 2-405; *with illus.,* 3-340-41

Laënnec, René-Théophile-Hyacinthe, French physician. 7-371-72, *illus.,* 370

Lafayette, troopship. See **Normandie**

Lagena, of fish's ears. 4-381

Lagomorpha, order of mammals. *with illus.,* 7-15; 8-168, 170

Lagoons. Coral islands, lagoons of, 4-136; 6-75, *illus.,* 77

Lagoons, sewage. 5-334

Lake, Simon, American naval architect.
  Submarine development, 5-32

Lake District, England. Mountains eroded, 10-221

Lake Superior district. Iron ore center, *with illus.,* 1-340-41

Lake trout, fish. 4-98

Lake Washington Bridge, Seattle. 2-342, *illus.,* 341

Lakes. *7-55-66
  Streams may be dammed to form, 8-17
  Titicaca, Lake, *illus.,* 6-115
  Volcanic craters, lakes in, 8-298
  See also **Great Lakes; Great Salt Lake**

Lamarck, Jean-Baptiste, Chevalier de, French naturalist. *with illus.,* 4-388-90
  Evolution, theory of, 8-258

Lamb, Charles, English essayist. Quotation from, 5-350

Lamb, Sir Harold, English geophysicist.
  Earth's magnetic field, explanation of, 4-176

Lamb. Cuts of, *with illus.,* 5-170-71

Lamb vultures. 6-156

Lambert, Count de, French inventor. 4-6

Lambot, Joseph-Louis, French inventor.
  Reinforced concrete boat built by, 3-119

Lamellae, gill-like spore-producing plates of mushrooms. *with illus.,* 3-29-30

Lamellibranchs, mollusks. 2-196-200, *illus.*, 193, 196, 197, 199, 201
　　Shell collecting, *with illus.*, 2-99-104
Laminated glass. Manufacture, 3-313
Laminating, layering. Plastics used in, 8-232, *diagram*, 233
Lamont Geological Observatory. 5-189, 190, 193, 194
Lamp shells. *illus.*, 1-293
　　Unchanged for millions of years, 6-283
Lampblack. 3-324
Lampreys. 4-98, *with illus.*, 94
　　Migration of, 9-427, *illus.*, 430
Lamps.
　　Ancient, 4-232, *illus.*, 233
　　Bolton lamp, 4-238
　　Discharge lamps, 4-239-40
　　Edison's first practical incandescent lamp, *illus.*, 4-235
　　Electric lighting, 9-239, 344-47
　　Electric lighting in nineteenth century, 5-246-47, *illus.*, 244
　　Incandescent, 2-187
　　Incandescent lamp, homemade model of, *with illus.*, 6-291
　　Tungsten-filament lamp, 4-238-39
　　See also **Electric lighting**
Lancelets (Amphioxus). *illus.*, 1-297; *with illus.*, 4-4
　　Heart of, 1-277, *illus.*, 278
Land, Edwin H., American inventor (1909–　　　). See **Land theory of color vision; Polaroid Land cameras**
Land.
　　Land habitats, 10-135-37, *illus.*, 136-40
　　Populations and, 3-227-28, 231-33
　　Temperature of, affects air circulation, 2-90-91
　　See also **Agriculture; Soil**
Land breezes. 2-90-91
Land theory of color vision. *8-178-80
Landes, lowlands of southwestern France. *with illus.*, 6-111
Landing gear, of airplanes. Retractable gear, development of, 9-218
Landing pods, of space vehicles. *illus.*, 10-52-53
Landscapes.
　　Photography of, 6-314, *illus.*, 314-16
　　See also **Geology; Geomorphology**
Landscaping, for roads. *illus.*, 3-298c
Landslides. 2-352-53
　　Lakes formed by, 7-55
　　Streams dammed by, 8-17
Landsteiner, Karl, Austrian pathologist. 9-35
　　Blood groups discovered by, *with table*, 3-333-34
Lange, Carl, Danish physiologist. 9-50
Langemarck, Belgium. Poison gas in warfare first used at, 9-212
Langen, Eugen, German engineer. 6-254, *illus.*, 252-53
Langerhans, islands of, clumps of pancreatic cells that secrete insulin. 5-13, 18-19, *illus.*, 19
Langevin, Paul, French scientist.
　　High-frequency-sound experiments, 8-105
Langford, Nathaniel, American park superintendent. 8-289
Langley, Samuel Pierpont, American scientist (1834–1906). He devoted most of his life to astronomy and his discoveries and inventions did much to enrich that science. He became director of the Allegheny Observatory in 1867, secretary of the Smithsonian Institution and president of the American Association for the Advancement of Science in 1887. He established the Astrophysical Observatory in Washington, D. C. He

Langley, Samuel Pierpont (*continued*)
was one of the pioneers in powered heavier-than-air flight.
　　Bolometer invented by, 7-201
　　Powered model plane developed by, 8-403, *illus.*, 402
　　Powered plane developed by, 6-182; 9-216
Langmuir, Irving, American chemist (1881–1957), second American to win the Nobel Prize in chemistry, 1932. He has made many outstanding discoveries in the field of surface chemistry; he is also noted for his work on the electron theory of matter and on the "seeding" of clouds in order to produce rain. Educated at Columbia University and at the University of Göttingen, Germany, he taught at Stevens Institute of Technology before joining the research laboratory of the General Electric Company in 1909. *illus.*, 10-303
　　Incandescent lamps, work on, 4-239
　　Quotation from, 10-224
　　Snow-making experiments of, 2-218
　　Television pioneer, 9-288
　　Valence theory of, 8-417
Langstroth, L. L., American beehive inventor. 3-370
Language. *1-107-21
　　Consequences of development of, 1-66
　　Multi-language typewriters, 1-274
　　See also **Printing**
Langurs, Old World monkeys. 9-255, 257, *illus.*, 254
Lanston, Tolbert, American inventor. 1-198
　　See also **Monotype machines**
Lantern fish, luminous fish. *illus.*, 2-190; *with illus.*, 4-97
Lanthanides, group of chemical elements. 4-308
　　Periodic series, position in, 4-310, *tables*, 307, 309
Lanthanum (La), chemical element. Atomic number, 57; atomic weight, 138.91; melting point, 826° C.; specific gravity, 6.155. One of the rare-earth metals, it was separated from the oxide, lanthana, by Mosander in 1839; name derived from Greek *lanthanein*: "to lie hidden." Found in ores cerite, orthite and monazite. White metal is prepared from the chloride by treatment with sodium or by electrolysis.
Lanthanum oxide. Gas-mantle experiments with, 4-237
Laplace, Pierre-Simon de, French astronomer and mathematician. 4-398-400
　　Nebular hypothesis, 1-29, *illus.*, 28
Lapp local race. 8-218
Lapps, northern European people.
　　Transportation methods on land, *with illus.*, 1-102
Lapse rate, of air. 2-214
Laramide Revolution, time of mountain making. 1-394-95; 6-374
Larch trees. 5-142, *illus.*, 143
Lard. Manufacture of, *with illus.*, 5-167-68
Larderello, Italy. Heat of earth yields power in, 8-304
Large calories. See **Calories**
Large intestine. See **Intestine, large**
Large Magellanic Cloud. *illus.*, 1-255
Large numbers. Exponents used in writing, 2-74
Larks. 6-100-01, *illus.*, 100, 105, 106
Larkspurs, birds.
　　Migration route of, *illus.*, 5-418e
Larvae, immature animal forms.
　　Acorn worms, 4-3, *illus.*, 2
　　Frogs, 5-159, *illus.*, 158-59
　　Insects, 2-407
　　　　Ants, *illus.*, 3-360
　　　　Beetles, 3-336-37, 341-42
　　　　Butterflies and moths, *illus.*, 2-408; 3-195, 197-98, *illus.*, 194, 197, 200
　　　　Flies, 3-283-84, *illus.*, 285-86
　　　　Social insects, 3-358, *with illus.*, 365-68, *illus.*, 363

Larvae *(continued)*
  Salamanders, *with illus.*, 5-160-61
  Sea squirts, 4-3
  Silkworms, 5-173, *with illus.*, 174-79, *illus.*, 180, 181
Laryngotomy. 4-201, 203
Larynx. *illus.*, 1-148g, *with illus.*, 282; 4-201, 203, *illus.*, 202
Lascaux Cave, France. Dating of sample from, 10-97
Laser ("Light Amplification by Stimulated Emission of Radiation"). Also known as the optical maser (see **Maser**), the laser is a device for producing a narrow light beam of a single wave length, the waves all being in phase, or in step with each other. Ordinary light consists of waves of varying lengths emitted at random and out of phase by the source. Such light is used to excite the atoms of the material being employed as the source of the laser beam. The electrons in the atoms of the laser material are raised to higher energy levels by the incoming light; as they fall back to their original states, they emit light of a single wave length. This light is reflected back and forth through the material for amplification before being passed out into the open. A solid-state laser uses a ruby crystal; a gaseous laser, a mixture of neon and helium. Laser beams are finding many applications: in communication, space research, chemistry and radar. A concentrated laser beam can burn a hole in the most resistant materials; it can also carry many signals at a time.
Lassell, William, English astronomer.
  Triton discovered by, 5-292
Last quarter, lunar phase. 4-278
Lateens, triangular sails. Early sailing ships used, 4-108
Latent heat.
  Heat of fusion, 3-416-17
  Heat waste in early steam engine due to, 4-40
Latent images, photographic. 9-401-02
Lateral buds. *with illus.*, 4-66
Lateral line system, of fishes. 4-382, *with illus.*, 102
Lateral undulatory movement, of snakes. *with illus.*, 5-354a
Laterites. See **Latosols**
Latex, milky fluid found in certain plant cells. 6-351
  Composition of, 6-355
  Plants producing latex for rubber, 6-353
  Processing of, *with illus.*, 6-354-55
  Tapping rubber tree to obtain, *with illus.*, 6-354-55
Lathes. 10-108-09
Latimeria chalumnae, primitive fish. 4-196, *with illus.*, 199
Latin.
  Living things named in Latin, 1-288, 291
  Prototype of modern Romance languages, 1-118-19
Latin America. See **South America; West Indies;** also names of individual countries
Latissimus dorsi, back muscle. 3-203, *illus.*, 205
Latitude, terrestrial. Latitude is a method of geographical reference to any point on the earth's surface. It is expressed in terms of angular distance from the equator. Thus the equator is at 0° latitude; the North Pole, at 90° north latitude. A point on the earth's surface that is midway between the North Pole and the equator would have a latitude of 45° north.
  Stars used in determining, 8-61
Latosols, soil type. 2-22, *map,* 20-21
Latreille, Pierre-André, French entomologist. 8-254-55
Lattice, arrangement of material in an atomic pile. 9-136
Lattices, crystal. *with diagrams,* 1-169-70, 171; *with diagrams,* 5-337-38
  Sodium chloride, *illus.*, 5-89

Laue, Max von, German physicist.
  Wave lengths of X rays discovered by, 7-144
Laughing gas (nitrous oxide). 3-318
Laughing jackass kingfishers. 6-310
Launching points and paths, of space vehicles and missiles. *diagrams,* 8-126, 127, 131
Laundering. Sickroom articles, 10-56, 66
Laundry center, of home. 4-269
Lava.
  Cave formations in, *with illus.*, 5-57
  Streams dammed by, 8-17
  Thermoluminescence, flows of lava dated by, 6-376
  Volcanic eruptions, flows of lava in, 8-301-02, 304, *illus.*, 300c
  See also **Igneous rocks; Volcanoes**
Laval, Carl Gustaf Patrik de, Swedish engineer and inventor.
  See also **Turbines**
Laveran, Charles-Louis-Alphonse, French Army surgeon.
  Malarial parasite discovered by, 10-31-32
Lavoisier, Antoine-Laurent, French scientist. *with illus.*, 4-356-57
  Conservation of matter, views on, 6-247
  Execution of, 4-34
Lawrence, Ernest Orlando, American physicist (1901–58) and developer of the atom-smashing cyclotron, used to free energy from the nucleus of the atom, to make chemical elements radioactive and to separate isotopes used in the production of atomic power. He was educated at the University of South Dakota and Yale University. In 1939 he received the Nobel Prize in physics. See also 8-420
  Cyclotron, development of, 9-244-45
Lawrence, John H., American physiologist. 8-81
Lawrencium (Lw), chemical element. Atomic number, 103; atomic weight, 257 (estimated). Half life about eight seconds; decays into mendelevium. Prepared by Ghiorso, Sikkeland, Larsh and Latimer at the Lawrence Radiation Laboratory of the University of California by bombarding californium with nuclei of boron. Named in honor of the American physicist Ernest O. Lawrence.
Laws, of science.
  *Parity law in physics, 7-107-10
  Avogadro's law, 5-76
  Bode's law, 4-420
  Conservation of energy and matter, 1-84-85
  Definite proportions, law of, 1-80; 5-74
  Einstein's equation, 1-84-85
  Experiments and observations testing scientific hypotheses and principles, 8-70-72, 74-77
  Gases, laws of, *with diagram,* 1-165-66, 172; 3-416
  Heredity, laws of, 8-339-42
  Machines, law of, 3-57
  Multiple proportions, law of, 5-74
  Periodic law of elements, 5-84
  Spectrum analysis, laws of, 5-86
Lawson, H. J., English inventor. 6-380
Laxatives. Natural laxative foods. 5-275
Layard, Sir Austen H., English archaeologist. 9-82
Layering, method of plant propagation. 9-8, *illus.*, 15
Layers, atmospheric. *with diagram,* 1-237-40
  See also **Strata**
Layout sheets, in photo-offset printing. 1-211
Lazear, Jesse, American biologist. 10-38
Leaching. Sewage disposal by leaching into soil, 5-333
  Soil formation and character, factor in, 2-17, 20, 22
Lead (Pb), chemical element. Atomic number, 82; atomic weight, 207.19; melting point, 327.4° C.; boiling point, 1,620° C.; specific gravity, 11.35. Blue-white, lustrous metal, very soft and malleable, poor conductor of electricity. Known at least since Biblical

Lead *(continued)*
days. Name derived from Anglo-Saxon *lead*; chemical symbol (Pb), from Latin *plumbum*: "lead." Widely found in nature, rarely uncombined; chief ore is galena, or lead sulfide, from which it is obtained by roasting. Used as corrosion-resisting lining; also in pipes, battery plates, bullets and paints. Lead alloys serve as Linotype metals, terneplate coatings, metals for fuses and so on. See also 3-40-41
    Alloys, 1-382
    Bone marrow poisoned by, 3-74
    Building material, 7-121
    Crystalline structure, 5-340, diagram, 339
    Earth's age determined by proportion of lead and uranium in rock deposits, 4-47
    Pyrophoric lead, *with diagram*, 7-174-75
    Smelting and refining, *with diagram*, 1-379
    Terneplate and steel, use in making, 1-350, **352**
Lead acetate.
    Experiments and tricks with, *with diagrams*, 7-174-77
Lead azide, explosive. 8-282
Lead telluride. Radioisotope-fueled thermoelectric generators, use in, 6-173-74
Leaders, preliminary lightning flashes. 1-399
Leaf axils. 4-66
Leaf beetles. 3-346-47
Leaf casts. Preparation of, *with illus.*, 10-210-11
Leaf-cutter bees. 3-368
Leaf-cutting ants. *with illus.*, 2-412b; 3-362, 364
Leaf fall. Causes of, 6-54-55
Leaf-footed bugs. 3-258
Leaf insects. *with illus.*, 3-149
    See also **Phasmida; Stick insects**
Leaf monkeys (langurs). 9-255, 257, *illus.*, 254
Leaf prints. Preparation of, *with illus.*, 10-209-10
Leaf scars, markings on surface of twigs. 4-67, *illus.*, 66
    Trees can be recognized by, 5-140
Leaf skeletons. Collecting and preparation of, 10-208-09
Leaf spots, plant diseases. 8-372
Leafhoppers. Grape leafhoppers, 9-195, *illus.*, 196
Leafy liverworts. 3-190
League of Nations.
    Calendar reform conference, 10-179-80
    Health Section, 9-42
Leap Years. 10-174-76, 178-80
Leaping. Mechanism in snow flea, *with illus.*, 1-284
Learning.
    *Animal intelligence, 2-26-29
    Ants, 3-359
    Birds, 5-424
    Psychology of, *with diagram*, 9-315-16
    See also **Binet, Alfred; Brain; Mind**
Learning curves, graphic description of learning progress. 9-316, *diagram*, 315
Least sandpipers, birds. *illus.*, 6-406
Least swamp frogs. 10-262
Leather. *7-231-35
    Human skin made into, 2-174
Leather (bracket) fungi. *with illus.*, 3-30
Leatherbacks, turtles. 5-388
Leavening, of bread. 9-294, *with diagrams*, 296-97
Leaves. *4-71-75
    Alternate, *with illus.*, 5-140
    Arrangement on stem, *with illus.*, 5-140; *with illus.*, 6-220, *illus.*, 221
    Collecting and preserving, *with illus.*, 10-206-12
    Compound, *with illus.*, 5-139
    Cross section of, *illus.*, 3-42b
    Falling of, 6-54-55, 57

Leaves *(continued)*
    Feather-compound, *with illus.*, 5-139-40
    Opposite, *with illus.*, 5-140
    Palmate (palm-veined), *with illus.*, 5-139
    Palmate-compound, *with illus.*, 5-139-40
    Pinnate (feather-veined), *with illus.*, 5-139
    Seed-plant leaves, *with illus.*, 3-400-04
    Simple, *with illus.*, 5-139
    Structure and functions of, 6-54
    Trees identified by, 5-140
    See also **Cotyledons**
Leavitt, Henrietta S., American astronomer. Cepheid variable studied by, 7-51
Le Bris, Jean-Marie. Man-carrying glider, development of, 6-181
Lechwes, antelopes. 8-386
Lecithin, complex substance found in bile. 5-14
Leclanché, Georges, French physicist. 5-94
Leclanché dry cells. *with illus.*, 5-94-95
Lecoq de Boisbaudran, Paul-Emile, French chemist. 5-85
Le Corbusier (Charles-Edouard Jeanneret), Swiss architect (1887–   ). 10-119
    Modern apartment house designed by, *illus.*, 3-125
Lederberg, Joshua, American biologist. 9-386
Lederer, L., American atomic scientist. 7-110
Lee, Tsung D., Chinese-American physicist. 7-110
Leeches. *illus.*, 1-294; *with illus.*, 2-161-62
    Fish in aquariums, leeches as menace to, 8-116
Leeuwenhoek, Anton van, Dutch microscopist. 3-272-73
    Cell structure, investigation of, 7-157
    Microscopes of, 3-16
Left auricle of heart. *illus.*, 1-148f
Left-handedness.
    Parity law and, *with illus.*, 7-107
Left ventricle of heart. *illus.*, 1-148f
Legal psychology. 9-321
Legends.
    Constellations, legends concerning, 1-325, 330, 331-32, 333, 335
    Kingfisher, myth of, 6-310
    Milky Way, 8-151
Legs.
    Birds' perching affected by leg tendon, *with illus.*, 1-284
    Blood vessels of, *illus.*, 1-148f
    Bones of, *illus.*, 1-148b; *with illus.*, 3-82-84, *illus.*, 74, 75
    Development in unborn human young, 8-29
    Fracture of bones, healing of, *illus.*, 7-352
    Human legs, action of, *with illus.*, 1-283
    Insects, 2-403-04, 406, *illus.*, 403
        Cockroaches, *with illus.*, 1-283-84
        True bugs, *with illus.*, 3-253-54
    Muscles of, *illus.*, 1-148c; *illus.*, 3-204, 205, 212, 213
    Sound conducted by front legs in newts, *with illus.*, 1-282
Legumes.
    Green manures, used as, 2-164
    Nitrogen fixed by nodule bacteria of, *with illus.*, 2-23
    See also **Nitrogen fixation; Vegetables**
Lehmann, Heinz E., Canadian psychiatrist. 9-104
Lehrs, ovens used in manufacture of glass containers. *with illus.*, 3-312; 4-156
Leibniz, Gottfried Wilhelm von, German philosopher and mathematician.
    Aneroid barometer, invention of, 3-17
    Binary system of calculation advocated by, 1-155
    Calculating machine of, 9-144
    Evolutionary views, 8-258

Leibniz, Gottfried Wilhelm von (*continued*)
Formation and structure of the earth, theory of, 4-392-93
Patronage of German Academy of Sciences, 3-268-69
Leica cameras. 9-405
Lemmings, rodents. 8-165, 167
Mass movements of, 9-422-23
Snowy owls prey on, 6-165
Lemon trees. Spraying of, *illus.,* 9-186
Lemons. Citric acid in, experiment with, *with illus.,* **4-231**
Lemurs, primates. *illus.,* 7-13; *with illus.,* 9-264-65
Length of life. Effect of increase, 8-79-80
Lenin, Russian nuclear-powered icebreaker. 4-118, *with illus.,* 114a
Lennox, William, American psychiatrist. 9-104
Lenoir, Etienne, French inventor.
Internal-combustion engine of, 2-130
Lenses. *with illus.,* 7-258-60, 261, 262
Camera, 9-397, 398, 405, 406-07, 411, *diagrams,* 405, 406, 407
Chromatic aberration in microscope lenses, overcoming of, 7-158
Compound microscope, *with illus.,* 9-86-93
Corrective, for eyes, 7-296
History of, 9-82-84, 86, 88
Manufacture, 3-314-15
See also **Leeuwenhoek, Anton van; Microscopes**
Lenses, crystalline, of eyes.
Function of, 7-294, 295, 296, *illus.,* 292, 294, 295, 296
See also **Eyes; Vision**
Lenticels, pores in stems of woody plants. 4-67, *illus.,* 66
Lenticular galaxies. 8-50
Leo (Lion), constellation of zodiac. 1-332
Leonardo da Vinci. See **Vinci, Leonardo da**
Leonids, meteor shower. 5-393, *illus.,* 395; 6-96, *table,* 97
Leopard frogs. *with illus.,* 5-154-55, 159
Leopards. *illus.,* 7-10; 8-203, 208, 210, *illus.,* 208
Cubs, *illus.,* 10-157
Fur, 7-238
See also **Snow leopards**
Lepidodendron, genus of ancient spore trees. *illus.,* 6-372
Lepidoptera, order of insects. 2-414; *3-193-202, *illus.,* 202a-d
See also **Moths**
Lepospondyls, primitive group of amphibians. 5-154
Leprosy. A chronic, mildly contagious disease, caused by the microorganism *Mycobacterium leprae.* It occurs chiefly today in tropical and subtropical regions, although there are occasional cases farther north. The disease is marked by external sores and by bone absorption of the fingers and toes. Chaulmoogra oil has been used to treat leprosy for centuries. Nowadays sulphone drugs, such as promin, diasone and promacetin, are preferred.
Bacteria that cause, *illus.,* 3-71
Lepus (Hare), constellation. 1-337
Lesions. Tubercular infection, 9-178
Lesseps, Ferdinand-Marie de, French diplomat.
Panama Canal, work on, 4-191, 192
Suez Canal, construction of, *with illus.,* 4-184
Lesser pandas. See **True pandas**
Letheon, name applied to sulfuric ether. 7-377
Letterpress, relief printing. *with illus.,* 1-197-98, 199-210
Lettuce. Diseases of, 8-374-75
Leucocidins, substances produced by bacteria. 8-366
Leucocytes. See **White blood cells**
Leucoplasts, cell structures. 2-9
Leukemias, cancers of white blood cells. 3-331; 8-267
Leukoplasia, precancerous condition of the tongue. 8-269

Lever House, New York City. 3-117; *illus.,* 8-388
Leverrier, Urbain-Jean-Joseph, French astronomer (1811-77); director of the Paris observatory. His studies of irregularities in the motion of Uranus led to the discovery of a new planet (Neptune). He traced and predicted the paths of storms by daily weather reports collected over a wide area; this led to the development of weather maps. His planetary and solar tables became standard in the *Nautical Almanac.*
Neptune, role in discovery of, 2-317; 3-164; 5-291; 6-392
Levers, simple machines. 3-57-59, *illus.,* 56-58
Experiments involving, *with illus.,* 7-214-16
Living examples of, *with illus.,* 1-283-84; 3-208
See also **Linkages**
Levy brothers, perfecters of halftone printing. 1-198
Lewis, Gilbert Newton, American chemist. 8-417
Lewis, Lee, United States Navy officer. Balloon ascent by, 1-235
Lewis, Meriwether, American explorer. 7-27-28
Lewis, W. Lee, American chemist. 9-213
Lewis and Clark Expedition. 7-28, *illus.,* 27
Lewis Falls, Yellowstone National Park. *illus.,* 6-412
Lewis River, western United States.
Dammed up by Yale Dam, *illus.,* 8-316c
Lewisite. Poison gas developed in World War I, 9-213
Ley, Willy, German-American rocket expert. 9-377
Leyden jars, electrical condensers. 4-359; *with illus.,* 6-122-23
Libby, Willard F., American chemist.
Radiocarbon dating, development of, *with illus.,* 10-93
Libraries. Microfilming in, *with illus.,* 10-72-74
Librations, of moon. 4-278
Libya, Africa. Artesian well in, *illus.,* 8-330
Lice. 2-413
Lice, plant. See **Aphids**
Lichens. *with illus.,* 3-32; 6-223, *illus.,* 139; 7-81
Algae form part of, 3-216, 217
Food chain involving, 10-187
Soil formation, importance in, 2-16, 21-22
Symbiosis, example of, 10-187
Lick, James, American financier, founder of Lick Observatory. 8-64
Lick Observatory, California. 8-64
Lick Observatory 120-inch telescope. 8-58
Liddar Valley, Kashmir. *illus.,* 10-26
Liddel, Urner, American physicist.
Flying saucers, explanation of, 9-19
Lie-detector tests. 9-321
Lieb, Clarence W., American researcher in nutrition. 5-172
Liébault, Ambroise, French physician. Influence on Freud, 9-99
Liebermann, Karl Theodor, German chemist. 5-80
Alizarin synthesized by, 8-183
Liebig, Justus von, German chemist. 5-80
Fermentation theory of, 9-73-74
Plant-nutrient experiments by, 8-34
Liebig condensers.
Construction of, for home laboratory, *with illus.,* 4-225-26
Liége, Belgium.
Smog damage (1930), 3-352-53
Life.
*Adaptations of plants and animals, 3-235-44
*Bioelectricity, 2-421-28
*Bioluminescence, 2-182-91
*Cells, 2-1-14, 287-92
*Classification of plants and animals, 1-287-306
*Communities of plants and animals, 10-181-90
*Evolution, 6-269-85

Life (continued)
  *Habitats, **10**-135-42
  *Nature of life, **1**-37-44
  *Seasonal changes and life, **5**-408-13
  *Senses, human, **7**-291-306
  *Time scale of evolutionary history, **6**-369-74
  Assimilation of radioactive carbon by plants and
      animals, **10**-94-95
  Cave-dwelling plants and animals, *with illus.*, **5**-58-60
  Extraterrestrial beings, radio signals from? **9**-225
  Increasing length of life, **8**-79
  Meteorites and, **6**-94-95
  Oldest things living, **2**-110
  Origin of, research and theory concerning, *with dia-*
      grams, **9**-383-86
  Petroleum formed from dead sea organisms, **4**-142
  Spontaneous creation, Pasteur's experiments disproving,
      9-75-76
  Venus, life on, **4**-30-31
  See also **Animals; Biology; Cells; Evolution; Fossils;**
      Heredity; Longevity of animals; Paleontology;
      Plants; Reproduction; Sex
Life expectancy. **9**-36
Life spans, animal. See **Longevity of animals**
Lift, of hydrofoils. *with illus.*, **4**-5-6
Lift, term used in aeronautics. *with illus.*, **2**-329; **6**-186-87
Lift bridges. *with illus.*, **2**-340, 341
Lift pumps. *with illus.*, **2**-37-38, 275
Lifts, hydraulic. *with illus.*, **2**-34
  Homemade version of, *with illus.*, **7**-222
Ligaments. *illus.*, **3**-204
  Tendons, distinguished from, **3**-210
Ligamentum patellae, kneecap ligament. *illus.*, **3**-204
Light. *Bioluminescence (living light), **2**-182-91
  *Color, **7**-277-90; **8**-178-80
  *Electroluminescence, **9**-344-47
  *Experiments with, **8**-117-24
  *Illumination, **4**-232-41
  *Optics, **7**-249-62
  *Photography, **9**-397-414
  *Solar battery, **7**-103-06
  Adaptations to lack of, **10**-142
  Aquariums, light requirements for, **8**-113
  Astronomy, analysis of light in, **8**-57, 60
  Atomic-bomb explosion produces visible light, **9**-351
  Bending of rays of, **4**-219; **9**-282
  Chemiluminescence, **2**-188-89
  Color separation for photography, *illus.*, **9**-400a-b
  Crystalloluminescence, **2**-188
  Diffraction grating analyses, **7**-144
  Deflection of, by gravitation, **3**-137
  Electromagnetic theory of, **7**-201, 205
    Light foreshadowed by Faraday, **5**-236
  Fishes that produce, **4**-103
  Galileo's attempt to measure the velocity of, **3**-5
  Magnetic properties of, **5**-236
  Mammals affected by, **7**-8
  Mass and energy, relation to, **1**-84-85
  Meteor glow, **6**-87, 88, 89, 95-96
  Minerals identified by reaction to, **5**-256
  Photoelectric devices for determining amount of, **8**-60
  Photon theory of, **9**-280
  Plane-polarized light, **5**-340-41, *diagram*, 339; **9**-71-72
  Plants affected by, *illus.*, **1**-47; **3**-52, *illus.*, 50; **6**-220-
      22
  Plants' utilization of sunlight energy, **3**-44-45
  Radio waves compared to light rays, **3**-85
  Scattering by dust, **7**-142
  Spectrum of, *with illus.*, **5**-85-86; **7**-205, *with diagram*,
      199-201
    Astronomical research, **9**-361

Light (continued)
  Study of, 1600–1765, *with illus.*, **3**-275-78
  Study of, in nineteenth century, *with illus.*, **6**-239-47
  Velocity of, **3**-278; **5**-21
  Water plants need, **8**-113
  See also **Incandescence; Lamps; Lighting;**
      Luminescence; Photoelectric cells; Sunlight; Vision
Light fuel oils. **4**-149
Light globes. See **Electric lighting**
Light meters. See **Photoelectric exposure meters**
Lighted buoys. **5**-71, *illus.*, 69
Lighter-than-air flight. **6**-177-81, *illus.*, 176, 178-81
  World War I, **9**-214, 215
Lighthouses.
  Pharos of ancient Alexandria, *illus.*, **1**-354
Lighting. *4-232-41
  Buoys, *illus.*, **4**-238
  Electric lighting, **9**-239
  Electric lighting in nineteenth century, *illus.*, **2**-244;
      5-246-47
  Fluorescent, *illus.*, **4**-237
  Good vision and, *with illus.*, **10**-78-79
  Homemade layouts for street and stage lighting, *with*
      illus., **6**-294
  Indirect incandescent, *illus.*, **4**-236
  Panelescent, uses of, **9**-345-46
  Photography, artificial lighting for, **9**-410-12
  Safety factor in home, **7**-194
  See also **Electricity; Lamps;** etc.
Lighting systems.
  Automobiles, **2**-144
  First practical electric lighting system for streets and
      homes, **4**-235
Lightning. *1-398-404
  Eruptions of volcanoes accompanied by, **8**-301
  Explanation of, **1**-245
  Franklin's experiment, **4**-360-61; *with illus.*, **6**-125
  Measuring distance from, *with illus.*, **5**-224
  Precautions at home against, **7**-191
  Trees protected from, **10**-150-51
Lightning bugs, beetles. **3**-342
Lightning rods. **7**-191
  Invented by Franklin, **1**-403
Lightweight passenger trains. **1**-188-89
Lignite, lowest-rank coal. **1**-408
Lilienthal, Otto, German pioneer in aeronautics. **6**-181-
      82, *illus.*, 183; **9**-216
Lilies. *illus.*, **1**-45; *illus.*, **3**-403
Lilius, Aloysius. See **Ghiraldi, Luigi Lilio**
Lima beans.
  Seeds of, *illus.*, **4**-131
Lime.
  Disease organisms in soil held in check by, **2**-206
  Hairs from hides removed by, **7**-232, *illus.*, 233
  Plastics, used in manufacture of, **8**-224, 225
  Soil component and fertilizer, *with illus.*, **2**-168-71
Lime juice.
  Scurvy treated by, **3**-380
Lime-soda ash process, for treating hard water. **2**-280-81
Lime spreaders, farm machines. *illus.*, **2**-169
Limelight. Invention of, **4**-235-36
Limestone, sedimentary rock. *illus.*, **1**-32; **3**-324, 425,
      illus., 424; **9**-308
  Caves in formations of, *with illus.*, **5**-51-56
  Construction and chemical industries, **3**-174
  Coral reefs form, **6**-72
  Deposition in sea, **2**-86
  Iron- and steelmaking, **1**-341-43, 345-46; **3**-174, *illus.*,
      173
  Plastics, used in manufacture of, **8**-224
  Reef-building corals from, **3**-179

Limestone (continued)
Soil fertilizer, use as, 2-168
See also **Quarrying; Rocks**

Limewater.
Carbon dioxide, reaction with, 4-231, illus., 230
Carbon dioxide, testing for, with illus., 7-130

Limit, in mathematics. 4-433-34

Limit gauges. Machined work tested by, 10-112

Limiting stress. 5-376

Limonite, mineral. 1-340; 5-254; 9-306, illus., 304

Limpets. 2-200-01
Light emission by, 2-185

Lin Yutang, Chinese author.
Chinese typewriter developed by, 1-274-75

Linacs. See **Linear accelerators**

Lincoln, breed of sheep. illus., 10-246

Lincoln Tunnel, New York City. with illus., 2-56-57

Lind, James, Scottish physician.
Scurvy prevention, contribution to, 3-380; 5-39

Lindbergh, Charles A., American aviator. 6-184, illus., 185; 9-217

Linden trees. with illus., 5-146
Fruits, illus., 5-141
Stem, cross section of, illus., 4-69

Line breeding. 10-242

Line-casting machines, for typesetting. with illus., 1-200-02

Line graphs. 2-72, illus., 70, 71

Line pack, pipeline storage of natural gas. 5-105

Linear accelerators (linacs). with illus., 9-242, 246-47

Linear expansion, coefficient of. 3-414-15

Linear measures.
Metric system, table, 10-296
United States, table, 10-295

Linen. 4-179-80

Lines, geometric. with illus., 3-430

Lines, straight. Analytic geometry, equations in, with diagrams, 4-426-27

Lines of force. Electrical and magnetic, with illus., 5-235-36; with diagram, 7-356-57

Linework, photoengraved illustrations in printing. with diagrams, 1-204-06

Linguistic stocks. 1-118-19

Linguistics. *1-107-21

Link jet trainers. illus., 2-235

Linkages, lever-and-gear systems. with illus., 3-437; with illus., 7-218

Linnaean Society. 3-377

Linnaeus, Carolus (Carl von Linné), Swedish naturalist. illus., 1-289; with illus., 3-374-77
Centigrade thermometer scale attributed to, 3-410
Classification of living things, 1-288

Linofilm machines, for typesetting. with illus., 1-203

Linoleum. Floor covering, 7-128

Linotype machines, for typesetting. with illus., 1-200-01

Linsangs, mammals. 8-245, 246

Linseed oil. 4-180

Lintels, horizontal members in construction. 7-119

Lions. illus., 1-300; with illus., 8-203-06
Zoo lions, illus., 10-154

Lipase, digestive enzyme. 4-328

Lipids, fatty substances. Protoplasm, lipid content of, 2-3, 5, 7-9
See also **Fats**

Lipmann, Fritz A., German-American biologist.
ATP research of, 9-385

Lipoproteins, complex lipids. 2-5

Lippershey, Hans, Dutch spectaclemaker. with illus., 3-14-15

Liquid diets. Sick persons', 10-64-65

Liquid-fuel rockets. 9-377, 381-82, illus., 376; 10-42, 44-46

Liquid measures.
United States, table, 10-295

Liquid smokes. See **Smokes, liquid**

Liquids.
*Blood, 3-325-34
*Petroleum, 4-140-52
*Solutions, 4-296-303
Allergenic substances, 4-260
Boiling of, 3-418
Colloidal particles, 5-296
Diffusion of, with illus., 5-373, 374
Emulsification by high-frequency sound, 8-109, illus., 110
Evaporation of, with illus., 3-417-18
Expansion, measurement of, 3-415
Experiments and tricks with, with diagrams, 7-173-80
Heat transfer by water, 4-10-13, 16, illus., 10, 12
Molecular behavior of, 1-170, with illus., 162-63, 171, 172, with diagram and illus., 166-69
Pressure of, with illus., 2-30-36
Protoplasm contains, 2-3, 6-7, 9-11
Solids, converted into, 3-416, 417
Superfluids, with illus., 5-208-09, illus., 207
Viscosity of, with illus., 5-369-70
Water pressure, experiments with, with illus., 7-221-22
See also **Matter; Molecules,** and names of liquids

Liquor, cooking, in paper-making. illus., 4-374b

Liquors, spirituous. with illus., 4-406

Lisbon, Portugal. Earthquake of 1755, 9-110

Lisse, Holland. Brick house, 7-119

Lister, Joseph, English surgeon. 7-385-87

Lithium (Li), chemical element. Atomic number, 3; atomic weight, 6.939; melting point, 186° C.; boiling point, about 1,336° C.; specific gravity, 0.534. Lightest alkali metal; soft, white, with salts similar to those of sodium and potassium. Discovered by Arfvedson in 1817; name derived from Greek lithos, "stone." Never occurs free in nature; traces found in almost all igneous rocks and in water of many mineral springs. Prepared from the fused chloride by electrolysis. Used in alloys as a hardening agent in bearing metals, adding tensile strength and resistance to corrosion; also as a "getter" in vacuum tubes to remove last traces of oxygen and nitrogen. See also 3-165-66
Atomic structure, 1-311, diagram, 312

Lithium carbide.
Decomposition of, in diamond synthesis, 4-275

Lithium carbonate.
Diamond-synthesis experiment using, 4-275-76

Lithographic printing. illus., 1-204a-d
See also **Planographic printing**

Lithosphere. 1-33; with illus., 4-46

Litmus paper, acid-base indicator. 4-231, 341, table, 339

Litter. Manures, absorbent of, 2-166

Litters, traveling couches. 1-98, illus., 99

Little, Clarence Cook, American medical researcher.
Lung cancer, research in, 5-350

Little Big Inch, pipeline. 4-147

Little Dipper, group of stars in Ursa Minor. 1-325

Live oak trees. 5-147

Live traps. See **Traps**

"Live" vaccines. Virus, 3-458

Liver. illus., 1-148d; 5-13-15, illus., 14
Alcoholism may be brought about by liver damage, 4-411
Blood partly regulated by, 3-327, 331
Development in human baby, 8-95

Liver *(continued)*
  Function of, 7-373
  Location in body, *illus.,* 4-322
Liver extracts, used in medicine. **9-35**
Liver flukes, flatworms. 2-155-56, *illus.,* 154
Liverworts. 3-189-90, *illus.,* 186
Livestock, farm and ranch animals.
  *Processing of livestock for food, 5-163-72
  Breeding improves, 5-165-66
  Manure of livestock fertilizes soil, 2-163, *with diagram,* 165-67
Livingston, M. Stanley, American physicist. **9-249**
Livingstone, David, Scottish missionary and explorer. 7-31, *illus.,* 32
  Crocodiles, experience with, 5-385
Lizard fishes. 4-99
Lizards. *5-196-206
  Desert-terrarium animals, 5-366
  Galápagos Islands, lizards of, *illus.,* 7-31
  Inactivity in cold weather, 5-411, 412
  Pets, 7-24
Llamas. 7-331-32, *illus.,* 330
  Adaptations for high altitudes, 7-8
  Transportation, use in, 1-102, *illus.,* 103
Lloyd barrage system, Pakistani irrigation project. 8-201
Load (resistance), resistance to action of lever. *with illus.,* 1-283; *with illus.,* 3-56-58; *with illus.,* 7-215
Load, stream, material carried by streams. 8-12-13, 16, 17, 18
Loaded circuits. Invention of, 2-392-93
Loading machines, in coal mining. 1-412, *illus.,* 413
Loadstones. 7-356, *with illus.,* 163-64, 167
Loams. 2-18
  See also Soil
Loaves, bread. 9-294, 295, *with diagrams,* 297-99
Lobachevsky, Nikolai Ivanovich, Russian mathematician (1793–1856). Geometry of, *with diagrams,* 4-439-41
Lobe-finned fish. 4-197; *illus.,* 6-372
Lobes of cerebrum. *with illus.,* 6-324-25
Lobster pots. 2-238
Lobsters. *illus.,* 1-295; 2-238-39, *illus.,* 236, 239
  Sounds made by, 8-43
LOBUND (Laboratories of Bacteriology, University of Notre Dame). *with illus.,* 7-151-55
Local Group, concentration of galaxies. 8-53, *diagram,* 52
Local races of mankind. 8-218-19
Local radioactive fallout. 9-355
Local Supercluster, concentration of galaxy clusters. 8-53-54
Localization, by eyes. 7-295-96
Locke, John, English philosopher. Innate ideas, denial of, 9-315
Lockheed Aircraft Corporation. 7-74
Lockheed Electra, American turboprop plane. 7-74
Lockjaw. See Tetanus
Lockup, stage in printing. *with illus.,* 1-206-07
Lockyer, Sir Joseph Norman, English astronomer (1836–1920). He served as director of London's Solar Physics Observatory and professor of astronomical physics at the Royal College of Science. He studied sun spots, developed a method of observing solar prominences (red flames around sun's disc) in daylight and discovered the presence of helium in the sun's atmosphere. In 1869 he established the British scientific journal *Nature.* See also 5-86
  Helium discovered by, 1-20; 6-391
  Solar observations, 3-105
Locomotion, animal. 1-54
  Bears, 7-308
  Bird flight, *with illus.,* 5-416-19

Locomotion, animal *(continued)*
  Cheetahs, 8-212
  Earthworms, *with diagram,* 1-279-80
  Elephants, 7-412
  Hippopotamuses, 7-412, 414
  Insect movement and flight, 2-403
  Marsupials, 7-422, 424
  Primates, 9-252, 255
  Seals, 7-86
  Snakes, 5-352-53, *with illus.,* 354a-d
  See also under names of various organs of locomotion such as Muscles
Locomotion, plant. Algae, *illus.,* 1-41; 3-215, 217, 221
  Slime molds, *with illus.,* 6-218a
Locomotives.
  Coal-burning, 1-89, 416, *diagram,* 90
  Compressed air for operating, 9-66
  See also Locomotives, diesel-electric; Locomotives, electric; Locomotives, steam; Locomotives, turbine-electric
Locomotives, diesel-electric. 1-185, *illus.,* 179-80, 184
Locomotives, electric. 1-186
Locomotives, steam. 1-186, *illus.,* 185
  Development of, 1-180-82, *illus.,* 179, 180, 181, 182; *with illus.,* 6-378-80
Locomotives, turbine-electric. *illus.,* 2-233
  Coal-burning power plant, 1-89, *diagram,* 90
Locus, path described by point in plane. *with illus.,* 3-437
Locust trees. *with illus.,* 5-148; 10-205
  Fruits, *illus.,* 5-141
  Leaves, *illus.,* 4-72; *illus.,* 5-139
Locusts. See Cicadas; Grasshoppers; Short-horned grasshoppers
Lodestones. See Loadstones
Lodge, Sir Oliver J., English physicist (1851–1940). He was physics professor at the University College, Liverpool, and principal of the University of Birmingham. He studied the propagation of electromagnetic waves, lightning, electrolysis and the relative motion of matter and the ether. He helped develop the coherer, used in wireless telegraphy. Interested in psychical research, Sir Oliver tried to reconcile science and religion.
  Radio emanations from sun studied by, 9-207
Loeb, Jacques, American physiologist whose researches into the origin of life attracted wide attention (1859–1924). He performed many experiments upon sea urchins and succeeded in artificially fertilizing their eggs. Born and educated in Germany, Loeb settled in the United States in 1891. After holding professorships at several universities, he became head of the department of experimental biology at the Rockefeller Institute, New York, in 1910. See also 7-326
Loeffler, Friedrich August Johannes, German bacteriologist. 3-452; 7-382
  Viruses discovered by, 8-405
Loess, soil deposit. 6-142; *with illus.,* 7-325-26, *illus.,* 140
Loewy, Raymond, American designer. 10-119, 120, 121-22, 123
Logarithms. 2-74-76
  Inventions of, 3-6, 19-20
Logging. 2-111-13, 115, *illus.,* 110, 111
  Elephants used in, 7-411, *illus.,* 413
Logographic writing. 1-113-14
Logs.
  Boats and rafts of, 4-106
  Building material, *with illus.,* 7-115
  Streams dammed by, 8-17
Logs, well. See Well logging
Lokman, Arabian king. Dam constructed by, 8-308
Lola giant silkworm moths. *illus.,* 3-202d

Lombardy poplar trees. 5-144
London, England.
　Smog damage (1952), 3-353
London plane trees. 5-146
Long, Crawford Williamson, American surgeon. 7-377
Long-day plants. 4-120
Long-distance telephony. with illus., 2-392-95
Long-eared owls. 6-165
Long-horned beetles. 3-346, illus., 346-47
Long-horned grasshoppers. with illus., 3-143-47; 10-262
Long-period variable stars. 7-48, 50
Long periods, of chemical elements. 4-306, 308, 310, tables, 307, 309
Long-playing records. 7-369, illus., 362
Long-range rockets. with illus., 10-2-4
Long-range weather forecasts. 1-254
Long records, red-filter photographs. 8-180, diagrams, 179
Longevity of animals.
　Aardwolves, 8-250
　Amphibians, 5-161
　Black bears, 7-315
　Camels, 7-329
　Cats, 8-204, 206, 208, 210
　Cockroaches, 3-147
　Elephants, 7-328
　Fossas, 8-249
　Genets, 8-249
　Insects, 2-407, 408
　Moles, 7-98
　Mongooses, 8-249
　Oriental civets, 8-249
　Polar bears, 7-310
　Primates, 9-260
　Snakes, 5-353
　Spotted hyenas, 8-250
　Striped hyenas, 8-250
Longitude, terrestrial. Longitude is a form of geographic reference to any point on the earth's surface. It is expressed in degrees of angular distance from the prime meridian, an imaginary line running from one pole to the other and through the city of Greenwich, England. Thus the longitude of New York City is 74° west of Greenwich. Longitude is also expressed in terms of the amount of time it takes the sun to travel between a point on the earth's surface and the prime meridian. New York is 4 hours 56 minutes west of Greenwich.
　Stars used in determining, 8-61
Longitudinal dunes. 7-322
Longitudinal waves.
　Earthquakes, 9-107
Longleaf pine trees. 5-142
Longspurs, sparrows. 6-108
Longwall mining, of coal. 1-411
Looms, for weaving. Silk, 5-184
Loons. 6-394, illus., 395
Loran. ("LOng-RAnge Navigation by radio"). It serves to determine the position of a ship or airplane and has a range of 750 nautical miles during the day and 1,400 miles at night. (On land, however, its range is much shorter.) Two different radio stations on land continuously send out pulsating signals that are picked up as a pair of lines on an oscilloscope screen inside a ship. The navigator measures the difference in time of arrival of the waves from the two separate stations. He then tunes in on another pair of Loran radio stations and in the same way determines their time difference. Using the two time differences and special tables, the navigator obtains two map lines, with which he fixes the exact position of his ship at sea independent of the weather.

Loran (continued)
　Hyperbola applied to, with illus., 3-439-40
　Ship's position checked by, 6-230, illus., 235
Lorentz, Hendrik, Dutch physicist (1853–1928). He was professor of mathematical physics at the University of Leiden. He tried to construct a consistent theory explaining electricity, magnetism and light. His explanation of the Zeeman effect (changes in spectral lines in a magnetic field) won for him the 1902 Nobel Prize in physics. (He shared it with P. Zeeman.) Lorentz's studies of electrical and optical phenomena in moving media paved the way for the relativity theory.
　Fitzgerald-Lorentz contraction, 4-214
Lorises, lemurlike primates. with illus., 9-265
Los Angeles, California.
　Mission San Fernando, illus., 7-121
　Smog problem, 3-350, 353-54, illus., 350, 354-55; illus., 5-294
　Water supply of, 2-275
Los Angeles, dirigible. 6-179-80
Lotuses. illus., 3-49; illus., 5-65
　Fruit of, illus., 5-3
Loud-speakers, in radio. with illus., 3-96-97
Loudness, of sounds. 5-124
Louis XIV, king of France.
　Patron of Academy of Sciences, with illus., 3-268
Louis, Pierre-Charles-Alexandre, French statistician. 7-375
Louisiana. Salt mines of, 5-318, illus., 312
Louisiana Purchase. 7-27
Lowe, T. S. Balloon observation corps in Civil War organized by, 6-177
Lowell, Percival, American astronomer (1855–1916). He taught astronomy at the Massachusetts Institute of Technology. Founding the Lowell Observatory at Flagstaff, Arizona, he made extensive studies of the planets Mercury, Venus, Saturn and, especially, Mars. He predicted the existence and position of planet X (Pluto, discovered in 1930). See also 6-392
　Mars, observations of, 4-419
　Pluto's position, calculations of, 5-292; 9-225
　Venus, theories about, 4-29
Lowell Observatory, Flagstaff, Arizona.
　Observations at, 5-292-93
Lows, atmospheric low-pressure areas. with diagrams, 1-242-44, illus., 250
Lubbock, Sir John, English science writer (1834–1913). Ants, observations of, 3-359-60
"Lubbock lights," alleged flying-saucer appearance. 9-18, 20
Lubricants.
　Graphite crystals, with diagram, 5-338
　Greases, 4-149
　Muscles and joints naturally lubricated, 3-211
　Plastics, used in manufacture of, 8-225
Lubricating oils. 4-148, 149
　Viscosity indicated by numbers, 5-370
Lubricating systems, of engines.
　Automobiles, 2-136, illus., 137
　Gasoline engines, 4-89
Lucerne, Lake of, Switzerland. illus., 2-219
Luciferase, compound formed in cells of luminous organisms. 2-188-89
Luciferin, compound formed in cells of luminescent organisms. 2-188-89; 3-342; 8-118
Lucite, acrylic plastic. 8-226
Lucky Dragon No. 5, Japanese fishing trawler. 9-353
Lucretius (Titus Lucretius Carus), Roman philosophical poet. 1-361
Ludlow machines, for typesetting. 1-202
Lumbago. 3-213

Lumbar nerves. 6-329, *illus.*, 328
Lumbar vertebrae, lower part of backbone. *illus.*, 3-75
Lumbering. *2-105-17
    Pulpwood logs, *illus.*, 4-374a
    Research in, 1-88
Lumbosacral plexus. 6-329
Lumen, standard unit of light intensity. 4-239
Luminescence. *Bioluminescence, 2-182-91
Luminescence, animal. *2-182-91
    Beetles, 3-341-42
Luminous mosses. 3-188
Luna moths. 3-200, *illus.*, 193
Lunar caustic, silver nitrate. 3-36
Lunar eclipses. 3-131-34
    Observation of, 6-83
Lung cancer.
    Smoking as cause of, *with diagrams*, 5-347-50; 8-268
Lungfishes. *illus.*, 5-411
    Estivation during dry season, 5-412-13, *illus.*, 411
    Evolution of, 4-197, *diagram*, 199
    Primitive forms, 1-389
Lungless salamanders. 5-156
Lungs. *4-200-09
    Air pollution's affect on, 3-351
    Amphibians use lungs as float mechanism, *with illus.*, 1-280
    Blood vessels of, *illus.*, 1-148f
    Lining tissue of, 1-145
    Man's, *illus.*, 1-148d-f
    Pumping action of, *with diagram*, 1-279
    Tuberculosis of, 9-176-77, 180-83, *illus.*, 178, 181
Luniks, Russian artificial satellites. 9-376, 380; 10-47
Lunulae ("half-moons") of fingernails. *with illus.*, 2-181
Lupines. Fruit of, *illus.*, 5-6
Luray Caverns, Virginia. *illus.*, 5-58a-d
Luster (sheen), identifying characteristic of minerals. 5-254
Lutetium (Lu), chemical element. Atomic number, 71; atomic weight, 174.97. Rare-earth metal. Discovered by Urbain in 1907; name derived from Latin *Lutetia*, ancient name for Paris. Found with other rare earths in the minerals gadolinite, euxenite, xenotime and others; usually separated by fractional crystallization of the bromates. Little practical use.
Lycopodium, genus of club mosses. 3-192, *illus.*, 190
Lycopodium powder, flammable spores of club mosses. 3-192; 7-178
Lye. See **Sodium hydroxide**
Lyell, Sir Charles, British geologist. 4-397-98
    Early man, study of, 9-21-22
Lygaeids, family of true bugs. *with illus.*, 3-258-59
Lying. Psychopathic personality, lying as symptom of, 9-200
Lymph. 3-388-89; 5-8
    Muscular exercise, role in, 3-207
Lymph glands. 5-8-9
    Body's defenses, role in, *with diagram*, 7-349
Lymph nodes. *illus.*, 1-148g; *with diagram*, 3-389-90
    Body's defenses, as part of, 5-8-9; *with diagram*, 7-349
Lymphatic nodes. *diagram*, 5-9
Lymphatic system. *illus.*, 1-148g; *with diagram*, 3-388-90; 5-8-9, *diagram*, 9
    Body's defenses, role in, *with diagram*, 7-349
Lymphatic vessels. 5-8, *diagram*, 9
    Development in unborn human young, 8-29
Lymphocytes, white blood cells. 3-328, *illus.*, 329; 5-8; 7-349
    Body's defenses, role in, *diagram*, 7-349
    See also **White blood cells**

Lymphomas, cancers of the lymph glands and other lymphatic tissues. 8-267
Lynxes. *with illus.*, 8-211-12
    Fur, 7-238
Lynxes, Society of the (Accademia dei Lincei). 3-265
Lyophilization. See **Freeze-drying**
Lyot, Bernard.
    Coronagraph, development of, 3-105
Lyra (Lyre), constellation. 1-333
Lyrids, meteor shower. 6-96, *table*, 97
Lysergic acid. 5-377
Lysosomes, cell structures. 2-8
Lyttleton, R. A., English astronomer.
    Origin of solar system, theory of, 1-29-30, *illus.*, 30

M

M42, gaseous nebula in Orion. 1-335
McAdam, John L., British engineer. 3-294, *with illus.*, 299
Macadamized roads. 3-299
Macaques, Old World monkeys. 9-257, 264, *illus.*, 256
MacCallum, William G., American pathologist. 10-34
McCandless, William, American manufacturer.
    Electron tube, development of, 8-85, 86, 87, 89
McCarthy, George L., American banker and inventor.
    Microfilming apparatus perfected by, 10-69
McCay, C. M., American physiologist. 8-82
McClendon, J. F., American biochemist. 2-292
McCormick, Cyrus Hall, American inventor and manufacturer. 6-383
McElroy, William D., American biologist. ATP research of, 9-385
McGill University, Montreal.
    Cyclotron at, *illus.*, 8-419
Mach, Ernst, Austrian physicist (1838–1916). 9-219; 10-228
Mach number. 7-72; 9-219; 10-228-30, 231, 233, 234
Mach waves (Mach cones or envelopes). *with diagrams*, 10-229-30, 231-32
Machine coating, process for providing smooth surface for paper. 4-375
Machine tools. *10-105-13
    Automobile industry, 2-145
    Industry, *illus.*, 1-92b
    Rise of machine-tool industry, 4-41
    See also **Machinery**
Machinery.
  *Automation, 10-235-38
  *Breadmaking, 9-293-99
  *Design of machines and machine-made goods, 10-117-26
  *Machine tools, 10-105-13
    Agricultural, *illus.*, 2-164, 168, 169; 9-291-92
    Cattle hides split by, 7-234, *illus.*, 233
    Coal-mining machinery, *with illus.*, 1-408-13
    Compressed-air operates, 9-66
    Cotton pickers, 4-178, *illus.*, 178-79
    History
        Industrial Revolution, *with illus.*, 4-35-41
        Development in nineteenth century, *with illus.*, 6-377-83
    Packing plants' use of, *with illus.*, 5-166-68
    Petroleum-industry, *with illus. and diagram*, 4-144-49
    See also **Boilers; Engines; Power; Printing;** etc.
Machines.
  *Animal mechanisms, 1-277-86
  *Simple machines, 3-56-62
    Muscles compared with, 3-207-08
    Plastic manufacturing, *with diagrams*, 8-230-33
    See also **Machinery**

Macintosh, Charles, English textile expert. **6-351**
Mackenzie, Alexander, Scottish explorer. **7-28-29**
MacKenzie River, Oregon.   Koosah Falls, *illus.,* **8-15**
Mackerel sharks. **4-288**
Mackerels. **4-315**
   Migration of, **9-427**
   Reproduction, **4-104**
Mackinac Straits Bridge, Michigan. *illus.,* **2-338**
McKinley, Mount, Alaska
   Glaciers of, *illus.,* **9-166**
   Highest peak of North America, **10-23**
McMillan, E. M., American physicist. **9-248, 249**
MacMillan, Kirkpatrick, Scottish inventor. **6-380**
Macrolepidoptera, large Lepidoptera. **3-202**
Macromolecules, giant molecules.
   Crystals made up of, *with diagrams,* **5-338**
Macronuclei, cell structures. **2-66**
Macrophages, giant splenic cells. **5-10**
Madder, dye plant.
   Alizarin (Turkey red), source of, **5-80-81; 8-183**
Maddox, Richard Leach, English photographer.
   9-403
Madrone trees. *with illus.,* **5-149**
Maelstrom, whirlpool. **6-207**
Maeterlinck, Maurice, Belgian poet and essayist.
   8-255-56
Magazines, publications. Microfilming for files of, *with
   illus.,* **10-72**
Magdeburg hemispheres. **3-18**
   Experiment with, **1-234,** *illus.,* **234-35**
Magellan, Ferdinand, Portuguese navigator. *with illus.,*
   2-365-66
Magellanic Clouds, nebulous appearances in southern
   skies. **1-337; 8-64**
   Distance from earth, **8-51**
Magendie, François, French physiologist (1783–1855).
   By attacking the traditions of medicine of his time, he
   became leader of an important new school of experi-
   mental medicine.   He introduced the medical use of
   bromine, iodine compounds, strychnine and morphine.
   His study of the nervous system and its functions won
   him his highest title to fame.   See also **7-373; 9-48**
Magenta. Printing color, **1-213**
Maggots. See **Flies; Larvae**
Magic. *Chemical magic, **7-173-80**
Magic squares, of numbers. *with diagrams,* **4-449-50**
Magma, molten rock. **3-419-22;** *diagram,* **7-334**
Magnes, mythical figure. Supposed to have discovered
   the loadstone, **7-164**
Magnesia. **3-172**
Magnesium (Mg), chemical element. Atomic number,
   12; atomic weight, 24.312; melting point, 651° C.; boiling point, 1,107° C.; specific gravity, 1.74. Alkaline-
   earth metal; light, white, fairly soft and tough, malleable and ductile.   Recognized as an element by Black
   in 1755, isolated by Davy in 1808.   Name derived
   from Magnesia, district in ancient Thessaly.   One of
   the most abundant metals, never occurring free but
   found combined with many carbonates and silicates,
   and in mineral springs and the ocean.   Obtained by
   electrolysis of the fused chloride, using brines from
   wells and sea water.   Alloys used in airplanes; also
   useful in deoxidizers in metallurgical operations, in
   flashlight powders, flares, perfumes and some medicines.
   See also **3-171-72,** *illus.,* **170**
   Diet, essential to, **4-59**
   Electrolytic production of, *illus.,* **5-93**
   Electron arrangement, *with illus.,* **3-247**
   Ions of, in protoplasm, **2-6**
   Photographic flashes with, **9-411**
   Plants' use of, **3-44**

Magnesium *(continued)*
   Salts of, in the sea, **6-30,** *chart,* **31**
   Soil magnesium available to plants, **2-24**
   Water hardened by magnesium compounds, **2-280-81**
Magnesium chloride. Sea water contains, **5-315**
Magnetic bottles, for confining plasmas. **1-175-78,**
   illus., **175, 176, 177**
Magnetic curves.
   Lines of force, *with illus.,* **5-235-36**
Magnetic drum separator, for separating iron and
   titanium ores.   *illus.,* **3-39**
Magnetic equator, of earth.   See **Magnetic field of the
   earth**
Magnetic field of the earth. **4-176**
   Atmospheric electricity affects, **1-240**
   Climate affected by, **3-185**
   Cosmic rays, *with diagram,* **8-394-95**
   See also **Geomagnetism**
Magnetic fields. *with illus.,* **7-164-68**
   Electric current generated by, *with illus.,* **9-227-28**
   Prospecting by measuring magnetic fields of rocks,
      with diagrams, **7-356-57, 361**
Magnetic loud-speakers, in radio. **3-96,** *illus.,* **97**
Magnetic ores. Prospecting for, **7-171,** *with diagram,*
   356-57
Magnetic poles. *with illus.,* **7-167-71**
Magnetic properties.
   Diamagnetic and paramagnetic, **5-236**
   Minerals, prospecting by analyzing magnetic proper-
      ties of, *with diagram,* **7-356-57**
Magnetic pumping, for creation of ultrahot plasmas.
   1-178
Magnetic recording. **7-368**
   Color-television signals recorded on magnetic tape,
      5-288
Magnetic separation, in ore dressing. **1-374-75**
Magnetic storms. **7-171-72**
Magnetic variables, variable stars. **6-268**
Magnetism. *7-162-72**
   *Experiments with, **8-142-50**
   Absolute zero, magnetic phenomena at temperatures
      near, **5-210,** *illus.,* **209**
   Charged particles affected by magnetic field, **9-241**
   Electricity, relation to, *with illus.,* **5-231-32**
   Force, magnetism as, *with illus.,* **1-83, 84**
   History
      Sixteenth century, **2-371**
      Electromagnetism in nineteenth century, *with illus.,*
         5-231-47
   Magnetic recording, **7-368**
   Magnetostriction, **8-107**
   Minerals identified by, **5-255-56**
   Natural-gas prospecting, magnetic devices used in,
      5-99, *illus.,* **101**
   Ore separation, use of electromagnets in, **1-374-75**
   Prospecting with magnetic methods, **7-361,** *with dia-
      gram,* **356-57**
   Relation of, to light and electricity, **6-239, 242-45**
   See also **Electromagnetism**
Magnetite, mineral. **3-422; 5-256; 7-356,** *with illus.,*
   163-64
   Iron ore contains, **1-340**
Magnetometers, instruments measuring the earth's
   magnetism. **5-99,** *illus.,* **101; 7-356-57**
Magnetosphere, radiation zone around earth. **1-240,**
   diagram, **239; 5-195**
Magnetostriction. **8-107**
Magnetrons, high-frequency electron tubes. **6-302**
Magnets.
   Alternating gradient accelerator magnets, **9-249**
   Bar magnets, *with illus.,* **8-142-43**

Magnets (continued)
 Betatron magnets, 9-247
 Cyclotron magnets, with illus., 9-244-46
 Electron synchrotron magnets, 9-248
 Ore separation, use of electromagnets in, 1-374-75
 See also **Magnetism**
Magnification.
 Galvanometric system, used in seismometers, 9-113
 Optical images, 7-256, 261, 262, illus., 260, 261
 Resolution as opposed to, 9-92
Magnifying lenses. 3-15-16; with illus., 7-258-61
Magnitude, absolute. See **Absolute magnitude**
Magnitude, apparent.
 Star magnitude, symbols for, illus., 1-325
 Stars and other heavenly bodies, 1-323; table, 10-299
 See also **Apparent magnitude**
Magnolia trees. 5-148, illus., 149
Magpies.
 Pets, 7-23
Maidenhair ferns. 3-192, illus., 189
Maidenhair trees. 3-402, illus., 401
Mail. Microfilming of, 10-74, illus., 73
Mail cars, of railroad trains. 1-186
Mail coaches. See **Stagecoaches**
Maimonides (Moses ben-Maimon), Jewish mathematician and philosopher, 2-302
Main-sequence stars. 6-264, 265, 266, table, 264
Maine. Granites in, 2-84
Mainmasts, principal masts of sailing ships. Ancient, 4-107
Mains, gas. Location by analytic geometry, with diagram, 4-430
Mains, transmission. 2-275-76, illus., 276-77
Mains, water. 2-275-76, 286, illus., 276-77, 285, 286
 Location by analytic geometry, with diagram, 4-430
Maintained vibration, of sound waves. 5-117
Major axis, of ellipse. 8-126-27, diagram, 126
Make-ready, in printing. 1-208-09
Make-up, bringing together of type and engravings in printing. with illus., 1-206
Make-up bank (stone), for imposition of printing material. 1-206
"Make-up" operations, in breadmaking. with diagrams, 9-297
Malagasy mongooses. See **Galidines**
Malania anjouanae, primitive fish. 4-196, with illus., 197
Malaria.
 *Mosquito as vector of malaria, 10-30-37
 Developments in control of, 9-39
 Mosquito shown to be vector of, 7-384
 Parasites
  Discovered by Laveran, 10-31
  Life cycle of, 9-431-32; 10-34
 See also **Mosquitoes**
Malayan sun bears (bruangs). 7-315
Male ants. illus., 3-360
Male ferns. 3-192
Male sex cells. See **Spermatozoa**
Malignancies. See **Malignant tumors**
Malignant tumors (malignancies).
 Benign tumors distinguished from, 8-265
 Bone, 3-84
 See also **Cancer**
Mallards, ducks. illus., 5-414; 6-402, illus., 401
 Banding a female, illus., 9-421
 Nest, with eggs, illus., 10-260
Malleability. 5-376
Malleus. See **Hammer**
Mallophaga, order of insects. 2-413

Malnutrition.
 Cancer entails, 8-266
 Causes and treatment of, 4-60-61
Malocclusion, tooth irregularities. 5-132-33, illus., 137
Malpighi, Marcello, Italian anatomist. with illus., 3-273-74
 Cell structure, investigation of, 7-157
Malt sugar. See **Maltose**
Malthus, Thomas R., English clergyman and economist. illus., 3-229; 4-403-04
 Darwin influenced by, 8-257
 Population theories of, 3-228-31
Malthusian theory. 3-228-31; 4-403-04
Maltose, malt sugar. 4-79
Mambas, snakes. 5-362
Mammallike reptiles. illus., 6-373; 7-2-3
Mammals. *7-1-16
 *Antelope family, 8-376-87
 *Apes, monkeys and kin, 9-250-65
 *Bears and kin, 7-307-17
 *Beasts of burden, 7-327-33
 *Beavers and others, 9-1-6
 *Cats, 8-202-12
 *Civets, mongooses and hyenas, 8-244-50
 *Deer family, 8-234-43
 *Dog family, 8-132-41
 *Domestication of, 10-239-50
 *Giant land mammals, 7-408-17
 *Human biology, 1-57-66
 *Insect-eaters, 7-94-102
 *Marine mammals, 7-181-89
 *Marsupials, 7-418-28
 *Rodents, 8-160-70
 *Seals and kin, 7-84-93
 *Weasel family, 8-171-77
 Adaptations for survival, 3-235-36, 238-39, 240, 242, illus., 235-36, 243
 Breathing mechanism of, with diagram, 1-279
 Classification of, 1-289, 291, 299-300
 Derivation of word, 7-1
 Ear and jaw structure, illus., 4-384
 Field study of, with illus., 10-259-61
 Fossil mammals, illus., 6-374
 Heart of, with illus., 1-278-79
 Migrations of, 9-415-16, with illus., 421-24
 Pets, with illus., 7-17-22
 Prehistoric, 1-393, 394, 395-96
 Seasonal changes affect mammals, 5-410-11, 413, illus., 412
 Seeds dispersed by, with illus., 5-5-6, illus., 4, 7
 See also **Animals; Apes; Man; Monkeys**
Mammary glands. See **Breasts**
Mammoth Cave region, Kentucky.
 Cave formation in, with illus., 5-51-53
Mammoths, extinct elephants. 1-384, 396-97, illus., 397; illus., 6-374; 7-408-09
Man. illus., 1-300
 *Aging problem, 8-78-83
 *Allergies, 4-257-64
 *Basic units of body, 1-143-48
 *Biology of, 1-57-66
 *Blood, 3-325-34
 *Body defenses, 7-346-53
 *Bones, 3-73-84
 *Cancer in man, 8-265-72
 *Circulatory system, 3-381-92
 *Digestive system, 4-321-35
 *Exercise and rest, 10-85-91
 *Food elements required by man, 4-76-79
 *Glands, 5-8-19
 *Growth, development and decline, 8-90-102

Man (*continued*)
 *Heredity in man, 8-333-47
 *Language, 1-107-21
 *Muscles, 3-203-13
 *Nervous system, 6-317-30
 *Population problems, 3-225-34
 *Psychology, 9-310-22
 *Races of mankind, 8-213-20
 *Reproduction, 8-19-33
 *Respiratory system, 4-200-09
 *Sense organs, 7-291-306
 *Skin, hair and nails, 2-173-80
 *Sleep, 6-143-51
 *Smoking, effects of, 5-343-50
 *Systems of human body, 1-148a-h
 *Teeth, 5-129-37
  Backbone, supporting function of, *with illus.*, 1-286, *illus.*, 60
  Balance of nature disturbed by, 3-235; 10-190
  Breathing mechanism of, *with diagram*, 1-279
  Caves, importance of, to man, 5-60
  Ear, *with illus.*, 4-379-81
  Evolution of, 1-56, 397
  High-frequency sound affects, 8-110
  Insect pests and allies of, 2-410-11, 412-14
  Limbs as levers, *with illus.*, 1-283
  Migration, human, distinguished from animal migration, 9-415
  Parasitic-worm infestations, 2-154-59
  Posture, upright, *with illus.*, 1-286
  Seeds dispersed by, 5-6
  Virus diseases of, 3-452, *illus.*, 454
  Voice production in, *with illus.*, 1-282
  See also **Anatomy; Archaeology; Biology; Body; Diet; Exercise; Health; Medicine; Physiology; Population; Primitive peoples; Society; Zoology**
Man-eating sharks. 4-288-89
Man-hours. 8-309-10
Manatees, aquatic mammals. 7-181-83, *illus.*, 182
Manchester Ship Canal, England. 4-186
Manchester University, Great Britain. Radio telescope at, 1-94
Mandalay Beach, California. Sea water converted into fresh water in, 2-283
Mandibles, jaws. Human lower jawbone, *with illus.*, 3-78-79, *illus.*, 74, 75, 77
  Insects, 2-403, *illus.*, 404
  See also **Beaks; Jaws**
Mandrills, Old World monkeys. 9-258, *illus.*, 259
Mangabeys, Old World monkeys. 9-258, 263
Manganese (Mn), chemical element. Atomic number, 25; atomic weight, 54.9380; melting point, 1,260° C.; boiling point, 1,900° C.; specific gravity, 7.2. Metal; gray-white, very hard and brittle, nonmagnetic. Discovered in 1774 by Gahn; name derived from Italian *manganese*, a corruption of Magnesia. (See **Magnesium**.) Widely distributed in earth's crust; principle source, the mineral pyrolusite. Obtained by reduction of the oxide or by electrolysis. Alloys with iron, copper and nickel industrially important; compounds useful as antiseptics and in quantitative analysis. The mineral pyrolusite has long given color to glass.
  Diet, manganese in, 4-60
  Steelmaking, use and control of manganese in, 1-344, 352-53
Manganin, alloy. 3-37
Mangrove swamps. 7-66
Mangrove trees. 4-65; *with illus.*, 5-146
  Coasts built up by, 8-358, *illus.*, 359
Manic-depressive psychosis, mental illness. 9-203

Manila hemp (Abaca).
  Plant and fiber, *with illus.*, 4-181
Mankind. See **Man**
Manly, Charles Matthews, pioneer aeronautical designer (1876–1927).
  Gasoline aircraft engine designed by, 6-182; 9-216
Mannogalactan mucilage, adhesive.
  Chemurgic development, 7-44
Manometers, measures pressure of gases. *with illus.*, 2-42
Manson, Sir Patrick, British physician.
  Parasites, research on, 10-32
Manta rays, fish. 4-295, *illus.*, 294
Mantell, Thomas F., United States Air Force pilot.
  "Flying saucer" sighted by, 9-17
Mantes, praying. *with illus.*, 3-150-51
  Experimental study of, 8-67-69, *illus.*, 68
  Field study of, 10-262
Mantids. See **Mantodea**
Mantissa, part of logarithm. 2-76
  See also **Characteristic**
Mantle, soil and rock waste.
 *Soil, 2-15-25
  Earth's crust covered by, 7-355
Mantle, earth's. 4-171, 173, *illus.*, 170, 172
Mantodea, order of insects. 2-412; *with illus.*, 3-150-51
Manual artificial respiration. 10-10, *illus.*, 11
Manufactured gas. Natural gas and manufactured gas, 5-106
Manufacturers Trust Company Building, New York City. *illus.*, 7-frontispiece
Manufacturing. See **Industry; Machinery; Wastes**
Manure spreaders. 2-166, *illus.*, 164
Manures. *with illus.*, 2-163-67
  See also **Fertilizers**
Manuscripts. Microfilming of, 10-73
Maple sap. See **Maple sugar**
Maple sugar. 4-79
Maple syrup. See **Maple sugar**
Maple trees. *with illus.*, 5-150
  Fruits of, *illus.*, 4-130; *illus.*, 5-3, 141
  Leaves, *illus.*, 1-304; *illus.*, 4-72; *illus.*, 5-140
  Seed dispersal of, 3-240
  Seeds, *illus.*, 5-63
  See also **Maple sugar**
Maps.
  Ancient world according to Eratosthenes, *illus.*, 1-359
  Ancient world according to Hecataeus, *illus.*, 1-130
  History
    Antiquity, 1-131, 359, *illus.*, 130, 359
    Mercator projection, introduction of, 2-367
  Iceberg routes, *illus.*, 9-336-37
  Magnetic surveys of earth, *with illus.*, 7-169-71, *with diagram*, 356-57
  Natural-gas prospecting, mapping used in, 5-99, *illus.*, 100
  Oceanic currents, *illus.*, 6-232-33
  Saracen empire, *illus.*, 2-299
  Similar triangles used in mapmaking, *with illus.*, 3-434
  Sixteenth-century conception of Old and New Worlds, *illus.*, 2-365
  Soil types of world, *illus.*, 2-20-21
  See also **Prospecting**
Maps, weather. 1-253-54, *illus.*, 250; *illus.*, 2-95
Marble, metamorphic rock. *illus.*, 1-32; 3-426, *illus.*, 425; 9-308
  Building material, *illus.*, 2-87; *with illus.*, 7-116, *illus.*, 118
  Sources of, 2-86, 87
Marchantia, genus of liverworts. 3-190, *illus.*, 186

Marconi, Guglielmo, Italian electrical engineer and inventor. *with illus.,* 6-245-46
   Radio-wave message, first, 7-202; 8-403
Mare Imbrium, lunar sea. *illus.,* 4-283
Maria. Plains on the moon, 4-280, 282
Marianas Trench. 6-74; 9-223
Marijuana (marihuana). 5-402-03, *illus.,* 400
   Hemp plant yielding marijuana introduced into America, 5-6
Marine biology. 6-29, 32-33, 35-36, *illus.,* 33-34
   Fossil sea organisms, *with illus.,* 6-370, 371, 372
   Petroleum formed from dead sea organisms, 4-142
   Sounds made by marine life, 8-41, 43
   See also **Algae; Crustaceans; Mollusks;** etc.
Marine carnivores. Teeth of, 7-10
Marine engineering. See **Boats; Ships**
Marine geology, scientific study of the ocean bottom and shores. *6-69-77
Marine mammals. *7-181-89
   Environmental factors affecting, 7-7-8
Marine photography. *with illus.,* 6-316
Marine plants. See **Algae**
Mariotte, Edme, French physicist. 3-278; 8-321-22
Maritime (seaside) earwigs. 3-152
Märjelensee, Switzerland. *illus.,* 7-56
Mark I, atomic submarine engine. *illus.,* 4-342d
Marketing. Livestock, *with illus.,* 5-165-66
Markets.
   Industrial designers analyze, 10-123, 125
   Packaging of products designed to stimulate buying, 10-123-25
Markowitz, W., American astronomer. 5-187-88
Markowitz moon camera. *with illus.,* 5-187-88
Marks, Arthur H., American chemist. 6-353, 360
Marmosets, monkeys. 9-259-60, *illus.,* 261
Marmots, ground squirrels. 8-162
   Fur, 7-238
Marrow, bone. See **Bone marrow**
Mars, planet. *4-415, 19, *illus.,* 421
   Backward motion is only apparent, *illus.,* 5-facing 1
   Canals on, *illus.,* 1-257; 6-392, *illus.,* 391
   Data, 10-298
   How to observe, 6-84
   "Invasion of earth by Martians"—instance of mass hysteria, 9-20
   Satellites of, 3-159
   Space flight to, 9-379; 10-54
Marsh deer. 8-241, *illus.,* 242
Marsh gas. See **Methane**
Marsh hawks. 6-160, *illus.,* 161
   Courtship behavior of, *with illus.,* 5-418b
Marsh treaders. *with illus.,* 3-262
Marsh wrens. 6-45
Marshall Islands, in the Pacific. Drilling exploration in, 6-77
Marshes. *with illus.,* 7-64, 66
Marsupial anteaters.
   Adaptations for feeding, 7-11
Marsupial moles. 7-426-27
Marsupial pouches, for offspring. 3-242, *illus.,* 243
Marsupialia, order of mammals. *with illus.,* 7-13
   See also **Marsupials**
Marsupials. *7-418-28
   Adaptations for survival, 3-242, *illus.,* 243
   Evolution of, 7-5, 6
Marsupium. 7-419-20
Martens.
   Description and habits of, 8-171
   Fur, 7-238
Martianus, Capella, Latin writer. 2-295
Martin, W. McK., inventor. 4-157

Martin aseptic process (HTST process). 4-157
Martins, swallows. 6-68
Mary the Jewess. Inventor of the water bath used in chemical laboratories, 1-360
Maser ("Microwave Amplification by Stimulated Emission of Radiation"). A device for amplifying weak incoming radio signals of very short wave length (microwaves) without any distortion or interference due to waves produced by the amplifier itself. The maser is based on the fact that when substances are at a high level of atomic or electronic activity, they reinforce by further emission several ranges of the electromagnetic waves that strike them. A gas-type maser electrostatically isolates high-energy ammonia molecules in a special chamber, where the radio waves are sent for amplification. A solid-state maser, consisting of a synthetic ruby immersed in liquid helium, raises the electrons in the atoms of ruby molecules to an energy peak by means of *artificially* produced microwaves. The most important application of the maser is in radio telescopes, for detecting faint radio signals from far out in space. It is also used in checking on the speed of light and in exact timing.
   Solid-state, 5-210
Mason bees. 3-367-68
Mass.
   Earth's mass, determination of, *with illus.,* 4-43-44
   Energy, relation to, 1-84-85; 9-131
   Fitzgerald-Lorentz contraction, 4-214
   Galaxies, masses of, 8-52-53
   Weight distinguished from, 2-318, 319
   See also **Gravitation**
Mass-energy conservation, law of.
   Applied to producing atomic energy, 9-131
Mass-energy equation. See **Einstein equation**
Mass hysteria.
   "Invasion of earth by Martians" as example of, 9-20
Mass number. Chemical elements, 9-125, 133
Mass production.
   *Design of products, 10-117-26
   Automobile manufacture by, 2-145
   Industrial Revolution, development of, 4-39, 41
   Machine tools have aided, 10-106
   Meat processing by, 5-164
   Synthetic diamonds, 4-276
   See also names of mass-production industries, such as **Metallurgy; Papermaking; Plastics; Printing;** etc.
Mass psychology.
   Le Bon's theory of, 9-56
Mass-ratio, of space rockets. 10-3, 42-43
Mass spectrograph. Invention, 8-418
Mass spectrometer. *illus.,* 10-200-01
Massachusetts. Granites in, 2-84
Massachusetts Constitution. Promotion of science, 4-34
Massachusetts Institute of Technology.
   Electronic computers, development of, 9-145
Massena quail. 6-334
Mast tops, ship observation platforms. Medieval ships, 4-108
Master gears, for automobiles, 2-141, *illus.,* 140
Mastiffs, dogs. 10-243
Mastigophora, class of protozoans. *with illus.,* 2-60-63
   Luminous, 2-183, 185, *illus.,* 184
Mastodons, extinct elephants. 1-396; 7-408
Mastrofini, Abbé Marco.
   Calendar reform proposed by, 10-178-79
Masts. 4-106-08
Matches.
   Manufacture with phosphorus, 3-321, *illus.,* 320
   Safe storage of, 7-193

Materials.
  *Builder's materials, 7-115-28
  See also **Concrete; Iron; Plastics; Silk; Steel; Wood; Wool;** etc.
Mathematicians. See **Mathematics;** also names of mathematicians
Mathematics. *1-73-78
  *Algebra, 2-67-80
  *Arithmetic, 1-149-61
  *Electronic computers, 9-143-52
  *Geometry (plane and solid), 3-427-46
  *Higher mathematics, 4-423-42
  *Recreations, mathematical, 4-443-54
  *Trigonometry, 3-446-50
  Astronomy, use in, 1-20; 6-258
  Binary system, 9-146-47
  Cartesian co-ordinates, 4-212-13
  Data, *with illus.,* 10-294
  Decimal system, 9-146
  History
      Antiquity, 1-126-27, 130, 133-34, 136, 355-58, 360, *illus.,* 129
      Arabic contributions, 2-298
      Arabic numerals, introduction of, to Western Europe, 2-310-11
      Seventeenth century, 3-19-20, 279-80
  Space-time concept, 4-213
  Statistics applied to problems of psychology, 9-313
Mating. Light affects, 7-8
  See also **Reproduction**
Mating flights. See **Nuptial flights**
Matrices (sing.: **matrix**), molds used in producing type faces. *with illus.,* 1-200-03
Matrix, medium existing in body. 1-145, 147
  Aging, connection with, 8-81
Matrix paper. 4-378
Mats, as casting molds. 1-207-08
Matte, primary product of ore smelting. 1-377-78, 379
Matter.
  *Acids, bases and salts, 4-336-42
  *Atomic structure, 1-307-14
  *Colloids, 5-294-304
  *Crystals, 5-337-42
  *Elements, periodic law of chemical, 4-304-10
  *Matter and energy, 1-79-86
  *Metallic elements, survey of, 3-33-42, 165-76
  *Molecules, 1-162-72
  *Nonmetallic elements, survey of, 3-317-24
  *Properties of matter, 5-369-76
  *Solutions, 4-296-303
  Atomic theory of, in nineteenth century, *with illus.,* 5-74-76
  Change of state, *with illus.,* 3-416-18
  Chemical elements, early efforts to classify, *with illus.,* 5-83-86
  Cosmic-ray-shower formation as conversion of energy into matter, 8-396
  Heat due to motion of, 3-408-09
  Heat, changes due to, *with illus.,* 3-414-18
  Interstellar space, 9-359-64
  Transformations of energy, 6-247-54
  See also **Atoms; Chemistry; Electrons; Elements, Chemical; Gases; Liquids; Molecules; Parity law; Physics; Solids**
Matterhorn, Alps. *illus.,* 10-18
Mature soils. 2-18, 21-23
Mature streams and valleys. 8-17, 18, *illus.,* 18
Maturity. Human body reaches, 8-100-01
Mauchly, J. W., American physicist.
  Electronic computers, work on, 9-145, 150
Mauna Kea, Hawaii. 7-344-45

Mauna Loa, Hawaiian volcano. **7-345**
  Caldera of, 8-298
Maury, Matthew Fontaine, American naval officer and oceanographer. 6-28-29
Mauve, purple dye. Discovery and history of, 8-186, 187
Max Planck Institute, Germany. 1-95
Maxillae, jaws. Insects, 2-403, *illus.,* 404
Maxim, Sir Hiram Stevens, American inventor (1840–1916). He went to England in 1883 and there invented the automatic rifle or machine gun. His next experiments resulted in improved types of explosives. He became a naturalized British citizen. The last years of his life were spent in the study of aeronautics; he built a heavier-than-air machine in 1894.
Maxim, Hudson, American inventor (1853–1927). He began his career in the publishing business but abandoned it to build a powder mill in New Jersey where he invented and manufactured the first smokeless gunpowder to be adopted by the United States Government. His later inventions in explosives include "maximite," "stabillite" and "motorite."
Maximum-minimum thermometers. 1-247, *illus.,* 246; *with illus.,* 3-412
Maximum Permissible Concentration. Strontium 90, 9-356
Maxwell, James Clerk, Scottish physicist. *with illus.,* 6-242-43, 254
  Color, work on, 8-179; 9-412-13
  Electromagnetic theory, 7-201-02
May beetles. 3-345
May flies. *illus.,* 2-405
Mayans.
  Calendar, 10-172-73
  Number system of, 1-156
  Pyramid constructed by, 9-29
  Rubber relics discovered in ruins of, 6-350
  Writing, system of, 1-112
Mayer, Julius Robert von, German physician and physicist. 6-252
Mayo, Charles, American physician and surgeon. 9-31
Mayo, William, American physician and surgeon. 9-31
Mazama, Mount, Oregon. Crater Lake, *illus.,* 8-299
Mead, Margaret, American anthropologist. 9-27
Mead, Lake, artificial lake formed by Hoover Dam 8-307, *illus.,* 316b
Meadow mice. 6-163
Meadowlarks. 6-105, *illus.,* 105, 106
Mean calories, heat units. 3-413
Mean solar time. 1-264
Mean temperature, 24-hour. 1-318
Meanders, stream windings. *with illus.,* 6-413-14
  Formation of, 8-14, 17, *illus.,* 14, 18
Measles. Vaccination immunizes against, 7-351
Measurement.
  *Noise meters, 8-38-46
  *Radiation thickness gauges, 9-43-46
  Electric current, devices for measuring, 6-130-33
  Ocean depths, 6-69, *diagram,* 70
  Oceanic currents, velocity and direction of, 6-229-31, *illus.,* 232, 234-35
  Tides, 6-207-08, *illus.,* 206-07
  See also **Measures**
Measures.
  Angstrom unit, 7-145
  Atomic weights, 1-308, 309-10, *with diagrams,* 312, *diagrams,* 313
  Electricity, *with illus.,* 6-130-33
  History
      Antiquity, 1-126-27, 130
      Metric system, establishment of, 4-34, *illus.,* 35

Measures (continued)
Molecules, 1-172
Pressure of gases, with illus., 2-42
Stellar distances, with diagram, 6-261, table, 262
Tables, 10-295-96
Measuring worms. 3-202
Meat.
Automatic frankfurter machines, illus., **10-237**
Balanced diets, meat in, 5-269, 274
Luminous bacteria on, 2-183
Preserved by gamma radiation, **10-116**
See also **Meat-packing industry**
Meat-packing industry. *5-163-72
Meat-packing plants. with illus., 5-166-69
Mechanical advantage. Simple machines, 3-57-62
Mechanical brakes, for automobiles. 2-144
Mechanical cotton pickers. with illus., 4-178-79
Mechanical energy. Transformations of, 6-247, illus., 248-49
Mechanical engineering. 1-218-19, 224-25
Mechanical equivalent of heat.
Joule's experiments to determine, 6-251-52
Mechanical work. 3-57
Mechanics, subdivision of physics.
*Animal mechanisms, 1-277-86
*Experiments in, 7-214-22
*Forces in liquids and gases, 2-30-42
*Gravitation, 2-315-22
*Matter, properties of, 5-369-76
*Motion, 2-118-28
Breathing mechanism, with illus., 4-205-06
Development in seventeenth century, with illus., 3-4
Force, energy and work, with illus., 1-82-83, 84-85
See also **Machinery; Physics**
Mechanistic theories of life.
Seventeenth century, 3-10, 13-14
Mechanists. 8-264
Mechanization.
Coal industry, 1-415-16
Earth-fill dams, factor in construction of, 8-309
Glassmaking, 3-308, 310-11, illus., 310-11
Meat-packing techniques, with illus., 5-166-68
Meckel's cartilage, 4-383, illus., 382, 383
Mecoptera, order of insects. 2-414
Media, sound. 5-119-20
Experiments concerning, with illus., 5-222-25
Medians. with illus., 3-433
Medicine.
*Allergies, 4-257-64
*Antibiotics, 10-130a-d
*Atomic medicines, 10-98-101
*Body defenses, 7-346-53
*Cancer, 8-265-72
*Diet, regulation of, 5-267-75
*First aid, 10-5-17
*Geriatrics, 8-78-83
*Microorganisms causing disease, 8-360-68
*Mosquito as vector of malaria and yellow fever, 10-30-39
*Nursing patients at home, 10-55-67
*Pasteur's contributions to bacteriology, 9-71-80
*Penicillin and streptomycin, 7-52-54
*Progress in medicine, 10-127-34
*Psychiatry, 9-197-205
*Smoking, effects of, 5-343-50
*Tranquilizers, 5-377-79
*Tuberculosis, 9-175-84
*Viruses, 3-451-58
*Vitamins, 5-38-49
Barium salts, used in, 3-174
Drugs, synthetic, 8-187-88

Medicine (continued)
Electric devices applied to, 9-240
Electromagnetic radiations, used in, 7-206
Gold used in, 4-250
History
Antiquity, 1-127-28, with illus., 363-67
Arabic contributions to, 2-301
Middle Ages, with illus., 2-311-13
Sixteenth century, 2-367-68
Seventeenth century, with illus., 3-10-12
Eighteenth century, with illus., 4-400-03
Nineteenth century, with illus., 7-370-89
Twentieth century, with illus., 9-31-42, 96-104, 327-28
Laboratory animals, use of, illus., 8-169
Morphine, 5-404
Neurology, study of nervous diseases, 6-330
Nobel prize winners in, 10-299-307
Petroleum used for medication in colonial America, 4-141
"Quacks" in practice of, 8-272
Radioactive isotopes used in, 9-142
Radium used in, 3-176
Sound microscopes, used in, 8-45
Strontium compounds used in, 3-175
Tooth disease and disorders, 5-130-33, illus., 135, 137
X rays, use of, with illus., 7-148-50
Zoo animals, care of, with illus., 10-157-59
See also **Diseases; Drugs; Health; Infectious diseases; Sickness; Surgery**
Medicine, preventive.
*Body defenses, 7-346-53
History
Antiquity, 1-128
Eighteenth and nineteenth centuries, with illus., 4-400-03; 7-384
See also **Diseases; Health; Laveran, Charles Louis; Lister, Joseph; Pasteur, Louis; Public Health**
Medicine men. 1-364
Medicines. Dosing procedure, with illus., 10-63-64
Mediterranean anemia. 8-220
Mediterranean local race. 8-218
Mediterranean Sea.
Ships of ancient and medieval times, 4-106-08
Medulla oblongata. 6-326, illus., 325
See also **Hindbrain**
Medusa, mythological figure linked with legends of constellations. 1-335
Medusas. with illus., 2-149-50
Meerkats, mongooses. 8-247
Megacycles. Definition, 3-91; 6-300
Megakaryocytes, bone-marrow cells forming blood platelets. 3-329
Megaloptera, order of insects. 2-414
Megamegameteorites, supergiant meteorites. 6-92
Megameteorites, giant meteorites. 6-91
Meigs, Charles, American physician. 7-374
Meiosis, sex-cell division. with illus., 6-270, with diagram, 8-335
Meitner, Lise, Austrian physicist. 9-330
Melamine-formaldehyde resin, plastic. Manufacture and uses of, 8-224-27
Melamine plastics. 8-224-27
Melamphids, fish. illus., 10-142
Melanesian geographical race. 8-217, illus., 216
Melanesian local race. 8-219
Melanin, coloring matter in skin and hair. 2-176, 179
Melanomas, cancers originating in pigmented moles on the skin. 8-267
Melanophores, skin-pigment cells. 5-156, 204
Meliponidae, stingless bees. 3-372

Mellon Institute. 1-88
Melody. Elements of, 5-213-15
Melotte, P. J., English astronomer.
  Jupiter's satellite VIII, discovery of, 5-24
Melting point. 3-416
  Molecular behavior at, 1-163, 171
Melvill, Thomas, Scottish scientific investigator. 5-85
Membrane theory of nerve conduction. 6-321, *illus.*, 320
Membranes. Water desalting, use in, 2-284
Membranes, cellular internal. See **Endoplasmic reticulum**
Memory.
  *Animal intelligence, 2-26-29
  Ants—do they rely on past experience? 3-359-60
  Ebbinghaus, work of, 9-56
  Nervous basis of, 6-318
  Psychology of, 9-316
  See also **Knowledge; Mind; Psychoanalysis**
Mendel, Gregor Johann, Austrian botanist (1822–84). He developed the Mendelian laws of heredity which became the foundation of experimental genetics. Mendel was a monk of the Augustinian monastery at Brünn and later became its abbot. He carried out his botanical experiments in the monastery garden. In a paper published in 1865, he discussed the laws of heredity revealed by his experiments in growing peas. The paper received scant attention, and it was only after Mendel's death that the importance of his work was fully realized. See also *illus.*, 8-340
  Laws of heredity, 8-339-42, *diagram*, 341
  Mechanism of heredity, 8-263
  Rediscovery of work of, 8-405-06
Mendel's laws, in genetics. 8-339-42, *diagram*, 341
Mendeleev, Dmitri Ivanovich, Russian chemist. *illus.*, 4-305; *with illus.*, 5-83-85
  Arrangement of elements in periodic table, 4-304; 9-124
Mendelevium (Md), chemical element. Atomic number, 101; atomic weight, uncertain but around 256. Chemical properties similar to those of the rare earth thulium; half life of about half an hour, decaying by spontaneous fission. Discovered in 1955 through the bombardment of about a billion atoms of einsteinium with alpha particles from a cyclotron; identified at Berkeley, California, by Ghiorso, Harvey, Choppin, Thompson and Seaborg. Named in honor of the Russian chemist Mendeleev, inventor of the periodic table of the elements.
Mendelism. See **Evolution; Heredity; Mendel, Gregor Johann**
Menes I, pharaoh of Egypt. Dam constructed by, 8-308
Meninges, membranes of brain and spinal cord. 6-327, 330, *illus.*, 327
  See also **Arachnoid; Dura mater; Pia mater**
Meningitis. 6-330
Menlo Park Laboratory, New Jersey. *illus.*, 5-245
Menopause. 8-101
Menstruation. 8-23
Mental deficiency. 9-198-99
  Goddard's work in, 9-56
Mental development.
  Gesell's studies of children, with *illus.*, 9-56-57
Mental hospitals. *illus.*, 9-205
Mental illness. *9-197-205
  Tranquilizers in treatment of, *with illus.*, 5-377-79
Menzel, Donald H., American astrophysicist.
  Flying saucers, explanation of, 9-19-20
Mepazine, synthetic tranquilizer. 5-379
Meprobamate, synthetic tranquilizer. 5-379
Mercaptan, foul-smelling substance. 7-303

Mercator, Gerardus (Gerhard Kremer), Flemish geographer. 2-367
Mercator projection. *with illus.*, 3-445
Mercedonius. Roman month, 10-174
Merchant marines. See **Ships**
Mercuric oxide. 3-245
  Chemical reaction under heat, 2-225-27, 229-30, *diagram*, 225-27; 4-230
Mercury (Hg), chemical element. Atomic number, 80; atomic weight, 200.59; melting point, —38.87° C.; boiling point, 356.58° C.; specific gravity, 13.546. Silver-white, shiny metal; only common metal that is liquid at ordinary temperatures. Known to ancients. Name derived from planet Mercury; chemical symbol (Hg), from Greek *hydrargyros:* "liquid silver" by way of neo-Latin form *hydrargyrum.* Occurs free in nature; chief source is the sulfide cinnabar, from which it is obtainable by heating in a current of air. Used for thermometers, barometers, hydrometers, vacuum pumps, liquid seals, electrical contacts, rectifiers, ultraviolet and fluorescent lamps; also serves as a cathode, catalyst and in many compounds. See also 3-41-42
  Air-pressure experiments, use of mercury in, 1-233; *with illus.*, 3-16-17
  Barometers, use of mercury in, 1-319, *diagram*, 320
  Color of mercury vapor when electrically excited, 8-118
  Converted into gold, 8-420
  Discharge lamps using mercury vapor, 4-240
  Electron tubes contain, *with illus.*, 6-301-02
  Experiments with, *illus.*, 1-89
  Gold ore treated with, 1-375; 4-248, 250
  Mercuric oxide, decomposition of, 4-230
  Photography, use in, 9-400
  Surface tension, *with illus.*, 5-371
  Thermometers, used in, 3-410
  Turbine use of, as source of vapor pressure, 5-312
Mercury, planet. *4-25-27
  Alteration of path, relativity calculations for, 4-220
  Data, 10-298
  How to observe, 6-83
  Transits of, 6-83
Mercury, Project. See **Project Mercury**
Mercury barometers. 1-319, *with diagram*, 247, 249, *diagram*, 320
  See also **Barometers**
Mercury cells, electric batteries. 5-95
Mercury fulminate, explosive. 8-282
Mercury thermometers. See **Thermometers**
Mercury vapor.
  Electron tubes contain, *with illus.*, 6-300-02
Mergansers, birds. *with illus.*, 6-400
Mergenthaler, Ottmar, inventor. *with illus.*, 6-381
Meridians. 1-261; 8-61
Merino, breed of sheep. 10-245, *illus.*, 246
Meristematic tissues, plant growth tissues. 3-49-50 *illus.*, 46; 9-7
Merlins, falcons. 6-159
Mermaids. Legends of, 7-182
Merrimac, Confederate warship.
  Battle between Monitor and Merrimac, *illus.*, 6-379
Mersenne, Marin, French scientist. 3-267
Mesabi Range, Minnesota.
  Conveyer belts on, 6-170
  Iron-ore deposits, discovery of, 6-383
Mescaline. 5-377
Mesenchyme, tissue. Sponge, *with illus.*, 2-146, 147
Mesentery, membrane connecting intestines with wall of abdominal cavity.
  Development in unborn human young, 8-28
Meseta, Spanish plateau. 6-109

Mesmer, Franz Anton, Austrian physician.
Mesmerism, introduction of, 9-99-100
Mesmerism. See **Hypnotism; Mesmer, Franz Anton**
Mesoderm, layer of cells in early development of embryo. 8-23, *illus.,* 24
Mesometeorites, meteorites of average to large size. 6-89-90
Mesons (mesotrons), atomic particles. 1-313, *with table,* 314
Detection by Geiger-Mueller counter, 9-343
Mu mesons, 4-215-16
Parity law of physics violated by, *with illus.,* 7-109-10
Secondary cosmic rays made up of, 8-398, *illus.,* 397
Mesophyll, leaf tissue. 4-73
Mesopotamia, ancient. Science in, 1-124
Writing in, 1-115, *illus.,* 114
Mesosphere, atmospheric layer. 1-238, *diagram,* 239
Mesothorax, middle part of insect chest. *illus.,* 2-403
Mesotrons. See **Mesons**
Mesozoa, animal phylum. 1-292
Mesozoic era, time in earth's history. 1-391-95; 6-373-74
See also **Geology**
Mesquite, plant. Underground water indicated by, 8-331
Messier, Charles, French astronomer.
Nebulae and star clusters catalogued by, 8-49
Messier 8, nebulosity in the constellation Sagittarius. *illus.,* 9-364
Messier 51, galaxy. *illus.,* 9-363
Messina, Sicily. Earthquake of 1908, 9-110, *illus.,* 111
Met. Measure of rate of energy transformation in body, 10-86, 88-89
Metabolism.
*Plant's metabolism, 3-43-55
Alcoholism may be due to disturbance in, 4-410
Cellular, 2-10-13
Definition, 3-43
Estivating animals, 5-412-13
Hormones control, 5-15-19
Lavoisier's experiment, *illus.,* 4-356-57
Lowered during sleep, 6-147
Metabolic processes duplicated in laboratory, 8-190
Radioisotopes used in testing of, 10-98, 99
Turtles, 5-386
Metacarpal bones, in hand. *illus.,* 1-148b; *with illus.,* 3-81, *illus.,* 74, 80
Metacarpus. See **Metacarpal bones**
Metal-forming tools. 10-107-08, *illus.,* 106-07
Metallic wood borers, beetles. 3-342
Metallography. Steel, 1-352-53
See also **Metallurgy; Metals**
Metalloids. Distinguished from metals, 3-33
Metallurgical engineering. 1-226
Metallurgy. *1-369-82
*Steel manufacture, 1-338-53
Beginnings, 3-269
Electrometallurgy, 9-240
Electronic detector, *illus.,* 10-170
Photomicrographs of ores, *illus.,* 10-164
Wear-testing auto parts, *illus.,* 4-342a
Metals.
*Gold, 4-242-50
*Preparation and processing, 1-369-82
*Steel, 1-338-53
*Survey of metals, 3-33-42, 165-76
Alloys defined, 1-81-82
Building materials, 7-121-22, *illus.,* 123
Buttons made from, 7-209, 213
Catalysts, metals as, 2-229, 231
Conservation of, 6-8

Metals *(continued)*
Crystalline structure, 5-340, *diagram,* 339
Electroplating, 5-91-92, *illus.,* 90
Formation of metal deposits through geologic time, 6-371, 372, 373, 374
Heat conductivity of, 4-10
High-frequency sounds used to detect flaws in, *with illus.,* 8-108-09
Mirrors made of, 7-252-53
Nonmetals distinguished from, 3-33; 4-304
Oxidation and reduction of, *with illus.,* 5-88-90
Photoengraving plates, metals used in, 1-205
Printing plates, metals used in making of, 1-207-08, 211, 212
Processing of, in nineteenth-century industry, *with illus.,* 6-383-85
Protoplasm contains salts and ions of, 2-6, 10, 11
Soils contain metallic compounds, 2-23, 24
Sound, speed of, in copper and aluminum, 5-119
Type-casting alloy, 1-200-01, 207-08
Voltaic cells, use of metals in, *with illus.,* 5-94-96
Metamorphic rocks. 3-419, 426, *illus.,* 425; 9-307-08
Origin of, 2-82
Metamorphism, formation of metamorphic rocks.
Factors in, 3-426
Minerals formed by, 5-251
Metamorphosis.
Insects, 2-407-08, *illus.,* 408-09
Beetles, *illus.,* 3-336
Butterflies and moths, *illus.,* 2-408-09; 3-195-96, *illus.,* 194-95, 197
Flies, 3-283-84, *illus.,* 285-87
Silkworms, *with illus.,* 5-174-79, *illus.,* 180
True bugs, 3-255
Metaphase, stage of cell division. 2-14, *illus.,* 13
Metaphysics.
Development in antiquity, 1-129, 132, 134-35, 137
Metastasis, transfer of disease from one part of body to another.
Cancer, 8-266
Metatarsal bones, in feet. *illus.,* 1-148b; 3-83, *illus.,* 74, 82-83
Metathorax, rear part of insect chest. *illus.,* 2-403
Metchnikoff, Elie, Russian biologist (1845–1916). He originated the theory that the congestion of blood at a wound is the result of a struggle between disease germs and the white blood corpuscles. Born in the province of Kharkov, he studied in Russia and Germany and was appointed professor of zoology at Odessa, 1870. In 1895 he became director of the Pasteur Institute, Paris. He shared the Nobel Prize in medicine with Paul Ehrlich in 1908. See also 7-388
Meteor, Russian hydrofoil boat. 4-7
Meteor Crater. See **Canyon Diablo meteorite crater**
Meteor showers. 6-96-97, *illus.,* 96, *table,* 97
Comet disintegrations produce, 5-393, *illus.,* 395
Meteor trails. 1-236; 6-95-96
Meteoric dust. 6-88, 90
Meteorite craters. 6-90, 91-92, 94, *diagrams and illus.,* 90, 91, *table,* 90
Meteorites. 3-161, *illus.,* 160; 4-36; *6-87-98
Composition of, as clue to earth's composition, *with illus.,* 4-175
Moon's craters caused by? 4-280
See also **Astronomy; Meteors**
Meteoritics, scientific study of meteorites and meteors. *6-87-98
Meteoroids. Discussion of term, 1-88
Meteorological Service of Canada. Voluntary observers for, 1-322

Meteorology, science of the atmosphere and its phenomena.
*Amateur meteorology, 1-315-22
*Atmosphere, 1-230-40
*Climates of the past, 3-177-85
*Clouds, 2-212-22
*Dust in the atmosphere, 7-137-42
*Jet streams, 2-358-60
*Lightning, 1-398-404
*Precipitation, 2-346-57
*Seasonal changes and life, 5-408-13
*Weather forecasting, 1-241-54
*Winds, 2-89-98; 7-318-26
Beaufort scale for gauging apparent strength of wind, 10-297
Flying saucers explained as meteorological phenomena, 9-19-20
Twentieth-century weather studies, 9-220, 223, illus., 221

Meteors. *6-87-98
Atmosphere's effect on, 1-232, 236, 238
Comet disintegrations produce, 5-393, illus., 395
Daylight showers discovered by radio methods, 9-208
Dust derived from, 7-141
Escape velocity of, 9-208
How to observe, 6-84-85
Showers of, 6-393
Solar energy due to? 3-109-10
Solar system, part of, 3-160-61
Space-travel hazard, 10-50
Velocity measured by radio methods, 9-208
See also **Meteorites**

Meters, measuring devices.
*Noise meters, 8-38-46
See also **Wattmeters**

Methadone, sedative. 5-404

Methane, or marsh gas (CH_4). 7-266-67, diagram, 267
Coal mines, methane gas in, 1-413
Graphic formula, 5-78
Jupiter's atmosphere contains, 5-20, 22
Molecule of, with illus., 3-246
Natural gas, methane in, 5-101
Structural formula, with illus., 7-267
See also **Digester gas**

Methane series, of hydrocarbons. 7-267-69

Methyl alcohol. 7-272
Formic acid derived from, 7-273

Methyl chloride. 7-271
See also **Chlorine**

Methyl isoprene. See **Synthetic rubber**

Methyl rubber, synthetic. 8-185

Methylene blue, dye.
Fish diseases treated with, 8-116

Metric system. tables, 10-296
Conversion table for, 10-296
Establishment of, 4-34, illus., 35

Metropolis Bridge, Ohio River. 2-335

Mexico.
Calendars of Mayans and Aztecs, 10-172-73, illus., 174
Mountain systems of, 10-23
Parícutin volcano, illus., 8-300b; 10-frontispiece
Plateau, illus., 6-114
Popocatepetl, volcano, illus., 8-300d
Primitive transportation of, illus., 3-295

Meyer, Julius Lothar, German chemist. 5-84

Miacids, extinct carnivores. 7-307; 8-171, 202

Miami Beach, Florida. Beach sands of, 8-352

Mica, mineral. 3-422
Beach sands contain, 8-353

Mice, rodents. 8-164
Golden mouse, illus., 8-160
Pets, 7-22
Tuberculous mice, illus., 9-184
White-footed mice, illus., 6-167

Michelson, Albert A., American physicist (1852–1931). He taught at the University of Chicago. In the course of his researches on light he invented the echelon spectroscope, which disperses light much better than the prism. Michelson measured the length of the standard meter in terms of the wave-length of light. He was the first to measure the diameter of a star (Betelgeuse). With E. W. Morley he found that the relative motion between the earth and the supposed medium "ether" is not measurable. His work in spectroscopy and metrology won him the 1907 Nobel Prize in physics. See also 6-246-47 (with illus.).
Experiment with light waves, 4-211-12
Light velocity determined by, 5-21

Michelson-Morley experiment. with illus., 6-246-47

Microbes.
*Germ-free animals, 7-151-55
*Pasteur's contributions to bacteriology, 9-71-80
*Protozoans, 2-58-66
*Viruses, 3-451-58
Agar as culture medium for, illus., 2-207
Bacterial forms, illus., 2-205
Body's defenses against, 7-347-51, diagrams, 348, 349
Carbon bacteria, 2-209
Coliform bacterium as indicator of water purity, 2-276
Food preservation as means of curbing, with illus., 4-153-68
Germ theory of disease, development, with illus., 7-387-85
Mineral bacteria, 2-208
Nursing precautions against germs, 10-55-57, 65-66
Soil, relation of microorganisms, 2-16, 23, 24, illus., 23, 25
Soil affected by, 2-205-11
Soil conditions favorable to growth of, 2-207
Soil contaminated by, 2-205
Tuberculosis, with illus., 9-175-78
White blood cells defend against bacteria, 3-328
See also **Bacteria; Protozoans**

Microfilming. *10-68-74
Use in Franco-Prussian War, 6-177-78

Microfossils, microscopic fossils. Meteorites contain?, 6-94-95

Micrographs. Specimen of toilet soap, illus., 10-169

Microlepidoptera, small Lepidoptera. 3-202

Micrometeorites, meteoritic dust. 6-88

Micron, unit of length. 2-59

Micronuclei, cell structures. 2-66

Microorganisms, organisms of microscopic or ultramicroscopic size.
Body's defenses against germs, microbes and bacteria, 7-347-51, diagrams, 348, 349
Soil, 2-16, 23-25
See **Algae; Bacteria; Diatoms; Microbes; Protozoans; Viruses**

Microphones.
Piezoelectric crystals used in, 2-294
Radio broadcasting, 3-88

Microscopes. *9-81-95
Beginnings of work with, with illus., 3-272-75
Blood cells counted and examined under, 3-329, with illus., 327
Bone, appearance of, illus., 3-75
Cancer cells detected under, 8-270
Chromatic aberration in lenses, overcoming of, 7-158, illus., 159

Microscopes (continued)

Compound microscopes, 7-261-62, illus., 260

Hooke's microscope (seventeenth century), illus., 2-2

Invention and development of, in seventeenth century, 3-16

Metallurgy, microscopes used in, illus., 4-342a

Prospecting, microscopes used to examine rocks in, 5-100, illus., 101

Ultramicroscopes, with diagram, 5-297-98

X-ray microscope, with diagram, 7-147

Dog flea magnified by, illus., 7-204

See also **Electron microscopes; Lenses**

Microseisms, small earthquakes. 9-115-16

Microspectroscopes. 9-81

Microwaves. 5-288

Chemical research, use in, 7-206

Radio relay systems used in carrier telephony, 2-394-95

Wave lengths of, diagram, 7-200

Midas satellites, American artificial satellites. 9-380

Mid-Atlantic Ridge, ocean-floor mountain range. 5-189

Midbrain. 6-323, 326

Middle Ages.

*Science, history of, 2-295-314

Aristotle as master, 1-138

Astronomical observatories, 8-64

Breadmaking in, 9-294-95

Bridges in, with illus., 2-333

Calendars, illus., 10-177-78

Coal, use of, 1-408-09

Engineering in, 1-217

Illumination in, 4-232

Irrigation in, 8-193

Ships and boats of, 4-107-08

Stone buildings, with illus., 7-117; with illus., 8-389

Transportation on land during, 1-98, 104, illus., 99

Waste disposal in, 5-326, illus., 327

Middle ear. 4-385, with illus., 380; with illus., 7-298-99

Middle East.

Petroleum industry and reserves, 4-140-41, 147

Middle English, language. 1-116-17

Middle stairway (scala media), of ear. with illus., 7-299, 300

Midgely, Thomas, Jr., American chemist (1889–1944).

Freon refrigerating fluids synthesized by, 4-310

Midges. 3-286, 289

Midwest Research Institute. 1-89

Midwife toads. 3-241; 5-160, illus., 152

Migrations.

*Animal migrations, 9-415-32

Adaptation for survival, with illus., 3-242-44

Ant armies, 3-364-65

Bird migrations, 5-423-24, with illus., 418d-e

Human populations, 3-226-28, 233-34

Swarming of bees, 3-372, with illus., 368

Migratory Bird Conservation Act, United States conservation measure. 9-274

Migratory Bird Law, United States conservation measure. 9-274

Migratory Bird Treaty, signed by United States and Great Britain. 6-406

Migratory Birds Convention, conservation agreement signed by United States and Canada. 9-274

Migratory locusts. See **Grasshoppers; Short-horned grasshoppers**

Migratory Waterfowl Hunting Stamp Act, United States conservation measure. 9-274

Milankovitch, M., geologist. Climatic theory of, 3-185

Military science. See **Warfare**

Milk. Adults' diets include, 8-82

Milk (continued)

Babies' and children's diets include, 5-273, 274

Breadmaking ingredients from, 9-295, 297, 299

Curdling, 5-302

Disease germs carried by, 7-382

Fiber synthesized from casein, 8-189

Homogenized by high-frequency sound, illus., 8-110

Mothers' milk, diet for breast feeding, 5-273

Pituitary gland controls secretion of, 5-17

Milk of magnesia, 3-172

Milk snakes. Pets, 7-25

Milk sugar. See **Lactose**

Milk teeth. 5-129-31, illus., 131-32, table, 130; 8-95, chart, 94

Milking. Machine for, illus., 9-62

Milks, fermented. 4-167

Milkweed bugs. 3-258

Milkweeds. illus., 7-113

Fruits, illus., 4-131

Seeds, illus., 5-63

Seeds dispersed by wind, illus., 5-2-3

Milky Way, galaxy. *8-151-59

Appearance from earth, 1-258-59, illus., 259

Discovery of radio-wave emanation from, 9-207

Features of, 6-259, 267, illus., 258

Formation of, according to Herschel, 4-399

Galileo's idea concerning, 3-2

Radio stars in, 9-208

Size of, 8-158; 9-359

Solid particles of matter in plane of, 9-361

Spiral structure of, 9-210

Mill, Henry, English engineer.

Typewriter patent granted to, 1-266

Millardet, Alexis, French mycologist. 3-25-26

Millepedes. with illus., 2-269

Development of, with illus., 6-278

Miller, S. L., American chemist.

Amino acids produced by, 8-190

Millikan, Robert A., American physicist (1868–1953). He served as physics professor at Chicago University and director of the physics laboratory at the California Institute of Technology. For his investigations on photoelectric phenomena and the determination of the charge on the electron, he won the 1923 Nobel Prize in physics. Millikan did important work on cosmic and X rays. See also 9-285

Cosmic-ray investigations, 8-393-94

Milling, in ore dressing. with diagrams, 1-371-75

Milling, tooling operation. 10-110, illus., 108, 112

Milling, grain.

Breadmaking, with illus., 9-295

See also **Flour; Grain; Wheat**

Mills, B. Y., Australian physicist. 9-210

Mills, Hannah. Case of, 9-102

Milo maize, type of corn. 7-38-39

"Miltown." See **Neprobromate**

Mimas, satellite of Saturn. 5-113

Mimi River, Japan.

Dammed up by Kamishiiba Dam, illus., 8-316b

Mimicry. Insects, 2-410, 412, illus., 410-11

Plants, 7-81

Mimosas, plants.

Turgor movements of, 3-54, illus., 53

Mind.

*Animal intelligence, 2-26-29

*Psychiatry, 9-197-205

*Psychology, 9-310-22

Aristotle's definition of, 9-47-48

Human growth and aging, mind in, 8-82-83, 97-98, 100-02

Psychology, history of, with illus., 9-47-57

Mindanao Trench. 6-74
Mineral oil. See **Petroleum**
Mineral separators. *illus.,* 3-38-39
Mineral springs. 8-326
Mineral wool, insulator. *with illus.,* 4-11
Mineralogy. See **Minerals**
Minerals. *5-248-56
 *Coal, 1-405-20
 *Diamond, 4-251-56
 *Gold, 4-242-50
 *Mineral and rock collecting, 9-300-09
 *Natural gas, 5-97-106
 *Ore discovery and processing, 1-369-82
 *Petroleum, 4-140-52
 *Prospecting for minerals, 7-354-61
 *Survey of metals, 3-33-42, 165-76
 Beach sands contain, 8-352
 Bone minerals, 3-73
 Bread enriched with, 9-299
 Classification according to external crystal structure,
  5-341-42, *diagrams,* 340-41
 Conservation of, 6-7-8
 Conserved in preparing foods, *illus.,* 5-38
 Diet, element of, *with table,* 4-55-57, 58-60
 Diet, essential to, 5-267, 272-73
 Erosion and precipitation by ground water, 8-328
 Flotation process, 5-303
 Formation of deposits through geologic time, 6-371,
  372, 373, 374
 Meat as important source of, 5-163
 Meteoritic, 6-92-93, 98
 Prospecting for magnetic ores, 7-171
 Protoplasm contains mineral elements, 2-6, 10, 11
 Salts in protoplasm, 1-43
 Silicon as an element in, 3-322
 Soil, relation of minerals to, 2-15-18, 20, 22-24, *illus.,*
  25
Miners.
 Coal miners, clothing of, 1-414, *illus.,* 405
 See also **Mining**
Miners' cramps. 10-91
Minerva Terrace, Yellowstone National Park. *illus.,*
 8-292
Mines.
 Canada, *illus.,* 3-35
 Minerals extracted in, 9-301
 United States, *illus.,* 3-38-39
 See also **Mining**
"Mini-pilots," gas-range pilot lights. 5-106
Miniature cameras. 9-405-06, *illus.,* 406
Miniature gardens. See **Terrariums**
Mining.
 *Coal mining, 1-405-20
 *Diamond mining, 4-251-56
 *Gold mining, 4-242-50
 *Prospecting, 7-355-61
 Compressed air used in mining operations, 9-66
 Development in sixteenth century, *with illus.,* 2-369
 Explosives used in, 8-182-83, 286
 Iron ore, *with illus.,* 1-340-41
 Machinery used in, *illus.,* 1-92d
 Ores, *with diagrams,* 1-370-71
 Safety measures in coal mining, *with illus.,* 1-413-15
 Salt mines, 5-316-17, 320, *illus.,* 317
 Strip mining for iron ore, 6-383-84
 Wood, used in, 2-105
 See also **Gold; Iron; Miners; Ores**
Mining engineering. 1-225-26
Mining pans. *with illus.,* 1-370
Minkowski, Hermann, German physicist.
 Space-time concept, 4-213

Minks. *illus.,* 8-175
 Fur, 7-238
 Relation to weasel, 8-174
Minnesota Spatial Relations Test, *illus.,* 9-199
Minor axis, of ellipse. 8-126-27, *diagram,* 126
Minor planets. See **Asteroids**
Minot, George R., American physician. 9-35
 Research on liver diet for pernicious anemia, 5-44
Miocene epoch, time in earth's history. 6-374
Mira, variable star. 1-355; 7-48, 50
"Miracle Decade" (1895–1905). *with illus.,* 8-400-10
Miraflores locks, Panama Canal. 4-194, *illus.,* 193
Mirages. Flying saucers thought to be, 9-20
Mirids, family of true bugs. *with illus.,* 3-261
Mirror galvanometers. See **Galvanometer**
Mirror machines, devices for confining plasmas. *with
 illus.,* 1-177
Mirrors. *with illus.,* 7-251-52, 256-58
 Cameras using, 9-405
 Manufacture, *with illus.,* 3-314
 Reflecting telescopes use, 6-387-88; 8-56-57, *with
  illus.,* 58-59; 9-365-67
  How to prepare and install mirrors, *with illus.,*
   9-367-70, 371, 372
Mirsky, Alfred E., American biologist.
 Nucleoprotein research of, 9-385
Miscible liquids, 4-301
Missiles.
 *Guidance of missiles and space vehicles, 8-125-31
 Torpedoes, *illus.,* 9-69
 See also **Jet planes; Rockets**
Mississippi flyway, bird migration route. *illus.,* 5-418e
Mississippi River. 8-13
 Discharge of, 6-415
 Load carried by, 8-13; 10-214
Mississippi River Bridge, Greenville, Mississippi. 2-343
Mississippian period, time in earth's history. 1-390;
 6-372
 Coal formation during, *with illus.,* 1-406-07
Missouri.
 Rain-eroded farm land, *illus.,* 2-352
Missouri River.
 Flood waters of, *illus.,* 6-417
 Formation of, at Three Forks, Montana, *illus.,* 6-410
Mistletoes.
 Habitat, 10-136
 Seed dispersal, 5-5
Mistral, a cold, dry wind. 2-94
Mitchell, Maria, American astronomer (1818-89). Astron-
 omy professor and director of the observatory of Vassar
 College, she was the first woman to be elected to the
 American Academy of Arts and Sciences. She discov-
 ered a comet (1847) and several nebulae, and she
 studied sunspots and satellites.
Mites. *with illus.,* 2-268-69
Mitochondria, cell structures. 1-143; 2-8, *illus.,* 4, 8,
 12b-c; 9-385
Mitosis, cell division. 1-144; 2-13-14, *with illus.,* 289-
 92, *illus.,* 13; *illus.,* 6-270
 See also **Cells**
Mitscherlich, Eilhardt, German chemist.
 Optical activity of substances, work on, 9-71
Mixed tides. 6-204
Mixers, used in breadmaking. *with illus.,* 9-296
Mixing, color. See **Color mixing**
Mixing basins. 2-279
Mixing houses, for gases. 5-106
Mixtures. *with illus.,* 1-81-82
 *Solutions, 4-296-303
 Alloys, 1-382
Mnium, genus of mosses. 3-188, *illus.,* 186

Moated-island zoo exhibits. 10-160-61, *illus.,* 154
Moccasin flowers. 7-245-46
Mocking birds. 6-46, 48
Model T, historic automobile model. 2-131
Modern alchemy. *with illus.,* 8-410-20; *with illus.,* 9-328-32
Modifiers, chemical additives. Plastics, used in manufacture of, 8-225
Modulation, in radio. *with illus.,* 3-89
    See also **Amplitude modulation; Frequency modulation**
Moebius, August Ferdinand, German mathematician (1790–1868)
    Strips, Moebius, *with diagrams,* 4-452-53
Moebius strips. *with diagrams,* 4-452-53
    Stellarator based on principle of, 1-176
Moeritherium, genus of extinct elephants. 7-408
Mohammedanism. Rise of, 2-298
Mohammedans. Calendar, 10-178
Mohave Desert. See **Mojave Desert**
Mohl, Hugo von, German botanist. 7-159
MOHOLE ("MOhorovičić-discontinuity HOLE"). A project to drill past the Mohorovičić discontinuity, which separates the crust of the earth from the underlying mantle —a layer of dense rock between the crust and the metallic core of the earth. Several sites in ocean areas are being considered, where the crust is thin and the mantle comes to about six or seven miles below the surface of the ocean bed. Preliminary test drillings with oil-well-type equipment have been made off the Pacific coast of Mexico. It is hoped that MOHOLE will provide samples of mantle rocks and answer many questions about the earth's origin and history.
Mohorovičić, A., geophysicist. Discovery of Mohorovičić discontinuity, 4-171
Mohorovičić discontinuity. 4-171, 173, *illus.,* 171
Mohs, Friedrich, German mineralogist (1773–1839).
    Hardness scale developed by, *with illus.,* 5-253-54
Mohs' scale, scale of hardness. *with illus.,* 5-253-54
    Testing minerals by, 9-303, 305
Moissan, Henri, French chemist, (1852–1907). He was chemistry professor at the School of Pharmacy in Paris and at the Sorbonne. He isolated fluorine and developed the electric arc furnace, for which he won the 1906 Nobel Prize in chemistry. With his electric furnace Moissan prepared new compounds of carbon, silicon and boron and discovered a simple method of making acetylene.
    Diamonds synthetically produced by?, 4-251, 274-75
Moisture. See **Humidity, relative; Soil; Water**
Mojave Desert, California.
    Alluvial fans in, *illus.,* 8-16
Molars, teeth. 5-129-30, *illus.,* 131-32, *table,* 130
    Mammals, adaptations in, 3-235, 236
    Man, development of molars in, 8-95, *illus.,* 94-95
    Rodents, found in, 8-161, 162
Molders, master printing plates. 1-207
Molding.
    Breadmaking operation, 9-297, *diagram,* 298
    Plastics, *illus.,* 7-211; *with diagrams,* 8-230-32, *illus.,* 220b
Molds. *with illus.,* 3-24-27, *illus.,* 23
    Antibiotics produced by, *with illus.,* 10-130a-d
    Food spoilage caused by, *with illus.,* 4-153, 154
    Gamma radiation affects, *illus.,* 10-116
    Penicillin, *with illus.,* 7-52-53
    Pink bread mold, hereditary studies of, 9-385
Molds, cavities in which objects are shaped.
    Papermaking, used in, 4-364-65
    Printing plates, molds used in preparation of, *with diagram,* 1-207-08
    See also **Molding**

Mole crickets, orthopteran insects. 2-412; 3-147
Mole shrews. 7-100
Molecular structure.
    Determination of, by microwaves, 7-206
Molecular weights. 2-227, 231; 5-76; 7-275
Molecules. *1-162-72
  *Chemical reactions involving molecules, 2-223-31
  *Properties of matter, 5-369-76
  *Valence, 3-245-51
    Atmospheric gas molecules, 1-231
    Carbohydrates, 4-76, 77, 78-79
    Change of state, *with illus.,* 3-416-18
    Colloidal particles and, 5-296, 300
    Crystals made up of, 5-337, *diagrams,* 338-39
    Definition and invention of word, 5-75-76
    Diamond structure, *with illus.,* 4-274
    Gaseous, behavior of, 3-416
    Heat due to motion of, 3-408-09; 4-17-19; 6-253-54
    Liquids and gases compared, 2-31
    Living molecules, *with diagram,* 9-383-86
    Magnetism, theoretical role in, 7-172; 8-143
    Molecular weight, 7-275
    Muscles, molecular structure of, 3-205
    Plastics, *with diagram,* 8-222
    Protoplasmic molecules, 2-3-7, 10-11
    Solutions, molecules in, *with diagram,* 4-297-98
    Sound waves, behavior in, 5-116-17, *illus.,* 116; 8-103-04
    X rays "fingerprint" arrangements of, 7-147
    See also **Atoms; Crystals; Energy; Matter**
Moles, mammals. 7-97-98, 102, *illus.,* 94
    Humidity affects, 7-7
    Pets, 7-20-21
    Tunnels of, 10-260
Molesworth, P. B., astronomer. Jupiter's markings studied by, 5-23
Moleyns, Frederick de, English inventor. 4-234-35
Mollies, tropical fish. 8-115
Mollusks. *2-192-202
  *Shell collecting, 2-99-104
    Classification of, 1-294
    Defense mechanisms, 3-239-40
    Luminous, *illus.,* 2-185
    Luminous secretion by, 2-185
    Pteropod ooze, 6-33
    Shells used for buttons, 7-210, *with illus.,* 212
Molochs, ant-eating lizards. 5-202, 204, 206
Molting.
    Light affects, 7-8
    Silkworms, 5-177
    Snakes, 5-353-54, *illus.,* 355
Molybdates.
    Minerals in the form of, 9-306
Molybdenum (Mo), chemical element. Atomic number, 42; atomic weight, 95.94; melting point, 2,620° C.; boiling point, 4,800° C.; specific gravity, 10.2. Metal; silver-white, very hard. Recognized by Scheele in 1778; first prepared in an impure form four years later; name derived from Greek *molybdos:* "lead." Not found in uncombined form; obtained from molybdenite and wulfenite. Prepared by reduction of the oxide with carbon, usually in electric furnace. Used widely in certain grades of tool steel and also in boiler plate and rifle barrels, increasing their toughness and tensile strength. Also serves in radio grids, filaments and screens.
    Salts of, used in facsimile transmission 7-392
    Steelmaking, use of molybdenum in, 1-352-53
Momentum. 2-122
Monadnocks, islandlike hills rising above the general surface of the land. 8-18; *illus.,* 10-20
Monadnock, Mount, New Hampshire. *illus.,* 10-20

Monarch butterflies. *illus.,* 2-408-10; 3-199, *illus.,* 193
　Migration of, 9-430-31
Monasteries.
　Centers of learning in Middle Ages, 2-295-97
Monel metal. 1-81-82, 382
Mongolia. Yurt, primitive dwelling of, *illus.,* 3-114
Mongolian ponies (Przewalski's horses). 10-250
Mongooses. *with illus.,* 8-247-48
　Jamaica, mongooses introduced into, 10-190
Monilia sitophila, bread mold. *illus.,* 10-130b-c
Monitor, American warship. 6-378, *illus.,* 379
Monitors, family of lizards. *with illus.,* 5-200, 204, 205,
　206
Monk seals. *illus.,* 7-87
Monkeys. *with illus.,* 9-254-64
　Adapted for tree-dwelling, 7-9
　Germ-free, *illus.,* 7-154
　Intelligence, *illus.,* 2-28
　Zoos, 10-161, *illus.,* 159
Monkfish. 4-290, *illus.,* 291
Monk's cloth. *illus.,* 9-93
Monkshoods. *illus.,* 7-77
Monoceros, constellation. Nebulosity in, *illus.,* 9-161
Monoclinic system, of external crystal structure. 5-342,
　diagram, 341
Monocotyledons, flowering plants. 2-415, *illus.,* 416;
　with illus., 3-403-04
　Classification of, 1-302-03
Monocytes, white blood cells. 3-328-29
　See also **White blood cells**
Monoliths, blocks into which dams are divided. 8-313
Monomers, molecular links. *with diagram,* 8-222
Mononucleosis, infectious disease. 3-331
Monosaccharides, sugar compounds. 4-51-52, 78-79
　Cells, sugars in, 2-5
Monotremata, order of mammals. 7-13, *illus.,* 12
　See also **Monotremes**
Monotremes, mammals. 7-4-5
Monotype machines, for typesetting. *with illus.,* 1-201-
　02
Monsoon drifts, oceanic currents. 6-234, 237, *map,*
　232-33
Monsoons, seasonal winds. 2-91
Mont Blanc, France. 10-21
Mont Cenis Tunnel. 2-44
Montagu, Lady Mary Wortley, English poet.
　Smallpox inoculation introduced into England, 4-401
Montana.
　Copper mine in, *illus.,* 3-39
Monte Bello Island, Australia.
　British atomic-bomb explosion at, 9-354
Monterey Canyon, oceanic canyon. 6-73
Montgolfier, Joseph-Michel and Jacques-Etienne.
　Pioneer balloon flights, 6-177, *illus.,* 176
Months.
　*Calendars, 10-171-80
Montreal Neurological Institute. 9-104
Monuments.
　See also **Marble; Sculpture**
Moon. *4-277-84
　Astronomical observatories on?, *illus.,* 1-25
　Calendars based on cycles of, 1-126; 10-171, 173-74,
　　178
　Data, 10-298
　Distances in heavens estimated with moon as guide,
　　6-79
　Earth, movement around, *with illus.,* 2-316
　Eclipse of, 3-131-34
　Galileo's observations of, 3-3
　Gravity on, 2-322

Moon (*continued*)
　Green appearance following Krakatoa's eruption,
　　7-342
　How to observe, 6-81-83
　Hydroponic farming on? 8-36, *illus.,* 37
　Illumination provided by, 9-344
　Origin of?, 1-29
　Phases of, 6-81-82
　Photograph of, first, 6-386
　Position determined by Markowitz moon camera, *with*
　　illus., 5-187-88
　Radar echoes from, 7-207
　Reproduction of, by planetarium projectors, 2-399,
　　illus., 401
　Shadow of, 3-135
　Space flight to, 10-53-54, *illus.,* 52-53
　Temperatures on, 1-232; 4-279
　Tides caused by moon's gravitational pull, *with*
　　diagrams, 6-201-04, 205
　See also **Moons of planets; Solar system; Universe**
"Moon shots," attempts to reach the moon with un-
　manned rockets. 9-376, 380, 382-83; 10-47
Moondogs, mock moons.
　Flying saucers thought to be, 9-20
Moonrats, insectivores. 7-99
Moons of planets.
　Jupiter, 5-21, 24
　　Observations of, 6-84
　Mars, 4-417-18
　Neptune, 5-292
　Origin, theories of, 1-29
　Saturn, 5-113
　Uranus, 5-289-90, *diagram,* 292
Moors, Moslems of North African origin.
　Contributions to culture in Middle Ages, 2-301-02
Moose. 8-240-41, *illus.,* 237
Moraines, debris carried or deposited by glaciers, 9-170,
　173, *illus.,* 166-67, 171
Moral imbecile. Psychopathic personality, 9-200
Morehead Planetarium, Chapel Hill, N. C. 2-398
Morels, pitted-cap fungi. 3-28
Morgan, Thomas Hunt, American geneticist.
　Fruit fly studied by, *with diagram,* 9-384-85
Morgan, William W., American astronomer.
　Galaxies spectrally classified by, 8-51
Morley, Edward W., American chemist and physicist
　(1838–1923). He was chemistry professor at Western Re-
　serve University, Cleveland. He conducted researches on
　the variations of oxygen content in the atmosphere, the
　thermal expansion of gases and the density of hydrogen
　and oxygen. He determined the speed of light in a mag-
　netic field. Morley was associated with A. A. Michelson
　in the famous experiment concerning the relative motion
　of the earth and the supposed medium "ether." See also
　6-246-47 (*with illus.*)
　Experiment with light waves, 4-211-12
Mormon crickets. *with illus.,* 3-145
Morning-glories, *illus.,* 4-123
　Movements of, *illus.,* 6-218b
　Weeds, 7-112
Morning star.
　Mercury as, 4-25
　Venus as, 4-28
Morphemes, linguistic forms. 1-108-09
Morphine, narcotic base. 5-404
Morphos, butterflies. 3-199
Morris, William, English poet and artist (1834–96). Arts
　and Crafts Movement, role in, 10-119
Morrison, Charles, Scottish physician. 2-378
Morrison Planetarium, San Francisco. *with illus.,* 2-398

Morse, Samuel Finley Breese, American inventor. 5-239-41, *illus.,* 238
  Photographic work, **9-400**
  Telegraph, development of, *with illus.,* 2-379-81
Morse code. 2-381, *diagram,* 380
  Developed by S. F. B. Morse, 5-239
Mortar. Construction material, 7-118-19
Morton, William T. G., American dentist. *with illus.,* 7-376-77
Morula, globular mass of cells developing from egg. 8-22, *illus.,* 21
Morus, mulberry tree. Silkworms cultured on, *with illus.,* 5-174-77
Mosaics.
  Roman floors, *with illus.,* 7-116-17
Mosasaurs, extinct marine lizards. 1-394; 5-198; *illus.,* 6-374
Moscow Canal. *with illus.,* 4-186-87
Moseley, Henry Gwyn-Jeffreys, English physicist. *with illus.,* 8-417
"Mosquito boats." *illus.,* 9-69
Mosquito control. Measures taken, *illus.,* 10-30, 36, 37, 39
Mosquitoes. 3-285, 287, 289-90, *illus.,* 283, 286-88
  *Vector of malaria and yellow fever, 10-30-39
  Anopheles, carrier of malaria, 8-405, *illus.,* 404
  Disease germs carried and transmitted by, 7-384-85
  Filarial worms transmitted by, 2-158
  Stegomyia, carrier of yellow fever, 8-405
  Sucking organs, 3-238
  Viruses transmitted by, 3-457
Moss animals. Unchanged for millions of years, 6-283
Mosses. 3-187-89, *illus.,* 186; *illus.,* 6-139
  Soil formation, importance in, 2-16, 21-22, 23
Moth balls. Experiment with, *with illus.,* 7-132-33
  See also Naphthalene
Mother-of-pearl. 2-196, 202
  Buttons made from, 7-210, *with illus.,* 7-212
Moths. *3-193-202
  *Silkworms and silk, 5-173-85
  Cecropia, *illus.,* 2-405
  Codling moths, *with illus.,* 9-192
  Pollen carriers, 7-247, *illus.,* 245
  Polyphemus moths, *illus.,* 9-190-91
Motion. *2-118-28
  *Relativity theory, 4-210-20
  *Stars, motions of, 7-223-29
  Bodies in solar system, motion of, 3-157-59, 162-64
  Doppler effect used to analyze motions of heavenly bodies, 6-391
  Earth's motion, *with diagrams,* 4-47-50
  Electricity and magnetism, relation to motion, 5-235-36
  Force and, *with illus.,* 1-82-83, 84
  Heat as motion of molecules, 1-163-66, 170-72, *with diagrams,* 167-69; 3-408-09; 4-17-18; 6-248-54
  Newton's laws of, *with illus.,* 2-122-26; 3-280
    Demonstration of third law, *with illus.,* 1-141; 2-329
  Pressure of moving liquids, 2-35
  Protoplasmic and cellular movements, 2-12, *illus.,* 10, 11
  Space flight, forces and motions in, 8-126-31
  Wave motion, 6-361-63
  See also Parity law; Stellar motions; Supersonics
Motion, animal. **See Locomotion, animal**
Motion pictures.
  Electroluminescent devices for, 9-347
  Photographic equipment, 9-403, 407, 408-09
Motivation. Psychology of, 9-319
Motor areas, of cerebrum. *with illus.,* 6-324-25
Motor nerves and fibers. 6-318, *illus.,* 322
  See also Cranial nerves

Motor transportation. **See Automobiles**
Motor trucks. **See Trucks**
Motorcycles. Invention of, 6-380
Motors. Airplanes, 6-187
  See also Electric motors; Engines; Servomotors
Moulton, Forest Ray, American astronomer.
  Planetesimal hypothesis, 1-29, *illus.,* 28; 9-225
  Quotation from, 10-224
Mount. For mountains preceded by "Mount," see names of mountains, as **Everest, Mount**
Mount Stromlo Observatory, Australia. *illus.,* 8-55, 62-63
Mount Wilson Observatory, California. *illus.,* 8-65; 9-156, *illus.,* 155
Mountain glaciers. 9-165, 168-70, *illus.,* 163, 166-67, 172
  Land forms produced by, *with illus.,* 9-168-70, *diagram,* 164-65
Mountain lions. **See Pumas**
Mountain making (revolutons and disturbances). 6-370, 371, 372, 373, 374
  See also Orogeny
Mountain of Heaven, Denmark. *illus.,* 10-20
Mountain quail. 6-333
Mountains. *10-18-29
  *Origin of mountains, 10-213-23
  Air circulation over, 2-94
  Lakes formed during mountain buildings, 7-56
  Precipitation affected by, 2-347-48
  Rivers, formation of, 6-409-10
  Roots of, 5-188-89
  See also Mountain making
Mountains, lunar. 4-280, 282, *illus.,* 281, 283
Mounts, telescope. *with illus.,* 9-372-74
Mourning doves. *with illus.,* 6-305
Mouth.
  Breathing through, 4-203
  Care of, 10-77-78
  Muscles of, 3-209-10
  Taking temperature by, *with illus.,* 10-57-58
Mouth rot, fish disease. 8-116
Mouth parts. Insects, 2-403, 406, *illus.,* 404
  True bugs, *with illus.,* 3-253
Mouth-to-mouth resuscitation. *with illus.,* 10-10
Mouth valves. Fish, breathing of, *with illus.,* 1-279
Mouth washes. 10-78
Mouton, fur. 7-238
Movable bridges. 2-340-41, *illus.,* 339-41
Movable dams. *illus.,* 8-316c
Movable palate. **See Soft palate**
Movable type. **See Printing**
Movement. See Motion
Movement, animal. **See Locomotion, animal; Muscles**
Movement, plant. *illus.,* 1-41, 47; 3-52-54, *illus.,* 51, 53, 55; *illus.,* 6-218a-d
  See also Locomotion, plant
Movements, population. 3-226-28, 233-34
Moynihan, Barkeley George Andrew, English surgeon. 9-31
Mu Draconis, star. Orbital motion of, *illus.,* 7-229
Mu Hercules, star. Solar system moving toward, 7-227-28
Mu mesons, particles emitted by cosmic rays. *table,* 1-314; 4-215-16
Mucilage, adhesive. Chemurgic development of, 7-44
Mucors, molds of bread and other foods. *with illus.,* 3-26
  Mucor racemosus, mold, *illus.,* 10-130b-c
Mucous glands. 5-10

Mucous membranes.
  Body's defenses, part of, 7-347-48; 9-177
  Nose, 4-203; *with illus.,* 7-303
Mucus. 5-10
Mud.
  Drilling mud, 4-145, *diagram,* 144
  Size of particles of, 3-424
  Streams carry and deposit, 8-13
  See also **Sediment; Sedimentary rocks**
Mud daubers.
  Black-and-yellow mud dauber and nest, *illus.,* 3-361
Mud floods. 2-351-52
Mud puppies, salamanders. Pets, 7-26
Mud volcanoes, 8-298
Mudskippers, fishes. 4-99
Mudstone, sedimentary rock. 3-424
Mueller, Johann, German astronomer and mathematician. 2-363
Mueller, Johannes, German physiologist. 9-48
Mueller, W., German physicist.
  Radiation detectors, development of, *with illus.,* 9-340-43
Mufflers, of automobiles. *with illus.,* 2-135
Muir, John, Scottish-born naturalist. 8-254
Muir Glacier, Alaska. *illus.,* 9-334
Mulberry trees. *with illus.,* 5-149
  Silkworms cultured on, *with illus.,* 5-174-77
Mulch. Soil moisture preserved by, *with illus.,* 5-29, *illus.,* 28
Mule deer. 8-241, *illus.,* 236
Mules. Transportation, use in, 1-102, *illus.,* 103
Mullard Radio Astronomy Observatory, England.
  Radio telescope of, *illus.,* 9-209
Muller, Hermann Joseph, American geneticist (1890–   ). In the course of experiments with fruit flies, he succeeded in bringing about the artificial transmutation of genes by means of X rays. He received his education in the United States and abroad and held various important scientific positions before becoming professor of zoology at the University of Indiana in 1945. A year later he was awarded the Nobel Prize in physiology and medicine.
  Mutations produced by X rays, 9-356; 10-251
Mullet, fish. Taste organs of, 4-101
"Multimatic Wall," gas kitchen-appliance center. 5-106
Multiple-arch dams. 8-315, *illus.,* 311
Multiple bank radial airplane engines. 6-187
Multiple freezer method, for freezing food. 4-162
Multiple fruits. *with illus.,* 4-129
Multiple-spindle bar machines. 10-109
Multiplex telegraphy. *with illus.,* 2-383
Multiplication, arithmetical operation. 1-157-58
Multiplication of living things. See **Reproduction**
Multistage rockets, rockets fitted into unit. 9-376, 381; 10-43, 46, 48, *illus.,* 44-45
  Satellites (artificial) placed into orbits by, *diagram,* 8-131
Multiwhistle, ultrasonic device. *illus.,* 8-111
Mumps, virus disease. *illus.,* 3-454
Municipal government. See **Cities**
Municipal parks, United States. 9-276-77
Munsell color atlas. 7-287-88
Muntjacs, deer. *with illus.,* 8-240
Muons. See **Mu mesons**
Murdock, William, British inventor. 4-233
  Steam-propelled vehicle of, 1-180
Muriate of potassium. See **Potassium chloride**
Murphy, George M., American chemist.
  Heavy hydrogen, discovery of, 8-418
Murphy, John B., American surgeon. 9-31

Murphy, William P., American physician. 9-35
  Research on liver diet for pernicious anemia, 5-44
Murray, Sir John, British marine zoologist. 7-34
  Coral reefs, theory of, 4-138-39
Murray meteorite, from Kentucky. 6-94
Murrayian local race. 8-219
Musangs, palm civets. 8-246, 248
Muscatel, sweet wine. 4-168
Muscatine, Iowa. Pearl-button manufacture at, 7-210
Muscle cramps. 6-150
Muscle sense. See **Kinesthesia**
Muscles.
  *Exercise, 10-85-91
  *Human muscles, 3-203-13
  Colloid gel, 5-301
  Birds', *with illus.,* 1-284-85; 10-138-39
  Body's defenses, role in, 7-346
  Breathing controlled by, *with illus.,* 4-204, 205
  Development in unborn human young, 8-27
  Human growth or aging, muscles in, 8-96-97, 100
  Insects, *with illus.,* 1-283-84
  Man's, *illus.,* 1-148c
  Mechanism of, in various animals, *with illus.,* 1-283-85, 286
  Parathyroid deficiency affects, 5-18
  Relaxation of, during onset of sleep, 6-143-44
  Strains, first aid for, 10-12
  Strong muscles not necessary for health, 1-70
  Tissue structure, *with illus.,* 1-144-45
Muscles of the eye. *illus.,* 7-292
Muscular system. See **Muscles**
Museum of Modern Art, New York City. Industrial design, fostering of, 10-126
Museums.
  Industrial design, museum departments devoted to, 10-126
"Mushroom cloud," of atomic bomb. 9-352
Mushrooms. *illus.,* 1-301; *with illus.,* 3-29-32, *illus.,* 23
  Edible mushrooms, *with illus.,* 3-30-31
  Light emission from, 2-182
  Poisonous mushrooms, *with illus.,* 3-31-32
  Toadstools, distinguished from, 3-30-31
Music.
  *Musical sounds, 5-211-20
  Analysis of sounds, 8-46
  Mathematics used in, 1-76
  Musical notations, 5-212
  Musical theory, development in antiquity, 1-134
"Music of the spheres." 1-134
  Kepler's belief in, 3-6
Music typewriters. *with illus.,* 1-275
Musical instruments.
  Acoustics ot, *with illus.,* and *tables,* 5-215-20
  Homemade, *with illus.,* 5-229-30
Musk (or civet), odoriferous secretion. 8-245
  Civets use musk to indicate range, 8-248
Musk deer. 8-240
Musk kangaroos. 7-425
Musk oxen. 8-378, *illus.,* 381
Musk shrews. 7-102
Muskingum River, Ohio. Conveyer belt crosses, 6-170
Muskrats, rodents. 8-164
  Fur, 7-238
  Home building, 9-6
Musschenbroek, Pieter van, Dutch scientist.
  Invention of Leyden jar, 4-359
Mussels. 2-199
  Parasitic, 8-368
  Shells used for buttons, 7-210, *with illus.,* 212
Mustard gas. World War I, used in, 9-213
Mustard plants. 7-112

Mutations. *with illus.,* 6-274-75; 8-343-44
  Radiation produces, 9-356; 10-252
  Viruses, mutations in, 3-455, 458
  See also **Heredity; Natural selection**
Muybridge, Eadweard, English inventor (1830–1904). He came to the United States and made a series of photographs in California with the purpose of analyzing the motions of a horse. He invented an apparatus that projected the animated pictures on a screen. This was an ancestor of the motion-picture projector.
Mycelium, mass of filaments of fungi. 3-22, *with illus.,* 27, 32; 4-63
  Light emission from, 2-182
Mycology, scientific study of fungi. *3-22-32
  See also **Fungi**
Mycorrhizal roots, association of fungi and green-plant roots. 3-28; 4-63
Myelin, sheath around axons. 6-318, 329, *illus.,* 318
  See also **White matter**
Myology. See Muscles
Myopia. See Nearsightedness
Myriapods, millepedes and centipedes. *with illus.,* 2-269
Mythology.
  Kingfisher, myth of, 6-310
  Legends linked with constellations, 1-325, 330, 331, 332, 333, 335
  Milky Way, 8-151
Myxamoebae, amebalike slime-mold cells. *with illus.,* 6-218a

N

n-butane. *with diagram,* 7-268
n-pentane. Structural formula, 7-269
N-type silicon.
  Solar battery, use in, 7-106, *illus.,* 104
NACA (U. S. National Advisory Committee for Aeronautics). 9-219
Nachmansohn, David, American physiologist. Impulse-conduction theory of, 6-321
Nacre, inner layer of shell of certain shellfish. 2-196, 202
  Buttons made from, 7-210, *with illus.,* 212
Nadir. 1-261, *diagrams,* 260, 261
Nafud, desert area of Arabia. 6-118
Nagasaki, Japan. Atomic-bomb explosion, 9-348, *illus.,* 122
Naiads, young forms of certain insects. 2-407, *illus.,* 408
Nail bed, part of fingernail. *with illus.,* 2-181
Nail root, part of fingernail. 2-181
Nails, of man. *2-180-81
  Care of, 10-81
Names, of geologic time units. Derivation, 6-370
Naming of animals and plants. *1-287-306
Nansen, Fridtjof, Norwegian explorer.
  Observations on oceanic currents, 6-234
Naphthalene, constituent of coal tar.
  Coal tar yields, *with illus.,* 1-419
  Indigo synthesized from, 8-183
  Sublimation of, 3-418
Napier, John, Scottish mathematician. *with illus.,* 3-20
Napier's bones, calculating device. *with illus.,* 3-20
Napoleon I (Napoleon Bonaparte). Interest in science, 4-34-35
Narcolepsy, "sleeping disease." 6-150
Narcosynthesis. Treatment for "shell shock," 9-327-28
Narcotics. *5-400-07

Narrative drawings. "Writing" by means of, *with illus.,* 1-112
Narrow-gauge railroads. 1-183
Narwhals, aquatic mammals. 7-189
NASA (National Aeronautics and Space Administration).
  Space program, 10-46-47
  Wind tunnel at Moffett Field, California, 10-233, 234
Nasal cavities, in skull. 3-79; *illus.,* 4-202
Nasal septum, nose partition. 3-79, *illus.,* 77
Nasturtiums. Flower structure, *illus.,* 7-242
National Academy of Sciences. 5-186
National Advisory Committee for Aeronautics.
  Wallops Island research station, *illus.,* 4-342c
National Aeronautics and Space Administration. See **NASA**
National Association for Mental Health. 9-103
National Audubon Society. Animal conservation work, 9-275, 278
National Bison Range, Montana. Bison in, *illus.,* 9-271
National Bureau of Standards.
  Standards Electronic Automatic Computer (SEAC), 9-145
National Center for Scientific Research, France. 1-95, 96
National Farm Chemurgic Council, Inc. 1-89
National Geographic Society-Palomar Observatory Sky Atlas. 8-62
National Livestock and Meat Board. 5-169
National Park Service, bureau of Department of the Interior. 9-276
National Pest Control Association, in the United States. Awards to young scientists by, 8-72
National Project Exposition, in the United States. Competitions for youthful scientists sponsored by, 8-73
National Reactor Testing Station.
  Atomic submarine engine tested in, *illus.,* 4-342d
National Reclamation Act. 8-199
National Research Council, of Brazil. 1-96
National Research Council, Canada. 1-92-93
  Activities in World War II, 9-323
National Research Council, of the United States.
  Bakery-product enrichment standards recommended by, 9-299
National Science Fair-International, competitions among young scientists. 8-72
National Science Teachers Association, in the United States. Competitions for youthful scientists sponsored by, 8-72-73
National Television System Committee (NTSC).
  Color-television specifications made by, 5-288
Nations. See **Civilization; England; Europe; France; Germany; Society;** etc.
Native cats, marsupials. 7-427
Native peoples. See **Anthropology**
Natural arches, geologic formations. 8-11
Natural bridges, geologic formations. Formation of, 5-54; *with illus.,* 8-15
Natural gas. *5-97-106
  Helium found in, 5-208
  Petroleum and, 4-146, *with diagram,* 142-43
Natural history.
  Beast and plant books of the Middle Ages, *with illus.,* 2-309
  Nineteenth-century studies of the world's fauna and flora, *with illus.,* 8-251-57
  See also **Animals; Biology; Botany; Flowers; Plants; Pliny the Elder; Zoology**
Natural History, magazine. Young biologists' researches published in, 8-74
Natural Immunity. 7-350-51
Natural levees, stream embankments. 8-17

Natural logarithms. 2-76

Natural resources. See Agriculture; Coal; Conservation of natural resources; Forests; Iron; Minerals; Mining; Oil; Petroleum; Timber; Water power; etc.

Natural selection. *6-269-85
  *Adaptations of plants and animals, 3-235-44
   Analyzed by Darwin, 8-260
   Hereditary endowments favored by, 8-346-47
   See also Darwin, Charles Robert; Evolution; Heredity; Mutations; Protective coloration; Weismann, August

Natural ventilation. 2-244, 245, 254

Naturalists. See Biology; Botany; Zoology; also names of individual naturalists.

Nature. See Animals; Biology; Botany; Flowers; Nature study; Plants; Seeds; Zoology; etc.

Nature study.
  *Ants, keeping colony of, 3-393-96
  *Exploring animal world, 10-254-64
  *Exploring plant world, 10-203-12
  *Insect collecting, 3-153-56
  *Mineral and rock collecting, 9-300-09
  *Nature photography, 6-311-16
  *Seasonal changes and life, 5-408-13
  *Shell collecting, 2-99-104
  *Terrariums, 5-363-68
  *Trees, how to recognize, 5-138-51

Nautical almanacs. 1-18, illus., 19

Nautical measures. table, 10-295

Nautical mile. See Nautical measures

Nautilus, atomic-powered submarine. with illus., 4-114a; 5-190, with illus., 35-36, 37
   Engine of, illus., 4-342d

Nautilus, Fulton's early submarine. 5-31-32, illus., 33

Nautiluses, cephalopods. with illus., 2-195-96
   Paper nautilus, shell of, illus., 2-101

Naval Observatory of the United States.
   Refracting 26-inch telescope at, illus., 8-61
   Time measured by, 8-61

Naval warfare. Hydrofoil boats in? 4-8

Navies. See Ships; World War I; World War II

Navigation.
  *Bathyscaphes, 6-74a-d
  *Buoys, 5-68-71
  *Guidance of missiles and space vehicles, 8-125-31
  *Ships, 4-106-18
   Astronomy basis of, 1-18, illus., 19
   Beaufort scale for gauging apparent strength of wind, 10-297
   Buoys powered with radioactive electric generators, with illus., 6-175
   Dams that improve, 8-307
   Inscribed angles used in, with illus., 3-436-37
   Magnetic compasses, 7-167-68
   Oceanic currents have effect on, 6-238
   Radar, use of, illus., 9-387-90
   Sonar, 8-105-06

Navigation, animal. External stimuli that may influence, 9-418

NC-4, transatlantic flying boat. 6-184; 9-217

Neanderthal man. 9-22

Neap tides. 6-203, diagram, 205

Nearsightedness (myopia). with illus., 7-296

Nebel, Bernard, American chemist. 9-291

Nebulae. *9-359-64
   Crab Nebula, illus., 8-156d-e
   Cygnus, nebula in, illus., 8-156b-c, 157
   Milky Way, 8-153, 155
   North American Nebula, illus., 8-156, 156h
   Orion, Great Nebula in, illus., 8-156f-g
   Ring Nebula, illus., 8-156a

Nebulae (continued)
   Spiral, Rosse's discovery of, with illus., 6-388-89
   Types of, illus., 9-161

Nebular hypothesis, of origin of solar system. 1-29, illus., 28; 4-400

Neck.
   Blood vessels of, illus., 1-148f
   Lymphatic nodes of, illus., 1-148g
   Muscles of, illus., 1-148c; illus., 3-204, 205

Neck bones. See Cervical vertebrae

Neck vertebrae. See Cervical vertebrae

Neckham, Alexander. Treatises on magnetic compass, 7-167

Nectar, flower secretion. 3-367

Nectaries, glands of flowers. 4-120

Needles, pine-tree. 7-80

Negative electricity. 1-398; 6-120
   Named by Franklin, 4-360

Negative integers, in arithmetic. 1-159-60

Negative numbers.
   Analytic geometry, with diagrams, 4-425-31

Negatives, photographic. 9-399, 401, 403, 406, 409, 412-14, with diagram, 410
   Microfilm, with illus., 10-70-71
   Photoengraving, negatives used in, with diagrams, 1-204-05

Negev, region in Israel. Irrigation in, 8-200, illus., 201

Negev Mountains, Israel. illus., 7-65

Negrito local race. 8-218

Negro bugs. 3-257

Negroes.
   Blood groups in Negro race, 3-334, with table, 333
   Hair of, illus., 2-178
   Skin color, 2-176

Negroid subspecies of man.
   Hair of, illus., 2-178

Neisser, Albert Ludwig Siegmund, German physician. 7-382

Nektonic organisms. 6-35

Nelson, George, American designer. 10-121

Nemathelminths, roundworms. illus., 2-153, 156-59, 160

Nematocysts, specialized cells. 2-148-49

Nematodes. See Nemathelminths

Nemertinea, phylum of flattened worms. 1-293

Neodymium (Nd), chemical element. Atomic number, 60; atomic weight, 144.24; melting point, 840° C.; specific gravity, 6.95. Yellowish, rare-earth metal. First reported by Mosander in 1843 as supposed element didymium, obtained from cerite. Von Welsbach, in 1885, separated didymium into two new elements, neodymium and praseodymium. The name is derived from Greek neos: "new," and didymos: "twin."

Neo-Hawaiian local race. 8-219

Neomycin, antibiotic. 10-128

Neon (Ne), chemical element. Atomic number, 10; atomic weight, 20.183; melting point, —248.67° C.; boiling point, —245.9° C.; specific gravity (air = 1), 0.69638. Inert, rare gas; spectrum shows marked red and green lines. Discovered by Ramsay and Travers in 1898; name derived from Greek neos: "new." Found in atmosphere in proportion of 18 parts per million; obtained by liquefaction of air and separation by fractional distillation. Widely used in electric signs and beacons, because of its red-orange glow in a vacuum tube.
   Atomic structure, 1-311, diagram, 312
   Color of, when electrically excited, 8-118
   Discharge lamps using neon gas, 4-240
   Electron tubes filled with, 6-301

Neopentane, a hydrocarbon. Structural formula, 7-269

Neoplatonic school, of philosophy. 1-368

Neoprene, plastic material. 6-359
  Piling wrapped with, *illus.,* 6-26d

Nephoscopes, instruments for observing drift of clouds. 2-92

Nephrons, excretory units of kidneys. *with diagram,* 5-12

Nepids, family of true bugs. *with illus.,* 3-263

Neprobromate ("Miltown"), synthetic tranquilizer. 9-104

Neptune, planet.
  Comet family of, 5-397
  Data, 10-298
  Discovery of and data, *with diagram,* 2-317;
    3-164; 5-290-92; 6-392

Neptunism, theory of earth formation. 4-394, 396-97

Neptunium (Np), chemical element. Atomic number, 93; atomic weight, 237(?). Discovered through tracer technique in 1940 at the University of California by McMillan and Abelson; name derived from the planet Neptune, next to Uranus in the solar system. Neptunium is the product of decay of the uranium isotope 239, which is formed through the capture of a neutron by uranium-238. Neptunium in its pure form has been prepared and studied.

Nerad, A. J., American physicist. 4-275

Nereid, satellite of Neptune. 5-292

Nerve cells (neurons).
  *Nervous system, 6-317-30
  Development in study of, 9-56
  Irreplaceable after destruction, 7-353

Nerve cords. Insect nervous system, *with illus.,* 2-406

Nerve deafness. 5-125

Nerve fibers (axons). *6-317-30
  Body's defenses, role in, 7-346, 353

Nerve-gap theory of sleep. 6-148

Nerve impulses.
  Explanation of, 2-425-26, *diagram,* 424
  Light production in animals due to, 2-187
  Muscular activity, role in, 3-208, *illus.,* 206
  Nature and functions of, 6-317-18, 320-21, *illus.,* 320

Nerves. *6-317-30
  Body's defenses, role in, 7-346
  Heartbeat, nerves affecting, 3-387
  Nervous impulses, 2-425-26, *diagram,* 424
  Phrenic nerve, 9-182
  Sense organs in the skin, 2-177-78
  Swallowing and breathing, nervous control of, 4-203, 209
  Tissue structure, 1-147
  See also **Nerve cells; Nervous system**

Nervous system. *6-317-30; *illus.,* 1-148h
  *Senses, 7-291-306
  Bird's, *with illus.,* 5-421-22
  Body's defenses as part of, 7-346-47, *diagram,* 347
  Chordates all have, 4-1-2
  Control of body during muscular exercise, 10-88
  Development in human baby, 8-97
  Development in unborn human young, 8-26-27
  Insect's, *with illus.,* 2-406
  Lobster's, *with illus.,* 2-239
  Man's, see main articles, above
  Muscular activity, role in, 3-208, *illus.,* 206
  Pavlov's discovery of conditioned reflex, *with illus.,* 9-51-52
  Phrenic nerve, 9-182
  Sleep, relation of nervous system to, 6-147-49
  Studies of, and rise of modern psychology, 9-48
  See also **Senses**

Nestorians, heretical Christians.
  Science in the early Middle Ages, 2-297-98

Nestorius, Patriarch of Constantinople. 2-297

Nests, ant. Artificial nests for keeping ant colony, *with illus.,* 3-393-96

Nests, bird. *with illus.,* 5-418f-h
  Bluebirds, 6-38
  Cowbirds' use of other birds' nests, 6-104-05.
  Creepers, 6-44
  Hermit thrushes, 6-38
  Hornbills, *with illus.,* 3-242-43
  Mallards, *illus.,* 10-260
  Nuthatches, 6-42
  Pigeons, 10-258
  Robins, 6-38; 10-258
  Starlings take woodpeckers', 6-210
  Swifts, 6-214
  Vireos, 6-64
  Woodpeckers, 6-210
  See also **Birds**

Nests, fish. 8-116

Nests, insect. See **Social insects**

Nests, wasp. *with illus.,* 2-412d

Nets. Insect-collecting nets, *with illus.,* 3-153-55

Neumann, John von, American physicist.
  Electronic computers developed by, 9-145

Neural arches, around spinal cord. 3-75

Neural tube, early structure in development of nervous system. 8-26-27

Neurasthenia, psychoneurosis. 9-202

Neurilemma, nerve-cell membrane. 6-318, 320, *illus.,* 318

Neuroglia, type of nerve tissue. 6-324, 330

Neurology. 6-330

Neurons (nerve cells).
  *Nervous system, 6-317-30
  Developments in study of, 9-56

Neuroptera, order of insects. 2-414

Neuroses, mental illnesses. 9-202
  Alcoholism as result of, 4-410

Neurospora, bread mold. 3-28
  Hereditary studies of, 9-385

Neutral buoyancy float, device for sounding depth of ocean. 5-191, 192, *illus.,* 193

Neutral coasts. 8-355

Neutral equilibrium. 2-322, *illus.,* 321

Neutralization of acids and bases. 4-231, 338-40
  Soil acidity neutralized by basic fertilizers, 2-168-69

Neutrinos. It was observed that when the neutron, an atomic nuclear particle, decayed into a proton and an electron, some of its mass remained unaccounted for. This mass was equal to 1.5 times the mass of the electron or 780,000 electron volts of energy. W. Pauli suggested a theory (developed by E. Fermi) that the decay produced an additional, yet undiscovered, particle that took up part of the missing mass and carried off the excess energy. Fermi called it the neutrino. *table,* 1-314

Neutrons, atomic particles. 1-310-11, *with diagrams,* 312-13, *table,* 314; 9-126, 131-33, 135-38
  Detection by Geiger-Mueller counter, 9-342
  Discovery of, 8-419
  Subatomic bullets, 9-330-31

Neutrophils, white blood cells. 3-328, *illus.,* 329
  See also **White blood cells**

New Bogoslof Island, islet produced by volcanic action. 8-303

New Brunswick.
  Herring catch, *illus.,* 6-21

New General Catalogue (NGC), classification of nebulae and star clusters. 8-49

New Hampshire. Granite quarries of, 2-83

New Jersey Turnpike. *illus.,* 3-306

New Mexico.
Sandstone formations, *illus.*, 2-350
New moon, lunar phase. 4-277
New Stone Age.
Breadmaking in, 9-293
Bridges, *with illus.*, 2-332
New World monkeys. *with illus.*, 9-258-63
New York Central System, American railroad.
No. 999, famous locomotive, *illus.*, 1-182
New York City.
Blizzard of 1888, 2-355
Central Park, repairing sidewalks of, *illus.*, 3-300
Roads leading to, *illus.*, 3-305
Rockefeller Center, *illus.*, 3-118
Secretariat Building, United Nations, *illus.*, 3-123
Skyscrapers of, 3-114-15, 117, 119, *illus.*, 117-18
Tunnels of, *with illus.*, 2-54-57
Water supply of, 2-48-50, *illus.*, 47
New York International Airport. 3-305; *illus.*, 6-199
New York State. Black River, *illus.*, 6-414
Natural gas, early use of, 5-98-99
New York State Barge Canal. 4-191
New York State Thruway. *illus.*, 3-298a
New York World's Fair (1939–40).
Artificial-lightning generator, 1-401
Time Capsule, Westinghouse, 10-73
New Zealand.
Champagne Cauldron (hot spring), *illus.*, 8-327
Geysers, *with illus.*, 8-291
Papakura, *illus.*, 8-293
Pohutu, *illus.*, 8-291, 300b, 327
Glowworms, 2-183
Newcomb, Simon, American astronomer (1835–1909). Newcomb served as director of the American *Nautical Almanac* office and as mathematics professor in the U. S. Navy and at Johns Hopkins. He studied planetary motions, and his lunar and planetary tables led to revision of nautical almanacs. Newcomb directed eclipse expeditions and wrote a number of popular works on astronomy.
Mercury's transits, calculations of, 6-83
Venus' gleam, theory of, 4-29
Newcomen, Thomas, English blacksmith and inventor. 4-39-40
Steam engine, development of, *with illus.*, 4-81
Newlands, John A. R., English chemist. *with illus.*, 5-83-84
News cases, in printing. 1-199
News photography. 9-14
Newspapers.
Microfilming, *with illus.*, 10-72
Paper, use of, 2-107
Pictures transmitted by wire and radio, *with illus.*, 7-390-92
Printing of, 1-208, 210
Newsprint. 4-378
Newton, Sir Isaac, English scientist. *with illus.*, 3-276-81
Color experiments of, *with illus.*, 7-277; *with illus.*, 8-178-79
Corpuscular theory of light proposed by, 6-239
Differential calculus, invention of, 1-20-21
Kinship of natural phenomena discussed by, 6-239
Law of gravitation, 2-315-16; 3-163
Motion, laws of, *with illus.*, 2-122-26; 3-280
Demonstration of third law, 2-329
Observatory sites, statement on, 8-56
Reflecting telescope of, 3-15; 9-154, *illus.*, 153
Spectrum, discovery of, 6-390; 7-199
See also **Gravitation**

Newtonian reflectors, telescopes. 7-262, *illus.*, 261; 8-57
*Building of, by amateur astronomer, 9-365-74
Newts, amphibians. 5-156, 161, *illus.*, 153, 160-61
Hearing of, *with illus.*, 1-282
Lungs used as float mechanism, *with illus.*, 1-280
Migration of, 9-428
NGC. See **New General Catalogue**
Niacin, B-complex vitamin. 5-42-43
Bread enriched with, 9-299
Daily requirement and sources of, *table*, 4-55-57
Niagara Falls, New York. Bridge across, 2-335
Formation of, 8-15
Measure of sound of, 8-40
Nicaragua. Canal project, 4-192
Niches, roles played by animals and plants in habitats. 10-183
Nicholas of Cusa, German churchman and philosopher. 2-364
Nicholson, Seth B., American astronomer.
Jupiter's satellites IX, X, XI and XII, discovery of, 5-24
Nicholson, William, English scientist.
Electrolysis, discovery of, 4-363
Nichrome wire heater replacement coil.
Glass cut by, 4-227, *illus.*, 226
Nickel (Ni), chemical element. Atomic number, 28; atomic weight, 58.71; melting point, 1,455° C.; boiling point, 2,900° C.; specific gravity, 8.90. White, hard metal; malleable and ductile. Discovered in 1751 by Cronstedt; name derived from German *Kupfernickel:* "demon's copper," so called because the ore seemed to contain copper, but yielded none. Associated in nature with ores of cobalt, copper, iron and magnesium; obtained chiefly from the ores pyrrhotite and garnierite by roasting to the oxide, reducing with carbon or carbon monoxide and finally decomposing by heat. Alloys of nickel, valued because of their ability to resist corrosion, are widely used in ships, chemical plants, table covers, sinks and household utensils, and for wires and cables.
Alloys, 1-382
Electronic filaments and plates, nickel used in, 6-296
Meteorites containing, 6-92-93
Nickel-iron as part of earth's composition, 4-175
Properties and uses, 3-41
Steels, nickel used in, 1-352-53
Nickel-cadmium storage batteries. 5-96
Nicolaier, Arthur, German physician. 7-382
Nicot, Jean, French statesman. 5-343
Nicotiana, genus of plants. 5-343
Nicotine, poisonous alkaloid.
Effects of, *with diagram,* 5-344-46
Insects controlled by, 9-188
See also **Tobacco**
Nicotine sulfate.
Grape leafhoppers controlled by, 9-195
Psyllas controlled by, 9-194
Nictitating membranes, eyelids. Birds, 5-423
Niepce, Joseph Nicéphore. Born in Châlons, France, 1765; died near Châlons, 1833. In the course of his researches in lithography and photography, he succeeded in making a permanent image on a metal plate. He joined with Louis Daguerre to continue experiments on the process he invented. After his death Daguerre perfected the process and gave it his name. (See **Daguerre.**) See also 6-382; 9-399
Nigeria. Panning for tin concentrate in, *illus.*, 3-38
Niggerhead cacti. *illus.*, 6-228
Night blindness. 5-40, *illus.*, 41
Night photography. *with illus.*, 6-313-15

Night plane flying. 6-198

"Night soil," human wastes. Fertilizer, 5-327, *illus.*, 328; 8-36

Night terrors, attacks of anxiety. 6-150

Nighthawks. 6-218, *illus.*, 216; 8-386-87

Nightingale, Florence, English nurse and hospital reformer. *with illus.*, 7-388-89

Nights. Length changes with seasons, 1-263

Nightshades, plants. *illus.*, 7-77

Nile monitors, lizards. 5-205

Nile River.
  Boats of ancient Egypt, 4-106
  Calendar of ancient Egypt related to overflow, 1-126
  Delta of, *map*, 8-16
  Discovery of source of, 7-31

Nilgais, antelopes. *with illus.*, 8-383

Nilson, Lars Fredrik, Swedish chemist. 5-85

Nim, mathematical game. 4-448

Nimbostratus clouds. *diagram*, 1-317; 2-222

Niobium (Nb), chemical element. Atomic number, 41; atomic weight, 92.906; melting point, 2,500° C.; boiling point, 3,700° C.; specific gravity, 8.4. Gray metal. Discovered in 1801 by Hatchett in ore sent to England more than a century earlier by John Winthrop, first governor of Connecticut; name derived from Niobe, daughter of Tantalus, mythological Greek king. Rare; found associated with iron in the mineral columbite in pegmatite veins, volcanic intrusions through the earth's crust. After removal of tin from an African ore, the residue is reduced, giving ferro-niobium, useful in steelmaking.

Nipkow, Paul von, German inventor. Television system of, 5-278

Nipples, protuberances of breasts. 8-20-21

Nitrate of soda. See Sodium nitrate

Nitrates.
  Nitrogen fixation, 2-23, 211; 3-126, 127; 9-211-12
  Plants require, 2-171; 3-318
  See also Explosives; Fertilizers; Nitrogen

Nitric acid. Behavior as typical acid, 4-339
  Oxygen-source for rocket fuels, 10-45, *illus.*, 43
  Photoengraving, nitric acid used in, 1-205-06
  Uses of, 3-318

Nitriding, casehardening process for steel. 1-353

Nitrification, combination with nitrogen or nitrogen compound. By soil bacteria, 2-23

Nitrile rubber. 6-359

Nitrites, nitrogen-oxygen compounds with other elements. Soils contain, 2-23

Nitrocellulose. See Guncotton

Nitrogen (N), chemical element. Atomic number, 7; atomic weight, 14.0067; melting point, −209.86° C.; boiling point, −195.8° C.; specific gravity, gas (air = 1): 0.96724; liquid: 0.808; solid: 1.026. Colorless, inert gas at ordinary temperatures. Discovered in 1772 by Rutherford; name derived from Latin words for "niter forming." Composes 78 per cent by volume of earth's atmosphere; obtained by liquefaction and fractional distillation, or by heating a water solution of ammonium nitrite. Though highly inert, its compounds are very active in foods, fertilizers and explosives. Nitrogen enters into the formation of all living tissues. See also 3-317-18
  *Fixation of, 3-126-29
  Ammonia synthesis, *with diagram*, 2-230-31; 3-127, *illus.*, 128-29; 9-211-12
  Atmospheric, 1-231
  Bacteria involved in nitrogen transformations, 3-68
  Blood stream, nitrogen in, *with illus.*, 4-206-07
  Conversion of, into radioactive carbon, 10-93

Nitrogen (continued)
  Electrostatic generators use nitrogen, 9-244, *illus.*, 243
  Elimination rate as measure of age, 8-81
  Explosive compounds manufactured from, 9-211-12
  Interstellar space contains, 9-362
  Lightning makes nitrogen available to plants, 1-402
  Plants' use of, 2-163, 164, 168-71; 3-44
  Plastics ingredient, 8-222, 224, 225
  Rain, found in, 2-350
  Sea, nitrogen-gas content in, 6-32
  Soil nitrogen available to plants, 2-23, 25
  Steel, nitrogen used in casehardening of, 1-353
  Transformations of, *with illus.*, 2-209-11
  See also Explosives; Fertilizers; Nitrates; Nitrogen fixation; Nitroglycerin; etc.

Nitrogen cycle, series of chemical changes by which nitrogen returns to environment after taking part in metabolism of living things.
  Bacteria's role in, 3-318
  Tracing of, 5-80

Nitrogen fixation. *3-126-29
  Bacteria, nitrogen-fixing, *with illus.*, 2-23, 209-11, 4-75
  Haber process, 9-211-12
  See also Haber process

Nitroglycerin. 8-182-83, 276, 284, 286
  Chemical composition, 3-318
  Discovery and use of, in dynamite, 5-81-82

Nitrostarch, explosive. 8-282

Nitrous oxide (laughing gas), anesthetic. 3-318

Nobel, Alfred Bernhard. Born in Stockholm, Sweden, 1833; died in Italy, 1896. He was educated in Russia and worked in the United States under John Ericsson. He and his father engaged in the manufacture of nitroglycerin. Nobel discovered dynamite in 1866 and blasting gelatin about ten years later. He left a large fortune to be distributed in annual prizes to those who make signal contributions in the fields of physics, chemistry, medicine, literature and in the furtherance of peace. See also *with illus.*, 5-82
  Dynamite made from nitroglycerin by, 8-182, 276
  Nobel awards, 10-299

Nobel Prizes. List of winners in physics, chemistry and medicine or physiology, 10-299-307

Nobelium (No), chemical element. Atomic number, 102; atomic weight 254(?). Nobelium is a man-made element, created in the Nobel Institute for Physics, Stockholm, Sweden, in 1957 by bombarding the artificial element curium with ions of the rare carbon 13 isotope. Nobelium is very unstable, having a half-life of only 10 minutes. When it decays it emits alpha particles. It was named for the late Alfred Nobel, Swedish scientist. Some American scientists dispute both the discovery and name of nobelium, claiming that element 102 was discovered in 1958 by a team of scientists at the University of California at Berkeley.

Nobile, Umberto, Italian explorer.
  Polar airship flights, 6-180

Noble gases. See Inert gases

Noce, Robert H., American psychiatrist. 9-104

Noctiluca miliaris, luminous flagellate. 2-185, *illus.*, 184

Noctilucent clouds, in atmosphere. 1-238, *diagram*, 239

Nodule bacteria, nitrogen-fixing bacteria. *with illus.*, 2-23; 3-68-69

Nodules, of plant roots. Formed through bacterial action, 3-68

Noise meters. *8-38-46

"Noise thermometers." *with diagram*, 8-39-41

Noiseless typewriters. 1-273

Noises.
  *Noise meters, 8-38-46
  Abatement of, 8-43-44
  Devices for reducing, 5-128
  Health affected by, 8-43
  Speech sounds, 1-107-08, 110-11, 113-15, 116
Noises, animal. See Sounds, animal
Nomenclature, system of names in classification.
  *Living things, 1-287-306
Nonelectrolytes, substances whose aqueous solutions do
    not conduct electricity. with diagram, 4-298; 5-89
Nones, Roman date. 10-173
Non-Euclidean geometries. with diagrams, 4-438-41; 9-
    282
Nonferrous alloys, mixtures of metals other than iron.
    1-382
Nonferrous metallurgy. See under Copper, Lead, Zinc
    and other nonferrous metals
Nonleguminous green-manure crops. 2-164, 165
Nonmetals.
  *Nonmetallic elements, 3-317-24
  Metals distinguished from, 3-33; 4-304
Norge, airship. 6-180
Norkay, Tensing, Sherpa mountain climber. Everest
    scaled by, 4-209, illus., 208
Normal, in light reflection. with illus., 7-251
Normalizers. See Tranquilizers
Normalizing, heat-treatment process for steel.
    1-352-53
Normandie, ocean liner. 4-115, 117
Norms. Psychology, use in, 9-313
North America
  Explorations of, in nineteenth century, 7-27-29
  Geological time scale of, 6-370-74
  Glacier formerly covered Canada and United States,
    6-138
  Great Salt Lake Desert, 6-118
  Jet streams over, 2-360
  Mountain systems of, 10-23-24
  Petroleum production and reserves, 4-150
  Plant and animal life in, study of, 8-252-54
  Transportation on land, primitive and early, with il-
    lus., 1-99-100, 105-06, illus., 101
  Trees of North America, how to recognize, with illus.,
    5-138-51
  Volcanoes in, 8-299
  See also Alaska; Canada; Mexico; United States;
    and the names of the various states
North American colored local race. 8-219
North American corn snakes. with illus., 5-354d
North American Nebula. illus., 8-156, 156h
North Atlantic Current, oceanic current. 6-238,
    map, 232-33
North Chinese local race. 8-219
North circumpolar stars. 1-324-25, 330, map, 325
North Equatorial Current, oceanic current. 6-237,
    238, map, 232-33
North Pacific Current, oceanic current. 6-238, map,
    232-33
North Pole.
  Conquest of, 7-34
  Pioneer flights in north-polar regions, 6-178, with
    illus., 180
  Shift of, as cause of ice ages, 5-193
  Submarines that have reached, 5-37; 9-220
  See also Arctic; Polar regions
North star. 1-264
  Change of, due to earth's precession, with diagram,
    4-50
Northeast European local race. 8-218
Northeast trades, wind belt. 2-93, diagram, 92

Northeasterlies, wind belt. 1-244, diagram, 243
Northern constellations. 1-324-25, 330, map, 325
Northern Cross, name given to constellation Cygnus.
    1-333
Northern Hemisphere.
  Atmospheric circulation in, with diagrams, 1-243-44,
    diagram, 242
  Jet-stream circulation in, 1-237-38
Northern lights. See Aurora borealis
Northern pike, fish. illus., 4-103
Northrop, Jack, American aeronautical engineer. 6-
    193, illus., 192
Northwest European local race. 8-218
Norton Company. Diamond-making, role in, 4-275
Norway.
  Fisheries, illus., 6-20
  Pottery-making, illus., 7-400
Norway maple trees. 5-150
Norway rats. 8-165, illus., 163
Norwegian Current, oceanic current. 6-238, map,
    232-33
Nose.
  Bones of, illus., 3-77
  Care of, 10-80-81
  Respiration, role in, 4-201, 203, illus., 202-03
Nose, of supersonic aircraft. with diagram, 10-232
Nose breathing. Advantages of, 4-203
Nose cones, of missiles. with diagrams, 10-232-33, 234
  Moon rockets, illus., 10-52-53
Nosema bombycis, sporozoan parasite. 2-66
Nostoc, blue-green algae. 3-214, illus., 215-16
Notochord, structure found at some time or other in
    all chordates. 4-1
  Acorn worms, with illus., 4-2
  Lancelets, with illus., 4-4
  Man, development in, 8-27
  Sea squirts, with illus., 4-3
Notre Dame University.
  Laboratories of bacteriology, with illus., 7-151-55
Nova Aquilae 1918, star. 7-47, illus., 49
Nova Cassiopeia 1572, star. 7-47
Novae, exploded stars. 6-268; 7-46-47, illus., 49
Novocain, synthetic drug. 8-188
  See also Procaine
Noyes, Eliot, American designer. 10-121
Nozzle throats. See Test sections
Nozzles.
  Damper-controlled, illus., 1-69
  Glass nozzles for home laboratory, with illus., 4-225
Nu Draconids, meteor shower. See Giacobinids
Nuclear bombs.
  *Perils of Atomic Age, 9-348-58
  *Precautionary measures, 9-391-96
  Cloud formed by atom-bomb explosion, 4-frontis-
    piece
  Development, 9-135-38, 141, 329-31, illus., 122
Nuclear energy. See Atomic energy
Nuclear membranes, parts of living cells. 2-2, illus.,
    2, 10
Nuclear radiation, accompanying nuclear explosion. 9-
    393-94
Nuclear reactors. 1-frontispiece; 9-136-38, illus.,
    138a-b, diagram, 357; illus., 10-227
  Atomic submarines, nuclear reactors for, illus.,
    4-342d; 5-35-37
  Electricity generated indirectly by, 9-358, illus., 357
  First one to be operated, 9-331, illus., 330
  Medical radioisotopes produced in, 10-98
  Power for industry provided by, 9-142, 231
  Savannah, nuclear reactor for, with illus., 4-114b-c
Nuclear sap, in cells. 2-9, illus., 4, 10

Nuclei, cell structures. *with illus.*, 1-143-44; 2-2, 9-10, 14, *with illus.*, 290-92, *illus.*, 4, 12b-d, 13, 425-26
    Chromosomes, role of, in heredity, 8-334-44
    Ciliates, nuclei of, 2-66
Nuclei, dense portions of comets. 5-391-92
Nuclei, atomic. 1-310-11, *with diagrams*, 312-13, *table*, 314
  *Cosmic rays, 8-393-99
Nucleic acids, organic substances of the cell. 2-5; *with diagram*, 9-383-86
    Viruses, found in, 3-453, 455, 457
Nucleoli, cell structures. 2-9, 14, 290, *illus.*, 4, 12b-d, 289
Nucleonics, science dealing with all the phenomena of the atomic nucleus.
  *Atomic energy, 9-120-42
  *Atomic farming, 10-251-53
  *Atomic medicines, 10-98-101
  *Atomic structure, 1-307-14
  *Food preservation, 10-114-16
  *Perils of Atomic Age, 9-348-58
  *Radiation thickness gauges, 9-43-46
  *Radiocarbon dating, 10-92-97
  *Radioisotope-fueled thermoelectric generators, 6-172-75
    Civil engineering and, 1-223
    Development of science of, *with illus.*, 8-410-20; *with illus.*, 9-328-32
    Possibilities in science of, 10-225, *with illus.*, 226
    Research in, 1-90, 93, 96, 97, *illus.*, 94
    See also **Parity law**
Nucleons, atomic particles. 1-310-11
Nucleoproteins. 9-385-86
    Heredity, factor in, 8-339
    Viruses, found in, 3-453, 455, 456
Nucleotides, nucleic molecules. 9-383, 386
    Heredity, factor in, 8-339
Null sets. See Empty sets
Number Eight, Dam, Ohio River. *illus.*, 8-316c
Number 999, famous locomotive. *illus.*, 1-182
Numbers.
  *Algebra, 2-67-80
  *Arithmetic, 1-149-61
  *Higher mathematics, 4-423-42
  *Mathematical recreations, 4-443-54
    Exponents used in writing large and small numbers, 2-74
    See also **Numerical systems**
Numbers, atomic. See Atomic numbers
Numerical systems. *1-149-61
    Development in antiquity, 1-127, 133
Nun buoys. 5-70, *illus.*, 69, 71
Nuptial flights, matings of social insects. 3-357-58
Nurse sharks. 4-287-88
Nursing.
  *First aid, 10-5-17
  *Home nursing, 10-55-67
    Nineteenth-century developments in, *with illus.*, 7-388-89
Nursing (breast feeding). Proper diet before and during, *with table*, 5-272-73
Nut trees. 5-146
Nutcrackers. Levers, combination of, 3-57, 58
Nuthatches, birds. 6-42, *illus.*, 41, 43
Nutrias (coypus), aquatic rodents. *with illus.*, 8-167
    Fur, 5-263; 7-238
Nutriculture. See Soilless agriculture
Nutrients, soil. 2-16-17, 20, 23-25
Nutrition.
  *Basic food elements, 4-51-61
  *Bread as food, 8-265-70

Nutrition *(continued)*
  *Carbohydrates, 4-76-79
  *Diet, regulation of, 5-267-75
  *Meat as food, 5-163-72
  *Plant nourishment in soil, 2-163-72
  *Preservation of food, 4-153-68
  *Vitamins, 5-38-49
    Anemias due to poor nutrition, 3-330
    Health, affected by, 10-77
    Ill person, *with illus.*, 10-64-66
    Older persons, 8-81-82
    Plant nutrition, experiments in, 8-35
    Tubercular patients, 9-183
    Zoo animals, 10-159-60, *illus.*, 158
    See also **Carbohydrates; Diet; Fats; Proteins; Vitamins**
Nuts, dry fruits. *with illus.*, 4-131
    Dispersal of, 3-240, *illus.*, 241; 5-4-6, 7, *illus.*, 7
    Vegetable-ivory nuts, 7-210, 212, *illus.*, 213
Nylon, synthetic material. 8-231, *with illus.*, 228
    Manufacture of, 8-189
Nymphs, young forms of orthopterous insects. 2-407, *illus.*, 408; 3-139, *illus.*, 138-39

O

Oak salamanders, amphibians. *illus.*, 5-152
Oak trees. *with illus.*, 5-147
    Acorns, *illus.*, 4-131; *illus.*, 5-63, 141
      Dispersed by rodents, *illus.*, 5-7
    Classification of, 1-291
    Leaves, *illus.*, 1-304; *illus.*, 4-72; *illus.*, 5-139
Oakum, kind of hemp fiber. 4-180
Oars. Ships and boats driven by, 4-106-07, *with illus.*, 109
Oases. Sahara Desert, *with illus.*, 6-117
Oats. Chemical compounds from hulls and straw, 7-35-36
Obelisks. *illus.*, 1-151
Oberth, Hermann, German rocket expert. 9-377; 10-42
Obesity, fatness.
    Effects and dietary control of, *with tables*, 5-268-71, *diagram*, 267, 269
    Relation to health, 8-82
Objectives, of microscopes. 7-262
Oblique sphere, in astronomy. 1-262
Obliquus externus abdominis, belly muscle. *illus.*, 1-148c
Obliquus internus abdominis, belly muscle. *illus.*, 1-148c
Oboes. Sound production in, 5-218
Observatories.
  *Astronomical observatories, 8-55-66
    List of, 8-66
    See also names of astronomical observatories, as **Lowell Observatory**
Observation cars, of railroad trains. 1-188
Obsidian, igneous rock. *illus.*, 1-31; 3-423-24
    Glassymeteorites (tektites) distinguished from, 6-93
Obtuse angles. *with illus.*, 3-431
Occipital bone, in skull. *illus.*, 3-75, 77
Occipital lobes, of cerebrum. *with illus.*, 6-324-25
Occluded fronts. See Fronts
Occupational therapy. Mental illness, used for, *illus.*, 9-204
Ocean. *6-26a-36
  *Bed, 6-69-77
  *Buoys, 5-68-71
  *Currents, 6-229-38
  *Icebergs in, 9-333-39
  *Shoreline changes, 8-348-59

Ocean (continued)
*Tides, 6-201-08
*Waves. 6-361-68
Bathyscaphes used in exploration of, with illus., 6-74a-d
Bioluminescence, 2-182-83
Circulation pattern, 5-191, illus., 192
Coconuts distributed by sea waves and currents, 3-240, illus., 241
Density of sea water, 2-32
Earthquakes in, 9-109
Fertilizing sea for increasing fish growth, 4-312
Fish habits and migrations, 3-241, 242-44, illus., 242-44
"Floods" in, may affect climates, 5-192
Glaciers affect level of, 9-166
Habitat of water-dwelling organisms, with illus., 10-141-42
Ice ages, oceans during, 3-183
Limestone, deposition of, 2-86
Mountains of, 5-189; 10-213-15, 218-20
Nineteenth-century explorations of depths, with illus., 7-32-34
Petroleum formed from dead sea organisms, 4-142
Salinity of, with chart, 6-30-32
Salt dust from, 7-140
Scuba diving in ocean exploration, illus., 6-26d
Sediments giving rise to natural-gas deposits, 5-97
Seeds and fruits transported by ocean currents, 5-4-5, 7
Temperature, density and pressure of, 6-34-35
Twentieth-century studies of, 9-221-23
Underwater obstacles detected by high-frequency sound, 8-105-06
Underwater photography, illus., 10-167
See also **Fish; Lakes; Rivers; Ships; Water; Waves, ocean**
Ocean liners. with illus., 4-110-18
Hydrofoils as?, 4-8
Ocean waves. See **Waves, ocean**
Oceanic islands. 4-133-34
Beach sands of, 8-352
Oceanography, scientific study of the ocean and its life. See **Ocean**
Ocellated turkeys. 6-337
Ocelli, simple eyes. Insect's, 2-403, illus., 403, 404
Ocelots, carnivorous mammals. 8-210-11
Fur, 7-238
Ochoa, Severo, Spanish-American biologist. Nucleic acid synthesized by, 9-386
Octamethylphosphate, insecticide. 9-187
Octane. 7-269
Octane number. Octane number indicates the efficiency of a given fuel in an internal combustion engine; it is determined in the following manner. A sample of the fuel in question is used to operate a special test engine under controlled conditions. The compression ratio (rate of fuel compression) is then regulated until a knock is evident. The intensity of the knock is measured by a device called a knockmeter, and noted. The engine is then operated on mixtures of isooctane and normal heptane, which are both compounds of carbon and hydrogen. Isooctane is used because it does not knock readily; normal heptane, because it does. A mixture of isooctane and normal heptane is found that gives the same knock intensity as the original fuel. The percentage of isooctane in the test mixture is then given as the octane number. For example, the knock intensity of an automobile fuel might be given as 80 octane. This would represent the ratio of 80 per cent isooctane to 20 per cent normal heptane by volume.

Octopuses, mollusks. illus., 1-294; 2-194-95, illus., 192
Sucking apparatus, with diagram, 1-280
Oculomotor nerve. 6-328
Odd parity. See **Parity law**
Odessa meteorite crater, Texas. 6-91, 92
Odonata, order of insects. 2-413
Odors. Plants protected by evil-smelling, 7-78
Oedogonium, species of green algae. 3-218, illus., 216, 217
Oersted, Hans Christian, Danish physicist. with illus., 5-231-32, 235
Electromagnetism, experiments with, 6-128
Magnetic field, production of, 7-164
Oesophagus. See **Esophagus**
Office of Scientific Research and Development (OSRD). 9-323
Offices, industrial-design. 10-122, 125-26
Offset. See **Photo-offset lithography**
Offset lithography. illus., 1-204a-d
Offspring, preservation of. Adaptations of animals and plants for, with illus., 3-240-44
*Seed plant dispersal, 5-1-7
Ogden, Charles Kay, English educator. 1-120
Ohain, Hans von, German aeronautical engineer. Jet-aviation pioneer, 7-68
Ohio River.
Dam No. 8 on, illus., 8-316c
Shutter dams on, 8-315
Ohio State University.
Radio telescope of, illus., 9-209
Ohm, Georg Simon, German physicist. 5-233
Ohms, units of electrical resistance. 6-130
Ohm's law. 5-233
Oil.
Action on waves, 6-368
Coal, fuel oils manufactured from, with illus., 1-418
Coal-tar crude oils, with illus., 1-419
Cottonseed, 4-178-79
Insects controlled by, 9-187-88
Mosquito extermination, use in, 10-35
Ocean bottoms (continental shelves), oil extracted from, 6-72
Plant oils, chemurgic production of, 7-42, 43
Pumping station, automatic, illus., 10-236
Steamship fuel oil, 4-114
See also **Fuel oils; Lubricating oils; Petroleum**
Oil, skin. Defense of body, role in, 7-347
Oil Creek, Pennsylvania. Petroleum experiments at, 4-141
Oil derricks, well-drilling towers. with diagram, 4-145
Oil engineering. See **Engineering—Petroleum engineering**
Oil flotation. See **Flotation process**
Oil (sebaceous) glands. 2-177, 180, illus., 174, 179
Bird's, 5-419, illus., 421
Oil refineries. Automation in, illus., 10-234d
See also **Refining—petroleum**
Oil seepage. See **Seepage, oil**
Oil shales. 4-143
Oil traps, natural petroleum reservoirs. with diagrams, 4-142-43; with illus., 7-357
Oil wells. See **Wells, oil**
Oilbirds. See **Guacharos**
Okapis, mammals. 7-417
O'Keefe, J. A., American meteoriticist. 6-94
Oken, Lorenz, German naturalist and philosopher. 7-158
Oklahoma.
Erosion effects, illus., 5-29
Oklahoma City, Oklahoma. YMCA Building, illus., 7-127
Old age. *Geriatrics, 8-78-83
Old English, language. 1-116, 117

Old Faithful, geyser in Yellowstone National Park.   *illus.,* 8-288, 300a

Old streams and valleys.   8-17-18

Old World monkeys.   *with illus.,* 9-254-58, 260-63, *illus.,* 259

Olds, Ransom E., American automobile manufacturer.   Automobiles, mass manufacture of, 2-131

Oleic acid.   7-275

Olfactory cells, of nose.   *with illus.,* 7-302-03

Olfactory nerve.   6-328

Olfactory pits, smelling organs of insects.   Ants, 3-360

Oligocene epoch, time in earth's history.   6-374

Oliphant, M. L. E., British physicist.   9-289

Olive-backed thrushes, birds.   6-39

Olszenski, Polish scientist.   5-207

Omar Khayyam, Persian mathematician and poet.   2-298
   Algebraic equations solved by geometry, *with diagrams,* 4-423-24

Omasum, chamber of cows' stomach.   *illus.,* 7-10

Omnirange, for air traffic.   6-198

One-celled organisms.
   Reproduction, 8-80
   See also **Algae; Protozoans**

One-pipe system, of steam heating.   *with illus.,* 2-248

One-to-one correspondence, in mathematical sets.   4-442

Onions.   *illus.,* 1-303
   Cell, *illus.,* 2-1
   Diseases of, 8-375
   Food stored in bulbs of, 2-420
   Hybrid, 9-291

Onnes, Kamerlingh, Dutch pioneer in cryogenics.   5-207, 209

Ontogeny, life history of individual organism.   8-262

Oort, J. H., Dutch astronomer.   Comet-launching theory, 5-391-92

Oozes, ocean-bottom deposits.   2-65; 6-32-33

Opalina, genus of one-celled animals.   2-66

Opals.   *illus.,* 5-297

Open-dump method, of refuse disposal.   5-336, *illus.,* 335

Open-flash technique, in photography.   9-411-12

Open-hearth furnaces.   Metals other than iron, smelting of, 1-379

Open-hearth process, of steelmaking.   1-340, *with illus.,* 345-47, *illus.,* 348a, *diagram,* 348b; 6-384

Open-pit (strip) mining.
   Coal, 1-409, *illus.,* 408
   Iron ore, 1-340, *illus.,* 340-41
   Ores, *with diagram,* 1-370-71

Operation, as function of engineers.   1-227

Operations.   See **Surgery**

Opercles (opercula).   See **Gill covers**

70 Ophiuchi, star.   Orbital motion of, *illus.,* 7-229

Ophiuchus (Serpent Bearer), constellation.   1-332

Ophthalmoscopes, Instruments for viewing interior of eye.   6-253

Opium.   *with illus.,* 5-403-04

Opium poppy.   5-403, *illus.,* 402

Opium War.   5-404

Opossum rats, marsupials.   7-427

Opossums.   *with illus.,* 7-427-28, *illus.,* 423
   Adaptations for defense, 7-11
   Fur, 7-238
   Pets, *with illus.,* 7-20
   Unchanged for millions of years, 6-283
   Young of, *illus.,* 7-6

Oppolzer, Theodor, Austrian astronomer.   3-133-34

Opposing muscles.   3-209

Opposite leaves.   *with illus.,* 5-140

Opposition, orbital.   Jupiter, 5-21

Optic disc.   *with illus.,* 7-293-94

Optic nerve.   6-317; 7-293, *illus.,* 292
   Regrowth impossible if destroyed, *diagram,* 7-352

Optic tract.   6-317

Optical activity.   Pasteur's researches on, 9-71-72

Optical fibers.   Optical fibers are groups or bundles of fine, flexible glass or other smooth and highly transparent materials with a highly refractive surface.   These fibers, when properly aligned, are able to transport light and images along a sharply curved path.   Optical fibers conduct light by means of a phenomenon known as total internal reflection (see Index).   The fibers themselves are usually surrounded by a medium having a lower refractive index.   The light or image enters a fiber bundle at an angle; it is passed along, in a series of repeated reflections, to the other end of the bundle. The image seen at the far end is a faithful reproduction of the original one.   Optical fibers are employed in medicine, engineering and other fields.

Optical glass.   Manufacture, 3-314-15

Optical instruments.   *with illus.,* 7-260-62

Optical pyrometers, instruments for measuring temperatures.   8-117

Optical telegraphs.   5-239

Optics, science treating of light and its effects.   *7-249-62
   *Color, 7-277-90; 8-178-80
   *Microscopes, 9-81-95
   Development, 1600–1765, *with illus.,* 3-275-78
   Eye, human, *with diagrams,* 7-291-97
   History of lenses, 9-82-84, 86, 88
   See also **Leeuwenhoek, Anton van; Microscope**

Optimum moisture, correct moisture supply for plants.   5-27, *illus.,* 26

Optimum (ideal) population.   3-233

Oral cavity, part of mouth.   *illus.,* 4-202

Orange juice, preparation of, *illus.,* 4-154-55

Orange trees.   Spraying of, *illus.,* 10-152

Oranges.   *illus.,* 1-304

Orangutans, apes.   9-253-54, 260-61, 264, *illus.,* 252

Orb-web spiders.   2-266, *illus.,* 265

Orbital motions, of stars.   7-228-29, *illus.,* 226-27, 229

Orbits.
   Artificial satellites, 5-188, 189; 9-375-76, 382, *with illus.,* 379-81; 10-44, 46, 47, 50
   Comets, 5-394-96, *illus.,* 399
   Earth, 3-185
   Meteorites, 6-94, 97-98, *diagram,* 98
   Space flight, 8-126-28, 131, *diagrams,* 125, 126, 127, 131

Orchards.   See **Fruits; Trees**

Orchids.   4-65, *illus.,* 123
   Seed dispersal, 5-3
   Viability of, 5-65

Orders, groups in classification of living things.   1-289

Ordinary-analysis fertilizers.   2-171

Ordinates, Y-axis distances in analytic geometry.   *with diagrams,* 4-425-31

Ordovician period, time in earth's history.   1-387-88; 6-371

Ore dressing.   *with diagrams,* 1-371-76

Ores.
   *Discovery and processing, 1-369-82
   *Prospecting for ore, 7-354-61
   Formation of deposits through geologic time, 6-371, 372, 373, 374
   See also **Minerals; Mining; names of minerals**

Organ Mountains, Cuba   5-54

Organelles.   See **Organoids**

Organic acids.   4-58; 7-273

Organic ammoniates, natural nitrogenous materials.   Soil fertilizers, 2-171

Organic chemistry. *7-263-76
  *Carbohydrates in nutrition, 4-76-79
  *Chemurgy, 7-35-44
  *Plastics, 8-221-33
  *Products of, 8-181-90
  Nineteenth-century developments, with illus., 5-78-82
  Petroleum, origin and chemical treatment of, with illus., 4-142-43, 147-52
  See also Biochemistry; Carbon; Chemistry; Organic compounds
Organic compounds.
  *Organic chemistry, 7-263-76
  *Synthetics, 8-181-90
  Bacteria play part in production of, 3-67
  Elements in, 3-322, 324
  Life processes, part played in, 7-275
  Meteorites containing, 6-94
  Plant poisons made up of, 7-76
  Sea, organic compounds in, 6-32
  Study of, in nineteenth century, with illus., 5-78-82
  See also Organic chemistry and under names of various organic compounds
Organic insecticides. 9-186-87
Organic lakes. 7-57
Organic matter.
  Petroleum formed from, 4-142
  Soil fertilizer, with illus., 2-163-67
  Soils contain, 2-15-17, 19, 21-23
  Water supply, removal from, 2-276-78
Organic remains. See Fossils
Organizations. Industrial design, 10-126
Organizers (inductors), cells or tissues that affect neighboring cells. 2-289
Organoids (organelles), cell structures. 2-8-9
Organs, biological structures.
  Human body, *1-148a-h
    Sensory, with illus., 7-291-306
    Skin, hair and nails, *2-173-81
    Tissue constitution of, 1-44, 147
  Plant, 1-44, 46
  See also Man, and names of organs
Organs, musical instruments.
  Electronic (Hammond), 5-220, illus., 219
  Sound production in, with illus., 5-217
Organzine, silk thread. 5-182
Oribis, antelopes. 8-387
Orient. Transportation on land, primitive and early, 1-98, with illus., 100-01, 102-03, illus., 99, 104
Oriental civets. 8-245
Oriental cockroaches. with illus., 3-148
Oriental poppies.
  Adaptations for seed dispersal, with illus., 5-2
Oriental squirrels. 8-162
Origin, intersection of axes in analytic geometry. with diagrams, 4-425-31
Origin of species. See Evolution; Natural selection
Orioles, birds. with illus., 6-105
  Baltimore orioles, with illus., 5-418f
Orion, constellation. 1-335
  Great Nebula in, 8-156f-g; 9-360-61, illus., 359, 360
Orionids, meteor shower. 6-96, table, 97
Ornithology, science that treats of birds.
  *Birds as allies of man, 6-341-49
  *Common birds, 6-37-48, 60-68, 99-108, 152-66, 209-18, 304-10, 331-40, 394-408
  *Introduction, 5-414-26
Ornithopters, experimental flying machines. illus., 2-362; 6-181; 9-216
Orogeny, formation of mountains. *10-213-23
  See also Mountain making
Orographic rainfall. 2-347-48

Ortelius, Abraham, German geographer. 2-367
Orthochromatic camera film. 9-408
Orthoptera, order of insects. 2-412
  Grasshoppers and similar insects, with illus., 3-138-47
Orthopteroids, group of related insects. *3-138-52
Orthorhombic system, of external crystal structure. 5-342, diagram, 341
Orthosympathetic division, of autonomic nervous system. 6-329
Oryxes, antelopes. 8-383, 384
Os innominatum. See Innominate bone
Os sacrum. See Sacrum
Osage orange trees. with illus., 5-145
Osborn, Henry Fairfield, American paleontologist. 9-23-24
Oscillation, ocean's natural period of.
  Tides affected by, 6-203
Oscillatoria, blue-green algae. with illus., 3-215
Oscillators (oscillating circuits). See Electric oscillators; Electronic oscillators
Oscilloscopes, cathode-ray tubes used in radar. 9-387
Osiander, Andreas, German clergyman.
  Publication of Copernicus' work on astronomy, 2-373
Osler, Sir William, Canadian physician and medical teacher (1849–1919). He was a stimulating teacher; he also contributed to medical knowledge with his researches on typhoid fever, malaria, pneumonia and infant mortality. Osler taught medicine at McGill University, the University of Pennsylvania and Johns Hopkins University. In 1905 he became royal professor of medicine at Oxford University; he was made a baronet in the year 1911.
Osmium (Os), chemical element. Atomic number, 76; atomic weight, 190.2; melting point, 2,700° C.; boiling point, above 5,300° C.; specific gravity, 22.48. Bluish white, hard, crystalline metal of the platinum family. Heaviest known form of matter. Discovered in 1803 by Tennant; name derived from Greek osme: "odor." Found in small amounts in platinum ores, but obtained chiefly from natural alloy osmiridium. Oxide useful in making microscopic slides. Osmiridium has been used for tips of gold pen points and fine machine bearings. See also 3-42
  Electric-lamp filaments made of, 4-238
Osmosis. 4-164, with diagram, 301-03
  Cells, process in, 2-7
  See also Dialysis
Osmotic pressure. 4-302
Ospreys, birds. 6-160
Ossicles of ear. 4-381, with illus., 480; 7-299, illus., 298
Osteichthyes (bony fishes), major group of fishes. 4-95, illus., 94
  First appearance, 1-389
Osteomalacia, bone disease. 5-47-48
Osteomyelitis, bone disease. 3-84
Ostracoderms, primitive fishes. with illus., 1-388
Ostrich ferns. illus., 3-186
Ostriches. illus., 1-298; illus., 5-414
Ostwald, Wilhelm, German chemist (1853–1932). Noted as a teacher, he sent from his laboratory at Leipzig some of the world's greatest teachers and research men. A pioneer in physical chemistry, he determined the values (constants) of the force binding the atoms of acids (and bases) together. His work on catalysis, chemical equilibrium and reaction rates earned him the 1909 Nobel Prize in chemistry. He studied the chemistry of color and invented a method of preparing nitric acid by oxidizing ammonia.
Ostwald, Wolfgang, German chemist. Colloids, work on, 5-296

Otoliths, structures in inner ear. 4-381; 7-306, *illus.,* 305

Otter civets, carnivorous mammals. 8-246

Otter shrews, insect-eating mammals. 7-102, *illus.,* 101

Otter trawls, devices used in sea fishing. 6-16

Otters, fish-eating mammals. *with illus.,* 8-177
  Fur, 7-238
  Sea otters, *illus.,* 8-176

Otto, Nikolaus August, German technician. 6-254, 380, *illus.,* 252-53
  Internal-combustion engine of, 4-86

Outbreeding. 10-240

Outcrops, natural rock exposures. 7-355

Outer ear. 4-385, *with illus.,* 380

Outer space. See **Space**

Outwash, glacial deposits. 9-173-74, *illus.,* 171

Ova, female sex cells. *with illus.,* 8-20, 21-22

Oval window, of ear. *with illus.,* 4-380; 7-299, 300, *illus.,* 298, 299

Ovaries, female sex glands. 5-19, *illus.,* 16-17; *with illus.,* 8-20

Ovens. Breadmaking ovens, 9-294, 297-98, *diagram,* 299

Overbank stage, of streams. 8-12

Overhead proofers, bread humidifiers. *with diagram,* 9-297

Overhead-valve engines, for automobiles. *with illus.,* 2-133

Overland Mail, American stagecoach line. 1-106

Overpopulation. Danger of, 3-228-34; 4-403-04

Overtones (partials), sound frequencies. 5-124-25
  Musical sounds, found in, *with table,* 5-212-13, 218-20

Overweight.
  Relation to health, 8-82
  Symptoms and dietary control of, 5-268-71, 273, *diagram,* 267

Oviparous animals. Animals that produce their young from eggs that they have already passed from their bodies are said to be oviparous. Most lower forms of animal life are oviparous.
  Lizards, certain species of, 5-204, 205

Ovipositors, egg-laying tubes of insects. 2-404; 3-367

Ovules, immature seeds. 4-125

Owen, Robert, English paleontologist. 4-392

Owl butterflies. 3-200

Owlet moths. 3-202

Owls. *illus.,* 1-299; *with illus.,* 6-161-66
  Burrowing owls, *with illus.,* 5-418g
  Great horned owls, *with illus.,* 5-418g
  Pets, 7-23
  Saw-whet owls, *illus.,* 6-167
  Screech owls, *illus.,* 6-348

Oxbows, stream bends separated from the main stream. 6-414
  Formation of, *with illus.,* 8-14

Oxen. Domestication of, 7-328
  Transportation, use in, 1-100, 106

Oxford University.
  Low-temperature studies at, 5-210
  Roger Bacon, 2-306-07

Oxidation, process of giving off electrons. 3-317, 319-20; 5-88; 8-273
  Atmospheric gases involved and produced in, 1-231
  Cellular respiration as, 2-11-12
  Chemical combination with oxygen, 2-224, 227, 228, 229, 230, *diagram,* 228
  Experiment to show that oxidation takes place without fire, *with illus.,* 4-352
  Luciferin reactions to, 2-188-89
  Muscular energy furnished by "burning" of foods in body, 3-205-06

Oxidation *(continued)*
  Plants burn food reserves as fuel, 2-417
  Rocket and jet fuels, combustion (burning) of, 10-41-42, 45
  Rust resulting from, *illus.,* 1-37
  Soil formation, 2-16
  Water improved by oxidation of impurities, 2-278, 282
  See also **Oxygen**

Oxides, compounds with oxygen. 3-317, 321-24
  Minerals in the form of, *with illus.,* 5-249-50; 9-306

Oxidizing agents.
  Chlorine, 3-319-20
  Fluorine, 3-320
  Sulfuric acid, 3-321

Oxygen (O), chemical element. Atomic number, 8; atomic weight, 15.9994; melting point, —218.4° C.; boiling point, —183.0° C.; specific gravity, gas (air = 1): 1.10527, liquid: 1.14. As gas, is colorless, odorless and tasteless; in liquid and solid form, is pale blue and magnetic. Highly reactive. Discovered in 1774 by Priestley; name derived from Greek *oxys:* "acid" and *genes:* "forming." In free form and compounds, makes up one half of total material on earth's surface; forms by weight more than one fifth of air and high percentage of minerals. Obtained by liquefaction and fractional distillation, by electrolysis of water and by heating potassium chlorate with manganese dioxide as catalyst. Essential for respiration and practically all combustion. Plays all-important role in industry and medicine. See also 3-317
  Air, removal from: experiment, *with illus.,* 7-133
  Aquatic organisms, oxygen obtained by, 10-141
  Atmospheric, 1-231
  Atomic weight, 1-310
  Blood, transportation in, 3-326-27
  Cellular respiration, 2-11-12
  Climates of past indicated by analysis of isotopes of, 3-181-82
  Combines readily with other elements, 8-273
  Diffusion of, from capillary network, 3-385
  Discovery of, *with illus.,* 4-354-56
  Electrolytic preparation of, 5-92
  Fishes' requirements in aquariums, 8-112-13
  Germination after admission of, 5-63-64
  Interstellar space contains, 9-362, 363
  Muscular exercise, oxygen intake during. 3-205-07; 10-87-88, 90-91
  Oxygen gas, home preparation of, *with illus.,* 4-348-51
  Plants' use and release of, 3-45-49
  Plastics containing, *with diagram,* 8-222
  Rain, oxygen carried in, 2-350
  Respiration, fish, 4-100
  Respiration, human, 4-206, 209, *with illus.,* 200-01, *illus.,* 202
  Rocket fuels, 10-45
  Rust due to, *illus.,* 1-37
  Sea, oxygen-gas content in, 6-32
  Sewage purification, 5-328
  Soil, 2-25
  Spaceships and space suits use, 10-50, 52, *illus.,* 49
  Steelmaking processes, 1-344, 346
  Sun, oxygen found in, 3-109
  Thyroid controls oxygen consumption in body, 5-17-18
  Water-dwelling organisms require, 10-141
  Water molecules contain, 2-223-24, 225, *diagram,* 223-24
  See also **Breathing; Oxidation; Ozone; Respiration**

Oxygen chambers. 4-209

Oxygen debt. 10-90-91

Oxygen-deficiency theory of sleep. 6-148

Oxygen kits, used in mountain climbing. 4-209, *illus.,* 208

Oxygen tents. 4-209

Oxyhemoglobin, aerated hemoglobin. 3-326, 327

Oyashio, oceanic current. 6-238, *map,* 232-33

Oyster culture. 2-197-98, 202

Oyster drills, snails. 2-200

Oyster mushrooms. *illus.,* 3-30

Oysters. *illus.,* 1-294; 2-196-98, 202, *illus.,* 197, 201
  Reefs developed by, 8-358
  Reproductive rate of, 3-225
  Shell of, *illus.,* 2-101
  Unloading of, at processing plant, *illus.,* 6-17

Ozone, form of oxygen.
  Atmospheric, 1-231-32, 237, 238

Ozonides. Air pollutants, 3-354

P

P-type silicon. Solar battery, use in, 7-106, *illus.,* 104

P waves of earthquakes. See **Primary (P) waves of earthquakes**

Pacas, rodents. *with illus.,* 8-168

Pachycephalosaurus, herbivorous dinosaur. 1-394

Pacific coast. Canneries of, 6-26
  Giant trees of, 2-108, 110; *with illus.,* 5-260, *illus.,* 259

Pacific flyway, bird migration route. *illus.,* 5-418d

Pacific Ocean.
  Earthquake belt, 9-118
  Geologic and geographic features of, 6-74-75, 77
  Jet streams over, 2-360
  See also **Ocean**

Pacific tree frogs. 5-155-56

Pacinotti, Antonio, Italian physicist. 5-247

Pack ice. 9-334-35, 338

Packaging.
  Design important in, 10-123-25
  Printing of designs in, 1-211

Packets, ocean vessels.
  Sailing packets, 4-108, 110
  Steam packets, 4-110

Paddle-wheel steamers. *with illus.,* 4-109-11

Paedomorphosis, process by which sexually mature larvae are produced. *with illus.,* 6-278

Paez, Pedro, Portuguese missionary. 2-366

Pain.
  Anesthetics, development of, *with illus.,* 7-375-78
  Brain areas associated with, 6-325
  Cancer patients afforded relief from, 8-272
  Muscular, 3-213
  Sense of, 7-305, 346, 347, *illus.,* 304

Paint.
  Poisoning from paint containing radium, 9-349

Painting.
  Compressed air used in, 9-70, *illus.,* 63

Painting, art of. Mathematics and, 1-76
  See also **Paintings**

Paintings.
  Cave men, paintings by, *illus.,* 1-122
  Infrared-ray analysis of, *illus.,* 7-203
  X-ray analysis of, 7-147

Pairing, equivalence of objects. 7-110, *with illus.,* 107-08, *illus.,* 109

Pakistan. Irrigation in, 8-201

Palanquins, carrying chairs. 1-98, *illus.,* 99

Palate.
  Bones of, 3-79, *illus.,* 77
  Evolution of, 7-2-3

Paleobotany, science dealing with fossil plants. See **Botany — Fossil plants**

Paleocene epoch, time in earth's history. 6-374

Paleogeography, past geography of the earth. 6-370-74
  See also **Geology**

Paleontology, science dealing with life of past geological periods.
  *Coelacanths, 4-196-99
  *Prehistoric animals, 1-383-97
  *Time scale of evolutionary history, 6-369-74
  Elephants, extinct, 7-403-09
  Fossil study becomes a science, *with illus.,* 4-386-94
  Man, study of, *with illus.,* 9-21-24
  See also **Earth; Evolution; Fossils; Geology; Prehistoric times; Stratigraphic paleontology**

Paleozoic era, time in earth's history. 1-386-91; *with illus.,* 6-371-73

Paleozoology, science dealing with fossil animals. See **Paleontology; Zoology**

Palestine.
  Dating archaeological material from, 10-97

Palisade cells, of leaves. *with illus.,* 4-73
  See also **Palisade layer**

Palisade layer, of leaves. *illus.,* 3-42b
  See also **Palisade cells**

Palisades, bluffs along the lower Hudson River. 3-421

Palisades Disturbance, time of mountain making. 6-373

Palissy, Bernard, French potter. 7-398-99

Palladio, Andrea, Italian architect. 2-335

Palladium (Pd), chemical element. Atomic number, 46; atomic weight, 106.4; melting point, 1,549° C.; boiling point, 2,200° C.; specific gravity, 12.16. Steel-white metal, belonging to the platinum family; malleable and ductile. Discovered in 1803 by Wollaston; name derived from the asteroid Pallas. Always found in platinum ores, often in nickel ores, sometimes in osmiridium and combined with gold; obtained by igniting the precipitated cyanide. Used in nonmagnetic watches, in parts of delicate balances, in surgical instruments and (with its compounds) as a catalyst.

Pallas, asteroid. 4-421

Palm civets. 8-246

Palm trees.
  Coconut palms, 3-240, *illus.,* 241
  Date palms, *illus.,* 6-227
  Fossil palm leaf, *illus.,* 1-384
  Nuts dispersed by ocean currents, 5-4-5, 7
  Starch from, 4-78
  Underground water indicated by, 8-331-32

Palmate (palm-veined) leaves. *with illus.,* 5-139

Palmate-compound leaves. *with illus.,* 5-139-40

Palmella stage, stage in protozoan development. 2-61

Palmistry, pseudoscience of palm reading. 2-175

Palmitic acid. 7-275

Palms of hands.
  Bones (metacarpals) of, 1-148b; 3-74, *with illus.,* 81, *illus.,* 80
  Flexure lines, 2-175, *illus.,* 176
  Muscles and tendons of, *illus.,* 3-208

Palolo worms. 2-162

Palomar Observatory 200-inch telescope. 8-57, 59, *with illus.,* 58; 9-153, 159-60, 223-24, *illus.,* 157-58
  Pyrex used in mirror of, 3-415

Palpi, sensory organs of invertebrates.
  Insect's, *with illus.,* 2-403
  Spider's, 2-262, *illus.,* 261

Pamir plateau. 6-109, 115

Pampas, treeless plains of Argentina. 6-113

Panama. Panama Canal negotiations, 4-192

Panama, Isthmus of. 4-191

Panama Canal. 4-191, 192-94, *illus.,* 185, 193, *map,* 195
  Yellow fever, control of, 7-384-85
Panamanian poison frogs. *illus.,* 5-162
Panchromatic photographic film. 9-408, 409
Pancreas. *illus.,* 1-148d-e, 148g; 5-13, 18-19, *illus.,* 13, 16-17, 19
  Cell in guinea-pig pancreas, *illus.,* 2-8
  Development in human baby, 8-95
  Location in body, *illus.,* 4-322
Pancreatic duct. *illus.,* 1-148d; *illus.,* 5-13
Pancreatic juice. 4-328; 5-13
Pancreozymin, hormone that stimulates pancreatic juice secretion. 4-328
Pandaka pygmaea, tiny fish. 4-96
Pandas. 7-315, *illus.,* 313
Pandromic Strips. *with diagrams,* 4-452-53
Panel heating. *with illus.,* 2-250-51; 4-16, *illus.,* 14-15
Panel system, in telephony. 2-389
Panelescent lamps. 9-345-46, *illus.,* 345
Pangenesis. Darwin's theory of, 8-262-63
  See also **Darwin, Charles Robert; Evolution**
Pangolins, mammals. 7-14, *illus.,* 15
  Adaptations for feeding, 7-11
Panicles, flower clusters. *illus.,* 4-124
Pans, dough. Breadmaking, 9-297, *diagram,* 298
Pans, mining. *with illus.,* 1-370
Pansies. Flower parts of, *illus.,* 3-398
Pantheon, Rome. 3-114, *illus.,* 115
Pantherodes pardalaria, moth. *illus.,* 3-202d
Pantothenic acid, B vitamin. 5-43
  Deficiency as protection against malaria, 8-365
Pantotheres, primitive mammals. 7-5
Papakura Geyser, New Zealand. *illus.,* 8-293
Paper.
  *Papermaking, 4-364-78
  Experiments and tricks with, *with diagrams,* 7-177, 179-80
  Mucilage from guar plant used as ingredient, 7-44
  Photographic, 9-410
  Radiation thickness gauges used in manufacture of, 9-46
  Wasps that make, *with illus.,* 2-412d
  Wood as source of, 2-107; 5-266
Paper birch trees. 5-145, *illus.,* 144
Paper nautiluses, cephalopods. 2-196
  Shell of, *illus.,* 2-101
Paper trimmers ("guillotines"). *with illus.,* 4-377
Paper wasps. See **Papermaking wasps**
Papermaking. *4-364-78
Papermaking wasps (paper wasps). *with illus.,* 2-412d; *illus.,* 3-363
Papier-mâché, in molding mats. 1-207-08
Papin, Denis, French physicist. 4-39; 6-377
  Steam engine of, 4-81
Papinicolaou, George, American cancer researcher. 8-270
Papinicolaou technique, method of diagnosing cancer. 8-270
Papuan local races. 8-219
Papyrus.
  Writing material made from, 4-364
Parabolas, plane curves. *with illus.,* 3-439
  Analytic geometry, equations in, 4-428, *diagram,* 429
  Cometary orbits depicted as, 5-395, *illus.,* 396
Parabolic flights, of aircraft. Weightlessness produced by, 10-49-50
Paracelsus, Philippus Aureolus (Theophrastus Bombastus von Hohenheim), Swiss alchemist and physician. 2-368
  Drugs, use of, in disease treatment, 9-32

Parachutes. Royal Canadian Air Force para-rescue man, *illus.,* 6-187
  Seed and fruit "parachutes," 5-4, *illus.,* 2-3
  Space and rocket research uses, 9-381; *illus.,* 10-47
Paradichlorobenzene. Peach-tree borer controlled by, 9-195
  Sublimation of, 3-418
Paradise kingfishers. 6-310
Paraffin hydrocarbons. 7-267-69
Paraffin paper. 4-378
Parallax, optical. 7-295-96
Parallax, stellar. *with diagram,* 6-261; 7-228
Parallel electric circuits. 6-133, *illus.,* 134
  Home experiments with, *with illus.,* 6-293-94
Parallel-flow tunnels, devices for dehydrating food. *with illus.,* 4-165-66
Parallel lines, in different geometries. *with diagrams,* 4-439-41
Parallel rulers, draughtsman's tool. *with illus.,* 3-435
Parallel sphere, in astronomy. 1-262
Parallelograms, plane figures. *with illus.,* 3-434, 435
Paramagnetic materials. *with diagram,* 7-165
  Faraday identified, 5-236
Paramecium, genus of protozoans. *illus.,* 1-292; 2-66, *illus.,* 64-65
Paranitroaniline, chemical.
  Experiments and tricks with, *with diagram,* 7-175
Paranoia, mental illness. 9-203
  Alcoholism may cause, 4-412
Parapsychology, branch of psychology. 9-321
Parasite drag, term used in aeronautics. 6-186
Parasites. *8-360-68
  *Viruses, 3-451-58
  Animal and vegetable, 10-186
  Bacteria as, 3-65
  Birds, parasitic
    Cuckoos, 6-306, 308
  Filariasis, parasites causing, 10-32
  Fish diseases caused by, 8-116
  Insects, parasitism among, 2-410-11, 413-14; 3-360-61, 365, 367, 368, *illus.,* 362
  Malarial parasite, 10-32-34
  Mistletoe, 5-5
  Plants affected by, *with illus.,* 8-369-75
  Protozoans, 2-60
  True bugs, 3-256
  Worms, parasitic, *with illus.,* 2-153-59, *illus.,* 160, 161
  See also **Fungi; Pests; Spraying**
Paraskevopoulos' comet. *illus.,* 5-398
Parasol ants. See **Leaf-cutting ants**
Parasympathetic division, of autonomic nervous system. 6-329
Parathion, insecticide. Spraying of, *illus.,* 9-186, 187, 188
Parathyroid glands. 5-18
Parchment. 4-378
  Derivation of word, 1-355
Parchment worms. 2-162
Paré, Ambroise, French surgeon. 2-376
Paresis, form of.
  Syphilis as cause of, 6-330
Parícutin, volcano in Mexico. 8-302, *illus.,* 300b; 10-frontispiece
Parietal bones, in skull. *illus.,* 3-74, 77
Parietal lobes, of cerebrum. *with illus.,* 6-324-25
Paris, France.
  Avenue Denfert-Rochereau, *illus.,* 10-145
  Champs Elysées, paving of, *illus.,* 3-302
  Eiffel Tower, *illus.,* 7-123
  First balloon flight, 6-177, *illus.,* 176
  Pneumatic-tube communication system, 9-66-67

"Paris Code," system adopted for naming plants. 1-288

Parity law, principle in physics.   *7-107-10

Parker Dam, California-Arizona.   8-307
  Water supplied to Los Angeles by, 2-275

Parkes, Alexander, English chemist (1813-90). 8-223

Parks.   See Glacier National Park; Yellowstone National Park

Parlor cars, of railroad trains.   1-187

Parmentier, Antoine-Augustin, early French agronomist and dietitian. Bread, remarks on, 9-293

Parrot fever.   Microorganisms that cause, 1-40

Parrots.
  Jaws, with illus., 1-285
  Skull, illus., 1-285

Parsec, astronomical term.   6-261

Parsons, C. A., British inventor.
  Turbine of, 5-307

Parsons steam turbines.   5-307, 310

Parsons, William.   See Rosse, 3rd Earl of

Parthenocarpic fruits, fruits that have developed without pollination.   4-128

Parthenogenesis, birth from unfertilized eggs. Insects, 2-406

Partial eclipses.   3-134-35

Partials, sound frequencies.   See Overtones

Particle accelerators.   *9-241-49

Particles, atmospheric.   1-232, 236, 238
  Water vapor condensing on, 1-245

Particles, charged.   See Ionization

Particles, soil.   2-18-19, 24

Particles, subatomic.   See Nucleonics

Parting, identifying characteristic of minerals.   5-255

Partridge berries.   Terrarium plants, 5-368

Pascal, Blaise, French physicist, mathematician and philosopher.   3-17, 20-21
  Atmospheric pressure, experiments with, 1-233; 2-37
  Calculating machine of, with illus., 9-144
  Liquid pressure law, discovery of, 2-34

Pascal's law.   2-34

Passenger cars, of railroad trains.   with illus., 1-186-89

Passenger pigeons.   6-305-06; 9-267-68

Passenger planes.   with illus., 6-189-93
  Jet, 9-219

Passionflowers.   Tendrils of, illus., 3-55

Passive immunity.   7-351

Pasteur, Louis, French chemist.   *7-378-81; *9-71-80
  Relationship between microbes and higher animals discussed by, 7-151
  Silk industry of France saved by, 5-173
  See also Bacteria

Pasteur Institute, Paris, illus., 9-78
  Foundation of, 9-80, illus., 78

Pasteurization.   4-154, 157
  Invention of process of, 9-75
  Tuberculosis prevented by, 9-176

Patas monkeys, Old World monkeys.   9-258; illus., 10-159

Patch tests.
  Allergy detection, 4-263
  Tuberculosis diagnosed by, 9-180

Patella (kneecap).   illus., 1-148b; with illus., 3-82, illus., 74, 75

Patent bases (patent blocks), in printing presses. 1-210

Patent blocks.   See Patent bases

Patents.
  Telephone most valuable patent, 2-387
  Typewriters, 1-266

Pathological liars.   9-200

Pathology.
  Nineteenth-century advances in, 7-387-88
  See also Diseases

Patrick, Saint, patron saint of Ireland.   2-295

Pattern psychology, theory of.   9-54

Pauling, Linus, American chemist.   Protein structure investigated by, 9-386

Paulownia trees.   5-150, illus., 151

Pavement breakers, compressed-air drills.   9-66

Pavements.   See Concrete; Road building

Pavlov, Ivan Petrovich, Russian physiologist (1849–1936). He was famous for his work on conditioned reflexes; he showed that the original stimulus may be replaced by another stimulus in bringing about a given response. In 1904 he received the Nobel Prize in physiology for his researches in the physiology of digestion. He studied in both Russia and Germany; in 1890 he became director of the physiology department of the Institute of Experimental Medicine at St. Petersburg. He remained director of the institute under the Soviet regime.   See also 9-51-52
  Inhibition theory of sleep, 6-149

Paxton, Joseph, English horticulturist.   8-390

Pay load, rocket.   10-42, 45

PC(H) (patrol craft-hydrofoil), subchaser.   4-8, illus., 7

Pea family.   Trees of, with illus., 5-148

Peach-tree borers, insects.   with illus., 9-195

Peach trees.
  Fruits, illus., 4-130
  Peach-tree borers attack, 9-195
  Seeds, illus., 5-62

Peaches.   Brown-rot disease of, 3-28

Peano, Giuseppe, Italian mathematician and linguist. 1-120

Peanut worms.   illus., 1-294

Peanuts.
  George W. Carver's work with, 10-192-93
  Root nodules of peanut plant, illus., 2-23
  Seeds, illus., 5-62

Pear psyllas, insects.   with illus., 9-194

Pear trees.
  Fruits, illus., 4-130
  Pruning, illus., 10-149

Pearl, Dr. Raymond, American researcher in nutrition. 5-172

"Pearl" buttons.   7-210, with illus., 212

Pearls.   2-202

Pearly nautiluses.   with illus., 2-195-96
  Eyes of, 7-262
  Unchanged for millions of years, 6-283

Pearn, W., American geologist.   5-191

Pears.   Brown-rot disease of, 3-28

Peary, Robert Edwin.   First to reach North Pole, 7-34

Peas.   illus., 4-130
  Seeds, illus., 5-62

Peat.
  Bogs laid down in Carboniferous period, illus., 3-180
  Formation of, with illus., 1-406-07; 3-188-89; 7-66
  Peaty soils, formation of, 2-23
  Pits in Holland, illus., 6-112

Peat mosses.   3-188-89, illus., 186

Peattie, Donald Culross, American naturalist.   8-254

Peaucellier's Cell, device for changing circular motion into straight-line motion.   3-437

Pebbles.   Streams carry and deposit, 8-13

Pébrine, silkworm disease.   9-77

Pecan trees.   5-146

Peccaries, wild pigs.   10-244

Pecking order, social hierarchy among birds.   5-425

Pecten, structure in bird's eye.   5-423

Pectoral fins, of fishes.   4-98, with illus., 96

Pectoralis major, chest muscle.   illus., 1-148c; 3-209, illus., 204

Pectoralis minor, chest muscle.   illus., 1-148c

Peenemünde, Germany, rocket research center. 9-378-79; 10-45
Pegasus, constellation. 1-334, *illus.,* 256
Pegmatite, igneous rock. 3-423; 9-308
Peking man (Sinanthropus pekinensis). 9-23
Pelagic fish. 4-311
Pelamis platurus, sea snake. *with illus.,* 5-354c
Pelecypods. See **Lamellibranchs**
Pelée, Mount. 8-301
  Eruption of, *with illus.,* 7-343-44
Pele's hair, threads of lava. 7-345
Pelicans. *illus.,* 1-298
  Adaptations for obtaining food, *with illus.,* 3-236-37
  Flight of, *illus.,* 5-419
Pellagra, vitamin-deficiency disease. 5-43
Pellets. Owls disgorge, 6-164
Pellicle (cuticle), animal-cell envelope. 2-7
  Protozoa, 2-60
Peltier, Leslie, American amateur astronomer.
  Comets, discovery of, 5-399
Pelton water wheels, impulse turbines. 9-234, *illus.,* 233
Pelts.
  Furs, conversion into, *with illus.,* 7-235-38
Pelvic fins. See **Ventral fins**
Pelvic nodes, lymphatics in hip. *illus.,* 1-148g
Pelvis, hip bone. *illus.,* 1-148b; 3-82
  See also **Hip**
Pen shells, bivalves. *illus.,* 2-101
Pendulum. 2-319, *with illus.,* 121-22, *illus.,* 318
  Foucault demonstrates earth's rotation by means of, 4-47-48
  Prospecting with, 7-359
  Richter's work on, 3-268, *illus.,* 269
Peneplains, eroded land surfaces. 8-18
Penetration funnels, due to missile impacts. Meteorites may produce, 6-91, *diagram and illus.,* 90
Penguins. *illus.,* 1-298
Penicillin. 9-33-34; 10-128
  Preparation of, *with illus.,* 7-52-53
Penicillium, mold. *with illus.,* 3-27
  Penicillin, source of, *illus.,* 10-130a, 130b-c
Penis, male sex organ. 8-21, *illus.,* 20
Pennsylvania.
  Natural gas, early use of, 5-98, 99
  Oil well, first American, *with illus.,* 4-141
  Slate quarry in, *illus.,* 2-88
Pennsylvanian period, time in earth's history. 1-390; 6-372
  Coal formation during, *with illus.,* 1-406-07
Pentane, a methane hydrocarbon. 7-269
Pentatomids, family of insects. *with illus.,* 3-256-57
Pentodes, electron tubes. 6-300
Pentothal, anesthetic. 10-100
Penumbra, region of partial shadow in eclipse. 3-132
Pepperidge trees. 5-146
Peptic ulcers. See **Ulcers**
Peptization, breakdown of coarse particles into colloid dimensions. 5-300
Peranema, genus of one-celled animals. 2-62
Perception.
  Helmholtz' work on, 9-48
  Psychological study of, 9-315
  See also **Sensations; Sense organs; Senses**
Perched water bodies. 8-324, *illus.,* 325
Perching, of birds. Mechanism of, *with illus.,* 1-284
Percussion. Tuberculosis diagnosed by, 9-179
Percussion instruments. Sound production in, 5-218
Père David's deer. 8-239, 240
Peregrine falcons. *with illus.,* 6-159

Peregrinus de Maricourt, Petrus.
  Loadstones discussed by, 7-167
Perennials, plants. 2-420; 6-57
Perfect-gas laws. *with diagram,* 1-165-66
Perfect (Diabolic) magic squares. *with diagram,* 4-450
Perfect flowers. 4-122
Perfecting presses (perfectors), in printing. 1-210
Perfectors. See **Perfecting presses**
Perfumes.
  Synthesis of, 8-188-89
Perianths, flower structures. 4-120-21
Pericycle, layer of plant cells. 4-64, 68, *illus.,* 64, 69
Peridotites, igneous rocks. 3-423; 9-308
Périer, F. Barometer, experiment with, 3-17
Perigee, closest orbital point. 8-127, 128, *diagram,* 126
Perilymph, liquid of inner ear. 7-299
Period, orbital. 8-127
Periodic law, of chemical elements. *4-304-10
  Development of, nineteenth century, *with illus.,* 5-84-85
Periodic meteor showers. 6-97
Periodic phenomena.
  Trigonometry used in analysis of, *with illus.,* 3-449-50
Periodic springs. 8-326
Periodic table, of chemical elements. *4-304-10
  Long form, *table,* 4-307
  Mendeleev's arrangement, *with illus.,* 5-84-85; 9-124
  Newlands' arrangement, *with illus.,* 5-83-84
  Short form, *table,* 4-309
Periodontal diseases. 5-131-32
Periodontal membranes, tooth-supporting tissues. 5-129, 131-32, *illus.,* 134
Periodontitis, disease of the gums. 5-132
Periods, major geologic-time units. 6-370
  See also **Epochs; Eras**
Periods, cometary. 6-97
Periscopes. Submarine, 5-35
Perissodactyla, order of mammals. *with illus.,* 7-16
Peristalsis, wave motion in the intestine and other organs. *with illus. and diagram,* 1-279-80; 4-327, *with illus.,* 330
Peritonitis. 4-335
Peritrichida, order of ciliate protozoans. 2-66
Periwinkles, gastropods. 2-200
  Shell of, *illus.,* 2-100
Perkin, Sir William H., English chemist. 5-80
  Aniline dyes synthesized by, 8-186
Perkins, R. Marlin, American zoo director. *illus.,* 10-155
Permalloy, magnetic alloy. 2-389
Permanent magnets. 7-165-66
Permanent teeth. 5-129-31, *illus.,* 131-32, *table,* 130
Permanent waving. 10-82-83
Permeability. Rocks, permeability of, 8-322-23
Permian period, time in earth's history. 6-373
Perminvar, magnetic alloy. 2-389
Permissible explosives. 8-286-87
Pernicious anemia, anemia due to lack of antianemic factor. 3-330; 5-44-45
Peroneus longus, lower-leg muscle. *illus.,* 3-204, 213
Peroxides. Air pollutants, 3-354
Perrault, Pierre, French writer. 8-321-22
Perret, Frank Alvord, American volcanologist. 7-337
Perrine, Charles D., American astronomer.
  Jupiter's satellites VI and VII, discovery of, 5-24
Perseids, meteor shower. 1-252; *with table,* 6-97
Perseus, constellation. 1-334
Perseus, mythological figure linked with legends of constellations. 1-335

Persia, Ancient.
  Petroleum used in ancient period, 4-140
  Signal system, in antiquity, 2-377
Persian lamb, fur. 7-238
Persian wheels. See Sakias
Persimmon trees. with illus., 5-149
  Fruits, illus., 5-141
Personality.
  Ink-blot tests for personality structure, with illus.,
    9-57
  Psychology of, 9-319
  Psychopathic, 9-199-200, with illus., 96-102
  Traits, list of, 9-319
Perspective, in painting. 1-76, illus., 77
Perspiration. 5-10-11
  Muscular exercise and, 10-87-88
  Sleep, increased during, 6-147
  Sweat glands, 2-176-77, illus., 174, 177
Peru. Arid region of, illus., 6-237
  Quipus as recording device of ancient Peruvians,
    illus., 1-113
Peru Current, oceanic current. 6-236, 238, map,
  232-33, illus., 237
Pests.
  *Insect enemies of fruit crops, 9-185-96
  True bugs, 3-256
  See also Codling moths; Insects; Parasites
Petals. illus., 4-123
Petals, flower parts. 3-405, illus., 398; 4-120, illus., 121
Petechiae, tiny blood spots. 3-331-32
Petioles, leafstalks. 4-72, 73
Petrarch, Francesco, Italian poet and scholar. with
    illus., 2-361
Petri dishes, used for cultivation of bacteria. with
    illus., 3-72; illus., 10-130a
Petrie, Sir Flinders, English Egyptologist. 7-209
Petrifaction, replacement of organic material by min-
    erals. 8-328
Petrified wood. 1-385, illus., 384
Petrochemicals, compounds from petroleum and gas. 4-
  151
Petroglyphs. Dates in prehistoric culture established
    by analysis of, with illus., 9-29-30
Petroleum. *4-140-52
  *Prospecting for petroleum, 7-354-61
  Ocean bottoms (continental shelves), oil from, 6-72
  Origin and nature of, 3-407
  Processing plants, automatic, 10-237
  Prospecting for, with seismographs, illus., 6-7; 9-116
  Research in petroleum and natural-gas industries, 1-
    88, 89
  War material, 9-326
  See also Natural gas; Oil
Petroleum coke. 4-150
Petroleum engineering. 1-225-26
Petroleum gases. 4-148, 151
Petroleum-product poisoning. First aid for, 10-10
Petrology, scientific study of the composition of rocks.
    See Geology; Rocks
Petrous bone, in skull. 3-78
Pets.
  *Fish as pets, 8-112-16
  *Wild animals as pets, 7-17-26
Petty, Sir William, English political economist and
    statistician. 3-21, 266
Petunias.
  Air-pollution detected by means of, illus., 3-352
  Pollination of, 7-244-45
pH, measure of acidity or alkalinity. 2-424; 4-340-42

pH (continued)
  Food-preservation processes, pH as factor in, 4-156,
    157
  Indicators of, table, 4-339
Phaeophyta, phylum of algae. 1-301; with illus.,
    3-219-21
Phaetons, horse-drawn vehicles. illus., 1-104
Phagocytes.
  Tuberculosis, defense against, 9-177-78
Phalangers, marsupials. 7-9, 421, 425, illus., 423
Phalanges, finger and toe bones.
  Fingers, illus., 1-148b; with illus., 3-81, illus., 74, 80
  Toes, illus., 1-148b; 3-83, illus., 74, 82-83
Phalaropes, birds. 6-405
Phanotrons, gas-filled diodes. 6-301
Pharaoh's ants. 3-362
Pharos, lighthouse of Alexandria. illus., 1-354
Pharynx. illus., 1-148d-e; 3-78, 79; 4-323, illus., 202,
  322
Phases, particular appearances of heavenly bodies in
    recurring cycles.
  Mercury, 4-26
  Moon, 4-277-78; 6-81
  Venus, 4-28, illus., 30
Phasmida, order of insects. 2-412; with illus., 3-149-50
Pheasants. 6-338, 340, illus., 339, 340
  Raising of, 7-23
Phenobarbital. See Veronal
Phenol, crystalline compound. Coal tar yields, with
    illus., 1-419
Phenol-formaldehyde resin. diagram, 8-222
Phenolic resins, plastics. 8-223-24, with illus., 227, dia-
    gram, 222
Phenolphthalein, chemical indicator.
  Experiments and tricks with, with diagram, 7-176-77
Phenotypes, types determined by visible characters.
    with illus., 6-272-73
Phenyl-thio-carbamide (PTC).
  Inheritance of taste for, 8-341-42, 346
Philippine Islands.
  Terraces for farming in, illus., 6-1
  Water buffaloes of, illus., 10-249
Philolaus, Greek philosopher. 1-242
  Forerunner of Copernicus, 2-372
Philology. *Development of language, 1-107-21
"Philosophical instruments." with illus., 3-14, 19
Philosophical Transactions of the Royal Society. 3-267
Philosophy. Psychology, relation to, 9-311
Phlebitis, inflammation of the veins. 3-392
Phloem, conducting tissue of plants. with illus., 4-64,
  68, 69, 70, 73
Phlogiston theory. 3-271-72
Phobos, satellite of Mars. 3-159
Phoebe, satellite of Saturn. 5-113
Phoebes, American birds. 6-99
Phoenicians. Sea voyages of, 6-27, illus., 28
  Tyre, city of, illus., 3-228
Phoenix, mythical bird. Legend of, 1-362, illus., 363
Phoenix, steamboat. 4-110
Pholas dactylus, luminous mollusk. 2-185, 188, illus., 185
Pholidota, order of mammals. 7-14, illus., 15
Phonemes, phonetic units. 1-110-11
Phonetic alphabet. 1-110
Phonograph needles.
  Piezoelectric crystals used with, 2-294
Phonographs. *7-362-69
Phonology, science dealing with language sounds. 1-
  107-08, 110-11, 113-15, 116-17
Phoronidea, phylum of worms. 1-293
Phosphates.
  Bone minerals, 3-73

Phosphates (continued)
  Cells contain, **2**-6
  Minerals in the form of, with illus., **5**-250; **9**-306
  Soil fertilizers, **2**-171
  Soils contain, **2**-23
Phospholipids, complex lipids. **2**-5
Phosphorescence. 3-320
  Deep-sea animals, phosphorescent organs of, with illus., **10**-142
  Minerals identified by, **5**-256
Phosphoric acid. Soil-fertilizer content, **2**-171
Phosphors.
  Electric lighting, phosphors used in, **4**-240
  Electroluminescence, role in, **9**-344-45
Phosphorus (P), chemical element. Atomic number, 15; atomic weight, 30.9738; melting point, 44.1° C.; boiling point, 280° C.; specific gravity, yellow: 1.82, red: 2.20, black: 2.34. Nonmetallic element; three varieties —a yellow, very reactive, soft, poisonous; a red, non-poisonous, less active; and a black. Discovered in 1669 by heating white sand with evaporated urine. Name derived from Greek phosphoros: "light-bearing." Never found uncombined in nature; present in wide variety of minerals and in cell protoplasm, nervous tissue and bones. Prepared in the electric furnace. Used in pure form and compounds in fertilizers, detergents and safety matches. (Only red phosphorus is used for matches.) See also **3**-320-21
  Diet, phosphorus essential to, **4**-59
  Muscle contraction, role of phosphorus in, **3**-206
  Oxygen experimentally removed from air by, with illus., **7**-133
  Parathyroids control phosphorus metabolism in the body, **5**-18
  Plants' use of, **2**-170, 171; **3**-44
  Soil phosphorus available to plants, **2**-23, 24
  Steelmaking, **1**-344, 346, 353
  See also **Fertilizers**
Phosphorylated compounds. Insects controlled by, **9**-186
Photo-offset. See **Photo-offset lithography**
Photo-offset lithography. with illus., **1**-210-12
Photoblepharon, East Indian fish. **2**-186
Photochemistry. Nineteenth-century developments, **5**-83
Photocopying, photographic reproduction of records.
  *Microfilming, **10**-68-74
Photoelectric cells (phototubes).
  Development of, **9**-289
  Exposure meters (photographic) contain, **9**-409
  Pictures sent by wire and radio, **7**-390-92
  Television, use in, **5**-277-78
  Uses of, **6**-302-03
    Interstellar space studied with, **9**-361
    Starlight magnified by photoelectric current, **8**-60
Photoelectric emission. 7-250
  Electron tubes, **6**-302
  See also **Photoelectric cells**
Photoelectric exposure meters. with illus., **9**-409
Photoelectric Fosterite, plastic.
  Stress analyzed by, illus., **7**-284c
Photoengraving, preparation of printing plates from photographs and drawings. with diagrams, **1**-204-06
  Electrical circuits made by, with illus., **6**-50-51
  See also **Printing**
Photoflash equipment. 9-411
Photoflood bulbs. 9-410
Photogenic drawing, photographic process. **9**-401
Photographic (cold-type) machines, for typesetting. with illus., **1**-202-03

Photography. *9-397-414; *10-163-67
  *Microfilm, **10**-68-74
  *Nature photography, **6**-311-16
  Astronomy, use in, **1**-24; **6**-258, 386-87; **8**-49, 59, 60
  Boys' camera, **1**-402
  Development of, in nineteenth century, with illus., **6**-382
  Eclipses, use in, **3**-136
  Engineering problems solved by, **5**-312
  High-frequency sound, photography of, illus., **8**-104, 106
  Home experiment to show principle on which photography is based, with illus., **4**-346-47
  Markowitz moon camera, with illus., **5**-187-88
  Meteors, **6**-95-96
  Printing, photography in, **1**-210-14, with illus., 202-06
  Star trails, photography of, with illus., **6**-85-86
  Telescopic, **4**-421
  Vision experiments with photographic transparencies, **8**-180, diagrams, 179
  X-ray photography, **7**-143, 146, 148, illus., 144, 150
  See also **Lenses; X rays**
Photolithographic printing. See **Photo-offset lithography**
Photometry, science dealing with measurement of light intensity.
  Star brightness, determination of, **6**-256-57, 260-62, table, 262
Photomicrographs, enlarged photographs of microscopic objects. **9**-414, illus., 93, 397; illus., **10**-164
Photomultiplier tubes. with illus., **6**-376
Photon machines, for typesetting. **1**-203
Photon theory of light. 7-205, 249; **9**-280
Photons, electromagnetic units. with table, **1**-314
Photoperiods, periods of light duration.
  Flowering affected by, **3**-55; **4**-120
Photophores, reflectors or lenses found in animals. **2**-186
Photosensitizing poisons. 7-76
Photosphere, bright disk of sun. **3**-100, illus., 101
Photosynthesis, manufacture of food in plants. **2**-11; **3**-45-46, 48, 398-99, illus., 42a-d; **6**-54; **7**-129
  Bacteria that engage in, **3**-65
  Coal's energy due to photosynthesis in ancient plants, with illus., **1**-406
Phototrollers, electronic finger-saving devices. illus., **10**-168
Phototropism, movement of an organism in response to light. illus., **1**-47; **3**-53, illus., 51
  Beans, illus., **6**-218c
Phototubes. See **Photoelectric cells**
Phreatophytes, well plants. Underground water indicated by, **8**-331-32
Phrenic nerve.
  Tuberculosis treated by crushing of, **9**-182
Phrenology. with diagram, **9**-317
Phycocyanin, algal pigment. **3**-214
Phycoerythrin, algal pigment. **3**-224
Phyla, groups in classification of living things. **1**-291
Phyllirrhoë, luminous snail. with illus., **2**-185
Phyllite, rock formation. **3**-426
Phylogeny, race history of plant and animal type. **8**-262
Phylum. See **Phyla**
Physical changes. 3-245
  Chemical changes distinguished from, with illus., **1**-81, 86; with diagram, **2**-223-24
  See also **Change of state**
  Examples of, with water, with illus., **4**-229-30
Physical chemistry. 1-86
  *Acids, bases and salts, **4**-336-42
  *Colloids, **5**-294-304

Physical chemistry (continued)
  *Molecules, 1-162-72
  *Solutions, 4-296-303
   Muscular exercise, chemistry of, 3-205-07
   Nineteenth-century developments in, 5-82-83
Physical constants. 10-295
Physical geography. See **Physiography**
Physicians. See **Diseases; Health; Infectious diseases;
   Medicine**
Physicists. See **Physics;** also names of physicists
Physics.
  *Air, experiments with, 2-323-31
  *Animal mechanisms, 1-277-86
  *Atomic energy, 9-43-46, 120-42, 241-49, 348-58, 391-
     96; 10-98-101, 114-16, 251-53
  *Atomic structure, 1-307-14
  *Audion, development of, 8-84-89
  *Bioelectricity, 2-421-28
  *Color, 7-277-90; 8-178-80
  *Compressed air, 9-58-70
  *Cosmic rays, 8-393-99
  *Cryogenics, 5-207-10
  *Crystals, 5-337-42
  *Diamond synthesis, 4-273-76
  *Electricity, 1-398-404; 2-377-95, 421-28; 6-49-51,
     119-35; 9-226-40
  *Electricity, experiments with, 6-286-94
  *Electrochemistry, 5-87-96
  *Electroluminescence, 9-344-47
  *Electromagnetic radiation, 7-199-207
  *Electronic computers, 9-143-52
  *Electronics, 2-169-72; 3-85-98; 5-276-88; 6-295-303;
     7-390-92; 9-387-90; 10-102-04, 168-70
  *Facsimile transmission, 7-390-92
  *Forces in liquids and gases, 2-30-42
  *Geiger-Mueller counters, 9-340-43
  *Gravitation, 2-315-22
  *Heat, 3-407-18
    *Engines, heat, 4-80-92
    *Experiments with, 4-17-24
    *Transmission of, 4-9-16
  *International Geophysical Year, 5-186-95
  *Light, 7-249-62
    *Experiments with, 8-117-24
  *Lightning, 1-398-404
  *Machines, simple, 3-56-62
  *Magnetism, 7-162-72
  *Matter, properties of, 5-369-76
  *Matter and energy, 1-79-86
  *Mechanics, experiments in, 7-214-22
  *Metallurgy, 1-369-82
  *Microscopes, 9-81-95
  *Molecules, 1-162-72
  *Motion, 2-118-28
  *Noise meters, 8-38-46
  *Optics. See **Light**
  *Parity law, 7-107-10
  *Photography, 9-397-414; 10-163-67
  *Piezoelectricity and electrostriction, 2-293-94
  *Plasmas, 1-173-78
  *Radar, 9-387-90
  *Radio, 3-85-98
  *Radiocarbon dating, 10-92-97
  *Radioisotope-fueled thermoelectric generators, 6-172-
     75
  *Relativity theory, 4-210-20
  *Solar battery, 7-103-06
  *Solutions, 4-296-303
  *Sound, 5-114-28
    *Experiments with, 5-221-30
    *Musical sounds, 5-211-20

Physics (continued)
  *Space travel, 10-40-54
  *Telescopes, 9-153-61
  *Television, 5-276-88
  *Thermoluminescence, dating by, 6-375-76
  *Transistors, 10-102-04
  *Turbines, 5-305-12
  *Ultrasonics, 8-103-10
  *Water, experiments with, 8-1-8
  *X rays, 7-143-50
   Astronomy, use in, 6-258
   Calculus used to measure physical quantities and
     changes, with diagrams, 4-433-39
   Fields of physics differentiated, 1-86
   History
     Antiquity, 1-138, with illus., 357, 359-60
     Arabic contributions, 2-300-01
     1600–1765, with illus., 3-275-82
     1765–1815, with illus., 4-358-63
     Nineteenth century, with illus., 6-239-54
     Twentieth century, with illus., 9-279-89
   Job opportunities in field of, with illus., 10-201-02
   Mathematics and, 1-77
   Nobel Prize winners in, 10-299-307
   Space-time concept, 4-213
   See also **Atoms; Biophysics; Electricity; Electrons
     Energy; Molecules; Motion; Periodic law of
     chemical elements; Physical chemistry; Tele-
     graphs, electric; Telephones;** etc.
Physiculus japonicus, fish harboring luminous bacteria.
   with illus., 2-186
Physiography, geography treating of exterior physical
   features and changes of earth.
  *Caves, 5-50-60
  *Earthquakes, 9-105-19
  *Flattened areas of earth, 6-109-18
  *Geysers, 8-288-92
  *Glaciers, 9-162-74
  *Ground water, 8-321-32
  *Icebergs, 9-333-39
  *International Geophysical Year, 5-186-95
  *Islands, 4-133-39
  *Lakes, 7-55-66
  *Mountains, 10-18-29, 213-23
  *Ocean bottom, 6-69-77
  *Rivers, 6-409-18
  *Shoreline changes, 8-348-59
  *Soil, 2-15-25
  *Volcanoes, 8-293-304
  *Water, erosive action of, 8-9-18
  *Wind, erosive action of, 7-318-26
   See also **Earth; Geology; Rivers; Soil; Volcanoes**
Physiological psychology. 9-320
Physiology.
  *Aging in man, 8-78-83
  *Basic units of body, 1-143-48
  *Blood, 3-325-34
  *Body defenses, 7-346-53
  *Bones, 3-73-84
  *Cellular physiology, 2-1-14, 287-92
  *Circulatory system, 3-381-92
  *Comparative, 1-57-66
  *Digestive system, 4-321-35
  *Exercise and rest, 10-85-91
  *Glands, 5-8-19
  *Growth, development and decline of human body,
     8-90-102
  *Mechanisms, animal, 1-277-86
  *Muscles of human body, 3-203-13
  *Nervous system, 6-317-30

Physiology (continued)
  *Plant physiology, 3-43-55
    *Photosynthesis, 3-42a-d
    Experiments in, 8-35
  *Reproduction, human, 8-19-33
  *Respiratory system, 4-200-09
  *Senses, 4-379-85; 7-291-306
  *Skin, hair and nails, 2-173-81
  *Sleep, 6-143-51
  *Smoking, effects of, 5-343-50
  *Systems of human body, 1-148a-h
  *Teeth, 5-129-37
  Acceleration, human body affected by, 10-48
  Alcoholic beverages, effects of, with illus., 4-406-12
  Estivating animals, 5-412-13
  History
    Seventeenth century, with illus., 3-10-12
    1700–1775, with illus., 3-379-80
    Nineteenth century, with illus., 7-372-73
  Human hearing, limits of, 8-104
  Narcotics, effects of, 5-401-05
  Nobel Prize winners in, 10-299-307
  pH of body fluids, 4-341
  Psychology, relation to, 9-311, 320
  Seed plants, 3-398-99
  See also **Blood; Body; Brain; Breathing; Circulatory systems; Digestion; Stomach;** etc.
Phytophthora infestans. 8-370
Phytoplankton. 9-222
Pi (π), geometric ratio. 3-435; 4-444-45
Pi mesons, atomic particles. 1-313, with table, 314
Pia mater, membrane found in brain and spinal cord. with illus., 6-327-28
Pianos. Sound production in, 5-216
Piazzi, Giuseppe, Italian astronomer (1746–1826). He was mathematics professor at Palermo where he founded and directed the observatory, and he became director of the government observatory at Naples. In 1801 he discovered the first known asteroid, or minor planet, naming it Ceres. He catalogued the fixed stars and contributed to the knowledge of comets. See also 3-159; 4-420; 6-393
Picard, Casimir, French student of early man. 9-23
Piccard, Auguste, Swiss scientist.
  Balloon flight into stratosphere, 6-179, illus., 180
  Bathyscaphe invented by, 2-191; with illus., 6-74a; 9-222-23
Piccard, Jacques, Swiss scientist. Bathyscaphe exploration by, 9-223
Piccolos. Sound production in, 5-217
Pickering, Edward Charles, American astronomer (1846–1919). Professor of physics at the Massachusetts Institute of Technology, he was also astronomy professor at Harvard and directed its observatory. He pioneered in the measurement of stellar light, in stellar spectroscopy and in the photography of the skies. Pickering established an observation station in Peru for the study of the southern heavens.
Pickering, William Henry, American astronomer (1858–1938). Brother of E. C. Pickering, William taught astronomy at Harvard. He led solar-eclipse expeditions and worked on planetary photography and on measurements of planetary brightness. The discoverer of Saturn's ninth satellite (Phoebe), he predicted the position of Pluto. He made important studies of the moon and Mars, aided his brother in establishing an observation station in Peru and founded another station in Jamaica.
  Martian canals studied by, 4-419
Pickling.
  Hams processed by, 5-167

Pickling (continued)
  Leather and furs processed by, 7-232, 237
Picks. Geologist's pick used in collecting minerals, with illus., 9-302
Pictographic writing. with illus., 1-112
Picture windows, clear large windows. illus., 8-389
  See also **Daylight walls**
Pictures.
  Reproduction for printing purposes, with diagrams, 1-204-06
  Writing developed from, with illus., 1-112
  See also **Photography**
Pied-billed grebes. 6-395
Piedmont glaciers. 9-165
Piedmont Plateau. 6-109
Pierce, George Washington, American physicist.
  Sound magnifier of, 8-45
Piercing process, for manufacture of seamless steel tubing. 1-351
Piezoelectricity. *2-293-94
  High-frequency sound produced by, 8-107
  Minerals identified by, 5-256
  Radio transmission, 3-88
Piezoluminescence. 2-188
Pig iron. Manufacture and uses, 1-343, 346
  See also **Cast iron; Iron; Steel**
Pig manure, as soil fertilizer. 2-165
Pigeon hawks. 6-159
Pigeon milk. 6-304
Pigeons. illus., 1-298; 6-304-06, illus., 305; 10-256
  Intelligence, illus., 2-28-29
  Message carriers, 5-239; 10-68, illus., 69
  Nests of, 10-258
  Passenger pigeons, 6-305-06; 9-267-68
Pigment metabolism, destruction of dead red blood cells, 5-13-14
Pigments.
  Bile, 5-13-14
  Blood contains iron pigment, 3-326, 327
  Scales of lepidopterous insects contain, illus., 3-202c
  Skin and hair coloring, 2-175-76, 179
Pigs. illus., 1-299
  Domestication of, 10-244
  Garbage as food for, 5-336
  Parasitic-worm infestations, 2-154, 156-57, illus., 161
  Processing of pigs for food, with illus., 5-166-68
  Wild, 10-243
Pigs, metal bars. Type casting, used in, 1-200
"Pigs," scrubbing devices for pipeline interiors. 5-102
Pigweeds. 7-112
Pikas, harelike mammals. 8-168, 170
Pike, fish. Northern pike, illus., 4-103
Pikes Peak, Colorado. 10-222
Pile drivers. 1-83, illus., 82
Pileated woodpeckers. 6-211
Piles, construction elements. 2-343
Pill bugs. 2-242
Pillars, geologic formations. Formation of, 2-353; 8-11
Pilobolus, genus of molds. illus., 10-130b-c
Pilot balloons, balloons for indicating upper-air conditions. 1-251-52
Pilot black snakes. Pets, 7-25
Pilot lights, in gas stoves. Cleaning, 7-191
"Piltdown man." Discovered by Dawson, 9-23
Pin cherry trees. 5-149
"Pinch effect," for confining plasmas. with illus., 1-177
Pinching bugs, beetles. 3-345
Pinchot, Gifford, American forester and conservation pioneer. 6-2-3, illus., 3
Pincushion mosses. 3-188

Pine grosbeaks. 6-108

Pine siskins, birds. 6-108

Pine trees.
Felling of, *illus.,* 2-109
How to recognize, *with illus.,* 5-141-43
Leaves, *illus.,* 4-72
Needles, *illus.,* 5-139
Needles as defense, 7-80
Pitch-pine sprouts, *illus.,* 10-144
Ponderosa pine, *illus.,* 3-400
Red-pine saplings, *illus.,* 5-265
Reproduction in, 3-402-03
Seeds, *illus.,* 5-3, 62
Sugar pine, 5-260

Pineal gland.
Function according to Descartes, 3-13

Pineapples. *illus.,* 1-303; *illus.,* 4-129
Fabrics made from pineapple leaves, 4-182

Pinel, Philippe, French physician. 9-102-03

Pinhole cameras. Experiments with, *with illus.,* 8-120

Pinions, automobile gears. 2-141, *illus.,* 140

Pinks, plants. Adaptations for dispersing seeds, 5-2

Pinnae. See **Auricles**

Pinnate (feather-veined) leaves. *with illus.,* 5-139

Pioneer, early steam locomotive. *illus.,* 6-380

Pioneer IV, artificial satellite launched by United States. 10-47

Pioneer V, artificial satellite launched by United States. 10-47

Pioneers. Wood used for building by, *with illus.,* 7-115

Pions. See **Pi mesons**

Pipe-organ wasps. *with illus.,* 2-412d

Pipe smoking. Lung cancer caused by?, *with diagram,* 5-347, 348, 349

Pipelines.
Natural gas 5-98-99, *with illus.,* 101-05, *illus.,* 98b-c
Petroleum and natural-gas, *with illus.,* 4-147
Water, 2-275-76, *illus.,* 276-277

Pipes.
Heat insulation of, 4-12
Petroleum industry uses, 4-145, *with illus.,* 146-47, *diagram,* 144
Sewage, 5-327-28, 336
Steel pipes, manufacture and uses of, 1-350-51

"Pipes of Pan." How to make, *with illus.,* 5-230

Piranhas, fishes. 4-105

Pisa, Italy.
Leaning Tower of Pisa, Galileo's experiments on, *with illus.,* 3-2

Pisaurids, fisher spiders. 2-266

Pisces (Fishes), constellation. 1-334

Piscis Austrinus (Southern Fish), constellation. 1-335

Pistillate flowers. *with illus.,* 4-122

Pistils, plant reproductive organs. 3-405-06, *illus.,* 398; *with illus.,* 4-121-22, 123

Piston engines. See **Diesel engines; Gasoline engines; Steam engines**

Piston pumps. Water supply, 2-284-85

Piston rings, of automobile engines. *with illus.,* 2-132

Pistons.
Automobile gasoline engines, pistons of, *with illus.,* 2-132-33, 134
Steam locomotives, pistons of, 1-186, *illus.,* 185
Steamship engines, early, 4-110, 111

Pit vipers, snakes. 5-364, *illus.,* 362-63

Pitch. Coal-tar residue, *with illus.,* 1-419
See also **Asphalt; Coal; Petroleum**

Pitch, of sound. 5-123-24, 127, *illus.,* 124, 126
Music, pitch in, *with illus.,* and *tables,* 5-211-20

Pitch, term used in aeronautics. 6-188, 194
Space vehicles and missiles undergo, 8-129, *diagram,* 130

Pitch pine trees. 5-142

Pitchblende. Polonium and radium, source of, 8-413-15

Pitcher plants. 3-238; 4-74, *illus.,* 73

Pitchstone, igneous rock. 3-423-24

Pith, plant tissue. 4-68, *illus.,* 69

Pithecanthropus erectus (Java man).
Discovered by Dubois, 9-23, *illus.,* 22

Pitot tubes. Invented by the French physicist Henri Pitot (1695–1771), they are devices for measuring the velocities of flowing liquids or gases. The Pitot meter consists of two tubes, bent at right angles; one is open against the direction of fluid flow and so builds up a high inner pressure. The other tube is closed but perforated around the middle by small holes that equalize its internal pressure with that of the outside fluid as a whole. A dial attached to the tubes gives either the pressure difference between them or the actual speed of the fluid. Pitot tubes are used in weather analysis and in aircraft wind tunnels.

Pitressin, a hormone. 5-17

Pittsburgh, Pennsylvania.
Alcoa Building, *illus.,* 7-126
Antismoke campaign, 3-356

Pittsfield, Massachusetts.
High Voltage Engineering Laboratory, *illus.,* 1-400

Pituitary gland. *illus.,* 1-148g; 5-15, 17, 19, *illus.,* 16-17
ACTH derived from, 10-133, *illus.,* 132
Cancer of, 8-266
First successfully operated upon, 7-387
Nicotine's effects on, 5-345

Pixii, Hippolyte, French instrument maker. 5-247

Place systems, for numbers. 1-152, 154-56

Placenta, plant seed attachment. *illus.,* 2-416

Placenta, structure by which unborn young is nourished in uterus. 7-419; 8-25, 26, 32, *illus.,* 24, 25, 32
Mammalian, 7-6

Placental mammals. 7-5, 6, 419

Placers, deposits containing particles of valuable minerals.
Gold found in, 4-245

Placid, Lake, New York. *illus.,* 7-60

Placodermi, major group of fishes. *with illus.,* 4-94

Placoderms, primitive extinct fishes. *with illus.,* 1-389; *illus.,* 6-372

Plague (Black Death).
Control of, 9-39
Flea, the carrier of, 7-383
Middle Ages, plague in, 2-312-13

Plain carbon steels. Composition and uses of, 1-353
See also **Steel**

Plains, level lands. 6-110-13
Stream terraces, or flood plains, 8-16

Plains Indians, of America. Writing of, *with illus.,* 1-112

Plan Position Indicator (PPI), system of radar reception. 9-387, 390

Planaria, genus of flatworms. *illus.,* 1-292; 2-156, *illus.,* 155

Planarians. See **Planaria**

Planck, Max Karl Ernst Ludwig, German physicist. *with illus.,* 9-283-84
Quantum theory of, 7-205; 8-406-07

Planck's constant. 9-283

Plane geometry. *3-429-40
Analytic plane geometry, *with diagrams,* 4-423-30

Plane-polarized light. 5-340-41, *diagram*, 339;
7-282-83, *illus.*, 285
Distant stars emit, **9**-364
Stress analyzed by, *illus.*, **7**-284c
Study of, in nineteenth century, **6**-240, 242
Plane trees. *with illus.*, **5**-146
Planers, blocks for leveling printing material. **1**-207
Planers, tools. **10**-110-11, *illus.*, 113
Planes, geometric. Distances on, **4**-440-41
Planes, inclined, simple machines. *with illus.*, **3**-59-60
Planet X. See **Pluto**
Planetaria. *2-396-401
Planetary motion, laws of. 3-5-6
Planetesimal hypothesis of origin of solar system.
1-29, *illus.*, 28; **9**-225
Planetoids. See **Asteroids**
Planets.
*Asteroids, **4**-419-22
*Earth, **4**-42-50
*Jupiter, **5**-20-24
*Mars, **4**-415-19
*Mercury, **4**-25-27
*Neptune. See *Uranus, Neptune and Pluto
*Pluto. See *Uranus, Neptune and Pluto
*Saturn, **5**-107-13
*Solar system, **3**-157-64
*Uranus, Neptune and Pluto, **5**-289-93
*Venus, **4**-28-31
Data, **10**-298
Galileo differentiates planets from stars, **3**-2
Meteorites reflect theoretical structure of, **6**-98
Movements of, **2**-316-17
Name, derivation of, **7**-223
Observation of, **6**-83-84
Origin, theories about, **9**-225
Pluto, discovery of, **9**-225
Radiations from, **9**-209-10
Reproduction of, by planetarium projectors,
2-399-400, *illus.*, 401
Search for, in solar eclipses, **3**-137
Sizes (relative) and distances from sun, **5**-20
Theories about formation of, *with illus.*, **1**-27-30
See also **Asteroids; Earth; Mars; Moon; Neptune;
Saturn; Solar system; Universe; Uranus;** etc.
Planing, tooling operation. **10**-110-11, *illus.*, 113
Planisphere, projection of celestial sphere and stars on
a plane. **6**-78
Plankton. 2-243; **4**-312; **6**-35-36
Diatoms form part of, **3**-224
Luminescence, **2**-185
Natural gas derived from fossilized plankton, **5**-97
Sharks that feed on, **4**-289
Planning, as function of engineers. **1**-227
Planographic (lithographic) printing. 1-197, 198, 266,
with diagram, 210-12
Plant ammoniates, nitrogenous vegetal materials.
Soil fertilizers, **2**-171
Plant bugs. *with illus.*, **3**-260-61
Plant diseases. *8-369-75
Bacterial diseases of plants, **2**-205
Weeds spread, **7**-111-12
Plant hormones. 3-50, 53-55
Plant kingdom. See **Botany**
Plant lice. See **Aphids**
Plant movements. *illus.*, **1**-47; **3**-52-54, *illus.*, 51, 53,
55; *illus.*, **6**-218a-d
Plant presses. *with illus.*, **10**-207
Plantations. Rubber, **6**-352-53
Plants. *1-45-50
*Adaptations, **3**-235-44; **6**-219-28

Plants *(continued)*
*Algae, **3**-214-24
*Amateur botany, **10**-203-12
*Bacteria, **3**-63-72
*Bioluminescence, **2**-182-91
*Cells, **2**-1-14
*Classification, **1**-287-91, 300-05
*Communities, **10**-181-90
*Defenses, **7**-75-83
*Diseases, **8**-369-75
*Fibers, vegetable, **4**-177-82
*Flowers, fruits and seeds, **4**-119-32
*Food storage in plants, **2**-415-20; **6**-52-59
*Fungi, **3**-22-32
*Germination, **5**-61-67
*Habitats, **10**-135-42
*Insect enemies, **9**-185-96
*Mosses, liverworts, club mosses, horsetails and ferns,
3-186-92
*Movements of plants, **6**-218a-d
*Photosynthesis, **3**-42a-d
*Physiology of, **3**-43-55
*Pollination by insects, **7**-239-48
*Propagation, **9**-7-15
*Roots, stems and leaves, **4**-62-75
*Seed and fruit dispersal, **5**-1-7
*Seed plants, **3**-397-406
*Soil, **2**-15-25, 203-11; **5**-25-30; **6**-136-42
*Fertility, **2**-163-72
*Soilless agriculture, **8**-34-37
*Terrariums, **5**-365-68
*Treatment, **10**-143-53
*Trees, **5**-257-66
*How to recognize trees, **5**-138-51
*Weeds, **7**-111-14
Air-pollution detection, use in, **3**-351-52, 354, *illus.*,
352
Allergic reaction to pollen from, **4**-259-60
Animals and plants, differences between, **1**-40-42
Animals dependent upon, **7**-8
Aquariums, plants suitable for, **8**-114
Beneficial to man, **1**-50
Cave-dwelling species, **5**-58, 59
Cell theory, development of, *with illus.*, **7**-160-61
Classification of, by Linnaeus, **3**-375-76
Coal formed from plants, *with illus.*, **1**-405-07
Coasts modified by, **8**-358, *illus.*, 359
Diseases, virus, **3**-452-53
Erosion of land curbed by plant cover, **8**-10
Fossil plants, *with illus.*, **6**-370, 371, 372
Ground water brought to surface by, **8**-331-32
Harmful to man, **1**-50
Industrial research on agricultural products, **1**-89,
illus., 91, 92
Insecticides from, **9**-188
Insects harming, **2**-410-14
Nitrogen cycle traced by Liebig. **5**-80
Nitrogen fixation, *with illus.*, **2**-209-11
Organic compounds derived from, **7**-263
Parasitic-worm infestations, **2**-159, *illus.*, 156
Peat formed from, *with illus.*, **1**-406-07
Preserved as fossils, **4**-387
Protected by insect-eating birds, **6**-341
Radiation affects, **10**-252, *illus.*, 253
Seasonal changes affect, **5**-409, *illus.*, 408
Soil as habitat of, *with illus.*, **2**-205-11
Soil organisms, *with illus.*, **2**-205-11
Struggle for existence among, **3**-225
Virus diseases of, **3**-451-53, 455, 456, 457, 458, *illus.*,
454, 456

Plants *(continued)*
See also **Agriculture; Biology; Cells; Evolution; Fertilizers; Plant diseases; Reproduction; Seeds; Soil**

Plaskon, plastic. Buttons made from, 7-210, *illus.,* 211

Plasma, blood. See **Blood plasma**

Plasma banks, stored blood plasma. 3-334

Plasma diagnostics. 1-178

Plasma instabilities. 1-178

Plasma membranes, cell surfaces. 2-2, 6, 7, 8, 425-26, *illus.,* 7

Plasmas, ionized gases. 1-173-78

Plasmodium, naked mass of noncellular protoplasm. *with illus.,* 3-25

Plasmodium malariae, parasitic protozoan. 8-365, 366
Life cycle of, 9-431-32; 10-34
Malaria caused by, 2-65-66

Plaster. Building material, 7-120-21

Plasticizers, additives. Plastics, used in manufacture of, 8-225-26

Plastics. *8-221-33
Aquariums, plastic covers for, 8-112
Building material, 7-128
Buttons made from, 7-210, 212, *illus.,* 211
Colloidal phenomena in manufacture of, *with illus.,* 5-303
Dynel fibers, *illus.,* 2-233
Farm products used in manufacture of, 9-292
Heat-resistant, for food containers, 4-155
Objects made of, *illus.,* 8-220c-d
Polyethylene balloon, *illus.,* 2-235
Printed circuits on plastic bases, *with illus.,* 6-50-51
Printing plates and molds of plastic, 1-207, 208
Teeth fillings made of, 5-136-37
Vinylite records, 7-369, *illus.,* 362

Plastids, cell structures. 2-9, *illus.,* 4, 9

Plate, steel. Manufacture and uses of, 1-349, *illus.,* 338

Plate girders, construction elements. *with illus.,* 2-334-35

Plate glass. Manufacture of, 3-311, *illus.,* 310-11, 314b-c

Plateaus. *6-109-13
Mountains formed from, 10-213
Tibetan, 10-22
See also **Physiography**

Platelets. See **Blood platelets**

Platen presses, in printing. *with diagram,* 1-209

Platens, typewriter cylinders. *with illus.,* 1-269-71

Plates (anodes).
Electron tubes, plates in, *with illus.,* 6-295-302
with illus., 6-295-302

Plates, dental. 5-135

Plates, photographic. 9-399, 400, 402, 403, 404

Plates, printing. 1-210-14, *with diagrams,* 207-08

Platforms, in oil derricks. 4-145, *diagrams,* 144

Platforms, island. 6-77

Plating. See **Electroplating**

Platinum (Pt), chemical element. Atomic number, 78; atomic weight, 195.09; melting point, 1,773.5° C.; boiling point, 4,300° C.; specific gravity, 21.37. White, soft, heavy metal; very malleable and ductile with high tensile strength. Discovered in 1735 in South America; name derived from Spanish *platina*: "little silver." Usually occurs free in nature, associated with other members of the platinum group. Very useful in electrical devices, as a catalyst in the chemical industries, in jewelry, dentistry, X-ray and laboratory apparatus, heating units and for many other purposes. See also 3-42

Platinum *(continued)*
Catalyst, use as, 2-229
Electrolytic use of, 5-89

Plato, Greek philosopher. 1-136-37

Platy soils. *with illus.,* 2-19

Platyhelminths, flatworms. *with illus.,* 2-153-54
Classification of, 1-292-93

Platypuses. The platypus, or duckbill (genus *Ornithorhynchus*), is a primitive, semiaquatic mammal of eastern Australia and Tasmania. Several of its skeletal and muscular features are reptile-like, and its body temperature is lower and varies more than that of other mammals. Adults do not possess true teeth. The platypus has webbed feet and a flattened tail; its muzzle forms a leathery, flattened bill and is a sensitive organ of touch. Soft and short fur covers the body. The platypus feeds on mollusks and other small aquatic animals, which it scoops from sand and mud by its bill. It lives in a burrow excavated in the bank of a stream, pond or lake. The female reproduces by laying two large-yolked, soft-shelled eggs in the burrow nest. The young nurse on milk secreted by specialized sweat glands on the female's belly. See also *illus.,* 1-299; 7-13, *illus.,* 12

Play. See **Exercise**

Playfair, John, Scottish mathematician and geologist. 4-396

Plecoptera, order of insects. 2-412-13

Pleiades, group of stars in Taurus. 1-335-36; 7-223; *illus.,* 9-362-63
Nebula in, 9-361

Pleistocene epoch, period of ice ages. 3-185; 6-374; 9-163, 171, 174
North-Pole shift during, 5-193, *illus.,* 194

Plesiosaurs, primitive marine reptiles. 1-392, *illus.,* 390

Pleurococcus. See **Protococcus**

Plexiglas, acrylic plastic. *with illus.,* 8-226

Plexuses, networks of nerves. 6-329, *illus.,* 319

Pliny the Elder (Gaius Plinius Secundus), Roman scholar and militarist. *with illus.,* 1-362-63
Luminous mollusks described by, 2-185

Pliny the Younger (Gaius Plinius Caecilius Secundus). Description of eruption of Vesuvius, 7-335-37

Pliocene epoch, time in earth's history. 6-374

Plotinus, Roman Neoplatonic philosopher. 1-368

Plough, name given to Big Dipper in England. See **Big Dipper**

Plovers, family of birds. 6-407-08, *illus.,* 408
Migration of golden plover, 9-420

Plowing.
Green-manure crops, 2-163-65
Soil moisture released by, 5-27
See also **Agriculture; Soil**

Plum curculios, insects. *with illus.,* 9-194

Plumage. See **Feathers**

Plumbago. See **Graphite**

Plume mosses. 3-188

Plumed quail. 6-333

Plums. Curculios attack, 9-194

Plungers, plumber's suction devices. *with illus.,* 7-220

Pluto, planet. *with diagram,* 5-292-93
Data, 10-298
Discovery of, 9-225

Plutonism, theory of earth formation. 4-396-97

Plutonium (Pu), chemical element. Atomic number, 94; atomic weight, 242(?). Radioactive metal. Discovered in 1940 at the University of California by Seaborg, McMillan, Kennedy and Wahl by the bombardment of uranium with deuterons in a cyclotron. Name derived from planet Pluto. The metal is highly electropositive and reacts with chlorine, bromine and iodine at mod-

Plutonium (continued)
erate temperatures. Used for the plutonium bomb.
  Atomic bombs, production of, 9-331
  Atomic energy, production of, 9-137-38
  Radioisotope-fueled thermoelectric generators, use in, 6-174

Plywood.
  Construction, use in, *illus.,* 4-268; 7-125, 128

Pneumatic caissons. 2-343, *illus.,* 344; 9-67-68

Pneumatic tools. 9-66, *illus.,* 61, 65
  Drill, measurement of noise produced by, *illus.,* 8-42
  See also **Guericke, Otto von**

Pneumatic troughs. *with illus.,* 4-353
  Oxygen and hydrogen gas, home preparation of, *with illus.,* 4-350-51

Pneumatic tubes. 9-66-67

Pneumatics, science dealing with mechanical properties of air and other gases. See **Air; Compressed air; Gases**

Pneumococci, bacteria. *illus.,* 8-363

Pneumonia. Bacteria that cause, *illus.,* 8-363

Pocket gophers, rodents. 8-163; 10-137, *illus.,* 140

Pods, dry fruits. *with illus.,* 4-130

Podsols, soil type. 2-22, *map,* 20-21

Pogson, N., English astronomer. 6-389

Pohutu Geyser, New Zealand. *illus.,* 8-291, 300b, 327

Point Ayliff meteorite, from South Africa. Age of, 6-95

"Point of no return," beyond which action is unprofitable. Ore dressing, 1-375-76

Pointers, dogs. 10-242

Points, geometric. *with illus.,* 3-429-30

Poison gases.
  Chlorine, 3-319
  Danger from, in home, 7-197
  Military use of, *with illus.,* 9-212-13

Poison ivy. *illus.,* 1-49; 7-76
  Allergic reaction to contact of, 4-260
  Fruits, *illus.,* 5-7
  How to recognize, 5-139, *illus.,* 138
  Spraying an infested field, *illus.,* 7-114

Poison oak. How to recognize, 5-139, *illus.,* 138

Poison sumac. How to recognize, 5-139, *illus.,* 138

Poisoning.
  First aid for, 10-10, 116
  Prevention of, in home, 7-197
  See also **Chemical warfare**

Poisoning, food.
  *Prevention through food preservation, 4-153-68

Poisonous fishes. 4-105

Poisonous insects. 2-409-10

Poisonous mushrooms. *with illus.,* 3-31-32

Poisonous plants. 1-50; 7-76, *illus.,* 77
  How to recognize, *with illus.,* 5-138-39
  Poison ivy, *illus.,* 1-49

Poisonous snakes. *with illus.,* 5-360-64

Poisons.
  Amphibians' venom, 5-162
  Bacterial toxins, body's defense against, 7-348-49
  Insects, 2-409, 411
  Nervous system, effects on, 6-330
  Nicotine as poison, 5-345
  Snake venom, 5-360
  Spider venom, 2-261, 264, 265, 266

Poland. Wieliczka salt mine, 5-316-17

Polar air masses. 9-223

Polar axis, of telescopes. 8-57

Polar bears. *with illus.,* 7-308-10

Polar centers, plant cell structures. 2-14

Polar continentals, air masses lying over polar lands. 2-95

Polar exploration and research. See **Antarctic; Arctic; International Geophysical Year; North Pole; South Pole**

Polar lights. See **Auroras**

Polar maritimes, air masses lying over polar oceans. 2-95

Polar orbits, parallel to earth's axis. *with diagram,* 8-127

Polar regions.
  Atmospheric circulation and phenomena over, 1-238, *with diagrams,* 242-44
  IGY investigations of, 5-190-91
  Weather stations in, *with illus.,* 6-174-75
  See also **North Pole; South Pole**

Polar winds, wind belts. 1-238; 2-94, *diagram,* 92

Polaris, star. 1-260, 264

Polaris missiles, American military rockets. *with illus.,* 4-114d; *illus.,* 9-382

Polarized light.
  Faraday's electromagnetic experiment, use in, 5-236
  Sugars affect, 4-78
  See **Plane-polarized light**

Polarizing monochromators, devices for producing monochromatic (one-color) images of sun. 3-104

Polaroid Land cameras. 9-410

Polecats. 8-174-75

Poles, of magnets. *with illus.,* 7-164-65

Poles, magnetic, of earth. *with diagrams,* 7-168-71

Poles, true. See **North Pole; Polar regions; South Pole**

Polestar (Polaris). 1-324-25, 330

Polhem, Christopher, Swedish engineer and inventor. 6-383

Poliomyelitis. 6-330; *with illus.,* 10-129-31, 133
  Vaccination against, *illus.,* 7-350-51
  Virus of, 3-453; *illus.,* 8-363

Political arithmetic. 3-21

Pollarding, method of trimming trees. *illus.,* 10-145

Pollen. 3-405-06, *illus.,* 398; *with illus.,* 4-124, 125, 126, 127, 128
  Allergies caused by, 4-259-60
  Collection of, by bees, 3-367
  Insect distribution of, *with illus.,* 7-239-48

Pollen baskets, of bees. 3-367

Pollen brushes, of bees. 3-367

Pollen tubes. 3-397, 406

Pollination. 3-406, *illus.,* 405; *with illus.,* 4-125-27
  Bumblebee pollinating hibiscus, 8-frontispiece
  Self-pollination, prevention of, 7-240-41

Pollio, Marcus Vitruvius, Roman architect. 1-363

Pollution.
  *Air pollution, 3-349-56
    Cancer may be caused by, 8-268
  Ground-water pollution, prevention of, *with illus.,* 8-332
  Streams and rivers polluted by sewage, 5-328; 6-6
  Water pollution, elimination of, 2-276-82, *illus.,* 278-79, 282-83

"Polly-noses," samaras. 5-150

Polo, Marco. Oil fields in Asia described by, 4-140-41

Polonium (Po), chemical element. Atomic number, 84; atomic weight, approximately 210. Radioactive; half life, 138 days; gives off alpha particles, passing to radioactive lead, radium G. Discovered by Mme. Curie in 1898; named for Poland, her native land. Present in all uranium minerals; recovered from uranium residues or from discarded radon tubes.
  Discovery of, 8-413
  Radioisotope-fueled thermoelectric generators, polonium 210 used in, 6-174

Polyamide resins, plastics. *with illus.,* 8-228

Polycarbonate resin, plastic. 8-228

Polycythemia, overproduction of red blood cells. 3-331
Polyester resins, plastics. 8-228
Polyethylene, plastic. 8-231, with illus., 228
    Balloon of, illus., 2-235
Polyhedral angles, in solid geometry. with illus., 3-441
Polymerization, molecular synthesis. Petroleum refining
    uses, 4-148
Polymers, chains of molecules. 7-270
    Natural rubber as polymer, 6-357
    Nucleoproteins, 9-385-86
    Plastics, with diagram, 8-222
    Synthetic rubbers as, 8-185
Polymethylmethacrylate, acrylic plastic.   with illus.,
    8-226
Polymorphism. Insects display, 2-408-09
    See also Ants; Bees; Dimorphism; Wasps
Polynesian geographical race. with illus., 8-217
Polynesian local races. 8-219
Polyneuritis, alcoholic, disease of nervous system.
    4-411
Polynomial nomenclature, many-term naming of living
    things. 1-288
Polyphemus moths. 3-200; illus., 9-190-91
Polyploidy, condition favoring development of new
    species. 6-280
Polypodies, ferns. illus., 3-188
Polyporus Hanedai, luminous fungus. illus., 2-182
Polypropylene, plastic. 8-228
Polyps. with illus., 2-148-51
Polysaccharides, complex carbohydrates. 4-51-52, 76-
    78; 7-276
    Cells' use of, 2-5, 11
Polystyrenes, plastics. 8-228-29, 233
Polytrichum, genus of mosses. illus., 3-186
Pomes, fleshy fruits. with illus., 4-130
Pompeii, Italy.
    Breadmaking in, 9-294
    Destruction of, with illus., 7-335-37
    See also Volcanoes
Ponderators, big atom smashers. 4-217
Ponderosa pine trees. illus., 3-400; 5-141, illus., 143
Pons, Jean-Louis, French astronomer.
    Comets discovered by, 5-399
Pons, part of hindbrain. 6-326, illus., 325
    See also Hindbrain
Pons-Brooks' comet. 5-397
Pons-Winnecke's comet. 5-392
Pont du Gard Aqueduct, France. 2-332, illus., 333
Ponte Vecchio (Old Bridge), Florence. 2-333
Pontifex Maximus, Roman official. 10-173-74
Pontoon bridges. See Floating bridges
Pony, fur. 7-238
Poor Law Commission.
    Sanitary reform in England, contributions to, 9-37
Poplar trees. with illus., 5-144
    Leaves of, illus., 4-72
Popocatepetl, dormant volcano in Mexico.   illus.,
    8-300d
Popov, Aleksandr Stepanovich, Russian inventor.
    6-245
Poppies.
    Adaptations for seed dispersal, with illus., 5-2
    Fruits, illus., 4-131
    Seeds, illus., 5-62
Poppy, opium. 5-403, illus., 402
Population. *3-225-34
    Density of population, table, 3-232
    Figures for representative areas, 3-231
    Overpopulation, danger of, 4-403-04; 9-328

Population (continued)
    Soilless agriculture may help meet needs of growing
        population, 8-34, 36
    See also Malthus, Thomas Robert
Population analysis.   Statistical method, development
    of, 3-21
"Population explosion." 6-12; 9-328
Populations, of living things. 6-275, 276, 277, illus.,
    279
Porcelain. 7-396
    Teeth fillings made of, 5-136
Porcupine grass.   Spikelet of, illus., 5-5
Porcupines, rodents. 8-163-64
    Adaptation for defense, with illus., 3-239
    Pets, 7-22
Pore fungi. with illus., 3-30
Pores.   Cell membranes contain, 2-7
Pores of skin, sweat-gland openings. 2-176, illus.,
    173, 177
Pores, plant.   Seed dispersal through, with illus., 5-2
Porifera, sponges. *2-146-48
    Classification of, 1-292
    See also Sponges
Pork, flesh of hogs used for food.
    Cuts of, with illus., 5-170-71
    Preparation of, with illus., 5-166-68
Pork tapeworms. 2-155
Porosity.
    Petroleum trapped in porous rocks, with diagram, 4-
        142-43
    Rocks, 8-322-23
Porphyry, igneous rock formation.   2-82; with illus.,
    3-423; 9-308
Porpoises, aquatic mammals. 7-189, illus., 185
Port, sweet wine. 4-168
Port Jackson sharks. 4-287
    Unchanged for millions of years, 6-283
Portable radio receivers. with illus., 3-98
Portable typewriters. with illus., 1-273
Portachuelo Pass, Venezuela.
    Insect mass movement through, 9-432
Portal mines.   Ores, with diagram, 1-371
Portland cement. 7-123
    Building, use in, 3-122
    Highway construction, 3-301-02
Portraits.   Photographic, 9-400-01, 402, 414, illus.,
    399-401
Portugal.
    Lisbon earthquake, 9-110
    World exploration, contributions to, 2-364, 366
Portuguese men-of-war. 2-150
Positions.   Scientific fields, available in, with illus.,
    10-197-202
Positions in space.
    Parity law of physics and, with illus., 7-108
Positive checks, against population growth. 3-229-30
Positive electricity.   1-398; 4-360; 6-120
Positives, photographic. 9-399, 401, 410, 413, 414,
    diagram, 411
    Microfilm, 10-71
Positrons, atomic particles.   1-313, table, 314; 9-128,
    132
    Cosmic-ray showers, components of, 8-396, 397
Post coaches.   See Stagecoaches
Postnatal development.   Pre-man, 1-66
Postulate of parallels. 9-282
Postulates, mathematical assumptions.   3-429
Posture of the body.
    Erect stance important factor in man's evolution,
        1-65
    Health affected by, 10-82, illus., 76

Posture of the body (continued)
  Muscles help maintain, 3-212
  Sleep, posture during, illus., 6-144
  Space travel, best posture for, 10-48
Pot furnaces, used in glassmaking. 3-309
Potash, name given to several carbonates. 3-169
  Dead Sea as source of, illus., 7-65
Potassium (K), chemical element. Atomic number, 19; atomic weight, 39.102; melting point, 62.3° C.; boiling point, 760° C.; specific gravity, 0.87. Alkali metal; soft, bright, silvery, very compressible, low-melting, highly reactive. Discovered in 1807 by Davy; name derived from English word "potash." Widely distributed in the earth's crust, found in potash and sea deposits. Never occurs in pure state; obtained by electrolysis of the oxide. Potassium compounds are used for soaps, fertilizers, matches, hard glass, explosives, medicines and other products. See also 3-168-69
  Diet requires, 4-59
  Interstellar space contains, 9-363
  Protoplasm, function of potassium ions in, 2-6
  Salts of, in the sea, with chart, 6-31
  Soil potassium available to plants, 2-24, 169-71
Potassium chloride (muriate of potassium).
  Soil fertilizer, used as, 2-171
Potassium ferrocyanide. Experiments and tricks with, 7-179, with diagram, 177
Potassium hydroxide. 4-339
  Protein, used in testing for, 7-136
Potassium nitrate. Experiments and tricks with, with diagram, 7-179-80
Potassium sulfocyanate (thiocyanate). Experiments and tricks with, with diagram, 7-177
Potassium thiocyanate (sulfocyanate). Experiments and tricks with, with diagram, 7-177
Potato virus X. 3-452-53, 456
Potatoes.
  Blight (late) of, 3-25; 8-370
  Food storage in, 2-420
  Starch from, 4-77, 78
  Tubers in soil, illus., 4-68
  Water required by, 5-25
Potatoes, sweet. Rot caused by mold, 3-26
Potential, electrical. See **Electrical potential**
Potential energy. with illus., 1-82-83
  Kinetic energy, distinguished from, 6-247
Potter, Nebraska. Giant hailstones found in, 2-357
Potter wasps. with illus., 2-412d
Potter's wheel. 7-393-94, 401
Pottery. *7-393-407
  Ancient Greek, illus., 1-131
  Colloidal phenomena in, with illus., 5-302-03
  Dating pottery by thermoluminescence, with illus., 6-375, 376
Pottos, lemurlike primates. 9-265
Pouched mammals. See **Marsupials**
Pouched mice, marsupials. 7-427
Poudre B, smokeless powder. 8-278, 280
Poulsen, Valdemar, Danish inventor. 7-368
Poultry bugs. 3-260
Powder. Flaming-powder trick, with diagram, 7-174-75
Powdered coal.
  Ignition of powdered coal and coal dust, 2-229
  Locomotives, use in, 1-89, diagram, 90
Powdery mildews. 3-28
Powell, John Wesley, American geologist and explorer. 7-29
Power.
  *Atom smashers, 9-241-49
  *Atomic energy, 9-120-42

Power (continued)
  *Electricity, 6-49-51, 119-35; 9-226-40
  *Electronics, 6-295-303; 8-84-89; 10-102-04, 168-70
  *Forces in liquids and gases, 2-30-42
  *Heat engines, 4-80-92
  *Magnetism, 7-162-72
  *Matter and energy, 1-79-86
  *Radioisotope-fueled thermoelectric generators, 6-172-75
  *Simple machines, 3-56-62
  *Solar battery, 7-103-06
  *Turbines, 5-305-12
  *Ultrasonics, 8-103-10
  Agricultural machinery, 9-292
  Aircraft, power for, 6-178, 182, 187-88
  Electric power in nineteenth century, with illus., 5-247
  Electrical transmission of, illus., 9-234b-c
  Industrial, during Industrial Revolution, with illus., 4-39-41
  Nuclear reactors as sources, 9-358, illus., 357
  Sound waves, 5-118-19, illus., 118
  Submarine power plants, 5-31-37
  Volcanoes yield, 8-304
  See also **Coal; Diesel-electric power; Electricity; Engines; Locomotives, steam; Steam; Turbines; Water power**
Power-dive subs, used in scuba diving. with illus., 6-26b
Power-driven tools. *10-105-13
Power looms. Invention of, with illus., 4-37-38
Power plants. See **Diesel engines; Electric Generators; Gasoline engines; Steam engines**, etc.
Powers, James, American inventor.
  Punched-card tabulating system developed by, 9-144
Powers, of numbers. 1-158
  Squares and cubes, with diagrams, 4-424
PPI. See **Plan Position Indicator (PPI)**
Pragmatism. See **James, William**
Prairie chickens. 6-337, illus., 334, 336
  Courtship behavior of, with illus., 5-418b
Prairie dogs, rodents. 8-162-63
  Home building, 9-6
Prairie fires. 2-350
Prairie soils, soil type. 2-22
Praseodymium (Pr), chemical element. Atomic number, 59; atomic weight, 140.907; melting point, 940° C.; specific gravity, 6.5. Yellowish rare-earth metal. Isolated in 1885 by Von Welsbach; name derived from Greek prasinos: "green," and didymos: "twin." Found, with other rare earths, in monazite, cerite and allanite; usually separated by fractional crystallization, and prepared by electrolysis of the fused chloride. See **Neodymium.**
Pratt, Joseph, British clergyman and mathematician. 7-32
Praying mantes. See **Mantes, praying**
"Preacher birds." 6-64
Pre-Cambrian era, time in earth's history. 1-386; 6-370
  Ice ages of, 3-183
Precancerous conditions. 8-269-70
Precast concrete. 7-124
Precession, change in direction of axis of rotating body.
  Earth's, 1-264; with diagram, 4-49-50
  Location of stars affected by, 7-224
Precious stones. See **Diamonds; Gems**; etc.
Precipitates, chemical. See **Precipitation, chemical**
Precipitation, water deposition on earth. 1-245
  Ground, effects on, 8-9-11
  Ground water derived from, 8-322
  Measuring and recording, 1-251, with diagram, 321-22, illus., 248, 250, diagram, 316
  Mountains, affect, 10-26-27

Precipitation (continued)
Radioactive fallout and, 9-355
World distribution of, with diagram, 2-247-49
See also **Rain; Snow**
Precipitation, chemical.
Examples of, with illus., 4-230-31
Precipitators. See **Electrostatic precipitators.**
Predators, animals that prey on other animals.   10-185-86
Predictions of weather. See **Forecasting**
Preforming, rough molding.   Plastics, 8-230, 233
Pregnancy. 8-23
Diet during, with table, 5-272-73
Preheating. Plastics, 8-233
Prehistoric times.
*Coelacanths, 4-196-99
*Geological time scale of earth's history, 6-369-74
Human populations in, 3-226-27
Language of primitive man, 1-107-08
Mathematics in, with illus., 1-149-50; 3-427
Pottery in, 7-393
Prehistoric man, study of, with illus., 9-21-30
Tunnel-digging in, 2-43
See also **Evolution; Fossils; Geology; Paleontology**
Prejudices.   Scientific progress obstructed by, 3-8
Premolars (bicuspids), teeth.   3-235, 236; 5-129, illus., 132, table, 130
"Prenatal influences."   8-22
Prenderol, drug.   5-345
Preparation plants, for coal.   with illus., 1-415-16
Prescriptions, medical.   10-63-64
Preservation of food.   *4-153-68
Quick-freezing, illus., 4-318-19
Preservation of offspring.
*Seed plant dispersal, 5-1-7
Adaptations of animals and plants for, with illus., 3-240-44
Press brakes, machine tools.   illus., 10-106
Presses, in paper manufacture.   illus., 4-374a
Presses, printing.   1-197-99, with diagrams, 208-14
Pressing.
Glass products shaped by, 3-311, illus., 314a, 314b-c
Tooling operation, 10-107, illus., 106
Pressure.
*Pressures within liquids and gases, 2-30-42
Adaptation to, by deep-sea organisms, with illus., 10-142
Air circulation affected by air pressure, with diagrams, 1-242-44; 2-89-91, 93, 95-96
Air pressure, experiments with, with illus., 7-220-22
Ammonia synthesis requires high pressures, with diagram, 2-231
Atmospheric
Experiments with, 1-233-34, illus., 234-35; with illus., 2-324-29; with illus., 7-220
Isobaric lines indicate air pressures, 9-223
Measuring and recording, 1-318-19, with diagrams, 247, 249, 254, diagrams, 316, 320
Boiling of liquids and, with diagrams, 1-168-69
Cartesian diver illustrates changes in, with diagram, 1-281
Deep-sea organisms' adaptation to, with illus., 10-142
Diamond synthesis requires high pressure, 4-275-76
Experiments on, with carbon dioxide, with illus., 7-132
Experiments with, with illus., 7-220-22
Gases: relation to volume and temperature, with diagram, 1-165-66, 172; 3-416
Liquids, relation to boiling point of, 3-418
Maintenance in high-altitude planes, 6-191
Oceanic, 6-35
Oil-well pressures, 4-143, 146

Pressure (continued)
Plastic products formed by, with diagrams, 8-230-33
Respiration, air pressure in, with illus., 4-204-07
Seed dispersal by, 5-2
Water animals use changes in, with illus. and diagrams, 1-280-81
Water pressure, experiments with, with illus., 7-221-22
Water pressure on dams, 8-316
See also **Atmospheric pressure**
Pressure, population. 3-228-29
Pressure, sense of.   with illus., 7-304
Pressure anemometers, wind gauges.   1-249
Pressure compounding turbines.   5-307
Pressure cookers.   3-418
Canning, used in, with illus., 4-156-57
Safety precautions with, 7-196
Pressure gauges.   See **Gauges**
Pressure vessels, for nuclear reactor.   illus., 9-120
Pressure waves, rhythmic waves in fluid medium.
Sound, with illus., 5-114-28
Sound waves produced in air by moving bodies, with diagrams, 10-228-32
Pressures, steam-engine.   Ships, 4-111
Pressurized-water reactors.
Savannah, pressurized-water reactor for, with illus., 4-114b-c
Pre-stressed concrete. 3-122
Prevailing westerlies, wind belts.   1-244, diagram, 243; 2-93-94, diagram, 92
Prevention, accident.   *7-190-98
Preventive checks, against population growth.   3-229-30
Preventive medicine.   See **Medicine, preventive**
Preying mantes.   See **Mantes, praying**
Priapuloidea, phylum of worms.   1-295
Pribilof Islands, Alaska.   Home of fur seals, illus., 6-14; with illus., 7-89
Price Tower, Bartlesville, Oklahoma.   illus., 3-124
Prickles, defensive devices of plants.   7-78, 80
Prickly pears. 7-113-14
Priestley, Joseph, English clergyman and scientist.
Electricity, work on, 4-361
Oxygen discovered by, with illus., 4-355
Respiration of animals and plants, work on, 3-380
Rubber, experiments with, 6-351
Primary batteries.   with illus., 5-94-95
Primary bow, of rainbows.   7-279, illus., 278
Primary coils, in electrical transformers.   with illus., 6-134-35
Primary colors. 7-285-86, illus., 287
Maxwell's color triangle, 9-412-13, diagram, 412
Primary cosmic rays.   See **Cosmic rays**
Primary roots, of plants.   with illus., 4-62-63
Primary treatment of sewage. 5-330-31, illus., 330
Primary (P) waves of earthquakes. 4-171, 173, illus., 170; 9-107, 114
Primates, order of mammals.
*Apes, monkeys and kin, 9-250-65
*Human biology, 1-57-66
Fossil primates, illus., 6-374
Rise of, 1-396
Summary, with illus., 7-14
See also **Man**
Primitive chordates (protochordates).   *4-1-4
Primitive Germanic, ancient ancestral language.   1-118
Primitive peoples.
Boats and ships of, 4-106
Language and writing, development of, 1-107-08, 111-15, illus., 112

Primitive peoples (continued)
Populations of, 3-225-28
Study of, *with illus.,* 9-21-30
Time measurements by, 1-17, *illus.,* 18
See also **Indians, American**
Primitive quadrupeds. *with illus.,* 4-384
Primroses, flowering plants.
Flowers of, *illus.,* 4-126
Princeton, American naval steamship. 4-111
Principles. See **Laws**
Printed circuits. *6-49-51
Printing, photographic process. 9-402, 410, 413, *diagrams,* 411
Printing, typographic process. *1-196-214
Color, *illus.,* 7-284b
History
Middle Ages, *with illus.,* 2-313-14
Nineteenth century, *with illus.,* 6-381
See also **Gutenberg, Johann; Newspapers**
Printing inks. 1-209, 211, 213-14
Printing presses. 1-197-99, *with diagrams,* 208-14
Hand lithograph, *illus.,* 1-204a
Medieval, *illus.,* 2-314
Photo-offset, *illus.,* 1-204a-d
Rotary press, invention of, *with illus.,* 6-381
Prints, leaf. Preparation of, *with illus.,* 10-209-10
Prism spectroscopes. 7-279, *illus.,* 280
Prismatic (columnar, or pillarlike) subsoils. *with illus.,* 2-19
Prisms, common solids. *with illus.,* 3-441-42
Light refracted as it passes through, *with illus.,* 7-277, 279; *with illus.,* 8-178-79
Spectrum analysis through use of, 5-85, *illus.,* 86
Pritchard, Thomas, English bridgebuilder. 2-333
Prizes. Nobel Prize winners in science, 10-299-307
Pro-men, forerunners of men. 1-65-66
Probability theory.
Binomial series used to calculate probabilities, 2-79-80, *illus.,* 78, 79
Development of, in seventeenth century, 3-21
Genetics, use in, 1-78
Problem-solving.
Equations used to solve problems, 2-72-73
Psychology of, 9-317
Problems, arithmetical. 4-453-54
Problems, scientific. Experiments and observations solving, 8-70-72, 74-77
Proboscidea, order of mammals. *with illus.,* 7-16
See also **Elephants**
Proboscis monkeys. 9-257, *illus.,* 255
Procaine, anesthetic. 5-402
Dentistry, use in, 5-136
Process color printing. See **Color printing**
Proctor, Richard Anthony, English astronomer.
Mars, map of, *illus.,* 4-419
Procyon, star in Canis Minor. 1-337
Producer gas, industrial fuel. *with illus.,* 1-418
Producers, in ecosystems. 10-184
Production.
*Design of products, 10-117-26
Automation, effects of, 10-237-38
Engineers engaged in, 1-227
Industrial Revolution, production during, *with illus.,* 4-35-41
Petroleum and petroleum products, 4-148-52
Radiation thickness gauges cut cost of, 9-46
See also **Economics; Labor**
Productivity, soil. *2-163-72
Products, chemical. Equations representing formation of, 2-226, 230, *diagram,* 226

Profiles, soil. 2-17-18, *illus.,* 17
Profiles, topographic. Ocean bottom, 6-71
Progesterone, hormone. 8-22, 23
Prognostic charts, weather charts. 1-254
Progress, in evolutionary development. *with illus.,* 6-284-85
Progressions. See **Arithmetic progressions; Geometric progressions**
Project Apollo, United States moon program. 9-382-83; *illus.,* 10-52-53
Project Bumper No. 5, early American multistage rocket. 10-46
Project Mercury, United States space program. 9-382; *illus.,* 10-40-41
Projectiles.
Galileo's work on, 3-4
Rockets, *with illus.,* 10-1-4
Projection, of images. Vision experiments with photographic transparencies, 8-180, *diagrams,* 179
Projectors.
Microfilm, *with diagram,* 10-70-71
Reproducing heavenly bodies in the Zeiss Planetarium, *with illus.,* 2-398-401
Photographic, 7-261
Projects. Definition and description of, 1-139-40
Projects and experiments.
*Air, experiments with, 2-323-31
*Animals, study of, 10-254-64
*Ants, keeping colony of, 3-393-96
*Astronomy for amateurs, 6-78-86
*Telescope making, 9-365-74
*Birds, attracting, 6-341-49
*Chemical magic, 7-173-80
*Chemistry for amateurs, 4-221-31, 343-52; 7-129-36
*Electricity, experiments with, 6-286-94
*Fish as pets, 8-112-16
*Heat, experiments with, 4-17-24
*Insect collecting, 3-153-56
*Introduction, 1-139-42
*Light, experiments with, 8-117-24
*Magnetism, experiments with, 8-142-50
*Mathematical recreations, 4-443-54
*Mechanics, experiments in, 7-214-22
*Meteorology for amateurs, 1-315-22
*Mineral and rock collecting, 9-300-09
*Nature photography, 6-311-16
*Plants, study of, 10-203-12
*Science competitions for youth, 8-67-77
*Shell collecting, 2-99-104
*Sound, experiments with, 5-221-30
*Terrariums, 5-365-68
*Trees, how to recognize, 5-138-51
*Water, experiments with, 8-1-8
*Wild animals as pets, 7-17-26
Prometaphase, stage of cell division. 2-14, *illus.,* 13
Promethium (Pm), chemical element. Atomic number, 61; atomic weight, uncertain, probably around 147. Discovered in 1947 by Marinsky and Glendenen at Oak Ridge, Tennessee, by fission of uranium and neutron bombardment of neodymium. Named after Prometheus, figure in Greek mythology.
Prominences, feature of sun's atmosphere. *illus.,* 1-23; *with illus.,* 3-102, 106
Promontory, Utah. 1-182
Pronghorned antelopes (pronghorns). 8-235; 9-270, *illus.,* 272-73
Pronghorns. See **Pronghorned antelopes**
Prontosil, medical drug. 9-33; 10-127
Proof presses. *illus.,* 1-196
Proofing, breadmaking operation. *with diagram,* 9-297, *diagram,* 298

Proofs, trial printings from type or plates. 1-199, 206, 208, 210, 212, 214, *illus.,* 196

Prop roots. 4-65

Propagation, plant. *Artificial, 9-7-15
See also **Reproduction**

Propane, a methane hydrocarbon. 7-268
Graphic and structural formulas, 5-79

Propellants, explosives. 8-278

Propeller shafts, for automobiles. 2-141

Propellers. Airplane propellers, 6-187-88
Wind-tunnel propellers, *with diagram,* 10-233
See also **Screw propellers**

Proper motions, of stars. 1-264; *with illus.,* 7-224-25

Properties.
*Matter, properties of, 5-369-76
Glass, 3-312-16, *illus.,* 314d, 316
Substances, properties of, 1-85-86

Prophase, stage of cell division. 2-14, *illus.,* 13

Propjets. 6-195

Propolis, bee cement. 3-367

Proportion, inverse. 2-315

Prospecting.
*Scientific prospecting, 7-354-61
Natural gas, *with illus.,* 5-99-100
Ores, *with illus.,* 1-370
Petroleum, 4-144-45, *diagram,* 143

Prostate gland, gland surrounding the urethra. 8-21, *illus.,* 20

Protactinium (Pa), chemical element. Atomic number, 91; atomic weight, 231(?). Radioactive element; half life, 3.43×10^4 years. Forms actinium by losing alpha particle. Discovered in 1917; later prepared from its pure pentoxide by Grosse in 1934.

Protective adaptations. Insects, 2-409-10
Mammals, 7-11

Protective coloration. Insects, 2-409-10, *illus.,* 410-11
Mammals, showing, 7-11
Seasonal changes and, 5-413, *illus.,* 412

Proteins.
Balanced diet, content in, 5-268, 269, 271, 272
Blood proteins, 3-326
Bread, 9-299
Chemical structure of, 7-275; *with diagram,* 9-383-86
Daily requirements and sources of, *table,* 4-55-57
Deaminization of proteins takes place in liver, 5-14
Digestion and assimilation of, 2-10-11
Endocrine control of protein metabolism, 5-18, 19
Essential food elements, *with illus.,* 4-53-54
Meat as important source of, 5-163, illus., 172
Muscle proteins, 3-205
Nitrogen in, 3-318
Older persons need, 8-82
Plants, found in, 2-417, 418
Plastics from, 8-222, 223, 227
Protoplasm, protein content of, 1-43; 2-3, 5-7
Recovery by colloidal action, 5-302
Test for, 7-136
Viruses, proteins of, 3-453, 455-57
See also **Fibrinogen; Globulins**

Proterozoic era. See **Pre-Cambrian era**

Prothalli, sex-cell-bearing fern plants. 3-191, *illus.,* 188

Prothorax, forepart of insect chest. *illus.,* 2-403

Prothrombin, blood-clotting protein. 3-330, 331
Vitamin K essential in formation of, 5-48

Protochordates. See **Primitive chordates**

Protococcus, genus of green algae. 3-218, *illus.,* 42d, 216

Proton-proton reaction.
Solar energy derived from? 3-111

Proton synchrotrons, atom smashers. 9-249

Protonemata (singular, **protonema**), primary growth stage of moss gametophytes. 3-187

Protons, atomic particles. 1-310-11, *with diagrams,* 312, 313, *table,* 314; 6-286; 9-126, 132
Acceleration of, *illus.,* 4-342b-c; 9-247
Discovery of, 8-416
Equivalent to hydrogen ions in acids, 4-338
Primary cosmic rays made up of, 8-397

Protoplasm.
*Structure and function of cells, 2-1-14
Bacteria, protoplasm of, 3-64
Composition of, 1-43
Living things, characteristics of, 1-37
Nature of, *with illus.,* 2-287-92
Nitrogen in, 3-318
Organic substances contained in, 7-275

Protospongia, colony of one-celled animals. 2-63

Protozoans. *2-58-66
Ameba, *illus.,* 1-42
Bacteria, formerly grouped with, 3-63
Classification of, 1-292
Luminous, 2-183, 185
Malarial parasites, life cycle of, 9-431-32
Marine deposits made up of shells of, *with illus.,* 6-33
Termites, partnership with, 10-188
See also **Leeuwenhoek, Anton von**

Protractors, devices for measuring angles. *with illus.,* 3-431

Protura, order of insects. 2-412

Proust, Joseph-Louis, French chemist. 5-74

Prout, William, English physician. 5-75
Atomic particles, ideas about, 9-121

Provitamins D. 5-46

Proxima Centauri, star in Centaurus. 1-337

Pruning. Methods, *with illus.,* 10-147-50, *illus.,* 149

Prussian Tables, astronomical tables. 3-5

Prussic acid. 7-76

Przewalski's horses. See **Mongolian ponies**

Pseudoplasmodium, elongated mass of slime mold cells. *with illus.,* 6-218a

Pseudopods. 2-12, 60, 64, 65
White blood cells may display, 3-328-29

Pseudospheres. *diagram,* 4-439

Psilopsida, phylum of land plants. 1-301

Psittacosislike microorganisms. 1-40; 3-458

Psychiatry. *9-197-205
Background of, *with illus.,* 9-96-104
Neurology, relation to, 6-330
Tranquilizers in treatment of mentally ill, *with illus.,* 5-377-79

Psychics. Psychic phenomena, study of, 9-57

Psychoanalysis. 9-202
Development of theory of, *with illus.,* 9-96-102
Psychiatry distinguished from, 9-197

Psychoanalytic theory of sleep. 6-149

Psychological conflict. 4-410

Psychology. *9-310-22
*Animal intelligence, 2-26-29
*Nervous system, 6-317-330
Color, psychology of, 4-270-71; *illus.,* 7-284d
History
Nineteenth and twentieth centuries, *with illus.,* 9-47-57
Freud's contributions to, *with illus.,* 9-96-102
Intelligence tests, *illus.,* 9-198
Mind development in human growth, 8-97-100
See also **Brain; Instincts; Mental illness; Mind; Nerves; Nervous system; Sensations; Spencer, Herbert**

Psychoneuroses, mental illnesses. 9-202

Psychopathic personality. 9-199-200

Psychoses, severe mental illnesses. 9-201-03

Psychosurgery, for relief of mental illness. 9-204
Psychotherapy, mental treatment of illness.
  Alcoholism treated by, 4-413
Psychrometers, humidity gauges. 1-249-50, with diagram, 320-21, illus., 248
Psyllas. Pear psyllas, with illus., 9-194
PT boats. illus., 9-69
Ptarmigans, birds. 6-335, illus., 333
  Snowy owls prey on, 6-165
  Willow ptarmigans change color with seasons, with illus., 5-413
PTC. See Phenyl-thio-carbamide
Pteranodon, primitive flying reptile. 1-394
Pterodactyls, primitive flying reptiles. 1-393, 394, illus., 393
Pteropod ooze, marine deposit. 6-33
Pteropsida, phylum of plants. 1-302-05
Pterotype, early writing machine. 1-266
Pteroylglutamic acid. See Folic acid
Ptiliidae, family of beetles. 3-348
Ptolemaic astronomy. 1-358-59, illus., 360
  Attacked by Galileo, 3-4
  Revised by Al-Battani, Arab astronomer, 2-299
Ptolemy, Claudius, Alexandrian astronomer, mathematician and geographer. 1-358-59, illus., 360
  Stars arranged according to brightness by, 6-389
Ptolemy I Soter, Egyptian pharaoh. with illus., 1-355-56
Ptolemy III, Egyptian pharaoh.
  Calendar reform, 10-172
Ptomaine poisoning. 4-153
Ptyalin, digestive enzyme. 4-323
Puberty. Brown bears, 7-311
  Critical stage in human development, 8-98-99
  Primates, 9-260
Pubis, bone of hip. illus., 1-148b; 3-81, 82, illus., 75
Public bakeries. Rome, Ancient, 9-294
Public health.
  *Sewage disposal, 5-326-36
  *Waste disposal, 5-326-36
  *Water supply, 2-270-86
  Cancer: causes, treatment and prevention, with illus., 8-265-72
  Drug addiction, treatment of, with illus., 5-406-07
  Nursing and, 10-56-57
  Red Cross organization, founding of, 7-389
  Twentieth-century developments in public-health movement, with illus., 9-36-42
  See also Infectious diseases; Insects; Mosquitoes
Public health agencies. 9-41-42, illus., 40
  Canada, 9-41, 42, illus., 40
  International, 9-42
  United States, 9-41, 42
Public ownership. See Economics
Public transportation. Early forms of, with illus., 1-104-05
Publishing. Microfilming in, with illus., 10-72
  See also Newspapers; Printing
Puddling process. Development of, in steelmaking, 6-383
Puerperal fever. Bacteria that cause, illus., 9-73
  Developments in control of, with illus., 7-374-75
Puerperal period, period following childbirth.   8-33
Puffballs, fungi. with illus., 3-30
Pulleys, simple machines. with illus., 3-61-62
  Bird wings, examples of pulleys in, with illus., 1-284-85
  Homemade versions of, with illus., 7-216-17
Pullman, George M., American industrialist. 1-187
Pullman cars. 1-187
Pulmonary artery, leading to lung. illus., 1-148f
Pulmonary tuberculosis. 9-176-77, 180-83, illus., 178, 181
Pulmonary vein, leading from lung. illus., 1-148f

Pulmonic circulation, blood circulation. 3-382
  Blood clot in pulmonary artery, 3-332
  See also Circulation of blood
Pulp, tooth tissue. 5-129, 131, illus., 134-35
Pulp, wood. illus., 4-347a
  Used in papermaking, with illus., 4-365-71
Pulsating variables, stars. 6-268; 7-47-48, 50
Pulsation theory, accounting for changes in Cepheid variables. 7-50
Pulse. 3-387
  Counting of, with illus., 10-58
  Hibernating animals, pulse rate of, 5-410
  Rate decreases during sleep, 6-147
  Rate in health, 10-76
Pulverizing, in ore dressing. with diagrams, 1-371-72
Pumas. illus., 3-236; 8-210, illus., 209
Pumping stations. Petroleum, illus., 10-236
Pumps.
  Air pumps, with illus., 2-40; with illus., 9-59-60
  Automobile fuel pumps, 2-135
  City water supplies, pumps for, 2-34
  Homemade water pump, with illus., 8-6-7
  Jet water pumps, with illus., 2-35-36
  Lift pumps, with illus., 2-37-38
  Living, with illus., 1-277-79
  Natural gas, compressor stations for, 5-103-04
  Petroleum industry, use in, 4-146, diagram, 144
  Sewage-disposal systems, pumps in, 5-328
  Vacuum pumps, with illus., 2-40-41
  Water supply, 2-284-86, with illus., 274-75, illus., 284, 286
  Well water brought up by, 8-195
  See also Machinery
Puna, Hawaiian volcano. illus., 8-300c
Punched-card computers. 9-149
Punching, tooling operation. 10-108
Punkies, midges. 3-287, 289
Pupae, immature forms of insects. 2-407-08, illus., 408
  Ants, illus., 3-360
  Beetles, illus., 3-336
  Butterflies and moths, illus., 2-408, 3-195-96, illus., 195, 197
  Flies, 3-284, illus., 285-86
  Polyphemus moths. illus., 9-190
  Silkworm, 5-174, 179
  Social insects, 3-358, 368
  Wasps, with illus., 2-412d
Pupils of the eyes. Function of, 7-293
Pupin, Michael I., American physicist and inventor (1858–1935). He taught physics at Columbia and helped revolutionize the telegraph, telephone, and radio industries by his inventions in long-distance telephony, electrical-wave propagation, electrical resonance, iron magnetization and multiplex telegraphy. He investigated X rays; he developed a method of short-exposure X-ray photography (using a fluorescent screen) and he discovered secondary X-ray radiations. His book Immigrant to Inventor won a Pulitzer Prize in 1924.
  Loaded circuits invented by, 2-392-93
Pupipara, suborder of flies. 3-292, illus., 291
"Pure races." Fallacy of concept of, 8-345
Purification.
  Metallurgical, with diagrams, 1-371-82
  Sewage, 5-328, illus., 330-32, 334
  Water supply, with illus., 2-276-82
Purkinje, Johannes Evangelista, Czech physiologist. 7-159
Purkinje system, fiber network of the heart. 3-387, diagram, 386
Purple finches, sparrows. 6-108
Purple martins, swallows. 6-68

Pus. 7-348
Bone disease, 3-84
Formation of, 3-328
Pussy willow trees. 5-144
Puy-de-Dôme, extinct volcano in France. *illus.,* 4-394
Barometrical experiments, site of, 3-17
Puzzles, mathematical. *4-443-54
Pyemia, blood poisoning. 3-332
Pygmy locusts, insects. 3-143, *illus.,* 144
Pygmy nuthatches, birds. 6-42
Pygmy owls. 6-165
Pygmy shrews, mouselike mammals. 7-1, 100
Pyloric sphincter, ringlike muscle. 4-326
Pylorus, part of stomach. 4-324, *illus.,* 324
Pynchon, William, first American meat packer. 5-164
Pyorrhea, disease of gums. 5-132
Protozoan is cause of, 2-64
Pyramids, common solids. *with illus.,* 3-443
Pyramids, geological formations. Formation of, 2-353
Pyramids, massive structures.
Cheops' pyramid, 3-115
Mayan pyramids, *illus.,* 9-29
Step Pyramid, *illus.,* 1-127
Pyramids, of kidney. *illus.,* 1-148e
Pyranometers, devices for recording radiation from sun. *illus.,* 1-21
Pyrenees, mountain range. 10-21, *illus.,* 22
Pyrex glassware. 3-415
Pyrheliometers, solar-heat instruments. *illus.,* 1-246
Pyridoxine, vitamin B$_6$. 5-43
Pyrite, mineral. *with illus.,* 5-249; *illus.,* 9-304
Pyrite tetrahedrite.
External structure of crystal, 5-341, *diagram,* 340
Pyroelectricity, production of electricity through heating.
Minerals identified by, 5-256
See also **Piezoelectricity**
Pyrophoric lead. Experiments and tricks with, *with diagram,* 7-174-75
Pyrosoma, tunicate. 2-185
Pyroxene, mineral. 3-422
Pyroxylin, cellulose nitrates. 8-223
Pyrrhocorids, family of true bugs. *with illus.,* 3-259
Pyrrolazote, synthetic tranquilizer. 5-379
Pyrrophyta, phylum of algae. 1-301; 3-215-16
Pyruvic acid, metabolic compound. 2-12; 3-48
Pythagoras, Greek philosopher. *with illus.,* 1-132-34
Pythagorean theorem. *with illus.,* 3-432-33
Pytheas, Greek navigator and geographer. 6-27-28
Pythonomorphs. See **Mosasaurs**
Pythons, snakes. 5-357-58, *illus.,* 353, 357
Adaptation for obtaining food, 3-237

Q

Quack grass, weed. 4-68
"Quacks." Cancer treated by, 8-272
Quadrantids, meteor shower. *table,* 6-97
Quadrants, in analytic geometry. *with diagrams,* 4-425-31
Quadrate bone, of vertebrates. 4-382, 384
Quadratic equations. 2-73
Quadrilaterals, four-sided plane figures. *with illus.,* 3-434-35
Quaggas, zebras. 7-333
Quail. 6-332-34, *illus.,* 337
Raising of, 7-23
Qualifications, personal.
Scientific career, required for, 10-193-94
Quality, sound. 5-124-25

Quantitative analysis, measurement of quantity in chemistry.
Electrochemical analysis, 5-91
Quantum mechanics. 9-283
Quantum theory. 9-283
Electromagnetic radiation and, 7-205
Planck, proposed by, 8-406-07
Quarantine.
Insects, 2-411
Introduction of, in Middle Ages, 2-312-13
Nursing and, 10-56-57, 59
Plants, 7-113-14
Quarries.
Collecting minerals at, 9-301
Quarrying. *2-81-88
Quartz (silica), mineral. 3-422; 5-251, 255, *illus.,* 250; 9-303, *illus.,* 304
Beach sands contain, 8-352
Crystals of quartz, passage of light through, 5-340-41, *diagram,* 339
Properties and uses of, 3-322
"Quartz glass." 3-315
Quartzite, metamorphic rock. 3-426; 9-308
Quaternary period, time in earth's history. 1-396-97; 6-374
Quebec Bridge, Quebec. *illus.,* 2-336
Queen ants. 3-365, *with illus.,* 357-58, *illus.,* 360
Queen bumblebees. 3-372
Queen Elizabeth, ocean liner. 4-117
Queen honeybees. 3-368, 370, *illus.,* 366, 372
Queen Mary, ocean liner. 4-115, 117
Queen termites. 3-362
Queen wasps. 3-365-66
Queens-Midtown Tunnel, New York City. 2-56
Quench-hardening steels. 7-166
Quenching, stopping an electrical discharge in a Geiger-Mueller counter. 9-342
Question-and-answer boards. Homemade, *with illus.,* 6-290-91
Quick-freezing of foods. *with illus.,* 4-160-63, *illus.,* 318-19
Quicklime (burned lime). Soil fertilizer, employment as, 2-168
Quiescence, period of, in plants. 2-418; 5-65
Quills. Porcupines', *with illus.,* 3-239; 8-164
Quinine. Drug for malaria, 10-37
Quinine hydrochloride.
Fish diseases treated with, 8-116
Quipus, knotted cords used by ancient Peruvians to record information. *illus.,* 1-113
Quoins, wedges for holding printing material. 1-207, *illus.,* 206

R

Rabbits. *illus.,* 7-15; 8-170
Adaptations for feeding, 7-9
Cottontail rabbit, *illus.,* 10-257
Experiments, use in, *illus.,* 8-169
Field study of, 10-259
Fur, 7-238
Homes of, 10-260
Pets, 7-22
Snowshoe rabbits (varying hares), 5-413, *illus.,* 412
Trained to play simplified basketball, *illus.,* 9-318
Rabi, Isidor Isaac, American physicist (born 1898). Taught physics at Columbia University. A researcher in nuclear physics and quantum mechanics, he was awarded the 1944 Nobel physics prize for his work on the magnetic properties of atoms and atomic nuclei. He discovered certain atomic radiations and he devised ways to

Rabi, Isador Isaac *(continued)*
measure them. He was one of the founders of the Brookhaven National Laboratory.
Rabies.
  Pasteur's work on, **7**-381; **9**-80
  Vaccination against, **7**-351
Raccoons. 7-307, *with illus.,* 316-17
  Fur, **7**-238
  Hibernation, **5**-411
  Pets, **7**-21, *illus.,* 22
Racemes, flower clusters. **4**-123, *illus.,* 124
Racemic acid. Optical properties of, **9**-71-72
Racers, snakes. *illus.,* **5**-358
  Pets, **7**-25
Races. ***8**-213-20
  Blood groups in human races, **3**-334, *with table,* 333
  Formation of, **3**-226
  Heredity and, **8**-346, *illus.,* 347
  Primitive races and early man, *with illus.,* **9**-21-30
  See also **China; Civilization; Indians, American;
      Japanese; Primitive peoples; Society;** etc.
Races, tidal currents. **6**-207
Racker, Efraim, enzymologist.
  Glucose produced by, **8**-190
Radar, electronic detection device. **9**-387-90
  Astronomy, use of radar in, **9**-207
  Comets tracked by, **9**-207
  Detection device for navigation, *illus.,* **6**-298c
  Development of, **9**-288-89, *illus.,* 287
  Electroluminescent military devices, **9**-347
  Ground Control Approach, **6**-200
  Magnetrons used in, **6**-302
  Meteor trails detected by, **6**-96
  Radio waves, use in, **7**-207, *illus.,* 200, 204
  Radiosonde signals received by, *illus.,* **1**-230
  Space and missile flights guided by, **8**-128, 131, *diagram,* 129
  Weather forecasting, role of radar in, **1**-252
Radar astronomy. 9-207
Radial airplane engines. 6-187
Radial motions, of stars. **7**-226
Radial symmetry. Flowers, 4-122, *illus.,* 123
Radial wells. 2-274
Radiant energy. *with illus.,* **1**-83, 84
  See also **Electromagnetic radiation; Electrons; Radio-
      activity; Radium; Thorium**
Radiant heat. 4-15-16, *illus.,* 9, 14-15
  Experiments with, *with illus.,* **4**-20-22
  Solar, *with illus.,* **1**-83
Radiant heating, 2-249-50
Radiants, apparent meteor-shower sources. **6**-96
Radiation.
  ***Atomic energy, 9**-120-38
  ***Cosmic rays, 8**-393-99
  ***Electroluminescence, 9**-344-47
  ***Electromagnetic radiation, 7**-199-207
  ***Food preservation by, 10**-114-16
  ***Geiger-Mueller counters, 9**-340-43
  ***Light, 7**-249-62, 277-90
  ***Perils of radiation, 9**-348-58
  ***Radiation thickness gauges, 9**-43-46
  ***Radioisotope-fueled thermoelectric generators, 6**-172-75
  ***X rays, 7**-143-50
  Air circulation due to heat radiation, *with diagrams,* 1-241-44
  Atmosphere affected by solar and space radiation, 1-231-32, 237, 238, 240, *with illus.,* 236
  Atomic-bomb explosion releases, **9**-348, 351-52, 391-92
  Cancer caused by, **8**-268

Radiation *(continued)*
  Cancer treated by, **8**-270, *illus.,* 269
  Diagnosis by, *illus.,* **8**-271
  Electronic computer used for analysis of, **9**-151
  Energy, radiant, *with illus.,* **1**-83, 84
  Exposure limits for safety, **9**-350
  Glass that minimizes effect of solar radiation, **10**-392
  Heat, **4**-15-16, *with illus.,* 20-22, *illus.,* 9, 14-15
  Heating, part played in, **2**-246
  Preserving food by, *with illus.,* **4**-168
  Solar radiation, measurement of, **1**-247, *illus.,* 246
  Space-travel hazard, **10**-50
  Study of, in nineteenth century, *with illus.,* **6**-239-47
  Sun's radiation affects climate, **3**-184-85
  Treatment by, *illus.,* **8**-271
  Van Allen belts of radiation surrounding earth, *with
      illus.,* **5**-195
  Weather changes in upper atmosphere may be due
      to sun's, **5**-193
  See also **Atomic energy; Gamma rays; Parity law;
      Radioactivity; Van Allen radiation belts; X
      rays;** etc.
Radiation belts. See **Van Allen radiation belts**
Radiation detectors.
  ***Radiation thickness gauges, 9**-43-46
  Medical uses of, **10**-99, *illus.,* 100
  Prospecting with, **7**-361
  See also **Fluoroscopes; Geiger counters**
Radiation sickness. 9-351-52, 353, 356, 364
Radiation thickness gauges. *9-43-46
Radiators.
  Automobile cooling systems, *with illus.,* **2**-136
Radiators, steam. 2-247
  Heat by convection current, **2**-247-48; **4**-14
Radio. *3-85-98
  Development of, **9**-287-88
  Flying, use in, *with illus.,* **6**-198-200
  Frequency regulated by electrostriction crystals, **2**-294
  Ionosphere affects radio communication, **1**-240
  Railroads served by, **1**-194
  Solar emissions affect radio, **3**-106-07
  Tuner and loudspeaker, *illus.,* **10**-121
  Wave lengths used, **7**-202, *diagram,* 200
  Weather forecasting, role of radio in, **1**-252; **9**-223, *illus.,* 221
  See also **Communication; Electronics; Radio astron-
      omy; Radio telescopes; Radio waves; Radio-
      sondes; Television**
Radio astronomy. *9-206-10
  Electrical engineering and, **1**-224
  History of, **9**-224-25
  Radio waves used in, **7**-207
  See also **Radio telescopes**
Radio-beam networks. 2-383
Radio-command guidance systems, for missiles and
      space vehicles. **8**-128-30, 131, *diagram,* 129,
      illus., 125
Radio Corporation of America (RCA).
  Electronic music synthesizer of, *with illus.,* **5**-220
Radio cosmology. 9-210
Radio engineering. Observation of sunspots affects,
      1-22
Radio relay. 2-383, 389
Radio-relay towers. 2-383, *illus.,* 393, 395; *illus.,* **5**-285
Radio stars. 9-224
Radio telescopes. *9-206-10
  Development of, *with illus.,* **6**-257; *illus.,* **8**-62; **9**-224-25, *illus.,* 222
  Interstellar space studied with, **9**-361
  Manchester University, Great Britain, **1**-94
  See also **Radio astronomy**

Radio waves.
Astronomy, use of radio waves in, 9-206-10
Broadcasting and receiving with electron tubes, 6-296-98
Discovery of, 6-245
Prospecting with, 7-361
Short-wave radio waves used to detect meteors, 6-96
Telegraph messages sent by, 2-383
Telephony, use in, *with illus.,* 2-394-95
Wave lengths and uses, discovery of, 7-202, 206-07, *illus.,* 200, 204, 207
See also **Electromagnetic waves; Radar; Radio; Television**

Radioactive elements.   Age of earth determined by, 4-47; 10-223

Radioactive fallout.   9-141, 354-55, 392, 394-96, *illus.,* 394
Cancer may be caused by, 8-268
Food chains affected by, 10-187
Maximum Permissible Concentration of, 9-356

Radioactive isotopes.
*Atomic medicines, 10-98-101
*Food preservation, 10-114-16
*Radiation thickness gauges, 9-43-46
*Radiocarbon dating, 10-92-97
*Radioisotope-fueled thermoelectric generators, 6-172-75
*Thermoluminescence, dating by, 6-375-76
Archaeological materials, use in dating, 9-30
Atomic farming, use in, 10-251-52
Dentistry, use in, 5-137
Tracers, use as, 9-142, 332
Uses of, 9-142

Radioactive wastes.   9-358

Radioactivity.
*Geiger-Mueller counters, 9-340-43
*Radiation thickness gauges, 9-43-46
*Radioisotope-fueled thermoelectric generators, 6-172-75
*Thermoluminescence, dating by, 6-375-76
Atomic-energy production, relation to, 9-126-28, 132-33, 136-37
Atomic farming, *with illus.,* 10-251-53
Discovery of, 9-348-49
Dusts, radioactive, 1-236
Food preservation by radiation, *with illus.,* 10-114-16
Heavy-water reactor, *illus.,* 1-94
Minerals: explanation for earthquakes, 9-106
Minerals identified by degree of, 5-255-56
Mountain building, radioactive minerals possibly causing, 10-219-20
Particles, atomic, 1-313, *with table,* 314
Prospecting and, 7-361
Radioactive carbon, 10-93-96
Rocks dated by, 4-37; 5-191
Rutherford's and Soddy's contributions to study of, 8-415-16
See also **Parity law; Radioactive isotopes; Radium; Thorium; Uranium**

Radiocarbon dating.   *10-92-97
Anticoincidence counters used in, 9-343
Development of, 9-30

Radiochromium.   Medical uses of, 10-99

Radiocobalt.   Tumors treated with, 10-100

Radiogold.   Medical uses of, 10-100

Radiographs.   See **X rays**

Radioiodine.   Medical use of, 10-98, 99, *illus.,* 100

Radioisotope-fueled thermoelectirc generators   *6-172-75

Radioisotopes.   See **Radioactive isotopes**

Radiolarian ooze, marine deposit.   6-33

Radiolarians, marine protozoans.   2-65; *with illus.,* 6-33

Radiophotos.   7-392

Radiosondes (sounding balloons).   *illus.,* 1-230
Balloons that carry meteorological instruments, 1-106
Stratosphere research, 6-179
Weather observations through agency of, 1-235, 252; 9-223, *illus.,* 221

Radiotelephones.   2-394-95

Radium (Ra), chemical element.   Atomic number, 88; atomic weight, 226(?); melting point, 700° C.; boiling point, 1,140° C.; specific gravity, 5(?).   Alkaline-earth metal.   Brilliant, luminescent white, oxidizes rapidly in air and decomposes water.   Discovered by Pierre and Marie Curie in 1898; first isolated by Mme. Curie and Debierne in 1911.   Name derived from Latin *radius:* "ray."   Never found free in nature; present in uranium ores, chiefly carnotite and pitchblende or uraninite.   Obtained commercially as the bromide or chloride.   Used to treat cancer, in luminous paints and in radiography.   See also *with illus.,* 3-174-76
Cancer treated with, *illus.,* 10-132
"Cold" light given off by radium paint, 8-118
Damage caused by, 9-349-50
Discovery of, 8-414-15
Maximum Permissible Amount, 9-350
Radioactivity, amount of, 9-126-27

Radius, bone of forearm.   *illus.,* 1-148b; 3-80, *illus.,* 74, 75, 81

Radon (Rn), chemical element.   Atomic number, 86; atomic weight, 222(?); melting point, −71° C.; boiling point, −61.8° C.; specific gravity (air = 1), 7.526.   Heavy, inert gas, colorless, condensing to a transparent liquid and an opaque, glowing solid.   Discovered and called radium emanation in 1900; isolated in 1908.   Name indicates that it is derived from radium.   Formed by disintegration of radium; as a gas, it is pumped off from radium and kept in tubes or capsules for use in medicine.   Less expensive than radium, it commonly serves as a replacement to help conserve the radium supply, but it has a far shorter life.

Rafinesque, Constantine Samuel, naturalist of French parentage.   8-252

Rag paper.   4-378

Rag stock.   Paper made from, 4-370

Rags.   Papermaking materials, 4-364

Ragweed.   10-205
Allergic reactions to, 4-259-60

Rail-diesel cars (RDC).   1-185-86

Railroad associations.   1-195

Railroad companies.   Organization of, 1-195

"Railroad worms," luminous female beetles.   *with illus.,* 2-189-90

Railroad yards.   1-192, *illus.,* 194

Railroads.   *1-179-95
Coal and locomotives, 1-89, 146, *diagram,* 90
Meat-packing industry aided by development of, 5-164
Petroleum carried in tank cars, 4-146, *illus.,* 147
Steam locomotive, invention and development of, *with illus.,* 6-378-80
See also **Locomotives; Trains; Transportation; Tunnels**

Rails.   *with illus.,* 1-191
Early use of, 1-179
Steel-rail manufacture, 1-349

Rails, marsh birds.   *with illus.,* 6-403-05

Rain.   1-245; *2-346-53
Measuring and recording, 1-251, *with diagram,* 321-22, *diagram,* 316, *illus.,* 248, 250
Red rain, 7-139
Solar heat causes, 1-83
See also **Clouds; Rainfall; Weather**

Rain gauges. 1-251, *with diagram*, 321-22, *illus.*, 248
Rain making. 2-216, 218
Rainbow Bridge, Utah. 8-15
Rainbows. 7-279, *illus.*, 278
    Photography of, 6-316
Raindrops.
    Formation of, 1-245
    Photography of, 6-316
    Snow is not frozen raindrops, 2-354
Rainfall. *2-346-53
    Amount at different places of the earth's surface, 8-9-10
    Measuring and recording, 1-251, *with diagram*, 321-22, *diagram*, 316, *illus.*, 248, 250
    Mountains affect, 10-26-27
    Plains, rainfall of, 6-111
    Water cycle, part of, 6-409
Raleigh, Sir Walter, English man of letters.
    Pipe smoking introduced in England by, 5-343
Raman, Sir Chandrasekhara, Indian physicist (born 1888). Physics professor at Calcutta University, he also lectured at other Indian colleges. In 1930 he won the Nobel physics prize for his work on light diffusion, especially the discovery of the Raman effect. (The Raman effect occurs when part of a beam of monochromatic light scatters as the beam passes through a transparent medium. The scattered light differs in wave length and frequency from the original beam.)
Rambouillet, breed of sheep. *illus.*, 10-246
Rameses II. Temple at Abu Simbel, *illus.*, 7-116
Rami, hinges of lower jawbone. 3-79
Ramie, plant yielding fiber. 4-182
Ramjet engines, jet engines. 7-72, *illus.*, 70-71; *illus.*, 10-43
    Principle of, 4-92
Ramjets. 6-195
Ramon y Cajal, Santiago, Spanish histologist. 9-56
Rams. *illus.*, 10-246-47
Ramsay, Sir William, British chemist (1852–1916). A chemistry professor at University College, London, Ramsay was a brilliant teacher and investigator. He studied the properties of liquids and discovered the inert gases argon (with Lord Rayleigh), neon, krypton and xenon (with M. W. Travers) and helium. His work on inert gases won him the 1904 Nobel Prize in chemistry. Later, he showed that helium was a gaseous emanation product of the atomic disintegration of radium. See also 5-86
Rana, genus of frogs. 5-154
Ranatra, genus of aquatic insects. *illus.*, 3-240
Range finders, camera. 9-405
Ranges, of various animals. Mammals, 7-12-13
Ranges, gas, stoves. 5-106
Rank, Otto, Austrian psychiatrist. 9-102
Ranks, of coal. 1-408
Rapid etching, of photoengraved plates. 1-206
Rapid sand filter, used in water purification. 2-272, 277, *with illus.*, 279-80
Rapids. Formation of, 8-15
Rapture of the deep, sensation felt by free divers. 6-26c
Rare-earth elements. Name applied to fourteen elements — cerium, praseodymium, neodymium, promethium, samarium, europium, gadolinium, terbium, dysprosium, holmium, erbium, thulium, ytterbium and lutetium — with atomic numbers from 58 to 71, inclusive. They usually occur in nature together with scandium, yttrium and lanthanum, belonging to Group IIIa of the periodic table. The rare-earth elements are found in very small quantities, particularly in the mineral monazite. As they are very electropositive, they are hard to pre-

Rare-earth elements (continued)
pare. For more details, see individual entries in Index for the different rare-earth elements.
    Periodic series, position in, 4-310, *tables*, 307, 309
Rare gases. See Inert gases
Rarefaction. Sound waves, *with illus.*, 5-116, 117
Ras Algethi, star in Hercules. 1-333
Raspberries.
    Pests of, *illus.*, 8-373
    Raspberry cane-borers attack, 9-196
    Runners of, *illus.*, 4-67
Raspberry cane-borers. 9-196
Rasses, oriental civets. 8-245
Rat guards, on mooring lines of ships. *illus.*, 7-383
Rat kangaroos. 7-425
Rat shrews, insect-eating mammals. 7-100
Rat snakes. Pets, 7-25
Ratels, badgerlike mammals. 8-175
Rates of change, in calculus. *with diagrams*, 4-436-39
Rational numbers. 1-160
Rats, rodents. 8-164-65, *illus.*, 163
    Body temperature of, 7-7
    Cave rats, *with illus.*, 5-59
    Experiments, use in, *illus.*, 8-169
    Nutrition experiments on, *illus.*, 5-42; 8-82
    Pets, 7-22
Rattails, fishes. *with illus.*, 4-97
Rattlesnakes. 5-364, *illus.*, 363
    Inactivity in cold season, 5-411-12
    Sidewinders, *with illus.*, 5-354b
    Skull and jaws, *with illus.*, 1-285
    Venom apparatus, *with illus.*, 1-285; 3-237
Ravens. 6-103
Raw silk. 5-180, 182
Rawinsondes, weather balloons carrying radar reflectors. 1-252
Ray, John, English biologist. 3-375
Ray-finned fish. 4-196
Ray flowers. *with illus.*, 4-124
Rayleigh, Baron (John William Strutt), English physicist (1842–1919). Professor at Cambridge and the Royal Institution, he became chancellor of Cambridge in 1908. He did research in optics (color vision and polarization) and in sound phenomena (resonance, absolute pitch and vibration). He investigated the propagation of waves, surface tension and the flow of liquids; he studied electricity and magnetism. Working on the densities of gases, he discovered argon (with Sir W. Ramsay); this achievement won him the Nobel physics prize in 1904.
Rayon.
    Cellulose, made from, *with illus.*, 5-303
    Manufacture of, *with illus.*, 8-189
Rays. See Cosmic rays; Incident rays; Heat; Light; Radiation; Refracted rays; Ultraviolet rays; X rays.
Rays, bands on surface of moon. 4-284
Rays, fish. *illus.*, 1-297; 3-237-38; 4-285-87, 293, 295, *illus.*, 293
    Reproduction, 4-104
Rays, in geometry. *with illus.*, 3-430
RDC. See Rail-diesel cars
Reactants, chemical. Equations representing interactions of, 2-226, 230, *diagram*, 226
Reaction engines. See Jet propulsion; Rockets
Reaction turbines. 9-234, *illus.*, 232
Reactions, chemical. *2-223-31
    Electrolytic, *with illus.*, 5-88-94
    Examples of, 4-230-31
Reactors, chemical. Petroleum refining uses, 4-148
Reactors, electrical. 9-235, *illus.*, 236, 238

Reactors, nuclear. illus., 9-138a-b
  Atomic fission brought about by, 1-frontispiece;
    9-136-38; illus., 10-227
  Heavy-water reactor, illus., 1-94
  Nuclear power for generating electricity, 9-231
Reade, T. Mellard, English geologist. Mountain-build-
  ing forces, theory of, 10-219
Readers, microfilm. with diagram, 10-70-71
Real number axis. 1-161
Real number system. 1-161
Reaming, tooling operation. 10-109
Reaping machines. Development of, in nineteenth
  century, 6-383
Rear-fanged snakes. 5-360-61
Reason. *Animal intelligence, 2-26-29
  Indications of, in apes, with illus., 9-52-54
  See also **Mind; Psychology**
Réaumur, René-Antoine Ferchault de, French physicist
  and naturalist. 3-19
  Réaumur thermometer scale developed by, 3-410,
    illus., 411
Réaumur scale. 3-410, illus., 411
  Compared with centigrade and Fahrenheit scales,
    illus., 3-411; 10-297
  Introduction of, 3-19
Reber, Grote, American pioneer in radio astronomy. 9-
  207
  Radio telescope first constructed by, 9-224
Rebus method. Writing developed through use of,
  1-113
Receivers, radio. with illus., 3-93-98
Recent epoch, time in earth's history. 6-374
Receptors, sense organs.
  Body's defenses, role in, 7-346
  Importance of receptors to animals, 4-379
  Nerve stimulation, role in, 6-320-21
  Skin, with illus., 7-304
Recessiveness, phenomenon of inheritance. 8-340-44,
  diagram, 341
Reciprocating compressors, air compressors. 9-61-63
Reciprocating engines.
  Steam, with illus., 4-81-85
    Compared with turbines, 4-86; 5-311
  See also **Diesel engines; Gasoline engines**
Reclaimed rubber. with illus., 6-360
Reclus, Jean-Jacques-Elisée, French geographer.
  Cloud description, 2-218, 220
  Cloud-zone description, 2-348
  Dry and rainy seasons described, 2-349
  Lake Geneva's regulating action described by, 7-61
  Sahara vegetation described by, 6-117
Recoil, backward reaction. Rockets and jets, 10-41,
  illus., 43
Recollection, part of thinking process. 9-317
Recordak Lodestar Reader, for microfilm. 10-70-71
Recorders, magnetic. 7-368
Recording. *7-362-69
Records.
  Bird observations, keeping records of, 10-259
  Duplication by microfilming, with illus., 10-68-74
  Home medical care, records of, with table, 10-66
Recreation.
  Aged, recreation for, 8-83
  Dams that supply water for, 8-307
Recreations, mathematical. *4-443-54
Rectangles, plane figures. 3-435, illus., 434
Rectifiers, electron tubes.
  Diodes, 6-298, 301, illus., 297
  Ignitrons, 6-302, illus., 301
  Television sets, rectifiers used in, illus., 6-298d
Rectilinear motion. 2-118-20, illus., 120, 121

Rectum, part of the large intestine. illus., 1-148d; 4-
  330-31, illus., 332
  Taking temperature by, 10-58
Rectus abdominis, belly muscle. illus., 1-148c
Rectus femoris, thigh muscle. illus., 1-148c; illus., 3-204
Recurrent turns, in bandaging. 10-16, illus., 17
Red alder trees. 5-145
Red algae. with illus., 3-224; 6-221
Red and yellow podsolic soils, soil types. 2-22
Red-backed shrikes.
  Courtship behavior of, with illus., 5-418b
Red bats. Migration of, 9-422
Red-bellied snakes. Pets, 7-25
Red blood cells (erythrocytes). 3-330-31, 333, with
  illus., 326-28, illus., 329; illus., 7-348
  Altitude affects number of, 7-8
  Bone marrow, manufactured in, 3-74
  Destruction of dead red blood cells, 5-13-14
  Life-span of, determined with radioisotopes, 10-99
  Respiration, function in, 4-200-01, 206
  Spleen as source of, 5-10
Red-breasted nuthatches, birds. 6-42
Red bugs. 2-268
Red cedar trees. with illus., 5-143
Red clay, marine deposit. 6-34
Red-cockaded woodpeckers. 6-211
Red Cross.
  Founding of societies, 7-389
  Home-nursing courses offered by, 10-67
Red deer. 8-236, 238, 239, illus., 234
Red efts, immature spotted newts. Pets, 7-26
Red-eyed vireos, birds. 6-63, illus., 65
Red filters, for light.
  Vision experiments with, 8-180, diagrams, 179
Red foxes. 8-141
Red grouse. 6-335
Red-headed woodpeckers. 6-210
Red maple trees. with illus., 5-150
Red oak trees. 5-147
Red phosphorus. 3-320-21
  See also **Phosphorus**
Red pine. Saplings, illus., 5-265
Red ramshorns, snails. illus., 8-115
Red river hogs. 10-244
Red salamanders. illus., 5-156
Red shift, displacement of spectrum lines toward red.
  8-54; 9-225
Red-shouldered hawks. 6-156
Red Spot, of Jupiter. See **Great Red Spot**
Red squill, plant. illus., 1-41
Red squirrels. 8-162
Red-tailed hawks. 6-156
Red-winged blackbirds. with illus., 6-104
Red wolves. illus., 8-135
Redbud trees. 5-148
Redi, Francesco, Italian embryologist. 3-265, 274-75
Redistribution, of printing type. 1-199-200
Redondo, California. Beach destruction, 8-351
Redpolls, sparrows. 6-108
Redstarts. illus., 6-62
Redstones, American rockets. with illus., 9-381
Reducing diets. with tables, 5-268-71
Reduction, in metallurgy. See **Smelting**
Reduction, process of taking on electrons. 5-88
  See also **Valence**
Reduviids, family of true bugs. with illus., 3-259
Redwood. Building material, illus., 7-126
Redwood trees. 2-108, illus., 106; 5-142, illus., 143
Reed, Walter, American bacteriologist and surgeon
  (1851–1902). Medical officer in the United States
  Army. As head of a board sent to Cuba to study

Reed, Walter *(continued)*
yellow fever, Reed discovered that this disease is transmitted by the bite of an infected mosquito. By showing how the disease might be controlled, he made an important advance in modern medical research. The Army's Walter Reed General Hospital, Washington, D. C., is named in honor of this soldier-scientist. See also **3**-452; **7**-384
Mosquitoes as vectors of yellow fever, **8**-405; **10**-38-39
Reed instruments. Sound production in, **5**-217-18
Reedbucks, antelopes. 8-386, *illus.,* 385
Reeds. Papyrus, **4**-364
Reefs, coral. *with illus.,* **4**-134-39; **6**-71-72, 75, *with illus.,* 77
Reels, rolls of photographic film. Microfilm, **10**-69-73, *illus.,* 70-73
Formation of, **8**-358-59
Re-entry of missile, into earth's atmosphere. **10**-232-33
Refining.
Metals, **1**-376, 379, 382, *with diagrams,* 378, 380
Petroleum, *with illus.,* **4**-147-52
Reflecting telescopes. *****9**-153-61; **8**-56-57
*Building of, by amateur astronomer, **9**-365-74
Amateurs, for use of, **6**-86
Development of, **6**-256, *illus.,* 257
Nineteenth century, **6**-387-88
Reflection.
Diffuse, *with illus.,* **7**-252
Earth and atmosphere reflect much incoming radiation, **1**-237
Heat, **4**-16
Internal, total, *with illus.,* **7**-254-55
Light, reflection of, *with illus.,* **7**-250, 251, 252
Experiments concerning, *with illus.,* **8**-120-23
Photography, color reflection in, **9**-413
Prospecting with reflected ground waves and currents, **7**-358, 361
Seismic surveys, **4**-145, *diagram,* 143
Sound, **5**-120-21, 128, *illus.,* 121, 127
Experiments on, *with illus.,* **5**-225
See also **Parity law**
Reflection, angle of. *with illus.,* **7**-251
Reflectoscopes.
Ultrasonic devices, *with illus.,* **8**-108-09
Reflex angles. *with illus.,* **3**-431
Reflex arcs. Nature and properties of, **6**-321, 323, 327, *illus.,* 322
Reflex cameras. 9-405, *illus.,* 405, 406
Reflexes.
Body's defenses, role in, **7**-346-47, *diagram,* 347
Nature of, **6**-321, 323, 326-27, *illus.,* 322
Pavlov's discovery of conditioned reflex, *with illus.,* **9**-51-52
Sleep, changes in reflexes during, **6**-147
Reforestation. 5-261; *illus.,* **6**-9
Refracted rays. *with illus.,* **7**-253-55
Refracting crystals. See **Crystals**
Refracting telescopes. 6-86, *with illus.,* 256; **7**-262, *illus.,* 261; **8**-56, *with illus.,* 57, *illus.,* 55; *diagram,* **9**-366
Nineteenth century, *with illus.,* **6**-387-88
Refraction.
Colors isolated by, **7**-278-80, *illus.,* 277, 280
Light, *with illus.,* **7**-253-55
Experiments concerning refraction of, **8**-122, 124, *with illus.,* 178-79, *illus.,* 123-24
Prospecting with refracted ground waves and currents, **7**-358, 360-61, *diagram,* 357
Sound waves, **5**-121-22, *illus.,* 121, 122-23
See also **Vibration; Waves**
Refraction, angle of. *with illus.,* **7**-254, 255

Refraction, index of. *with illus.,* **7**-254
Refrigeration. Food preservation by, **4**-159-63, *illus.,* 158, 159
Freon chemicals used in, **4**-159, 310
Refrigerator cars, freight cars. **1**-190
Meat-packing industry aided by development of, **5**-164
Refrigerators.
Cryogenic-range temperatures (see **Cryogenics**) produced by, **5**-210
Design improved by Raymond Loewy, **10**-120
Refuse disposal. 5-334-36, *illus.,* 334, 335
See also **Wastes**
Regal hairstreaks, butterflies. *illus.,* **3**-202d
Regeneration.
Nerve fibers, **6**-320
Plant tissues, **10**-143
Regenerators. Open-hearth furnaces, *with diagram,* **1**-345
Petroleum refining uses, **4**-148
Reggio, Italy. Earthquake of 1908, **9**-110
Regional research. United States, **1**-89-90, *illus.,* 91, 92
Register, in color printing. **1**-213, 214
Registers (grilles), heating. **2**-246, 247
Regolith, parent material of soil. **2**-15-16, 18
Regular flowers. 4-122, *illus.,* 123
Regular World Days. 5-187
Regular World Intervals. 5-187
Regulator stations, controlling natural-gas flow from pipelines. *with illus.,* **5**-105-06, *illus.,* 98c
Regulators, used in scuba diving. *with illus.,* **6**-26b
Regulus, star in Leo. **1**-332
Reindeer. 7-332-33
Transportation, use in, *with illus.,* **1**-102
Reinforced concrete. 3-119, 122, 123-24
Bridges made of, **2**-333-34, 337
Building material, **7**-123-24
Reinforced plastics. *with diagram,* **8**-233
Reis, Philipp, German physicist. **2**-386; **5**-243
Telephone of, **2**-386, 388
Rejuvenation, geographic cycle. **8**-18
Relative humidity
Measuring and recording, **1**-249-51, *with diagram,* 320-21, *diagram,* 316, *illus.,* 248
See also **Humidity, relative**
Relativity theory. *****4**-210-20
Development of, *with illus.,* **9**-279-82
Tests of, **3**-137
See also **Einstein, Albert**
Relaxation. Muscular relaxation, **3**-209
Relaxing jars, for softening collected insects. **3**-156
Relay towers, for television. *illus.,* **2**-393, 395; *illus.,* **5**-285
Relief printing. See **Letterpress**
Religion.
Astronomy and, **1**-16
Calendar reforms of religious bodies, **10**-172-76, 178
Remaining mass, rocket. **10**-42
Remington Rand Inc. Electronic computers developed by, **9**-145
Remington typewriters. Development of, *with illus.,* **1**-267-68
Remote control. See **Automation**
Remsen, Ira, American chemist and educator (1846–1927). In 1876 he became the first chemistry professor at the newly founded Johns Hopkins University; later he became its president. He won fame for his researches in organic and inorganic chemistry and especially for his discovery of saccharin—a coal-tar product. He founded and edited the *American Chemical Journal.*

Renaissance, revival of learning in Europe.
  *Science in Renaissance, 2-361-76
  Engineering in, 1-217
  Illumination in, 4-232
  Living things, classification of, 1-288
Renal artery, leading to kidney. *illus.,* 1-148e; with diagram, 5-12
Renal pelvis. *illus.,* 1-148e; with *diagram,* 5-12
Renal vein, leading from kidney. *illus.,* 1-148e; diagram, 5-12
Renard, Charles, French pioneer in aeronautics. **6-178**
Repeater stations, telephone. 2-393
Repletes, food-holding ants. 3-364
Reproducer circuit, in radio. with *illus.,* 3-96-97
Reproduction.
  *Artificial propagation of plants, 9-7-15
  *Flowers, fruits and seeds, 4-119-32
  *Germination, 5-61-67
  *Heredity in man, 8-333-47
  *Human reproduction, 8-19-33
  *Population problems, 3-225-34
  *Seed and fruit dispersal, 5-1-7
  Animal reproduction, 1-54
    Acorn worms, 4-2-3
    Amphibians, 5-157-61
    Bears, 7-309, 310, 311, 312, 313
    Birds, see articles on birds
    Cats, 8-204, 206, 208
    Civets, mongooses and hyenas, 8-249, 250
    Coelenterates, 2-149, 150, 151
    Crocodilians, 5-383
    Crustaceans, 2-238
    Deer, 8-238, 239, 240
    Dog family, 8-138, 140
    Echinoderms, 2-152
    Elephants, 7-412
    Fishes, with *illus.,* 4-104-05, 286, 314, 315, 316, 317, 320
    Hippopotamuses, 7-414
    Insects, 2-406-08, *illus.,* 408-09; 3-139, 144, 148, 195, 255, 284, 362, 368, 370, 372, with *illus.,* 357-59, 365-67
    Lancelets, 4-4
    Lizards, 5-204-05
    Marine mammals, 7-87-88, 93, 186, 188
    Marsupials, 7-424
    Marsupials and placental mammals, differences between, 7-419
    Mollusks, 2-197-98
    Primates, 9-260
    Rabbits and hares, 8-170
    Rhinoceroses, 7-414
    Sea squirts, 4-3
    Snakes, 5-355, *illus.,* 354
    Spiders, 2-262
    Sponges, 2-147
    Turtles, 5-386
    Worms, with *illus.,* 2-154-58
  Asexual, 6-271
  Cells, nineteenth-century developments in study of, 7-160-61
  Glands of, 5-19, *illus.,* 16-17
  Human heredity, with *illus.,* 8-91-92
  Light affects, 7-8
  Mitosis (cell division), 2-13-14, *illus.,* 13
  Plant reproduction
    Algae, 3-217, 218-21, 223-24, *illus.,* 218
    Bacteria, 3-64-65
    Ferns, club mosses and horsetails, 3-190-92
    Fungi, 3-22-23
    Liverworts, 3-189-90

Reproduction, Plant reproduction *(continued)*
    Mosses, 3-187
    Pine trees, 3-402-03
    Seed plants, 3-397, 399, 401-06, *illus.,* 398
  Preservation of offspring, with *illus.,* 3-240-44
  Viruses, reproduction in, 3-455, 457
Reproduction, in printing and photography. **See Duplication**
Reptiles.
  *Crocodilians and turtles, 5-380-89
  *Lizards, 5-196-206
  *Snakes, 5-351-64
  Adaptations for survival, 3-237, 240
  Amphibians compared to, 5-153
  Birds evolved from, 5-415-16, *illus.,* 417
  Classification of, 1-298
  Ear and jaw structure, with *illus.,* 4-381
  Evolution of, 6-282-83
  Field study of, 10-261
  Heart of, 1-278
  Jaws, with *illus.,* 1-285
  Lizards of the Galápagos Islands, *illus.,* 7-31
  Migration of turtles and sea snakes, 9-415, *illus.,* 429-30
  Pets, reptiles as, with *illus.,* 7-23-25
  Prehistoric, *illus.,* 4-386; with *illus.,* 6-372, 373, 374
  Seasonal changes affect, 5-411-12
  See also **Lizards; Snakes; Turtles;** etc.
Republic Aircraft Corporation.
  Low-pressure conditions for plant growth, **researches** in, *illus.,* 8-37
Research.
  *Chemical synthesis and products, 8-181-90
  *Chemurgic research and production, 7-35-44
  *Industry and scientific research, 1-87-97
  *International Geophysical Year, 5-186-95
  *Modern research projects, 4-342a-d
  Cancer research today, 8-272
  Engineers who take part in, 1-227, *illus.,* 229
  Meat-packing industry, with *illus.,* 5-169, 172
  Space vehicles, scientific research aboard, 10-53
  See also **Atoms; Chemistry; Energy; Life; Physics; Power; Radium;** etc.
Reserpine, drug. 5-378-79; 9-104
Reserves, natural-gas. United States, 5-99
Reserves, petroleum. World, 4-143, 150-52
  See also **Oil traps**
Reservoirs.
  Impounding, 2-272-73, 276-77, *illus.,* 272, 281, 282
  Water-distribution systems, with *illus.,* 2-285-86
  See also **Dams; Water power; Water supply**
Residual (heavy) fuel oils. 4-149
Residual soils. 6-141
Resina, Italy. Disaster of, 2-351-52
Resins. 3-400-01
  *Plastics, 8-221-33
  Dynel fibers, *illus.,* 2-233
Resistance, electrical. 5-233; 6-133
  Disappearance of, in some metals, 5-209
  See also **Resistivity, electrical**
Resistance, forces of. with *illus.,* 2-122-23
Resistivity, electrical.
  Prospecting, measurement of rock resistivity in, 7-360-61
  See also **Resistance, electrical**
Resistors, variable. Principle of and **experiments with** rheostats, with *illus.,* 6-292-93
Resolution, optical property. Magnification as **opposed** to, 9-82
Resonance, chemical phenomenon. **4-274**

Resonance, group of phenomena associated with sympathetic vibration. 5-118, with illus., 227-28; 7-300
Resonance, in radio. 3-94
Resonators. See Electric resonators
Respiration. *4-200-09
 Bacteria, respiration in, 3-65-66
 Breathing, demonstration of, 2-331, illus., 330
 Cellular respiration, 2-10-11
 Diaphragm and abdominal muscles play part in, 3-209, diagram, 211
 Estivating animals, breathing of, 5-412
 Fermentation, relation to, 9-75
 Fish, with illus., 1-279; with illus., 4-100
 Hibernating animals, breathing of, 5-410, 411
 Human, how to measure, 10-58-59
 Mammals, mechanism of, with diagram, 1-279
 Mechanism, with illus. and diagram, 1-279
 Plant respiration, 3-47-49, 399; 5-64
 See also Air; Breathing; Lungs; Respiratory systems; Ventilation
Respirators, artificial. with illus., 4-205-06
Respiratory systems.
 Birds, with illus., 5-420-21
 Insects, 2-405
 Man's, illus., 1-148d-e
 Spiders, 2-261
 Turtles, 5-386
 See also Respiration
Rest.
 *Exercise and rest, 10-85-91
 Tubercular patients, 9-181-82
 See also Sleep
Retailing, selling products to consumers. Petroleum products, 4-152
Reticulo-endothelial system, cell networks and linings. 3-328
Reticulum, chamber of cow's stomach. illus., 7-10
Retinal fatigue. 7-289, illus., 284d
Retinas, membranes of eyes. 7-293-94, 295, 296, illus., 292, 294, 295, 296, 297
 See also Blindness; Eyes; Vision
Retinene, substance in eyes. 7-293
Retirement. Older persons, 8-83
"Retort zinc," distilled and condensed zinc. with diagram, 1-380
Retorts, pressure cookers used in canning. illus., 4-157
Retrorockets, rocket brakes. 9-381; illus., 10-52-53
Retting.
 Bacteria play part in, 3-67-68, illus., 69
 Process in preparation of flax fibers, with illus., 4-179-80
Return passages, for air circulation in wind tunnels. with diagram, 10-233
Retzius, Anders, Swedish anatomist and anthropologist. 9-24
Re-usable ice. 4-160
Reverberation. 5-120, 128
Reverberatory furnaces, in ore smelting. with diagrams, 1-377, 379
Reversible chemical reactions. 2-229-30, 231, diagram, 231
Reversing layer, layer of sun's atmosphere. 3-100-01
Revillagigedo Islands, Mexico.
 Volcanic eruptions on San Benedicto, illus., 7-339
Revolution of the earth. with diagrams, 4-48-49, diagram, 46
Revolutions, periods of geologic change. 1-385
 See also Mountain making
Rey, Jean, French physician. 3-18, 269
Reyniers, James A., American bacteriologist. with illus., 7-151-55

Rh factor, blood agglutinogen. 3-333-34
 Race, importance in study of, 8-214
Rhazes, Persian alchemist and physician. 2-300-01
Rhea, satellite of Saturn. 5-113
Rheims, France. Cathedral at, illus., 3-116
Rhenium (Re), chemical element. Atomic number, 75; atomic weight, 186.2; melting point, about 3,167° C.; specific gravity, 20.53. Metal, discovered in 1925 by Noddack, Tacke and Berg in the minerals columbite, tantalite and wolframite. Name derived from Latin Rhenus: "Rhine." Metal can be hot forged or rolled; is readily dissolved in nitric acid. Rhenium is useful as a catalyst for dehydrogenation.
Rheostats. Principle of, and experiments with, with illus., 6-292-93
 Radio sound volume controlled by, 3-98
Rhesus monkeys. illus., 5-378-79; 9-257, 262
Rheumatic fever. Treatment with adrenal hormones, 10-134
Rheumatism, name applied to various pains. 3-213
 See also Arthritis
Rhine, Joseph B., American psychologist. 9-57
Rhinoceros beetles. illus., 2-407
Rhinoceros vipers. illus., 5-362
Rhinoceroses. 7-414, illus., 715
 Drawing by Duerer, illus., 2-370
 Tick birds, partnership with, 10-188, illus., 189
 Woolly, 3-179
Rhizoids, rootlike, anchoring filaments of lower plants. 3-187, 189
Rhizomes, modified stems. with illus., 4-67-68; 6-58
 Ferns', 3-190-91
Rhodium (Rh), chemical element. Atomic number, 45; atomic weight, 102.905; melting point, about 1,966° C.; boiling point, above 2,500° C.; specific gravity, 12.5. Silver-white metal of the platinum family. Discovered in 1803 by Wollaston; name derived from Greek rhodon: "rose." Found native in river sands of the Urals and in the Western Hemisphere. Alloy with platinum used together with pure platinum in some pyrometers. Rhodium is useful in electroplating; it provides a surface that is not affected by strong acids or alkalies or by exposure to air. See also 3-42
Rhododendrons. illus., 1-305; illus., 7-77
Rhodophyta, phylum of algae. 1-301; illus., 3-294
Rhodopsin. See Visual purple
Rhomboids, plane figures. 3-435, illus., 434
Rhombuses, plane figures. 3-435, illus., 434
Rhyolites, igneous rocks. 3-423; 9-308
Rialto Bridge, Venice. with illus., 2-333
Rib cartilages. 3-77
Ribbon glass. illus., 3-316
Ribbon kelps. with illus., 3-220
Ribbon snakes. Pets, 7-25
Ribbons, typewriter. 1-270, illus., 271
Riboflavin, vitamin B₂. with illus., 5-42
 Bread enriched with, 9-299
 Daily requirement and sources of, table, 4-55-57
Ribonucleic acid (RNA). 9-383-86
Ribonucleoproteins, biochemical substances. illus., 2-12d
Ribosomes, cell structures. 2-8
Ribs. illus., 1-148b; 3-77-78, illus., 74, 75
 Bellows, ribs as, with illus., 1-279
Riccia, genus of liverworts. 3-190, illus., 186
Rice. Starch from, 4-77
Rice bugs. 3-258
Richards, Theodore W. American chemist (1868–1928). He served as chemistry professor at Harvard and director of the Gibbs Memorial Laboratory there. He determined, with an accuracy never before attained,

Richards, Theodore W. (continued)
the atomic weights of many chemical elements, for which he received the 1914 Nobel Prize in chemistry. He did outstanding research in thermochemistry, chemical thermodynamics, surface tension and electrochemistry.
Richer, Jean, French scientist. 3-268, illus., 269
Rickets. 5-46-47
Cause, effects and treatment of, 3-84
Rickettsiae, microorganisms. 1-40; 3-458
Ridges, oceanic. 6-74-75, diagrams, 73, 76-77
Riemann, G. F. Bernhard, German mathematician (1826-66). Geometry of, with diagrams, 4-439-41
Rift Valley. See **Great Rift Valley**
Rigel, star in Orion. 1-335
Right angles. with illus., 3-431
Right ascension, position of a star. with diagram, 1-260; 6-81, diagram, 80
Right auricle of heart. illus., 1-148f
Right axillary nodes, lymphatics in armpit. illus., 1-148g
Right-handedness. Parity law and, with illus., 7-107
Right of way, railway. with illus., 1-191-94
Right sphere, in astronomy. 1-262
Right subclavian artery and vein, in shoulder. illus., 1-148f
Right ventricle of heart. illus., 1-148f
Right whales. illus., 7-15, 184
Rigi, mountain of Swiss Alps. illus., 2-219
Rigid airships. with illus., 6-179-80
Riker mounts, display cases for insects. 3-156, illus., 154
Riley, Charles V., American entomologist. 9-290
Rill marks, on beaches. with illus., 8-354
Rills, crevices in moon's surface. 4-284
Rimstone, calcium-carbonate formation in caves. 5-55
Ring Nebula. illus., 8-156a
Ring-necked ducks. Migration route of, 5-418e
Ring-necked pheasants. 6-340, illus., 339
Ring-necked snakes. illus., 5-358
Pets, 7-25
Ring rot, disease of potato. 8-371
Ring stand. Home laboratory, found in, with illus., 4-222-23
Ring-tailed cats. 7-317
Ringed kingfishers. 6-310
Ringelmann Chart. Smoke density measured by, with illus., 3-351
Rings, Saturn's. with illus., 5-109-13; 6-94
Ringworm diseases. Fungi cause, 3-32
Rio de Janeiro, Brazil. Lights of, illus., 4-241
Rip currents. with illus., 8-349-50
"Rip tides." 8-349
Ritter, Johann Wilhelm, German physicist.
Ultraviolet rays, discovery of, 7-200
Ritual. Smoking as, 5-346, 347
River snakes. 5-358
Rivers, William Halse, English physiologist and anthropologist. 9-28
Rivers. *6-409-18
*Land erosion by running water, 8-9-18
Delta formation, 5-301-02
Lakes, action of, in forming, 7-55
Mountain making, role in, 10-214
Origin of, 10-27
Pollution of streams, 5-328
Principal rivers of world, table, 6-418
Sea fish migrating into streams, with illus., 3-242-44
Soil movement and formation, factors in, 2-16
Submarine canyons, action of, in carving, 6-73

Rivers (continued)
Water supply from, 2-272-73
See also **Dams; Water power;** and names of rivers
Riverside Hospital, New York City. Drug-addiction, treatment and research on, with illus., 5-406-07
Riveting. Skyscraper construction, illus., 7-124b
RNA. See **Ribonucleic acid**
Roaches. See **Cockroaches**
Road building. See **Roads**
Road cuts. Collecting minerals at, 9-301
Road rollers. illus., 3-300
Road runners, birds. with illus., 6-308-09
Roads. *3-293-306
Primitive, 1-98-99
Roan antelopes. 8-383-84
Roaring forties, wind belt. 2-94
Roaring Spring, Pease River, Texas. illus., 8-327
Roasting, of ores. 1-376
Robber crabs. 2-242
Migration of, 9-430
Robber flies. illus., 2-410
Robert, Louis, inventor of papermaking machine. 4-365
Robins. with illus., 6-37-38
Nest of, 6-38; 10-258
Robot miners, in coal mining. with illus., 1-409
Roche, Edouard, French astronomer. 5-112
Roche's limit, astronomical constant. 5-112
Roches moutonnées, glaciated rocks. 9-171
Rock, cap, dense rock layer trapping oil or gas. 5-98
Rock doves. 6-306
Rock-fill dams. 8-312, illus., 310
History of, 8-308-09
Rock fragments. Streams carry and deposit, 8-12-13
Rock oil. See **Petroleum**
Rock salt. See **Sodium chloride**
Rock sections, standard rock-bed sequences. 6-369
Rock wrens. 6-46
Rockefeller Center, New York City. illus., 3-118
Rocker arms, of automobile engines. with illus., 2-133
Rocket, Stephenson's locomotive. 6-379, illus., 380
Rockets. *10-1-4
*Guidance of missiles and space vehicles, 8-125-31
*Space travel, 10-40-54
Atmospheric and space research with, 1-236
Cosmic-ray research, illus., 8-396
Development, 9-218-19
Firing station, illus., 1-97
Photographs of earth taken from, 4-42, illus., 42-43
Pilotless missile research, illus., 4-342c
Planes powered by, 6-195
Power plants for planes, 7-69-71
Rocket engine, principle of, 4-92
Twentieth-century developments, with illus., 9-375-83
V-2, 6-185
Weather observations by means of, 1-252
World War II use of, with illus., 9-326-27
See also **Supersonics**
Rocks.
*Formation of rocks, 3-419-26
*Mineral and rock collecting, 9-300-09
*Minerals, 5-248-56
*Mountain-building forces, 10-213-23
*Quarrying, 2-81-88
Bacteria help break down, 2-208
Caves in limestone and other rock formations, with illus., 5-51-58
Coal beds and associated rocks, formation of, with illus., 1-406-07
Erosion and formation by ground water, 8-328
Formations suitable for wells, 8-330-31

Rocks (continued)
  Glaciers' effects on, 9-168-70, 171-73, illus., 164-65, 169
  Ground water held in rock formations, with illus., 8-322-25
  Lake basins formed by erosion of, 7-56
  Metamorphic, 2-82
  Microscopic study of rocks in natural-gas prospecting, 5-100, illus., 101
  Natural gas, rocks containing, 5-97, 99-100
  Oceanic mountains, rocks of, 5-189-90
  Petroleum, rocks containing, with diagrams, 4-142-43
  Sandblasting effects on, 7-320, illus., 320-21
  Soil composed of weathered rock particles, 2-15-19, illus., 17, 18, 19, 25; 6-136
  Water erodes and deposits, 8-10-11
  See also **Deposits; Geological time; Geology; Limestone; Marble; Quarrying; Prospecting**
Rockweeds, brown algae. 3-220-21, illus., 223
Rocky Mountain goats. 8-378, illus., 380; 9-270
  Glacier National Park, found in, 9-276
Rocky Mountain sheep (bighorns). illus., 9-275
Rocky Mountains. 10-23
  Glaciers in Canadian Rockies, illus., 9-162
  History of, 10-215, 216, 218, 221
  Laramide Revolution helped form, 6-374
Rod mills, in ore dressing. with diagram, 1-372
Rodentia, order of mammals. 7-14-15
  See also **Rodents**
Rodents. *8-160-70
  *Beavers and kin, 9-1-6
  Adaptations for feeding, 3-236; 7-9
  Hibernation of, 7-7
  Nature's control of, 6-153
  Seeds dispersed by, 5-5-6, illus., 7
  Survival, adaptations for, 3-236, with illus., 239
  See also **Beavers; Rats; Squirrels; etc.**
Rods, nucleonic devices. Radioisotope-fueled thermo-electric generators, use in, 6-173-74, illus., 172-74
Rods, steel shapes. Manufacture and use in wiremaking, with illus., 1-350-51
Rods and cones of eye. 7-293-94, illus., 292; 8-179
  Stimulate optic nerves in vision, 6-317
Roe deer. 8-243
Roemer, Olaus, Danish astronomer. 3-278; 5-21
Roentgen, Wilhelm Konrad, German physicist.
  Discovery of X rays, 7-143, 202-03; 8-402, 411-12; 9-348-49
Roentgen rays. See **X rays**
Roentgens, units of exposure to external radiation. 9-350
Roll, axial rotation of craft or vehicles. Space vehicles and missiles undergo, 8-129, diagram, 130
Rolled-fill construction, for earth-fill dams. 8-312
Roller dams. 8-315
Rollers, for inking paper in printing presses. 1-208, with diagrams, 209, 211-12
Rollers, used to move heavy objects. with illus., 7-219
Rolling of steel. 1-347-49
Roman Catholic Church. Calendar reform, 10-176, 178, illus., 175
Roman Empire. Signal system, 2-377
Romance languages. 1-119
Romanes, George J., British biologist. 9-51
Rome, Ancient.
  Architecture, 3-114, illus., 115
  Breadmaking in, 9-294
  Bridges, 2-332-33
  Calendars, 10-173-76, illus., 172
  Engineering in, 1-216-17
  Glassmaking, 3-308

Rome, Ancient (continued)
  Illumination in, 4-232
  Irrigation in, 8-193
  Mosaic floors, with illus., 7-116-17
  Number system of, with illus., 1-153-54
  Overthrow of Western Empire, 1-368
  Pottery of, 7-398
  Refrigeration of food in, 4-159
  Roads of, 3-296, 298, illus., 294, 297
  Scientific contributions, with illus., 1-361-63
  Ships and boats of, 4-107
  Transportation in Roman world, with illus., 1-103-04, illus., 105
  Tunnels of, 2-43
  Water supply in, 2-271
Romney, breed of sheep. illus., 10-246
Roof membrane, of ear. with illus., 7-300
Roof tanks, for water-supply systems. with illus., 2-286
Room-and-pillar mining, of coal. with illus., 1-411
Roomettes, Pullman sleeping cars. 1-188
Rooms, in underground coal mines. 1-410, illus., 411
Roosevelt, Franklin Delano, U. S. President.
  Conservation measures in administration of, 6-4
Roosevelt, Theodore, U.S. President.
  Conservation movement supported by, 6-3-4
  Game-protection work, 9-275
Root hairs. with illus., 4-63
Root pressure. 4-71
Roots. *4-62-65
  Bedrock cracked by, illus., 6-140
  Flowering plants, roots of, 3-404
  Food storage in, 2-420
  Nodules and nitrogen binding, with illus., 2-210-11
  Soil in relation to, 2-20-21, 24-25
  Water absorbed by, 5-25, 26
Roots, of numbers. 1-158
Rope-stretchers, Egyptian surveyors. 3-427-28
Rorschach, Hermann, Swiss psychiatrist. 9-57
Rorschach test. with illus., 9-57, illus., 310
Roses. illus., 1-304
  Fruit of wild rose, illus., 5-7
  Wild rose stems, illus., 6-220
Rosin.
  Source of, 2-106
Ross, Malcolm, United States Navy officer. Balloon ascent by, 1-235
Ross, Sir Ronald, British physician (1857–1932). While in the medical service in India, he began a series of special investigations on the causes of malaria. He verified by experiments the theory that the microorganisms that cause the disease are spread by mosquitoes, and he studied the life history of these microorganisms. Ross later made a study of the malaria-bearing mosquitoes of West Africa. He was awarded the 1902 Nobel Prize in medicine in recognition of his services in the field of tropical medicine. See also 7-384
  Life cycle of malarial parasite, discovery of, 10-32-33, illus., 35
Ross, Wayne M., American engineer. Sonar invention, 8-106-07
Ross Dam, Washington (state). illus., 8-316d
Ross Shelf Ice, Antarctica.
  Icebergs produced from, with illus., 9-339
Rosse, 3rd Earl of (William Parsons), British astronomer (1800–67). A member of parliament and a peer of Ireland, he was more inclined toward astronomy than politics. With his powerful telescope, having an improved speculum (reflecting mirror) six feet in diameter, he found that certain nebulae were really groups of stars. He discovered binary and triple stars (stars revolving around a common center of gravity) and described the

Rosse, 3rd Earl of (William Parsons) *(continued)*
moon more fully. See also **6**-388-89
Reflecting telescope of, **9**-156
Rossi, Bruno, Italian-born physicist.
Coincidence counters, development of, **9**-340-41
Cosmic-ray investigations, **8**-395
Rotary compressors, air compressors. **9**-63, *illus.,* 60
Rotary presses, in printing. **1**-210, 214, *diagrams,* 209, 213
Invention of, *with illus.,* **6**-381
Rotary tables. See **Turntables**
Rotary well drilling. Oil wells, **4**-145-46, *diagram,* 144
Water wells, **2**-274
Rotary-wing airplanes. *illus.,* **6**-182, 193-94; *with illus.,* **9**-219-20
See also **Helicopters**
Rotating-arm filters. Sewage purified by, *illus.,* **5**-331
Rotation of earth. **4**-47-48, *diagrams,* 46-47
Atmospheric circulation affected by, *with diagrams,* **1**-243-44
Tidal effects on, **6**-205
Rotation of galaxies. *with diagram,* **8**-51-53
Rotation of Jupiter. **5**-21, 23
Rotation of particles. *with illus.,* **7**-108, *illus.,* 109
Rotation of sun. *with illus.,* **3**-107-08
Rotifers. *illus.,* **1**-293
Rotogravure, printing process. **1**-212-13, *diagram,* 211
Rotors, of dynamo. *illus.,* **5**-309
Rotors, revolving switches of automobile ignition systems. **2**-138
Homemade, *with illus.,* **8**-148-49
Rots, plant diseases. **3**-26; **8**-372
Rough-legged hawks. **6**-156
Roughage. Importance of, in diet, **4**-54, 76; **5**-267, 275
Round window, of ear. **7**-299, 300, *illus.,* 298, 299
Rounding, breadmaking operation. *with diagram,* **9**-297
Roundworms. **2**-156-59, *illus.,* 153, 156, 160
Rousseau, Jean-Jacques, French philosopher.
Educational theory, **9**-52
Rove beetles. *with illus.,* **3**-339-40
Royal antelopes. **8**-387
Royal Canadian Air Force.
Para-rescue man, *illus.,* **6**-187
Photographing Canada from the air, *illus.,* **10**-163
Royal cells, in bees' nests. **3**-368
Royal ferns. **3**-192
Royal Greenwich Observatory.
Founding of, **3**-281
Royal jelly, of bees. **3**-368
Royal Jennerian Society. Work with smallpox, **4**-402
Royal Meteorological Society, in Canada. Weather hobbyists may join, **1**-322
Royal Society, British scientific society. *with illus.,* **3**-266-67
Royal William (Canadian steamship). **4**-110; **6**-378
Rozier, Pilâtre de. Pioneer balloon flight, **6**-177, *illus.,* 176
RR Lyrae stars. **7**-50
Rub'al Khali, desert area of Arabia. **6**-118
Rubber. *****6**-350-60
*****Conveyer belts of rubber, **6**-168-71
Isoprene units in, **7**-270
Molecule, *diagram,* **6**-357
Printing plates of, **1**-208
Radiation thickness gauges
Manufacture of rubber, use in, **9**-46, *illus.,* 44
Sheet rubber, use in measuring, *illus.,* **9**-44
Synthetic rubbers, development of, **8**-185
War material, **9**-325
See also **Synthetic rubber**

Rubber, reclaimed. See **Reclaimed rubber**
Rubbing, friction causing heat. *with illus.,* **7**-219
Rubbing posts, of certain animals. **7**-13
Rubidium (Rb), chemical element. Atomic number, 37; atomic weight, 85.47; melting point, 38.5° C.; boiling point, 700° C.; specific gravity, 1.53. Rare alkali metal; soft and white. Discovered in 1861 by Bunsen and Kirchhoff; name derived from Latin *rubidus:* "red," because of two dark red lines in spectrum. Found in the minerals lepidolite, petalite, and in mica and carnallite; also in some mineral waters and in tea, cocoa, coffee, tobacco and beetroot ash. Prepared by electrolysis of the cyanide. Sometimes used to remove all traces of oxygen from electron tubes. See also **3**-169
Ruby-crowned kinglets. **6**-42
Ruby-throated hummingbirds. **6**-214, *illus.,* 213
Migration of, **9**-420
Rudders. Airplanes, **6**-188-89
Ship rudders, advent of, **4**-108
Rudolphine Tables, astronomical tables. **3**-5
Ruffed grouse. **6**-335, *illus.,* 332
Rufous hummingbirds. **6**-214
Rufus, Roman medical writer. **1**-366
Rugae, folds of the stomach lining. *with illus.,* **4**-325
Rugs. Interior decoration, **4**-271
Rumen, chamber of cow's stomach. *illus.,* **7**-10
Rumford, Count (Benjamin Thompson), American-born British physicist. *with illus.,* **6**-248-50
Heat, experiment showing kinetic nature of, **3**-408
Ruminants, cud-chewing animals. *with illus.,* **7**-10
See also **Cows; Goats; Sheep;** etc.
Rumsey, James, American mechanical engineer. **6**-377
Rundle, Mount, Canada. *illus.,* **10**-21
Runners (stolons), modified stems. *with illus.,* **4**-67
Running, human. *illus.,* **10**-88, 89
World records, **10**-89
Runoff, excess ground water. See **Drainage**
Rural Electrification Administration (REA). **6**-6
Rush, Benjamin, American physician and political leader. **4**-33
Ruskin, John, English essayist. Quotation from, **2**-220
Russell, Bertrand Arthur William (1872-   ), English mathematician and philosopher. Quotation from, **1**-75
Russell, Majors and Wadell, early American freighting company. **1**-106
Russia. See **Union of Soviet Socialist Republics**
Russian thistles. **7**-113
Adaptations for dispersal of seeds, **5**-4
Introduction of, in United States, **5**-6
Rust, iron oxide. **3**-37
Oxygen forms, *illus.,* **1**-37
Rustication, in masonry. **7**-118
Rusting. Oxidation, form of: experiment, *with illus.,* **4**-352
Rusts, fungi. **3**-29
Ruthenium (Ru), chemical element. Atomic number, 44; atomic weight, 101.07; melting point, 2,450° C.; boiling point, above 2,700° C.; specific gravity, 12.2. Gray metal of the platinum group; hard and brittle. Discovered by Klaus in 1844; name derived from the Ukrainian province of Ruthenia. Found native with other members of the platinum group. No practical uses at present. See also **3**-42
Rutherford, Ernest, British physicist. **8**-415-17, *illus.,* 414
Energy derived from atom, writing on, **9**-329
Radiation detectors, development of, **9**-340
Transmutation of light elements, discovery of, **9**-128
Rutledge Gulley, Georgia. *illus.,* **8**-10
Ryle, M., British physicist. **9**-210

S

S-3 satellite. Solar cells in, *illus.*, 7-105

S Waves of earthquakes. See Secondary (S) waves of earthquakes

Saber-toothed cats, extinct carnivores. *with illus.*, 1-397; *illus.*, 6-374; 8-202

Sabin, Albert B., American medical researcher. Polio vaccine developed by, 10-133

Sabin vaccine (antipolio). *illus.*, 7-351

Sabine, Wallace C., American physicist. 5-128

Sable, fur. 7-238

Sable antelopes. 8-383, 384, *illus.*, 386

Sabre jets (F-86), U.S. Air Force planes. *illus.*, 7-67; *illus.*, 9-218

Sac fungi. *with illus.*, 3-26-28

Sacajawea, American Indian woman interpreter and guide. 7-28, *illus.*, 27

Saccharides. See Carbohydrates.

Saccharin, synthetic sweetener. 4-79

Saccule (sacculus), structure in inner ear. *with illus.*, 4-380-81; *with illus.*, 7-305, 306

Sacculina, genus of crustaceans. 2-243
Degeneration, example of, *with illus.*, 6-284

Sachs, Julius von, German botanist. Water-culture experiments by, 8-35, *illus.*, 34

Sacral nerves. *illus.*, 1-148h; 6-329, *illus.*, 328

Sacral plexus. See Sacral nerves

Sacramento River, California. Dammed up by Shasta Dam, *illus.*, 8-316a

Sacrobosco, Johannes de (John of Holywood), English mathematician. 2-309-11

Sacroiliac joints. 3-76

Sacrum, lower part of backbone. 3-76, 81-82, *illus.*, 74

Sadd-El-Aali irrigation project, Egypt. 8-200

Saddleback, lepidopterous insects. 3-202

Safety.
*Accident prevention in home, 7-190-98
*First aid, 10-5-17
*Nuclear-bomb precautions, 9-391-96
Chemical experiments, safety in, 7-180
Coal mining, safety measures in, *with illus.*, 1-413-15
Machine tools constructed for, 10-113

Safety factor, in engineering. 5-376

Safety glass. 3-313

Safety lamps, in coal mines. *with illus.*, 1-413-14

Safflower, thistlelike herb. 7-43, *illus.*, 42

Sage grouse. Courtship display of, *illus.*, 5-422

Sagitta (Arrow), constellation. 1-334

Sagittarius (Archer), constellation. 1-333
Dark area in, 8-153
Messier 8 (nebulosity) in, *illus.*, 9-364

Sago palms. 3-401
Starch storage in, 2-420; 4-78

Sahara Desert. 6-113, *with illus.*, 116-18
Spread of dust from, 7-138-39

Sahuaro, Lake, in Arizona. Evaporation in, 2-273

Sahuaro cacti. *illus.*, 6-228

Saigas, goat antelopes. 8-379, *illus.*, 382

Sail-fin reptiles (Dimetrodon). *illus.*, 6-373; *illus.*, 7-2

Sailboats. Hydrofoil, 4-8
See also Sailing ships

Sailing. See Navigation

Sailing packets. See Packets—Sailing packets

Sailing ships. 4-106-09

Sailplanes. 6-196

Sails. See Sailing ships

Saint Bernards, dogs. 10-243

St. Catherine's Monastery, in Egypt. Manuscripts microfilmed, 10-73

St. Elmo's fire, electrical discharge. 1-399

St. Gotthard Tunnel, Switzerland. 2-44, 48, *illus.*, 46

Saint-Hilaire, Etienne Geoffroy, French naturalist. 4-390

St. Lawrence, Gulf of. Icebergs in, 9-336, *map*, 336-37

St. Lawrence Seaway project. 4-189

St. Martin, Alexis, French-Canadian trapper. Experiments on, 7-372, *illus.*, 373

St. Mary of Bethlehem, London hospital. 9-197

St. Mary's River Dam, Alberta, Canada. *illus.*, 8-199

St. Pierre, Martinique. Destruction of, by eruption of Mount Pelée, *with illus.*, 7-343-44

Sakel, Manfred, Austrian physician. 9-103

Sakia, Persian water wheel. *with illus.*, 8-193

Salamanders. *illus.*, 1-297; 5-156-57, 161, 162, *illus.*, 152, 153, 156, 157, 161
Cave salamanders, *with illus.*, 5-59
Hearing of, *with illus.*, 1-282; *with illus.*, 4-383
Migration of, 9-428-29
Pets, 7-25-26
Terrarium animals, 5-366-67

Salem limestone (Bedford oölite). 2-86

Salerno, Italy. School of medicine at, 2-311-12

Sales, as function of engineers. 1-227

Salinity of sea. *with chart*, 6-30-32
Fish distribution influenced by, 4-97

Salisbury Cathedral, England. Choir, *illus.*, 7-117

Saliva.
Nature and function, 4-321, 323
Reflex secretion of, 6-323

Salivary glands. Human baby, 8-95 .

Salk, Jonas E., American medical researcher. Antipolio vaccine developed by, 10-131, 133, *illus.*, 130

Salk vaccine (antipolio). *illus.*, 7-350; *with illus.*, 10-131, 133

Salmon.
Fishing industry, 6-26, *illus.*, 24-25
Loss because of water pollution, 5-328
Migrations, 3-242-43, *illus.*, 244; 9-425, *illus.*, 426, 428
Reproduction, 4-104, *illus.*, 105
Smell, sense of, 4-101

Salmon flies. See Plecoptera

Salmon ladders. *illus.*, 9-426

Salmonella, genus of bacteria. *with illus.*, 4-153

Salt, common. See Sodium chloride

Salt, table. See Sodium chloride

Salt blocks, source of salt for livestock. 5-324, *illus.*, 325

Salt domes.
Formation of, 5-318
Oil located by, 4-143; *with illus.*, 7-357

Salt flats. 2-23

Salt grass. Underground water indicated by, 8-331

"Salt-making" trick. *with diagram*, 7-180

Salt mines. 5-316-17, 320, *illus.*, 317

Salt water. Buoyancy of, 8-8
Density of, 2-32
Fresh water, conversion of salt water into, 2-283-84

Salt-water crocodiles. *illus.*, 5-383

Salt-water fish.
*Sharks, rays, swordfish and kin, 4-285-95
See also Fish

Salt wells. See Wells, salt

Salterns, saltworks. *with illus.*, 5-314-15

Saltpeter (potassium nitrate). 3-169
See also Fertilizers; Nitrogen

Salts.
*Acids, bases and salts, 4-336-42
Bile, 5-14
Blood-plasma salts, 3-326
Definition of, 2-423
Electrical conductivity of, testing, *with illus.*, 4-345
Formation of, 4-231

Salts (continued)
   Protoplasmic, 2-3, 6, 11
   Sea, presence in, with chart, 6-30-32
Salukis, dogs. 10-240
Salvaging operations. Waste materials collected for sale or use, 5-335
Salvarsan. Development of, for treatment of syphilis, 9-33
Samaras, dry fruits. with illus., 4-130-31; 5-150
Samarium (Sm), chemical element. Atomic number, 62; atomic weight, 150.35; melting point, above 1,300° C.; specific gravity, 7.7-7.8. Grayish white rare-earth metal. Radioactive, emitting alpha particles very slowly. Discovered in 1879 in the mineral samarskite, named in honor of a Russian mine official. Found in very minute amounts in samarskite, cerite and certain Scandinavian minerals; separated from neodymium and europium by reduction or fractional crystallization, or prepared by electrolysis of the fused anhydrous chloride.
Samarkand, U.S.S.R., site of astronomical observatory in Middle Ages. 8-64
Sambars, deer. with illus., 8-239
Samos satellites, American artificial satellites. 9-380
Sampson posts, walking-beam supports. Well drilling, use in, diagram, 4-144
San Benedicto Island, Mexico. Volcanic eruption on, illus., 7-339
San Diego, California.
   Highway 101 at, illus., 3-304
San Francisco, California. Earthquake of 1906, with illus., 9-110
San José scale, insect. 8-368, illus., 367; with illus., 9-193
San Stefano, Italy.
   Destruction by landslide, 2-352
Sanarelli, Guiseppe, Italian scientist. 3-452
Sanatoria. Tubercular patients, with illus., 9-183-84
Sanctuaries, bird and game. *9-266-78
Sand.
   Aquariums, sand for use in, 8-114
   Beach sands, origin and characteristics of, with illus., 8-351-53
   Frosting of grains, 3-178
   Glassmaking uses of, 3-308-09
   Lakes formed by drifting sand, 7-57
   Particles of, size of, 3-424
   Sewage contains, 5-329, 330
   Soil texture, 2-18, 19, illus., 18
   Streams carry and deposit, 8-13
   Tar sands, 4-143
   Wind distribution of, 7-319-24, illus., 318, 322-24
Sand beds, filtered. Sewage, purification of, 5-331
   Water purification by, 2-277, 279-80, illus., 279, 283
Sand crabs.
   Diamond patterns on beach sands produced by, 8-354
Sand crickets. with illus., 3-145-46
Sand dollars, flat, circular sea urchins. illus., 1-293; 2-152
   Fossil form, illus., 1-384
Sand flies. 3-287, 289
Sand lizards. illus., 5-199
Sand sharks. 4-288
Sandblasting, type of wind erosion. 7-319-20, illus., 320-21
Sandglasses. See Hourglasses
Sando Bridge, Sweden. illus., 2-337
Sandpaper. Industrial research on, 1-88
Sandpipers. with illus., 6-405-07
   Migration of, 9-420
Sandstone, sedimentary rock. illus., 1-32; 3-424; 9-308
   Cross-bedding in, illus., 3-179

Sandstone (continued)
   Distribution in United States, 2-85, 86
   Formation of, 2-85
   New Mexico, formations in, illus., 2-350
   Tar sands, 4-143
Sandworms. illus., 1-294
Sanitary fill, method of refuse disposal. 5-336, illus., 335
Sanitation.
   *Sewage disposal, 5-326-36
   *Waste disposal, 5-326-36
   *Water supply, 2-270-86
   Ground-water supplies, sanitation of, with illus., 8-332
   Public-health movement, rise of, with illus., 9-37-40
   Sickroom, 10-56, 59, 61-63, 65-66, illus., 56, 62-63
   Zoos, 10-157-58
   See also **Ventilation**
Santa Trinità (Holy Trinity) Bridge, Florence. 2-333
Santos-Dumont, Alberto, Brazilian aviator.
   Dirigibles, development of, 6-178, illus., 179
Sap. Rise of, 4-71
Sapphire, precious stone.
   Solar cells protected by slices of, 7-106, illus., 105
Saprophytes.
   Bacteria as, 3-65
   See also **Fungi**
Sapsuckers, birds. 6-212, illus., 211
Sapwood, outer wood of trees. with illus., 4-70
Sarcodina, class of protozoans. 2-63-65, illus., 62, 63
Sarcomas, cancers of the muscles, bones, cartilages and connective tissues. 8-266
Sardines. 4-314
   Migration of, 9-427
   Reproduction, 4-104
Sargasso Sea. 3-221; 6-238
Sargassum, genus of brown algae. illus., 1-301; 3-221
Saroses, time periods between eclipses of a series. 3-134
Sartorius, thigh muscle. illus., 1-148c; illus., 3-204
Sassafras trees. 5-148, illus., 149
Sastrugi, snow ridges. 9-171
Satellites, artificial, of earth. 9-382, with illus., 375-76, 379-81; 10-44, 46, 50, 52-54, illus., 47, 51
   *Guidance of missiles and space vehicles, 8-125-31
   Electronic computers used for estimates of time aloft, 9-151
   Radioisotope-fueled thermoelectric generators, with illus., 6-174
   Vanguard I, 5-188
   Vanguard II, 5-188
   Weather study by means of, 1-252, illus., 241, 253; 9-223
Satellites, of planets. 3-158-59, illus., 160, 162
   Jupiter, 5-21, 24
   Mars, 4-417-18
   Neptune, 5-292
   Saturn, 5-113
   Uranus, 5-289-90, diagram, 292
   See also **Moon**
"Satelloons," American satellite-balloons. with illus., 9-380
Saturated solutions. 4-298-99
Saturation, color quality. 7-287
Saturation, condition of atmospheric moisture. 1-244-45
Saturation, zone of. Ground-water accumulation, 8-323-24, 328-29, 332, illus., 322-25, 329, 332
Saturn, planet. *5-107-13
   Comet family of, 5-397
   Conceptions of, illus., 3-164
   Data, 10-298
   Galileo's observations of, 3-2

Saturn (continued)
How to observe, **6**-84
Model of, *illus.*, **2**-400
Rings of meteoritic material, **6**-94
Satellites of, **3**-159
Sauba ants. See **Leaf-cutting ants**
Saudi Arabia. Desert, *illus.*, **6**-113
Sauerkraut. Fermentation of, **4**-167
"Sausage," chemical trick. *with diagram*, **7**-175
Sausages. Preparation of, **5**-167, *illus.*, 168
Savannah, nuclear-powered ship. **4**-118, *with illus.*, 114b-c
Savannah, steamship. **4**-110; **6**-378
Save River Bridge, Yugoslavia. **2**-335
Savery, Thomas, English military engineer. **4**-39
Saw-whet owls. **6**-165, *illus.*, 152, 167
Sawdust. Heat insulation by, **4**-12
Sawfish. **4**-292, *illus.*, 291
Sawmills. **2**-115-17, *illus.*, 114, 115, 116
Saws. Kinds used in lumbering, *with illus.*, **2**-115-16
Sawtooth Mountains, Idaho. *illus.*, **10**-24
Saxonia, early locomotive. *illus.*, **1**-179
Saxophones. Sound production in, **5**-218
Scabs. Potatoes, **8**-371
Scala media. See **Middle stairway**
Scala tympani. See **Stairway of the tympanum**
Scala vestibuli. See **Stairway of the vestibule**
Scalar quantities. **2**-127
Scalds. Prevention of in home, **7**-196
Scale insects. See **San José scale**
Scale of hardness. See **Mohs' scale**
Scaled quail. **6**-334
Scales, animal.
Lepidopterous insects, scales of, **3**-193, *illus.*, 194, 202c
Lizards, scales of, **5**-197
Snakes, scales of, *with illus.*, **5**-354b, 354d
Scales, barometric. **1**-247, 249
Scales, musical. *with table*, **5**-214-15
Scales, temperature. *with diagram*, **1**-164
Scallops. **2**-199, *illus.*, 196
Shell of, *illus.*, **2**-101
Scaly anteaters. See **Pangolins**
Scandinavia.
Ancient wood calendar, *illus.*, **10**-174
Scandium (Sc), chemical element. Atomic number, 21; atomic weight, 44.956; melting point, 1,200° C.; boiling point, about 2,400° C.; specific gravity, about 3.02. This metal forms colorless salts. It was discovered by Nilson in 1879; named after Scandinavia. Obtained from various ores, including those of tin, tungsten and beryllium.
Discovery of, **5**-85
Scanning, technique used in reproducing images. **6**-278, 281-82; **7**-391
Facsimile transmission, **7**-391, *illus.*, 390
Printing plates made by electric scanning, **1**-208
Television, **5**-278-79, 282
Scaphopods, mollusks. **2**-201
Shell collecting, *with illus.*, **2**-101
Scapula, shoulder blade. *illus.*, **1**-148b; **3**-79-80, *illus.*, 74, 75
Sound conducted by shoulder blades in newts, *with illus.*, **1**-282
Scar tissue. **7**-352, 353, *illus.*, 353
Scarab beetles. **3**-345
Scarlet fever.
Baldness due to, *illus.*, **2**-180
Recovery from, **7**-352
Scarlet oak trees. **5**-147

Scarlet tanagers, birds. **6**-108
Migration of, **9**-421
Scattering, of light. **7**-283
Clouds' colors due to, **2**-220
Scaup ducks. **6**-402, 403
Scavengers.
Bacteria as, **2**-206
Plants and animals serving as, **10**-186
Sea gulls, **6**-395
Scent glands. Defensive use by animals, *with illus.*, **3**-238-39
True bugs, **3**-255
Schaefer, Vincent J., American scientist.
Rain- and snow-making experiments of, **2**-218
Schaudinn, Fritz, German zoologist.
Spirochete causing syphilis, discovery of, **8**-409
Scheele, Karl Wilhelm, German scientist.
Oxygen, discovery of, **4**-355-56
Scheiner, Christoph, German astronomer. **3**-15
Scheiner, Julius, German astronomer.
Galactic spectrogram first obtained by, **8**-51
Schiaparelli, Giovanni, Italian astronomer (1835–1910). Director of the Milan Observatory he was famed as an astronomical observer. He gave the name *canali* (channels) to the markings on Mars. He showed the relationships between cometary orbits and meteor swarms and discovered the asteroid Hesperia. See also **6**-392
Venus' period of rotation, theory of, **4**-30
Schindleria, tiny fish. **4**-96
Schists, metamorphic rocks. **3**-426; **9**-308
Schizocarps, dry fruits. **4**-131
Schizomycophyta, bacteria. *3-63-72
See also **Bacteria**
Schizophrenia, mental illness. *with illus.*, **9**-203
d-lysergic acid used to study, **9**-104
Tranquilizers used in treatment of, **5**-378
Schleiden, Matthias Jakob, German botanist. *with illus.*, **7**-159-61
Cell theory, **2**-2
Schleyer, Johann Martin, German priest. **1**-119-20
Schliemann, Heinrich, German businessman and archaeologist. **9**-28-29
Schlieren photography. *illus.*, **10**-165
Schmidt telescopes. *with illus.*, **8**-59; *with illus.*, **9**-160
Schmutzdecke, slime mat forming on slow sand filter. **2**-277
Schoenbein, Christian Friedrich, German chemist. **5**-81
Schoenbein, J. L., Swiss physician. **9**-175
Scholarships.
Scientific education, available for, **10**-195
Psychology study, **9**-322
Scholasticism. Medieval universities influenced by, **2**-304-05
Schonland, B. F. J., South African meteorologist. **1**-399
Schools.
Health services in, **9**-41
Industrial design, training in, **10**-126
See also **Education**
Schott, Otto, German glassmaker. **9**-82, 92
Schram, Gustav, German biologist. Virus experiments of, **9**-385
Schroedinger, Erwin, Austrian physicist. **9**-283
Wave mechanics, theory of, **7**-205
Schroeter, J. H., German astronomer. **4**-30
Schulze, Johann Heinrich, German physicist.
Experiments with sunlight and silver salts, **9**-398-99
Schurz, Carl, American general and politician.
Conservation movement supported by, **6**-2
Schwabe, Heinrich Samuel, German astronomer. **6**-393
Schwann, Theodor, German naturalist. **7**-159-61
Cell theory, **2**-2

Schwassmann-Wachmann's comet. 5-397
Sciatic nerve. illus., 1-148h
Science.
 *Industry and scientific research, 1-87-97
 *Youth competitions in science, 8-67-77
 Careers in, with illus., 10-191-202
 Chemistry and physics, relationships between, 1-86
 Engineering as applied science, with illus., 1-215-29
 Mathematics and, 1-76-78
 Nobel Prize winners in, 10-299-307
 See also Astronomy; Chemistry; History of science;
  Medicine; Physics; Projects and experiments;
  Research; etc.
Science Clubs of America, Washington, D. C. Competi-
  tions among young scientists, information on, 8-72,
  73
Science Projects Handbook. Young scientists' researches
  described in, 8-74
Science Service, in the United States. Competitions and
  science fairs for youngsters sponsored by, 8-72, 73
Science Talent Search. See Westinghouse Science
  Talent Search
Science World, magazine. Young scientists' researches
  published in, 8-74
Scientific American, magazine. Young scientists' re-
  searches described in, 8-74
Scientific collections. See Projects and experiments
Scientific method.
  Applied to psychology, 9-312
  Bacon and Descartes, contributions of, 3-6-10
  Newton's rules, 3-280
Scientific notation. 2-74
Scientists. *Youth competitions in science, 8-67-77
  See also Astronomy; Chemistry; Geology; Medicine;
   Physics; etc.; also names of scientists
Scincids (Scincidae), family of lizards. 5-199
Scintillation counters. See Scintillometers
Scintillometers, radiation counters. Prospecting with,
  7-361
Scissors. Levers, combination of, 3-58
Sclerotic layer, of the eye. 7-293, illus., 292
Scorpion flies. See Mecoptera
Scorpions. 2-267-68, illus., 258
Scorpius (Scorpion), constellation. 1-332
Scotland. Uplift of, 10-223
Scott, Leon. Invented the phonautograph, 7-365
Scouring rushes, horsetails. 3-192
Scrap, steel. Steelmaking, used in, 1-345-46
Scrapers, horse-drawn. 8-309, illus., 308
Scratch tests, in allergy detection. 4-262-63
Scratches. Prevention of, in home, 7-197-98
  Treatment of, 10-7
Screech owls. 6-165, illus., 162, 348
Screening.
  Ore dressing, with diagram, 1-372
  Papermaking, illus., 4-374b
  Sewage purification, with illus., 5-330
  Water purification, 2-273
  Wood fibers, screening of, 4-368
Screens, for halftones in printing. with illus., 1-204
Screw propellers, in boats and ships. 4-111; 6-378
Screw worms, blowflies. 3-287
Screws, simple machines. with illus., 3-60
Scripps Canyon, oceanic canyon. 6-73
Scrotum, pouch containing testes. 8-21, illus., 20
Scrubbers, gas-trapping devices. 3-355
Scrubbing towers, gas-cleaning devices. 5-101
Scuba diving. with illus., 6-26a-d
Scully, Frank, American author. Flying saucers, account
  of, 9-18
Scurvy. 5-39, 45-46

Scutellum, triangular plate found in true bugs. with
  illus., 3-252, 253
Sea. See Lakes; Ocean
Sea, name given to area in southern region of sky.
  1-333
Sea anemones. illus., 1-292; 2-150-51, illus., 148; 6-34
Sea animals. See Fish; Octopuses; Seals; Squids;
  Whales; etc.
Sea arrows. See Squids
Sea bass, fish. 4-314, 320
Sea breezes. 2-90-91
Sea catfish. illus., 4-104
Sea cliffs.
  Beach sand along base of, with illus., 8-353
Sea cows. See Manatees
Sea cucumbers. 2-152
Sea elephant. 7-92-93, illus., 91
Sea fans. 2-151
Sea gulls. 6-395-96
Sea horses, fishes. illus., 1-297
  Reproduction, 3-241; 4-104, illus., 105
Sea lettuce, green algae. 3-217, 218
Sea level. Instability of, 6-75, 77; 8-355
Sea lilies. 2-152
  Fossil crinoids, 1-388, illus., 387; illus., 6-372
Sea lions. 7-86, illus., 87; illus., 9-424-25
  Herds of, 7-12
Sea mice, marine worms. 2-162
Sea monsters. Whale, sixteenth-century artist's concep-
  tion of, illus., 6-29
Sea mosses. illus., 1-301
Sea otters. 8-177, illus., 176
Sea palms, brown algae. with illus., 3-220
Sea plants.
  Light received by, 6-221
  See also Algae
Sea plumes. 2-151
"Sea pusses." 8-349
Sea reptiles (sea "serpents"). illus., 6-374
Sea snakes. 5-363, with illus., 354c
  Migration of, 9-429-30
Sea squirts (tunicates). with illus., 4-3
  Luminous, 2-185
Sea stars (starfish). illus., 1-293; 2-152, illus., 150
"Sea trout." See Squeteague
Sea turtles, 5-386, 388
Sea urchins. illus., 1-293; 2-152, illus., 151
Sea weeds. See Algae
Sea whips. 2-151, illus., 148-49
Sea Wings, hydrofoil test boat. illus., 4-7
Seaborg, Glenn T., American research chemist (1912-
). In 1940, at the University of California, he and
  his associates discovered element 94 — plutonium; later
  they discovered other transuranic elements. (A tran-
  suranic element is one that has an atomic number
  greater than that of uranium: that is, 92.) Seaborg
  won the Nobel Prize in chemistry in 1951, was named
  Chancellor of the University of California in 1958 and
  appointed Chairman of the Atomic Energy Commission
  in 1961.
Seals. *7-85-93
  Fur, 7-238
  Herds of, 7-12
  Migration of, 9-423
  Refuge in Pribilof Islands, illus., 6-14
Seals, concrete, for cofferdams. 2-343, illus., 342
Sealskins.
  Fur seals, illus., 7-89-90, 93
Seam-welders, ultrasonic. illus., 8-111
Seamless tubing, steel.
  Manufacture and uses of, 1-351

Seamounts, oceanic peaks. *with diagram*, **6-75**

Searchlights.
Parabolic surfaces of, *with illus.*, **3-439**

Seas, lunar. **4-282, 284**

Seascapes. Photography of, **6-314**

Seaside (maritime) earwigs. **3-152**

Seasonal dimorphism. See **Dimorphism**

Seasons. *Calendars, **10-171-80**
*Life and seasonal changes, **5-408-13**
Circulation changes in stratosphere, **1-237, 238**
Crop growing according to, **1-164-65**
Jupiter, possible seasons on, **5-22**
Mars, seasons on, **4-416, 417, 418**
Seasonal changes, causes of, **4-49**, *diagrams*, **47-49**
Sleep patterns vary during, **6-146**

Seawater. Body fluids resemble, **2-6**
Fresh water, conversion into, **2-283-84**

Seawolf, atomic submarine. **5-36, 37**

Sebaceous (oil) glands. **2-177, 180**, *illus.*, **174; 5-19**

Sebum, sebaceous-gland secretion. **5-11**

Secchi, Pietro Angelo, Italian astronomer (1818–78). A Jesuit, he was an astronomy professor and the director of the observatory at the Roman College, Rome. As a pioneer in the field of astrophysics, he was the first to make a systematic spectroscopic study of the skies. He made noteworthy solar-eclipse photographs, studied the constitution of the sun and the nature of sun spots and made important meteorological observations. See also **6-391**

Second-class levers. *with illus.*, **1-283; 3-58**, *illus.*, **57**; *with illus.*, **7-215**

Secondaries, bird feathers. **6-210**

Secondary anemias, anemias due to certain underlying conditions. **3-330-31**

Secondary (storage) batteries. **5-94**, *with illus.*, **95-96**

Secondary bow, of rainbows. **7-279**, *illus.*, **278**

Secondary coils, in electrical transformers. *with illus.*, **6-134-35**

Secondary colors. **7-285-86**, *illus.*, **287**

Secondary cosmic rays. See **Cosmic rays**

Secondary roots, of plants. **4-62, 64**, *illus.*, **65**

Secondary (S) waves of earthquakes. **4-171, 173**, *illus.*, **170; 9-107, 114**

Secretariat Building, United Nations, New York City. *illus.*, **3-123**

Secretin, hormone that stimulates pancreatic-juice secretion. **4-328**

Secretions, cellular. **2-12-13**

Secretions, human glandular. *5-8-19**
Skin, **2-176-77**

Secretions, insect. Defensive and offensive, **2-409**
Food secretions, **3-360-61**

Secretions, internal. See **Endocrine glands**

Secretions, plant. Protection against insects, **7-82**

Sectors, parts of linkages or lever-and-gear systems. *with illus.*, **7-218**

Secular variations, in earth's magnetic field. **7-169-71**

Sedan chairs, for transportation. **1-98**, *illus.*, **100**

Sedatives, drugs. **5-401, 403-05**, *illus.*, **400**
Alcoholic beverages as, **4-408-09**

Sedges, grasslike plants. *illus.*, **6-223**
Rhizomes of, *illus.*, **4-67**

Sedgwick, Adam, English geologist (1785–1873). He was a professor at Cambridge and a founder of the Cambridge Philosophical Society. He is most famous for his investigations of the geology of Devonshire; he showed that certain rock formations were of an early geologic age, which he named Devonian. He also founded the Cambrian system of dating geological deposits.

Sediment.
Color in warm, moist climate, **3-179**
Mountain building, role in, **10-213-14, 218-20**
Ocean bottom, **6-73-74, 75**
Soil formed from, **2-16**
Stream transportation and deposition of, **8-12-13, 16-17**
Varves, **3-180**
Water supply, removal of silt and other solids from, **2-273, 277-80**, *illus.*, **278-79, 282-83**
See also **Soil**

Sedimentary rocks. **3-419**, *with illus.*, **424-26; 9-307-08**
Coal beds and associated rocks, formation of, *with illus.*, **1-406-07**
Fossils found in, **1-383**
Mountain building, role in, *with illus.*, **10-213-20**
Natural gas, sedimentary rocks containing, **5-97**
Origin of, **2-82**
Petroleum, sedimentary rocks containing, *with diagrams*, **4-142-43**
Sequence and correlation of, **6-369**
See also **Deposits**

Sedimentation, deposition of particles.
Red blood cells, sedimentation rate measured in, **3-327-28**

Seebeck, Johann, German physicist. **6-172-73**

Seebeck electromotive force. **6-172-73, 174**

Seed coats, seed parts. **2-415, 418, 419; 5-63**, *illus.*, **62**

Seed diamonds. Diamonds synthesized by using, **4-276**

Seed ferns. **3-401**

Seed plants. *3-397-406**
*Flowers, fruits and seeds, **4-119-32**
*Food storage in seed plants, **2-415-20**
*Germination, **5-61-67**
*Roots, stems and leaves, **4-62-75**
*Seed and fruit dispersal, **5-1-7**

Seeding, cloud. **2-218**

Seedlings, immature plants. Bean, *illus.*, **1-38**

Seeds.
*Dispersal, **5-1-7**
*Germination, **5-61-67**
Bean seed, germination of, *illus.*, **1-38**
Coral islands, introduced into, **4-136**
Description of, **4-131-32**
Distribution of, *with illus.*, **3-240-41; 6-53-54**
Food reserves in, **2-415, 417, 418-19, 420**, *illus.*, **416**
Formation of, **3-55, 406**
Preservation of, **10-211-12**
Structure of, **5-62-63; 6-53**
Transportation of weed seeds, *with illus.*, **7-112-13**
Trees can be recognized by, **5-140-41**
Uses of, **4-132**

Seeds, imperfections in glass. **3-312**

Seeing. See **Vision**

Seepage, gas. Natural gas, **5-98**

Seepage, oil. **4-140-42**

Seepage, water.
Dams affected by, **8-317**
Springs, **8-325**

Seepage springs. **8-325**

Segmented worms. *with illus.*, **2-159-62**, *illus.*, **153, 158**

Segregation, law of heredity. **8-340**, *diagram*, **341**

Seiches, oscillations of lake surfaces. **7-57, 60**

Seismic methods. Ore and petroleum deposits located by, **4-145**, *diagram*, **143**; *with illus.*, **7-357-58**
Natural-gas prospecting, used in, **5-99**, *illus.*, **100**

Seismographs. *with illus.*, **9-112-16**
Earth's interior, use in study of, **4-170-71, 173**
Natural-gas prospecting, seismographs used in, **5-99**, *illus.*, **100**

Seismographs *(continued)*
Oil prospecting, use in, 4-145, *diagram,* 143; *illus.,* 7-354
See also Earthquakes
Seismology. *9-105-19
See also Earthquakes
Seismometers. See **Seismographs**
Seistan, inland lake depression of Iran. **7**-57
Selden, George B., American inventor.
Automobile patent granted to, 2-130
Selection, natural. See **Natural selection**
Seleniferous plants. 7-76
Selenium (Se), chemical element. Atomic number, 34; atomic weight, 78.96; melting point, 220° C.; boiling point, 688° C.; specific gravity, 4.8. **Nonmetal; re**sembles sulfur chemically. Conductivity increases with brightness of light playing on it. Discovered in 1817 by Berzelius; name derived from Greek *selene:* "moon," as it was associated with tellurium, named for the earth. Traces are found in sulfur deposits, either free or as the sulfide. Prepared in red amorphous form by reduction of selenic acid. Used chiefly in glass and ceramic industries, as well as for photoelectric cells.
Self-pollination. 4-125
Prevention of, 4-125-26
Self-potential, electrical. Prospecting, detection of rock potentials in, 7-359-61
Self-regulation machines. See **Automatic machines**
Self-service stores (supermarkets). Design of products and packages important in, 10-123-25
Sella turcica, bone cavity into which pituitary gland fits. 5-15
Semantics, science of word meanings. 1-116-17
Semaphore arms, railway signaling devices. 1-192, *illus.,* 193
Semaphore communication. History of, 2-378
Semen, fluid produced in male reproductive organs. 8-21
Semiarid (nearly desert) regions. Soils of, 2-19, 22
Water erosion in, 8-11
Semicircles, geometric figures. *with illus.,* 3-436
Semicircular canals. 4-381, *illus.,* 380; 7-305-06, *illus.,* 298, 305
Semiconductors. Electronics, used in, 6-303
Radioisotope-fueled thermoelectric generators, used in, 6-173
Semidiurnal tides. 6-204, 205
Semifinishing. Plastics, 8-233
Semihydraulic method, for constructing earth-fill dams. 8-312
Seminal vesicles, bladderlike vessels. 8-21, *illus.,* 20
Semipermeable membranes. *with illus.,* 5-373-74
Cells contain, 2-7
Semitic peoples. Alphabet developed by, 1-115
Semmelweis, Ignaz Philipp, Hungarian obstetrician. *with illus.,* 7-374-75
Seneca, Lucius Annaeus, Roman philosopher and statesman. 1-361-62
Senefelder, Alois, Bavarian inventor of lithographic printing. 1-197
Senile psychosis. 9-201-02
Senility.
Mental illness in, 9-201-02
Tranquilizers used in treatment of, 5-378
Sensations. *7-291-306
Body's defenses, role in, 7-347-48
Hearing and sound waves, 5-114-15, 118-19, 122-23, 125
Musical sounds, *with illus. and tables,* 5-211-15
Nerve impulses, relation to, 6-320
Psychological study of, 9-314-15
See also **Brain; Cerebrum; Hearing; Senses; Vision**

Sense organs, animal.
Ants, 3-360
Birds, 5-421-23
Cats, 8-203
Crustaceans, 2-237, *illus.,* 239
Fishes, *with illus.,* 4-101-02
Importance to animals, 4-379
Insects 2-402-03, 406
Flies, *with illus.,* 3-284-85
Primates, 9-251
Man, *with illus.,* 7-291-306
Snakes, 5-352, 364
Spiders, *with illus.,* 2-261-62
Senses. *7-291-306
Adaptations to environment, 10-140, 142
Body's defenses, sense organs as part of, 7-346-47
Hearing and sound waves, 5-114-15, 118-19, 122-23, 125, *illus.,* 114-15, 119, 123, 125
Helmholtz' work on perception, 9-48
Psychological study of, 9-314-15
Skin, organs in the, 2-177-78
See also **Hearing; Sensations; Vision**
Sensitive plants. Turgor movements of, 3-54, *illus.,* 53
Sensitization.
Alcoholism treated by, 4-413-14
Antibodies and, 4-259
Sensitometry. Measurement of effect of light on photographic emulsions, 9-403-04
Sensors, space-flight path detectors. 8-128, 130, 131
Sensory areas, of cerebrum. *with illus.,* 6-325, *illus.,* 324
Sensory nerves and fibers.
Body's defenses, role in, 7-346-47
Definition and functions of, 6-318, 320, 325, *illus.,* 322
See also **Cranial nerves; Spinal Cord**
Sentences. Language, make-up of, 1-108
Sepals, flower parts. 3-405, *illus.,* 398; 4-120, *illus.,* 121
Separating, in ore dressing. *with diagrams,* 1-373-75
Separators, cream. 2-126
Separators, mineral. *illus.,* 3-38-39
Separating diamonds from baser materials, 4-254
Sepia, pigment. 2-195
Sepias. See **Cuttlefish**
Septic tanks. Sewage disposal, 5-333-34, *illus.,* 334
Sequences, in numbers. 4-436-37
Sequences, algebraic. *with illus.,* 2-77-80
Sequoia trees, giant cone-bearing trees. **2**-108, 110; *with illus.,* 5-142-43; *illus.,* 8-333
Sericin, silk-cementing secretion. 5-178
Sericteries, silk-spinning organs. 5-178
Series, rocks of particular geologic epochs. 6-370
Series electric circuits. *with illus.,* 6-133
Home experiments with, *with illus.,* 6-293
Serotonin, hormone. 5-377
Serows, goat antelopes. 8-377
Serpens (Serpent), constellation. 1-332
Serpent stars. 2-152
Serpentine, mineral. *illus.,* 9-304
Serpentine movement, of snakes. *with illus.,* 5-354a
Serpents. See **Snakes**
Serpulids, family of worms.
Coastal formations due to, 8-358
Serum albumin, blood-plasma fraction. 3-326, 334
Radioactive albumin used in determining blood volume, 10-99
Serums. 7-351
Bacteria used in preparation of, 3-70
See also **Blood serum; Vaccines**
Servals, cats. 8-212
Service stations. 4-152

Serviceberry trees. 5-149, *illus.,* 148
Servomotors, automatic variable-speed motors. 10-235-36
Sesostris III, king of Egypt.
    Funerary ship from tomb of, *illus.,* 10-92
Seton, Ernest Thompson, English-born writer. 8-254
Sets (mathematical), theory of. *with diagrams,* 4-441-42
Settling basins, for water purification. *with illus.,* 2-279
Settling chambers. Smoke particles trapped by, 3-354-55
Settling tanks, for purifying sewage. *with illus.,* 5-330
Severn River, England. Bridge over, 2-333
Sewage disposal. *5-326-36
Sewage treatment. *with illus.,* 5-328-34, *illus.,* 326, 330-32, 334
Sewers. 5-327-28, 335-36, *illus.,* 334
Sewing, of printed matter. 1-214
Sewing machines.
    Early typewriters incorporate many features of, 1-267
    Electronic, *illus.,* 10-168
Sex.
    Freud's ideas on, 9-99
    Growth and aging, 8-98-101
    See also Reproduction
Sex cells. *with illus.,* 6-270
    Eggs and sperm, *illus.,* 1-43
    Heredity, role in, *with illus.,* 8-334-37
Sex determination. 8-337-39, *diagram,* 338
Sex glands. *illus.,* 1-148g; 5-19, *illus.,* 16-17
Sex-linked inheritance. 8-342-43
Sextants, navigation instruments. *illus.,* 1-19
Sexual dimorphism. See Dimorphism
Sexual reproduction. See Reproduction
Sexual selection. See Natural selection
Shad, fish.
    Catches of, 6-22
    Food, source of, 4-314
    Introduction of, into new localities, 4-312
    Migration of, 9-425, 427
Shadbush trees. 5-149
Shadoofs, irrigation devices. *with illus.,* 8-192
Shadow (X-ray) photography. 7-143, 146, 148, *illus.,* 144, 150
Shaft mines.
    Coal, *with illus.,* 1-410
    Ores, *with diagram,* 1-371
Shafts, bone. 3-73-74
Shagbark trees. 5-146
Shaking tables (vanners), in ore dressing. *with diagram,* 1-373
Shale, sedimentary rock. 3-424, *illus.,* 425; 9-308
    Oil shales, 4-143
Shallows, oceanic. 6-70, 71
Shane, Charles D., American astronomer.
    Galaxies catalogued by, 8-49
Shapers, planing tools. 10-110-11
Shapley, Harlow, American astronomer.
    Galaxies catalogued photographically by, 8-49
    Galaxy, theories concerning, 8-156, 158
Sharks. *with illus.,* 4-285-90, *illus.,* 294
    Cow sharks, 6-283
    Ear and jaw structure, *with illus.,* 4-382-83
    Fossil sharks, *illus.,* 6-372
    Frilled shark, *illus.,* 4-291
    Heart of, 1-277
    Port Jackson sharks, 6-283
    Reproduction, 4-104
    Soupfin shark, *illus.,* 4-94
    Whale sharks, 4-96-97
Sharp-shinned hawks. 6-157, 158

Shasta Dam, California. *illus.,* 8-316a
Shatter cones, fracture features. Meteorites, evidence of, 6-92
Shattuck, Lemuel, American stationer and sanitary reformer. 9-37-38
Shaw, George Bernard, British author. Quotation from, 9-279-80
Shear waves, of earthquakes. 9-107, 114-15
Shearing, tooling operation. 10-108
Shearing strain. 5-375, *illus.,* 376
Shedding of hair. 2-179
Sheen. See Luster
Sheep.
    Altitude affects number of blood cells, 7-8
    Domestication of, 10-244-45, *illus.,* 246-47
    Goats distinguished from, 10-245, 248
    Mutations in, *illus.,* 6-274
    Parasitic-worm infestations of, 2-155-56, 159, *illus.,* 154
Sheep manure, as soil fertilizer. 2-156
Sheep ticks. 3-292, *illus.,* 291
Sheet and strip, steel. Manufacture and uses of, *with illus.,* 1-349-50
Sheet-fed presses, in printing. 1-209
Sheet floods. 8-10-11
Sheet papers. 4-377
Sheet rubber. 6-355
Shell concept, of atomic structure. *with diagrams,* 1-311-12, *diagram,* 313; 3-246; 4-310
    Proposed by Bohr, 8-417
Shells, nose bones. See Turbinate bones
Shells, of atoms. See Shell concept
Shells, animal.
    *Shell collecting, 2-99-104
    Beach sands made up of wave-ground shells, 8-352
    Fossil shells, *with illus.,* 6-371
    Turtle, 5-386
Shells, missiles. See Explosives
Shelter belts, for protection of soil. 6-5-6
Shelters, for weather instruments. 1-317, *diagram,* 318
Shelters, to protect against effects of nuclear bombs. 9-392, 394-96, *illus.,* 395
Shepard, Alan B., Jr., United States naval officer. Space flight by, *with illus.,* 9-381
Shepard, Francis P., American geologist.
    Shoreline classification proposed by, *with illus.,* 8-355-58
Sherrington, Sir Charles S., English physiologist. 9-56
Sherwood, Project, for achieving controlled nuclear fusion. 9-332
Shield bugs. 3-257
Shield ferns. *illus.,* 3-188
Shield-tailed snakes. 5-358
Shields, used in tunnel excavations. 2-52, *illus.,* 50, 52, 53, 56
Shift locks, typewriter. 1-272
Shigella, genus of bacteria. Bacillary dysentery, *with illus.,* 4-333
Ship Rock Peak, New Mexico. 8-11
Shipbuilding. *4-106-18
Ships. *4-106-18
    *Bathyscaphes, 6-74a-d
    *Hydrofoils, 4-5-8
    *Submarines, 5-31-37
    Beagle, British ship, 7-31, *illus.,* 30
    Biremes, type of galley, *illus.,* 6-28
    Cable-laying steamer, *illus.,* 5-241
    Cutters of United States Coast Guard, *illus.,* 6-363
    Displacement of water, 2-33
    Freighters, *illus.,* 4-187-89; *illus.,* 7-61
    French frigate, *illus.,* 3-373

Ships (continued)
Icebergs a menace to, 9-337-38, illus., 336, 338
Magnetization of metal, 8-143
Nuclear power plants, 9-358
Oceanographic research vessels, 6-29-30, 69-70, 74, illus., 30, 36, 70
Steamboat, invention and development of, 6-377-78, illus., 378-79
Tankers, 4-146, illus., 147; 6-362
Turbines used to propel, 5-312
See also **Canals**; **Submarines**; **Turbines**
Shipworms. See **Teredos**
Shishaldine, Mount, Aleutian Islands. illus., 8-295
Shivering, of body. 3-208
Shoals of fish. 4-312-13
Shock.
Serum albumin treatment for, 3-334
Symptoms, signs and first aid for, with illus., 10-10-11
Shock, electric. Prevention of, in home, 7-196-97
Shock absorbers, automobile. 2-142
Shock treatment, for mental ills. 9-103
Shock tubes, apparatus for testing model nose cones. with diagram, 10-234
Shock waves.
Aircraft may produce, with diagrams, 10-231-32
Atom-bomb explosion produces, 9-391, 392
Explosions produce, with illus., 8-274
Meteors producing, 6-89, 91
See also **Earthquakes**; **Seismographs**
Shoe manufacturing.
Leather used in, 7-232
Shoes. Care of feet, 10-81-82
See also **Leather**
Sholes, Christopher Latham, American inventor. 6-381
Typewriter developed by, with illus., 1-266-67
"Shooting stars." See **Meteors**
Shoran. Short-range detection device used in navigation and mapping. It was first used, and still serves, to locate a ship's position within 200 miles of the shore; hence the name (SHOrt RAnge Navigation). The ship determines its position by sending out radar impulses to two stations on shore. In measuring distances on land, the shoran set is installed on a plane; it also sends out signals to two stations.
Shore bugs. 3-261
Shore flies. 3-291
Shorelines. *8-348-59
Short circuits. Precautions against in electric generating stations, 9-234-35
Short-day plants. 4-120
Short-eared owls. 6-165
Short-horned grasshoppers. 3-140, 142-43, illus., 140, 142, 144; 10-262
Short-period variable stars. 7-50
Short periods, of chemical elements. 4-306, 308, 310, tables, 307, 309
Short records, green-filter photographs. 8-180, diagrams, 179
"Short-short" period, of chemical elements. 4-308, 310, tables, 307, 309
Short-winged hawks. 6-157-59
Shoulder blade. See **Scapula**
Shoulders.
Blood vessels of, illus., 1-148f
Bones of, 3-79-80, illus., 74, 75
Muscles of, illus., 1-148c; 3-209, illus., 204, 205, 207
Shrew moles. 7-98-99
Shrews. with illus., 7-100-02, illus., 13, 97
Pets, 7-20-21
Shrikes, birds. with illus., 6-66
Courtship behavior of, with illus., 5-418b

Shrimps. 2-240, illus., 236; 6-34
Sounds made by, 8-43
Shrinking crust theory, of mountain building. 10-216
Shrubbery. Attractive to birds, 6-345-46
Shrubs. Trees, how shrubs differ from, 4-66
Shutter (wicket) dams. 8-315
Shutters, camera. 7-260; 9-405, 407, 411
Siamangs. 9-252, 254
Sickle-cell anemia. 8-220; 9-386
Sickness.
*First aid, 10-5-17
*Geriatrics, 8-78-83
*Mosquitoes as vectors of malaria and yellow fever, 10-30-39
*Nursing patients at home, 10-55-67
*Psychiatry, 9-197-205
*Tuberculosis, 9-175-84
Radiation sickness, 9-394
Zoo animals, 10-157-58
See also **Bacteria**; **Colds**; **Diseases**; **Drugs**; **Flies**; **Immunity to diseases**; **Malaria**; **Medicine**; **Surgery**; **Yellow fever**
Side-booms, movable beams for handling pipes. 5-102-03
Side-lever steam engines. 4-110
Side-necked turtles. 5-389
Sidereal month. 4-278
Sidereal time. 1-264
Sidereal year. 4-48
Siderites, meteorites composed chiefly of iron. 6-92-93, 98, illus., 93
Siderolites, stony-iron meteorites. 6-93, 98
Sidewalks, moving. 6-170, illus., 169
Sideward erosion, by streams. 8-14, 17, 18
Sidewinders (horned rattlesnakes). with illus., 5-354b
Sidewinding, movement used by snakes. with illus., 5-354b
Siedentopf, H. F. W., German physicist.
Development of ultramicroscope, 5-297; 8-408
Siemens, Sir William, German-born electrical engineer. 5-247
Sierra Madre, mountain system of Mexico. 10-23
Sierra Nevada, mountain range of western United States. 10-23
Granite in, 2-83
Uplifts of, 8-18
Sieve tubes, conducting cells of plants. 4-64
Sifakas, lemurs. 9-265
Sifting mechanisms. Role in seed dispersal, with illus., 5-2
Sight. See **Vision**
Signal systems, railway. with illus., 1-192-93
Signaling, of bees. with illus., 2-412c; 3-370
Signaling devices.
Before telegraph, 2-377-79
Early history of, 2-377-78
Homemade electrical signalers, with illus., 6-289-90
Signals, electronic. Space and missile flight guided by, 8-128-31
Signatures, in bookbinding. 1-214
Significant figures. 2-319
Signs, of illness. Symptoms of illness distinguished from, 10-5
Sikorsky, Igor I., Russian-American aeronautical engineer. 9-220
Silence, zone of, preceding bodies moving at supersonic speeds. with diagram, 10-229
"Silent" dog whistles. 8-104
"Silent sound" (ultrasonics). *8-103-10
"Silent zone," in atmosphere. 5-121, illus., 122-23

Silica (silicon dioxide).
   Meteorites producing silica glass, 6-92, 94
   Properties and uses, 3-322
Silica dust. Tuberculosis, effect of inhalation on, 9-179
Silica gel. Water absorbed by, 4-343
Silica glasses (impactites). 6-92, 94
Silica sand, used in glassmaking. 3-308
Silicate rock. Earth's mantle composed of, 4-174-75
Silicates.
   Minerals in the form of, 5-251, *illus.*, 250; 9-306
   Occurrence of, 3-322
Silicon (Si), chemical element. Atomic number, 14; atomic weight, 28.086; melting point, 1,420° C.; boiling point, 2,355° C.; specific gravity, 2.42. Nonmetal; resembles carbon in having several allotropic forms and in the nature of its compounds. First prepared in 1823 by Berzelius; name derived from Latin *silex:* "flint." Second most abundant element; found in all important rocks except carbonates, composing one fourth of the earth's crust. Not found uncombined; occurs chiefly as silica (silicon dioxide), either free or combined with metallic oxides to form silicates. Obtained as powder or crystal by chemical means. As silicate, it forms basis of glass, cement and clay-working industries. Silicones — organic silicon compounds — are used widely as electric insulators, lubricants, binders and so on.
   Iron and steel, use and control in, 1-344, 346, 352-53
   Occurrence, properties and uses, *with illus.*, 3-322-23
   Sea, content in, 6-31
   Solar battery, role in, *with illus.*, 7-103-06
   Transistors, function in, 6-303
Silicon carbide (Carborundum).
   Abrasive, 3-322
   Ignitrons, used in, *with illus.*, 6-301-02
   Semiconductor used in electronics, 6-303
Silicon dioxide. Structure of crystal, 5-341, *diagram*, 339
Silicone rubbers, synthetic rubbers. 6-360
Silicones, plastics. *with illus.*, 3-322-23; 8-232, *with illus.*, 229
   Breadmaking uses, 9-297
Silk. *5-173-85
   Spiders produce, *with illus.*, 2-262-66
Silk, artificial. See **Rayon**
Silk-screen printing. 1-214
Silk-spinning moths. 3-200, *illus.*, 194-95, 200
Silkworm moths. Lola giant silkworm moth, *illus.*, 3-202d
Silkworms. *with illus.*, 5-173-79, 180
   Pasteur's work on diseases of, 7-380; 9-76-77
   Virus diseases of silkworm larvae, 3-456
Silliman, Benjamin, American scientist (1779–1864). He was a successful professor of chemistry and natural history at Yale and a popular public lecturer. He founded and edited the important *American Journal of Science and Arts.* Silliman made a geological survey of part of Connecticut, the first study of its kind in the United States.
   Petroleum experiments, 4-141
Sills, geologic formations. 3-421, *illus.*, 420
Silting basins, for removal of silt. 2-273
Silts.
   Size of particles of, 3-424
   Soil texture, 2-18, *illus.*, 19
   Water-supply problem, 2-273
Siltstone, sedimentary rock. 3-424
Silurian period, time in earth's history. 1-388; 6-371
Silver (Ag), chemical element. Atomic number, 47; atomic weight, 107.870; melting point, 960.5° C.; boiling point, 1,950° C.; specific gravity, 10.50. White, lustrous metal; highly malleable and ductile. Best me-

Silver *(continued)*
tallic conductor of heat and electricity. Known to ancients. Name derived from Anglo-Saxon *soelfor;* chemical symbol (Ag), from Latin *argentum:* "silver." Found in native state and with many nonmetallic elements in ores; prepared commercially from its ores by lead or copper smelting, cyanidation or amalgamation with mercury. Used in photographic equipment, as a medical antiseptic and for coins, jewelry and tableware.
   Compounds darkened by light, 9-398-401, 403, 408, 409, 410, *illus.*, 400a
   Crystalline structure, 5-340, *diagram*, 339
   Electroplating of, 5-91
   Experiments involving, *with illus.*, 7-134
   Properties and uses, 3-34, 36
   Sterling silver, 1-382; 3-36
   Teeth fillings made of silver amalgam, 5-136
   Telescopes, silvering surface of, 9-156
Silver bromide. Crystal analysis, *with diagram*, 5-297-98
Silver chloride.
   Homemade photographic plates, used in preparation of, *with illus.*, 4-346-47
   Visible and invisible light detected with, 7-200-01
Silver-haired bats. Migration of, 9-422
Silver leaf, smog-symptom of vegetation. 3-354, *illus.*, 352
Silver maple trees. *with illus.*, 5-150
   Leaves, *illus.*, 4-72
Silverfish. *illus.*, 1-295
   See also **Thysanura**
Silviculture. 5-260
Similar solids. *with illus.*, 3-444
Similar triangles. *with illus.*, 3-433-34
Simon, Théodore, French psychologist. 9-54-55
   Intelligence tests, 9-198
Simons, David, United States Air Force officer. Balloon ascent by, 1-235
Simoom, a hot, dust-laden wind. 2-94
Simple fractures. 3-84
   First aid for, *with illus.*, 10-11
Simple fruits. *with illus.*, 4-129
Simple harmonic motion. 2-121
Simple leaves. *with illus.*, 5-139
Simple machines. *3-56-62
Simplification. Design of products, simplification as factor in, 10-121
Simplon No. 2 Tunnel, between France and Italy. 1-192
Simplon Tunnel, between Switzerland and Italy. 2-45
Simpson, James, English engineer. Slow sand filter for water purification designed by, 2-271
Simpson, Sir James Young, Scottish physician. 7-377-78
Sinanthropus pekinensis. See **Peking man**
Sind, province of Pakistan. Irrigation in, 8-201
Sine, trigonometric function. 3-448, *with illus.*, 447, 449, 450; 7-254
Sine curves. *with illus.*, 3-450
Sinews. See **Tendons**
Singapore. Harbor at high and low tides, *illus.*, 6-204
Single-lens reflex camera. *with illus.*, 9-405
Sinkholes, water-erosion formations. 5-52, *illus.*, 52-53
Sinkin, part of underground water. 8-9
Sinkings, by submarine.
   World War I, tonnage losses in, 9-215
   World War II, tonnage losses in, 9-326
Sinnott, Edmund Ware, American botanist. Quotation from, 10-227
Sino-auricular node, tissue in which heartbeat impulses originate. *with diagram*, 3-386
Sintering, heating of ores. 1-376

Sinuses.
  Brain, found in, 6-328
  Skull, sinuses found in, 3-79, *illus.*, 77; **10-81**
Siphon recorders. 2-384
Siphonaptera, order of insects. 2-414
Siphons. *with illus.*, 2-38-39
  Experiment with, *with illus.*, 2-327-28
  Water conveyed by, 2-276, *illus.*, 277
  Water-siphon jug for home laboratory, *with illus.*,
    4-221-22
Siphons, tubular organs of animals.
  Clams, 2-198
  Sea squirts, 4-3
Sipunculoidea, phylum of worms. 1-294
Sirenia, order of mammals. *with illus.*, 7-16
Sirenians. 7-181-83
  See also **Sirenia**
Sirens. Experiments with, *with illus.*, 5-222
Sirens, salamanders. 5-157
Sirius (Dog Star). 1-336-37
  Calendar of ancient Egypt related to appearance of,
    1-126; 10-171
  Changes in aspect of, 7-45
Sirius, steamship. 4-110
Sirocco, a hot, dust-laden wind. 2-94
Sisal, plant fiber. *with illus.*, 4-182
Sites, building. Suitability of, 4-266
Sitka bears. 7-312
Size.
  Insects, 2-408-09, *illus.*, 407
  Meteorites and meteorite craters, size of various,
    6-88-92
  Strength of animals, size as factor in, 1-284
Skagit River, western United States.
  Dammed up by Ross Dam, *illus.*, 8-316d
Skate, atomic-powered submarine. 5-37, 190
Skates, fish. 4-285, 286, 292-93, *illus.*, 292
Skeins, of silk. 5-182, 184
Skeletal muscles. See **Striped muscles**
Skeletal system. See **Skeleton**
Skeleton, human.
  *Bones of body, 3-73-84
  Development in
    Human baby, 8-96
    Unborn human young, 8-27
  Invertebrate, supporting strength of skeleton of,
    1-286
  Man's, *illus.*, 1-148b
    Compared with skeletons of other vertebrates, *illus.*,
      1-57
  Muscles and ligaments hold bones together, 3-211-12
  Vertebrate, supporting strength of skeleton of, *with
    diagram*, 1-286
  See also **Bones; Muscles**
Skeletons, animal.
  Ape, *illus.*, 1-57
  Man, see **Skeleton, human**
  Snake, *illus.*, 5-353
  Sponge, 2-147
  Turtles, 5-386
Skew lines, in solid geometry. 3-440
Skids, platforms.
  Breadmaking industry, 9-295
  Paper industry, 4-377
Skids, sideslips.
  Causes and prevention of, *with illus.*, 2-125-26
Skimmers, birds. 6-396-97
Skin. *2-173-78
  *Allergies, 4-257-64
  Aging, effect of on, 8-101
  Body's defenses, role in, 7-346, 347-48

Skin *(continued)*
  Breathing through, 4-200, *illus.*, 201
  Cancer of, 8-267
  Care of, 10-83-84
  Development in unborn human young, 8-30
  Glands of, 5-10-11
  Human and reptilian skin, comparison of, *illus.*, 7-5
  Muscular control of, 3-210
  Precancerous conditions of, 8-270
  Processing of animal skins, *with illus.*, 7-230-38
  Protozoan, 2-60
  Sensations of (cutaneous), *with illus.*, 7-303-05
  Shark's skin, 4-285-86
  Virus diseases of, 3-453
Skin, outer wall of skyscraper. *illus.*, 7-124c
Skin beetles. 3-341
Skin color. Inheritance of, 8-343, 346
Skin friction, term used in aeronautics. 6-187
Skin senses. Sensations of touch, *with illus.*, 7-303-05;
  9-314
Skin shedding. Snakes, 5-353-54, *illus.*, 355
Skin tests, in allergy detection. 4-262-64
Skinks, lizards. 5-199, *illus.*, 198
Skipjack, atomic submarine. 5-37
Skippers, lepidopterous insects. 3-196, 200
Skjellerup's comet. 5-398
Skobeltsyn, D. V., Russian physicist.
  Cosmic-ray investigations, 8-394
Skull. *illus.*, 1-148b; *with illus.*, 3-78-79, *illus.*, 74, 75,
  77
  Birds, *with illus.*, 1-285
  Development in
    Human being, 8-96, *illus.*, 99
    Unborn human young, 8-29
  Evolution of, *illus.*, 7-3
  Phrenologist's map of, *with diagram*, 9-317
  Races, use of in classifying, 9-24-25
  Snakes, *with illus.*, 1-285
Skunk cabbages. 10-204
Skunks. 8-176, *illus.*, 173
  Fur, 7-238
  Hibernation, 5-411
  Pets, 7-21
  Scent glands, *with illus.*, 3-238-39
Sky.
  Cloudiness and visibility, 1-251
  Colors in, caused by dust, 7-142, 342
  Colors in, due to atmospheric phenomena, 1-232;
    7-283
  Photography of, 6-315
  See also **Astronomy; Clouds; Planets; Stars; etc.**
Sky charts. 6-78; 8-62-63
Sky cover, extent of clouds. *with diagram*, 1-315-16,
  diagram, 317
"Sky watch," by artificial satellites. 10-53, *illus.*, 51
Sky waves, in radio. 3-92
Skyhook balloons. Cosmic-ray research, *illus.*, 8-396-97
Skyscraper. *3-113-25
  Construction of, *illus.*, 7-124a-d
  Hydroponicums established on?, 8-35, 36
Slabbing mills. 1-348, *diagram*, 348d
Slabs, rolled steel shapes. 1-347-49, *diagram*, 348d
Slag, waste product in ore smelting. 1-377, 379
  Iron and steel industry, 1-341, 343, 346, *illus.*, 345
Slang-Kop, South Africa, site of astronomical observa-
  tory. 8-64
Slate, metamorphic rock. *illus.*, 1-32; *with illus.*, 2-88;
  3-426; 9-308
Slaughterhouses. See **Meat-packing plants**
Slavery, among ants. 3-365
Sledges, for transportation. 1-98, 100, *illus.*, 99, 101

Sleds. See Sledges
Sleep. *6-143-51
  Hibernation and estivation resemble, *with illus.,* 5-410-13
  Restorative effect, 10-91
  Silkworm larvae, dormant periods of, 5-177
Sleep movements, in plants. 3-54
Sleeping accommodations, on railroad trains. 1-187-88
"Sleeping disease," narcolepsy. 6-150
Sleeping postures. *illus.,* 6-144
Sleeping sickness.
  African trypanosomiasis, *with illus.,* 6-151
  Lethargic encephalitis, 6-151
  Protozoans that cause, 2-62-63
Sleet. 2-355-56
Sleighs. See Sledges
Slicing and wrapping, breadmaking operation. 9-298, *diagram,* 299
Slime molds. *with illus.,* 3-24-25
  Locomotion of, *with illus.,* 6-218a
Slimes, bacterial. Sewage purified by, *with illus.,* 5-331, 332
Slipher, Vesto M., American astronomer.
  Galactic velocities measured by, 8-54
Slippery surfaces. Safety precautions, 7-194
Slips, used in pottery. 7-398
Slitter knives, devices for trimming paper sheets. 4-373, *illus.,* 374d
Slope mines, for coal. *with illus.,* 1-410
Sloth bears. 7-315
Sloths. 7-9, *illus.,* 14, 15
  Adaptations to environment, 10-136, *illus.,* 138
Slotters, planing tools. 10-110-11
Slow breeders, nuclear reactors. 9-138
Slow sand filter, used in water purification. 2-271, 277
Sludge, formed in treatment of sewage. 5-331-33, 334, *illus.,* 330, 332-34
Slug-eating snakes. 5-360
Slugs, cast lines of printing type. 1-201
Slugs, mollusks. 2-200, *illus.,* 198
Sluice gates. 2-273
Slurries, thin, watery mixtures. 4-166
Slush molding. Plastics, 8-231
Small calories. See Calories
Small circles. 3-444, *illus.,* 445
Small intestine. See Intestine, small
Small numbers. Exponents used in writing, 2-74
Smallpox.
  Preventing and controlling, *with illus.,* 4-400-03
  Vaccine used against, 3-458; 7-350
Smeaton, John, English engineer. 1-218
Smell, sense of. *with illus.,* 7-302-03
  Ants' sense of, 3-360
  Body's defenses, role in, 7-346
  Fishes, 4-101
  Insects, 2-402, 403, 406
Smelters. See Smelting
Smelting. *with diagrams,* 1-376-82
  Identifying minerals by use of home smelter, *with illus.,* 9-305
  See also under various metals
Smelts. Migration of, 9-427
Smeroe, volcano of Java. *illus.,* 8-297
Smilodon, saber-tooth cat. *with illus.,* 1-397
Smith, F. G., British physicist. 9-210
Smith, Theobald, American pathologist. 7-383-84
Smith, William, English geologist. 4-397, *illus.,* 398
Smith, William A., early American well driller.
  Petroleum first drilled for in United States by, *with illus.,* 4-141

Smith's larkspurs, birds.
  Migration route of, *illus.,* 5-418e
Smithsonian Institution. 5-237
Smog. *with illus.,* 3-349-50, 352-54
  Colloidal suspension, example of, *illus.,* 5-294
  Demonstration of, 2-330-31
Smoke.
  Air pollution by, *with illus.,* 3-349-51, 354-56
  Control by high-frequency sound, 8-109
  Honeybees calmed by, 3-370, *illus.,* 369
  Particles, motion of, 1-163-64
  Precipitation by electricity, *with diagram,* 5-304
Smoke screens.
  World War I, 9-213
Smokeless powders. 8-278, 280
Smokers, bee. See Bee smokers
Smokes, liquid, food preservatives. 4-164
Smoking, method of food preservation. 4-164
  Hams processed by, 5-167, *illus.,* 168
Smoking, tobacco. *5-343-50
  Cigar smoking
    Lung cancer caused by?, *with diagram,* 5-347, 348, 349
  Cigarette smoking
    Lung cancer caused by?, *with diagrams,* 5-347-50; 8-268
  Danger of fire, 7-193
  Virus diseases of plants spread by, 3-456
Smooth muscles (involuntary muscles). *with illus.,* 3-204-05
  Tissue structure, 1-145, 147
Smuts, fungi. *with illus.,* 3-29
Smyth, Henry D., American physicist. 9-331
Snails. *illus.,* 1-294; 2-200, *illus.,* 193
  Aquariums, snails useful in, 8-115
  Intermediate hosts of liver flukes, 2-155, *illus.,* 154
  Land snails, 2-103
  Luminous, *with illus.,* 2-185
  Migration of, 9-430
  Red ramshorn, *illus.,* 8-115
  Shell of, *illus.,* 2-100
  Sperm cell, *illus.,* 2-8
Snake-eaters, birds. 6-309
Snake-necked turtles. 5-389
Snake River, western United States.
  Dammed by Bliss Dam, *illus.,* 8-316d
Snakeheads, fishes. 4-99
Snakeroots, plants.
  Reserpine, tranquilizer, derived from, 5-378-79; **9**-104
Snakes. *illus.,* 1-298; *5-351-64
  Adaptations for survival, 3-237, 240
  Birds that prey on, 6-308
  "Children's Zoo," *illus.,* 10-162
  "Collecting," for zoo, *illus.,* 10-156
  Exhibiting, 8-70
  Inactivity in cold season, 5-411-12
  Lizards, distinguished from, 5-197
  Locomotion of, *with illus.,* 5-354a-d
  Migration of sea snakes, 9-429-30
  North American corn snakes, *with illus.,* 5-354d
  Pets, *with illus.,* 7-24-25
  Prehistoric, 1-394
  Symbols of the god of healing, 1-364
SNAP (System for Nuclear Auxiliary Power), device for converting atomic energy directly into electricity. *6-172-75
Snapdragons. *illus.,* 4-123
Snappers (snapping turtles). 5-388, *illus.,* 389
Snapping turtles. See Snappers

Sneezing.
Allergy as cause of, 4-261
Spread of tuberculosis, *with illus.,* 9-176
Snell, Willebrord, Dutch mathematician. 3-277
Snoring. 6-146
Snorkels, submarine air devices. *illus.,* 2-234
Development of, 5-34; 9-326
Snout beetles. *with illus.,* 3-347-48
Snow, John, English physician. 7-378-79
Snow. 1-245; *with illus.,* 2-354-55
Blasting an overhang, *illus.,* 8-285
Climates of past indicated by accumulation rate of, 3-180-81
Crystals, *illus.,* 2-354
Glacier formation and flow, role in, 9-163-65, 168, 170-71
Ice age stages caused by variations in fall of, 3-185
Measuring and recording, 1-251, 322, *diagram,* 316, 321
Sounds absorbed by, 1-122
Snow buntings, birds. 6-108
Snow fleas. *with illus.,* 1-284
See also **Collembola**
Snow geese. 6-400, *illus.,* 399
Migration route of, *illus.,* 5-418e; 9-420
Snow leopards. 8-210, *illus.,* 209
Snow scenes. Photography of, *with illus.,* 6-315
Snowfall. Measuring and recording, 1-251, 322, *diagrams,* 316, 321
Snowflakes. *illus.,* 2-354
See also **Snow**
Snowplows. *illus.,* 3-301
Snowshoe rabbits (varying hares). 5-413, *illus.,* 412; 8-170
Molting cycle controlled by light, 7-8
Snowy owls. *illus.,* 6-152, 166
Snub-nosed monkeys. 9-257
Snyder, H., American physicist. 9-249
Soaking pits, heating furnaces for ingots. 1-347, *diagram,* 348c
Soap bubbles. Colors of, *with illus.,* 7-281-82
Soapmaking. By-products of meat animals used in, 5-169
Soaps.
Body cleanliness, 10-82-84
Hard-water, action of, 4-348
Tests of, *illus.,* 2-232
Wetting agents, *with illus.,* 8-3-4
Soapwort, weed. Asiatic transplant, 5-6
Sobrero, Ascanio, Italian chemist. 5-81
Nitroglycerin prepared by, 8-182
Social bees. *with illus.,* 3-367-72, *illus.,* 366
Social development.
Adolescents', 8-98-100
Social insects.
*Ants, wasps and bees, 3-357-72
Polymorphism among, 2-409
See also **Hymenoptera; Isoptera**
Social life, animal.
Antelopes, 8-384, 386
Ants, bees and wasps, 3-365-66, 368, 370, *with illus.,* 357-60
Beavers, 9-5
Birds, 5-424-25
Deer, 4-236, 238, 239, 240
Lions, 8-204-05
Lizards, 5-205
Mammals, 7-11-13
Primates, 9-260-62
Seals, 7-86, 88
Termites, 3-362

Social psychology. 9-321-22
Social wasps. *with illus.,* 3-365-66, *illus.,* 363, 364
Social weavers, birds.
Nesting activities of, *with illus.,* 5-418h
Societies, engineering. 1-229
Societies, scientific. *with illus.,* 3-265-69
Society.
*Language as cornerstone of society, 1-107-21
*Population problems, 3-225-34
*Races of mankind, 8-213-20
Automation's effects on, 10-237-38
Industrial Revolution's effects on, 4-41
Nineteenth-century spirit of progress, 5-73-74
Prehistoric and primitive, developments in study of, *with illus.,* 9-25-30
Society for Space Travel (German).
Early rocket experiments, 10-44
Society for Study of Psychical Research. 9-57
Society of the Lynxes. 3-265
Sociology, scientific study of societies.
*Population problems, 3-225-34
Older persons, problems of, 8-83
Socony Mobil Oil Building, New York City. 3-117
Socrates, Greek philosopher. 1-136
Magnetic powers of loadstone, 7-163
Opinion of a treatise on mind, 9-47
Soda process, for preparation of wood pulp. 4-365, 366, 367
Soda straws, calcium carbonate deposits in caves. 5-54, *illus.,* 55
Soddy, Frederick, English chemist. 8-415-16, *illus.,* 414
Energy derived from atom; 9-329
Sodium (Na), chemical element. Atomic number, 11; atomic weight, 22.9898; melting point, 97.5° C.; boiling point, 880° C.; specific gravity, 0.971. Most common of the alkali metals; malleable, ductile, bright and silvery, highly active and an excellent conductor of electricity. First isolated by Humphry Davy in 1807 by the electrolysis of sodium hydroxide, a method still used. Name derived from English soda; chemical symbol (Na), from *natrium,* the Latin name for the substance now called sodium carbonate. Never occurs free in nature; found in many ores. Particularly common in form of sodium chloride, or common salt. Compounds of sodium are used for food, fertilizers and in a great many industrial processes. See also *with illus.,* 3-166-68
Bright-line spectrum of, *illus.,* 7-284a
Diet, essential in, 4-59
Electron arrangement of, *illus.,* 3-247
Interstellar space contains, 9-363
Oxidation of, 5-88-89
Produced from salt (NaCl), 5-325
Protoplasm, function of sodium ions in, 2-6
Salt electrolysis produces, 5-89
Separation of, from table salt, 7-134
Spectral lines of, 7-280
Sodium acetate. Experiments and tricks with, 7-175
Sodium benzoate, food preservative. 4-164
Sodium carbonate. 3-166
Preparation by Solvay process, 5-325
Sodium chloride (common salt, table salt). *5-313-25
Atmospheric dust, found in, 5-167
Composition of, 4-230
Crystal structure of, *with diagram,* 1-170; *with diagrams,* 2-422-23; 5-338-40, *with illus.,* 374
Deposits in arid climate, 3-166
Diet, essential in, 4-59
Electrolysis of, 5-89, 92-93
Food preservation by, 4-163-64
Formation of, 3-249

Sodium chloride *(continued)*
  Freezing point of solutions lowered by, *with illus.,* 4-301
  Leather processing, use in, 7-232
  Loss from body in exercise, 10-91
  Perspiration contains, 5-11
  Protoplasm contains, 2-6
  Sea, presence in, 3-166; 6-30, *chart,* 31
  Separation into elements, 7-134
  Soil fertilizer, used as, 2-169, 171
  Solutions of, 4-297
  Stockpile, *illus.,* 5-frontispiece
  Sweat contains, 2-177
  Water softened by, in zeolite process, 2-281
  See also **Salt domes; Salts; Wells, salt**
Sodium cyanide. Preparation of, 5-325
Sodium fluoride, for prevention of dental caries, *illus.,* 10-77
  Formation of, *with illus.,* 3-248-49
Sodium hydroxide (lye, caustic soda).
  Behavior as typical base, 4-338-39
  Experiments and tricks with, *with diagram,* 7-176-77
  Industrial uses, 3-168
  Production of, 5-93
Sodium nitrate (Chile saltpeter). 3-166, *illus.,* 167
  Soil fertilizer, used as, 2-171
Sodium sulfide. Formation of, *with illus.,* 3-249
Sodium thiosulfate.
  Experiments and tricks with, *with diagram,* 7-176
  Photography, used (as "hypo") in, 9-400-02, 410
Soft coal, bituminous coal. 1-408
Soft diets. Sick persons', 10-65
Soft palate. 3-79
  Function in swallowing food, *with diagram,* 4-323
Soft rubber. Uses of, 6-356
Soft-shelled clams. 2-198
Soft-shelled crabs. 2-240
Soft-shelled turtles. 5-388
Soft water. Hard water converted into, 2-280-81
Soft X rays. 7-145
Softwoods. Construction, use in, 7-120
Soil. *2-15-25, 203-11; 5-25-30; 6-136-42
  *Fertility, 2-163-72
  *Formation, 6-136-42
  *Organisms in soil, 2-203-11
  *Water of soil, 5-25-30
  Analysis by Department of Agriculture on request, 4-266
  Conservation of, 6-4-6
  Coral islands, 4-136
  Erosion prevented by plants, 1-50
  Fertility increased by bacterial activity, 3-68
  Germination without, 5-64
  Habitat of animals and plants, 10-136-37, *illus.,* 140
  Mountains as a source of, 10-28
  Plant's absorption and use of soil nutrients, 3-44-45
  Red-soil deposits, 3-178-79
  Water-holding capacity variations, 8-191
  See also **Bacteria; Clay; Fertilizers; Irrigation; Loams; Loess; Sand; Silts**
Soil acidity. See **Acid soils**
Soil conservation. Practices of, *illus.,* 6-137
Soil Erosion Service. 6-4
Soil organisms. Antibiotics, source of, *with illus.,* 10-130a-d
  Formation and fertility of soils, factors in, 2-16, 20-25
Soil structures. *with illus.,* 2-19
Soil textures. 2-18, *illus.,* 18-19
Soil types. 2-21-23, *map,* 20-21
Soilless agriculture. *8-34-37
  Substitute for conservation of soil?, 6-14

Solar battery. *7-103-06
Solar eclipses. *3-130-37
  Observing, method of, 6-82-83
Solar energy. *with illus.,* 3-109-12; 9-224
  Plants' utilization of, 3-44-45
  Restoration of, 6-254
  Solar battery run by, *with illus.,* 7-103-06
  Transformations of, *with illus.,* 6-248
Solar engines, in space flight. 10-4
Solar flares, disturbances on sun. Atmosphere affected by, 1-238
Solar heating. *with illus.,* 2-252-53
Solar observatories. 8-63
Solar radiation.
  Atmosphere affected by, *with illus.,* 1-236
  Chemical effects of, experiments to show, 8-118
  Glass that minimizes effect of, 8-392
  Measuring quantity and intensity of solar radiation reaching the earth, 1-247, *illus.,* 246
  Space travel and, 10-50, 52
Solar system. *3-157-64
  *Comets, 5-390-99
  *Earth as planet, 4-42-50
  *Jupiter, 5-20-24
  *Mars and asteroids, 4-415-22
  *Mercury and Venus, 4-25-31
  *Meteorites and meteors, 6-87-98
  *Moon, earth's, 4-277-84
  *Saturn, 5-107-13
  *Uranus, Neptune and Pluto, 5-289-93
  Atomic structure compared with, *with diagram,* 1-311
  Formation, theories about, *with illus.,* 1-27-30; 9-225
  Relative distances in, 5-20
  Relative sizes of sun and planets, 5-20
  See also **Meteorites**
Solar time. 1-264
Soldier ants. 3-357, 358
Soldier termites. 3-362
Solenodons, insectivorous mammals. *with illus.,* 7-102
Solenoids. 7-164
  Typewriters operated by, 1-276
Soles, flatfish. 4-317
Soleus, lower-leg muscle. *illus.,* 1-148c; *illus.,* **3**-205, 213
Solid fuels, for rockets. 10-42, 45, *illus.,* 43
Solid geometry. *3-440-46
  Analytic solid geometry, *with diagram,* 4-430-32
Solid-medium technique, for cultivating bacteria. *with illus.,* 3-72
Solid-state physics. The branch of physics dealing with the structure, characteristics and behavior of matter in the solid state, particularly crystalline matter, under a variety of conditions. See **Atoms; Cohesion; Crystals; Dielectric; Elasticity; Electricity; Heat; Kinetics; Magnetism; Metals; Minerals; Molecules; Photoelectric cells; Semiconductors; Solids; Tensile strength; Valence; Vibrations**
Solids.
  *Crystals, 5-337-42
  Analysis of, 5-374-75
  Colloidal particles, 5-296
  Expansion due to heating, *with illus.,* 3-414-15
  Floating bodies, 2-32-34
  Gases, converted into, 3-418
  Heat conductivity of, 4-10
  Liquids, converted into, 3-416-17
  Molecular structure and behavior of, *with illus.,* 1-162-63, *with diagrams,* 169-71
  Physical properties of, *with illus.,* 5-375-76
  Sewage contains, 5-328-31, 334
  See also **Matter; Molecules**
Solitary (nonsocial) bees. 3-367-68

Solitary (nonsocial) insects. 3-357, 366-68, *illus.,* 362
Solitary (nonsocial) wasps. 3-366-67, *illus.,* 362
Solitary sandpipers. 6-406
   Migration of, 9-420
Sollas, W. J., English geologist.
   Coral-reef formations study, 4-139
Sols, forms of colloidal suspension. *with illus.,* 5-297
   Living matter, found in, **2**-6, *illus.,* 10; 5-301
Solstices. 1-263
Solubility. 4-299-300
Solutes. *with diagram,* 4-297-98
Solutions. *4-296-303
   Ammoniated solutions as soil fertilizers, 2-171
   Colloids in, 5-295
   Definition of, 1-81-82
   Experiments with solutions of various chemical compounds, *with illus.,* 4-344-48; *with diagrams,* 7-173-77, 179-80
   pH of, measurement of, 4-341-42
   Protoplasm, solutions in, 2-3, 6, 10-11
   Soil, 2-16-17, 22-25
   Soil water a food solution for plants, 5-25, 26
Solvay process, method of preparing sodium carbonate. 5-325
Solvents. 4-297-98
   Dissolving-powers of solvents, tests of, 4-344-46
Somerset, Edward, English inventor. 4-39
Somites, structures that develop into vertebrae or muscles. 8-27
Somnambulism, sleepwalking. 6-150
Somniloquism, sleep talking. 6-150
Sonar. 8-105-06
Song box, of birds. See **Syrinx**
Song sparrows. 6-108
Songbirds.
   Insect-destroying habits, 6-153
   Migrations of, 9-420-21
Songs, bird. See **Calls, bird**
Sonic barrier. See **Sound (sonic) barrier**
Sonic boom. 10-230
Sonic sounding. See **Echo sounding**
Sonic velocity, equal to velocity of sound in air. *with diagrams,* 10-230
Sorac, birds. 6-403
Sorbic acid, food preservative. 4-164
Sorghum, cereal. Sugar from, 4-79
Sori, clusters of sporangia. Ferns, 3-191
Sosigenes, Greek astronomer. Calendar reform, 10-174
Soule, Samuel, American inventor. 1-266-67; 6-381
Sound. *5-114-28
   *Experiments with, 5-221-30
   *Hearing, 4-379-85
   *Musical sounds, 5-211-20
   *Noise meters, 8-38-46
   *Phonographs, 7-362-69
   *Ultrasonics, 8-103-10
   Bathyscaphe used to analyze sound phenomena in water, *with illus.,* 6-74d
   Conduction in ear, *with illus.,* 1-282; *with illus.,* 7-298-301
   Hearing in humans and newts compared, *with illus.,* 1-282
   Insect detection and production of, 2-406
   Loudest, explosions at Krakatoa, 7-342
   Measuring ocean depths, used in, 6-69-70, *diagram,* 70
   Sine curves used in analysis of, *with illus.,* 3-450
   Speech sounds, 1-107-08, 110-11, 113-15, 116
   Thunder, explanation of, 1-399
   Velocity of, at different altitudes, 9-219

Sound *(continued)*
   See also **Ears; Hearing; Sound waves; Sounds; Supersonics**
Sound (sonic) barrier. 10-231
   Broken by experimental aircraft, 9-219
Sound buoys. 5-71, *illus.,* 69
Sound-imitative theory. Origin of language explained by, 1-107
"Sound microscopes." 8-44-45
Sound production. Orthopterous insects, 3-140, 142, 143-44, *illus.,* 141
Sound recording.
   *Phonographs, 7-362-69
Sound waves. *5-114-28
   *Experiments with, 5-221-30
   Animals make use of, *with illus.,* 1-281-83
   Earthquakes, 9-107-08
   See also **Sound; Supersonics; Ultrasonics**
Sounding, of oceanic depths. 6-69-70, 74, *illus.,* 70; 9-221-22
   See also **Echo sounding**
Sounding balloons, for studying weather. 1-251
   See also **Radiosondes**
Soundproofing. 5-128; 8-44
   Glass blocks in soundproofing, 8-392
Sounds, animal.
   Alligators, 5-384
   Amphibians' hearing of, *with illus.,* 1-282
   Ants produce and detect, 3-360
   Bats, hearing of, **10**-140
   Beetles, 3-335
   Click beetles produce, 3-341
   Deathwatch beetles produce, 3-342
   Dolphins, 7-186
   Fishes, 4-102
   Grasshoppers produce, 3-140, 142, 144, 146
   Grouse, 6-335
   Human hearing of, *with illus.,* 1-282
   Marine animals, 8-41-43
   Mosquitoes, 3-290
   Snakes, 5-364
   True bugs produce, 3-255
   Turtles, 5-386
   Voices of man and other vertebrates, *with illus.* 1-282-83
   Whales, 7-186
   See also **Songs, bird; Sound; Voices, animal**
Soupfin sharks, fishes. *illus.,* 4-94
Sour gum trees. 5-146
South Africa.
   Astronomical observatories, 8-64
   Diamond mining in, *with illus.,* 4-253-56
   Gold mine in, *illus.,* 4-249
   Johannesburg, *illus.,* 6-114-15
South-African Colored local race. 8-218
South America.
   Atacama Desert, Chile, 6-118
   Explorations of, in nineteenth century, *with illus.,* 7-29-31
   Marsupial mammals formerly found in, 7-420
   Mountain systems of, 10-24
   Petroleum production and reserves, 4-150
   Plains of, 6-113
   Plant and animal life in, study of, 8-252
   Rivers of, 6-418
   Transportation on land, primitive and early, 1-102, *illus.,* 103
   Volcanoes in, 8-299
South Atlantic. Pressure distribution in, 5-192
South Carolina Railroad, early railroad. 1-181
South Dakota. Dust storm in, *illus.,* 7-138

South Equatorial Current, oceanic current.   6-236, *map*, 232-33
South Pacific Ocean.
Plant and animal life in islands of, 8-252
South Pole. Conquest of, 7-34
See also **Antarctic; Polar regions**
South Tropical Disturbance, surface feature of Jupiter. 5-23-24
Southeast Asiatic local race. 8-219
Southeast trades, wind belt. 2-93, *diagram*, 92
Southeasterlies, wind belt. 1-244, *diagram*, 243
Southern circumpolar stars. 1-337, *map*, 330
Southern constellations. 1-337, *map*, 330
Southern Cross (Crux), constellation. 1-337
Southern Hemisphere.
Atmospheric circulation in, *with diagrams,* 1-243-44, *diagram*, 242
Jet-stress circulation in, 1-237, 238
Southern lights. See **Aurora australis**
Southern Regional Research Laboratory, of the United States Department of Agriculture. *illus.*, 1-92
Southern Research Institute. 1-89-90, *illus.*, 91
Soviet Union. See **Union of Soviet Socialist Republics**
Sowerby whales. *illus.*, 7-184
Soybeans. Industrial materials from, 7-42-43, *illus.*, 40-41
Space.
*Interstellar space, 9-359-64
IGY studies of outer, 5-194-95
Intergalactic, atoms in, 9-364
Three-dimensional-space axes, 7-109, *illus.*, 108
See also **Astronomy; Cartesian co-ordinates**
Space charge, electron-tube phenomenon. 6-300-01
Space exploration. *10-40-54
History of, *with illus.*, 9-375-83
Solar batteries used in, 7-106, *illus.*, 105
Space motions, of stars. 7-226-27
Space ships. See **Rockets; Space travel**
Space stations. *with illus.*, 9-379, 380; 10-48-49, 50, 52-54, *illus.*, 51
Hydroponic farming in?, 8-36
See also **Satellites, artificial**
Space suits. 10-50, 52, *illus.*, 49
Space-time, important concept in relativity theory. 4-213; 9-281-82
Space travel. *10-40-50
*Flying saucers, 9-16-20
*Guidance of missiles and space vehicles, 8-125-31
Future possibilities in, 10-225
Rockets as craft for, 10-4
See also **Space exploration**
Spacebands, in type casting. *with illus.*, 1-200
Spain.
Exploration, contributions to, *with illus.*, 2-364-66
Talgo, lightweight train, 1-188
Spandrels, wall spaces between windows. Glass used for, 8-391-92
Spaniels. 10-242, *illus.*, 241
Spanish bayonets. See **Yuccas**
Spanish flies, beetles. 3-348
Spans, bridge elements. 2-334
Spar buoys. 5-70, *illus.*, 69
Spark plugs, for automobile engines. *with illus.*, 2-137, 138; *illus.*, 407
Sparks. Electromagnetic disturbances, 6-244
Sparrow hawks. 6-159, *illus.*, 158
Sparrows. *with illus.*, 6-106-08
Cowbirds' young reared by, 6-104-05
Eastern chipping sparrows, *illus.*, 5-418e
English sparrows, 10-256
Spawning. Migrations for, *with illus.*, 3-242-44

Special Committee of the International Geophysical Year. 5-186-87
Special theory of relativity. *with illus.*, 4-212-18
Special World Days. 5-187
Special World Intervals. 5-187
Specialization. Social insects show, 3-357
Species, groups in classification of living things. 1-289
Hymenopterous insects, number of species of, 3-357
New species, development of, *with illus.*, 6-278-81
Specific gravity. 2-31-33
Minerals identified by, 5-254
Specific heat, heat unit. 3-413-14
Spectacled bears. 7-315
Spectra. See **Spectrum**
Spectral lines. Discovery and meaning of, 5-85-86
Shifts predicted by relativity theory, 4-220
Spectrograms, records of light spectra.
Nebulae, 8-51
Xenon gas, converted into plasma, *illus.*, 1-173
Spectrographs. 7-279
Astronomy, uses in, *illus.*, 1-21; 6-257; 8-57, 59
Ultraviolet rays studied with, 7-201
See also **Mass spectrograph**
Spectroheliograms, photographs of sun made by monochromatic (one-color) light. 3-103, *illus.*, 104
Spectroheliographs, devices for taking photographs of sun. 3-103, *illus.*, 104
Spectroheliokinematographs, devices for taking moving pictures of sun. 3-104
Spectrohelioscopes, devices for observing sun. 3-103
Spectrophotometers, instruments for comparing color intensities.
Hemoglobin content of blood measured by, 3-327
Spectroscopes. 7-279, *illus.*, 280, 284
Astronomy, uses in, 9-361
Properties of stars, analysis of, 8-122
Radial motions of stars, analysis of, 7-226
Invention of, 5-85
Spectroscopic binaries. 7-46, 229
Spectroscopy. Development of, in nineteenth century, 6-390-91
Spectrum. 7-280
Continuous emission, *illus.*, 7-284a
Diffraction grating used to produce, 7-144, *illus.*, 284a
Discovery of, by Newton, 3-277; *with illus.*, 8-178-79
Nebulae and galaxies, spectra of, 8-47, 49, 51-52
Sodium, bright-line spectrum of, *illus.*, 7-284a
Sun's, *illus.*, 3-109; 7-284a
Visible, 7-199-201, 205, *illus.*, 284a, 284c, *diagram*, 201; 8-122, *illus.*, 123
Spectrum analysis.
Development of, in nineteenth century, *with illus.*, 5-85-86
Matter in interstellar space, spectrum analysis of, 9-361
Red shift (displacement of spectrum lines toward red), 8-52, 54; 9-225
Spectrum, electromagnetic. See **Electromagnetic spectrum**
Speech. *Development of spoken and written language, 1-107-21
Visible Speech Translator, 5-127
Speed.
Average, *with illus.*, 2-118-19
Chemical reactions, speed of, 2-227-29, 230, 231
Constant, 2-118
Nineteenth-century measurements of velocity of light, 6-241-42, 246-47

Speed (continued)
Heavenly bodies, speed of, determined by Doppler effect, **6**-391
Human runners, world records of, **10**-89
Light, **7**-249
Nerve impulses, **6**-320, 323
Rates of change, with diagrams, **4**-436-39
Sound, **5**-119-20
Velocity, different from, **2**-120-21
Wind speeds, measuring and recording, **1**-249, 320, illus., 248, 250, diagrams, 316, 321
Speiss, by-product of lead smelting. **1**-379
Speke, John Hanning, English explorer. **7**-31
Speleologists, cave scientists. **5**-58
Speleology, scientific study of caves. *__*5**-50-60
Speleothems, limestone deposits in caves. with illus., **5**-54-56
Spelter, condensed zinc. **1**-380
Spelunkers, cave explorers. **5**-58
Spencer, Herbert, English philosopher.
Evolution, contributions to theory of, **8**-262
Sperm. See **Spermatozoa**
Sperm whales. 7-183, 186, 187, illus., 184
Spermatozoa (sperm), male sex cells. **8**-19, 21, illus., 21, 22
Heredity, role in, **8**-334-37
Human, illus., **1**-43
Snail sperm cell, illus., **2**-8
Spermophiles, ground squirrels. Hibernation of, **5**-410
Sphagnum, genus of mosses. illus., **1**-301; **3**-188-189, illus., 186
Sphalerite, mineral. **5**-256
Sphere fungi. 3-28
Spheres, common solids. with illus., **3**-444-46
Analytic geometry, equations in, **4**-431
Sound waves as, with illus., **5**-116
Spherical aberration. with illus., **7**-257; **9**-91
Sphexes, wasps. **3**-367
Sphincters, ringlike muscles. Gastrointestinal tract, sphincters of, **4**-323, 324, 330-31, illus., 331
Sphinx moths. 3-200
Sphygmomanometers, apparatus for measuring blood pressure. with illus., **3**-388
Spica, star in Virgo. **1**-331
Spicebush moths. 3-200
Spicebush swallowtail butterflies. illus., **3**-202a
Spider beetles. 3-344
Spider crabs. 2-241, illus., 240
Spider monkeys. illus., **7**-9; with illus., **9**-259-62
Adapted for swinging through trees, **7**-9
Spiders. illus., **1**-295
*__*Spiders and kin, **2**-258-69
Spike-tooth harrows, farm machines. illus., **2**-168
Spikes, flower clusters. **4**-123, illus., 124
Spillways, of dams. **8**-306, 316, illus., 315, 316d
Spin, of atomic particles. **1**-313
Spinach. Air-pollution detected by, illus., **3**-352
Spinal accessory nerves. 6-328
Spinal column. See **Backbone**
Spinal cord.
*__*Nervous system, **6**-317-30
Backbone protects, **3**-75
Body's defenses, role in, **7**-346-47
Muscular activity, role in, **3**-208, illus., 206
Spinal fluid. See **Cerebrospinal fluid**
Spindle shells, gastropods. illus., **2**-100
Spindles, formations in cells that are undergoing division. **2**-14, 290, illus., 13, 291
Spine. See **Backbone; Spinal cord**
Spines, animal. Lizards, **5**-206
Turtles, **5**-386

Spines, plant.
Cactus, with illus., **6**-227-28
Protective devices of various plants, **7**-78, illus., 79
Seed and fruit spines, **5**-5, 6, illus., 4, 5
Spinnerets, spinning organs. Spiders', **2**-262, illus., 261-62
Spinning, of silk. with illus., **5**-178-82, illus., 183, 185
Spinning jennies. Invention of, with illus., **4**-36-37
Spinning mules. Invention of, with illus., **4**-37
Spinning wheels. with illus., **4**-36
Spiny anteaters. Spiny anteaters are primitive mammals closely related to the platypuses. Several species (genus Tachyglossus and Zaglossus) occur in rocky and scrub areas of Australia, Tasmania and New Guinea. They possess spiny bristles, scattered among the hairs, on the back and sides of the body. The toothless muzzle is elongated into a slender and pointed beak, and the long, narrow tongue can be thrust out some distance from the tip of the muzzle. The strong and stout claws are used to tear up the nests of ants and termites upon which the spiny anteaters feed. The females lay but a single egg, which is carried in a brood pouch specially formed at breeding time. The young feeds on milk produced by glands on the mother's belly. See also illus., **7**-12
Adaptations for feeding, **7**-11
Spiny lizards. illus., **5**-205
Spiny sharks. 4-290
Spiny-tailed lizards. illus., **5**-202
Spiracle, passage leading from fish's throat to outside of body, **4**-382-83
Spiracles, breathing pores of insects. **2**-405, illus., 403; **4**-200, illus., 201
Spiral galaxies. illus., **6**-259; **8**-50, 155, diagrams, 48; **9**-363
Spiral nebulae. 8-153, 156
See also **Galaxies; Milky Way**
Spiral of Archimedes. 1-357
Spiral turns, in bandaging. with illus., **10**-16
Spirilla, bacteria. illus., **1**-301; **3**-64, illus., 63
Spirochetes. Discovery of spirochete causing syphilis, **8**-409
Spirogyra, genus of green algae. illus., **1**-45; **3**-218-19, illus., 216, 219
Spirometers, for measuring lungs' vital capacity. **4**-207
Spirostomum, genus of ciliated protozoans. **2**-66
Spirotrichida, order of protozoans. **2**-66
Spitteler, Adolph, German chemist. **8**-223
Spitzer, Lyman, American physicist.
Plasma researches of, **1**-176
Spleen. illus., **1**-148d-e; **5**-9-10, illus., 11
Location in body, illus., **4**-322
Spoilage of food. *__*Prevention of, **4**-153-68
Sponge, breadmaking mixture. with diagram, **9**-296
Sponge cells, of leaves. with illus., **4**-73
Sponges, animals. **2**-146-48
Classification of, **1**-292
Fossil sponge spicules, illus., **6**-370
Sponges, rubber. Manufacture of, illus., **6**-356
Spongy layer, of leaves. illus., **3**-42b
Spontaneous combustion. 2-228; **7**-193
Spontaneous generation of life. Disproved by Pasteur, **9**-75-76
Nonliving matter does not give rise to living things, **1**-38-39
Spookfish. 4-295
Sporadic meteors. 6-96, illus., 94-95
Sporangia, spore cases. Ferns, **3**-191
Fungi, with illus., **3**-25
Spore cases. See **Sporangia.**

Spore trees, early trees reproducing by spores. *illus.,* 6-372

Spores.
  Animal reproduction
    Sporozoa, 2-65-66
  Plant reproduction
    Algae, 3-217, 220
    Bacteria, 3-64-65
    Fungi, 3-22-23
      Mosses, liverworts, ferns, club mosses and horsetails, 3-187, 190-92
    Lycopodium powder, experiments with, 7-178
    Meteorites once thought to carry, 6-94

Sporophytes, spore-producing generations of plants.
  Mosses, 3-187
  See also **Alternation of generations; Reproduction**

Sporozoa, class of protozoans. 2-65-66

Sporozoites, spores. **2-65**

Sports. *Exercise,* 10-85-91

Sports, biologic. See **Heredity; Mutations**

Spotlights, photographic. 9-410-11

Spotted hyenas. 8-250, *illus.,* 249

Spotted newts, amphibians. 5-156, 161, *illus.,* 153, 160-61
  Pets, 7-26

Spotted sandpipers. 6-406-07

Spotted whip rays, fish. 4-295

Sprague, Frank J., American electrical engineer and inventor. 6-380

Sprains. 3-213
  First aid for, **10-12**

Sprats, fish. 4-314

Spratt, Thomas, English prelate and historian. 3-8

Spray driers, devices for dehydrating foods. 4-166, *illus.,* 167

Spray guns. 9-70.

Spraying.
  Coal mines, spraying to lay coal dust in, 1-414
  Compressed air used for, 9-70
  Plant parasites destroyed by, *illus.,* 10-152
  Sewage treated by, 5-332, *illus.,* **331**

Spreading boards, for preparing collected insects. 3-156, *illus.,* 154

Sprengel explosives. 8-287

Spring.
  Atmospheric circulation during, 1-238
  Exploring plant world in, 10-204-05

Spring beauties. *illus.,* 7-242

Spring constellations.
  Seen from middle northern latitudes, *map,* 1-326

Spring peepers, frogs. 5-155

Spring tides. 6-203, *diagram,* 205

Springboks, antelopes. 8-387, *illus.,* 385

Springers, distorted cans. 4-158

Springs, automobile. *with illus.,* 2-142

Springs, seepage. See **Seepage springs**

Springs, water streams issuing from earth.
  Formation of, 8-325-26, *illus.,* 327

Springtails, insects. See **Collembola**

Sprinkler irrigation. 8-196-97

Sprinkling. Irrigation water distributed by, 5-30

Spruce grouse. 6-335

Spruce trees. *with illus.,* 5-142
  Fruits, *illus.,* 5-141
  Sitka spruce, 5-260

Spun silk, inferior silk. 5-180

Spurges. Linnaeus' classification of, 1-288

Sputniks, Russian artificial satellites. *with illus.,* 9-375; 10-46, *illus.,* 47

Sputum. Tuberculosis, 9-176, 179

Spying. See **Espionage**

Squamata, order of reptiles.
  *Lizards, 5-196-206
  *Snakes, 5-351-64

Square measure.
  Metric system, *table,* **10-296**
  United States, *table,* **10-295**

Square rigging. See **Square sails**

Square sails. 4-106-08

Squares, of numbers. *with diagram,* 4-424

Squares, plane figures. 3-435, *illus.,* 434
  Graphs used to analyze, *with illus.,* 2-70-71

Squares, magic. See **Magic squares**

Squash bugs. *with illus.,* 3-258

Squeteagues, fish. 4-314

Squids. *with illus.,* 2-194
  Defense mechanism, 3-239-40
  Flying, 2-194
  Luminous, *illus.,* 2-191
  Sucking apparatus, *with illus.,* 1-280
  Young squid, *illus.,* 6-34

Squill, plant. *illus.,* 1-41

Squirrels. 8-162-63, *illus.,* 160
  Field study of, 10-259
  Flying squirrels, *illus.,* 8-166
  Fur, 7-238
  Gray squirrel, *illus.,* 8-160
  Hibernation of ground squirrels, 5-410
  Nest of, 10-260
  Pets, 7-22, *illus.,* 21

Squirting cucumbers. Adaptations for seed dispersal, 5-2, *illus.,* 6

Stabilizers, anti-deterioration compounds. Plastics, used in manufacture of, 8-225

Stable atomic particles. 1-313, *with table,* 314

Stable equilibrium, 2-322, *illus.,* 321

Stable flies. 3-292

Stacking, of planes at airports. 6-198

Stadler, L. J., American geneticist.
  X rays used to produce mutations, 10-251

Stag beetles. 3-344-45, *illus.,* 343

Stage lighting. Homemade layout, 6-294

Stagecoaches. 1-106, *with illus.,* 104-05

Stages, rocket. 10-43, 46, 48

Stagg Field, University of Chicago.
  Site of first self-sustaining chain reaction, **9-331,** *illus.,* 330

Stahl, Georg Ernst, German physician and chemist.
  Sponsor of phlogiston theory, 3-272

Stained-glass windows. *with illus.,* 8-389

Stainless steels. 1-352-53
  Smoking operation, *illus.,* 5-168

Stairs. Accident prevention on, 7-194

Stairway of the tympanum (scala tympani), of ear. *with illus.,* 7-299, 300

Stairway of the vestibule (scala vestibuli), of ear. *with illus.,* 7-299, 300

Stalactites, calcium carbonate deposits in caves. *with illus.,* 5-55

Stalagmites, calcium carbonate deposits in caves. *with illus.,* 5-55, *illus.,* 58a

Stamens, flower parts. 3-405-06, *illus.,* 398; *with illus.,* 4-121

Staminate flowers. *with illus.,* 4-122

Stamp batteries, in dressing gold ore. 1-375

Standard of living. Population and, 3-230-33

Standing. See **Posture of the body**

Stanley, Henry Morton, explorer. 7-31, *illus.,* 32

Stanley, Wendell M., American biochemist.
  Virus, research on, 1-40; 3-453

Stapes. See **Stirrup**

Staphylococci, bacteria.
  Bone disease caused by, 3-84
  Food spoilage by, *with illus.,* 4-153
Star atlases. 6-78
Star Carr, Yorkshire, England.
  Relic from human occupation site at, *illus.,* 10-92
Star catalogs. 6-259-60
  Bonner Durchmusterung (Bonn Catalog), 6-389
Star clusters. Formation of, *with illus.,* 6-266-67
Star groups. *with illus.,* 6-266-67
Star maps. *illus.,* 1-325-30
  Use of, 1-324, 331
Star names. 6-260
Star streaming. 6-263
Star trails. Photography of, *with illus.,* 6-85-86
Starch grains. Color photography, former use in, 9-413
Starches.
  *Sugars and starches, 4-76-79
  Cells contain, 2-5, 9, 11
  Grains on chloroplast, *illus.,* 3-42c
  Muscular energy furnished by, 3-205
  Nitrostarch, 8-282
  Older person's diet, 8-82
  Plant-food storage, 2-417, 420
  Polysaccharides, 7-276
  Tests for, *with illus.,* 7-135-36
Starfish. See **Sea Stars**
Starlings. *with illus.,* 6-103
  Migrations of, *illus.,* 10-256
  Woodpeckers' nests taken by, 6-210
Stars. *6-255-68
  *Constellations, *6-323-37
  *Galaxies, 8-47-54
  *Interstellar materials, 9-359-64
  *Milky Way, 8-151-59
  *Motions of, 7-223-29
  *Planetaria show positions of, 2-396-401
  *Sun, 3-99-112
  *Variable stars, 7-45-51
  Apparent magnitude, *table,* 10-299
  Astronomical time measured by, 1-17-18
  Brightness, see **Apparent magnitude**
  Common space motion of, 7-228
  Laboratories for testing physical and chemical theories,
    1-19
  Latitude and longitude calculated by observation of
    stars, 8-61
  Light from stars analyzed, 8-57, 59, 60
  Meteorites derived from?, 6-98
  Number visible to unaided eye, 1-323
  Observation of, *with diagrams,* 6-79-81
  Orbital motions of, 7-228-29, *illus.,* 226-27, 229
  Planets differentiated from, by Galileo, 3-2
  Plasmas in, 1-174
  Positions determined, 8-61-63
  Proper motions of, *with illus.,* 7-224-25
  Radial motions of, 7-226
  Reproduction of, by planetarium projectors, *with illus.,*
    2-398-99
  Space motions of, 7-226-27
  Studies of, in nineteenth century, 6-389-91, *illus.,* 388
  Time measured by passage of stars, 8-61
  See also **Astronomy; Solar system; Stellar dimensions;
    Stellar temperatures; Universe;** names of stars
Starvation. Survival time in, 4-331
"Starved" beaches. 8-351
Stassfurt, Germany. Salt mines at, 5-317
State, change of, in matter. 1-171, *with diagram and
    illus.,* 166-69, *with illus.,* 162-63; *with illus.,* 3-
    416-18
State parks, United States. 9-276

Static electricity. 6-119-21
  Experiments with, *with illus.,* 6-286-88
  Research on, between 1765-1815, *with illus.,* 4-358-62
Static stability, response of aircraft to wind. 10-231
Statics. 7-214
Stationary fronts. See **Fronts**
Stations, compressor, for natural gas. *illus.,* 5-98b
Stations, pumping. Petroleum, *illus.,* 10-236
Stations, railway. 1-192
Stations, regulator, for natural gas. *illus.,* 5-98c
Statistical method. Origin and development of, in
    seventeenth century, 3-21
Statistics. 1-75; 2-80
  Electronic computers used for compilation of, 9-152
  Psychology problems, applications to, 9-313
Stators, of dynamo. Assembly of, *illus.,* 5-309
Statues. See **Sculpture**
Stature. See **Growth**
Staurolite, mineral. 5-253
Steam.
  Canning, used in, 4-156, 157
  See also **Boilers; Locomotives; Power; Steam engines;
    Steam stations; Transportation; Turbines; Water
    vapor**
Steam, superheated. Turbines, use in, 5-311
Steam engines. 1-186, *illus.,* 185; 4-80-86; *with illus.,*
    5-305-12
  Aircraft powered by, 6-178, 182
  Development of, during Industrial Revolution, *with
    illus.,* 4-39-41; 6-254
  Forerunners of, *with illus.,* 1-359-60
  Ships powered by, *with illus.,* 4-109-18
  See also **Locomotives, steam**
Steam generators. Diesel-electric locomotives often
    supplied with, 1-185
Steam-heating systems. *with illus.,* 2-247-48
Steam inhalation. 10-66, *illus.,* 67
Steam locomotives. See **Locomotives, steam**
Steam navigation. Development of, in nineteenth
    century, 6-377-78, *illus.,* 378-79
Steam packets. See **Packets—Steam packets**
Steam power.
  Inventions using steam power, *with illus.,* 4-39-41
  See also **Railroads; Steam; Steam stations**
Steam shovels. See **Mining**
Steam stations, electricity-generating plants. 9-229,
    231, *illus.,* 230
Steam turbines. *5-305-12
  Atomic submarines, power for, 5-36
  Electricity generated by, 9-229, 231, *illus.,* 230
  See also **Turbines**
Steam Vac, canning process. 4-157
Steamships. *with illus.,* 4-109-18; 6-377-78, *illus.,* 378-79
  See also **Fulton, Robert; Steam navigation**
Stearic acid. 7-275
Steel. *1-338-53
  Bridges made of, 2-333, 344, *with illus.,* 336-37
  Building material, 7-122-23
  Developments in nineteenth century, *with illus.,*
    6-383-85
  Piping made of, 2-276
  Quench-hardening steels, 7-166
  Radiation thickness gauges used in manufacture of,
    9-46
  Skyscraper construction, 3-114, 115, 117
  War material, 9-324
  Water required in manufacture of, 2-271
  See also **Bessemer, Sir Henry; Iron; Mining**
Steel-frame buildings. Safety in electrical storms, 1-403
Steel manufacture. See **Steel**
Steel mills. See **Steel**

Steering assembly, automobile. *with illus.*, 2-142-43
Stefansson, Vilhjalmur, Arctic explorer. 5-172
Stegocephalians, primitive land vertebrates. 1-390
Stegosaurus, genus of giant dinosaurs. 1-393; *illus.*, 6-373
Steinboks, antelopes. 8-387
Steinheil, Karl August. German physicist, 9-156
Steinheim Basin, in Germany. Meteorite crater?, 6-92
Steinmetz, Charles P., German-born electrical engineer (1865–1923). He was educated at the universities of Breslau, Berlin and Zurich. He came to the United States in 1889 and from 1894 was consulting engineer of the General Electric Company. Steinmetz made many outstanding contributions to electrical research, including the theory and calculation of alternating current. He was famous for his experiments in the generation of artificial lightning. See also *with illus.*, 8-408
    Lightning, investigation of, 1-401
Steles, stone pillars. *illus.*, 1-118
Stellar dimensions. *with table*, 6-263-64, *diagram*, 266
Stellar distances.
    Developments in measuring, in nineteenth century, 6-389-90
    Measurement of, *with diagram*, 6-260-61, *table*, 262
Stellar energy. 6-265-66
Stellar evolution. 6-265-66, 267, 268
Stellar motions. *with diagram*, 6-262-63
Stellar structure. 6-265
Stellar systems. See Galaxies; Stars
Stellar temperatures. *with table*, 6-263-64
Stellarators, devices for confining plasmas. *with illus.*, 1-176
Steller's jays. 6-102
Stelvio Road. *illus.*, 10-25
Stemposts, ship timbers. 4-106
Stems, of plants. *4-65-71
    Cactus, *with illus.*, 6-228
    Cross section, *illus.*, 10-164
    Flowering plants, 3-404
    Food storage in, 2-420
    Thorns, arrangement of, *illus.*, 6-220
Stencils. Typewriters prepare, 1-276
Steno, Nicolaus, Danish clergyman and physician. 3-265; 4-387
Stentor, figure in Greek legend. 8-41
Step-and-repeat machines, photographic duplicators in printing. 1-211
Step-by-step system, in telephony. 2-389, *illus.*, 390
Step principle, of space-rocket design. 10-43, 46, *illus.*, 44-45
Step Pyramid. *illus.*, 1-127
Stephenson, George, English inventor (1781–1848). He studied at night school while he worked in a colliery. In 1814 he built his first locomotive to transport coal. He supervised the construction of the steam railway between Stockton and Darlington and designed its engine. It opened in 1825 and was the first railway in England to carry passengers as well as freight. Stephenson built the famous locomotive called the Rocket in 1829. See also 6-379, *illus.*, 380
    Railroad built by, 1-180
Stephenson, Robert, English inventor (1803-59). The son of George Stephenson, he was educated at Edinburgh University. He was his father's assistant in many of his engineering projects. Robert is especially notable for his construction of bridges. The high-level bridge at Newcastle, the tubular-plate bridge over the Menai Straits and Victoria Bridge over the St. Lawrence are examples of his work. See also 1-219
Stereochemistry.
    Founding of, 5-83

Stereochemistry *(continued)*
    Pasteur's contributions to, 9-72
Stereoisomers. 9-72
Stereophonic sound systems, for phonographs. 7-369
Stereotypes, in printing. 1-207-08
Sterilamps, electronic devices. *illus.*, 10-170
Sterilization.
    Autoclave, *illus.*, 9-79
    See also Food—*Preservation of
Sterling silver. This is silver of a standard quality; there is English sterling silver, Java sterling and others. The silver is alloyed with another metal, usually copper. In every 1,000 parts of English sterling silver there are 925 parts of silver and 75 parts of copper, and it is said to be 925 "fine." In other words, fineness denotes the number of parts of silver present in every 1,000 parts of the silver alloy.
    See also 1-382; 3-36
Stern, Wilhelm, German psychologist.
    Intelligence testing, 9-55
Sternberg, George Miller, American physician. 7-382
Sternomastoids, neck muscles. *illus.*, 1-148c
Sternposts, ship timbers. 4-106
Sternum, breastbone. *illus.*, 1-148b; 3-77, 78, 79, *illus.*, 74-75, 207
    Development in unborn human young, 8-28
Steroids, complex lipids. 2-5; 5-14
    Allergies controlled by, 4-264
Stethoscopes.
    Invention of, 7-371-72, *illus.*, 370
    Homemade, *with illus.*, 5-225
Stevens, Albert W., American explorer of stratosphere. 1-235
    Flight to stratosphere, 6-179
Stevens, John, American inventor (1749–1838). Steamboat of, 4-110
Steward, Julian, American archaeologist. 9-30
Stick-and-slip action, sound production by strings. 5-117, 216
Stick insects (walking sticks). *illus.*, 2-411; *with illus.*, 3-149-50
    See also Leaf insects; Phasmida
Sticklebacks, fishes. Reproduction, *with illus.*, 4-104
Sticks, trays of printing type. *with illus.*, 1-199
Sticks, forked. Prospecting, former use in, 7-355
Stieglitz, Edward J., American physician.
    Aging process, explanation of, 8-81
Stiff neck. 3-213
Stigmas, parts of pistils. *with illus.*, 4-121
Stilts, shore birds. 6-405
Stimulants, drugs. 5-401-03, *illus.*, 400
Stimulation of nerves and receptors. *with illus.*, 6-320-22
Stimuli.
    Breathing, factors stimulating, 4-207-09
    Living things respond to, 1-37-38
    Plants sensitive to various stimuli, 3-52-54, *illus.*, 51, 53, 55
    Sense organs affected by, 4-379
    Skin senses, 2-177-78
    Sleep-preventing, 6-144
Stimulus-response relationships.
    Development of study of, *with illus.*, 9-51-52
    Nerve impulses, study of, 6-320-21
Sting rays, fish. 4-293, 295, *illus.*, 293
Stinging nettles, plants. 7-80-81
Stingless bees. 3-372
Stings, model-holding booms in wind tunnels. 10-234, *diagram*, 233
Stings (stingers), of insects. 2-404
    Bees, *illus.*, 2-405; 3-367
Stinkbugs. *with illus.*, 3-256-57, *illus.*, 254

Stinkhorns, fungi. 3-30, *illus.,* 31
 Spores of, spread by insects, 7-239
Stipules, appendages at base of leaves. 4-72
Stirrup (stapes), bone of ear. *with illus.,* 4-380; 7-299, 300, *illus.,* 298
Stjerneborg, astronomical observatory. *illus.,* 1-24
Stocks, geologic formations. 3-422
Stockyard pens. *illus.,* 5-165
Stoics, Greek philosophers. 1-138
Stokes, Sir George Gabriel, English mathematician and physicist. Ultraviolet light, research in, 7-200
Stokes-Adams disease. Treatment with barium salts, 3-174
Stolons. See **Runners**
Stomach. *illus.,* 1-148d; 4-324-26, *illus.,* 322, 324-25, 334
 Complex stomachs in certain mammals, *with illus.,* 7-10
 Cow's, *illus.,* 7-10
 Human baby's, 8-95
 Muscle tissue, 1-147
 See also **Digestion; Food**
Stomach worms. 2-159
Stomadaeum, primitive mouth. 8-29
Stomata, pores of leaf epidermis. 3-44; *with illus.,* 4-72-73
Stommel, Henry, American oceanographer. 5-191-92
Stommel theory of deep-water flow. *with illus.,* 5-191-92
Stone.
 *Quarrying, 2-81-88
 Building material, *with illus.,* 7-116-18
 Dam construction, 8-313
 Soil texture, 2-18
 See also **Rocks**
Stone (make-up bank), for imposition of printing material. 1-206
Stone Age.
 Art of, *illus.,* 9-25, 30
 Breadmaking in, 9-293
 Bridges, *with illus.,* 2-332
 Picture writing in, *illus.,* 1-110-11
 Reconstructed by Osborn, 9-23-24
Stone flies. See **Plecoptera**
Stonehenge, ancient monument in England. Determining date of sample from, 10-97, *illus.,* 92
Stones, imperfections in glass. 3-312
Stoneware. 7-396, 399
Stoney, George Johnstone, Irish physicist. 9-285
Stony corals. See **Corals**
Stony Creek Bridge, British Columbia. *illus.,* 1-183
Stony-iron meteorites. See **Siderolites**
Stony meteorites. See **Areolites**
Storage, manure. 2-166
Storage, natural-gas. *with illus.,* 5-104-05, *illus.,* 98b-c
Storage, petroleum. 4-146
Storage, water. *Dams, 8-305-20
 Water supply, 2-272-73, 276-77, *illus.,* 282-83, 285, 286
Storage batteries. See **Batteries, storage**
Storage facilities. Kitchen, 4-267
 Records and documents, 10-69, 71-72, 73, *illus.,* 72-73
Storage of coal. 1-416
Storage of food. See **Food storage**
Storage tanks. Petroleum, 4-146
Storks. *illus.,* 1-299
Storm, W. M. Internal-combustion engine of, 2-130
Storm sewers. 5-328
Storms. 1-245, 252, *illus.,* 241
 See also **Weather**
Stourbridge Lion, early locomotive. 1-181, *illus.,* 180
Stovepipe drilling. See **California drilling**

Stoves.
 Heating by means of, 2-245
 Heating units for blast furnaces, *with illus.,* 1-342-43
 Safety procedures with, 7-191, 196, 197, 198
Straight angles. *with illus.,* 3-431
Straight lines. See **Lines, straight**
Strains. *with illus.,* 5-375, 376
 First aid for, 10-12
Straplike muscles. *diagram,* 3-210
Strassmann, Fritz, German physicist. 9-330
Strata, layers of rock.
 Beach sands display, 8-353
 Formation and study of, 6-139-40
 Investigation of, *with diagram,* 7-357-58
 Mountain building, stratified rocks in, *with illus.,* 10-213-21
 Petroleum in stratified rocks, *with diagrams,* 4-142-43
 Study of, in eighteenth century, *with illus.,* 4-397-98
Stratigraphic column, geologist's historical yardstick. 3-425-26; 6-369
Stratigraphic paleontology, science dealing with fossils in relation to rock beds.
 *Time scale of earth's history, 6-369-74
 See also **Evolution; Geology**
Stratigraphy, science dealing with rock layers of earth's crust.
 *Time scale of earth's history, 6-369-74
 See also **Geology; Paleontology**
Stratocruisers, airplanes. *illus.,* 6-189
Stratocumulus clouds. *diagram,* 1-317; 2-222, *illus.,* 215
Stratosphere. 1-237-38, *diagram,* 239; 4-45
 Research into, by means of balloons, 6-179, *illus.,* 180
Stratospheric radioactive fallout. 9-355
Stratotanker-Stratoliner, jet tanker-transport plane. *illus.,* 7-69
Stratus clouds. *diagram,* 1-317; 2-222
Strawberries. *illus.,* 4-129
Strawberry leaf spot, disease of strawberry. *illus.,* 8-373
Streak, identifying characteristic of minerals. 5-254
Stream discharge. 8-12-13
Stream load, material carried by streams. 8-12-13, 16, 17, 18
Stream velocity. Factors determining, 8-12, 13, 14, 16
Streamlining.
 Airplanes, streamlining of, 6-186-87
Streams. See **Rivers**
Streams, air. See **Winds**
Street lighting. Homemade layout, *with illus.,* 6-294
Street railways. Introduction in nineteenth century, 6-380
Strength.
 Insects compared with larger animals, 1-284, 286, *illus.,* 283
 Size of animals as factor in, 1-284
Streptococci, bacteria.
 Food spoilage caused by, *with illus.,* 4-153
 Streptococcus pyogenes, illus., 9-73
Streptomyces, mold. *illus.,* 10-130b-c
Streptomyces scabies, common-scab fungus. 8-371
Streptomycin, drug. 10-128
 Preparation of, *illus.,* 7-54
 Tuberculosis treated with, 9-183
Stressed-skin construction. 7-128
Stresses. 5-375, 376
 Compression, 3-312-13, *illus.,* 313
 Polarized light used to analyze, *illus.,* 7-284c
 Skeleton sustains various, *with diagrams,* 1-286
 Tension, 3-312-13, *illus.,* 313
Striae, in butterfly wings. *illus.,* 3-202b
Striae, glacial, rock scratches due to glaciers. 3-179-80; *with illus.,* 9-169, 171

Strigils, insect noisemaking organs. Ants, 3-360

String galvanometers. See **Galvanometer**

"String of colors," gold concentrate. 1-370

Stringed instruments. Sound production in, *with illus.,* 5-215-17

Stringfellow, John, English inventor. Steam-driven plane, 6-182

Strip mining. See **Open-pit mining**

Strip steel. See **Sheet and strip, steel**

Striped bass. 4-314

Striped hyenas. 8-250

Striped (skeletal, voluntary) muscles. *with illus.,* 3-204-13

   Development in human beings, 8-96-97

   Tissue structure, *with illus.,* 1-145

Strips, Moebius. See **Moebius Strips**

Strips, Pandromic. See **Pandromic Strips**

Stroboscopic photography. 9-411-12, *illus.,* 397, 412; *illus.,* 10-166

Stroke (apoplexy). First aid for, 10-14

Strokkr, geyser of Iceland. 8-291

Stroma, framework of red blood cell. 3-326

Stromatolites, fossil plants. 1-386

Stromboli, island of Mediterranean. Volcano of, *illus.,* 7-338; 8-298

Strömgren, Elis, Swedish astronomer.

   Tribute to Zeiss planetarium, 2-397

Strong, H. M., American physicist. 4-276

Strontium (Sr), chemical element. Atomic number, 38; atomic weight, 87.62; melting point, 800° C.; boiling point, 1,150° C.; specific gravity, 2.54. Alkaline-earth metal; hard, silver-white, tarnishing quickly in air. Discovered by Crawford in 1790; first isolated by Davy in 1808. Name derived from Scottish town of Strontian where strontianite, a source of strontium, was first discovered. Found chiefly in the minerals celestite and strontianite; also in various rocks, soils and mineral waters. Prepared by the electrolysis of the fused chloride. Used in fireworks, in a compound to remove sugar from molasses and in a bromide to treat certain nervous disorders. See also 3-174-75

   Radiation thickness gauges use strontium-90, 9-43, 45

   Radioactive, 9-352, 355-56

   Radioisotope-fueled thermoelectric generators, strontium 90 as fuel for, 6-174, 175

Strontium 90, radioactive isotope. 9-352, 355-56

   Lichen-caribou-Eskimo food chain affected by, 10-187

Strontium titanate. Radioisotope-fueled thermoelectric generators, use in, 6-175

Structural formulas.

   *Organic chemistry, 7-263-76

   *Valence, 3-245-51

   Definition, 3-246

   Methane, *with illus.,* 7-267

   See also specific compounds

Structural geology, scientific study of natural structures in rocks. See **Anticlines; Faults; Folds; Geanticlines; Geosynclines; Mountains; Prospecting; Synclines**

Structural steel. Manufacture of, 1-349, *illus.,* 348a

Structuralism. Wundt's psychological theory of, 9-48

Struggle for existence.

   *Adaptations of plants and animals, 3-235-44; 6-218-28

   *Seasonal changes and life, 5-408-13

   Darwin's analysis of, 8-259-60

   Primitive man's, 3-225-26

   See also **Adaptations; Darwin, Charles Robert; Evolution; Natural selection; Population**

Struthiomimus, ostrichlike dinosaur. 1-394

Strutt, John William. See **Rayleigh, Baron**

Struve, Friedrich Georg Wilhelm von, Russian-German astronomer (1793–1864). He served as director of observatories in the cities of Dorpat (Tartu) and Pulkovo. He discovered many double stars and he studied various nebulae. Struve was one of the first to measure stellar parallax; he also measured an arc of the earth's meridian. See also 6-390

Struve, Otto, Russian-American astronomer (born 1897). Great-grandson of Friedrich von Struve, Otto Struve served as astrophysics professor of the universities of Chicago and California and as director of the Yerkes and Leuschner observatories. He measured the radial velocity of stars (the rate at which the distance between star and observer is changing) and determined the rotation speed of stars around their own axes. He also studied interstellar matter.

   Radio astronomy in search for extraterrestrial life, 9-225

Struve, Otto Wilhelm von, Russian astronomer (1819–1905). He succeeded his father, Friedrich von Struve, as director of the observatory at Pulkovo. He discovered many double stars and estimated stellar magnitudes, the sun's velocity and the mass of Neptune. He studied nebulae, comets and the ring-system of Saturn and developed new methods of stellar measurement.

Stucco. Building material, *with illus.,* 7-121

Sturgeon, fish. Taste organs of, 4-101

Styles, stalks of pistils. *with illus.,* 4-121

Styling. *Industrial design, 10-117-26

Stylonychia, genus of ciliated protozoans. 2-66

Stylus engraving. Printing plates made by, 1-208

Styrene, plastic material.

   Synthetic rubber, use in, 6-358

Subatomic reactions. See **Nucleonics**

Subbituminous coal, low-rank coal. 1-408

Subclasses, groups in classification of living things. 1-289

Subclavian artery and vein, in shoulder. *illus.,* 1-148f

Subconscious mind.

   Freud and Breuer reveal presence of, 8-403

   Freud's exploration of, *with illus.,* 9-96-102

Subgenera, groups in classification of living things. 1-288

Subgroups, of chemical elements. 4-308, *tables,* 307, 309

Subirrigation. 5-30

Sublimation, a change of state. 1-171; 3-418

Submarine canyons. 6-72-74, *illus.,* 76

Submarine pipelines, natural-gas. 5-103

Submarines. *5-31-37

   *Bathyscaphes, 6-74a-d

   Atomic engine for, *illus.,* 4-342d

   Atomic-powered, *with illus.,* 4-114d

   Detection of submerged submarines, 7-356; 8-105-06

   Displacement of water, 2-33

   First practical submarine, 9-214

   Nautilus, atomic submarine, *illus.,* 4-114a

   Snorkel, *illus.,* 2-234; 5-34

   World War I, *with illus.,* 9-214-15

   World War II, 9-326

   See also **U-boats**

Submergence of land. 6-73-75, 77, *diagrams and illus.,* 75, 77

Submerging coasts. 8-354-55

Subphyla, groups in classification of living things. 1-291

Subshells, atomic. 1-311, *diagrams,* 312

Subsidiary ("parasitic") cones, of volcanoes. 8-296

Subsoil. *with illus.,* 2-17

Subsonic velocities, less than velocity of sound in air. 10-233, *with diagrams,* 229, 230, 231

Subsonic wind tunnels. *with diagram,* 10-233

Subspecies, groups in classification of living things. 1-288

Substations, for transmission of electricity. **9-236-37,** *illus.,* 234c, *diagram,* 237

Subsurface geology, scientific study of underground rocks. See **Geology; Prospecting**

Subsurface irrigation. 8-197-98

Subsurface water. See **Ground water**

Subtraction, arithmetical operation. 1-157

Subtractive color mixing. 7-286, *illus.,* 284b; 9-413-14

Subtractive principle, applied to number systems. 1-153-54

Subways. Tunnel construction, *illus.,* 2-45, 50

Succession, series of changes in plant and animal communities. 6-224; 10-188-90, 205-06

Succus entericus, intestinal juice. 4-327

Sucrose, ordinary sugar. 4-79

Suction. Experiments with force cups, *with illus.,* 7-220
Tentacles of squid and octopus use, *with diagram,* 1-280

Suction boxes, in Fourdrinier paper machines. *illus.,* 4-374b

Suction-type fans. 2-255

Suctorea, class of protozoans. 2-66

Sudanese local race. 8-218

Suede leather. 7-232

Suez Canal. 4-184
Malaria wiped out in Ismailia, **10-34-35**

Suffolk, breed of sheep. *illus.,* **10-247**

Sugar-beet nematodes, parasitic roundworms. **2-159,** *illus.,* 156

Sugar beets. See **Sucrose**

Sugar cane. 2-420
Industrial products from waste fibers of, **7-39**

Sugar maple trees. 5-150

Sugar pine trees. 5-141

Sugars.
*Starches and sugars, 4-76-79
Breadmaking ingredients, 9-295, *with diagrams,* 296, 299
Essential food elements, 4-51-52
Food preservation by, 4-163
Glucose regulation in blood, 5-15
Muscular energy furnished by, 3-205
Older person's diet, 8-82
Protoplasm contains, 2-5, 11
Solution of, 4-297-99, *diagrams,* 298-99
Tungsten filaments, use of sugar in production of, 4-238
See also **Fermentation**

Sulci, cerebral cortex. 6-324

Sulfa drugs (sulfonamides). **10-127**
Development of, 9-33

Sulfanilamide. Discovery of antibiotic properties, 10-127

Sulfate of ammonia. See **Ammonium sulfate**

Sulfate process, for preparation of wood pulp. 4-365, 366, 367

Sulfates.
Minerals in the form of, 5-250, *illus.,* 249; 9-305-06
Soil fertilizers, used as, 2-171
Soils contain, 2-24
Water hardness due to calcium and magnesium sulfate, 2-280-82

Sulfides.
Copper-sulfide ores, smelting of, *with diagrams,* 1-377-78
Minerals in the form of, *with illus.,* 5-249; 9-305-06

Sulfite process, for preparation of wood pulp. 4-365, 366, 367

Sulfite pulp. Plastics, used in manufacture of, 8-225

Sulfonamides. See **Sulfa drugs**

Sulfur (S), chemical element. Atomic number, 16; atomic weight, 32.064; melting point, rhombic: 112.8° C., monoclinic: 119.0° C.; boiling point, 444.6° C.; specific gravity, rhombic: 2.07, monoclinic, 1.957. Nonmetal; pale yellow, odorless, brittle solid, readily forming compounds, called sulfides, with many other elements. Known to the ancients; name derived from Latin *sulfur.* Found widely in nature in an uncombined state and in numerous sulfides and sulfates. Chief source: wells driven into salt domes on the Gulf coast; also obtained from sulfide ores by heating in presence of oxygen. Sulfur and its compounds are very important industrial materials; among other things, they are used for fertilizers, insecticides, explosives, paper, plastics, paints and dyes.
Atomic weight, 1-310
Bacteria that help make sulfur available to higher plants, **3-65**
Cells, found in, 2-6
Diet, essential in, 4-60
Electron arrangement of, 3-249, *illus.,* 248
Frasch process for extraction of, 3-321, *illus.,* 318
Fumes of, used as food preservative, 4-165
Interstellar space contains, 9-362
Iron, reaction with, 4-230
Properties and compounds of, 3-321
Sea, content in, *with chart,* 6-30-31
Silver, reaction with, 7-134-35
Soil sulfur available to plants, 2-24
Steelmaking, control of sulfur in, 1-344, 346, 353
Vulcanization process, sulfur used in, 6-351-52

Sulfur dioxide.
Air pollutant, 3-352, 353
Catalyzed reaction with oxygen, 8-190
Food preservative, 4-164
Thermostats, use in, 2-253
Uses of, 3-321

Sulfur trioxide. Sulfur dioxide, production of sulfur trioxide from, 8-190

Sulfuric acid.
Experiments and tricks with, *with diagram,* 7-175
Uses of, 1-207; 3-321

Sulkies, horse-drawn vehicles. *illus.,* 1-104

Sulphur. See **Sulfur**

Sulphuric acid. See **Sulfuric acid**

Sulphurs, butterflies. 3-198-99

Sumacs. Fruits of, *illus.,* 5-7
How to recognize, 5-139, *illus.,* 138

Sumer (Sumerian civilization).
Irrigation in, 8-192
Science in, 1-124-25
Writing of, 1-115

Summer.
Animals affected by, 5-412-13
Atmospheric circulation during, 1-238
Exploring plant world in, 10-205-06

Summer constellations, seen from middle northern latitudes. *map,* 1-327

Summer tanagers, birds. 6-108

Sumner, William Graham, American economist and sociologist. 9-26

Sun. *3-99-112
*Eclipses, 3-130-37
*Solar system, 3-157-64
Absorption spectrum of, *illus.,* 7-284a
Age of, 3-112
Air circulation of earth affected by solar radiation, *with diagrams,* 1-241-44; *with diagram,* 2-89-91
Apparent path, 1-262-63

Sun (continued)

Atmosphere affected by, 1-231-32, 237-38, 240, with illus., 236

Calendars based on apparent movement of, 1-126; 10-171-72, 176, illus., 172, 174-75

Cancers of skin may be caused by overexposure to, 8-267

Chemical composition of, 3-108-09

Color apparently altered following Krakatoa's eruption, 7-342

Comets affected by, 5-392-93

Data, 10-298

Description of, 3-157-58

Distance from earth, 3-99-100

Earth's revolution about, 4-48-49, diagrams, 46, 48-49

Energy of, 9-139-41, 224

Galileo's observations of, 3-3

Guide for estimating distances in the heavens, 6-79

Heat, sun as source of, 3-407-08

Heating, modern use of sun in, with illus., 2-252-53

Helium discovered in chromosphere of, 5-86; 6-391

IGY program for study of, 5-186

Light reaching earth, measuring quantity and intensity of, 1-247, illus., 246

Living things affected by, 3-177-78

Metallic atoms in, 9-364

Meteorites and comets, relationship to, 6-97-98, diagram, 98

Observation of, with illus., 6-82-83

Planets, relative distances from, 5-20

Planets probably derived from, 9-225

Radiation and climate, 3-184-85; 9-209

Radio storms originating in, 9-209

Reproduction of, by planetarium projectors, 2-399, illus., 400-01

Revolves around center of galaxy, 6-263

Rotation of, with illus., 3-107-08

Solar battery run by energy of, 7-103-06

Space motion of, 7-227

Space vehicles and solar radiation, 10-50, 52

Studies of, in nineteenth century, with illus., 6-393

Sunrise and sunset colors caused by dust, 7-142

Temperature of, 3-100

Tides caused by sun's gravitational pull, 6-201, 203, diagram, 205

Typical star, 6-255-56, 262, table, 262

Weather changes in upper atmosphere may be due to radiation from, 5-193

See also **Astronomy; Climate; Eclipses; Solar system; Sunlight; Universe; Weather**

Sun-drying, method of food preservation. with illus., 4-165

Sunburn. First aid for, 10-13

Sunday. Established as first day of week, 10-175

Sundews, carnivorous plants. 4-74, illus., 73

Sundials. 1-17, 264, illus., 18

Sundogs, mock suns. 7-279

Flying saucers thought to be, 9-20

Sunflowers. illus., 3-402

Stem, cross section of, illus., 4-70

Sunis, antelopes. 8-387

Sunlight.

*Solar battery, 7-103-06

Chemical effects of: experiment, 8-118

Fish in aquariums affected by, 8-113

Glass that helps keep out sunlight, 8-392

Measuring quantity and intensity of sunlight reaching earth, 1-247, illus., 246

Silver compounds affected by, 9-398-99, 412

Skin and, 2-176

See also **Light; Sun**

Sunrises. Photography, 6-316

Sunsets.

Beautiful sunsets due to volcanic dust, 7-342

Photography of, 6-316

Sunspots. 3-100, 105-06, 107, illus., 101, 105, 107, 108

Atmosphere affected by, 1-240

Climate influenced by, 3-185

Cycles of, 6-393

Earth's magnetic field influenced by, 7-172

Galileo's observations of, 3-3

Observation of, 6-83

Practical applications of knowledge of, 1-22

Radio telescopes detect, illus., 1-22

Superboxes, parts of artificial beehives. 3-370

Supercalenders, devices for providing high gloss for papers. 4-373-74

"Supercavitating" foils, for hydrofoil craft. 4-8

Superchargers.

Airplane construction, feature of, 6-187, 191

Superclusters, concentrations of galaxy clusters. 8-53

Superconductors. with illus., 5-209-10

Superficial lymph channels. illus., 1-148g

Superfluids. with illus., 5-208-09, illus., 207

Superfortresses, B-29 planes. 6-185, illus., 186

Supergiants, stars. 6-264, 265, table, 264

Superheating units, of steam locomotives. 1-186, illus., 185

Superheterodyne principle, in radio. with illus., 3-95

Superimposition, of images. Vision experiments with, 8-180, diagrams, 179

Superior, Lake. with illus., 7-61

Superior vena cava, great vein in chest. illus., 1-148f

Supermarkets. See **Self-service stores**

Supernovae, exploding stars. 6-268; 7-47-48

Cosmic-ray particles emanate from? 8-399

Crab Nebula and Cassiopeia A as suspected remnants of, 9-210

Superphosphates, soil fertilizers. 2-171

Supersaturated solutions. 4-303

Supersonic boom. 10-230

Supersonic velocities, greater than velocity of sound in air. 9-219; 10-233-34

Supersonic wind tunnels. with diagram, 10-233-34

Supersonics. Science dealing with flight at speeds exceeding that of sound waves in air. The term is also applied to the study of sound waves having a frequency range greater than that detectable by the human ear. The latter study is also known as ultrasonics and is indicated by that name in *The Book of Popular Science.* In the present entry, the word "supersonics" is used in the first meaning given above. *10-228-34

Superstitions.

Ancient peoples', 1-24, 26; 5-98

Comets as source of, 5-391

Medicine men, 1-364

Palmistry, 2-175

See also **Taboos**

Supramar, A. G., Swiss company. 4-7

Surface (external) breathing. 4-200, illus., 201

Surface condensers, in ships' steam engines. 4-111

Surface irrigation. 8-196-97

Surface tensions, of liquids. with diagram, 1-166-67; with illus., 5-371

Experiments involving surface tension of water, with illus., 8-2-3

Surface washing, method of cleaning rapid sand filters. 2-280

Surfboard riding. 6-367

Surgeons. See **Medicine; Surgery**

Surgery.

Cancer detection by biopsy, 8-270

Surgery (continued)
  Cancer removal by, **8**-270
  High-frequency sound beams used in, **8**-110
  History
    Antiquity, **1**-127-28
    Sixteenth century, **2**-376
    Nineteenth century, with illus., **7**-375-78, 385-87
    Twentieth century, **9**-31
  Psychosurgery, for mental illness, **9**-204
  Tranquilizers used to prepare patient for, **5**-379
  Tuberculosis treated by, **9**-182-83
Surinam toads. with illus., **3**-242; **5**-160
Surveying. Natural-gas map surveys, **5**-99, illus., 100
  Trigonometry used in, **3**-449
  See also **Prospecting**
Survival of the fittest.
  *Adaptations of plants and animals, **3**-235-44
  *Seasonal changes and life, **5**-408-13
  Man and animals, competition between, **3**-225-26
  Pangenesis, theory of, **8**-262-63
  See also **Darwin, Charles Robert; Heredity; Natural selection**
Susliks, rodents. **9**-6
Suspended solids, sanitary engineer's measure of wastes. **5**-329, 330
  Water supply, removal of silt and other solids from, **2**-273, 277, 278-80, illus., 278-79, 282-83
Suspenders, components of suspension bridges. **2**-339, illus., 338
Suspension bridges. 2-344, with illus., 338-40
Swainson's hawks. 6-156; illus., **10**-258
Swainson's warblers. illus., **6**-63
Swallow, J. C., British oceanographer. **5**-191
Swallow bugs, parasites. **6**-68
Swallowing mechanism. with illus., **4**-203
Swallows. with illus., **6**-67-68
  Barn swallow, illus., **5**-414
Swallowtail butterflies. 3-198, illus., 197, 199, 202a, 202c
Swammerdam, Jan, Dutch scientist. **3**-274
Swamp bay trees. 5-148
Swamp terrariums. 5-366-68
Swamps. illus., **10**-182
  Cypresses in, illus., **1**-48
  Field study of animals in, **10**-264
  Soil development in swamps and bogs, **2**-20, 23
Swan, Sir Joseph W., English physicist.
  Electric lighting, contributions to, **4**-235
Swans. with illus., **6**-398-99
Swarming of bees. 3-372, with illus., 368
Swash marks, on beaches. **8**-354
Sweat glands. 2-176-77, illus., 174, 177; **5**-10-11
  Deodorants, use of, **10**-84
Sweating. See **Perspiration**
Sweden. Uplift of, **10**-223
Swedish language. 1-117-18
Sweepback. See **Swept-back wings**
Sweet cicelies. Fruit of, illus., **5**-4
Sweet clover. Germination: dormant period, **5**-63
Sweet gum trees. with illus., **5**-145
  Fruits, illus., **5**-141
  Leaves, illus., **5**-139
  Winter buds, illus., **6**-58
Sweet potatoes. George W. Carver's work with, **10**-192-93
  Rot caused by mold, **3**-26
Sweet wines. 4-168
Swells, distorted cans. **4**-158
Swept-back wings, in supersonic aircraft. with diagrams, **10**-231-32

Swifts. 6-214-16
  Migration of chimney swifts, **9**-420
Swim bladder, in bony fish. **4**-313, with illus., 98-99
  See also **Air bladder**
Swimming. Dangerous in thunderstorm, **1**-404
  Fishes, **4**-98-99
  Rip currents as a hazard, **8**-350
  Snakes as swimmers, with illus., **5**-354c
  Surf swimming hazardous, **8**-349
Swimming-pool reactors. illus., **9**-138b
Swine. See **Pigs.**
Swine erysipelas, bacteria-caused disease.
  Pasteur's work with, **9**-80
Swing bridges. 2-340, illus., 339
Swiss Lake Dwellers, Stone Age people. Breadmaking of, **9**-293
Switchboards, telephone. 2-391, illus., 390
Switches, electric.
  Disconnecting switches used in transmission and distribution of electricity, **9**-235, 237, illus., 236, 238
  Homemade electrical circuits, switches in, with illus., **6**-289-90
Switzerland.
  Hydrofoil development in, **4**-7
  Lake of Lucerne and the Rigi, illus., **2**-219
  Märjelensee and Aletsch Glacier, illus., **7**-56
  Nineteenth-century naturalists, **8**-254
  Veisch Glacier, illus., **9**-162
  Weisshorn, illus., **10**-217
  See also **Alps; Swiss Lake Dwellers**
Swordfish. 4-315
Swordtails, tropical fish. **8**-115, illus., 116
  Reproduction, **4**-104
Sycamore trees. 5-146
Sydney Harbor Bridge, Australia. **2**-337
Syenite, igneous rock. **3**-423
Syllabaries, systems of writing. **1**-115, illus., 114
Sylvania Electric Products Inc.
  Electroluminescent devices developed by, **9**-345
Sylvatrons, electroluminescent devices. with illus., **9**-346-47
Symbiosis. 7-81; **10**-187-88, illus., 188-89
  Bacteria and fish, **2**-185-86
  Fungi and green plants associated in, **3**-24, with illus., 32
  Lichens as example of, **8**-362
  Roots and nodule-forming bacteria, relations between, **3**-68
  Termites and bacteria, relations between, **8**-362
Symbolic behavior.
  Apes display, **9**-263-64
Symbols, language. *Development of spoken and written speech, **1**-107-21
Symbols, mathematical. 10-294
Symbols for chemical elements. 2-224-26, 227, 229, 230, 231, diagrams, 224, 226
  Alchemical symbols, illus., **5**-76
  Development in nineteenth century, **5**-77
  List of, **10**-293
Syme, James, Scottish surgeon. **7**-385
Symington, William, Scottish engineer and inventor.
  Steamboat of, with illus., **4**-109; with illus., **6**-377-78
Symmetry. Pairs and images, **7**-110, with illus., 107-08, illus., 109
Sympathetic nervous system. See **Autonomic nervous system**
Sympathetic resonance, in ear. **7**-300
Symptoms of illness. 10-5, 55, 57-59, illus., 57-58
  Blood diseases, symptoms of, **3**-330, 331-32
  Cancer, **8**-270

Synapses, in nervous system. **6**-318, 323
Synchrocyclotrons, atom smashers. **9**-248, *illus.,* facing 248
Synchrotrons.
Relativistic speed of particles in beams of, **4**-216-17
Synclines, downfolds of rocks. **10**-215, 221, *illus.,* 219
Synodic month. 4-278
Synoptic charts, weather maps. **1**-253-54, *illus.,* 250
Synthetic chemical elements. 5-86
Synthetic diamonds. *4-273-76
Synthetic drugs. Development of, **8**-187-88
Synthetic dyes. Development of, **8**-183-84, 186-87
Synthetic fibers and fabrics. *with illus.,* **8**-189
Silk industry, effects of synthetic fibers on, **5**-184
Synthetic furs. 7-238
Synthetic materials.
*Organic chemists at work, **8**-181-90
*Plastics, **8**-221-33
Crystals used for electrostriction and piezoelectricity, **2**-294
Farm products that yield, **7**-35-36, 38-39, 40, 42, 43, 44, *diagrams* and *illus.,* 36-37, 38, 40-41, 42, 43
First attempts to synthesize organic compounds, *with illus.,* **5**-80-81
Meat animal by-products replaced by, **5**-169
Silicones, **3**-322, *illus.,* 323
See also **Synthetic rubber**
Synthetic rubber. *with illus.,* **6**-357-60
Development of, **8**-185
World War I, use in, **9**-213
World War II, use in, **9**-325
Synthetic vitamins. 5-42, 46, 49
Syphilis.
Nervous system, effects on, **6**-330
Salvarsan, Ehrlich's development of, **9**-33
Spirochete that causes, discovery of, **8**-409
Syrinx, vocal organ of birds. *with illus.,* **1**-282-83; **5**-421
System for Nuclear Auxiliary Power. See **SNAP**
System of Nature (Systema Naturae), work by Linnaeus. **1**-288
Systemic circulation, blood circulation. **3**-382
See also **Circulation of blood**
Systems, of human body. *1-148a-h
Organization of, **1**-147-48
See also **Anatomy; Circulation; Digestion; Endocrine glands; Excretion; Muscles; Nervous system; Skeleton**
Systems, rocks of particular geologic periods. **6**-370
Systole, phase in pumping action of heart. **3**-383

T

T2 bacteriophage, virus. *illus.,* **3**-454
Taal, Mount, Philippine Islands. **7**-57
Table Mountain, Cape Colony.
"Tablecloth," cloud formation. **2**-214
Table rolls, in Fourdrinier paper machines. *illus.,* **4**-374b
Table salt. See **Sodium chloride.**
"Tablecloth," cloud formation at Table Mountain, Cape Colony. **2**-214
Tables, shaking or **concentrating,** in ore dressing. *with diagram,* **1**-373
Tables of values, in mathematics. **2**-70
Taboos. 9-26
Tachina flies. 3-292
Tacoma Narrows Bridge, Washington. **2**-339-40
Taconic Disturbance, time of mountain making. **6**-371
Tadpoles. 5-159, *illus.,* 158-59

Tagua palms. Nuts used for buttons, **7**-210, 212, *illus.,* 213
Tahiti. Tides at, **6**-205
Tahrs, goat antelopes. **8**-377, *illus.,* 378
Tail rot, fish disease. **8**-116
Tailed spiders. Web of, *illus.,* **2**-263
Tailorbirds. Nesting activities of, **5**-418g
Tails, animal.
Insect appendages (bristles, filaments, pincers, stings), **2**-404, 406, *illus.,* 405
Lizards, detachable tails of, **5**-206, *illus.,* 205
Tails, comet. 5-391-93, *illus.,* 392, 397
Taine, Hippolyte, French scholar. **5**-73-74
Take-off mass, rocket. **10**-42, 43, 45
Takeuchi, H., Japanese geophysicist.
Earth's rigidity calculated by, **4**-174
Takins, goat antelopes. **8**-378, *illus.,* 380
Talbot, William Henry Fox, English inventor. **6**-382
Photographic process devised by, **9**-401-02
Talbotypes, early photographs. **9**-401-02
Talgo, lightweight train. **1**-188-89
Talking machines. *7-362-69
Talus, bone of ankle. *with illus.,* **3**-83, *illus.,* 82
Tamaracks, eastern larch trees. **5**-142
Tamarins, New World monkeys. **9**-259
Taming of animals. *7-327-33; *10-239-50
Tanagers, birds. **6**-108, *illus.,* 98
Migration of scarlet tanager, **9**-421
TANCAN (Tactical Air Navigation). *illus.,* **6**-298b-c
Tangent, trigonometric function. *with illus.,* **3**-447, 448
Tank cars, freight cars. *with illus.,* **1**-190
Petroleum carried in, **4**-146, *illus.,* 147
Tank farms, petroleum-storage centers. **4**-146
Tank furnaces, used in glassmaking. *with illus.,* **3**-309
Tankers, ships.
Petroleum carried in, **4**-146, *illus.,* 147
Tanks, earth-fill dams of India. **8**-308
Tanks, electrolytic, for refining metals. *with diagram,* **1**-378
Tanks, filtering, in ore dressing. *with diagram,* **1**-374
Tanks, military vehicles.
World War I, use in, *with illus.,* **9**-214
World War II, use in **9**-326, *illus.,* 324
Tanks, water. 2-285-86, *illus.,* 282, 283, 285, 286
Tannin, astringent substance.
Leather tanning, use in, **7**-233
Tanning, processing of leather. *with illus.,* **7**-232-34
Tantalum (Ta), chemical element. Atomic number, 73; atomic weight, 180.948; melting point, 2,996° C.; boiling point, above 4,100° C.; specific gravity, 16.6. Metal; can be drawn into wire with very high point of fusion and great tenacity. Discovered in 1802 by Ekeberg; name derived from Tantalus, a figure of Greek mythology. Found chiefly in the mineral tantalite; prepared by the reduction of potassium tantalum fluoride with hydrogen, followed by fusion in a vacuum. Used in electron tubes, as catalyst in manufacturing synthetic rubber, in cutting tools, aerial camera lenses, chemical equipment and so on. See also **3**-42
Electric-lamp filaments made of, **4**-238
Tape.
Coded tape used in typesetting, **1**-201-02, 203
Teletype machines using, **1**-276
Tape grass, aquatic plant. *illus.,* **8**-114
Tape recording. 7-368
Novel effects produced by, **5**-220
Tapeworms. *illus.,* **1**-292; **2**-154-55, *illus.,* 153
Degenerate forms, **6**-284
Fish tapeworms, **8**-361
Tapioca, starch product. **4**-78
Tapirs, large mammals. *illus.,* **7**-16

Tappets, of automobile engines. *with illus.,* 2-133

Tapping, of rubber trees. *with illus.,* 6-354-55

Tapping, of smelting and steelmaking furnaces. 1-343, 346, *illus.,* 345

Tapping, tooling operation. 10-109

Taproot systems, of roots. *with illus.,* 4-64-65

Tar. Valuable by-products of, 8-187

Tarantulas, spiders. 2-263-64, *illus.,* 265

Targhee, breed of sheep. *illus.,* 10-247

Tarnished plant bugs. *with illus.,* 3-261

Tarpans, extinct horses. 10-250

Tarpons, fish. 4-315, *illus.,* 314

Tarsal bones, in ankle. 3-83, *illus.,* 74, 75, 82-83

Tarsiers, arboreal mammals. *with illus.,* 9-264

Tartar, deposit on teeth. 10-78

Tartaric acid. Pasteur's work on optical activity of, 9-71-72

Tarugas, deer. *illus.,* 8-241

Tasmanian devils, marsupials. 7-427, *illus.,* 426

Tasmanian wolves, marsupials. 7-427

Taste, sense of. *with illus.,* 7-301-02; 9-314
Birds, taste sense in, 5-422
Fishes, 4-101
Inheritance of taste for phenyl-thio-carbamide (PTC), 8-341-42, 346

Taste buds. *with illus.,* 7-301

Tatum, Edward L., American biologist. Bread-mold heredity studied by, 9-385

Tatum, R. L., American archaeologist. 9-30

Taurids, meteor shower. *table,* 6-97

Taurus (Bull), constellation of zodiac. 1-335-36
Pleiades, star group in, *illus.,* 9-362-63

Taurus moving cluster, stellar group. 7-228

Taxonomy, classification of animals and plants. *1-287-306

Taylor, A. H., American physicist. 9-289

Tayras, carnivorous mammals. 8-172, *illus.,* 174

Teaching.
Engineers engaged in, 1-227, *illus.,* 228
Industrial design, training in, 10-126
Job opportunities in science teaching, 10-197-98, *illus.,* 196

Teague, Walter Dorwin, American designer. 10-119, 120, 123

Teams, scientific. 10-224

Tear gas.
World War I, use in, 9-213

Technetium (Tc), chemical element. Atomic number, 43; atomic weight, 99(?). Metal. Discovered in 1937 by Perrier and Segrè at the University of California by bombarding molybdenum with deuterons or neutrons; later isolated in large quantities from fission products of uranium. Named after Greek *technetos:* "artificial," as it was the first artificially made element. A number of isotopes, all radioactive, are known.

Technology.
*Chemical synthesis, 8-181-90
*Electronic computers, 9-143-52
*Engineering, 1-215-29
*Science and industrial progress, 1-87-97
Developments in, during Industrial Revolution, *with illus.,* 4-33, 35-41
Populations influenced by, 3-227, 232-34
Twentieth-century developments in, 8-410
See also **Engineering; Industry**

Tectonic earthquakes. 9-105-06

Teddington Physical Laboratory, England. 1-93

Teeming, pouring molten metal into molds.
Steel ingots, teeming of, 1-347, *illus.,* 348b

Teeth. *5-129-37
Adaptations for obtaining food, *with illus.,* 3-235-36

Teeth *(continued)*
Care of, *with illus.,* 10-77-78
Decay, in germ-free animals, 7-155
Development in human being, 8-95, *chart,* 94-95
Unborn human young, 8-30
Fossil remains, 1-384-85
Gum of newborn baby in cross section, *illus.,* 10-164
Lizards, egg teeth of, 5-205
Mammalian, 7-10
Evolution of, 7-2
Man's, compared with those of other vertebrates, *illus.,* 1-59
Man's digestive tract, part of, *illus.,* 1-148d
Origin of, 1-62
X-ray pictures of, *illus.,* 7-150

Tegmina, forewings of orthopterous insects. 3-139

Tegus (tejus), lizards. *with illus.,* 5-199

Teiids (Teiidae), family of lizards. 5-199

Tejus. See **Tegus**

Tektites, "glass meteorites." 6-93-94, 98, *illus.,* 93

Telecar, equipped for radiophoto transmission. *with illus.,* 7-392

Telefax, facsimile machine. 7-392
Railroads served by, 1-194

Telegrams.
Transmission of, by facsimile transmission, 7-392, *illus.,* 390, 392

Telegraph keys. *illus.,* 2-380
Homemade, *with illus.,* 8-145-46

Telegraph sounders. *illus.,* 2-380

Telegraphs, electric. *2-377-85
Automatic recorder invented by Edison, 7-363
Harmonic telegraph of Alexander Graham Bell, 2-386-87
Invention and development, *with illus.,* 5-238-41, 244
See also **Cables; Wireless telegraphy**

Telegraphs, optical. 5-239

Teleostei, important group of true bony fishes. *with illus.,* 4-95-96

Telepathy, thought transference. 9-57

Telephone exchanges. *with illus.,* 2-388-91

Telephone poles. Protection of, against sandblasting, 7-319, *illus.,* 320

Telephone repeater stations. 2-393

Telephones. *2-386-95
Design improved by Henry Dreyfus, 10-120
Electrical engineering in development of, 1-224
Homemade, *with illus.,* 5-224
Invention and development of, *with illus.,* 5-242-44
Long-distance lines, improvements, 2-392-95
Pictures transmitted through telephone circuits, 7-391-92
Ships, 4-117, 118
Transoceanic telephone cable, *with illus.,* 8-226

Telephoto lenses. 9-406

Teleprinters. *with illus.,* 2-381-82

Telescopes. *9-153-61
*Astronomical telescopes, 8-55-66
*Making a telescope, 9-365-74
Amateur astronomy, use in, 6-86
Astronomical observatories, list of, 8-66
Baker-Schmidt telescope, *illus.,* 10-226
Herschel, Sir William, and his telescopes, *illus.,* 4-339; *illus.,* 5-291; 9-154
History, 6-256, *illus.,* 256-57
Seventeenth century, *with illus.,* 3-2, 14-15
Nineteenth century, *with illus.,* 6-387-89
Reflecting, 7-262, *illus.,* 261
Refracting, 7-262, *illus.,* 261
Solar observation, use in, *with illus.,* 6-82-83
Spectroscopes, telescopes of, 7-279, *illus.,* 280

Telescopes (continued)
  Telescopic photography, 4-421
  Time measured by, 1-18
  Tower telescopes, with illus., 3-103
  See also **Astronomy; Radio telescopes**
Teletype machines. with illus., 1-276
Teletypesetters, coded type-casting machines. 1-202
Teletypewriter exchange system (TWX). 2-382
Teletypewriters. with illus., 2-381-82
Television. *5-276-88
  Cathode-ray tubes, used in, 6-302
  Color cameras, illus., 6-298c
  Development of, 9-288
  Marine research, use in, illus., 6-36
  Monitoring of, illus., 7-207
  Photographing televised images, 6-311
  Portable television set, illus., 10-121
  Radio waves used in, illus., 7-207, diagram, 200
  Relay tower, illus., 2-393
  Tubes, analytic geometry used to test, 4-432
  Weather study by, illus., 1-241, 253
Telford, Thomas, Scottish civil engineer. 3-294, with illus., 299
Telluric currents, natural earth electricity. Prospecting, measurement in, 7-360
Telluric lines. 3-108
Tellurium (Te), chemical element. Atomic number, 52; atomic weight, 127.60; melting point, 452° C.; boiling point, 1,390° C.; specific gravity, 6.24. Metal; brittle, silver-white, forming tellurides with hydrogen and various metals. Discovered by von Richenstein in 1782; name derived from Latin *tellus:* "earth." Found in pure form and also as the telluride of gold and other metals; obtained by reduction of telluric oxide. Serves as coloring agent in glass, giving blue-brown color; also in certain alloys to give high electrical resistance.
Telophase, stage of cell division. 2-14, illus., 13
Telstar, communication satellite. Solar cells used in, 7-106, illus., 105
Temperate zones. Precipitation in, with diagram, 2-348
Temperature. with illus., 3-410-13
  Atmospheric, 1-232, 237-38, 240
    Air circulation affected by, with diagram, 2-89-91
    Measuring and recording, 1-247, with diagrams, 316, 317-18, illus., 246, 250
    Seasonal changes and life, with illus., 5-408-13
  Barrier to plant and animal communities, 10-182
  Body temperature, 10-75-76
    Babies', 8-94
    Hibernating animals, 5-410, 411
    Lizards', 5-203
    Methods of taking, with illus., 10-57-58
    Regulation of, 2-176-77, 180; 5-10; 10-87-88, 90
    Regulatory devices, evolution of, 7-4
    Reptiles', illus., 7-4
  Chemical reactions influenced by, 2-230, 231, with diagram, 227-29, diagram, 226
  Cryogenics, science of very low temperatures, with illus., 5-207-10
  Dams affected by varying, 8-317
  Diamond synthesis requires high, 4-275-76
  Earth's internal, 4-174
  Extremes of, in deserts, 6-117-18
  Fish affected by temperature of aquarium water, 8-113
  Fish distribution influenced by, 4-97
  Flowering, effects on, 3-55
  Gases: relation to volume and pressure, with diagram, 1-165-66, 172; 3-416

Temperature (continued)
  Ground-water temperatures, 8-324-25
  Incandescence and, 2-187
  Jupiter, 5-20, 22
  Mach number and air temperature, 10-231
  Measurement of, with diagram, 1-164; 3-409-12, illus., 410-13
  Molecular motion and, 1-170-72, with diagrams, 164-66, 167-69
  Moon, 4-279
  Mountain building, earth's internal heat in, 10-216, 218-20, 223
  Ocean waters, temperature of, 6-34
  Seed germination and, 5-63, 64
  Soil formation partially due to temperature variations, 2-15, 21, 22
  Solubility of substances affected by, 4-299-300
    Water-temperature effects on solubility, testing for, 4-344
  Sound and, 5-120-22, illus., 121, 122-23
  Sound wave, 5-119
  Surface tension affected by, 5-372
  Thermometers, development of, 3-18-19
  Variations in past, 3-181-82
  Viscosity depends on, 5-370
  Weathering effects of, 6-137
  See also **Heat; Kindling temperature; Weather**
Temperature-humidity index (THI). 1-250
Temperature inversion. Smog caused by, with illus., 3-350
Temperature scales. 3-19
  Kelvin or "absolute" scale, 5-242
  See also **Thermometers**
Tempered scales, musical. 5-215
Tempering.
  Glassmaking, use in, 3-313
  Steel, manufacture, used in, 1-353
Temporal lobes, of cerebrum. with illus., 6-324-25
Temporalis, temple muscle. illus., 3-204, 209
Tenacity, identifying characteristic of minerals. 5-255
Tenaplate, aluminum alloy. 1-207
Tenaya, Lake, California. illus., 7-59
Tendon patches. 3-211
Tendon sheaths. 3-211, illus., 212
Tendons. 1-283, with illus., 284; 3-203, with illus., 210-11, illus., 204, 207-09, 212-13
Tendrils, plant parts. illus., 1-47; 4-67, 74
  Morning-glory, illus., 6-218b
  Passion flower, tendrils of, illus., 3-55
Tenite, cellulose-acetate plastic. illus., 8-227
  Buttons made from, 7-210
Tenite Butyrate, plastic material. Objects made of, illus., 2-148d
Tenite Polyethylene, plastic. illus., 8-220a
Tennant, Smithson, English researcher. 4-274
Tennessee. Cypress swamp in, illus., 7-66
  Analysis of stroke by stroboscopic photography, illus., 10-166
Tennessee Valley Authority (TVA). 6-12-13, illus., 11, 13
Tennis. Analysis of stroke by stroboscopic photography, illus., 10-166
Tenrecs, insectivorous mammals. 7-102, illus., 101
Tensile strain. 5-375
Tensile strength. 5-376
Tension, surface. See **Surface tensions**
Tensor fasciae latae, thigh muscle. illus., 1-148c
Tentacles. Suction in tentacles of squid and octopus, with diagram, 1-280
Terbium (Tb), chemical element. Atomic number, 65; atomic weight, 158.924. Rare-earth metal; not yet iso-

Terbium (continued)
lated. Discovered by Mosander in 1843 in the Swedish town of Ytterby; hence the name. One of the most difficult rare earths to purify; best separated by fractional crystallization of the bromides.

Teredos. with illus., 2-199-200

Terman, Lewis M., American psychologist. 9-55

Terminal buds. with illus., 4-66

Terminology, system of names and words in science.
 *Living things, 1-287-306

Termites. 3-362
 Nuptial flight of, 10-254
 Protozoans, partnership with, 2-63; 8-362; 10-188

Terneplate, coated iron or steel.
 Manufacture and uses of, 1-350

Terns, birds. 6-396, illus., 397
 Arctic tern, illus., 9-418
 Migration of, 9-420, diagram, 419
 Courtship behavior of, with illus., 5-418c

Terra cotta. Building construction, use in, 7-119

Terraces, used in farming. with illus., 6-1
 Crops grown on, 8-196

Terraces, of beaches. with diagram, 8-352

Terraces, stream. 8-16-17

Terraces, submarine. 6-71, 75, 77

Terrain-clearance altimeters. 6-192

Terramycin. 10-128, 129
 Fish diseases treated with, 8-116
 Food preservation, used in, 4-164

Terrapins. illus., 5-387

Terrariums. *5-365-68
 Home gardens, preparation of, 10-212

Terriers, dogs. 10-243, illus., 241

Tertiary period, time in earth's history. 1-395-96; 6-374

Tessera, vinyl plastic. illus., 8-229

Test sections, parts of wind tunnels holding airplane models. with diagram, 10-233-34

Test tube holders. For home laboratory, with illus., 4-222

Test tube rack. Home laboratory, use in, with illus., 4-222

Testes, primary sex organs of male. illus., 1-148g; 5-19, illus., 16-17; 8-21, illus., 20

Testosterone, hormone. 5-19

Tests.
 Acidity-alkalinity pH, tests for, 4-341-42, table, 339
 Acids and bases, tests for, with illus., 4-231
 Aerodynamic ground tests on model aircraft and missiles, with diagrams, 10-233-34
 Carbon dioxide, tests for, with illus., 7-130
 Extrasensory perception, tests for, illus., 9-321
 Food tests made at home, with illus., 7-135-36
 Intelligence tests, 9-320, illus., 310
 Machined work, tests for, 10-112
 Minerals, tests for, 9-302-03, 305-06
 Soil analysis, 2-172, illus., 165, 171
 Starch, test for, 4-77
 Substances, testing properties of, 1-85-86
 Wear test on auto parts, illus., 4-342a

Tetanus (lockjaw).
 Infection by, 8-366

Tetany, general tightening of muscles when blood is deficient in calcium. 5-18

Tethys, satellite of Saturn. 5-113

Tetraethyl lead. 3-168; 5-325

Tetragonal system, of external crystal structure. 5-342, diagram, 340

Tetrapods, four-legged backboned animals.
 Skeleton, supporting strength of, with diagram, 1-286

Tetrodes, electron tubes. 6-300

Tetryl, explosive. 8-282

Teutonic, British steamship. 6-378

Texas.
 Coasts, formation of, 8-358
 Sandstorm, illus., 7-139

Texas (cattle) fever.
 Germs of, carried by ticks, 7-383-84
 Sporozoan parasite is cause of, 2-66

Textiles.
 *Silk industry, 5-173-85
 *Vegetable fibers, 4-177-82
 Developments in textile industry during Industrial Revolution, with illus., 4-36-39
 Dynel fibers, illus., 2-233
 Printed by machine, illus., 1-92c
 Synthetic fibers and fabrics, with illus., 8-189
 See also **Cotton; Nylon; Plastics; Silk; Wool**

Thackeray, William M., English man of letters.
 Smoking, remarks on, 5-343

Thales, Greek philosopher. with illus., 1-129-30
 Eclipse of 585 B.C. predicted by, 3-134
 Loadstone's magnetic properties discovered by, 7-163
 Mathematical contributions, with illus., 3-428
 Static electricity discovered by, 6-119

Thalli, simple plant bodies.
 Fungal, 3-22
 Lichens, with illus., 3-32
 Liverworts', 3-189, illus., 186

Thallium (Tl), chemical element. Atomic number, 81; atomic weight, 204.37; melting point, 302° C.; boiling point, about 1,457° C.; specific gravity, 11.85. Blue-white, soft metal. Discovered in 1861 by Crookes by means of spectroscope; isolated the next year. Name derived from Greek thallos: "budding twig." Found in pyrites. Metal prepared by heating thallium iodide with metallic sodium. Thallium salts are poisonous and are used to control squirrels and other rodents.
 Radiation thickness gauges use thallium-204, 9-43, 45

Thalloid liverworts. 3-190, illus., 186

Thallophyta.
 *Algae, 3-214-24

Thames River Bridge, London. 2-333

Theodore Roosevelt Sanctuary, New York State.
 School group in, 9-277

Theophrastus, ancient Greek botanist. 1-138, 287, 288

Theorems, in mathematics. 3-429

Theriodonts, reptilian ancestors of mammals. 1-391

Thermal cracking, molecular breakdown. Petroleum refining uses, 4-148

Thermal expansion. 3-315

Thermal springs. See **Hot springs**

Thermals, ascending currents of air. 6-196

Thermionic emission.
 Electron tubes based on, 6-295-302

Thermochemistry. Nineteenth-century developments, 5-83

Thermoclines, masses of ocean water differing in temperature from surrounding masses. with illus., 6-74d

Thermocouples (thermopiles), devices used to measure slight differences in temperature. 3-412, illus., 413

Thermodynamics, science treating of mechanical actions or relations of heat.
 *Transmission of heat, 4-9-16
 Rise of, 6-253-54

Thermoelectric couples, devices for converting heat energy into electric energy. 9-228
 Radioisotope-fueled thermoelectric generators, with illus., 6-172-75
 Solar radiation measured by, 1-247

Thermographs, recording thermometers. 1-247

Thermoluminescence. *Dating by thermoluminescence, 6-375-76
Minerals identified by, 5-256
Rocks dated by, 5-191

Thermoluminescent glow. 6-375, 376

Thermometers. with diagram, 1-164; 3-409-12, illus., 410-13
Accademia del Cimento, thermometer developed by, with illus., 3-266
Atmospheric temperatures measured with, 1-247, 317, illus., 246
Beckman differential, 3-411
Bimetallic, 3-415
Clinical, with illus., 3-411; 10-75, with illus., 57-58
Experiments with, 4-24
Humidity of atmosphere measured by, 1-249-50, with diagram, 320-21, illus., 248
Invention and development of, in seventeenth and eighteenth centuries, 3-18-19
Maximum-minimum, with illus., 3-412
Mercury for thermometers, introduction of, 3-19
Thermocouple (thermopile), 3-412, illus., 413
Thermometer scales, comparison of, 10-297

Thermonuclear bombs. See Hydrogen bombs

Thermopane, insulating double-pane glass. illus., 8-389

Thermopiles. See Thermocouples

Thermophilic bacteria. 4-157

Thermoplastics. with diagram, 8-222-23

Thermos bottles. See Vacuum bottles

Thermoscope, early thermometer of Galileo. with illus., 3-410

Thermosets. See Thermosetting plastics

Thermosetting plastics (thermosets). with diagram, 8-223

Thermostats, temperature-regulating mechanisms. 2-252-53, illus., 253; 3-415
Breadmaking uses, 9-298

Thiamine, vitamin B₁. 5-41-42
Bread enriched with, 9-299
Daily requirement and sources of, table, 4-55-57

Thighbone. See Femur

Thinking. Psychology of, 9-316-17
See also Mind

Thiokol, synthetic rubber. 6-359-60

Third-class levers. with illus., 1-283; with illus., 3-58; with illus., 7-215

Thirst.
Cause of, 4-331-32
Muscular exercise and, 10-91
Sensation of, 9-314
Survival time without water, 4-331-32

Thirteen-Month Calendar. with illus., 10-179

Thirty-five-millimeter cameras. See Miniature cameras

Thistles.
Flowers and leaves of, illus., 7-79
Weeds, 7-113
See also Russian thistles

Thompson, Benjamin. See Rumford, Count

Thomsen, Julius, Danish chemist. 5-83

Thomson, Sir Charles Wyville, Scottish naturalist. 7-32, 34

Thomson, Elihu, English-American inventor. 5-246-47
Electromagnetic waves produced by, 7-202

Thomson, Sir Joseph John, English physicist.
Electrons discovered by, 8-403-04; 9-285

Thomson, Sir William (Baron Kelvin), British mathematician and physicist. 5-241-42
Siphon recorder development, 2-384
Thermodynamics, contributions to, 6-254

Thoracic nerves. 6-329, illus., 328

Thoracic vertebrae, backbone in chest area. with illus., 3-75-76

Thoracoplasty, surgical removal of ribs. 9-183

Thorax.
Insects, with illus., 2-403
Beetles, with illus., 3-336
True bugs, 3-253

Thorium (Th), chemical element. Atomic number, 90; atomic weight, 232.038; melting point, 1,845° C.; boiling point, 4,500+° C.; specific gravity, 11.3. Metal; heavy, gray, hard to fuse, emits radiations similar to those of radium. Discovered in 1828 by Berzelius; name derived from Thor, Scandinavian god of war. Found chiefly in thorite and other rare minerals; obtained commercially from monazite sand. Free element prepared by heating the double chloride or fluoride of thorium and potassium with metallic sodium or potassium. Thoria, the oxide, has been used in making incandescent gas mantles. Can be changed into a fissionable fuel in a breeder type of nuclear reactor.
Uses of
Atomic-energy production, 9-128, 138
Electronic filaments, with illus., 6-296

Thorium oxide. Gas-mantle experiments with, 4-237

Thorn-headed worms. illus., 2-161

Thorns, defensive devices of plants. 7-78, 80

Thorpe, Thomas E., Chemical historian. 5-78

Thought. See Mind; Psychology

Thrashers. 6-48, illus., 47

Thread cells. See Nematocysts

Thread-legged bugs. 3-260, illus., 254

Threads. See Fibers; Filaments

Three-dimensional space. with illus., 7-108-09

Three Forks, Montana. Missouri River formed at, illus., 6-410

Three-way switches. with illus., 6-290

Thresher sharks. 4-290, illus., 294

Threshing, of grain. 9-295, diagram, 294

Threshold, of sensation. 7-291, 302

Thrips, insects. See Thysanoptera

Throat.
First aid for foreign bodies in, 10-15

Thrombin, blood-clotting protein. 3-330

Thrombocytopenia, deficiency in blood platelets. 3-331-32

Thrombokinase, blood-clotting substance. 3-329, 330, 331

Thromboplastin. See Thrombokinase

Thrombus, clot in blood vessel. 3-332

Throttles, for automobiles. 2-135, illus., 134

Through bridges. with illus., 2-334

Throwing, silk-twisting process. 5-180, 182

Thrown silk, twisted silk. 5-180, 182

Thrush, human disease caused by a yeast. 3-27

Thrush family. with illus., 6-37-40

Thrust, term used in aeronautics. 2-124, illus., 123; 6-187-88; 10-41, 45

Thuban, star in Draco. 1-330-31

Thulium (Tm), chemical element. Atomic number, 69; atomic weight, 168.934. Rare-earth metal. Discovered in 1879 by Cleve; first isolated by James in 1911, as a pure compound, thulia. Named after Thule, the northernmost part of the habitable world according to ancient belief. Occurs in very slight amounts in gadolinite, euxenite, xenotime and other minerals; prepared in form of thulia by fractional crystallization. Free element has not yet been isolated.

Thumb, General Tom. Dwarf, illus., 8-94

Thumbs. Bones of, with illus., 3-81, illus., 80
Muscles of, illus., 3-208

Thunder. 1-399; 5-120-21
  Cause of, 1-245; 2-216, 218
  Eruption of a volcano, 8-301
  Timing of, to locate lightning, *with illus.*, 5-224
Thunderclouds, and lightning. 1-398-99
Thunderjet P-84. *illus.*, 6-194
Thunderstorms.
  Hail produced in, 2-356-57
  Lightning, *with illus.*, 6-123-26
Thurstone, Louis L., American psychologist.
  Originator of factor analysis, 9-313
Thymus gland. *illus.*, 1-148g; 5-9, *illus.*, 10
Thyratrons, gas-filled triodes. 6-301
Thyroid cartilage (Adam's apple). 3-79
Thyroid gland. *illus.*, 1-148g; 5-17-18, *illus.*, 16-17
  Human development, role in, 8-94-95
  Radioiodine used to treat diseases of, 10-98, 99, *illus.*, 100
Thyroxine, thyroid hormone. 5-17, 18
  Iodine found in, 10-98
Thysanoptera, order of insects. 2-413
Thysanura, order of insects. 2-412
Tibet. Plateau of, 6-109; 10-22
Tibeto-Indonesian local race. 8-219
Tibia, bone in lower leg. *illus.*, 1-148b; 3-83, *illus.*, 74, 75, 82
  Fracture, healing of, 7-352
Tibialis anterior, lower-leg muscle. *illus.*, 1-148c; *illus.*, 3-204, 213
Tick birds. Rhinoceroses, partnership with, 7-414; 10-188, *illus.*, 189
Tick flies. 3-292, *illus.*, 291
Ticks. *with illus.*, 2-268-69; 8-368
  Transmitters and carriers of disease germs, 7-383-84
Tidal movements of the earth. 4-174
Tidal theory, of mountain building. 10-216, 218
Tidal theory, of origin of solar system. 1-29, *illus.*, 28
"Tidal waves." 6-74, 205-06, 368; 8-350; 9-109-10
  See also **Tsunami**
Tide gauges, measuring devices. 6-207-08, *illus.*, 206-07
Tide-predicting machines. 6-208, *illus.*, 206
Tide staffs, tide-measuring devices. *with illus.*, 6-207
Tide tables. 6-208
Tides, atmospheric. 1-240, 319
Tides, oceanic. *6-201-08
  Electrical energy generated from tidal flow, 9-229
  Knowledge of, from astronomy, 1-18
  Newton's explanation, 3-280
  Tidal currents, 6-231-32
  Utilization as power source, 6-208
Tiercels, falcons. 6-159
Tiger beetles. 3-337
Tiger moths. 3-200
Tiger salamanders. *illus.*, 5-156
Tiger sharks, *with illus.*, 4-288
Tiger snakes. 5-363
Tigers. 8-203, 206, 208, *illus.*, 207
Tilaiya Dam, India. *illus.*, 8-201
Tilden, Sir William A., English chemist.
  Isoprene obtained from turpentine by, 6-357
Tile drains. Soil drainage, *with illus.*, 5-27-28
Tiles.
  Acoustical, 5-122
  Building material, *with illus.*, 7-118-19, *illus.*, 127
  Ceramic tiles, *illus.*, 7-407
Till, glacial deposit. 9-173, *illus.*, 171
Timber. *2-105-17
  *United States, 5-257-66
  Alpine type, 5-259
  United States, 5-257-66
  See also **Forests; Trees**

Timber slides. 2-113
Timber wolves. 8-136-37, *illus.*, 134
Timbre. See **Quality, sound**
Time.
  *Calendars, 10-171-80
  *Geological time scale of earth's history, 6-369-74
  Calculations of time, 1-264
  Development of measurement of, 1-17-18
  Measures, *table*, 10-295
  See also **Clocks**
Time Capsule, New York World's Fair (1939–40).
  Microfilm records in, 10-73
Time-division multiplex. *with illus.*, 2-383
Time stars. 8-61
Time zones. 1-182
Tin (Sn), chemical element. Atomic number, 50; atomic weight, 118.69; melting point, 231.89° C.; boiling point, 2,270° C.; specific gravity, gray: 5.75, rhombic: 6.55, tetragonal: 7.31. Ordinarily silver-white, malleable metal, with low tenacity. Known to ancients. Name derived from Anglo-Saxon "tin"; chemical symbol (Sn), from Latin *stannum*: "tin." Found chiefly in the mineral cassiterite, in association with granitic rocks; obtained by roasting to remove sulfur and arsenic and smelting with powdered anthracite in a reverberatory furnace. Two thirds of tin produced is used for tin plate or tin-lead solder; other industrial alloys are important.
  Electroplating of, 5-91
  Properties and uses, 3-40-41
  Steelmaking, use in, 1-350, 352
Tin cans. 1-350; 4-155-56
  Radiation thickness gauges used in manufacture of, 9-46
Tin plate.
  Manufacture and uses of, 1-350
  Radiation thickness gauges used in manufacture of, 9-46
Tintoretto, Il (Jacopo Robusti), Italian painter.
  Painting—The Doge Alvise Mocenigo Presented to the Redeemer, *illus.*, 7-203
Tipples, preparation plants for bituminous coal. *with illus.*, 1-415-16
Tiredness. See **Fatigue**
Tires, automobile. 2-143
  Detection of flaws by high-frequency sound, 8-109
  Manufacture of, *illus.*, 6-356
  Radiation thickness gauges used in manufacture of, 9-46
Tiros satellites, artificial satellites launched by United States. 9-223, 380; 10-46-47
  Weather study by, *illus.*, 1-241, 253
Tissue paper. 4-378
Tissues.
  *Blood, 3-325-34
  *Bones, 3-73-84
  *Muscles of human body, 3-203-13
  *Skin, hair and nails, 2-173-81
  *Systems of human body, 1-148a-h
  Aging of, 8-80-81
  Cancer cultures, 8-272
  Cellular composition of, *with illus.*, 1-44; 2-2-3
  Human body, *with illus.*, 1-144-45, 147; 2-287, *illus.*, 288
  Plant tissues, *with illus.*, 1-46
    Food storage, *with illus.*, 2-415-20
  X rays' effects on living tissue, 7-146, 148-50
  See also **Blood; Bones; Muscles; Histology; etc.**
Tissues, carbon. See **Carbon tissues**
Titan, satellite of Saturn. 5-113
Titan missiles. illus., 8-125
Titanic, ocean liner. Destruction by iceberg, 9-337

Titanium (Ti), chemical element. Atomic number, 22; atomic weight, 47.90; melting point, 1,800° C.; boiling point, above 3,000° C.; specific gravity, 4.5. White, lustrous metal; only element which burns in nitrogen. Discovered by Gregor in 1791; first prepared in pure form in 1910. Name derived from Titans, primeval deities in Greek mythology. Almost always found in igneous rocks and their sediments, occurring as an oxide in titanates and many iron ores. Prepared by heating the oxide with aluminum or by electrolysis. Oxide used in high-grade white pigments. Added to steel alloys to provide added strength.
  Interstellar space contains, 9-363
Titchener, Edward Bradford, American psychologist. 9-49
Titicaca, Lake, Bolivia-Peru. *illus.,* 6-115; 7-57
Titmice. *with illus.,* 6-40-42
Titov, G. S., Russian astronaut. 10-47-48
Titration, chemical measurement method.
  Acids and bases, 4-342, *illus.,* 341
Titusville, Pennsylvania. Oil well, first American, *with illus.,* 4-141
TNT (Trinitrotoluene). 8-282
  Structural formula, 7-275
  World War I, use of, 9-212
Toads. 5-155, 159, 160, 161, 162, *illus.,* 152, 155, 158
  Adaptations for survival, *with illus.,* 3-241-42
  Inactivity in cold weather, 5-411
  Migration of, 9-428
  Pets, 7-26
  Terrarium animals, 5-367
Toadstools. Mushrooms, distinguished from, 3-30-31
Tobacco. *Smoking, effects of, 5-343-50
  Cancer may be caused by smoking, 8-268
Tobacco Industry Research Committee. 5-350
Tobacco mosaic, virus disease of plants. 1-39, 40; 3-451-53, 455-56, *illus.,* 454
Tobacco plants.
  Mutations in, *illus.,* 6-274
  Virus diseases of, 3-451-52, 453, 455, 456, *illus.,* 454
Tobacco tar. Effects of, 5-350
Tobacco worms. 3-198
Tocopherols, vitamin E. 5-48
Toddy cats. See **Musangs**
Toe biters, true bugs. 3-263
Toes. Bones (phalanges) of, *illus.,* 1-148b; *with illus.,* 3-83, *illus.,* 74, 82
  Nails of, 2-180-81
Tokyo, Japan.
  Earthquake of 1923, 9-111
Tolerance for nicotine. 5-346
Toll-road system. 3-298
Toluene. Coal tar yields, *with illus.,* 1-419
Tom Thumb, early locomotive. *with illus.,* 1-181
Tomato bushy stunt virus. Crystals of, *with illus.,* 3-456
Tomato fruit worms, pests.
  Protecting tomato plants against, *illus.,* 10-152
Tomatoes. *illus.,* 4-130
  Diseases of, 8-372
    Tomato fruitworm, prevention of, *illus.,* 10-152
  Leaf spot of, 8-372
  Production without soil, 8-35
Tombaugh, Clyde W., American astronomer
  Discovery of Pluto, 5-292-93; 9-225
Tone, muscle. See **Tonus**
Tones. 5-117, 123, 124-25
  *Musical sounds, 5-211-20
  Sensitivity of ear to, *chart,* 8-40
Tonga Trench, oceanic deep. 6-74
Tongs. Third-class levers, *with illus.,* 3-58
  Metal, for home laboratory, 4-225

Tongue.
  Adaptations among animals, 3-236, 237
  Insects (butterflies), 2-403, *illus.,* 404
  Leukoplasia as precancerous condition of, 8-269
  Lymphatics of, *illus.,* 1-148g
  Man's digestive tract, part of, *illus.,* 1-148d
Tonus. Muscle tone, 3-211-12; 6-323
Tools.
  *Machine tools, 10-105-13
  *Simple machines, 3-56-62
  Importance of, in man's evolution, 1-66
  Machine-tool industry, 4-41
  Pneumatic, 9-66, *illus.,* 61, 65
  Populations influenced by, 3-227
  Primitive tools as aid in study of early man, 9-23-24
  Pruning tools, 10-148
  See also **Machinery**
Tooth-cutting devices. 5-137
Tooth decay. 5-130-31, 133-34, *illus.,* 135
Tooth shells. 2-201, *with illus.,* 101
Toothbrushing. Care of teeth by, 5-133
Toothed whales. 7-187, *illus.,* 184-85
Toothpicks.
  Mathematical recreations with, 4-445, *diagrams,* 445-46
Topography, physical descriptive geography.
  *Water erosion of land, 8-9-18
  Soil formation influenced by, 2-20
  Submarine topography, *with illus.,* 6-69-77; 9-221-22
Topology, branch of geometry.
  Recreations, topologic, *with diagrams,* 4-451-53
Topsails, of sailing ships. Ancient, 4-107
Torches. 4-232
Tornadoes. *with illus.,* 2-97-98
  Erosive agents, not important as, 7-319
  See also **Monsoons; Winds**
Torpedo rays, fish. 3-237-38; 4-293
Torpedoes.
  Launching a torpedo, *illus.,* 9-69
  Primary submarine weapons, 5-35
Torque. Control in helicopters, 6-194
Torquemada, Juan de, Spanish Franciscan monk and historian.
  Rubber, early use described by, 6-350
Torricelli, Evangelista, Italian physicist and mathematician. *with illus.,* 3-16-17
  Atmospheric-pressure experiment, 1-233
  Mercury barometer, 2-37, *illus.,* 36
Torsion balances. Mass of earth determined by, 4-44
  Prospecting with, 7-358-59
Tortoises. See **Turtles**
Torus, doughnut-shaped device. Plasmas confined in, *with illus.,* 1-176
Toscanelli, Paolo dal Pozzo, Italian physicist and mathematician. 2-364
Total eclipses. 3-134-35
Total internal reflection. *with illus.,* 7-254-55
Touch, sense of. *with illus.,* 7-304; 9-314
  Birds', 5-422
  Body's defenses, role in, 7-346
  Insects, 2-402, 403, 406
Touch typing. 1-269, *with illus.,* 272
Tourmaline, mineral. 5-256, *illus.,* 255
  Black, 5-254
  Light plane-polarized by, 7-282-83, *illus.,* 285
Tourniquets. *with illus.,* 10-6-7
Tow, straw. Paper from flax straw, *illus.,* 7-38
Tower telescopes. *with illus.,* 3-103
Towers, fractionating. See **Fractionating**—petroleum
Towhees, sparrows. 6-108
Townsend's solitaires, thrushes. 6-39

Toxins.
Body's defense against bacterial toxins, **7**-348-49
Nervous system, effects on, **6**-330
Toxoids, toxins treated so as to destroy poisonous qualities. **7**-351
Toys. Precautions in selecting, **7**-198
Trace elements, elements occurring in minute quantities.
Soil, **2**-23
Trachea (windpipe). *illus.,* **1**-148d-e; **4**-201, 204, *illus.,* 202
Tracheae, insect breathing tubes. **2**-405; **4**-200, *illus.,* 201
Tracheids, conducting cells of plants. **4**-64
Tracheophytes, vascular plants.
*Seed and fruit dispersal, **5**-1-7
*Seed plants, **3**-397-406
*Storage of food in plants, **2**-415-20
Ferns, club mosses and horsetails, **3**-190-92, *illus.,* 186, 188-91
Tracheotomy, incision into trachea. **4**-201, 203
Tracks, animal. *with illus.,* **10**-260-61
Tracks, railway. *with illus.,* **1**-191-92
Tractors. *illus.,* **2**-164, 168, 169; **9**-290
Saltworks, found in, **5**-frontispiece
Trade.
Populations influenced by, **3**-227-28, 232
See also **Economics; Waterways**
Trade winds. **1**-244; **2**-93, *diagram,* 92
Traffic. Regulating air routes, *with illus.,* **6**-197-200
Training.
Engineering, training in, **1**-228
Industrial design, training in, **10**-126
Science career, training needed, **10**-194-95
Trains.
Air brakes, **9**-68
See also **Locomotives; Transportation**
Trajectories, paths of flying objects.
Meteorites, **6**-95-96, 97, *diagram,* 89
Space travel, **8**-126-28, *diagrams,* 125, 126, 127, 131
Tram, silk thread. **5**-182
Tramways, early railroads. **1**-179
Tranquilizers, drugs that produce a calming effect.
*5-377-79
Alcoholism treated with, **4**-409
Development of, **9**-104
Transatlantic ship crossings. *with illus.,* **4**-108-11, 115, 117-18
Transcontinental railroads.
Canada, **1**-184
United States, **1**-182
Transfer molding. Plastics, *with diagram,* **8**-230
Transformations, energy-matter. **1**-84-85
Transformers, electric. *with illus.,* **6**-134-35; *illus.,* **9**-234b
Radio, use in, **3**-94
Use in transmission and distribution of electricity, **9**-235, 237, *illus.,* 236, 238-39
Transfusions. See **Blood transfusions**
Transistors. *10-102-04
Development of, **9**-289, *illus.,* 288
Electronic computers, use in, **9**-148, 289
Radio receivers that use, *with illus.,* **3**-98
Telephone system use of, **2**-389
Transit **satellites,** atificial earth satellites. Radio-isotope-fueled thermoelectric generators, use in, *with illus.,* **6**-174
Transits, passages of celestial bodies across disks of larger bodies.
Mercury, **4**-27; **6**-83
Venus, **4**-28, 31; **6**-83
Transits (theodolites), surveying instruments.
Tunnel construction, use in, **2**-50-51

Translucence. **7**-253
Transmission, natural-gas. **5**-98-99, *with illus.,* 101-05
Transmission, radio. *with illus.,* **3**-87-91
Transmission deafness. **5**-125
Transmission lines. **9**-frontispiece, 235-36, *illus.,* 236-38
Natural gas, *illus.,* **5**-98b
Protection of, *with illus.,* **1**-403
Transmission systems, for automobiles. *with illus.,* **2**-138-42
Transmissions, for automobiles.
Automatic, *with illus.,* **2**-140
Semiautomatic, **2**-139-40
Standard, *with illus.,* **2**-138-39
Transmitting stations, in radio. **3**-86-88
Transmutation, of chemical elements. *with illus.,* **8**-410-20; **9**-123, 125-26, 128, 131-32, 140, *with illus.,* 328-32
Transonic velocities, approximately equal to velocity of sound in air. **10**-231
Transparencies, black-and-white. Vision experiments with, **8**-180, *diagrams,* 179
Transparencies, color. **9**-413, 414
Principles in making of, *illus.,* **9**-400a-b
Transparency, in optics. **7**-253
Transparency, to heat. **4**-16
Transpiration, water evaporation from plants. **5**-25
Plant adaptations for controlling, *with illus.,* **6**-226-27
Sap, rise of, **4**-71
Transportation. *illus.,* **1**-92b
*Air transportation, **6**-176-200
*Automobiles, **2**-129-45
*Bridges, **2**-332-45
*Buoys, **5**-68-71
*Canals, **4**-183-95
*Flying saucers, **9**-16-20
*Guidance of missiles and space vehicles, **8**-125-31
*Hydrofoils, **4**-5-8
*Jet planes, **7**-67-74
*Land transportation in the past, **1**-98-106
*Railroads, **1**-179-95
*Roads, **3**-293-306
*Rockets, **10**-1-4
*Ships, **4**-106-18
*Space travel, **10**-40-54
*Submarines, **5**-31-37
*Tunnels, **2**-43-57
Bakery ingredients and products, **9**-298, *diagrams,* 294, 299
Civil engineering and, **1**-222-23
Coal mines, transportation systems in, *with illus.,* **1**-410-11, 412-13
Coal transportation from mine to consumer, **1**-416
Electrical engineering and, **1**-223
Mechanical engineering and, **1**-224-25
Nineteenth century development, *with illus.,* **6**-377-82
Petroleum, *with illus.,* **4**-146-47
Space travel, *with illus.,* **9**-375-83
Water, transportation of, **2**-275-76, *with illus.,* 284-86, *illus.,* 276-77
See also **Aeronautics; Canals; Railroads; Ships; Supersonics; Tunnels**
Transuranic chemical elements. **5**-86
Transverse crural ligaments, in ankles. *illus.,* **3**-212, 213
Transverse dunes. **7**-320-21, *illus.,* 322-23
Transverse waves.
Earthquakes, **9**-107
Light, **6**-241
Trap-door spiders. **2**-263-65, *illus.,* 264
Trapeziums, plane figures. *with illus.,* **3**-434

Trapezius, shoulder and neck muscle. *illus.,* 1-148c; *illus.,* 3-205
Trapezoids, plane figures. *with illus.,* 3-434-35
Traps. Catching wild animals alive, *with illus.,* 7-19-20
Travel, space. See **Space travel**
Traveling blocks. See **Block and tackle**
Traveling ovens. Breadmaking, 9-297-98, *diagram,* 299
Travois, primitive hauling devices. *with illus.,* 1-100
Trawls, fishing. 6-16
Demersal fish caught with, 4-311
Trays (sticks), of printing type. *with illus.,* 1-199
Treatment, medical. Nursing treatment at home, 10-63-64, 66-67, *illus.,* 63-64, 67
Tree care. *10-143-53
Tree crickets. *with illus.,* 3-146-47
Tree-dwellers, mammalian. 7-8-9
Tree ferns. 3-191-92
Tree frogs. *with illus.,* 5-155-56
Tree hoppers, insects. *illus.,* 2-411
Tree kangaroos. 7-424, *illus.,* 421
Tree moving. 10-151, *illus.,* 153
Tree-ring method, for dating ancient ruins. 9-29
Tree shrews. 7-100; 9-265
Tree snakes. *illus.,* 5-360
Tree sparrows. 6-108
Tree surgery. See **Tree care**
Trees. *5-257-66
*Care of trees, 10-143-53
*How to recognize trees, 5-138-51
*Lumber industry, 2-105-17
Adaptation to environment, 10-135, *illus.,* 137
Ants protect from other insects, 7-81
Danger spots in thunderstorm, *with illus.,* 1-403-04
Fossil trees, *illus.,* 6-372
Gymnosperms and angiosperms, *with illus.,* 3-400-04
Insect enemies of fruit crops, 9-185-96
Mulberry trees in silkworm cultivation, *with illus.,* 5-174-77
Rainfall, effect on, 2-349, 350
Sapsuckers cause damage to, 6-212
Seed and fruit dispersal, 5-3-6, 7, *illus.,* 3-4
Shrubs, how trees differ from, 4-66
United States, forests of, *map,* 2-107
United States and Canada, forests of, 2-108, 110
See also **Pine trees; Timber; Wood**
Trematodes, flatworms. 2-155-56, *illus.,* 154
"Trembles," disease of grazing animals. 7-76
Tremetol, active ingredient in plant poisons. 7-76
Trench mouth, disease of mouth and throat. 5-132
Trenches, oceanic. 6-74
Trevithick, Richard, English engineer and inventor. 6-379
Steam locomotive of, 1-180
Triangle spiders. Webs of, *illus.,* 2-263
Triangles, three-sided plane figures. 2-334; *with illus.,* 3-431-34
Euclidean and non-Euclidean, *with diagrams,* 4-440-41
Triassic period, time in earth's history. 1-392; 6-373
Triatoma, genus of true bugs. *with illus.,* 3-260
Triboluminescence, "light through rubbing."
Minerals identified by, 5-256
Tributaries, stream. 8-12, 14-16
Triceps (triceps brachii), upper-arm muscle. *illus.,* 1-148c; 3-209, *illus.,* 205
Trichina worms. 2-156-57, *illus.,* 153
Trichinosis. 2-156-57
Danger from undercooked pork, 5-336
Prevented by freezing of foods, 4-163
Trichomonas, genus of one-celled animals. 2-63
Trichoptera, order of insects. 2-414
Trickling filters, for purifying sewage. *with illus.,* 5-331

Triclinic system, of external crystal structure. 5-342, *diagram,* 341
Tricuspid valve, of heart. 3-383
Trieste, bathyscaphe of United States Navy. 2-191; 6-74b, 74c; 9-223
Trigeminal nerve. 6-328
Trigger force. Producing earthquakes, 9-107
Trigonometry. *3-466-50
Trihedral angles, in solid geometry. *with illus.,* 3-441
Trilobites, extinct crustacean shellfish. 1-387, *illus.,* 383, 386; *illus.,* 6-371
Trinitrotoluene. See **TNT**
Triodes, electron tubes. *with illus.,* 3-87-88; *with illus.,* 6-298-301, 303
*Audion, development of, 8-84-89
Triparanol, drug. 10-134
Triplanes, three-winged aircraft. 9-216, *illus.,* 217
Tripods, for home laboratory. *with illus.,* 4-223
Tritium, hydrogen isotope. 1-312, *diagram,* 313; 3-319
Lithium isotope yields, 3-166
Triton, satellite of Neptune. 5-292
Trochlea, lower part of upper-arm bone. 3-80
Trochlear nerve. 6-328
Troglodytes, human cave dwellers. 5-60
Trombones. Sound production in, 5-219
Trommels, in ore dressing. *with diagram,* 1-372
Troopships, military transports. 4-117, 118
Troost's terrapins. *illus.,* 5-387
Trophallaxis, food exchange among social insects. 3-360-61
Tropical continentals, air masses lying over tropical lands. 2-94-95
Tropical cyclones. 2-96, *diagram,* 98
Tropical diseases. See **Malaria; Trypanosomiasis; Yellow fever**
Tropical fish. 8-115
Tropical maritimes, air masses lying over tropical oceans. 2-94
Tropical orioles. See **Caciques**
Tropics.
Atmospheric circulation in, *with diagrams,* 1-242-44
Precipitation in, *with diagram,* 2-348
Tropisms, innate animal and plant movements.
Plants, found in, 3-52-54, *illus.,* 51, 55
Tropopause, division zone between troposphere and stratosphere. 4-45
Troposphere, lowermost layer of atmosphere. 1-237, 241, *diagram,* 239; 4-45; 5-193
Tropospheric radioactive fallout. 9-355
Trost, A., Swiss physicist.
Self-quenching radiation detectors, development of, 9-342
Troughs, containers. Breadmaking, *with diagram,* 9-296
Troughs, of beaches. *with diagram,* 8-352
Troughs, of ocean waves. *with illus.,* 6-362; 8-348, *illus.,* 349
Trout. *illus.,* 1-297
Lake trout, 4-98
Troy, ancient city of Asia Minor.
Archaeological studies, 9-29
Troy weights. *table,* 10-295
Trucks. First use of, 8-407
Petroleum carried by, 4-146, *illus.,* 147
Refuse collected in, 5-335, *illus.,* 334
True bugs. *3-252-64
True hawks. *with illus.,* 6-156-61
True pandas (lesser pandas). 7-315
True parasites. *8-360-68
True ribs. 3-77, *illus.,* 74-75
Truffles, edible underground fungi. *with illus.,* 3-28

Truman, Harry S., U.S. President.
Atomic bomb, announcement of, **9**-329
Trumpeter swans. 6-398
Trumpets. Sound production in, **5**-219
Truss bridges. with illus., **2**-335-36
Trusses. with illus., **2**-335
Truth serums. 5-405
Trychonympha, genus of one-celled parasites of termites.
2-63, illus., 62
Trypanosoma, genus of one-celled animals. **2**-62-63,
illus., 61
Trypanosomiasis, African sleeping sickness. **2**-62-63;
with illus., **6**-151
Trypsin, digestive enzyme. **4**-328
Ts'ai-Lun, Chinese official and pioneer papermaker. **4**-364
Tsetse flies. 3-287, 292, illus., 291; **8**-364
Tsientang River, China. Tidal bores in, **6**-205
Tsiolkovsky (Ziolkovsky), Konstantin Eduardovich, Rus-
sian schoolteacher. Rocket space flight proposed in
1903 by, **9**-377; **10**-42
Tsu Ch'ung-Chih, Chinese astronomer (fifth century A.D.).
Pi, method of determining, **4**-445
Tsunamis, tidal waves. **6**-368; **8**-350; **9**-109-10
Origin of, **6**-74
Tu-104, Russian turbojet plane. **7**-74
Tu-114, Russian turboprop plane. **7**-74
Tuataras, reptiles.
Unchanged for millions of years, with illus., **6**-283
Tubas. Sound production in, **5**-219
Tubercle bacilli. illus., **3**-67; **9**-175-78; illus., 176
Tubercles, tuberculosis nodules. **7**-349; **9**-178
Tuberculin, alleged cure for tuberculosis. **7**-382
Tuberculin test. 9-180
Tuberculosis. *9-175-84
Bacterium of, illus., **3**-67, 71
Bone, tuberculosis of, **3**-84
Lymph nodes affected by, **7**-349
X-ray units used in mass surveys, **7**-148-49
Tubers, underground stems. with illus., **4**-68; **6**-58
Food storage in, **2**-420
Plants propagated by, **9**-7, illus., 15
Tubes. See **Vacuum tubes**
Tubes, pneumatic. 9-66-67
Tubing.
Steel, manufacture and uses of, **1**-350-51
Well drilling, use in, **4**-146
Tubules, kidney. with diagram, **5**-12
Tubulidentata, order of mammals. with illus., **7**-16
Tudor, Frederic, American ice-trade pioneer. **4**-159
Tuff, sedimentary rocks. **7**-326
Tufts, of bristle or hair. Seeds and fruits, **5**-4, illus.,
2-3
Tuke, William, English reformer. **9**-102
Tulip trees. 5-148, illus., 149; **10**-205
Fruits, illus., **5**-141
Tulipwood. Photomicrograph of, illus., **9**-93
Tumbleweeds. 7-113
Adaptations for dispersal of seeds, **5**-4
Tumors.
*Cancer, **8**-265-72
Bone, **3**-74, 84
Brain, **6**-330
Cancerous tumors removed by surgery, **8**-270
Parathyroid glands, **5**-18
Radiation used to diagnose and treat, illus., **8**-271
Radioisotope treatments, **10**-98, 99-100
Strontium 90 may cause, **9**-355
Thyroid, **5**-18
Virus caused, **3**-453
X-ray treatment for, with illus., **7**-149-50
Tuna fish.   See **Tunnies**

Tundra.
Soils of, **2**-21-22, map, 20-21
Tung nuts. Oil from, **7**-43, illus., 42
Tungabhadra Dam, India. **8**-313
Tungsten (W), chemical element; also known as wolfram.
Atomic number, 74; atomic weight, 183.85; melting point,
3,370° C.; boiling point, 5,900° C.; specific gravity, 19.3.
Metal; hard, brittle, nonmagnetic, forming oxide when
heated in air. Recognized and named by Scheele in
1781; discovered two years later. Tungsten means
"heavy stone" in Swedish. It is found in tungstates,
such as wolframite, scheelite and huebnerite; obtained by
reduction of the oxide with hydrogen, carbon or aluminum.   90 per cent of world production used in manufacture of steel products, such as high-speed cutting tools,
projectiles and armor plate. Because of high melting
point, used for light filaments, targets of X-ray tubes
and electric wiring for furnaces.
Electric-light filaments of, **4**-238-39
Electronic filaments, use in, with illus., **6**-296
Properties and use of, **3**-42
Steelmaking, use in, **1**-352
Tungsten carbide. Diamond synthesis, use in, **4**-275
Tunicates. See **Sea Squirts**
Tunicin, secretion that forms coat of sea squirts. **4**-3
Tuning circuit, in radio. with illus., **3**-94-95
Tuning forks. 5-115-17, illus., 116, 117
Sine curves described by vibrating tuning fork, with
illus., **3**-450
Sound production in, **5**-218
Tunnel diodes. Electronic devices resembling transistors.
The tunnel diode consists essentially of a tiny crystal of
semiconducting material, such as silicon, germanium,
gallium or indium, which normally does not pass electricity particularly well. Certain impurities that conduct
currents are introduced into it. When the diode is connected to an electrical circuit, the electrons, which are
particles of negative electricity, "jump" through the
crystal with the speed of light, by "tunneling" through
a thin barrier in the crystal. This action is many times
faster than the electron movement in a transistor or a
vacuum tube. The tunnel diode is small enough to fit inside a small paper clip. It is not damaged by radiation
and can operate in extreme heat or cold, with a fraction
of the voltage needed for transistors and tubes. It is believed that the tunnel diode will find its greatest application in radio, electric switches, computing machinery,
nuclear projects and space vehicles. See also **Semicon-
ductors; Transistors**
Tunneling.
Dam construction, tunneling used in, **8**-309
Tunnels. *2-43-57
Irrigation water carried in, **8**-195
Railway, **1**-192
Tunnies (tuna, tuna fish). 4-315
Swimming movement of, **4**-98
Tupaias, tree shrews. **7**-100
Tupelo trees. with illus., **5**-146
Turbellarians, flatworms. **2**-156, illus., 155
Turbidity currents, in the ocean. **6**-73-74, 75
Turbinate bones, of nose. **3**-79; illus., **7**-302
Turbines.
*Steam turbines, **5**-305-12
Electricity generated by use of steam, gas and water
turbines, with illus., **9**-229-34
Gas, **4**-92; **5**-305
Jet engines, incorporated in, **4**-92
Locomotives driven by, **1**-89, 186, diagram, 90
Ships, use on, **4**-114
Steam, **4**-80, 81-82, with illus., 85-86
Water pumps, illus., **2**-275

Turbinia, British ship. 5-312
Turbocompressors, air compressors. 9-63-64
Turbojet engines. 4-92; 7-17, 73, 74, illus., 67-69
Turbojets. 6-194-95
Turboprop jet engines. 4-92; with illus., 7-71-73
Turbulence, irregularities of air circulation. 2-91-92
Turgor movements of plants. 3-52, 54, illus., 53
Turkey. Earthquake in, 9-119
Turkey red, dye. See Alizarin
Turkey vultures. with illus., 6-155
Turkeys. 6-337-38, illus., 336
Turkic local race. 8-218
Turner's formula, for determining atmospheric humidity. 1-321
Turning, tooling operation. 10-108
Turning vanes, for air circulation in wind tunnels. with diagram, 10-233
Turntables (rotary tables). Well drilling, use in, 4-145, diagram, 144
Turpentine. Source of, 2-106
Turret lathes. 10-109
Turret shells, gastropods. illus., 2-100
Turtle, Bushnell's early submarine. with illus., 5-31
Turtle doves. 6-305
Turtles. illus., 1-298; *5-386-89
    Migration of, with illus., 9-429
    Pets, 7-23, illus., 24
    Rib structure, evolution of, illus., 1-60
    Terrarium animals, 5-367-68
Turton, R. H., British Minister of Health.
    Cigarette smoking and lung cancer, remarks on, 5-350
Tusk shells. 2-201, with illus., 101
Tuskegee Institute. Work of G. W. Carver at, 10-192-93
Tutankhamen, Egyptian Pharaoh. Gold objects found in tomb of, 4-244
Tuve, Merle A., American physicist.
    Coincidence counters, development of, 9-340-41
Twain, Mark. 6-381
    First typewritten manuscript prepared by, 1-268
Tweezers. Third-class levers, 3-58
Twigs. Collection of, 10-211
Twilight. Cause of, 1-236; 7-142, 283
Twin-lens reflex cameras. 9-405, illus., 406
Twiners, modified stems. 4-67
Twining, of plants. illus., 1-47
Twinning, crystalline phenomenon. 5-253
Twins. Identical and fraternal, 8-22, with illus., 336-37
Twisters. See Tornadoes
2,4-D. Weed-killer, 7-114
    Plant hormone, 9-291
Two-pipe system, of steam heating. 2-248
TWX, teletypewriter exchange system. 2-382
Tympanum of ear. with illus., 4-380
    Birds', reptiles' and frogs'. illus., 4-381
    See also Eardrum
Tyndall, John, British physicist (1820–93). Professor of natural philosophy at the Royal Institution, he later became superintendent of the Institution. He studied various phenomena of light and sound and the transmission and absorption of radiant heat by gases and vapors. He investigated alpine glaciers, showed the blue of the sky to be due to tiny particles in the atmosphere and demonstrated that spontaneous generation does not occur in germ-free air.
    Experiments showing that dust carries microbes, 9-76
Tyndall effect. 5-297
Type I, star population. 8-50
Type II, star population. 8-50

Type bars, typewriter. 1-269-70, illus., 270, 271
Type casting, casting of printing type. with illus., 1-200-02
Type-high, exactly as high as type used in printing. 1-201
Type styles. Typewriter, 1-272
Typesetting. with illus., 1-199-203
Typewriters. *1-265-76
    Development of, in nineteenth century, with illus., 6-381
    Electronic computers, typewriters used with, 9-147, 148-49
Typhoid fever.
    Antibodies and immunization against, 7-350
    Bacteria that cause, illus., 3-64
    Germs of, carried by flies, 7-383
    Human carriers of, 8-365-66
"Typhoid Mary," human carrier of typhoid fever. 8-365-66
Typhoons. See Hurricanes
Typhus fever. Developments in control of, 9-39
Typography, printing with type. *1-196-214
Tyrannosaurus rex, carnivorous dinosaur. 1-394, illus., 383, 395
Tyre, ancient Phoenician city. illus., 3-228
Tzolkin, calendar of Mayan priests. 10-173
    Cycle used for Mayan calendar, 1-24

U

U-boats.
    World War I, use in, 5-32; with illus., 9-214-15
    World War II, 5-33
    See also Submarines
U-shaped valleys, land forms due to glacial erosion. 9-169, 172, diagram, 164-65
Ulcers.
    Peptic ulcers, with illus., 4-334-35
    Smoking may aggravate, 5-346
Ulna, bone of forearm. illus., 1-148b; 3-80, illus., 74, 75, 81
Ulothrix, genus of green algae. 3-217
Ultramicroscopes. 9-94
    Development of, with diagram, 5-297-98; 8-408
Ultrasonics. *8-103-10
    Bats' use of ultrasonic waves, 1-283; 8-104-05
    Vibrations produced by quartz crystal, illus., 2-294
Ultraviolet rays. 7-200-01, 205-06, diagram, 201
    Atmosphere affected by, 1-231-32, 237-38
    Atomic-bomb explosion produces, 9-351
    Dentistry, use in, 5-137
    Microscopy with, 9-92
    Radioactivity detection, use in, 10-99
    Space-travel hazard, 10-50
Ulugh, Beg, Persian ruler. 8-64
Umbra, region of complete shadow in eclipse. 3-132
Umbrella trees. 5-148
Unavailable water, soil water that cannot be used by plants. 2-24; with illus., 5-27
Uncertainty principle. 9-284-85
Unconsciousness. First aid for, 10-15
Undercutting, factor in etching photoengraved plates. 1-205-06
Underground natural-gas storage. 5-104-05
Underground Railroad, system of refuges for escaping slaves. 5-60
Underpopulation. Dangers of, 3-232-34
Underwater blimps, cameras. illus., 10-167
Underwater photography. with illus., 6-316; illus., 10-167

Underweight.
Symptoms and dietary control of, **5**-271-72, *diagram,* 267

Ungulates, hoofed mammals.
  *Antelopes, **8**-376-87
  *Deer, **8**-234-43
  *Elephants, hippopotamuses and giraffes, **7**-408-17
"Unheard sound." **5**-115
Unicorn beetles. *illus.,* **3**-344
Unified field theory. **4**-220
Uniflow steam engines. **4**-84
Union, in mathematical sets. *with diagram,* **4**-442
Union of South Africa. See **South Africa**
Union of Soviet Socialist Republics.
  Atomic bombs, **9**-352, 354
  Atomic-powered vessels of, **4**-118, *with illus.,* 114a
  Hydrofoil development in, **4**-7
  Industrial research in, **1**-96
  Irrigation in, **8**-201
  Jet-plane development, **7**-74
  Lakes in, **7**-56
  Moscow Canal, *with illus.,* **4**-186-87
  Petroleum industry and reserves, **4**-147, 150
  Space and rocket research in, *with illus.,* **9**-375-76, 379-81; **10**-42, 46
Union Pacific Railroad Company.
  Central Pacific, tracks joined with, **6**-379
Uniservo units, of electronic computers. *illus.,* **6**-298b-c; **9**-148, *illus.,* 147
Unit-type presses, in printing. **1**-210
United Nations.
  Narcotics, attempt at control of, **5**-406
  Public-health movement, contributions to, **9**-42
  Secretariat Building, *illus.,* **3**-123
  Security Council meeting, telecast of, *illus.,* **5**-286
United Nations Children's Fund. **6**-14
United States.
  *Science competitions for youth, **8**-67-77
  Athletics in, **10**-90
  Atomic bombs, **9**-348, 351-54
  Atomic-powered ships of, *with illus.,* **4**-114a-c
  Bird and game conservation in, *with illus.,* **9**-270-78
  Bridges; see main article on **Bridges**
  Button industry of, **7**-209-10
  Canals of, **4**-187, 190, 191, 192-94, *illus.,* 193, 195
  Chemurgic developments in, *with illus.,* **7**-35-44
  Coal, early use of, **1**-409
  Coal deposits and production of, *with illus.,* **1**-420
  Dating archaeological materials from, **10**-97
  Fisheries of, **6**-21
  Fissure eruptions in, **8**-304
  Forests of, **2**-108, 110, *map,* 107; **5**-257-66
  Granites of, **2**-83-84
  Hydrofoil boats in, **4**-7, 8
  Hydroponic farms in, **8**-35-36
  IGY program, **5**-186-88, 190, 191, 193-95
  Industrial design in, *with illus.,* **10**-118-26
  Industrial scientific research in, *with illus.,* **1**-87-92
  Irrigation in, *with illus.,* **8**-198-99
  Jet stream over, **2**-359, *illus.,* 358
  Life expectancy in, **8**-79-80
  Limestones of, **2**-86
  Meat-packing industry of, *with illus.,* **5**-163-72
  Mining operations in, *illus.,* **3**-38-39
  Narcotics, illicit traffic in, **5**-406
  Natural gas, discovery and use of, **5**-98-99, *with illus.,* 105-06
  Navigation, development of, *with illus.,* **4**-108-10
  Petroleum industry and reserves, **4**-140, 146-47, 152, *with illus.,* 141-42
  Pipeline systems for natural gas, *with illus.,* **5**-101-05

United States *(continued)*
  Plastics industry, development of, *with illus.,* **8**-223-33
  Plateaus and plains, **6**-109
  Psychology in, **9**-322
  Railroads of, *with illus.,* **1**-181-95
  Railway stations in, **1**-192
  Railway tunnels in, **1**-192
  Rainfall statistics for, **2**-347
  Roads and highways of, **3**-306, *illus.,* 305-06
  Salt mining in, **5**-320, *illus.,* 317
  Sandstones of, **2**-85, 86
  Science, contributions to
    1765–1815, **4**-359-61, *illus.,* 358
    Nineteenth-century electrical inventions, **5**-239-47
    Development of synthetic chemical industry in twentieth century, **8**-187
    Jet aviation developments, **7**-69-72, *illus.,* 67, 69
  Ships and boats of, **4**-111, 117-18
  Space and rocket research in, *with illus.,* **9**-375-76, 378-79; **10**-42, 44, 46-48, *illus.,* 40-41
  Transportation on land, early, *with illus.,* **1**-105-06
  Volcanoes in, **8**-299
  Water supply in, **2**-272-75, 283
  See also **Government**
United States, ocean liner. **4**-117, 118
United States Air Force.
  Flying saucers, investigation of, **9**-18
United States Army.
  Hydroponic farms in Japan established by, **8**-36
United States Bureau of Mines. Safety in mines enforced by, **1**-414-15
United States Civil Service Commission.
  Jobs in science provided by, **10**-198-99
United States Coast and Geodetic Survey.
  Tidal wave warning system of, **6**-368
United States Coast Guard.
  Cutters of, *illus.,* **6**-363
  Ice patrol of, **9**-338, *illus.,* 333, 338
United States Constitution. Science promoted by, **4**-34
United States Department of Agriculture. **9**-290
  Southern Regional Research Laboratory, *illus.,* **1**-92
United States Federal Communications Commission (FCC).
  Color television systems approved by, **5**-288
United States Fish and Wildlife Service.
  Marine fishes, contributions to conservation of, **4**-312
United States Food and Drug Administration.
  Bakery-product enrichment standards set by, **9**-299
United States Hydrographic Office.
  Ice forecasting service provided by, **9**-336-37, 338
United States Maritime Administration. **4**-8, *illus.,* 5
United States National Advisory Committee for Aeronautics (NACA). **9**-219
United States National Bureau of Standards.
  Ionospheric conditions studied by, **8**-63
  Time measured by, **8**-61
United States Naval Research Laboratory. Radio telescope, *illus.,* **8**-62
United States Navy. Microfilming of blueprints for, **10**-74
United States Navy radio telescope, in West Virginia. **9**-225
United States Public Health Service.
  Antipolio vaccine studies and program, **10**-131, 133
  Industrial waste, analysis of, **5**-329
United States Railroad Administration. **1**-183
United States Weather Bureau. Voluntary observers for, **1**-322
UNIVAC, electronic computer. *illus.,* **6**-298a, 298b-c; **9**-145, 147-49, *illus.,* 147

UNIVAC (continued)
Space and missile flights guided by UNIVAC ATHENA, 8-128, diagram, 129
Universal antidote. How to make and use in treating poisoning, 10-10
Universal blood donors. 3-334
Universal blood recipients. 3-334
Universal joints, for automobiles. 2-141, illus., 140
Universal languages. 1-119-21
Universal sets (universes), in mathematics. with diagram, 4-442
Universe.
*Stars and galaxies, 8-47-54
Continuous-creation theory, 9-210
Curved universe theory proposed by Einstein, 4-220
Ether and light, early theories of, 4-210-11
Evolution theory, 9-210
Expanding universe, theory of, 9-225
Origin and nature of universe, theories of, with illus., 4-398-400
Universities.
Industrial research in, 1-89, 90, 94, 95
Rise of, in Middle Ages, 2-304
University of California Radiation Laboratory.
Bevatron at, 9-249, illus., facing 248
Linear accelerator at, illus., 9-246
University of Chicago. Atomic-energy research, 1-90
University of Michigan.
Food preservation by atomic radiation, research on, with illus., 10-114-16
Unleavened bread. Prehistoric, 9-293
Unrestricted submarine warfare.
World War I, 9-214-15
World War II, 9-326
Unsaturated hydrocarbons. 7-270
Unstable atomic particles. 1-313, with table, 314
Unstable equilibrium. 2-322, illus., 321
Updrafts, air currents. 1-242
Upflow, suspended-solids contact basins, for water purification. 2-279
Upland game birds. *6-331-40
Upper atmosphere. with illus., 1-235-40
Research, 1-251-52, illus., 253; 9-223, illus., 221
Uprush, forward motion of ocean waves. 8-349, 351
Uraniborg, observatory built by Brahe. 2-373-74
Uranium (U), chemical element. Atomic number, 92; atomic weight, 238.03; melting point, about 1,150° C.; specific gravity, 18.68. White and hard metal. Discovered by Klaproth in pitchblende in 1789; first prepared in 1841 by reduction of the chloride with metallic potassium, a method still used. Chief ore is uraninite, or pitchblende, found in various other ores. Used largely since World War II for manufacture of atomic missiles and other work based on nuclear fission. See also 3-42
Atomic energy derived from, 9-132-38, 330-31
Atomic fission after explosion, 9-351
Earth's age determined by proportion of uranium and lead in rock deposits, 4-47
Isotopes of, 1-313; diagram, 9-134
Radioactivity of uranium, discovery of, 8-403, 412-13; 9-349
Radium as disintegration product of, 3-175
Ships' reactors may use, 4-118
U-235 separated from other isotopes by diffusion, 5-373
Uranus, planet. 5-289-90, diagram, 292
Data, 10-298
Discovery of, 4-398
Neptune discovered as result of irregular motion of, 2-317

Urea, waste product eliminated by kidneys. 5-11
Ammonium cyanate yields, 7-264
Sweat contains, 2-177
Synthesis of, 5-78
Urea-formaldehyde plastics. 8-227
Ureters, urinary ducts. illus., 1-148e; diagram, 5-12
Urethan resins, plastics. 8-229, 233
Urethra, canal of urogenital system. 8-21, illus., 20
Urey, Harold Clayton, American chemist and one of the leading figures in America's World War II atomic-bomb project (1893–). In 1932 he discovered heavy hydrogen, or deuterium, which is present in heavy water. He received the 1934 Nobel Prize in chemistry for this achievement. Urey taught at Columbia University for a number of years; in 1945 he became professor of chemistry at the University of Chicago. illus., 10-facing 303
Geologic thermometer developed by, 3-181-82
Heavy hydrogen discovered by, 8-418
Urinary bladder. illus., 1-148d-e
Urine, fluid excretion from kidneys. 5-11-13
Urochordates, class of chordates. with illus., 4-2, 3
Urodela, order of amphibians. See **Salamanders**
Urogenital system, urinary and reproductive organs.
Development in unborn human young, 8-28
Ursa Major (Greater Bear), constellation. 1-324
Spiral nebula in, illus., 1-256
Ursa Major group, group of stars with common space motion. 7-228
Distance from earth, 8-51
Ursa Minor (Lesser Bear), constellation. 1-325
Urus, extinct wild ox. 10-248
Use and disuse. Lamarck's theory of, 4-390
Ussuri (Sikhote-Alin) meteorite, in Siberia. 6-89-90, 91, 92
Utah. Rainbow Bridge, 8-15
Uterine mucosa, mucous membrane of uterus. 8-22-23
Uterus, organ for containing the unborn young. 8-20, 21, 22, 23, 24, 32, 33, illus., 20, 21, 25
Utricle (utriculus), structure in inner ear. 4-381, illus., 380; with illus., 7-305, 306
Utterances. Language, role in, 1-108
Uvarov, B. P., zoologist.
Migratory locusts, study of, 9-432

V

V-1, German pilotless jet plane. 6-185; 7-68; 9-218; 10-229
V-2 rockets. 6-185; 7-69; 9-218, 219; 10-2, 45, 46, 229, illus., 1, 2, 47
World War II, used in, with illus., 9-378
V-mail, American system of microfilmed mail. 10-74, illus., 73
V-type airplane engines. 6-187
Vaal rheboks, antelopes. 8-386
Vacant lots. Teem with life, 10-255-56
Vaccination. with illus., 7-350-51
Antipolio, illus., 7-350-51
Vaccines. 7-350-51
Antipolio vaccines, illus., 7-350-51; with illus., 10-131, 133
Bacteria used in preparation of, 3-70
Pasteur's work with, 9-79-80
Virus vaccines, 3-458
Vaccinia virus. 3-455, illus., 454
Vacuoles, cell structures. 2-8, 9, 61, 62, illus., 4
Vacuum bottles. 4-16, illus., 15
Vacuum cleaners. with illus., 9-70
Design of, 10-123, illus., 124-25
Vacuum driers, devices for dehydrating foods. 4-166

Vacuum evaporators. 3-418
  Beverage concentration by, 4-167
  Salt extraction by, 5-315, 322, 324, *illus.,* 322-23
Vacuum molding. Plastics, *with diagram,* 8-232
Vacuum pumps. *with illus.,* 2-40-41; *illus.,* 9-60
Vacuum tubes, electronic. *6-295-303
  *Audion, development of, 8-84-89
  See also **Diodes; Cathode-ray tubes; Crookes tubes; Electron tubes; Triodes;** etc.
Vacuums.
  Canning, use of vacuums in, 4-156-57
  "Nature abhors a vacuum," 3-5
  Rockets operate best in, 10-41-42, 45
  Sound absent in, 5-119
Vadose circulation, shallow circulation of ground water. 8-324
Vagabond spiders. 2-266-67
Vagina, female sexual organ. *with illus.,* 8-20
Vagus nerves. 6-328
  Heartbeat, effect on, 3-387
Vail, Alfred, American pioneer in telegraphy. 5-240
Vakil, Rustom Jal, Indian physician. 9-104
Valence, combining power of atoms. *3-245-51; 1-312
  Introduction of concept of, 5-78
  Lewis-Langmuir theory of, 8-417
  Periodic table, progressive change of valence in, 4-305, 306
Vallarta, Manuel S., Mexican mathematician.
  Cosmic-ray investigations. 8-395
Valley quail. 6-334
Valley sinks, water-erosion formation. 5-52, *illus.,* 53
Valleys.
  Drowned river valleys, *with illus.,* 8-358
  Formation of, 8-12, 14, 15, 17, *with illus.,* 18
Values, of color. 4-269, 271
Valves.
  Engine cylinders, valves of
    Diesel engines, *with illus.,* 4-90-91
    Gasoline engines, *with illus.,* 2-133, 134; 4-87-88, 89, *illus.,* 86-89
    Steam engines, *with illus.,* 4-81, 83-84
  Water mains supplied with, 2-286
Valves of the heart. *with illus.,* 1-277-78; 3-383, 387, 390, *diagrams,* 383, 391
Van Allen, James A., American physicist. 5-195
Van Allen radiation belt. *with illus.,* 5-195
  Plasma in which high-energy particles are trapped, 1-177
  See also **Magnetosphere**
Van de Graaff, Robert J., American physicist. 8-419-20
Van de Graaff electrostatic generators (accelerators). *diagram,* 1-309; 8-419-20; 9-242, *illus.,* 129, 241, 243
Van der Hulst, H., Dutch physicist. 9-210
Van der Waals, Johannes Diderik, Belgian chemist. 1-166
Van der Waals' equation. 1-166
Van der Waals' forces. 1-166
Van Maanen's star. Radial velocity of, 7-226
Vanadates. Minerals in the form of, 9-306
Vanadium (V), chemical element. Atomic number, 23; atomic weight, 50.942; melting point, 1,710° C.; boiling point, 3,000° C.; specific gravity, 5.96. Soft, white metal; malleable and ductile. Discovered in 1830 by Sefstrom; isolated in 1869 by Roscoe; name derived from the Scandinavian goddess Vanadis. Relatively rare, but found in a variety of minerals, such as vanadinite and patronite. Obtained by the reduction of the chloride in hydrogen and by electrolysis of sodium

Vanadium *(continued)*
vanadate in hydrochloric acid. Vanadates (salts or esters of vanadic acid) useful in preparation of aniline black, for coloring glass and in manufacture of steel alloys.
  Steelmaking, use in, 1-352
Vanes, turbine. 5-307, 308
Vanes, wind. See **Wind vanes**
Vanguard I, United States artificial satellite. 5-188
Vanguard II, United States artificial satellite. 5-188
Vanishing point, in perspective. 1-76, *illus.,* 77
Vanners (shaking tables), in ore dressing. *with diagram,* 1-373
Van't Hoff, Jacobus Hendricus, Dutch physical chemist. 5-83
Vapor. See **Evaporation; Gases; Water** vapor
Vapor inhalation. 10-66, *illus.,* 67
Vapor lamps. 9-344
Vapor pressure. Solutions affected by, 4-300-01
Vaporization. See **Boiling; Evaporation**
Vaporization, heat of. 3-418
Varanids (Varanidae), family of lizards. 5-200
Vari-Typers, typewriters with removable type fonts. *with illus.,* 1-274
Variable stars. *7-45-51
  Description of, 6-267-68
  Mira, in Cetus, 1-335
Variation, biological. 6-272
Varicose veins. 3-392, *diagram,* 391
Varied thrushes. 6-39-40
Varro, Marcus Terentius, Roman scholar. 1-361
Varves, deposits due to glaciers. 3-180; 9-174
Varying hares (snowshoe rabbits). 5-413, *illus.,* 412
Vas deferens, duct for transporting sperm. 8-21, *illus.,* 20
Vasco da Gama. See **Gama, Vasco da**
Vascular bundles, plant conducting tissues. *with illus.,* 4-70, 71, 73, 74
Vascular diseases, diseases of blood vessels.
  Nervous system affected by, 6-330
Vascular rays, plant conducting tissues. 4-68, *illus.,* 69
Vascular systems of plants. *diagram,* 3-47
Vasculums, plant-specimen containers. 10-207, *illus.,* 206
Vat dyes. 8-186
Vaucheria, genus of green algae. 3-219
Vectors, *with illus.,* 2-126-28
Vedette, aircraft of Royal Canadian Air Force. *illus.,* 10-163
Veery thrushes. 6-39
Vega, star in Lyra. 1-264, 333
  Distance from earth, calculation of, 6-390
Vegetable ivory.
  Buttons made from, 7-210, 212, *illus.,* 213
Vegetable kingdom. See **Botany**
Vegetables. 4-132
  Food stored by, 2-420
  Preserved by gamma radiation, 10-116
  Soilless-agriculture methods applied to, 8-35-36
Vegetation.
  Air-pollution detection, use in, 3-351-52, 354, *illus.,* 352
  Climate type indicated by, 3-180
  Coal formed from vegetation, *with illus.,* 1-405-07
  Dunes controlled by growth of, 7-323-24
  Peat formed from, *with illus.,* 1-406-07
  Protected by insect-eating birds, 6-341
  See also **Plants**
Vegetative activities, of plants. *4-62-75
Vegetative organs. Seed plants', 3-397-98

Vegetative reproduction.
 *Artificial propagation of plants, **9-7-15**
 Banana plants, **5-62**
Veil Nebula. *illus.*, **8-156b-c**
Veins. *illus.*, **1-148e-f**; **3-381, 382, 383, 386**, *diagrams*, **381, 382, 385**
 Bleeding from veins, control of, *with illus.*, **10-5-7**
 Diseases of, **3-392**, *diagrams*, **391**
 Kidney, *diagram*, **5-12**
Veins, mineral deposits. **5-251**
Veksler, V., Russian physicist. **9-248**
Velocities, of earthquake waves. **7-357-58**
 See also **Earthquakes**
Velocities, galactic. 8-54
Velocity.
 Light, energy and matter, significance of velocities in, **1-84-85**
 Space vehicles and rockets, **10-43-46, 48**
 Speed, different from, **2-120-21**
 See also **Supersonics**
Velocity compounded turbines. 5-307
Vema, Lamont Geological Observatory vessel. **5-194**
Vena cava, great vein. *illus.*, **1-148e-f**
Venable, James. 7-377
Venezuela.
 Salt harvesting in, *illus.*, **5-316**
Venice, Italy. Glassmaking in medieval Venice, *with illus.*, **3-308**
Venn, John, English logician (1834–1923). Diagrams of mathematical sets, *illus.*, **4-442**
Venn diagrams, of mathematical sets. *with diagrams*, **4-442**
Venom.
 Amphibians', **5-162**
 Lizards', **5-206**
 Scorpions', **2-267-68**
 Snakes', *with illus.*, **1-285; 3-237; 5-360**
 Spiders', **2-261, 264-66**
Ventifacts, wind-cut stones. *with illus.*, **7-320**
Ventilation. *2-244-45, 254-57
 Coal mines, ventilation of, **1-414**
 Holland Tunnel, ventilation of, **2-55-56**
 Paper making process, required in, **4-372**
 See also **Air; Oxygen**
Ventral fins (pelvic fins), of fishes. *with illus.*, **4-96**
Ventricles of heart. *with illus.*, **1-277-79**; *illus.*, **148f; 3-383, 386-87,** *illus.*, **382, 383**
Venules, small veins. **3-386,** *illus.*, **385**
Venus, planet. *with illus.*, **4-28-31**
 Data, **10-298**
 Galileo's observations of, **3-2**
 Observation of, **6-83-84**
 Space flight to, **10-54**
 Transits of, **6-83**
Venus's-flytraps, carnivorous plants. **3-238; 4-74,** *illus.*, **73;** *illus.*, **6-218d**
 Turgor movements of, **3-54**
Venus's girdles, jellyfish. *illus.*, **1-292**
Verdins, birds. **6-42**
Vermeer, Jan, Dutch painter. **1-268**
Vermiform appendix. *illus.*, **1-148d; 4-329,** *illus.*, **322, 329**
 Appendicitis, **4-334**
Vermillion Lake, Canada. *illus.*, **10-21**
Vermont. Granites in, **2-83**
Vermont (Green Mountains) Disturbance, time of mountain making. **6-371**
Vernix caseosa, covering of embryo and fetus. **8-33**
Veronal, drug. Developed by Fischer, **8-408**
Vertebrae, segments of backbone. *with illus.*, **3-75-77**
Vertebral column. See **Backbone**

Vertebrates.
 *Ears, development of, **4-379-85**
 Backbone, supporting strength of, *with diagrams*, **1-286**
 Brains, comparison of, *illus.*, **1-63**
 Cave-dwelling species, *with illus.*, **5-58-59**
 Classification of, **1-289, 291, 297-300**
 Heart, evolution of, **1-277-79**
 Invertebrates distinguished from, **3-74-75; 4-1**
 Skeleton, supporting strength of, *with diagram*, **1-286**
Vertical circle.
 Determining star position, *with diagram*, **6-80**
Vertical-circle telescopes. *illus.*, **8-55**
Vertical-lift bridges. *with illus.*, **2-340, 341**
Vertical turbine pumps. 2-274-75
Verticillium wilt, disease caused by a fungus. **8-371**
Vesalius, Andreas, Flemish physician. *with illus.*, **2-374-76**
Vesper sparrows. 6-108
Vespidae, family of wasps. Social wasps, *with illus.*, **3-365-66**
Vespucci, Amerigo, Italian navigator. **2-365**
Vessels, conducting cells of plants. **4-64**
Vesta, asteroid. **4-421**
Vesuvius, Mount, Italy. *with illus.*, **7-335-38**
 Changes in shape, **8-294, 296**
 Crater, *illus.*, **8-294**
 Pliny the Elder's death caused by eruption of **1-362**
Veterinary medicine. Zoos, practiced in, *with illus.*, **10-157-59**
Viability, of plants. **5-65-66**
Vibrating screens, in ore dressing. *with diagram*, **1-372**
Vibrations.
 Animals make use of, *with illus.*, **1-281-83**
 Molecular vibration, **1-170, 171**
 Sound, *with illus.*, **5-114-28**
  Experiments with, *with illus.*, **5-221-23, 226**
  Musical instruments, *with illus.*, **5-215-20**
 See also **Earthquakes; Seismographs**
Vibrato, effect in musical sounds. **5-212, 220**
Viceroy butterflies. *illus.*, **2-410**
Vickers Vanguard, British turboprop plane. **7-73**
Vickers Viscount, British turboprop jet plane. *with illus.*, **7-72-73**
Victoria, Lake, Africa. **7-61**
Victoria Desert, Australia. **6-118**
Victoria Falls, Africa. Discovery of, **7-31**
Victoria regia, plant. **7-80,** *illus.*, **81**
Vicuñas, wild ruminating mammals. **7-331-32,** *illus.*, **328**
 Adaptations for high altitudes, **7-8**
Vielle, Paul-Marie-Eugène, French engineer.
 Poudre B (smokeless powder) invented by, **8-278**
Viesch Glacier, Switzerland. *illus.*, **9-162**
Vieta, François, French mathematician. **2-68**
View cameras. 9-404-05, *illus.*, **404**
View finders, camera. *with illus.*, **9-405**
Viking, American rocket. **10-46**
Vikings, ancient Nordic people. Ships and navigation of, **4-107, 108**
Villemin, Jean-Antoine, French physician. **9-175**
Villi, outpouching of intestinal wall. **4-329,** *illus.*, **327**
Villi, chorionic. 8-22, *illus.*, **23**
Vincent's infection, "trench mouth." **5-132**
Vinci, Leonardo da, Florentine artist, engineer and scientist. *with illus.*, **2-362-63**
 Camera obscura described by, **9-398**
 Engineering accomplishments of, **1-217**
 Fossils, theory of, **4-387**

Vinci, Leonardo da (continued)
  Human flight, plans for, 6-181
  Ornithopter of, illus., 2-362; 9-216
Vinegar, acetic acid solution.
  Experiments with, 4-231; with diagram, 7-173-74
  Food preservative, 4-164
Vinegar flies. with illus., 3-290-91
Vinyl plastics. Dynel fibers, illus., 2-233
Vinyl resins, plastics. with illus., 8-229
  Dynel fibers, illus., 2-170
Vinylite, plastic.
  Molds of Vinylite used in preparation of printing
    plates, 1-207
  Records (phonographic) made of, 7-369, illus., 362
Violets. Structure, 7-243
Violins.
  Sound production in, 5-117-18, 124, 216, illus., 124
Viomycin, antibiotic. 10-128
Vipers, snakes. 5-363-64, illus., 362
Virchow, Rudolf, German scientist (1821–1902).
Founder of modern pathology. Although his most
notable work was done in the study of disease, he
also distinguished himself as an anthropologist, archae-
ologist and politician. He became lecturer at the Uni-
versity of Berlin in 1847, and in 1856 he was appointed
professor of pathological anatomy. See also 7-387-88
Vireos, birds. 6-63-65, illus., 65
Virginia. Petroleum found in early brine wells, 4-141
Virginia City, Nevada. Gold rush, 4-243
Virginia deer. 8-241
Virginia rails, birds. 6-403, 404, illus., 403, 405
Virgo, constellation. 1-331
Virgo cluster, group of galaxies. 8-51, 53, 54
Virtual foci. 7-257, 259, illus., 257, 258
Virtual images.
  Formation of, with illus., 7-256, 257, 258, 259, 260,
    261, 262
  Optical illusion created by, with illus., 8-121
Virus diseases of plants. Potatoes, 8-372
  Tomatoes, 8-372
Viruses. *3-451-58
  Blood diseases caused by, 3-331
  Body's defenses against, 7-351
  Bushy stunt crystals, illus., 5-342
  Cancer may be caused by, 8-268
  Infection by, illus., 9-84
  Living matter, relation to, 1-39-40
  Loeffler and Frosch, discovered by, 8-405
  Molecular nature of, 9-385
  Nervous disease caused by, 6-330
  Poliomyelitis, viruses that cause, illus., 8-363;
    10-129-31, 133
  Yellow fever caused by, 10-39
Viscachas, rodents. Adaptations for high altitudes, 7-8
Visceral muscles. Tissue structure, 1-145, 147
Visceral nervous system. See **Autonomic nervous
  system**
Viscosity. with illus., 5-369-70
  Protoplasm, consistency of, 2-6
Viscount, British turboprop plane. with illus., 7-72-73
Visibility, degree of atmospheric clearness.
  Measuring and recording, 1-251, 322, diagram, 316
Visible spectrum. See **Spectrum**
Visible Speech Translator. 5-127
Vision. *7-291-97
  *Land theory of color vision, 8-178-80
  Birds', 5-422-23
  Blindness of deep-sea animals, 10-142
  Color, perception of, with diagram, 7-288-90, illus., 287
  Fishes, with illus., 4-101-02
  Insects', 2-403

Vision (continued)
    Flies, 3-284-85
  Nervous processes involved in, 6-317
  Nuclear blast may imperil, 9-393
  Optic-nerve destruction, diagram, 7-352
  Smoking may affect, 5-345-46
  See also **Cerebral cortex; Color blindness; Eyes**
Visual binaries, stars. 7-229
Visual cortex, of cerebrum.
  Vision, function in, 6-317
  See also **Cerebral cortex; Vision**
Visual purple (rhodopsin), eye pigment. 7-251, 293
Vital capacity, breathing capacity of lungs. 4-207
"Vital force." Theory of, used to define organic matter,
  5-77-78
Vital statistics.
  Development of statistical method, 3-21
  Increasing life expectancy, 8-79
  Public-health agencies, 9-41
  See also **Population**
Vitalists. 8-264
Vitamin A. with illus., 5-40-41
  Daily requirement and sources of, table, 4-55-57
  Function of, 7-293
  Test for, 7-136
Vitamin B$_1$, thiamine. 5-41-42
  Bread enriched with, 9-299
  Daily requirement and sources of, table, 4-55-5
Vitamin B$_2$, riboflavin. with illus., 5-42
  Bread enriched with, 9-299
  Daily requirement and sources of, table, 4-55-57
Vitamin B$_6$, pyriodoxine. 5-43
Vitamin B$_{12}$, cyanocobalamin. 5-44-45
  Anemia (pernicious), role in, 3-330
Vitamin-B complex. 5-40-45, illus., 42
Vitamin C, ascorbic acid. 5-45-46
  Daily requirement and sources of, table, 4-55-57
  Food preservative, 4-164
  Test for, 7-136
Vitamin D. 5-46-48
  Daily requirement and sources of, table, 4-55-57
  Derived from cholesterol, 5-14
  Ultraviolet rays create, 1-231-32
Vitamin E, the tocopherols. 5-48
Vitamin K. 5-48-49
  Blood clotting, essential for, 3-331
Vitamins. *5-38-49
  Bread enriched with, 9-297, 299
  Cells of plants and animals, function in, 2-3
  Daily requirement and sources of, table, 4-55-57
  Diet, essential in, 4-60; 5-267-68, 272-73
  Eijkman first reveals, 8-404
  Meat as important source of, 5-163
  Sunlight and, 1-232
Vitrified clay. Sewer pipes made of, 5-328
Vitreous humor, of eye. 7-294, illus., 292
"Vitrolux" spandrel glass. 8-392
Vivariums. See **Terrariums**
Viverrids, mammals. *8-244-50
Viviparous animals. Animals that bring forth their young
alive from their bodies instead of hatching them from
eggs are said to be viviparous. All mammals with
the exception of the monotremes are viviparous; so are
certain forms of amphibians and reptiles.
  Lizards, certain species of, 5-198, 204
Vocabulary. Language, make-up of, 1-108
Vocal cords. with illus., 1-282; with illus., 4-203
  Musical sounds, production of, 5-219-20
Vocational psychology. 9-321
Vogel, Hermann, early photographer. Orthochromatic
  photography invented by, 9-408

Voice, human. Larynx, role of, *with illus.*, 1-282
  Musical sounds, produced by, 5-219-20
Voice box. See **Larynx**
Voices, animal.
  Bird's voice, production of, *with illus.*, 1-282-83
  Cats, 8-210
  Deer, 8-238, 240
  Dholes, 8-140
  Frogs, 5-155-56, 158
  Gibbons, 9-254
  Giraffes, 7-416
  Howling monkeys, 9-259, 262, 263
  Hyena, 8-250
  Lions, 8-205
  Lizards, 5-198
  Moose, 8-240
  Orangutans, 9-264
  Pandas, 7-315
  Pikas, 8-170
  Primates, 9-262
  Seals, 7-88
Volapük, artificial language. 1-119-20
Volcanic ash. Climate affected by, 3-184
  Deposition of, 7-326
Volcanic islands. *with illus.*, 4-133-34
  Coral reefs and lagoons around, 6-75, 77
Volcanic necks, geologic formations. 3-421
  Erosion of, 8-11
Volcanism (vulcanism), movement of molten rock matter and its transformation into rock. 1-34, 36, *illus.*, 35
  See also **Volcanoes**
Volcanoes. *8-293-304
  *Volcanic catastrophes, 7-334-45
  Climates of past affected by, 3-183
  Coasts modified by, *with illus.*, 8-356
  Cross section of, *diagram*, 7-334
  Dust from, 7-140
  Earth formation. action in, 4-395. *illus.*, 394
  Earthquakes associated with, 9-106
  Lakes formed by action of, 7-57
  Moon's craters formed by volcanic action? 4-280
  Mountains formed by volcanic action, 10-213
  Parícutin, Mexico, 10-frontispiece
  Streams dammed by products of, 8-17
  Submarine, 6-75
  Volcanic-ash deposition, 7-326
  Volcanic islands, formation of, *with illus.*, 4-133-34, 362-63
Volta, Alessandro, Italian physicist. *with illus.*, 4-362-63
  Electricity, experiments with, 6-125-26
Voltage. 9-227, 235
Voltage multipliers, atom smashers. 9-242
Voltaic cells (electric batteries). *with illus.*, 5-94-96; *with illus.*, 6-288, *illus.*, 127
Voltaic piles. *with illus.*, 4-362-63; 6-125-26
Voltaire (François-Marie Arouet), French writer.
  Quotation from, 3-281
Volts, units of electromotive force. 6-131
Volume.
  Gases: relation to temperature and pressure, *with diagram*, 1-165-66, 172; 3-416
  Molecular, of water, 1-172
Voluntary muscles. See **Striped muscles**
Volutes, gastropods. Shells of, *illus.*, 2-100
Volvae, wrappers of mushroom spore cases. *with illus.*, 3-29
Volvox, genus of green algae. *illus.*, 1-300; *with illus.*, 3-218
Vomiting. 4-332
Vorticella, genus of protozoans. 2-66

Vostok I, Russian manned space vehicle. 9-382, *with illus.*, 380-81; 10-47
Vostok II, Russian manned space vehicle. 10-47-48
Vulcanism. See **Volcanism**
Vulcanist theory, of earth formation. 4-395-96
Vulcanization, process of treating rubber. 6-351-52
Vultures. *with illus.*, 6-155-56

W

Waals, Johannes van der, Dutch physicist (1837–1923). He was a professor at the University of Amsterdam. He stressed the continuity of the liquid and gaseous states of matter and formulated the law of corresponding states, which aided Dewar in liquefying gases. For this work, Waals received the 1910 Nobel physics award.
Wade, L. A. B., Australian engineer. 8-308
Wagner von Jauregg, Julius, Austrian psychiatrist. 9-103
Wagons (carts). Development of, *with illus.*, 1-103, 105-06
  See also under names of different vehicles drawn by animals
Waialeale, Mount, Kauai, Hawaiian Islands. Rainfall on, 2-348
Waksman, Selman A., American biochemist.
  Streptomycin isolated by, 9-34
Waldseemueller, Martin, German geographer. 2-365
Walking beams, swinging engine levers. Well drilling, use in, *diagram*, 4-144
Walking ferns. 3-192
Walking fishes. 4-99-100
Walking-leaf insects. 3-240
Walking sticks (stick insects). *illus.*, 2-411; *with illus.*, 3-149-50
  See also **Leaf insects; Phasmida**
Wallabies, kangaroos. 7-424, *illus.*, 13
  Adaptation for preservation of offspring, 3-242
Wallace, Alfred Russel, English naturalist. 8-252, 258-60, *illus.*, 259
  See also **Natural selection**
Wallace, Robert, Scottish scholar. 4-403
Wallaroos, kangaroos. 7-424
Wallboards. Construction, use in, 7-125
Wallis, John, English mathematician. 3-266
Wallop's Island, Virginia.
  Rocket research station, *illus.*, 4-342c
Walls. Glass in wall construction, *with illus.*, 8-391-92
Walnut trees. *with illus.*, 5-146
  Seeds, *illus.*, 5-63
Walruses. 7-86, *with illus.*, 90-91, *illus.*, 15, 84
  Feeding habits of, 7-10
Walsh, Don, United States naval officer. Bathyscaphe exploration by, 9-223
Walton, Ernest T. S., English scientist. 8-419
  Voltage multiplier, development of, 9-242
Wapitis, American elks. *with illus.*, 8-238; 9-270-71
  See also **Elks**
Wapping-Rotherhithe Tunnel, England. *illus.*, 2-52, 53
War production. World War II, production in, *with illus.*, 9-323-27
Warble flies. 3-287, 291-92
Warblers, birds. *illus.*, 6-60, 63
  American wood warblers
    Migration of, 9-421
  Cowbirds' young reared by, 6-104-05
Warbling vireos. 6-64
Warfare.
  *Nuclear-bomb precautions, 9-391-96
  Aircraft used in, 6-177-79, 181, 183-85, *illus.*, 181, 184, 186-87, 194, 196-97

Warfare (*continued*)

Animals and primitive weapons used in, **1**-100-01, 103, *illus.*, 104

Ants engage in, **3**-365

Atomic bombs, perils of, *with illus.*, **9**-351-58

Chemical industry and, **8**-187

Chemurgic developments affect strategic materials, **7**-44

Elephants used in, **7**-410

Explosives used in, **8**-278, 280, 282

Microfilm uses in, **10**-68, 73-74, *illus.*, 69, 73-74

Overpopulation relieved by invasion and conquest, **3**-233

Photographs, early military, **9**-403

Rocket weapons, **9**-376-77, 382, *with illus.*, 378-79; **10**-45-46, *illus.*, 47

Rubber used in, **6**-357

Science and technology applied to, **1**-91-92, *illus.*, 97; *with illus.*, **9**-211-15, 218, 323-29

Typewriters used in, **1**-265

See also **Civil War; Warships; World War I; World War II**

Warm fronts. See **Fronts**

Warm-moist climate. **3**-179

Warmings, stratospheric. See **Explosive warmings**

Warren, John Collins, American surgeon. **7**-376

Warships. Blueprints microfilmed, **10**-74

See also **Aircraft carriers; Galleys; Ships; Submarines; Warfare**

Wart hogs. *illus.*, **7**-16; **10**-244

Warts. Toads, wartlike structures of, **5**-155

Wasatch Mountains, Idaho and Utah. **10**-218

Wash-off relief color photographs. **9**-413

Washers. Plastic, *illus.*, **8**-220d

Washing. Coal from mine, washing of, **1**-415

Colored rinsing trick, **7**-179

Nursing, role in, **10**-56, 58, 61-63, 65-66, *illus.*, 56, 62-63

Wood pulp, washing of, **4**-367

See also **Laundering**

Washing machines. Spinners of, **2**-126

Washington, Booker T., American Negro educator. G. W. Carver inspired by, **10**-192

Washington, D. C. Jefferson Memorial, *illus.*, **7**-118

U.S. Naval Hospital at, *illus.*, **3**-119

Washington, Mount, New Hampshire. Life zones of, **10**-182

Wasps. *illus.*, **1**-296; **3**-365-67, *illus.*, 361, 363-65

Figs pollinated by, *illus.*, **3**-405

Nests serve to protect nests of caciques (birds), *with illus.*, **5**-418h

Papermaking wasps, *with illus.*, **2**-412d; **4**-364

Pipe-organ wasps, *with illus.*, **2**-412d

Potter wasps, *with illus.*, **2**-412d

Tarantulas, enemies of, **2**-264, *illus.*, 265

Wastes. *Air pollution, **3**-349-56

*Disposal of wastes, **5**-326-36

Agricultural wastes as sources of products, **7**-35-37, 39

Animal wastes used as soil fertilizer, **2**-163, 171, *with diagram*, 165-67

Cellular, **2**-13

Leather processing, waste products derived from, **7**-235

Muscular activity, waste products of, **3**-206-07

Radioactive waste materials, **9**-358; **10**-115-16

Rubbish accumulation, hazards of, **7**-193

Sickroom, disposal of, **10**-56

Skin disposes of, **2**-176-77, *illus.*, 177

Water. *Erosive action of, **8**-9-18

*Experiments with, **8**-1-8

*Geysers, **8**-288-92

*Glaciers, **9**-162-74

Water (*continued*)

*Ground water, **8**-321-32

*Icebergs, **9**-333-39

*Irrigation, **8**-191-201

*Lakes, **7**-55-66

*Oceanography, **6**-26a-36, 69-77, 201-08, 229-38, 361-68

*Precipitation, **2**-346-57

*Rivers, **6**-409-18

*Soil, water contained in, **5**-25-30

*Storage by dams, **8**-305-20

*Water supply, **2**-270-86

Air circulation affected by temperature of large bodies of, **2**-90-91

Atmospheric pressure affects, **1**-233

Atmospheric water vapor, **1**-244-45

Experiment with, *with illus.*, **2**-330-31

Measuring and recording, **1**-249-51, *with diagram*, 320-21, *illus.*, 248, *diagram*, 316

Carbohydrates and water, **4**-76, 77, 78-79

Chemical structure of, **9**-121-22

Coal mining, water a problem in, **1**-413, 414

Conservation of, **6**-6-7

Density of, **2**-31-32

Desalting of, **6**-6-7, *diagram*, 5

Desert plants conserve, **3**-238

Diet, essential in, **4**-58

Electrical energy generated by force of running water, **9**-229, 233-34, *illus.*, 232-33

Electrolysis of, **5**-92

Experiments with, *with illus.*, **1**-89, *with illus.*, **4**-343-50; *with diagrams*, **7**-173-77, 179-80

Fish affected by temperature of, **8**-113

Fluoridation of, **5**-133

Freezing causing expansion of, **3**-417

Habitat of animals and plants, *with illus.*, **10**-140-42

Heat transfer by, **4**-10-13, 16, *illus.*, 10, 12

Heavy-water reactor, *illus.*, **1**-94

Hydrosphere, as part of earth, *with illus.*, **4**-45-46

Ice, relation to, **3**-417

Index of refraction of, **7**-254

Ionization of, **4**-340

Jupiter contains frozen, **5**-22

Limestone caves, water as erosive agent in formation of, *with illus.*, **5**-51-54

Loss during muscular exercise, **10**-87-88, 91

Mammals dependent on, **7**-7-8

Manures, moisture in, **2**-163-66

Molecular behavior of, **1**-172, *with illus.*, 162-63, *with diagrams and illus.*, 167-69, *illus.*, 171; **2**-223-24, 225, *diagram*, 223-24; *with illus.*, **3**-251

Moon has no, **4**-279

Nuclear blasts may cause contamination of, **9**-396

Osmotic flow of, in cells, **2**-7

Perspiration contains, **5**-11

Petroleum and, *with diagram*, **4**-142-43

Physical changes of, *with illus.*, **4**-229-30

Plants' absorption and use of, **3**-44, 45, 54, *illus.*, 47; **5**-63, 64, 65

Plants' adaptations to aquatic environment, *with illus.*, **6**-223-25

Plastics, used in manufacture of, **8**-225

Pressure changes used by water animals, *with illus. and diagrams*, **1**-280-81

Protoplasm, water content of, **2**-3, 6, 7, 10, 11, 12

Seeds dispersed by, **5**-4-5, 7

Skin and, **2**-176, 177

Soil, relation of water to, **2**-15, 16, 17, 18, 20-22, 24-25, *diagram*, 25

Soil deposition by, **6**-142

Soil formation by action of, **6**-136-37

Water *(continued)*
Solubility of gases in, *with diagram,* 4-300
Solvent action in soil formation, 6-141
Sound, speed of, in water, 5-119, 120
Surface tension, *with illus.,* 5-371
Vapor pressure of, 4-300
Volcanoes yield, 8-300
Volume affected by temperature changes, 3-415
Waves compared to sound waves in air, 5-116-17, *illus.,* 116
See also **Ice; Irrigation; Mineral springs; Precipitation; Rain; Sleet; Snow; Transportation; Water supply; Water vapor**
Water beetles. *with illus.,* 3-338
Water boatmen, true bugs. *with illus.,* 3-264
Water buffaloes. *with illus.,* 10-248-49
Water civets. 8-245
"Water crickets," true bugs. 3-264
Water culture. Plant growing method, 8-35, *illus.,* 34
Water (hydrologic) cycle. 2-272, *illus.,* 271; 9-233
Water debt. 10-91
Water deer. 8-240, *illus.,* 242
Water dogs, true bugs. 3-263; 5-156
Water ferns. 3-191
Water fleas, crustaceans. *with illus.,* 2-243
Water frames, textile machines. 4-37
Water gas, fuel. *with illus.,* 1-418
Water heaters. 4-13
Water hyacinths. 7-111, *illus.,* 112
Water kingfishers. 6-309
Water lilies. *illus.,* 1-45, 304; *illus.,* 6-226; *illus.,* 10-141
Leaves of, *illus.,* 4-72
Viability of, 5-65
Water-meadow irrigation. 8-193
Water moccasins, snakes. 5-364
Water moles, aquatic mammals. 7-98
Water mosses. 3-188
Water pipes. Corrosion in, 5-96
Water power.
Electricity, generation of, 9-233-34, *illus.,* 232-33
See also **Hydroelectric power**
Water pressure.
Animals use changes in, *with illus. and diagrams,* 1-280-81
Dams affected by, 8-316
Experiments, *with illus.,* 7-221-22
Fish distribution influenced by, 4-97
Hydrofoil lift because of reduced, 4-5
Seed dispersal by internal water pressure, 5-2
Water pumps. *with illus.,* 2-274-75, 284-86
Homemade water pump, *with illus.,* 8-6-7
Water purification. *with illus.,* 2-276-82
Water-release controls, for dams. 8-316
Water requirements. Plants', 5-25
Water scavengers, beetles. 3-338
Water scorpions. *with illus.,* 3-263
Water shrews, aquatic mammals. *illus.,* 7-101
Water-slaked lime. Soil fertilizer, use as, 2-168
Water snakes. 5-359, *illus.,* 358
Pets, 7-25
Water striders, true bugs. *with illus.,* 3-262
Water supply. *2-270-86
Dams store water for, 8-306
Mountains provide, 10-26-27
Plants help conserve, 1-50
Pollution from sewage, 5-328
Pumping system, 2-34
Sanitary protection of, 9-38
Wells, *with illus.,* 8-328-32

Water table, upper limit of ground saturated with water. 8-323-24, 328-29, 332, *illus.,* 322-25, 329, 332
Water-tube boilers. *with illus.,* 4-82
Ships, used in, 4-111, 114
Water turbines. See **Turbines**
Water vapor.
Atmosphere contains, 1-231, 237-38, 244-45, 249-51, *with diagram,* 320-21; 2-231, *with illus.,* 330-31
Molecular behavior of, *with illus.,* 1-163, 168
Rain formed from, 2-347
Water witches, persons who use divining rods. 8-331
See also **Divining rods**
Waterbucks, antelopes. 8-386, *illus.,* 385
Waterfalls.
Caves formed by action of, *with illus.,* 5-56-57
Formation of, 8-15, *illus.,* 9, 15
See also **Water power**
Waterfowl. 6-398-403
Waterhouse, Benjamin, American physician.
Smallpox, research on, 4-402
Watermelons. *illus.,* 1-305
Waterscopes. Homemade, *with illus.,* 10-264
Watersheds. 6-410, 412
Waterspouts, maritime tornadoes. 2-98
Waterways. *Canals, 4-183-95
Water supply, used for, 2-275-76
Watson, James D., English biologist. Nucleic-acid model of, 9-386, *diagram,* 385
Watson, John B., American psychologist. 9-52, 312
Watson, Thomas Augustus, American telephone technician. 2-387; 5-243-44
Watt, James, Scottish inventor and mechanical engineer. *with illus.,* 4-40-41
Automatic governor for steam engine, 10-235
Steam engine of, 4-81
Wattmeters. 6-132-33; 9-238, *illus.,* 239
Watts, units of electric power. 6-131
Wave function, amplitude of wave. 7-109
Wave lengths.
Electromagnetic spectrum, use in construction of, 6-245
High-frequency sounds', 8-105
Ocean waves, 8-348, *diagram,* 349
Radiations, wave lengths of, 7-250, 253, 255
Sound waves', 5-117, 127, *illus.,* 117, 126
Visible light, wave lengths of, 7-278; *with illus.,* 8-178-80
See also **Color; Spectrum; Vision**
Wave mechanics, theory of matter-energy. 7-205; 9-283
See also **Parity law**
Wave periods. 8-348
Wave theory of light. 7-199, 201, 205, 249, 250; *with illus.,* 8-119
Nineteenth-century developments, *with illus.,* 6-239-45
Waves, earthquake. 4-170-71, 173, *illus.,* 170; *with diagram,* 7-357-58; 9-107, 114
Prospecting, earthquake waves induced in, 4-145, *diagram,* 143
Waves, electromagnetic. See **Electromagnetic waves**
Waves, Mach. See **Mach waves**
Waves, ocean. *6-361-68
*Shoreline changes produced by waves, 8-348-59
Caves formed by action of, *with illus.,* 5-57
Destructiveness of, 6-205
Erosive and other effects of, 6-74, 75, 77
Height, *with illus.,* 6-363-64
Waves, peristaltic, in animal bodies. *with diagram,* 1-279-80
Waves, pressure. See **Pressure waves**
Waves, radio. See **Radio waves**
Waves, river. Dams affected by, 8-317

Waves, sound. See **Sound waves**
Wax glands, of ear. 5-11
Waxes.
  Beeswax, 3-368, 372, *illus.*, 371
  Molds of wax used in preparing printing plates, 1-207
  Paraffin wax, 4-150
Waxwings, birds. 6-65-66, *illus.*, 64; 9-421
Weakfish. 4-314
Wealth. *Gold and diamonds, 4-242-56
Weapons.
  *Guidance of missiles and space vehicles, 8-125-31
  Development of, in World War I, *with illus.*, 9-211-15
  Development of, in World War II, 9-218, *with illus.*, 326-27
  Remote-control, 10-238
  Rocket weapons, 9-376-77, 382, *with illus.*, 378-79, 10-45-46, *illus.*, 47
  Scientific research and, 1-91-92, *illus.*, 97
  World War II, designed to human standards in, 10-121
Wear-test machines. *illus.*, 4-342a
Weasels. *Weasel family, 8-171-77
  Color changes with seasons, 5-413; *illus.*, 8-173
  Evolutionary progress, example of, *illus.*, 6-285
  Fur, 7-238
  Molting cycle controlled by light, 7-8
Weather.
  *Amateur meteorology, 1-315-22
  *Atmosphere, 1-230-40
  *Climates of past, 3-177-85
  *Clouds, 2-212-22
  *Forecasting weather, 1-241-54
  *Jet streams, 2-358-60
  *Lightning, 1-398-404
  *Precipitation, 2-346-57
  *Seasonal changes and life, 5-408-13
  *Winds, 2-89-98
  Dams affected by, 8-317
  IGY studies of, 5-192-94
  Migrations of animals influenced by, 9-416, 418
  Radiosondes used in analysis of, 6-179
  Snow, *with illus.*, 2-354-55
  Sunspot cycles affect, 3-107
  Thunderstorms, hail produced in, 2-356-57
  Twentieth-century study of, 9-220, 223, *illus.*, 221
  See also **Climate**
Weather balloons. See **Radiosondes**
Weather charts. 1-253-54, 315, *illus.*, 316
  See also **Weather maps**
Weather forecasting. *1-241-54
  Jet-stream study aids in, *with illus.*, 2-358-60
  Twentieth-century developments, 9-223
Weather maps. 1-253-54, *illus.*, 250; *illus.*, 2-95
Weather records. *Amateur meteorology, 1-315-22
Weather satellites. 1-252, *illus.*, 241, 253; 9-223
Weather stations. *Amateur meteorology, 1-315-22
  *Forecasting weather, 1-241-54
  Radioisotope-fueled thermoelectric generators for weather stations, *with illus.*, 6-174-75, *illus.*, 173
  See also **Radiosondes**
Weather stripping. 7-125
Weather vanes. See **Wind vanes**
Weatherglasses, for indicating atmospheric pressure. 1-319, *diagram*, 320
Weathering.
  Chemical weathering of rocks as evidence of warm, moist climates, *with illus.*, 3-179
  Minerals formed by, 5-251
  Soil formed by, 2-15-17, 20, *illus.*, 17, 25; 6-136
  See also **Soil**

Weaver finches. 6-108
Weaving. Silk, 5-184
Web-fed presses, in printing. 1-209
Web-footed shrews. 7-102
Weber, Ernst Heinrich, German anatomist. 9-48
Weber's law. 9-48
Webs. Spiders', 2-263, 265-66, *illus.*, 263
Weddell seals. *illus.*, 7-93
Wedges, simple machines. *with illus.*, 3-59-60
  Logging operations, use in, 2-111
Wedgwood, Josiah, English potter. 7-401, 406
Weeds. *7-111-14
  Dispersal of, 5-6
Weeks Law, for forest conservation. 6-4
Weeping willow trees. 5-144
Weevils. *with illus.*, 3-347-48
Weighing rain gauges. 1-251
Weight. Dams affected by, 8-316-17
  Diet and, *with tables*, 5-268-72, *diagrams*, 267, 269
  Energy, relation to, 1-83, *illus.*, 82
  Health, weight as index of, 10-76-77
  Health and diet, relation to, *with tables*, 5-273
  Human brain, weight of, 6-323-24
  Human growth, relation to, 8-93
  Mass distinguished from, 2-318, 319
  Meteorites, weights of, 6-88, 89, 90, 91, 93
  Skeleton sustains bodily weight, *with diagrams*, 1-286
  See also **Gravity**
Weight belts, used in scuba diving. *with illus.*, 6-26b
Weighting, of silk. 5-182
Weightlessness, condition in space travel. 10-48-50
Weights.
  Chemical calculations involving, 2-227, 231
  Homemade balance, for use with, 4-227-28
Weights, atomic. See **Atomic weights**
Weights, molecular. See **Molecular weights**
Weights and measures. Conversion table for, 10-296
  Metric system, establishment of, 4-34, *illus.*, 35
  Metric system, *tables*, 10-296
  United States, *tables*, 10-295-96
Weinrich, M., American atomic scientist. 7-110
Weismann, August, German biologist.
  Germ-plasm theory, contributions to, 8-263
Weisshorn, Swiss peak. *illus.*, 10-217
Weizmann, Chaim, Israeli chemist. 9-212
Weizsäcker, C. F. von, German astronomer.
  Nebular hypothesis of, 1-30
Welch, William H., American pathologist (1850–1934). He helped to organize the Johns Hopkins Medical School and also furthered the cause of medical education throughout the country. His researches included studies of embolism, thrombosis, diphtheria and pneumonia; he investigated the bacterium causing gas gangrene, which was named Welch bacillus.
Well-being. Sleep, relation to, 6-148, *chart*, 149
Well logging, record of drilling progress.
  Electric logging, 7-361
  Radioactivity logging, 7-361
Welland Canal. *with illus.*, 4-187-89
Wells, Horace, American dentist. 7-376-77
Wells, brine. See **Wells, salt**
Wells, natural-gas. 5-98, 100-01, *illus.*, 98a
Wells, oil. 4-140, 143, *with illus.*, 141, *with diagrams* 144-46
  See also **Well logging**
Wells, salt. Petroleum in, 4-141
Wells, water. *with illus.*, 8-328-32
  Irrigation water supplied by, 8-195
  Water supply, source of, *with illus.*, 2-273-75
Welsbach, Baron Carl Auer von, Austrian chemist. 4-236

Welsbach, Baron Carl Auer von (continued)
Electric-lighting experiments, 4-238
Gas illumination, contributions to, 4-236-37
Welsbach gas mantles. 4-236-37
Wenatchee Valley, Washington. Orchard in, *illus.,* 9-185
Wenham, Francis H., English inventor. 9-88
Went, Fritz W., Dutch-American botanist. 9-291
Wentorf, R. H., American physical chemist. 4-275
Werner, Abraham Gottlob, German geologist and mineralogist. *with illus.,* 4-393-94
Wernicke's disease, disease of nervous system. 4-411
West, American. Transportation on land, early, *with illus.,* 1-106
West Australian Current, 6-236, *map,* 232-33
West Indies. Petroleum production and reserves, 4-150
West Spitsbergen, island in Arctic Ocean.
Gerard de Geer Glacier, *illus.,* 9-334
West Virginia Turnpike. Bridge over, *illus.,* 2-335
West Wind Drift, oceanic current. 6-236, 237, *map,* 232-33
Westerlies, prevailing winds. 1-244, *diagram,* 243
Western Fish (Circlet), group of stars in Pisces. 1-334
Western Germany. Industrial research in, 1-95
Western tanagers. 6-108
Western Union. Facsimile transmission, 7-392, *illus.,* 390
Telephone field entered by, in 1870's, 2-388
Western vine maple trees. 5-150
Westinghouse, George, American inventor and manufacturer. 1-189; 6-380
Westinghouse Science Talent Search. 8-73-74, *illus.,* 67, 71, 73, 75, 76
Westinghouse Time Capsule. See **Time Capsule**
Wet assays, analyses of ores. 1-376
Wet concentrating (or shaking) tables, in ore dressing. *with diagram,* 1-373
Wet (cold) manures, soil fertilizers. 2-165
Wet-plate process, in photography. 6-382; 9-402-03, *illus.,* 402
Wet suits, used in scuba diving. *with illus.,* 6-26b
Wetas, crickets. 3-146
Wetting agents. 4-347-48; *with illus.,* 8-3-4, 6
Weyer, Johann. See **Wier, Johann**
Whakarewarewa, region in New Zealand.
Pohutu, geyser in, *illus.,* 8-300b
Whale sharks, fishes. 4-96-97, 289, *illus.,* 287
Whales. *illus.,* 1-299; 7-181, *with illus.,* 183-89, *illus.,* 15
Migration of, 9-423-24
Sixteenth-century artist's conception of, *illus.,* 6-29
Whaling. 6-21; 7-187-88
Wheat. *illus.,* 1-303
Breadmaking utilizes, *with diagrams,* 9-294-95
Grains of, *illus.,* 2-416; *illus.,* 4-131
Rust, wheat-barberry, 3-29
Smuts attack, *with illus.,* 3-29
Water required by, 5-25
Wheatstone, Sir Charles, English physicist. Born in Gloucester, England, 1802; died in Paris, 1875. He began his career as a maker of musical instruments and became interested in experiments with acoustics. He was appointed professor of experimental philosophy in King's College, London. The theories he formulated on the transmission of sound and the instruments he devised form the basis of modern telegraphy. See also 5-238
Wheatstone's bridge, device for measuring electrical resistance. 5-238
Wheel and axle, simple machine. *with illus.,* 3-60-61
Wheels.
Origin and development of wheels and wheeled vehicles. *with illus.,* 1-100, 102-06, *illus.,* 101
Well drilling, use in, 4-145, *illus.,* 144

Wheels (continued)
See also **Gears;** and under names of various machines and vehicles
Whelks, marine snails. 2-200
Whip snakes.
Locomotion of, 5-354a
Pets, 7-25
Whip-tailed lizards. *illus.,* 5-199
Whipple, F. L., American astronomer.
Dust cloud hypothesis of, 1-30; 9-225
Icy conglomerate theory of comets, 5-393
Whipple, George H., American physician. 9-35
Whippoorwills, birds. 6-218, *illus.,* 217
Whirled psychrometers, humidity gauges. 1-249-50, *illus.,* 248
Whirlers. See **Turbinate bones**
Whirligig beetles. 3-338
"Whirlpool," spiral galaxy. *illus.,* 9-363
Whirlpools. 6-207
"Whispering galleries." Explanation of, 3-438
Whistle buoys. 5-71, *illus.,* 69
Whistles. "Silent" whistles, 8-104, *illus.,* 105
Whistling swans. 6-398-99
White ants. See **Termites**
White ash trees. *illus.,* 5-151
White birches. *illus.,* 5-261
White blood cells (leucocytes). 3-331, *with illus.,* 328-29; 9-177-78
Body's defenses, role in, *with illus.,* 7-348; 8-366
Spleen as source of, 5-10
White-breasted nuthatches, 6-42, *illus.,* 43
White-crowned sparrows. 6-108
White dwarf stars. 6-264, 265, 266, 268, *table,* 264
White-eyed vireos, birds. 6-64
White-footed mice. *illus.,* 6-167
White gold. 1-382
White light. Breaking up white light into colors of visible spectrum, 8-122, *illus.,* 123
Colored light, relation to, *with illus.,* 7-277; *with illus.,* 8-178-80
See also **Spectrum**
White matter, of nervous system. 6-324, 326-27
See also **Myelin**
White mulberry trees. 5-149
White oak trees. *with illus.,* 5-147
Classification of, 1-291
Leaves, *illus.,* 4-72
White phosphorus. 3-320-21
White pine trees. *illus.,* 1-302; 5-141, *illus.,* 142
White race. See **Caucasoid subspecies of man**
White rats. Body temperature of, 7-7
White rhinoceroses. 7-414
White Sands Proving Ground, New Mexico.
Rocket research at, *illus.,* 10-2
White sharks. 4-288-89
White-tailed deer. 8-241
White-throated sparrows. 6-108
White whales. *illus.,* 7-185
White-winged doves. 6-305
Whitebait, fish. 4-313-14
Whitefish. Cells of blastula undergoing mitosis, *illus.,* 2-13
Whites, butterflies. 3-198-99
Whitney, Eli, American inventor. *with illus.,* 4-38-39
Whittle, Frank, English jet-plane engineer. 7-68; 9-218
Whooping cranes. *illus.,* 9-266
Wicket dams. See **Shutter dams**
Wickham, Sir Henry, English botanist.
Rubber industry, contributions to, 6-352
Wide-angle lenses. Photographic, 9-406
Wide-angle telescopes, in astronomy. 8-59

Wideröe, R., Swiss physicist.
  Linear accelerator, development of, **9**-246
Widmanstätten figures, figures appearing on etched
    meteoric iron. *illus.,* **4**-175; *illus.,* **6**-93
  Meteoritic iron identified by means of, **6**-92, 93
Wieliczka salt mine, Poland. **5**-316-17
Wien, Wilhelm, German physicist.
  Displacement law of radiant energy, **7**-201
Wier (Weyer), Johann, Dutch physician. **9**-102
Wigglesticks, fraudulent oil-prospecting devices. **7**-355
Wilberforce, Samuel, English prelate. **8**-256
Wild Carrots. Fruit of, *illus.,* **5**-5
Wild cats. **8**-211
Wild dogs. **8**-140, *illus.,* 139
Wild geraniums. *illus.,* **4**-123
Wild roses. Fruit of, *illus.,* **5**-7
  Stems of, *illus.,* **6**-220
Wild turkeys. **6**-337, *illus.,* 336
Wildebeests, antelopes. **8**-386, *illus.,* 387
Wildlife. *Exploring animal world, **10**-254-64
  Conservation of, **6**-8, 10; *with illus.,* **9**-266-78
Wildt, Rupert, American astronomer.
  Jupiter, structure of, **5**-22
Wiley, Harvey W., American physician, **9**-290
Wilkinson, William B., English inventor. **3**-119
Willamette meteorite. *illus.,* **6**-87
Williams, A. Stanley, astronomer. Jupiter's belts
    studied by, **5**-22
Williams, Greville. Isoprene isolated by, **6**-357; **8**-185
Willow ptarmigans, birds. Color changes with seasons,
    with illus., **5**-413
Willow trees. *with illus.,* **5**-144
  Buds, *illus.,* **5**-140
Wilson, Charles Thomson Rees, Scottish physicist
1869-   ). About 1912 he perfected the cloud chamber
used in photographing the paths of subatomic particles.
This device plays an important part in researches in
modern atomic physics. In 1918 he was appointed pro-
fessor of natural philosophy in the field of atmospheric
electricity at Cambridge. He shared the Nobel Prize in
physics with A. H. Compton in 1927. See also **9**-285
Wilson, Mount. See **Mount Wilson Observatory**
Wilson cloud chamber, device that shows paths of
    atomic particles. *with illus.,* **9**-127
Wilson's snipes. **6**-407
Wilting.
  Plant wilting due to lack of water, *with illus.,* **5**-25-26
Wilts, plant diseases. **8**-372
Wind belts. **2**-93-94, *diagram,* 92
Wind drifts, oceanic currents. **6**-232, 234, 235, 236-37
Wind instruments. Sound production in, *with illus.,*
    5-217-18, 219
Wind pollination. **7**-239
Wind socks. *with diagram,* **1**-320
Wind tunnels. **9**-217-18; *with diagrams,* **10**-233-34
Wind vanes. **1**-249, *with diagram,* 319-20, *diagram,*
    321, *illus.,* 248
Winders, in papermaking. *illus.,* **4**-374c
Window glass.
  Heat insulation of windows, **4**-11-12
  History of use, *with illus.,* **8**-388-91
  Manufacture of, **3**-311
Windpipe (trachea). **4**-200, 201, 204, *illus.,* 202
  Lining tissue of, **1**-145
Winds. *with diagrams,* **1**-242-44; *2**-89-98
  *Erosive effects of winds, **7**-318-26
  *Jet streams, **2**-358-60
  Atomic-bomb explosion, caused by, **9**-393
  Beaufort scale for gauging apparent strength of,
    10-297

Winds *(continued)*
  Cancers of skin may be caused by overexposure to,
    8-267
  Caves formed by action of, *with illus.,* **5**-56
  Direction. See Velocity and direction (below)
  Lakes formed by action of, **7**-57
  Mountains' effects on, **10**-28
  Oceanic currents caused by, **6**-232, 234, 235, 236-37
  Patterns of, **1**-236-38, 240
  Plants affected by, **6**-222-23
  Pollination, wind as factor in, **4**-127
  Sailing ships and winds, **4**-107-08
  Seeds dispersed by, **3**-240; *with illus.,* **5**-2-4
  Soil formation partially due to, **2**-16, 21
  Soils formed by, **6**-138-39, 142
  Spores of fungi spread by, **3**-22
  Velocities and directions of, measuring and record-
    ing, **1**-249, *with diagrams,* 319-20, *diagrams,*
    316, 321, *illus.,* 248, 250
Windshields, automobile. Construction of, **3**-313
Wines. **4**-405, *illus.,* 406
  Fermentation of, **4**-168
Wings. Birds', *with illus.,* **1**-284-85; **5**-416-17
  Insects', **2**-404, *illus.,* 403, 405
    Beetles, **3**-335, *illus.,* 336
    Butterflies and moths, **3**-193-94
    Flies, **3**-283, 285-86, *illus.,* 285, 287
    Orthopterous insects, **3**-138, 139, *illus.,* 141
  Seed and fruit "wings," *with illus.,* **5**-3-4
  True bugs, **3**-255, *with illus.,* 253
Winkler, Clemens Alexander, German chemist. **5**-85
Winter.
  Animals affected by, *with illus.,* **5**-409-13
  Atmospheric circulation during, **1**-238
  Exploring plant world in, **10**-203-04
  Plants affected by, **5**-409, *illus.,* 408
Winter constellations. *map,* **1**-329
Winter wrens. **6**-45
Winton, Alexander, American automobile manufac-
    turer. **2**-130-31
Wire, steel. **1**-350
Wire recording. **7**-368
Wireless telegraphy.
  Development of, **5**-244; *with illus.,* **6**-245-46
  First wireless messages, **8**-403
Wirephotos. *with illus.,* **7**-390-92
Wiring, electrical. Safety measures with, **7**-192
Wisdom teeth. **5**-129-30, *illus.,* 132, *table,* 130
Wisents, buffaloes. **10**-249
Wistar, Caspar, American button manufacturer. **7**-209
Witch hazels. Fruit of, *illus.,* **5**-6
Witches'-brooms, symptoms of virus infection. **3**-453
Withdrawal, deprivation of addicting drugs or liquors.
  Alcohol, withdrawal of, **4**-412
  Heroin, withdrawal of, **5**-405
Withering, William, English physician.
  Digitalis, preparation of, **3**-380
Woehler, Friedrich, German chemist. **5**-78; *with illus.,*
    7-264; **8**-181
Wolf, Henry, American engraver. **1**-268
Wolf, Max Franz Joseph Cornelius, German astronomer.
  Astronomical photography, contributions to, **4**-421
Wolf, Rudolf, Swiss astronomer. **6**-393
Wolf spiders. **2**-266, *illus.,* 258, 260
Wolff, Kaspar Friedrich, German anatomist. **7**-157
Wolfhounds. **10**-242
Wolfram. See **Tungsten**
Wollaston, William, English chemist and physicist.
  Dark-line spectra discovered by, **5**-85· **6**-390
Wolverines. *with illus.,* **8**-172

Wolves. *with illus.,* 8-135-38, *illus.,* 134
  Color changes with seasons, 5-413
  Dogs (domestic) derived from, 6-275-76, *illus.,* 269
Wombats, marsupials. *with illus.,* 7-426
Women. Typewriter's role in emancipation of, 1-269
Wood. *Lumber industry, 2-105-17
  *Trees, 5-257-66
  Advantages of, 5-266
  Bacteria that decompose wood, 3-67
  Building material, *illus.,* 4-268; 7-115, 119-20, 125, 128, *illus.,* 115, 120, 126
  Chemistry of, 5-266
  Decay of wood caused by fungi, *with illus.,* 3-30
  Insects attacking, 3-362
  Pipes made of, 2-276
  Research in lumber industry, 1-88
  Ships and boats of, 4-106-10
  Strength of, 5-262-64
  Uses of, 4-75
  Xylem of mature woody stems, *with illus.,* 4-69-70
  See also **Forests; Lumbering; Timber**
Wood borers, insects. *illus.,* 9-95
Wood Buffalo National Park, Canada. 9-270
Wood kingfishers. 6-309
Wood-Neumann scale of earthquake intensity. 9-111-12
Wood peewees, birds. 6-99
Wood thrushes. 6-39
Woodchucks. *illus.,* 5-409; *illus.,* 10-261
  Field study of, 10-259
  Pets, *with illus.,* 7-21
Woodcocks. 6-407, *illus.,* 407
Woodland nightjars, birds. 6-218
Woodpeckers, birds. *with illus.,* 6-209-12; *illus.,* 10-258
  Adaptations for obtaining food, 3-237
  Downy woodpeckers, *illus.,* 6-344
  Flickers, *illus.,* 6-347
Wood's metal, uses of. 3-416
Woodward, Sir Arthur Smith, English paleontologist. 9-23
Woodward, John, English geologist. 4-387
Woody fibers. *with illus.,* 5-263-64
Woody stems. *with illus.,* 4-66-70
Wool.
  Sheep giving different grades of, *illus.,* 10-246-47
Woolly aphids, insects. *with illus.,* 9-192-93
Woolly bears, lepidopterous insects. *with illus.,* 3-200
Woolly mammoths, extinct elephants. *illus.,* 1-397
Woolly monkeys. 9-259
Woolly rhinoceroses. 3-179
Woolly spider monkeys. 9-259
Words. *Language, 1-107-21
Work, in physics. 1-82, 83
  Force related to, 3-56-57
  See also **Energy; Power**
Worker ants. 3-357, 358, 359, 364, 365, *illus.,* 360
Worker honeybees. 3-368, 370, *illus.,* 366, 372
Worker termites. 3-362
Worker wasps. 3-366
Workers, printing plates. 1-207
World. See **Astronomy; Earth; Geology; Physiography; Soil; Universe**
World Calendar. *with illus.,* 10-179-80
World Health Organization (WHO). 6-14
  Antimalaria campaigns of, 10-37
  Establishment of, 9-42
World population. 3-230-33, *map,* 230-31
World War I. Aircraft uses in, 6-179, 183, *illus.,* 184
  Chemical industry, effect on, 8-187
  Railroads of United States affected by, 1-183
  Science and technology in, *with illus.,* 9-211-15

World War II.
  Aircraft used in, 6-181, 184-85, *illus.,* 181, 186; 7-68-69
  Digester gas, use of, 5-332-33
  Forecasting of ocean waves in, *with illus.,* 6-366-67
  Microfilm uses in, *with illus.,* 10-73-74
  Railroads of United States affected by, 1-184
  Rocketry in, *with illus.,* 9-378-79
  Science and technology in, *with illus.,* 9-323-29
  Silk industry affected by, 5-184
  Soilless-agriculture advances during, 8-36
  Weapons engineered to human standards, 10-121
World Warning Agency (WWA). 5-186-87
World's petroleum. 4-152
Worm lizards. *illus.,* 5-200
Worms. *2-153-62
  Earthworms, soil development aided by, 2-204
  Luminous, 2-183, 185
  Prehistoric forms, 1-387
  Ridges on beach sands produced by, 8-354
  See also **Larvae**
Wounds. Bodily reactions to, 7-348, 351-53
Wounds, tree. Care of, *with illus.,* 10-143, 146-47
Wrapping, of bread. See **Slicing and wrapping**
Wrapping paper. 4-378
Wrasses, fishes. *illus.,* 4-314
Wrens. 6-44-46, *illus.,* 44
Wright, Frank Lloyd, American architect.
  Glass architecture advocated by, 8-390
  Price Tower, Bartlesville, Oklahoma, designed by, *illus.,* 3-124
Wright, Orville and Wilbur, American pioneers in aviation. *with illus.,* 6-182-83; 9-216, *illus.,* 217
Wright, Russel, American designer. 10-125
Wrinkles, formation in skin. 2-174-75, *illus.,* 175
Wrists. Bones of, *with illus.,* 3-81, *illus.,* 74, 80
  Muscles and tendons of, 3-210-11, *illus.,* 208
Writing. *Development of spoken and written language, 1-107-21
  Development in antiquity, 1-124-25, *illus.,* 127
  Fire-writing trick, *with diagram,* 7-179-80
  See also **Printing**
Wrought iron. Nature of, 1-339-40
Wu, Chien S., physicist.
  Parity law of physics tested by, 7-110
Wundt, Wilhelm, German physiologist and psychologist. 9-48-49
Wüst, George, German oceanographer. 5-192
WWA. See **World Warning Agency**
Wynch Bridge, England. 2-338
Wynder, E. L., American surgeon. 5-348, 350
Wyoming. Landslide in Gros Ventre Valley, 2-353

X

X-1, experimental rocket plane. 7-70; 9-219
X-1A, experimental rocket plane. 7-70
X-2, experimental rocket plane. 7-70
X-15, experimental rocket plane. 6-195; 7-71; 9-219
X axis, in analytic geometry. *with diagrams,* 4-425-31
X chromosomes, female sex chromosomes. 8-337-38, 342, *diagram,* 338
X-ray diffraction. Crystal structure analyzed by, 7-206
X-ray diffractometers. *illus.,* 7-358
X-ray microscopes. Flea photomicrograph, *illus.,* 7-204
X-ray tubes.
  Beryllium used for "windows" of, 3-171, *illus.,* 168
  Principle of, 6-302
X rays. *7-143-50
  Atmosphere affected by solar X rays, 1-238, 240
  Barium sulfate in X-ray diagnosis, 3-174, *illus.,* 175

X rays *(continued)*
Betatrons produce high-energy X rays, 9-247
Cancer and, 8-268, 270, *illus.,* 269; *illus.,* 10-132
Crystal structure analyzed by, 5-341; 9-151
Damage caused by, 9-349
Description of, 7-202-03, 204, 205-06, *illus.,* 201
Discovery of, 8-402, 411-12; 9-348-49
Food preserved by, 4-168
Hazards of, 9-358
Mutations due to, 9-356
Space-travel hazard, 10-50
Tuberculosis detected by, 9-180, *illus.,* 178-79, 181-82
X series, experimental jet and rocket craft.   9-219
See also **X-1; X-1A; X-2; X-15**
Xanthophyll, leaf pigment.   4-73, 74; 6-55
Xenon (Xe), chemical element.   Atomic number, 54;
atomic weight, 131.30; melting point, —112° C.; boiling
point, —107.1° C.; specific gravity, gas (air = 1):
4.525, liquid: 3.52.   Inert gas; forms no stable compounds.   Discovered by Ramsay and Travers in 1898;
name derived from Greek *xenon:* "stranger."   Found
with krypton in certain mineral springs; obtained from
the atmosphere, of which it forms one part in twenty
million.   Prepared by condensation, as liquid or solid,
as slow stream of dry air is passed through tube
cooled by liquid air.   Used in high-speed photographic
tubes and vacuum tubes.
Gas-filled electron tubes, use in, 6-300-01
Plasma created from xenon, *illus.,* 1-173
Xerographic printing.   1-214
Xerophytes, plants living under extremely dry conditions.
Adaptations of, *with illus.,* 6-226-28
Xylem, conducting tissue of plants.   *with illus.,* 4-64,
69, 70, 73
Seed plants, xylem of, 3-399-400

Y

Y axis, in analytic geometry.   *with diagrams,* 4-425-31
Y chromosomes, male sex chromosomes.   8-337-38, 342,
diagram, 339
Yakima River, Washington.   Roller dam across, 8-315
Yaks.   7-333, *illus.,* 330
Yale Dam, Oregon.   *illus.,* 8-316c
Yang, Chen N., physicist.
Parity law of physics tested by, 7-110
Yankee bugs.   3-257
Yankee machines, for making glazed papers.   4-373
Yards, of homes.   Safety practices in, 7-195
Yarkon-Negev project, Israeli irrigation project.   8-200
Yaw, right-and-left motion of craft and vehicles.   Space
vehicles and missiles undergo, 8-129, *diagram,* 130
Yaws, disease.   Microorganisms that cause, *illus.,* 8-363
Yeager, Charles E., American test pilot.   X-series ex-
perimental rocket planes, 9-219
Yeasts.   3-26-27
Anaerobic respiration of, 3-48
Breadmaking utilizes, 9-294, *with diagrams,* 296-97
Fermentation caused by, 4-168; *with illus.,* 7-135;
9-73-76
Food spoilage caused by, *with illus.,* 4-153, 154
Yellow.   Printing color, 1-213
Vision experiments with, 8-180
Yellow-bellied sapsuckers.   *illus.,* 6-211
Yellow-bellied turtles.   Migration of, 9-429
Yellow-billed cuckoos.   6-306, 308, *illus.,* 307
Yellow fever.   Control of, 9-39
Mosquitoes as vectors of, 8-405; 10-38-39
Nineteenth-century developments, 7-384-85
Vaccine used against, 3-458
Yellow-headed blackbirds.   6-104

Yellow pine trees.   Leaves of, *illus.,* 4-72
Yellow sharks.   *illus.,* 4-288
Yellow-throated vireos, birds.   6-63
Yellow-throated warblers, birds.   *illus.,* 6-60
Yellow trumpets, flowering plants.   Pollination of,
illus., 4-127
Yellows, butterflies.   3-198-99
Yellowstone National Park, Wyoming.
Bison in, *illus.,* 9-271
Geysers and hot springs of, 8-289-90, *illus.,* 288,
292, 300a, 300d
Lewis Falls, *illus.,* 6-412
Minerva Terrace, *illus.,* 8-292
Wildlife sanctuary, 9-275
Yellowstone River, Wyoming and Montana.   Grand
Canyon of, *illus.,* 8-18
Yerkes, Robert, American psychobiologist.   9-52
Yerkes Observatory 40-inch refracting telescope.
8-56, *illus.,* 57
Yersin, Alexandre-Emile-John, Swiss bacteriologist.   7-
383
YMCA Building, Oklahoma City, Okla.   *illus.,* 7-127
Yogurt, fermented milk.   4-167
Yolk sac, early structure in product of conception.
8-23, *illus.,* 22
Yosemite National Park, California.
Bridalveil Falls, *illus.,* 10-29
Young, L. C., American physicist.   9-289
Young, Thomas, English physician and physicist.   *with
illus.,* 6-239-40
Color-vision theory, *with diagram,* 7-288-89, *illus.,* 787
Ether theory, 4-211
Young-Helmholtz theory of color vision.   *with illus.,*
7-288-89
Young streams and valleys.   8-17, *with illus.,* 18
Young's modulus, ratio of tensile stress to tensile strain.
5-376
Ytterbium (Yb), chemical element.   Atomic number, 70;
atomic weight, 173.04; melting point, 1,800° C.   Rare-
earth metal; solutions are colorless.   Separated by
Marignac in 1878.   Name derived from Swedish village
of Ytterby.   Best sources gadolinite, xenotime, poly-
crase and blomstrandine.
Yttrium (Y), chemical element.   Atomic number, 39;
atomic weight, 88.905; melting point, 1,490° C.; boiling
point, 2,500° C.; specific gravity, 5.51.   Rare-earth
metal.   Forms small scales with metallic luster and
iron-gray color; readily oxidizes in air.   Discovered in
1794 by Gadolin; name derived from Ytterby, Swedish
village.   Found in almost all rare-earth minerals; has
been obtained by reduction of the chloride with potassium and by electrolysis of a mixture of the chloride
and sodium chloride.
Yucca moths.   3-202; *with illus.,* 4-126-27
Yucca night lizards.   5-205
Yuccas (Spanish bayonets), plants.
Pollinated by yucca moths, *with illus.,* 4-126-27
Yukawa, Hideki, Japanese physicist.
Meson's existence predicted by, 8-398
Yurts, primitive dwellings.   *illus.,* 3-114
YWCA, New York City.   Typing courses introduced at,
with illus., 1-268-69

Z

Z axis, in analytic geometry.   4-430, *diagram,* 431
Zamenhof, Lazarus Ludwig, Russian philologist.   1-120
Zea Mays, species of corn.   Stem, cross section of,
illus., 4-70
Zebras.   *with illus.,* 7-333
Zeiss Company, German optical firm.
Planetarium projectors manufactured by, **2-397-98**

Zeiss Planetarium. See Planetaria
Zeller, E., American geologist. 5-191
Zenith. 1-261, *diagrams*, 260, 261; 8-61
Zeno's paradox. 4-433-34, *diagram*, 432-33
Zeolite. Hard water treated by, 2-181-82
Zeppelin, Count Ferdinand von, aeronautical pioneer. 6-179
Zeppelins, dirigibles. 6-179, *with illus.*, 180; 9-214
Zero, in mathematics. 1-159
Zero, absolute. See Absolute zero
Zeta Aurigae, eclipsing binary. 7-46
Zeuglodonts, primitive whales. 7-181
Zick-zack plovers. 6-408
Zimmerman, Percy W., American botanist. 9-291
Zinc (Zn), chemical element. Atomic number, 30; atomic weight, 65.37; melting point, 419.5° C.; boiling point, 907° C.; specific gravity, 7.14. Metal; blue-white, brittle at ordinary temperatures. Recognized as separate metal by Marggraf in 1746; name derived from German *Zink*. Chief ores are sphalerite, smithsonite and calamine. Obtained by heating roasted ore with carbon in a retort and by electrolysis. Used to coat other metals, especially iron, to prevent corrosion; as a negative electrode in electric batteries; in compounds for paints, antiseptics and many other purposes.
    Alloys of, 1-382
    Building material, 7-121-22
    Corrosion of, 5-96
    Galvanizing of steel, use in, 1-350, 352
    Living cells, found in, 2-6
    Plants' use of, 3-44
    Properties and uses of, 3-40-41
    Smelting and refining of, *with diagram*, 1-380
Zinc sulfide. Phosphor in electroluminescence, 9-345
Ziolkovsky, Konstantin Eduardovich. See Tsiolkovsky, Konstantin Eduardovich
Zirconium (Zr), chemical element. Atomic number, 40; atomic weight, 91.22; melting point, 1,857° C.; boiling point, above 2,900° C.; specific gravity, 6.4. Metal. Discovered in zircon by Klaproth in 1789; isolated by Berzelius in 1824. Name derived from Arabic *zargun:* "gold color." Found in various igneous rocks; usually occurs in zirconium orthosilicate. Pure metal prepared by heating the tetrachloride with sodium in a bomb. Metal can be drawn into wire or pressed into rods. Zirconium alloys have been used in steel manufacture; the oxides serve in paints, lacquers and abrasives.
Zirconium oxide. Gas-mantle experiments with, 4-237
Zodiac. 1-264, *illus.*, 263
Zodiacal light. 1-240; 3-161
"Zone of audibility," in atmosphere. 5-121-22, *illus.*, 122-23
Zone of silence, preceding bodies moving at supersonic speeds. *with diagram*, 10-229
Zones of Jupiter. See Belts of Jupiter
Zoning laws, for buildings. Private dwellings must conform to, 4-266
Zonurus giganteus, lizard. *illus.*, 5-197
Zoologists. See Zoology; Biology; Botany; also names of individual zoologists
Zoology.
  *Adaptations, 3-235-44
  *Amphibians, 5-152-62
  *Antelope family, 8-376-87
  *Ants, keeping colony of, 3-393-96
  *Apes, monkeys and kin, 9-250-65
  *Bears and kin, 7-307-17
  *Beavers and others, 9-1-6
  *Beetles, 3-335-48

Zoology (continued)
  *Bioluminescence, 2-182-91
  *Birds, 5-414-26; 6-37-48, 60-68, 99-108, 152-66, 209-18, 304-10, 331-40, 341-49, 394-408
  *Cat family, 8-202-12
  *Cells, 2-1-14
  *Civets, mongooses and hyenas, 8-244-50
  *Classification, 1-287-300
  *Coelacanths, 4-196-99
  *Coelenterates, 2-148-51
  *Communities, 10-181-90
  *Crocodilians, 5-380-85
  *Crustaceans, 2-236-43
  *Deer family, 8-234-43
  *Dog family, 8-132-41
  *Domestic animals, 7-327-33; 10-239-50
  *Echinoderms, 2-151-52
  *Exploring animal world, 10-254-64
  *Fishes, 4-93-105, 285-95, 311-20; 8-112-16
  *Germ-free animals, 7-151-55
  *Giant land mammals, 7-408-17
  *Glands, 5-8-19
  *Habitats of animals, 10-135-42
  *Hearing of animals, 4-379-85
  *History of animal life, 1-383-97
  *Human biology, 1-57-66
  *Insect collecting, 3-153-56
  *Insect eaters, 7-94-102
  *Insects, 2-402-14; 3-138-52, 193-202, 252-64, 283-92, 335-48, 357-72; 9-185-96; 10-30-39
  *Intelligence in animals, 2-26-29
  *Introduction to study of zoology, 1-51-56
  *Lizards, 5-196-206
  *Mammals, 7-1-16
  *Marine mammals, 7-181-89
  *Marsupials, 7-418-28
  *Mechanisms, animal, 1-277-86
  *Migration of animals, 9-415-32
  *Mollusks, 2-192-202
  *Muscles of the human body, 3-203-13
  *Primitive chordates, 4-1-4
  *Protozoans, 2-58-66
  *Rodents, 8-160-70; 9-1-6
  *Sanctuaries, bird and game, 9-266-78
  *Seals and kin, 7-84-93
  *Seasonal changes that affect animals, 5-409-13
  *Senses, human, 7-291-306
  *Snakes, 5-351-64
  *Spiders and kin, 2-258-69
  *Sponges, jellyfish and sea stars, 2-146-52
  *Systems of human body, 1-148a-h
  *Turtles, 5-386-89
  *Weasel family, 8-171-77
  *Wild animals as pets, 7-17-26
  *Worms, 2-153-62
  *Zoo animals, 10-154-62
  Fossil animals, *with illus.*, 6-370-74
  Plants and animals, differences between, 1-40-42
  See also Animals; Biology; Evolution; Fossils; etc.
Zoos. *10-154-62
  Photographing animals at, 6-313
Zsigmondy, R., German chemist.
  Ultramicroscope, development of, 5-297; 8-408
Zuñi Indians. Pottery-making, *illus.*, 7-400
Zwicky, Fritz, American astronomer.
  Galaxies studied by, 8-49, *with diagram*, 54
Zworykin, Vladimir K., Russian-American inventor. 5-280
Zygotes, cells due to reproductive union. 6-270
Zytel, nylon plastic. *illus.*, 8-228